The Caledonian–Appalachian Orogen

Geological Society Special Publications

Series Editor K.COE

GEOLOGICAL SOCIETY SPECIAL PUBLICATION NO 38

The Caledonian–Appalachian Orogen

EDITED BY

A. L. HARRIS
Department of Earth Sciences
University of Liverpool
Liverpool

D. J. FETTES
British Geological Survey
Edinburgh

1988
Published for
The Geological Society by
Blackwell Scientific Publications

OXFORD LONDON EDINBURGH

BOSTON PALO ALTO MELBOURNE

Published for
The Geological Society by
Blackwell Scientific Publications
Osney Mead, Oxford OX2 0EL
  (*Orders*: Tel. 0865-240201)
8 John Street, London WC1N 2ES
23 Ainslie Place, Edinburgh EH3 6AJ
3 Cambridge Center, Suite 208
  Cambridge, Massachusetts 02142, USA
667 Lytton Avenue, Palo Alto,
  California 94301, USA
107 Barry Street, Carlton, Victoria 3053,
  Australia

First published 1988

Typeset, printed and bound in Great Britain by
William Clowes Limited
Beccles and London

DISTRIBUTORS

USA and Canada
  Blackwell Scientific Publications Inc.
  PO Box 50009, Palo Alto
  California 94303
  (*Orders*: Tel. (415) 965-4081)

Canada
  Oxford University Press
  70 Wynford Drive
  Don Mills
  Ontario M3C 1J9
  (*Orders*: Tel. (416) 441-2941)

Australia
  Blackwell Scientific Publications
  (Australia) Pty Ltd.
  107 Barry Street, Carlton,
  Victoria 3053
  (*Orders*: Tel. (03) 347-0300)

British Library Cataloguing in Publication Data

The Caledonian–Appalachian orogen.—
(Geological Society special publication,
  ISSN 0305-8719; no. 38).
1. Geology, Stratigraphic—Palaeozoic
I. Harris, A. L. II. Fettes, D. J.
III. Geological Society of London
IV. Series
551   QE654

ISBN 0–632–01796–1

Library of Congress Cataloging-in-Publication Data

The Caledonian–Appalachian orogen.

(Geological Society special publication; no. 38)
  1. Geology, Stratigraphic—Paleozoic—Congresses.
2. Orogeny—North America—Congresses. 3. Orogeny—
Europe—Congresses. I. Harris, A. L. (Anthony L.)
II. Fettes, D. J. III. Geological Society of London.
IV. Series.
QE654.C26 1987   551.7′32′091821   87–6382
ISBN 0–632–01796–1

Contents

Preface

This special publication of the Geological Society records papers read at the 5-day final symposium of IGCP Project 27 (the Caledonide Orogen) held at the University of Glasgow in September 1984 by courtesy of Principal Sir Alwyn Williams FRS and Professor Bernard Leake FRSE.

Special thanks are due to Dr D. S. Weedon, Glasgow, who ensured the high standard of the logistical and accommodation arrangements enjoyed by participants at the meeting.

Most previous symposia held under the auspices of IGCP 27 have focussed on the Caledonian–Appalachian geology of the various countries transected by the fragmented orogen and include that held in Dublin in 1978 and recorded in Geological Society Special Publication No. 8. The final symposium was intended to indicate the 'state-of-the-art' knowledge of the orogen in 1984, and this was attempted in the context of four time-periods. The periods were chosen to relate as closely as possible to significant (but commonly diachronous) stages in the complex history of the orogen. For each time-period, orogenic activity was treated in terms of process: cover–basement interaction, deformation, metamorphism, plutonism, volcanism, sedimentation, fauna and flora, which were integrated for each time-period by four synthesizing papers. Geophysical aspects of the orogen were treated separately, so that the importance of palaeomagnetism and of deep seismic experiments in understanding the orogen is explained. The papers published in this volume have in many cases been updated (July 1986) since the symposium.

The time-periods considered were convened and synthesized by Professor J. W. Skehan SJ, Boston Observatory, Dr W. S. McKerrow, Oxford, Professor R. D. Hatcher, S Carolina (now at University of Tennessee, Knoxville), and Professor John Rodgers, Yale. Dr R. T. Haworth, British Geological Survey, convened the section on geophysical aspects of the orogen.

The *pre-Arenig* described the pre-Iapetan and early Iapetan stages and includes the rifting of continental crust with related sedimentation, the products of early island arcs and the effects of their collision either with each other or with early oceanic margins to produce Grampian (early Caledonian), Finnmarkian, Penobscotian and Avalonian orogenesis. *Arenig–Wenlock* dealt largely with the main and waning stages of Iapetus as shown by the provinciality of fossils and the generation of island arcs by closure-related subduction. The period also saw the event,

important in N America, involving island-arc collision to produce Taconic deformation and metamorphism. The study of faunal provincialism was crucial in the recognition of the λ-shaped form of the orogen dating at least from this period and involving the still little known Tornquist Sea in addition to the Iapetan. The Wenlock–mid-Devonian was concerned with the major deformation and thermal activity (Acadian, Scandinavian and late Caledonian) related to the closing of Iapetus between Laurentia and Baltica and the attachment of Avalonia to N America and N Britain. Thrusting towards and onto the continental margins was of major importance in N America, Scotland and Greenland with the transport of previously deformed rocks and their cover sequences as major thrust nappes, an activity well documented in Scandinavia where the package of Finnmarkian nappes was reshuffled by Scandian thrusting. The *mid-Devonian–Permian* covered the waning of the orogeny after the final closing of Iapetus which is seen as a NE–SW diachronous wave. It is concerned with the history of rifted pull-apart basins whose fill was subsequently deformed by strike-slip movements and with the closure of the Theic Ocean lying between Laurentia and proto-Gondwana. The Upper Palaeozoic Variscan events in the southern part of the British Isles traditionally regarded by British workers as post-Caledonian are part of continuing Appalachian orogenesis (Alleghanian) in N America. The time periods used in the symposium are adhered to as far as possible in this volume. Inevitably, however, the time-based format could not always be used rigidly because activity in the orogen overlapped the somewhat arbitrarily determined time planes. Papers in which authors were obliged to ignore the time planes are clearly indicated.

The time-span of Project 27 has coincided with the blossoming of plate tectonic theory. As a result the project has seen the development of research into the Caledonian–Appalachian orogen from that of individuals who were concerned with small areas, largely in isolation, to the present when every worker can see his or her research in the context of a major orogen in which the full range of orogenic phenomena can be perceived as interrelated.

Mesozoic to present-day phenomena more obviously related to plate tectonic activity than those of the Caledonian–Appalachian chain have pointed to explanations of characteristics of the more ancient rocks. Fragments of crust of the major oceans hinted at by the pioneering work on faunal provincialism are preserved as ophiolite complexes; sediments, related to rifting or shed into basins formed ahead of continental or obducted ophiolitic nappe complexes, were deformed and metamorphosed by the continuation of the tectonic processes by which they were initiated; waning faunal provincialism may be linked to coeval subduction-related magmatism and metamorphism during the closure of oceans or marginal basins.

Of exceptional importance in understanding Caledonian–Appalachian activity has been the escape from the simplistic view of orthogonal convergence of plates, based on increasing knowledge of more recent plate configuration. Models involving oblique collision and subduction, or the impingement of irregular continental margins against one another, have led to interpretations of Caledonian–Appalachian diachronism on orogen-wide and local scale. Recognition of strike-slip accretion in such orogenic zones as western N America has led to the application of terrane concepts to account for hitherto unexplained contrasts in contemporary geological history between areas in the Caledonide–Appalachian belt which are now adjacent.

IGCP Project 233 has been designed to study Palaeozoic terranes in the circum-Atlantic area and might thus be seen as a natural successor to Project 27 whose organizers wish the new venture every success.

The organizers of the Glasgow symposium wish to thank the national correspondents of participating countries for their help in organizing the meeting, particularly the Project Leader, Professor B. A. Sturt, Bergen, and the Project Secretary, Dr D. Bruton, Oslo Museum.

Everyone who participated in Project 27 benefited from the wisdom and friendship of Professor David Wones, Blacksburg, Virginia, and Professor Leo Hall, Amherst, Massachusetts, whose deaths are sadly recorded in this preface. The help of David Roberts (NGU) and Krishna Sinha (VPI Blacksburg) in bringing their articles to publication is greatly appreciated by the editors.

The International Working Group for Project 27 have recorded their appreciation of the sustained high level of support enjoyed by the Project from the Royal Society and the Geological Society of London. The U.K. members wish to identify the help and encouragement received from Sir Kingsley Dunham FRS and the late Professor Janet Watson FRS through the U.K. National Committee for IGCP.

We thank Hilary Davies for her work in preparing the index.

The symposium was convened by Dr A. L. Harris, Liverpool, and Dr D. J. Fettes, British Geological Survey, Edinburgh, on behalf of the U.K. Working Group for Project 27. It was generously supported by the Royal Society, the Geological Society of London, UNESCO, B.P. Petroleum Development, B.P. Minerals International, Britoil, Esso Petroleum Company, Robertson Research International, Shell International Petroleum Company and Texaco.

Field symposium

The symposium in Glasgow was preceded by a field symposium which was supported by the NATO as Advanced Study Institute (984/83). The advice and cooperation of Dr Craig Sinclair of the NATO Scientific Affairs Division in organizing this symposium is gratefully acknowledged. The full proceedings of the field symposium have been published, and incorporate a detailed field guide to Caledonian and Precambrian rocks of Britain: *Synthesis of the Caledonian rocks of Britain* (eds D. J. Fettes and A. L. Harris) (Vol. C 175). Published by Reidel Publishing Company, Dordrecht, Holland.

Editors' notes

1 Individual authors were asked to make sure that their usage of Early/early and Late/late was consistent within individual papers. No attempt has been made to make the usage consistent throughout the book.
2 Because 'terrain' and 'terrane' are not distinguished by spelling in North America, it was decided to spell the word 'terrane' throughout the book, regardless of nuance.

A. L. HARRIS, University of Liverpool
D. J. FETTES, British Geological Survey, Edinburgh

Maps published under the auspices of Project 27

Scandinavia

Maps all available from the Geological Survey of Sweden, Box 670, S-751 28 Uppsala, Sweden and in *The Caledonide Orogen–Scandinavia and Related Areas* (eds Gee, D. G. & Sturt, B. A.) published by Wiley.

Scandinavian Caledonides: Tectonostratigraphic Map 1985 1:2M compiled by Gee, D. G., Kumpulainen, R., Roberts, D., Stephens, M. B., Thon, A. and Zachrisson, E.

Scandinavian Caledonides: Magnetic Anomaly Map 1985 1:2M compiled by Borg, K., Bergmark, T., Gee, D. G. and Kumpulainen, R.

Scandinavian Caledonides: Gravity Anomaly Map 1985 11:2M compiled by Henkel, H., Gee, D. G. and Kumpulainen, R.

Britain and Ireland

Maps all available separately from the Geological Society of London, Burlington House, Piccadilly, London W1V 0JU, UK and incorporated into Geological Society Memoir 9 (ed. Harris, A. L), coloured plates 1–3.

Plate 1: Caledonian Igneous Rocks of Britain and Ireland 1984 1:2M compiled by Brown, G. C., Francis, E. H., Keenan, P. S. and Stillman, C. J.

Plate 2: Time of Deformation in the Caledonide Orogen of Britain and Ireland 1984 1:1M compiled by Powell, D. and Phillips, W. E. A.

Plate 3: Grade and Time of Metamorphism in the Caledonide Orogen of Britain and Ireland 1984 1:2M compiled by Fettes, D. J., Long, C. B., Max, M. D. and Yardley, B. W. D.

Canada

All Canadian maps are available from the Department of Earth Sciences, Memorial University of Newfoundland, St Johns, Newfoundland A1B 3X5, Canada, attention Professor Harold Williams, apart from the map compiled by J. Hibbard which can be obtained from the Publications and Information Section, Mineral Development Division, Department of Mines and Energy, PO Box 4750, 95 Bonaventure Avenue, St Johns, Newfoundland A1C 5T7, Canada.

Tectonic lithofacies map of the Appalachian orogen (1978); Department of Geology, Memorial University of Newfoundland, Map 1, 1:1M; Map 1a, 1:2M. Compiled by Williams H.

Magnetic anomaly map of the Appalachian orogen (1980); Department of Geology, Memorial University of Newfoundland, Map 2 at scale 1:1M and Map 2a at scale 1:2M. Complied by Zietz, I., Haworth, R. T., Williams, H. and Daniels, D. L.

Bouguer gravity anomaly map of the Appalachian orogen (1980); Department of Geology, Memorial University of Newfoundland, Map 3 at scale 1:1M and Map 3a at scale 1:2M. Compiled by Haworth, R. T., Daniels, D. L., Williams, H. and Zietz, I.

Geology of the Baie Verte Peninsula (1982); Newfoundland Department of Mines and Energy, Map 82-2, scale 1:100 000. Compiled by Hibbard, J.

Structural map of the Appalachian orogen in Canada (1982); Department of Geology, Memorial University of Newfoundland, Map 4, scale 1:2M. Coordinated by Keppie, J. D.

Magnetic anomaly map of Atlantic Canada (1984); Department of Earth Sciences, Memorial University of Newfoundland, Map 5, scale 1:2M. Compiled by Williams, H. and Haworth, R. T.

Bouguer gravity anomaly map of Atlantic Canada (1984); Department of Earth Sciences, Memorial University of Newfoundland, Map 6, scale 1:2M. Complied by Williams, H. and Haworth, R. T.

USA

The following maps are in varying states of preparation, revision, review and publication.

Basement and basement/cover relations map of the Appalachian orogen in the United States, by Drake, A. A., Jr, Hall, L. M. and Nelson A. E.: US Geological Survey Miscellaneous Investigations Map, MI 1655, scale 1:1M. In press.

Time of deformation map of the Appalachian orogen in the United States, by Osberg, P. H. and others (under revision by Professor Osberg for publication by the US Geological Survey).

Metamorphism map of the Appalachian orogen in the United States and Canada, by Fisher, G. W. and Trzcienski, W. E., Jr. In preparation.

Plutonic rocks of the Appalachian orogen in the United States and Canada, by Wones, D. R. and Currie, K. L. In preparation (for publication by the US Geological Survey after review and revision).

Volcanic rocks of the Appalachian orogen in the United States, by Rankin, D. W. and Blackburn, W. H. In preparation.

Lithostratigraphy–faunal provinces maps, all for publication by the US Geological Survey. Status in January 1988:

Late Precambrian (Proterozoic Z; Hadrynian), by Schwab, F. L. Under revision after review.

Cambrian, by Gundersen, L. C. and Palmer, A. R. Three maps. Under revision after review.

Lower Ordovician (Tremadocian–Arenigian), by Dolfi, R. U. and many others. Under revision after review by Buyce, M. R.

Middle Ordovician (Llanvirnian–Caradocian), by Thompson, A. M. Final compilation in progress.

Late Ordovician (Ashgillan), by Thompson, A. M. Under revision after review.

Early Silurian (Llandoverian), by Thompson, A. M. Final compilation in progress.

Mississippi–Pennsylvanian, by Hines, R. A. and Thomas, W. A. Final compilation in progress.

Geophysics of the
Caledonian–Appalachian Orogen

CONVENOR
R. T. HAWORTH
British Geological Survey

Geophysical framework and the Appalachian–Caledonide connection

R. T. Haworth, R. Hipkin, R. D. Jacobi, M. Kane, J. P. Lefort, M. D. Max, H. G. Miller & F. Wolff

SUMMARY: Gravity and magnetic data from the Appalachian–Caledonide area demonstrate the overall continuity of the orogen while identifying its segmentation into areas of contrasting structural style. The extension of this segmentation into 'drift'-covered areas (e.g. the southern U.S.A.) and offshore areas (e.g. around Newfoundland and the British Isles) provides an orogen-wide framework into which structural detail established at outcrop can be accommodated. Linear gravity and magnetic anomalies often reflect contrasts within the Precambrian basement that have controlled tectonic events to the present. Such basement structure has been investigated by deep seismic profiling, which has also identified large-scale thrusting throughout the Appalachians and the Caledonides with some thrusts even extending into the upper mantle. Speculation to greater depths based on conductivity and P-wave travel-time residuals suggests that traces of the early Palaeozoic collision zone may still exist in the lower crust and upper mantle beneath the northern Appalachians. The loading imposed by thrust sheets during that collision produced foreland basins in the eastern USA whose form and sedimentary record indicate the magnitude and duration of thrusting. Palaeomagnetic results suggest transcurrent movement in Devonian–Carboniferous time, but the early Palaeozoic collisional choreography has not yet been uniquely defined.

Participation by geophysicists in the work of the International Geological Correlation Program Project 27 'The Appalachian–Caledonide Orogen' began in 1978, 4 years into the project. At that time it was recognized by all participants that many types of geophysical data available both onshore and offshore throughout the orogen could provide pictorial evidence for the continuity of the orogen which was not available as easily (or at all) with any of the geological data sets. Initially the efforts of the geophysicists were directed towards the compilation of gravity and magnetic data in the Appalachians of the USA and Canada (Haworth & MacIntyre 1975, Hood & Reveler 1977, Zietz & Gilbert 1980, 1981) and composite maps on the same scale and projection as the *Tectonic Lithofacies Map of the Appalachian Orogen* were published (Williams 1978, Haworth *et al.* 1980, Zietz *et al.* 1980). These served both to identify the geophysical characteristics of the tectonic lithofacies units hypothesized by Williams to be common along the length of the orogen and to demonstrate the extension of these units beneath the coastal plain cover and to the edge of the continental shelf.

From the earliest days of speculation about continental drift, continuity between the Appalachians and Caledonides had been hypothesized, but only in 1965 did Bullard *et al.* (1965) attempt to demonstrate physically the degree of fit by matching specified bathymetric contours from each side of the Atlantic. Unfortunately the edge of the continental crust as we now know it does

not coincide at all closely with a single bathymetric contour and is generally far seaward of the 500 m contour chosen by Bullard *et al.* (1965). In addition to trying to fit the real outlines of continental crust on both sides of the Atlantic, geophysicists have also attempted to match specific features within the continental crust. Continuity of features between the Appalachians and Caledonides is therefore both a consequence of and an aid to making pre- (Mesozoic) drift reconstructions of the N Atlantic.

Several reconstructions with little major difference have been used to demonstrate the continuity of geophysical lineations between Appalachia and Caledonia and to provide a framework within which the hypothesized continuity of structure could be examined (Lefort & Haworth 1978, Lefort 1980, 1983, 1984, Haworth 1981, Jacobi & Kristoffersen 1981, Lefort & Van der Voo 1981, Haworth & Jacobi 1983). Interpretation of these compilations suffered from three major problems: (i) the highly dissected nature of the European continental margin across which it was hoped to follow these lineations, and within which area the publicly available geophysical data were considerably less abundant than on the N American margin; (ii) the uncertainties regarding post-Caledonide, pre-Jurassic movements (e.g. Kent & Opdyke 1978, Swanson 1982); (iii) the overlap and low-angle divergence of trends associated with post-Caledonide tectonism. The latter problem is particularly severe when trying to use gravity and magnetic data for regional

From HARRIS, A. L. & FETTES, D. J. (eds), 1988, *The Caledonian–Appalachian Orogen,* Geological Society Special Publication No. 38, pp. 3–20.

extrapolation of Caledonide trends within the UK. Hipkin & Hussain (1983) have used the available seismic reflection data offshore from Scotland to strip the effects of post-Caledonide sedimentary basins and reveal Caledonide structural trends, the investigation of whose continuity between Britain and Scandinavia must be a prime target for future research.

Compilation of geological data in N America on which to demonstrate the continuity of Appalachian structure was no more easily accomplished than for the Caledonides in Europe—the number of U.S.A. state and Canadian provincial surveys to be coordinated were more numerous than the national surveys in Europe. However, the N American geophysical programmes were primarily national in origin so that compilation of geophysical data was easier in N America than in Europe. Differing national specifications in Europe made the situation even more difficult. In magnetics, for example, the aeromagnetic surveys of neighbouring countries in Europe have been flown at different heights, at different times and with different regional fields removed, making it almost impossible to merge the predominantly analogue data sets. Discontinuities along national boundaries therefore compound the problems associated with discontinuities onshore and between offshore data sets.

Major efforts within the U.K. have recently produced a uniform file of gravity data (Hipkin & Hussain 1983, Hipkin *et al.* 1986), and analogue magnetic field data are being digitized. 1 : 250 000 scale maps are available for all the surveyed land and marine areas of the UK except for a few coastal areas where merging of the two data sets has proved troublesome. Magnetic and gravity around Ireland, N of Scotland and in the North Sea is neither uniform nor universally releasable, covering as it does the hydrocarbon exploration areas of several countries. However, considerable progress has recently been made with the compilation and release of such data for Ireland and its neighbouring continental shelf (Max *et al.* 1982, 1983). In Scandinavia, high-level reconnaissance magnetic surveys (Geological Survey of Sweden 1983) have been succeeded by low-level high-resolution surveys (Wolff 1981) directed towards mineral and hydrocarbon exploration, and therefore restricted in their release. The efforts of the Bureau Gravimétrique International (1982) in assembling worldwide gravity data and the objectives of the European Geotraverse Project (Mueller 1983) are additional stimuli for the preparation of uniform geophysical maps of Europe which will have immediate benefits for Caledonide investigations. The compilations of data referred to here for the European Caledonides are therefore only preliminary in nature and can be expected to improve significantly in the next few years.

As the geophysical contribution to Project 27 has developed, so has recognition of the difference between the geophysical and geological definition of suture zones and terrane boundaries. The geophysical definitions are generally based upon the integration of a physical response over the thickness of the crust, whereas the geological definition is almost always as a line or zone at the Earth's surface. The geophysical definition has the advantage that it can often indicate the dip of the suture. However, the occasional 'disagreement' between the geophysical identification of the plan view of that dipping crustal zone and the geological identification of the outcrop of one boundary within it has been known to hamper communication between the disciplines. Greater emphasis will therefore be given in this paper to interpretation of deeper structure and the overall geophysical recognition of terrane boundaries within the orogen. Because deep seismic profiling is dealt with in the companion paper by Cook *et al.* (1988) we shall concentrate on techniques other than seismic reflection. Most geophysical techniques (palaeomagnetism and geochronology are the prime exceptions) do not yield data that can be interpreted to give the timing of tectonic activity. Since palaeomagnetism is also dealt with in a companion paper (Briden *et al.* 1988) and the chronological development of the orogen as a whole is the objective of the rest of this volume, interpretative remarks on these subjects will be kept to a minimum.

The Caledonide–Appalachian and Hercynian orogenies had two distinct phases, each with different temporal and geographical extents. The 'sutures' representing closure of the Iapetus and Theic Oceans are parallel in the southern and eastern U.S.A. with consequent Hercynian reactivation of Appalachian structures. The 'sutures' diverge in southeastern Canada so that in Europe–Africa the two elements are distinct. The southern (Appalachian–Hercynide–Mauritanide) connection is discussed by Lefort *et al.* (1988) and will therefore be avoided in this paper except where tectonic overprinting or rejuvenation necessitates mention of it. Some alternatives to the interpretations expressed in this paper about the Avalon terrane in particular are to be found in the paper by Lefort *et al.* (1988).

Continuity of geophysical character along the orogen

The gravitational expression of the Appalachians has long been recognized as primary evidence for

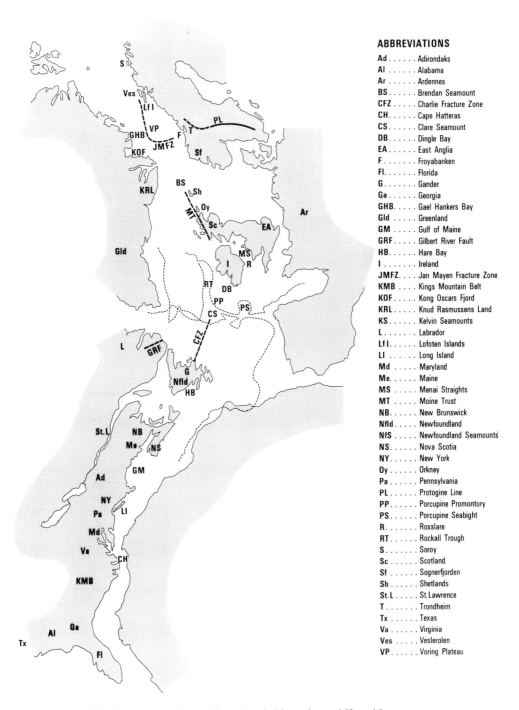

ABBREVIATIONS

Ad . . . . . . Adirondaks
Al . . . . . . Alabama
Ar . . . . . . Ardennes
BS . . . . . Brendan Seamount
CFZ . . . . . Charlie Fracture Zone
CH . . . . . . Cape Hatteras
CS . . . . . . Clare Seamount
DB . . . . . . Dingle Bay
EA . . . . . . East Anglia
F . . . . . . Froyabanken
Fl . . . . . . Florida
G . . . . . . Gander
Ga . . . . . Georgia
GHB . . . . Gael Hankers Bay
Gld . . . . Greenland
GM . . . . Gulf of Maine
GRF . . . . Gilbert River Fault
HB . . . . . Hare Bay
I . . . . . . Ireland
JMFZ . . . Jan Mayen Fracture Zone
KMB . . . . Kings Mountain Belt
KOF . . . . Kong Oscars Fjord
KRL . . . . Knud Rasmussens Land
KS . . . . . Kelvin Seamounts
L . . . . . . Labrador
Lfl . . . . . Lofoten Islands
Ll . . . . . Long Island
Md . . . . Maryland
Me . . . . . Maine
MS . . . . Menai Straights
MT . . . . Moine Trust
NB . . . . . New Brunswick
Nfld . . . . Newfoundland
NfS . . . . Newfoundland Seamounts
NS . . . . . Nova Scotia
NY . . . . . New York
Oy . . . . . Orkney
Pa . . . . . Pennsylvania
PL . . . . . Protogine Line
PP . . . . . Porcupine Promontory
PS . . . . . Porcupine Seabight
R . . . . . . Rosslare
RT . . . . . Rockall Trough
S . . . . . . Soroy
Sc . . . . . Scotland
Sf . . . . . Sognerfjorden
Sh . . . . . Shetlands
St. L . . . . St.Lawrence
T . . . . . . Trondheim
Tx . . . . . Texas
Va . . . . . Virginia
Ves . . . . Veslerolen
VP . . . . . Voring Plateau

FIG. 1. Features of the N Atlantic borderlands in their early Mesozoic pre-drift positions.

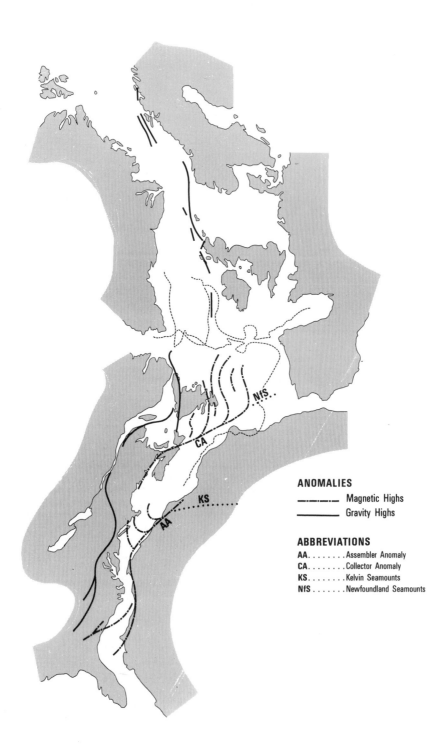

FIG. 2. Prominent gravity and magnetic anomalies of the N Atlantic borderlands (see text for details).

continuity of structure along the orogen. Recent maps for the entire conterminous USA (Simpson *et al.* 1982) show the Appalachian gravity high as the longest most continuous anomaly in the country and second only in prominence to the mid-continent gravity high. Despite such prominence and its more detailed presentation (Haworth *et al.* 1980) for direct correlation with the tectonic lithofacies map of the Appalachians (Williams 1978), the origin of this gravity anomaly remains unclear. The positive anomaly is paired with a negative anomaly on its western margin whose origin has been attributed amongst other things to a sedimentary basin covered by over-thrust crystalline rocks (Woollard 1939) or to a depression of the crust into the mantle (Diment 1968). The positive anomaly was correspondingly attributed to the uplift of dense lower-crustal rocks (Diment 1968). Thomas (1983), by comparison with the paired anomalies observed over suture zones in the Canadian Shield (Gibb & Thomas 1976), suggested that it marked a collisional suture zone dipping southeastward beneath the inner Piedmont. Despite the non-uniqueness of gravity modelling, Hutchinson *et al.* (1983) also support this interpretation. Following the interpretation of dipping seismic reflectors identified by deep seismic reflection programmes in the eastern USA and Canada as thrust planes (Cook *et al.* 1979, Granger *et al.* 1980), gravity interpretation has proceeded to identify the line of maximum gravity gradient with the eastern edge of Precambrian continental crust onto which the allochthonous sedimentary sequences were thrust (Cook 1984a, b). This is consistent with the situation in western Newfoundland where the gravity gradient follows the eastern edge of the Precambrian outcrop in the northern peninsula (Weaver 1967, Haworth 1975). However, gravity models for the central part of Newfoundland (Haworth & Miller 1982) have been interpreted as indicating that that part of the island is entirely allochthonous above the continental crust (Karlstrom 1983) which would require Precambrian basement to extend E of the line of gravity gradient, and this interpretation is supported by deep seismic reflection data (Keen *et al.* 1986). Miller (1984) disputes this, indicating that the gravity and refraction data for central Newfoundland are consistent with a thicker crust in that area indicative of a rooted or autochthonous 'oceanic' zone. We can therefore say that throughout eastern N America the line of maximum gravity gradient is the minimum eastward extent of Grenville crust.

N of Newfoundland the line of maximum gravity gradient swings sharply offshore and merges with anomalies associated with the continental margins of the Labrador Sea and the Rockall plateau in the vicinity of which it should have its landfall. A series of gravity and magnetic highs in northwestern Britain appear to be related to the northwestern (Grenville) continental margin. The most prominent of these highs is a lineation running SSW immediately to the W of the Shetlands (Tully 1983). This anomaly would at first sight appear to be a prolongation of the line of the Moine thrust, although the latter has little gravitational expression on land. However, the higher anomalies might indicate Mesozoic intrusions along this old line of weakness. Where this anomaly dies away at the shore it is replaced farther W by an equally large anomaly correlative with the Outer Isles thrust (McQuillin & Watson 1973) which continues SSW to become tangential with the continental margin on the southeastern margin of the Rockall trough. This two-element lineation is the most prominent of the linear highs on the NW British continental shelf. Approximately 60 km to the SW of each element is another linear high of about half the amplitude. In Shetland this high correlates with the zone of greenstones and serpentinized rocks (McQuillin & Brooks 1967) which is interpreted to form part of a post-Cambrian ophiolite suite (Flinn *et al.* 1979) and is bounded on its western margin by a thrust fault (Flinn 1977). On the mainland the correlative high lies over Lewisian basement rocks W of the Moine thrust. This double band of anomalies continues northeastward from the Shetlands merging with a gravity and magnetic anomaly apparently associated with the continental margin. This anomaly continues northeastward (Talwani & Eldholm 1972) until it is truncated at a point that lies approximately on a line that is the extension of the trend of the Jan Mayen fracture zone near Froyabanken.

The merging of the 'Shetland anomaly' with the 'edge anomaly' at 62°N, 0°W, the northeastward continuation of the 'merged' high along the trend of the 'edge anomaly' rather than following the Scottish trend, the disturbance of the merged anomaly by an ESE-trending low towards Sognefjorden and the location of the Brendan seamount (Smythe *et al.* 1983) suggest that this point marks the northeastern limit of the western edge of the Scottish Caledonides. Several reconstructions of the northern N Atlantic fit the Knud Rasmussens Land promontory into the embayment of the Norwegian margin off Trondheim. If this is correct there is excellent parallelism or continuity between the Outer Isles thrust trend, the Shetland trend and the western thrust margin of the Caledonian orogen in Greenland. Gravity data for eastern Greenland are unfortunately not available and the aeromagnetic data have not yet been published and so the geophysical character of that margin and its northward extension cannot be examined.

The western edge of the Appalachian–Caledonide orogen therefore has a geophysical expression that can be followed as a more or less continuous feature from the emergence of the Appalachians from beneath the coastal plain cover in Alabama to eastern Greenland.

The eastern margin of the orogen is by no means so clearly marked geologically nor so directly identifiable geophysically. It is known geologically in only scattered areas throughout the orogen: Virginia?, southern New England, eastern New Brunswick and Newfoundland, SE Ireland?, Wales? and then clearly in Scandinavia.

The base of the thrust sheet in Scandinavia can be seen along the coastal zone and this base is part of the 'southeastern' Caledonian continental margin. Inshore of the interpreted northwestern escarpment of the Voring plateau and seaward of the Lofoten Islands and Vesterolen lies a linear band of correlative magnetic and gravity anomalies, both positive and negative. The positive anomaly coincides approximately with what Talwani & Eldholm (1972) identify as the shelf edge at a water depth of approximately 200 m. Inshore of these linear anomalies is a second band of intense positive anomalies associated with the Proterozoic granulites in the Lofoten archipelago (Wolff 1983). Positive anomalies over Sørøy (Brooks 1970) are of similar amplitude to those over the Lofoten and Vesterolen islands. Talwani & Eldholm (1972) show that there is no direct continuity between the anomalies, but it seems likely that they have a common source in the basement rocks or the ultramafic elements of the allochthon thrust over them. The interpreted cross-sections of Sørøy (Brooks 1970) are extremely similar to those of the eastern margin of the northern peninsula of Newfoundland onto which the Hare Bay ophiolitic complex was thrust (Srivastava *et al.* 1977). It might therefore be implied that this anomaly marks the northwestern edge of the eastern continental margin of Caledonia.

Talwani & Eldholm (1972) suggested that the Lofoten–Vesterolen anomaly has a similar intrabasement source to that of the linear anomaly running from N of Shetlands to Froyabanken. They infer that the intra-basement structure has controlled the subsequent development of the shelf edge. If this is the situation and there is an offset between the two linear anomalies along a line trending NW from Trondheim, a similar offset might be anticipated in other elements of the Proterozoic basement of Scandinavia and Greenland. Such a line would be a landward extrapolation of the trend of the Jan Mayen

fracture zone NW of the Voring plateau and, according to the reconstruction by Talwani & Eldholm (1977), would have a landfall in Greenland between Kong Oscars Fjord and Gael Hankes Bay. Offsets are indeed recognizable as a change in the trend of the Greenland Caledonides and by contrasts within the Scandinavian Caledonides (Stromberg 1976) as discussed later.

Between southern New England and Newfoundland the eastern continental margin of Appalachia is the Avalon terrane (Williams & Hatcher 1982, Skehan & Rast 1983). This terrane has a clear geophysical signature in Newfoundland which can be used to define its extent throughout Atlantic Canada (Haworth & Lefort 1979). Such characteristics can also be used to interpret its extension into the USA, although Lefort *et al.* (1988) have inferred a history for the USA elements of the Avalon terrane that is an alternative to that described below.

The continental shelf S of Long Island has a geophysical character that is almost identical with that of the Avalon terrane of Newfoundland, including lineations that continue onshore into the Avalon terrane of southern New England (Haworth 1979). In both these areas the northwestern limit of the Avalon zone is marked by truncation of a series of linear sub-parallel positive magnetic anomalies indicating Precambrian volcanic highs. In some areas where the lineation is not oblique to the terrane boundary, the minimum westward extent of the terrane is marked by the westernmost anomaly band. In Newfoundland truncation of the anomalies is relatively clear and is emphasized by its juxtaposition against the Gander terrane with which a pronounced gravity and magnetic low is associated. This northwestern margin of the Avalon terrane is clearly marked geophysically to the edge of the NE Newfoundland shelf at the inshore edge of the Charlie fracture zone (Haworth 1977). Its southeastern margin is just as clearly followed by means of a major magnetic anomaly (the Collector anomaly (Haworth 1975)) trending E from New Brunswick, across Nova Scotia and the southern Grand Banks to the inshore end of the Newfoundland seamounts. A similar anomaly occurs at the southern edge of the geophysically defined Avalon terrane S of Long Island where the equivalent of the Collector anomaly, denoted here the Assembler anomaly, follows the edge of the continental shelf. Haworth (1979) infers that this 'edge anomaly' is therefore a precursor, rather than a consequence, of the development of the continental margin at a crustal discontinuity, similar to the interpretation by Talwani & Eldholm (1982) of Scandinavian 'edge anomalies'.

S of about 39°N the location of the Avalon zone is not clear on geophysical grounds. Magnetic and gravity anomalies in the Carolina Slate Belt are not atypical of those in the Avalon terrane of New England and Canada, but they tend to be lineated in far narrower zones and cut by N- and NW-trending dykes. The undoubted change in geophysical character at the Kings Mountain belt is perhaps the most likely correlative with that at the northwestern margin of the Avalon terrane farther N. Whereas on-land exposure of the Avalon terrane is widest in Newfoundland (approximately 150 km), its geophysically inferred width is considerably more (over 500 km). Extension of the Avalon terrane in the southern Appalachians eastwards to the 'shelf-edge' anomaly S of Cape Hatteras and southwards to the possible equivalent of the Collector anomaly that skirts the northern state boundary and northwestern coast of Florida would therefore seem possible. However, Williams & Hatcher (1982) have subdivided that area into two terranes: the Avalon terrane and the Brunswick terrane.

The eastern margin of Appalachia, presumably the western margin of the Avalon terrane, therefore has a more variable and less distinct geophysical character with which to trace its continuity or extrapolation. Fortunately, NE of Newfoundland the character is most pronounced, and since the boundary correlates with the western end of the Charlie fracture zone (Haworth 1977) the eastern end of the latter should mark its European landfall. The Clare lineament (Dingle *et al.* 1982, Megson 1983) is the most prominent feature at the eastern end that might be correlative with the northwestern edge of the Avalon terrane. The lineament has an associated magnetic high that can be traced ESE across the Porcupine Bank and the Porcupine Seabight to reach the 'stable' margin as a series of high-amplitude short-wavelength anomalies near 51°N 11°W. These anomalies have been regarded by Lefort & Max (1984) as an extension of the Mesozoic volcanics E of the elbow of the Porcupine Seabight or as representing upstanding magnetic basement. On the margin S and E of Ireland the gravity anomalies in particular are well lineated and trend northeastwards similar to those in the Avalon terrane of Canada. Although its continuity from 51°N 11°W is not as good as elsewhere in Avalon terrane, this boundary anomaly has its best continuity with a zone of high gravity and magnetic anomalies running almost along the S coast of Ireland and cutting its southeastern corner correlative with the Rosslare complex. However, the presence here of Mesozoic basic intrusions and volcanics (Roberts *et al.*

1981) renders interpretation of upstanding basement uncertain. This zone extends across the Irish Sea to the Lleyn Peninsula and N Wales, NE of which its continuity is concealed by the effects of the Palaeozoic cover, particularly the Cheshire basin and its northwestward extension. By comparison with the structure of eastern Canada this line could be the northeastward limit of the stable craton of 'Avalonia'. Max *et al.* (1983) have proposed that such a boundary to an imbricate tectonic zone involving slices of Avalon-related rocks lies 10–30 km farther N along a line from Dingle Bay to Rosslare. The deep seismic reflection profile WINCH (Brewer *et al.* 1983) shows a series of reflectors with a northwestward component of dip whose uppermost surface reaches the sea-floor at the southernmost of the two suggested boundaries. The Menai Straits line (Barber & Max 1979), which is regarded as the boundary between the stable craton margin and the imbricated marginal zone, may be the onshore continuation of the WINCH reflector.

Gravity and magnetic data are unable to demonstrate the continuity of the Avalon terrane farther to the E. Thorpe *et al.* (1984) report little geological or geochemical evidence for basement older than 900 Ma in this area. Skehan & Rast (1983) propose an extension of this Avalon terrane beneath E Anglia into the Ardennes, and although regional trends in the gravity and magnetic data do follow such an ESE line there is little evidence to suggest that their sub-surface origin is within Avalonian terrane.

E of or overlying the Avalon terrane in N America is the Meguma 'terrane' (Schenk 1983) whose lower Palaeozoic sequence may be equivalent, in the British Isles, to the Welsh basin (Kennedy 1979). Meguma and Avalon rocks in Nova Scotia are in fault contact, with several hundred kilometres of transcurrent movement postulated to have occurred along the contact in Devonian time (Keppie 1982). Continuity of magnetic and gravity anomalies associated with both the Meguma and Avalon terranes in the Gulf of Maine strongly suggests that the Meguma group overlies Avalonian basement. However, this could be the result of thrusting, the inferred transcurrent movement therefore being compatible with observations at the edge of the thrust sheet.

The along-strike continuity of the western edge of the orogen and the easternmost Appalachian terranes as proposed by Williams & Hatcher (1982) is therefore supported on geophysical grounds; indeed, geophysical data were the prime reason for their making the hypothesis. Further extension of those terranes and mapping of the

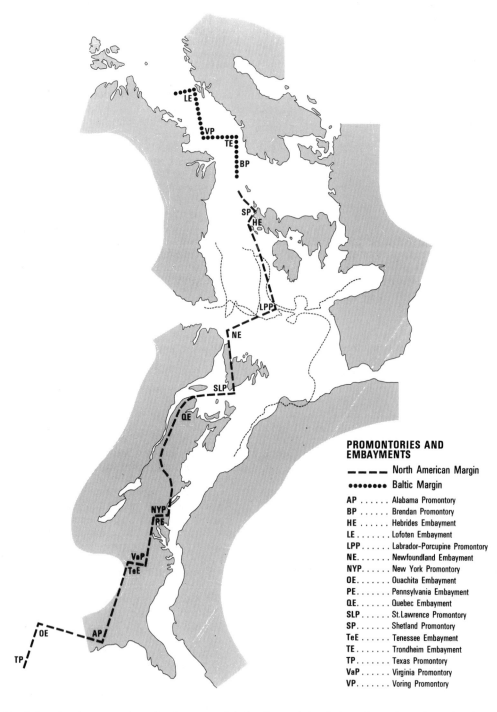

PROMONTORIES AND EMBAYMENTS

— — — North American Margin

••••••• Baltic Margin

AP . . . . . . Alabama Promontory
BP . . . . . . Brendan Promontory
HE . . . . . . Hebrides Embayment
LE . . . . Lofoten Embayment
LPP . . . . . . Labrador-Porcupine Promontory
NE . . . . . . Newfoundland Embayment
NYP . . . . . . New York Promontory
OE . . . . Ouachita Embayment
PE . . . . Pennsylvania Embayment
QE . . . . Quebec Embayment
SLP . . . . . . St. Lawrence Promontory
SP . . . . . . Shetland Promontory
TeE . . . . . . Tenessee Embayment
TE . . . . Trondheim Embayment
TP . . . . . . Texas Promontory
VaP . . . . . . Virginia Promontory
VP . . . . Voring Promontory

FIG. 3. Postulated promontories and embayments of the late Precambrian–Palaeozoic continental margins of the N Atlantic borderlands (see Thomas (1983) and text for details).

central Appalachian terranes is possible on the basis of compilations of gravity and magnetic data made on pre-drift reconstructions of the N Atlantic borderland. Such discussion has been published elsewhere (see the introductory section for references) and cannot be adequately described within the scope of this paper; we shall instead concentrate on the interruptions to the continuity of the terranes which are perhaps more important in deducing the tectonic evolution of the orogen.

Segmentation of the Appalachian–Caledonide orogen

The curvilinear continuity of the Appalachian orogen is believed to be the result of oceanic closure and convergence against a continental margin whose edge was irregular in plan, either because it developed along valleys between triple junctions (Rankin 1976) or because of its separation into rift and transform segments (Thomas 1977). The promontories and embayments (convex and concave respectively towards the ocean) on the ancient continental margin result in the development of recesses and salients (concave and convex respectively towards the craton) in the orogenic belt (Thomas 1980, 1983). In general, we prefer the precursive rift and transform 'interpretation' of evolution (Thomas 1977) but recognize, by analogy with the modern margin of eastern N America, that the ancient margin is unlikely to have been rectilinear in outline. Just as the present continental margin has geophysical anomalies associated with it which change character abruptly at each promontory or embayment, so we might expect to see these in the now cratonized margin. What we need not see, however, W of that ancient margin is offsets or recesses and salients unless the craton had been subject to much earlier faulting or continental collision/agglomeration respectively.

The major promontories on the ancient margin, now part of N America and each identified by a prominent change in trend of the Appalachian geophysical anomalies, are the Alabama, New York and St Lawrence promontories (Thomas 1983). The change in trend of the anomalies at the Virginia promontory is far less prominent. Between each of these promontories the style of Appalachian tectonic development was quite different, and the degree of deformation varies as does the width of the orogen along its length. Recognition of other promontories by geophysical means will therefore indicate where changes in tectonic style might be anticipated.

The Labrador–Porcupine promontory (new name) is the largest promontory N of Texas, with an offset of approximately 600 km (Haworth 1980, Williams & Max 1980). In much the same way that N of the Alabama promontory there are no more major promontories for approximately 1000 km, there are similarly few offsets within the Caledonides of the British Isles. Interruptions in continuity may have occurred close to the southern margin of the Rockall trough but these must be relatively minor. It might therefore be inferred that the style of Caledonide tectonism within Ireland and Scotland might be as uniform as that observed in the southern Appalachians. Immediately N of Scotland there is a distinct break in the gravity and magnetic lineations and a corresponding change in trend of the shelf edge that argues for a Hebrides embayment and a Shetland promontory. Transforms are also suggested by the interruption in trends in the vicinity of the Brendan seamount and NE from Trondheim. These would appear to be promontory and embayment respectively, although of the Baltic rather than the N American craton. The existence of a Voring promontory and Lofoten embayment might further be suggested on geophysical grounds.

Inheritance and rejuvenation

In N America the promontories and embayments on the ancient (Precambrian) margin controlled the development of the (Palaeozoic) Appalachian structure. This structure then provided foci for the subsequent development of the present (Mesozoic) continental margin. For example, the New York promontory on the ancient margin produced, as a result of collision, the Appalachian New York recess. Avalonian trends also follow that recess pattern suggesting that the Avalon terrane was deformed during collision (Lefort *et al.* 1988). The southern extent of Long Island Avalonia is indicated by an E–W magnetic high (here called the (American) Assembler anomaly, equivalent to the (Canadian) Collector anomaly on the southern Grand Banks) that subsequently acted as a locus for the development of a transform fault.

This mimicry of ancient margins by younger margins was discussed and modelled for the St Lawrence promontory (Haworth 1974, 1975, Haworth & Keen 1979), but in its case the modern transform margin leading into the Newfoundland fracture zone does not follow the Collector anomaly at the southern edge of the Newfoundland section of the Avalon terrane, possibly because of geometrical constraints on the early opening history (all transforms must be parallel to each other but not necessarily perpendicular to the rift zone). However, seamount chains did develop at the oceanward limits of the Collector and Assembler anomalies; these were the Newfoundland and Kelvin seamounts respectively. The northwestern edge of the Avalon terrane has clearly acted as the locus for the development of the Charlie fracture zone (Haworth 1977). It is probable that the terrane boundary on the European margin is likewise the reason for the marked dissection of the craton into the Rockall and Porcupine Banks. The Labrador–Porcupine promontory on the Grenville margin occurs where a major Precambrian gabbroic body mapped by Eade (1962) and bounded on its southern margin by the Gilbert River fault intersects the Labrador margin (Haworth *et al.* 1976). This might be an example of the situation proposed by Rankin (1976) in which embayments are created on the margin along the two active arms of a triple junction, with the gabbroic body in Labrador representing the failed arm (aulacogen).

Just as the modern margin of N America has developed in mimicry of the early Palaeozoic margin, so offsets in earlier margins might be recognizable within the craton. The St Lawrence Promontory, having developed within the Grenville Province along a line that is the projection of the trend of the boundary between the Superior and Churchill Provinces, is the most likely candidate. However, the Grenville Province, which has been inferred to have collided with the Superior–Churchill craton (Dewey & Burke 1973) shows little offset at that margin and no internal structure that might provide a locus for the subsequent development of the St Lawrence Promontory.

The pattern of offsets in the Scandinavian margin suggests several inherent boundaries within the craton. The most obvious of these follows the projection across Scandinavia of the trend of the Jan Mayen fracture zone (Riddihough 1972). This line follows a prominent boundary in the regional gravity field of Scandinavia (Wolff 1983) coincident with a prominent boundary in the magnetic map of Scandinavia (Eleman *et al.* 1969, Geological Survey of Sweden 1983). The lineament approximately coincides with an age boundary within the craton (Stromberg 1976) and a change in crustal thickness (Husebye & Bungum 1981). It also appears to coincide with the location of earthquakes recorded during the 1970s and has the same trend as the direction of their maximum horizontal compression (Slunga 1981). The trend is $10°–20°$ counterclockwise of the trend of topographic

lineaments, which are seen by Landsat (Lindh 1980) and which parallel the Klaralven line, part of the regionally defined Protogine zone (Gorbatschev 1980). The left lateral offset in the zones of crustal ages (Stromberg 1976), which is also inferred from an offset in the aeromagnetic anomaly pattern (Riddihough 1972), is entirely consistent with the angularity of the present continental margin along the Jan Mayen fracture zone and apparently reflects the latter's inheritance of cratonic discontinuities. Riddihough (1972) similarly notes the coincidence in trend and continuity in the boundary between the Karalian and Svecofennian fold belts and the Senja fracture zone off northern Norway (Talwani & Eldholm 1977), implying similar tectonic inheritance.

Few Caledonide trends are highlighted by plots of the seismicity of northern New England (Foley *et al.* 1984) or of the British Isles (Turbitt 1984, 1985). The most obvious of all the seismicity trends in the vicinity of Britain is associated with the graben structures of the northern North Sea, whose activity might be a consequence of relaxation along boundary faults following glacial loading (Browitt, personal communication). The general quiescence of the Caledonide orogen invites a sense of security that is periodically dispelled by events such as those in New Brunswick in 1982 and in Wales in 1984. Considerably more effort is needed to monitor the low-level earthquake activity of the orogen in order to locate those zones that have the potential for high-energy release and to develop seismotectonic models from which practical risk can be determined. Such models would demonstrate the extent to which rejuvenation of Caledonide structures is of modern practical concern.

Deep structure

The elements of the orogen discussed so far have primarily been deduced from potential field data which refer either to relatively shallow structures (less than 10 km) or to the characteristics of an entire cratonic block. Deep seismic reflection and refraction data (Cook *et al.* 1979, Brewer *et al.* 1983, Keen *et al.* 1986) which have had a revolutionary effect on the interpretation of Appalachian and Caledonide geology are dealt with elsewhere (Cook *et al.* 1988), but other techniques are available to provide clues to the deeper structure of these cratonic blocks.

Analysis of the inductive response to geomagnetic variations of different frequencies provides a means of deducing conductivity variations with depth (Gough 1983). For example, controlled-source induction experiments (Connerney *et al.* 1980) and gradient analysis of geomagnetic fluctuations (Connerney & Kuckes 1980) demonstrate the existence beneath the Adirondacks of a highly conductive layer whose upper surface lies at a depth of 22 km. The distribution of geomagnetic-variation stations throughout the eastern U.S.A. and Canada is now such that regional interpretations of these data are possible (Greenhouse & Bailey 1981). In the S central U.S.A. the coastal effect that dominates induction vectors elsewhere along the eastern seaboard is somewhat subdued, probably as a result of the extensive over-thrusting seen on deep seismic reflection profiles. A highly conductive zone in the middle to lower crust underlies Pennsylvania and southern New York. This zone is roughly coincident with the great thickness of Palaeozoic platform rocks, and the zone is relatively free of seismicity (Greenhouse & Bailey 1981). Its northern and western edges are best defined as the zone of highest conductivity, and its shape shows excellent parallelism with the Pennsylvania embayment. The existence of such a crustal block with significant geophysical properties is substantiated only by combining interpretations of diverse data, each of which may be quite tentative. That, however, is the normal situation when deducing deeper Earth structure.

Farther N in Atlantic Canada the complications of tectonics and the present coast line make interpretation of the induction vectors difficult. However, Cochrane & Wright (1977) tentatively identify a zone of enhanced deep conductivity in eastern Newfoundland. This corresponds to the location of an inferred subduction zone, for which there may be even deeper evidence on the basis of travel-time residuals for teleseismic PP waves (Stewart 1978). Neither of these techniques can be conclusive about the polarity of any residual effect of that subduction zone but each, together with other geophysical data, suggests that it dips to the SE (Haworth *et al.* 1978). A similar exercise conducted in the Scottish Caledonides indicated the presence of deeper conducting zones that correlate with ancient subduction zones deduced on geological grounds (Hutton *et al.* 1977). Travel-time delay analysis with which this might be correlated is only at a preliminary stage (El-Haddadeh & Fairhead 1984). Similar analyses of geomagnetic variation data for Scandinavia are not known to us, but interpretation is likely to be extremely difficult with the major conductivity contrast being close to the coast except in the S where further evidence for the offset on the ancient eastern margin of the Palaeozoic ocean might be discovered.

Geophysicists have also contributed to an understanding of the evolution of the Appalachians by pointing out the physical consequences for the loading of the craton by the extensive thrusting proposed, especially as interpreted for deep seismic reflection profiling. Cook (1984a) analysed the gravity data to indicate the location of crustal discontinuities beneath these thrust sheets in the southern Appalachians. Quinlan & Beaumont (1984) have instead deduced the load that must have been applied to the margin in order to produce the foreland basins W of the Appalachians. The stratigraphy of these basins is sufficiently well known that the magnitude of the thrust sheets and the time of their emplacement can be deduced, giving an independent check of the hypothetical geological models. Quinlan & Beaumont (1984) conclude that in middle Ordovician time the thrusting was widespread between the New York promontory and Georgia. By late Ordovician time the thrusting was confined to the Pennsylvania embayment and, following an early Silurian phase of widespread thrusting, the loads in this northern segment continued to increase, reaching a peak in the middle and late Devonian. During the early Carboniferous no over-thrust loads were imposed on the foreland, but the loading returned during the middle to late Carboniferous, particularly in the vicinity of the Virginia and Alabama promontories. The cumulative over-thrust load calculated using this method has a maximum thickness of 18 km in Virginia, Maryland and SE Pennsylvania.

Such quantification of loading is a powerful tool and is complementary to palaeomagnetic analyses which have been somewhat rare in these areas. The method can also be applied to marine basins such as the lower Palaeozoic basin of the Gulf of St Lawrence where Quinlan (personal communication) has shown that the subsidence of the basin is episodic, with the most significant of these episodes coming in the middle Ordovician at the time of emplacement of the ophiolite suites in western Newfoundland.

Transcurrent movement along the orogen

Although details of the palaeomagnetically derived movements of crustal blocks within the Appalachian–Caledonide orogen are presented elsewhere (Briden *et al.* 1988), a brief mention cannot be avoided in this introduction or its companion paper (Lefort *et al.* 1987).

Major movement of the eastern flank of the Appalachians has long been proposed (Roy & Robertson 1968) and has recently undergone more intensive scrutiny including interpretation in terms of transcurrent movement along the axis of the Appalachians (Kent & Opdyke 1978). Although details of timing and the boundaries and the extent of the crustal blocks involved in the movement are still subject to debate (Roy *et al.* 1983), movements of several tens to hundreds of kilometres in Devonian or Carboniferous time are credible. Several thousand kilometres of movement have been hypothesized. Independent evidence for the degree of offset along this fault zone by means of matching geophysical markers would be highly desirable, but as seen earlier most of the trends are parallel to the early Palaeozoic collision zone which has subsequently been the locus for much of the transcurrent movement. Indeed, where geological markers have been found to be offset, there seems to be no continuity of the faults or consistency between movement along them within any zone (e.g. the Great Glen debate (Kennedy 1946)). Whatever movement has taken place will undoubtedly remove any correlation between the structure observed within the continental blocks on each side of the transcurrent zone when the orogen is restored to its pre-Mesozoic form. It seems surprising that there is such a good correlation between structure on opposite sides of the orogen; in Newfoundland, for example, the Avalonian lineations, which have an oroclinal form, parallel the orthogonal form of the Grenville margin, yet it is hypothesized that the transcurrent fault zone passes between these two structures. Ziegler (1984) hypothesizes a reconstruction of the orogen in late Grenvillian time (1000 Ma?) in which the portion of the Porcupine promontory comprising northwestern Scotland and Ireland is mated with the St Lawrence promontory. Since the difference in scale of these promontories is not too great and the New York promontory would match in location with subsequently developed bending of the Avalonian lineations, this juxtaposition might be considered acceptable. However, evidence for the lineations along which the hypothesized transcurrent movement subsequently took place is not apparent. Unless such linear transcurrent faults were present, major 'rhombachasms', for which there is little evidence, would have developed as a result of movement transverse to the general trend of the highly serrated margin. It is therefore difficult to reconcile the postulated major transcurrent movement with the geology of the orogen.

Phillips *et al.* (1976) have used the hypothesized location of Ireland along a transform segment of the margin to explain the differences between the tectonic setting of Ireland and that of Scotland and Newfoundland. Their model, however, explains transcurrent movement along the transform segment as a result of convergence between the opposing plates. The transcurrent movement is considerably less than has been postulated palaeomagnetically and is localized. Similar analyses elsewhere in the orogen, where the geology is better exposed and where palaeomagnetic data are plentiful, must be a necessary precursor to any well-substantiated reconstruction for the early to middle Palaeozoic that incorporates pre-Jurassic transcurrent movement.

Conclusions

Geophysical data demonstrate the serrated continuity of the eastern margin of the Appalachian–Caledonide orogen. The western margin of the orogen does not display such continuity, but elements of Avalon-like terrane have been identified throughout the eastern flank of the orogen, S of the British Isles. N of the British Isles the western margin of the orogen shows more continuity, despite offsets that are apparently related to discontinuities in the bordering craton. Geophysical characteristics of the Appalachian and Caledonide terranes permit their extrapolation across continental shelves and beneath coastal plain cover, but work describing this has only been referenced in the paper. Investigation of conductivity variations in the crust coupled with teleseismic data shows evidence for southeastward-dipping structures that may be the fossil remnants of the Canadian Appalachian subduction zone. Similar evidence supported by deep seismic reflection profiling indicates southeastward subduction in the southern USA and northwestward subduction on the southern flank of the orogen in the British Isles. Gravity and magnetic data are now available for almost the entire orogen. Other data such as sedimentary isopachs, seismicity and heat flow collected for practical programmes (hydrocarbon exploration, seismic hazard and geothermal energy respectively) are becoming available and can form the basis for developing quantitative models for the evolution of the orogen. Models for the development of foreland basins and the pressure–temperature histories of their basement as a consequence of thrust loading and subsequent uplift/erosion are already being produced.

ACKNOWLEDGEMENTS: In this paper we have attempted to provide an overview of the activities of numerous earth scientists who have contributed to the geophysical aspects of Project 27. It is as impossible to acknowledge the contribution of each as it has been to review their work adequately within the scope of this paper. We hope, however, that sufficient references are provided to allow the interested reader to pursue individual aspects further. RTH absolves his co-authors completely from responsibility for the opinions that have crept into this review/overview paper. To have deleted those opinions would have been further to weaken the paper, to have claimed sole authorship would have been misrepresentation and to have ensured that every possible interpretation of every observation was covered would have been impossible. The contribution of RTH is made with permission of the Director, British Geological Survey (Natural Environment Research Council).

References

The asterisks indicate publications not referred to in the text but considered to be significant concerning the geophysics of the orogen.

*ANDO, C. J., COOK, F. A., OLIVER, J. E., BROWN, L. D. & KAUFMAN, S. 1983. Crustal geometry of the Appalachian Orogen from seismic reflection studies. *In*: HATCHER, R. D., JR, WILLIAMS, H. & ZIETZ, I. (eds) *Tectonics and Geophysics of Mountain Chains. Geological Society of America Memoir No. 158*, pp. 83–102.

BARBER, A. J. & MAX, M. D. 1979. A new look at the Mona Complex. *Journal of the Geological Society, London*, **136**, 407–32.

*BARRETT, D. L., BERRY, M., BLANCHARD, J. E., KEEN, M. J. & McALLISTER, R. E. 1964. Seismic studies on the eastern seaboard of Canada: the Atlantic coast of Nova Scotia. *Canadian Journal of Earth Sciences*, **1**, 10–22.

*BATH, M. 1979. The seismicity of Sweden. *Geologiska Föreningens i Stockholm Förhandlingar*, **100** (3), 295–9.

*BEAMISH, D. & BANKS, R. J. 1983. Geomagnetic variation anomalies in northern England: processing and presentation of data from a non-simultaneous array. *Geophysical Journal of the Royal Astronomical Society*, **75**, 513–39.

*BEAUMONT, C. 1981. Foreland basins. *Geophysical Journal of the Royal Astronomical Society*, **65**, 291–329.

*BEHRENDT, J. C. & GRIM, M. S. 1983. Structural elements of the U.S. Atlantic margin delineated by second vertical derivative of aeromagnetic data. *United States Geological Survey Map No. GP-956*.

*BLUNDELL, D. J. 1981. The nature of the continental crust beneath Britain. *In*: ILLING, L. V. & HOBSON, G. D. (eds) *Petroleum Geology of the Continental Shelf of North West Europe*, pp. 58–64.

*—— 1975. The geology of the Celtic Sea and southwestern approaches. *In*: YORATH, C. J., PARKER, E. R. & GLASS, D. J. (eds) *Canada's Continental Margins and Offshore Petroleum Exploration. Canadian Society of Petroleum Geologists Memoir No. 4*, pp. 341–62.

*BREWER, J. A. & SMYTHE, D. K. 1984. MOIST and the continuity of crustal reflector geometry along the Caledonian–Appalachian orogen. *Journal of the Geological Society, London*, **141**, 105–20.

——, MATTHEWS, D. H., WARNER, M. R., HALL, J., SMYTHE, D. K. & WHITTINGTON, R. J. 1983. BIRPS deep seismic reflection studies of the British Caledonides. *Nature, London*, **305**, 206–10.

BRIDEN, J. C., KENT, D. V., LAPOINTE, P. L., LIVERMORE, R. A., ROY, J. L., SEGUIN, M. K., SMITH, A. G., VAN DER VOO, R. & WATTS, D. R. 1988. Palaeomagnetic constraints on the evolution of the Caledonian–Appalachian orogen. *This volume*.

BROOKS, M. 1970. A gravity survey of coastal areas of West Finnmark, northern Norway. *Quarterly Journal of the Geological Society of London*, **125**, 171–92.

BULLARD, E. C., EVERETT, J. E. & GILBERT SMITH, A. 1965. The fit of the Continents around the Atlantic. *Philosophical Transactions of the Royal Society of London*, **258**, 41–51.

BUREAU GRAVIMÉTRIQUE INTERNATIONAL 1982. *BGI Data Collection Program. Bulletin d'Information No. 50*.

*COCHRANE, N. A. & HYNDMAN, R. D. 1974. Magnetotelluric and magnetovariational studies in Atlantic Canada. *Geophysical Journal of the Royal Astronomical Society*, **39**, 385–406.

—— & WRIGHT, J. A. 1977. Geomagnetic sounding near the northern termination of the Appalachian System. *Canadian Journal of Earth Sciences*, **14**, 2858–64.

CONNERNEY, J. E. P. & KUCKES, A. F. 1980. Gradient analysis of geomagnetic fluctuations in the Adirondacks. *Journal of Geophysical Research*, **85** (B5), 2615–24.

——, NEKUT, A. & KUCKES, A. F. 1980. Deep crustal electrical conductivity in the Adirondacks. *Journal of Geophysical Research*, **85** (B5), 2603–14.

COOK, F. A. 1984a. Variations of geophysical anomalies along the strike of the southern Appalachian Piedmont: implications for crustal structure. *Tectonics*, **3**, 45–61.

—— 1984b. Harmonic distortion on a seismic reflection profile across the Quebec Appalachians: relation to Bouguer gravity and implications for crustal structure. *Canadian Journal of Earth Sciences*, **21**, 346–53.

——, ALBAUGH, D. S., BROWN, L. D., KAUFMAN, S., OLIVER, J. E. & HATCHER, R. D., JR 1979. Thin-skinned tectonics in the crystalline southern Appalachians: COCORP seismic-reflection profiling of the Blue Ridge and Piedmont. *Geology*, **7**, 563–7; **8**, 211–6.

——, MATTHEWS, D. H. & JACOB, A. W. B. 1988. Crustal and upper mantle structure of the Appalachian–Caledonide orogen from seismic results. *This volume.*

*CUTT, B. J. & LAVING, J. G. 1977. Tectonic elements and geologic history of the South Labrador and Newfoundland continental shelf, eastern Canada. *Bulletin of the Canadian Society of Petroleum Geologists,* **25**, 1037–58.

*DAINTY, A. M., KEEN, C. E., KEEN, M. J. & BLANCHARD, J. E. 1966. Review of geophysical evidence on the crust and upper mantle structure on the eastern seaboard of Canada. *American Geophysical Union Geophysical Monograph No. 10,* pp. 349–69.

*DEWEY, J. F. 1982. Plate tectonics and the evolution of the British Isles. *Journal of the Geological Society, London,* **139**, 371–412.

—— & BURKE, K. C. A. 1973. Tibetan, Variscan and Precambrian basement reactivation: products of continental collision. *Journal of Geology,* **81**, 683–92.

DIMENT, W. H. 1968. Gravity anomalies in northwestern New England, N.Y. *In* ZEN, E-AN, WHITE, W. S., HADLEY, J. B. & THOMSON, J. B. (eds) *Studies in Appalachian Geology: Northern and Maritime,* pp. 399–413, Wiley-Interscience, New York.

DINGLE, R. V., MEGSON, J. B. & SCRUTTON, R. A. 1982. Acoustic stratigraphy of the sedimentary succession west of Porcupine Bank, NE Atlantic Ocean: a preliminary account. *Marine Geology,* **47**, 17–35.

*DONATO, J. A. & TULLY, M. C. 1981. A regional interpretation of North Sea gravity data. *In*: ILLING, L. V. & HOBSON, G. D. (eds) *Petroleum Geology of the Continental Shelf of North West Europe,* pp. 65–75.

*DYRELIUS, D. 1980. Aeromagnetic interpretation in a geotraverse area across the central Scandinavian Caledonides. *Geologiska Föreningens i Stockholm Förhandlingar,* **102** (4), 421–38.

EADE, K. E. 1962. Geology, Battle Harbour–Cartwright, Coast of Labrador, Newfoundland. *Geological Survey of Canada Map No. 22–1962.*

*EDWARDS, J. W. F. & BLUNDELL, D. J. 1984. Summary of seismic refraction experiments in the English Channel, Celtic Sea and St George's Channel. *British Geological Survey Report No. 144.*

ELEMAN, F., BORG, K., OQVIST, U. & SUCKSDORFF, C. 1969. *The Aeromagnetic Survey of Denmark, Finland, Norway, Sweden, 1965,* Swedish Board of Shipping and Navigation, Stockholm.

EL-HADDADEH, B. R. H. & FAIRHEAD, J. D. 1984. Teleseismic delay time study of the UK. *Geophysical Journal of the Royal Astronomical Society,* **77**, 299 (abstract).

*EWING, G. N., DAINTY, A. M., BLANCHARD, J. E. & KEEN, M. J. 1966. Seismic study of the eastern seaboard of Canada: The Appalachian system I. *Canadian Journal of Earth Sciences,* **3**, 89–109.

*FENWICK, D. K. B., KEEN, M. J. & LAMBERT, A. 1968. Geophysical studies of the continental margin northeast of Newfoundland. *Canadian Journal of Earth Sciences,* **5**, 483–500.

FLINN, D. 1977. A geological interpretation of the aeromagnetic map of east-central Shetland. *Journal of the Geological Society, London,* **133**, 111–21.

——, FRANK, P. L., BROOK, M. & PRINGLE, I. R. 1979. Basement cover relations in Scotland. *In*: HARRIS, A. L., HOLLAND, C. H. & LEAKE, B. E. (eds) *The Caledonides of the British Isles Reviewed. Special Publication of the Geological Society of London No. 8,* pp. 109–15.

FOLEY, J. E. *et al.* 1984. *Seismicity of the Northeastern United States,* Weston Observatory, Boston College, Weston, MA (coordinated by P. W. Pomeroy United States Geological Survey).

*GARDINER, P. R. R. & MACCARTHY, I. A. J. 1981. The late Paleozoic evolution of Southern Ireland in the context of tectonic basins and their transatlantic significance. *In*: KERR, J. W. & FERGUSSON, A. J. (eds) *Geology of the North Atlantic Borderlands. Canadian Society of Petroleum Geologists Memoir No. 7,* pp. 683–725.

GEOLOGICAL SURVEY OF SWEDEN 1983. Aeromagnetic anomaly map of Scandinavia. *Sveriges Geologiska Undersökning, Serie C,* **22**.

GIBB, R. A. & THOMAS, M. D. 1976. Gravity signature of fossil plate boundaries in the Canadian Shield. *Nature, London,* **262**, 199–200.

GORBATSCHEV, R. 1980. The Precambrian development of southern Sweden. *Geologiska Föreningens i Stockholm Förhandlingar,* **102** (2), 129–36.

GOUGH, D. I. 1983. Electromagnetic geophysics and global tectonics. *Journal of Geophysical Research,* **88**, 3367–77.

GRANGER, B., ST JULIEN, P. & SLIVITZKY, A. 1980. A seismic profile across the southwestern part of the Quebec Appalachians. *Geological Society of America Abstracts with Programs,* **12**, 435.

GREENHOUSE, J. P. & BAILEY, R. C. 1981. A review of geomagnetic variation measurements in the eastern United States: implications for continental tectonics. *Canadian Journal of Earth Sciences,* **18**, 1268–89.

*HALL, J. 1977. Crustal structure of the eastern North Atlantic seaboard. *In*: BOWES, D. R. & LEAKE, B. E. (eds) *Crustal Evolution in Northwestern Britain and Adjacent Regions. Special Publication of the Geological Society of London No. 10,* pp. 23–38.

*——, POWELL, D. W., WARNER, M. R., EL-ISA, Z. H. M., ADESANYA, O. & BUCK, B. J. 1983. Seismological evidence for shallow crystalline basement in the southern uplands of Scotland. *Nature, London,* **305**, 418–20.

HAWORTH, R. T. 1974. Palaeozoic continental collision in the Northern Appalachians in light of gravity and magnetic data in the Gulf of St Lawrence. *Geology of Offshore Eastern Canada. Geological Survey of Canada Paper No. 74–30,* Vol. 2.

—— 1975. The development of Atlantic Canada as a result of continental collision—evidence from offshore gravity and magnetic data. *In*: YORATH, C. J., PARKER, E. R. & GLASS, D. J. (eds) *Canada's Continental Margins and Offshore Petroleum Exploration. Canadian Society of Petroleum Geologists Memoir No. 4,* pp. 59–77.

—— 1977. The continental crust northeast of Newfoundland and its ancestral relationship to the Charlie fracture zone. *Nature, London,* **266**, 246–9.

—— 1979. Magnetic and Bouguer gravity anomaly

compilations for the Appalachians. *Geological Survey of Canada Open File No. 615.*

—— 1980. Appalachian structural trends northeast of Newfoundland and their trans-Atlantic correlation. *Tectonophysics*, **64**, 111–30.

—— 1981. Geophysical expression of Appalachian–Caledonide structures on the continental margins of the North Atlantic. *Geology of the North Atlantic Borderlands. Canadian Society of Petroleum Geologists Memoir No. 7*, pp. 429–46.

—— & JACOBI, R. D. 1983. Geophysical correlation between the geological zonation of Newfoundland and the British Isles. *In*: HATCHER, R. D., JR, WILLIAMS, H. & ZIETZ, I. (eds) *Contributions to the Tectonics and Geophysics of Mountain Chains. Geological Society of America Memoir No. 159.*

—— & KEEN, C. E. 1979. The Canadian Atlantic margin: a passive continental margin encompassing an active past. *Tectonophysics*, **59**, 83–126.

—— & LEFORT, J. P. 1979. Geophysical evidence for the extent of the Avalon zone in Atlantic Canada. *Canadian Journal of Earth Sciences*, **16**, 552–67.

—— & MACINTYRE, J. B. 1975. The gravity and magnetic fields of Atlantic offshore Canada. *Marine Science Paper No. 161: Geological Survey of Canada Paper No. 75–9.*

—— & MILLER, H. G. 1982. The structure of Palaeozoic oceanic rocks beneath Notre Dame Bay, Newfoundland. *In*: ST JULIEN, P. & BELAND, J. (eds) *Geological Association of Canada Special Paper No. 24*, pp. 149–73.

——, DANIELS, D. L., WILLIAMS, H. & ZIETZ, I. 1980. Bouguer gravity anomaly map of the Appalachian orogen. *Memorial University of Newfoundland Map No. 3.*

——, GRANT, A. C. & FOLINSBEE, R. A. 1976. Geology of the continental shelf off southeastern Labrador. *Geological Survey of Canada Paper No. 76–1C*, pp. 61–70.

——, LEFORT, J. P. & MILLER, H. G. 1978. Geophysical evidence for an east-dipping Appalachian subduction zone beneath Newfoundland. *Geology*, **6**, 522–6.

*HENKEL, H. & ERIKSSON, L. 1980. Interpretation of low altitude airborne magnetic and VLF measurements for identification of fracture zones. *In*: BERGMAN, M. (ed.) *Subsurface Space*, pp. 913–8.

HIPKIN, R. G. & HUSSAIN, A. 1983. Regional gravity anomalies. 1. Northern Britain. *Institute of Geological Sciences Report No. 82/10*, 45 pp.

——, LYNESS, D., CHACKSFIELD, B. C., GIBBERD, A. J. & REAY, D. 1986. Bouger Anomaly Map of the British Isles—Southern Sheet, British Geological Survey, Keyworth, Nottingham.

HOOD, P. J. & REVELER, D. A. 1977. Magnetic anomaly maps of the Atlantic Provinces. *Geological Survey of Canada Open-File Report No. 496.*

HUSEBYE, E. S. & BUNGUM, H. 1981. New crustal thickness results for Fennoscandia. *Geologiska Föreningens i Stockholm Förhandlingar*, **103** (1), 1–8.

HUTCHINSON, D. R., GROW, J. A. & KLITGORD, K. D. 1983. Crustal structure beneath the southern Appalachians: nonuniqueness of gravity modelling. *Geology*, **11** (10), 611–15.

*HUTTON, V. R. S., INGHAM, M. R. & MBIPOM, E. W. 1980. An electrical model of the crust and upper mantle in Scotland. *Nature, London*, **287**, 30–3.

——, SIK, J. M. & GOUGH, D. I. 1977. Electrical conductivity and tectonics of Scotland. *Nature, London*, **266**, 617–20.

*HYNDMAN, R. D. & COCHRANE, N. A. 1971. Electrical conductivity structure by geomagnetic induction at the continental margin of Atlantic Canada. *Geophysical Journal of the Royal Astronomical Society*, **25**, 425–46.

——, JESSOP, A. M., JUDGE, A. S. & RANKIN, D. S. 1979. Heat flows in the Maritime Provinces of Canada. *Canadian Journal of Earth Sciences*, **16**, 1154–65.

*IRVING, E. 1979. Paleopoles and paleolatitudes of North America and speculations about displaced terranes. *Canadian Journal of Earth Sciences*, **16**, 669–94.

—— & STRONG, D. F. 1984. Paleomagnetism of the early Carboniferous Deer Lake Group, western Newfoundland: no evidence for mid-Carboniferous displacement of Acadia. *Earth and Planetary Science Letters*, **69**, 379–90.

JACOBI, R. D. & KRISTOFFERSEN, Y. 1981. Transatlantic correlations of geophysical anomalies on Newfoundland, British Isles, France and adjacent continental shelves. *In*: KERR, J. W. & FERGUSSON, A. J. (eds) *Canadian Society of Petroleum Geologists Memoir No. 7*, pp. 197–229.

KARLSTROM, K. E. 1983. Reinterpretation of Newfoundland gravity data and arguments for an allochthonous Dunnage Zone. *Geology*, **11**, 263–6; Comment by H. G. Miller and Reply by K. E. Karlstrom, 1984, *Geology*, **12**, 60–1.

KEEN, C. E., KEEN, M. J., NICHOLS, B., REID, I., STOCKMAL, G. S., COLMAN-SADD, S. P., O'BRIEN, S. J., MILLER, H., QUINLAN, G., WILLIAMS, H. & WRIGHT, J. 1986. Deep seismic reflection profile across the northern Appalachians. *Geology*, **14**, 141–5.

KENNEDY, M. J. 1979. The continuation of the Canadian Appalachians into the Caledonides of Britain and Ireland. *In*: HARRIS, A. L. & LEAKE, B. E. (eds) *The Caledonides of the British Isles Reviewed. Special Publication of the Geological Society of London No. 8*, pp. 33–64.

KENNEDY, W. Q. 1946. The Great Glen fault. *Quarterly Journal of the Geological Society of London*, **102** (1), 41–73.

*KLITGORD, K. D. & BEHRENDT, J. C. 1978. Basin structure of the U.S. Atlantic Margin. *Geological and Geophysical Investigations of Continental Margins. American Association of Petroleum Geologists Memoir No. 29*, pp. 85–112.

KENT, D. V. & OPDYKE, N. D. 1978. Paleomagnetism of the Devonian Catskill red beds: evidence for motion of the coastal New England–Canadian Maritime region relative to cratonic North America. *Journal of Geophysical Research*, **83**, 4441–50.

KEPPIE, J. D. 1982. The Minas geofracture. *In*: ST JULIEN, P. & BELAND, J. (eds) *Major Structural*

Zones and Faults of the Northern Appalachians. Geological Association of Canada Special Paper No. 24, pp. 263–80.

LEFORT, J. P. 1980. Un 'fit' structural de l'Atlantique nord: arguments géologiques pour corréler les marqueurs géophysiques reconnus sur les deux marges. *Marine Geology*, **37**, 355–69.

—— 1983. A new geophysical criterion to correlate the Acadian and Hercynian orogenies of Western Europe and Eastern America. *In*: HATCHER, R. D., JR, WILLIAMS, H. & ZIETZ, I. (eds) *Contributions to the Tectonics and Geophysics of Mountain Chains. Geological Society of America Memoir No. 158*, pp. 3–18.

—— 1984. The main basement features recognized in the northern part of the North Atlantic area. *In*: DE GRACIANSKY, P. C., POAG, C. W. *et al.* (eds) *Initial Reports of the Deep Sea Drilling Project*, Vol. 80, Part II, pp. 1103–14, U.S. Government Printing Office, Washington, DC.

—— & HAWORTH, R. T. 1978. Geophysical study of basement fractures on the western European and eastern Canadian shelves—transatlantic correlations and late Hercynian movements. *Canadian Journal of Earth Sciences*, **15**, 397–404.

—— & MAX, M. D. 1984. Development of the Porcupine Seabight: use of magnetic data to show the direct relationship between early oceanic and continental structures. *Journal of the Geological Society, London*, **141**, 663–74.

—— & VAN DER VOO, R. 1981. A kinematic model for the collision and complete suturing between Gondwanaland and Laurussia in the Carboniferous. *Journal of Geology*, **89** (5), 537–50.

——, MAX, M. D. & ROUSSEL, J. 1988. Geophysical evidence for the location of the NW boundary of Gondwanaland and its relationship with two older satellite sutures. *This volume*.

LINDH, A. 1980. Correlation of Landsat lineaments in the south-western margin of the Baltic Shield. *Geologiska Föreningens i Stockholm Förhandlingar*, **102** (1), 1–12.

*MAX, M. D. 1979. Extent and disposition of Grenville tectonism in the Precambrian continental crust adjacent to the North Atlantic. *Geology*, **7**, 76–8.

——, INAMDAR, D. D. & McINTYRE, T. 1982. Compilation magnetic map. The Irish continental shelf and adjacent areas. *Geological Survey of Ireland Report Series No. RS 82/2 (Geophysics)*, 7 pp. and map.

—— RYAN, P. D. & INAMDAR, D. D. 1983. A magnetic deep structural geology interpretation of Ireland. *Tectonics*, **2** (5), 431–51.

*MBIPOM, E. W. & HUTTON, V. R. S. 1983. Geoelectromagnetic measurements across the Moine thrust and the Great Glen in northern Scotland. *Geophysical Journal of the Royal Astronomical Society*, **74**, 507–24.

McQUILLIN, R. & BROOKS, M. 1967. Geophysical surveys in the Shetland Islands. *Institute of Geological Sciences Geophysics Paper No. 2*.

—— & WATSON, J. 1973. Large scale basement structures of the Outer Hebrides in the light of

geophysical evidence. *Nature, London, Physical Science*, **245** (170), 1–3.

MEGSON, J. B. 1983. Marine geophysical investigation: Rockall Trough to Porcupine Seabight. *Thesis*, University of Edinburgh.

*MILLER, H. G. 1977. Gravity zoning in Newfoundland. *Tectonophysics*, **38**, 317–26.

—— 1984. Comment (and Reply) on 'Reinterpretation of Newfoundland gravity data and arguments for an allochthonous Dunnage Zone'. *Geology*, **12**, 60–1.

*MOREL, P. & IRVING, E. 1978. Tentative paleocontinental maps for the early Phanerozoic and Proterozoic. *Journal of Geology*, **86**, 535–61.

MUELLER, S. 1983. EGT Project. *Eos (Transactions of the American Geophysical Union)*, **64** (29), 458.

*PALM, H. & LUND, C. E. 1980. A seismic refraction study in the Caledonian front of Jauntland, Sweden. *Geologiska Föreningens i Stockholm Förhandlingar*, **102** (4), 561–8.

PHILLIPS, W. E. A., STILLMAN, C. J. & MURPHY, T. 1976. A Caledonian plate tectonic model. *Journal of the Geological Society, London*, **132**, 579–609.

QUINLAN, G. M. & BEAUMONT, C. 1984. Appalachian thrusting, lithospheric flexure and the Paleozoic stratigraphy of the Eastern Interior of North America. *Canadian Journal of Earth Sciences*, **21**, 973–96.

RANKIN, D. W. 1976. Appalachian salients and recesses: late Precambrian continental breakup and the opening of the Iapetus Ocean. *Journal of Geophysical Research*, **81** (32), 5605–19.

RIDDIHOUGH, R. P. 1972. Regional magnetic anomalies and geology in Fennoscandia: a discussion. *Canadian Journal of Earth Sciences*, **9** (3), 219–32.

ROBERTS, D. G., MASSON, D. G., MONTADERT, L. & de CHARPAL, O. 1981. Continental margin from the Porcupine Seabright to the Armorican marginal basin *In*: ILLING, L. V. & HOBSON, G. D. (eds) *Petroleum Geology of the Continental Shelf of North West Europe*, 455–73.

ROY, J. L. & ROBERTSON, W. A. 1968. Evidence for diagenetic remanent magnetization: the Maringourin Formation. *Canadian Journal of Earth Sciences*, **5** (2), 275–85.

——, TANCZYK, E. & LAPOINTE, P. 1983. The Paleomagnetic record of the Appalachians. *In*: SCHENK, P. E. (ed.) *Regional Trends in the Geology of the Appalachian–Caledonian–Hercynian–Mauritanide Orogen*, pp. 11–26, Reidel, Dordrecht.

*ROYDEN, L. & HODGES, K. V. 1984. A technique for analyzing the thermal and uplift histories of eroding orogenic belts: A Scandinavian example. *Journal of Geophysical Research B*, Paper 4B0610.

SCHENK, P. E. 1983. The Meguma terrane of Nova Scotia, Canada—an aid in trans-Atlantic correlation. *In*: SCHENK, P. E. (ed.) *Regional Trends in the Geology of the Appalachian–Caledonian–Hercynian–Mauritanide Orogen*, 121–30, Reidel, Dordrecht.

*SEGUIN, M. K. 1982. Geophysics of the Quebec Appalachians. *Tectonophysics*, **81**, 1–50.

*—— 1983. Tectonic style of the Appalachian allochthonous zone of southern Quebec. Seismic and gravimetric evidence. *Tectonophysics*, **96**, 1–18.

*SELLEVOLL, M. A. 1975. Seismic refraction measurements and continuous seismic profiling on the continental margin off Norway between 60°N and 69°N. *Norges Geologiske Undersøkelse*, **316**, 219–35.

*SHERIDAN, R. E. & DRAKE, C. L. 1968. Seaward extension of the Canadian Appalachians. *Canadian Journal of Earth Sciences*, **5**, 337–73.

SIMPSON, R. W., HILDENBRAND, T. H., GODSON, R. H. & KANE, M. F. 1982. A description of coloured gravity and terrain maps for the conterminous United States, shown on 35 mm slides. *United States Geological Survey Open-File Report 82–477*, 7 pp.

SKEHAN, J. W. & RAST, N. 1983. Relationship between Precambrian and lower Palaeozoic rocks of southeastern New England and other North Atlantic Avalonian terranes. *In*: SCHENK, P. E. (ed.) *Regional Trends in the Geology of the Appalachian–Caledonian–Hercynian–Maurtitanide Orogen*, pp. 131–62, Reidel, Dordrecht.

SLUNGA, R. 1981. Fault mechanisms of Fennoscandian earthquakes and regional crustal stresses. *Geologiska Föreningens i Stockholm Förhandlingar*, **103** (1), 27–31.

SMYTHE, D. K., CHALMERS, J. A., SKUCE, A. G., DOBINSON, A. & MOULD, A. S. 1983. Early opening history of the North Atlantic. I. Structure and origin of the Faeroe–Shetland escarpment. *Geophysical Journal of the Royal Astronomical Society*, **72**, 373–98.

*——, DOBINSON, A., McQUILLIN, R., BREWER, J. A., MATTHEWS, D. H., BLUNDELL, D. J. & KELK, B. 1982. Deep structure of the Scottish Caledonides revealed by the MOIST reflection profile. *Nature, London*, **299**, 338–40.

SRIVASTAVA, S. P., FALCONER, R. K. H., HAWORTH, R. T., PIERCE, J. W., CLARK, M. J. & CLARKE, D. B. 1977. Correlation between magnetic anomalies and the bedrocks in the offshore regions of eastern Canada. *Proceedings of the IAGA/IAMAP Joint Assembly, Seattle*, p. 106 (abstract).

STEWART, I. C. F. 1978. Teleseismic reflections and the Newfoundland lithosphere. *Canadian Journal of Earth Sciences*, **15**, 175–80.

STROMBERG, A. G. B. 1976. A pattern of tectonic zones in the western part of the East European Platform. *Geologiska Föreningens i Stockholm Förhandlingar*, **98**, 227–43.

SWANSON, M. T. 1982. Preliminary model for an early transform history in central Atlantic rifting. *Geology*, **10**, 317–20.

TALWANI, M. & ELDHOLM, O. 1972. Continental margin off Norway: A geophysical study. *Geological Society of America Bulletin*, **83**, 3575–606.

—— & —— 1977. Evolution of the Norwegian–Greenland Sea. *Geological Society of America Bulletin*, **88**, 969–99.

THOMAS, M. D. 1983. Tectonic significance of paired gravity anomalies in the southern and central Appalachians. *In*: HATCHER, R. D., WILLIAMS, H. & ZIETZ, I. (eds) *Contributions to the Tectonics and Geophysics of Mountain Chains. Geological Society of America Memoir No. 158*, pp. 113–24.

THOMAS, W. A. 1977. Evolution of Appalachian–Ouachita salients and recesses from reentrants and promontories in the continental margin. *American Journal of Science*, **277**, 1233–78.

—— 1980. Evolution of embayments and promontories of the continental margin. *Geological Society of America Abstracts with Programs*, **12** (7), 535.

—— 1983. Continental margins, orogenic belts, and intracratonic structures. *Geology*, **11**, 270–2.

THORPE, R. S., BECKINSALE, R. D., PATCHETT, P. J., PIPER, J. D. A., DAVIES, G. R. & EVANS, J. A. 1984. Crustal growth and late Precambrian–early Palaeozoic plate tectonic evolution of England and Wales. *Journal of the Geological Society, London*, **141**, 521–36.

TULLY, M. C. 1983. Bouguer gravity anomaly map: Northern North Sea sheet 1:1,000,000 series. *Institute of Geological Sciences Map*.

TURBITT, T. (ed.) 1984. Catalogue of British earthquakes recorded by the BGS seismograph network 1979, 1980, 1981. *Global Seismology Unit Report No. 210*, British Geological Survey, Keyworth, Nottingham.

—— (ed.) 1985. Catalogue of British earthquakes recorded by the BGS seismograph network 1982, 1983, 1984. *Global Seismology Unit Report No. 260*, British Geological Survey, Keyworth, Nottingham.

WEAVER, D. F. 1967. A geological interpretation of the Bouguer anomaly field of Newfoundland. *Publications of the Dominion Observatory*, **35** (5), 223–51.

WILLIAMS, H. 1978. Tectonic lithofacies map of the Appalachian orogen. *Memorial University of Newfoundland Map No. 1*.

—— & HATCHER, R. D. 1982. Suspect terranes and accretionary history of the Appalachian orogen. *Geology*, **10**, 530–6.

—— & MAX, M. D. 1980. Zonal subdivision and regional correlation in the Appalachian/Caledonide orogen. *In*: WONES, D. R. (ed.) *The Caledonides of the USA: Proceedings of the International Geological Correlation Program—Caledonide Orogen Project 27, Blacksburg, VA. Department of Geological Sciences, Virginia Polytechnic Institute and State University, Memoir No. 2*, pp. 57–62.

WOLFF, F. 1981. Magnetic and geologic correlation map of Norway. *1:1 000 000 Scale Map*, Scandinavian Caledonides Group of IGCP Project 27.

—— 1983. Crustal structure of the Scandinavian peninsula as deduced by wavelength filtering of gravity data. *In*: SCHENK, P. E. (ed.) *Regional Trends in the Geology of the Appalachian–Caledonian–Hercynian–Mauritanide Orogen*, Reidel, Dordrecht.

*WRIGHT, J. A. & COCHRANE, N. A. 1980. Geomagnetic sounding of an ancient plate margin in the Canadian Appalachians. *Journal of Geomagnetism and Geoelectricity*, **32**, 133–40.

*——, JESSOP, A. M., JUDGE, A. S. & LEWIS, T. J. 1980. Geothermal measurements in Newfoundland. *Canadian Journal of Earth Sciences*, **17**, 1370–6.

WOOLLARD, G. P. 1939. *Transactions of the American Geophysical Union*, Part III, pp. 317–23.

ZIEGLER, P. A. 1984. Caledonian and Hercynian crustal consolidation of western and central Europe—a working hypothesis. *Geologie en Mijnbouw,* **63**, 93–108.

ZIETZ, I. & GILBERT, F. P. 1980. Aeromagnetic map of part of the southeastern United States. *United States Geological Survey Geophysical Investigations Map No. GP-937* (in colour *Map No. GP-936*).

—— & —— 1981. Aeromagnetic map of the northeastern United States: in colour (scale 1:2,000,000). *United States Geological Survey Geophysical Investigations Map No. GP-942.*

——, HAWORTH, R. T., WILLIAMS, H. & DANIELS, D. 1980. Magnetic anomaly map of the Appalachian orogen. *Memorial University of Newfoundland Map No. 2.*

R. T. HAWORTH, British Geological Survey, Keyworth, Nottingham NG12 5GG, UK.

R. HIPKIN, Department of Geophysics, Edinburgh University, West Mains Road, Edinburgh EH9 3JZ, UK.

R. D. JACOBI, Department of Geological Sciences, State University of New York at Buffalo, 4240 Ridge Lea Road, Amherst, NY 14226, USA.

M. KANE, United States Geological Survey, Box 25046, Federal Center, Denver, CO 80225, USA.

J. P. LEFORT, Institut de Géologie, Université de Rennes, 35031 Rennes Cédex, France.

M. D. MAX, Geological Survey of Ireland, Beggars Bush, Haddington Road, Dublin 4, Eire. *Present address*: Naval Research Laboratory, Washington, DC 20375–5000, USA.

H. G. MILLER, Memorial University of Newfoundland, St John's, Newfoundland A1B 3X7, Canada.

F. WOLFF, Geological Survey of Norway, Liev Eriksons vei 39, PO Box 306, N-7007 Trondheim, Norway.

Crustal and upper mantle structure of the Appalachian–Caledonide orogen from seismic results

F. A. Cook, D. H. Matthews & A. W. B. Jacob

SUMMARY: The Appalachian–Caledonide orogen extending from the southeastern USA to northeastern Canada and Britain now has more crustal-scale seismic reflection profiles recorded across it than any other orogen in the world. From SW to NE these include the COCORP Ouachita traverse, the COCORP southern Appalachian traverse, the COCORP northern Appalachian traverse, the BIRPS Western Isles–North Channel (WINCH) offshore profile, the BIRPS Moine–Outer Isles Seismic Traverse (MOIST) profile and the BIRPS SW Approaches Traverse (SWAT) profile. In addition there are several seismic profiles in the eastern USA and Canada with data to mid-crustal (15–20 km) depth within the crystalline 'core' of the Appalachians. In eastern N America, where the Caledonian (Taconian) deformation is overprinted by Acadian and Alleghanian deformation, the seismic reflection data clearly indicate large-scale (several hundred kilometres) cratonward thrusting of shelf, off-shelf and basinal facies sediments and metasediments. The eastern limit of undeformed Precambrian (Grenville) basement is probably represented by a zone of E-dipping reflectors which, in New England, can be correlated with surface exposures of faults and metasediments. Two profiles offshore from Scotland cross the Caledonide orogenic front. The BIRPS MOIST profile indicates that the Moine thrust zone is also characterized by E-dipping reflectors which extend to mid-crustal depths. In contrast with the data from the Appalachians, the BIRPS MOIST, WINCH and SWAT data show remarkably continuous reflections from the crust–mantle transition, as identified on seismic refraction data both across strike (LISPB) and along strike (ICSSP and CSSP). The Moho is at a depth of about 30 km throughout much of Britain and is commonly overlain by a thick (4–5 s travel time or about 12–15 km) layered lower crust at depths between 15 and 30 km. In some areas the data offshore from Scotland show deep reflections which extend into the mantle. Additionally, many of the profiles in eastern N America and Britain provide strong evidence that late normal faults (Mesozoic) may be reactivated older compressional structures (Caledonian and Variscan in Britain; Alleghanian in the southern Appalachians).

The major results obtained from seismic studies of crustal structure in the Appalachian–Caledonide orogen are reviewed in this paper. The geological continuity of this orogen in a pre-Mesozoic drift reconstruction together with the large quantity of crustal seismic refraction and reflection data obtained (Figs 1 and 2) provide a unique opportunity for comparing crustal structure along strike and for delineating variations and similarities as they relate to geological structure.

Crustal seismic data of the orogen have been acquired by various methods, but can be generalized into three categories.

1 Crustal structure studies from teleseismic events (e.g. P-wave residuals).
2 Crustal structure studies from controlled-source long-range refraction profiles.
3 Crustal structure studies from controlled-source near-vertical reflection profiling.

Teleseismic and controlled-source refraction studies tend to produce similar kinds of information on crustal structure, although controlled-source studies are generally of higher resolution.

Major results from such studies include crustal thickness, generalized crustal velocity structure and some information on major intra-crustal discontinuities.

In contrast, near-vertical seismic reflection profiling provides information on the geometry of intra-crustal boundaries, the crust–mantle transition and the upper mantle. Because the scale of observed reflections is comparable with the visible scale of many geological structures, these types of data are more easily correlated with surface geology than are refraction and teleseismic results. However, many features such as the Moho may not be clearly discernible on near-vertical reflection data and are thus better delineated with refraction observations. Convincing models of crustal structure should thus incorporate information from both types of observations.

The general outline of the Appalachian–Caledonide orogen is shown in Figs 1 and 2 on a map depicting the pre-Mesozoic configuration of the continental lithospheric plates around the N Atlantic (after LePichon et al. 1977). Figures 1 and 2 also show the limits of the Caledonide and

From HARRIS, A. L. & FETTES, D. J. (eds), 1988, *The Caledonian–Appalachian Orogen*, Geological Society Special Publication No. 38, pp. 21–33.

21

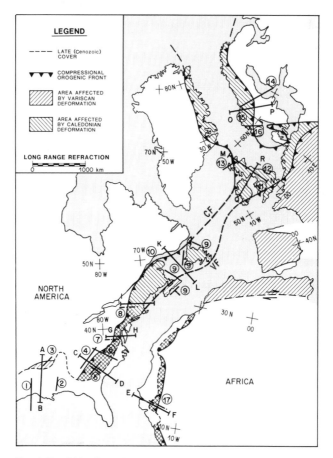

FIG. 1. Pre-drift orientation of the continents around the N Atlantic (after LePichon *et al.* 1977) with the Palaeozoic deformational fronts shown. Locations of seismic refraction (solid lines) and teleseismic (broken lines) crustal studies are indicated. The lettered profiles indicate the crustal structure sections in Fig. 3 and incorporate information from other methods (such as gravity) to constrain crustal thickness: CF, Caledonian front; VF, Variscan front. The sources of information are as follows: 1, Hales *et al.* 1970; 2, Warren *et al.* 1966; 3, McCamy & Meyer 1966; 4, Warren 1968, Prodehl *et al.* 1984; 5, Lee 1980, Lee & Dainty 1982; 6, Warren 1968; 7, Bollinger *et al.* 1980; 8, Taylor *et al.* 1980, Taylor & Toksoz 1982; 9, Dainty *et al.* 1966; 10, Berry & Fuchs 1973; 11, Bamford *et al.* 1976, 1978; 12, Bott *et al.* 1983, Jacob *et al.* 1985; 13, Smith & Bott 1975; 14, Vogel & Lund 1970; 15, Kanestrom & Haughland 1971; 16, Sellevoll & Warwick 1971; 17, Briden *et al.* 1981, Dorbath *et al.* 1983.

Variscan deformations. In general, the southern portions of the orogen (southern Appalachians–Mauritanides) are characterized by Caledonian (Taconian) deformation overprinted by Variscan (Acadian and/or Alleghanian–Hercynian) deformations; in Britain the Caledonian and Variscan fronts are separated by a considerable distance, and in Scandinavia there is no evidence for

Variscan deformation (Zwart & Dornsiepen 1980). Following the Palaeozoic compressional deformations, much of the area was affected by Mesozoic and Cenozoic extension culminating in the Atlantic opening.

One of the major problems in interpreting crustal-scale geophysical data is that of separating the effects of the various episodes of activity. For

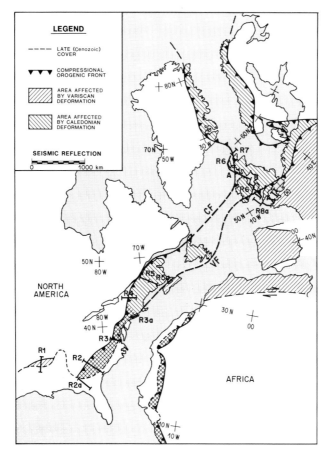

FIG. 2. As Fig. 1 but with locations of crustal reflection profiles indicated. Only the part of BIRPS WINCH between A and B (on R6) is shown in Fig. 4. Numbered profiles are prefixed with R to distinguish them from numbered refraction lines in Fig. 1. The subscript a indicates unpublished data. Sources of information are as follows: R1, Nelson *et al.* 1982, Lillie *et al.* 1983; R2, Cook *et al.* 1979, 1981, 1983; R2a, J. Oliver & L. Brown 1984, personal communication; R3, Clarke *et al.* 1978, Harris *et al.* 1981, 1983, Costain *et al.* 1984; R3a, Phinney *et al.* 1984; R4, Brown *et al.* 1983, Ando *et al.* 1983, 1984; R5, Seguin 1982, St Julien *et al.* 1983, LaRoche 1983; R5a, Green & Berry 1984; R6, Smythe *et al.* 1982, Brewer & Smythe 1984; R7, Brewer *et al.* 1983; R8a, BIRPS, unpublished.

example, in the southern Appalachians the entire orogen includes evidence of both Cambro-Ordovician and Devonian–Carboniferous compressional orogenies; however, evidence of Mesozoic extension is common only in the eastern portion. Thus, although the Mesozoic extension on the E and the compressional belts to the W are widely separated, it is difficult to delineate the effects of each of the individual compressional episodes. In contrast, the wide separation of the Caledonian

and Variscan fronts in Britain clarifies the effect of each compressional orogeny; however, the entire crust of Britain was probably subjected to extension in the Mesozoic (Kent 1980). Thus it may be difficult to separate the effects of late extension from those of earlier compression. Nevertheless, with these provisos in mind, much valuable information has been obtained from seismic results. We begin by examining crustal refraction and teleseismic observations.

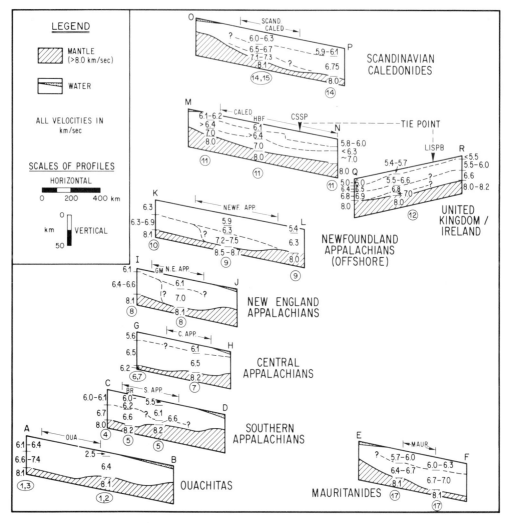

FIG. 3. Crustal cross-sections based on refraction and teleseismic results. The letters refer to the sections indicated in Fig. 1. Lines of correlations between velocity models are not intended as geological boundaries. The numbers beneath the velocity models refer to the numbered profiles in Fig. 1. Limits of orogens are indicated by bars at the top of the sections. Location abbreviations are as follows: BR, Blue Ridge; GM, Green Mountains; SUF, Southern Uplands fault; HBF, Highland Boundary fault.

Refraction and teleseismic results

The locations of refraction and teleseismic studies bearing on the crustal structure of the Appalachian–Caledonide orogen are shown in Fig. 1, and generalized crustal cross-sections based on these results are shown in Fig. 3. Most of the data from N America are from the 1960s (with the exception of the teleseismic results and some recent work in the southern Appalachians), whereas most of the data from Britain are 1970s vintage.

Comparison of the refraction models for N America reveals several important similarities along strike. In general, the major crustal change is the thinning from the continent into the Atlantic Ocean. Within the craton (N and NW sides of profiles A–B to K–L) the crust is generally depicted by a three-layer model. The near-surface layer typically has P-wave velocities of 5.5–6.3 km s^{-1}. The lower values (about 5.5 km s^{-1}) are found in the Valley and Ridge sediments (e.g. profile G–H), whereas the values of 6.1–6.3 km s^{-1} appear to be typical of shallow Grenville

(Precambrian) crust. The near-surface layer has a thickness range of 5–20 km.

The second (lower-crustal) layer appears quite variable with velocities of 6.4–6.9 km s^{-1} (Fig. 3) and probably reflects varying amounts of mafic material along strike. The base of this layer is the Moho, with a consistent depth of 36–40 km beneath the craton. Upper-mantle velocities P_n range from 8.0 to 8.2 km s^{-1}.

Major changes are observed in crustal velocities and/or crustal thickness across the strike of the Appalachian–Ouachita orogen. In the Ouachitas there may be a southward crustal thinning of about 9 km (from 38 km N of the mountains to 26 km in the southern Ouachitas (Lillie *et al.* 1983). S of the Ouachita belt the crust thins further to about 20 km in the Gulf of Mexico.

The southern and central Appalachians display similar changes in crustal thickness (Fig. 3): the craton on the W is typically 40 km thick (Warren 1968, Prodehl *et al.* 1984), the Appalachian mountains are generally about 45 km thick and the crust thins to near 33 km in the eastern part of the orogen (Fig. 3, sections C–D and G–H). Further E, the crust thins dramatically into the Atlantic Ocean basin (Hutchinson *et al.* 1983).

The causes of the crustal thinning beneath the orogen are not entirely clear. Present ideas centre around two models—a lithospheric suture zone related to either Caledonian or later orogenies (Hatcher & Zietz 1980), and a transition from Precambrian cratonal crust on the W to rifted or oceanic crust on the E. Such a transition would be Precambrian in age and would be buried beneath the craton-verging near-surface allochthons (Cook & Oliver 1981, Nelson *et al.* 1982, Lillie *et al.* 1983, Cook 1984a). Further thinning on the E side of the trans-Appalachian sections is likely to be a consequence of the Mesozoic rifting.

In the Mauritanides (Fig. 3, section E–F) Briden *et al.* (1981) and Dorbath *et al.* (1983) have measured teleseismic P-wave residuals and have concluded that there is a westward decrease of about 6 km in Moho depth beneath the Mauritanide fold belt. They suspect that the boundary is related to the orogenic development of the Mauritanides and may represent a buried subduction zone.

The crustal structure of New England and offshore Newfoundland appears to have some differences compared with the southern Appalachians (Taylor & Toksoz 1982). For example, there is no obvious eastward shallowing of the Moho beneath the orogen except that associated with the Atlantic area (Dainty *et al.* 1966, Taylor *et al.* 1980, Taylor & Toksoz 1982). However, there is a clear eastward increase in the lower crustal P-wave velocities from the craton into the orogen (Fig. 3, sections I–J and K–L). Beneath the craton the lower crust typically has velocities of 6.4–6.6 km s^{-1}, whereas beneath the northern Appalachian orogen the seismic velocities in the lower crust are 7.0–7.5 km s^{-1}. As in the southern Appalachians, two distinctly different conceptual models have been proposed to account for this change: Taylor & Toksoz (1982) have suggested that it represents a deeply-penetrating suture, whereas Ando *et al.* (1983, 1984) have interpreted the reflection data to be more consistent with a buried Precambrian–Ordovician rifted margin.

In Britain the refraction characteristics of the crust are different from those in the Appalachians. Bamford *et al.* (1976, 1978) have summarized results of the Lithospheric Seismic Profile in Britain (LISPB) experiment along the length of Britain (Fig. 1, M–N). In addition, a profile has recently been recorded across the strike of the orogen near the suspected Caledonide suture zone (Bott *et al.* 1983, Jacob *et al.* 1985). These are shown as Q–R in Fig. 1 and are referred to as the Caledonide Suture Seismic Profile (CSSP) and the Irish Caledonide Suture Seismic Profile (ICSSP).

Offshore experiments providing links to the structure on the British and Irish mainland have been carried out by Smith & Bott (1975) and Bott *et al.* (1979) with profiles mostly near the present continental margin in the Caledonian foreland. Smith & Bott's (1975) lines included one within the Caledonian belt across the mouth of the Moray Firth. All the lines in the foreland between the N of Scotland and Shetland found a remarkably constant depth to the Moho of 26 ± 2 km with P_n at 7.99 km s^{-1}. The upper crust has widespread Palaeozoic or earlier sediments and some local Mesozoic basins overlying an upper-crustal layer with a P-wave velocity of 6.10 km s^{-1} and thickness up to 10 km. Hall & Al-Haddad (1976) confirmed that this velocity of 6.1 km s^{-1} is due to Lewisian gneisses. The next layer, at about 6.5 km s^{-1}, is widespread at variable depths between 2 and 16 km and was tentatively identified by Smith & Bott (1975) as Lewisian granulites; the work of Hall & Al-Haddad (1976) in the Lewisian metamorphic complex of NW Scotland confirmed this. Smith & Bott (1975) also used Moho reflections to measure an average crustal velocity of 6.4 km s^{-1}. This indicated that there may be unobserved material at the base of the crust with velocities around 7 km s^{-1}. In the same region, although closer to the Scottish coast, Jacob & Booth (1977) estimated a crustal thickness of about 29 km. Their average velocity of 6.64 km s^{-1} was higher than that obtained by Smith & Bott (1975), but as this velocity was for the crust below the sediments it can be considered a similar result, indicating high velocities at the base of the crust. Sub-critical P-wave and converted-wave reflections from the Moho indicated a very sharp crust–mantle transition (Jacob & Booth 1977).

The sharp Moho transition was confirmed in profile LISPB by Assumpçao (1980) who also observed converted-wave reflections. He defined a Moho step which had been tentatively identified by Bamford et al. (1978). This was the first indication that there might be significant topography in the Moho. The LISPB profile runs S from the northern margin of the Caledonian fold belt and, neglecting shallow sediments, it shows the crust divided into the three zones (Fig. 3). As far S as the Southern Uplands faults (SUF) this pattern of three layers is followed with similar velocities in each layer. The crust thickens from about 26 km at the N end of the line to a maximum of about 36 km under the Highland Boundary fault and northern part of the Midland Valley (Bamford et al. 1978). A line across the Moray Firth and nearly parallel to the LISPB line showed considerably thinner crust under the Mesozoic basin (Smith & Bott 1975). This evidence suggests crustal thinning and stretching in the North Sea area and has been confirmed by more recent studies (Christie & Sclater 1980, Leeder 1983, Wood & Barton 1983, Barton & Wood 1984).

On the LISPB interpretation there seems to be a significant change in the crust in the neighbourhood of the SUF. One notable feature is that the Moho becomes less well defined (Bamford & Prodehl 1977, Bamford et al. 1978). Bamford & Prodehl (1977) suggest that the nature of the Moho varies significantly below different tectonic areas and features.

Hall et al. (1983) have re-interpreted some of the LISPB data in the Southern Uplands in conjunction with data from temporary and permanent arrays and a refraction line (Warner et al. 1982) along the Caledonian strike S of the SUF. They find no shallow discontinuity at the SUF, but they identify blocks of crystalline rocks of continental affinity at shallow depth (1–5 km) further S in the Southern Uplands.

The ICSSP profile runs fairly close to (between 5 and 40 km away from) the course of the Caledonian suture zone (Iapetus suture) as described by Phillips et al. (1976). All stations lie on the NW flank of the zone. There are at least two different crustal columns on the Irish line—at the NE end and at the SW end. A possible third column in the middle could not be defined because of the distribution of shots.

In general the crust can be divided into an upper zone including rocks with velocities less than 6.4 km s^{-1}, a mid-crustal zone with velocities between 6.4 and 6.6 km s^{-1}, and a lower-crustal zone with a velocity of 6.8 km s^{-1}. The boundary between the middle- and lower-crustal zones is at around 20 km depth through most of the ICSSP profile. There may be a slight depression in the velocity of the lower-crustal zone below the NE end of the line, but it is not conclusively established. Here also, the crust–mantle boundary is a transition zone extending over 3–4 km with the velocity increasing from about 7 to about 8 km s^{-1}. In contrast the SW end has a well-defined Moho at a slightly shallower depth. On the Irish Sea portion of the line an upper-crustal low-velocity layer may extend to 16 km depth. Beneath the Irish Sea there is a narrow transition zone leading to a lower-crustal velocity of about 6.8 km s^{-1}. This transition is slightly shallower than in Ireland and there is a relatively sharp Moho at about 29 km.

Refraction results from the Scandinavian Caledonides appear to be more similar to the Appalachians than they are to the British Caledonides. The Moho below the northern Caledonides in Norway has a fairly uniform depth of about 40 km, even though the profiles cross various tectonic units (Hirschleber et al. 1975, Avedik et al. 1984). Within the crust there may be a velocity increase from about 6.2 to 6.5 km s^{-1} at a depth of approximately 15 km.

Data from profiles further S have been summarized by Sellevoll (1973) (O–P in Fig. 3). The near-surface velocity in the uppermost crystalline layer within the Caledonian orogen in Scandinavia shows quite a lot of variation, but in the three lines shown (Fig. 1) it is between 6.0 and 6.3 km s^{-1} with an increase to 6.5–6.7 km s^{-1} generally observed for the mid-crust. In the more northern lines there is some evidence for deep-crustal velocities of over 7.0 km s^{-1}. In contrast with the data from the northern Caledonides, a good correlation generally exists between the surface elevation and the thickness of the crust, with the high mountains having thicker crust.

In summary, the refraction data display changes both along and across the strike of the Appalachian–Caledonide orogen. The most striking difference occurs with crustal thickness: in the Appalachians and Scandinavian Caledonides the crust is 35–45 km thick, whereas in Britain the crust is 25–35 km thick. It is not entirely clear whether this difference is due to Palaeozoic variations in crustal thickness or to variations in the amount of Mesozoic thinning.

Near-vertical seismic reflection results

Since 1978 there has been a rapid increase in the number of crustal-scale reflection profiles recorded in this orogen. Indeed, all the profiles illustrated in Figs 2 and 4 were obtained in 1978 or later; the impact that these data are having on our understanding of the architecture of this orogen is profound.

The Consortium for Continental Reflection Profiling (COCORP) has acquired data from the Ouachitas, southern Appalachians and New England Appalachians, the United States Geo-

logical Survey has obtained upper-crustal data from the central Appalachians, the group at Virginia Polytechnic Institute also has some shallow data from the central Appalachians and a joint Canadian–U.S.A. project has recently completed a traverse across the Quebec–Maine Appalachians. In Britain the BIRPS group has acquired over 3000 km of deep reflection data offshore across the Caledonide and Variscan orogens.

Reflection profiles in the Ouachita and southern Appalachian orogens image large-scale craton-verging thrust sheets (Fig. 4, profiles R1 and R2). In both areas the data traverse, on the surface, from the dominantly unmetamorphosed

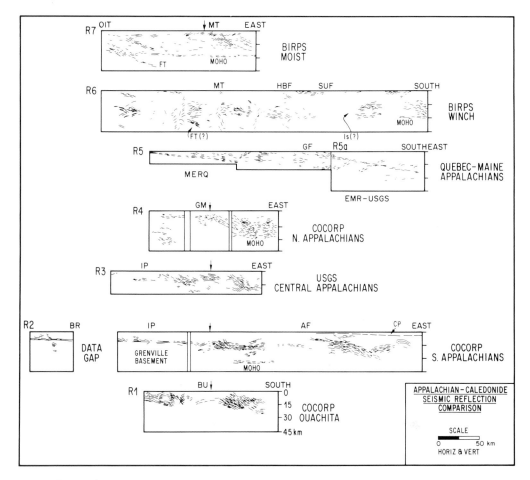

FIG. 4. Line drawings of seismic reflection sections throughout the orogen. Letters of the sections refer to the letters in Fig. 2. Abbreviations are as in Fig. 3 with the following additions: BU, Benton uplift; IP, inner Piedmont; AF, Augusta fault; GF, Guadaloupe fault; MT, Moine thrust; OIT, Outer Isles thrust; FT, Flannan thrust; IS, Iapetus suture; CP, Coastal Plain. Arrows indicate the E-dipping reflection zone seen throughout most of the orogen which probably marks the eastern limit of pristine Grenville crust. On profile R5a, only the most prominent reflection zone is illustrated for comparison with other data; this is not intended as a representative drawing of those data. Only the portion between A and B of the BIRPS WINCH data (profile R6) is shown.

foreland fold and thrust belt across the dominantly metamorphosed eugeoclinal belts. The
foreland belts of both the Ouachitas and the
southern Appalachians show characteristics of
thrust-faulted and folded layered sediments (Nelson *et al.* 1982, Cook *et al.* 1983, Lillie *et al.* 1983).
Data from the Ouachitas also show a large
antiformal structure S of the foreland thrust belt
which is likely to be a detached basement slice
(Nelson *et al.* 1982, Lillie *et al.* 1983).

In the southern and central Appalachians the
Blue Ridge and Inner Piedmont are characterized
by sub-horizontal reflectors in the shallow (less
than 10 km) crust which are probably Palaeozoic
and/or Precambrian (meta)sediments. In some
areas a remarkably continuous zone of detachment between the allochthon and underlying
layers at 5–10 km can be traced for up to 250 km
beneath the Blue Ridge and Piedmont (Cook *et
al.* 1979, 1983). Clark *et al.* (1978), Harris *et al.*
(1981, 1983) and Cook *et al.* (1979, 1981, 1983)
have interpreted very-high-amplitude layers beneath the Blue Ridge and Inner Piedmont belts
to be, at least in part, relatively undeformed low-
grade or even unmetamorphosed sediments of
late Precambrian or early Palaeozoic age. This
layering extends from Georgia to Virginia and
from the Valley and Ridge foreland to the centre
of the Piedmont (Figs 2 and 4, profiles R2–R3).
A recently acquired profile (Fig. 2, profile R2a)
in SW Georgia recorded by COCORP confirms
the presence of this layering beneath the Piedmont (J. Oliver and L. Brown 1984, personal
communication).

On the E side of the Inner Piedmont the
COCORP southern Appalachian traverse shows
major changes in reflection character from the
near-horizontal reflections beneath the Blue
Ridge and Inner Piedmont to a more steeply
(20°–30°) E-dipping zone on the E edge of the
Inner Piedmont (Cook *et al.* 1979, 1981, 1983). This
change in character has since been seen in the
Ouachitas (Nelson *et al.* 1982, Lillie *et al.* 1983),
the New England Appalachians (Ando *et al.*
1984) and the Scottish Caledonides (Brewer &
Smythe 1984). These zones in the Appalachians
and Ouachitas occur in the vicinity of both major
changes in surface geology and other geophysically inferred changes, including the change in
Moho depth and/or lower-crustal seismic velocities mentioned above. Hence they may be related
to lithospheric penetrating sutures (Hatcher &
Zietz 1980, Taylor & Toksoz 1982). However, in
places (such as the southern Appalachians) the
geophysical changes and surface geology changes
do not spatially coincide (Cook 1984a), and in
some areas the E-dipping reflecting boundaries
can be projected to surface outcrops of faults and

metasediments (Ando *et al.* 1984). Such observations do not appear to be consistent with
boundaries penetrating from the surface to deep
in the mantle. Cook *et al.* (1979, 1983), Lillie *et
al.* (1983) and Ando *et al.* (1984) have suggested
that the observations are more consistent with a
Precambrian–Palaeozoic continental margin
buried beneath the Appalachian allochthons.
Thus this zone probably marks the eastern limit
of pristine Grenville crust.

Two reflection traverses have been obtained in
the northern Appalachians: the COCORP New
England traverse (profile R4 in Fig. 4) (Ando *et
al.* 1983, 1984, Brown *et al.* 1983) and the
Ministère de l'Energie et des Richesses Naturelles
du Québec (MERQ) profile in Quebec (Fig. 4,
profile R5) (LaRoche 1983, St Julien *et al.* 1983).
The MERQ profile has recently been extended
across eastern Quebec and Maine through a
cooperative programme of the Department of
Energy, Mines and Resources, Canada, and the
United States Geological Survey (Green & Berry
1984, Stewart 1984).

The COCORP New England traverse crosses
a portion of the orogen in which the foreland
thrust belt shows the least development. Thus the
seismic expression of thrusted sediments is not as
pronounced as it is farther S. Nevertheless, the
data display shallow (about 4–4.5 km) horizontal
reflectors which may extend from the foreland
sediments to the E beneath the Green Mountain
anticlinorium. Hence the Green Mountains are
likely to be allochthonous. On the E side of the
Green Mountains the seismic data are characterized by the E-dipping zone mentioned above. E
of there, these reflections flatten into a strongly
layered lower crust (Ando *et al.* 1984).

The original MERQ profile in Quebec extends
from the St Lawrence lowlands to the Gaspé–
Connecticut Valley synclinorium. Most clearly
defined is a sequence of Palaeozoic sediments
dipping at about 4°–5° beneath the Quebec
allochthons to a depth of about 12 km (Seguin
1982, LaRoche 1983, St Julien *et al.* 1983). There
is no observed crustal-scale ramp such as that on
the E side of the Green Mountains and in the
southern Appalachians. However, it is not known
whether this is due to geological causes (e.g. non-
existence of the ramp) or to the choice of recording
parameters which prevented the acquisition of
data from below 12 km (Cook 1984b).

E of the major portion of the Caledonide
(Taconian) deformation, several profiles have
now imaged major crustal-penetrating low-angle
boundaries (thrusts?). The first of these was the
COCORP traverse in NE Georgia which crossed
the Alleghanian Augusta fault near the coastal
plain onlap (Fig. 4, profile R2). The Augusta fault

is seen to have a moderate E dip and can be traced to a depth of 25–30 km at a distance of about 80 km E of its outcrop (Cook *et al.* 1981, 1983). SE of this boundary, the reflections typically change to a more westerly orientation (Cook *et al.* 1981, 1983) (Fig. 4, profile R2). In the northern Appalachians, the eastward extension of the MERQ profile in Quebec and Maine has shown a remarkably similar E-dipping zone of reflections which probably correlate with the (Acadian?) Guadaloupe fault in Quebec (Green & Berry 1984). Recently, Phinney *et al.* (1984) (Fig. 2, profile R3a) have shown a profile from offshore New England (near Long Island) which also displays a strongly E-dipping zone penetrating the crust. Near the base of the crust, the orientation of reflections changes to a more westerly dip similar to that observed in the southern Appalachians by Cook *et al.* (1983). It is indeed possible that this major boundary represents a major lithospheric boundary (suture) as has been suggested for the southern Appalachians (Cook *et al.* 1983). It is important, however, to distinguish between this nearly crustal-penetrating zone and the E-dipping reflections which probably mark the edge of Precambrian basement farther W.

In Britain, BIRPS has recorded data across the offshore projections of nearly all the major structural features (Smythe *et al.* 1982, Brewer *et al.* 1983, Brewer & Smythe 1984). The first efforts were directed at the Moine and Outer Isles thrusts in northern Scotland. These data provided some important geometric information on the thrusts and on Mesozoic extensional basins. In addition they produced some startling new findings of lower-crust and upper-mantle structure. The Moine–Outer Isles Seismic Traverse (MOIST) line displayed a zone of E-dipping reflections which are strikingly similar to E-dipping reflections observed in the Appalachian–Ouachita belt (Figs 2 and 4, profile R7) (Brewer & Smythe 1984).

The Outer Isles fault shows a clear seismic reflection which is underlain by a very pronounced, parallel E-dipping reflection penetrating into the upper mantle. This deep reflector (called the Flannan thrust by Smythe *et al.* (1982)) has been observed on more recent BIRPS profiles (Brewer *et al.* 1983) and may not extend above the lower crust.

Throughout many of the BIRPS profiles the lower crust displays a prominent layered character which has rarely been seen in the Appalachians; exceptions include the eastern portion of the COCORP NE Georgia profile and the eastern portion of the COCORP New England profile. The Moho may be at the base of this layering

(Barton *et al.* 1984), as the depth at the base corresponds well to refraction interpretations. In contrast, the Moho is rarely seen on data from eastern N America.

Major structures which have been observed on the BIRPS Western Isles–North Channel (WINCH) traverse include the Flannan thrust, the Outer Isles thrust, a N-dipping Iapetus suture and the N-dipping S Irish Sea lineament (Brewer *et al.* 1983). The S Irish Sea lineament and the Outer Isles thrust are the only features which can be traced through the transparent upper crust and the layered lower crust on the WINCH data (Brewer *et al.* 1983). In addition, many of the crustal-penetrating boundaries such as the Outer Isles thrust are overlain in the hanging wall by Mesozoic sedimentary basins. Similar configurations have been observed in the Appalachians where Palaeozoic tectonized zones, such as the Augusta fault, were reactivated and overlain by Mesozoic basins (Cook *et al.* 1981, Brewer *et al.* 1983, Brewer & Smythe 1984, Petersen *et al.* 1984).

Recently acquired BIRPS profiles have crossed the Variscan front (SW Approaches Traverse (SWAT)) and have shown it to be characterized by a S-dipping boundary normal fault, which may also be a reactivated thrust. Meissner (1984) has reported data from northern Europe which show a S-dipping thrust near the Variscan front. The nature of the Variscan front is in many ways similar to the moderately E-dipping boundaries (Guadaloupe fault and Augusta fault) seen on the E flank of the Appalachians.

Comparison of reflection data from Britain and N America

The comparison of reflection results from Britain and N America (Fig. 4) suggests some generalizations. For example, the layered lower crust appears to be most easily seen on the reflection data in areas subjected to extension. This is likely to be the case in Britain, where Mesozoic extension was widespread, and it is also true beneath the eastern part of the Appalachian orogen where vestiges of Precambrian extension may be buried beneath the allochthons.

The layered lower crust, so commonly observed on BIRPS data, is not as common in the Appalachians, with the exceptions previously noted. Speculations on its significance will probably be made for some time, but some preliminary observations may be significant now. In some cases (e.g. on the E side of the Green Mountains and the Outer Isles fault) boundaries in the upper part of the crust may sole into the layered lower crust. Similarly, as Smythe *et al.* (1982) have suggested, the Moho-penetrating fault (Flannan thrust) appears to terminate upwards into the layering. Few boundaries may penetrate the entire crust. Examples of these could be, speculatively, the Augusta fault, the boundary observed off Long Island (Phinney *et al.* 1984) and possibly the Iapetus suture in Britain. The observation that many boundaries, both extensional and compressional, tend to terminate in the layered lower crust suggests that the lower crust has acted as a zone of detachment during the compressional orogenies and was reactivated during later extension.

Finally, the E-dipping layering observed on MOIST and along strike in the Appalachian–Ouachita orogen is probably due to a major pre-thrusting crustal boundary. It may mark the limit of 'normal' Precambrian crust which was later subjected to Palaeozoic compression. The boundary probably acted as a crustal-scale footwall ramp causing thrust splays and duplexes to form (Cook *et al.* 1979, 1983, Ando *et al.* 1984, Butler & Coward 1984). The evidence thus seems to indicate that, even on a large scale, the crust responds to compression as a generally layered medium, with its rheology dependent upon temperature, strain rate and composition.

Summarizing comments and conclusions

The Appalachian–Caledonide orogen of the N Atlantic has more crustal-scale seismic reflected data than any other orogen. When these data are supplemented by refraction information, they provide significant information on crustal structure throughout the orogen:

1 The crust in eastern N America is usually thickest (up to 45 km) where the greatest amount of shortening is observed. This is probably due to allochthons 5–10 km thick overlying older crust of relatively normal thickness.

2 The crust thins eastward, by 7–10 km, beneath the southern Appalachian–Ouachita segment of the orogen. This is probably an effect of Precambrian rifting. The crust thins again further toward the Atlantic owing to Mesozoic rifting.

3 The crust of Britain is thin (around 30 km). It is not known whether this is dominantly a late (Mesozoic) extensional effect or an early (Palaeozoic) effect.

4 Reflections from the Moho are rarely seen on data from the craton W of the Appalachians, but are much more common in the extended regimes (either Precambrian or Mesozoic).

5 The upper crust is often transparent, with only major boundaries such as faults being observed.

6 The lower crust is often layered, especially in Britain and the eastern part of the Appalachians. The layering may represent a zone of detachment into which both thrusts and normal faults sole.

7 Palaeozoic thrusts were commonly reactivated as Mesozoic normal faults.

8 The BIRPS data have imaged a boundary which penetrates well into the upper mantle (Flannan thrust).

9 Many tectonic fronts (e.g. Blue Ridge, Augusta fault, Variscan front, Iapetus suture, Guadaloupe fault) are apparently shallow-dipping features (30° or less).

New crustal seismic data and re-interpretations of existing data will clearly continue to provide critical information on the architecture of the Appalachian–Caledonide orogen.

ACKNOWLEDGMENTS: Partial support for this work was derived from the University of Calgary President's NSERC Research fund. The manuscript was prepared by Tari Forrest. Reviews and comments by D. Smythe and an anonymous reviewer are greatly appreciated.

References

ANDO, C., COOK, F., OLIVER, J., BROWN, L. & KAUFMAN, S. 1983. Crustal geometry of the Appalachian orogen from seismic reflection studies. *In*: HATCHER, R. D., JR, WILLIAMS, H. & ZIETZ, I. (eds) *Contributions to the Tectonics and Geophysics of Mountain Chains. Geological Society of America Memoir No. 158*, pp. 83–101.

——, CZUCHRA, B., KLEMPERER, S., BROWN, L., CHEADLE, M., COOK, F., OLIVER, J., KAUFMAN, S., WALSH, T., THOMPSON, J., JR, LYONS, J. & ROSENFELD, J. 1984. Crustal profile of a mountain belt: COCORP deep seismic reflection profiling in New England Appalachians and implications for architecture of convergent mountain chains. *Bulletin of the American Association of Petroleum Geologists*, **68**, 819–37.

ASSUMPÇAO, M. 1980. Determination of Moho dip using PS reflections. *Geophysical Journal of the Royal Astronomical Society*, **60**, 77–84.

AVEDIK, F., BERENDSEN, D., FUCKE, H., GOLDFLAM, S., HIRSCHLEBER, H., MEISSNER, R., SELLEVOLL, M. & WEINREIBE, W. 1984. Seismic investigations along the Scandinavian 'Blue Norma' profile. *Annals of Geophysics*, **2**, 571–8.

BAMFORD, D. & PRODEHL, C. 1977. Explosion seismology and the continental crust–mantle boundary. *Journal of the Geological Society, London,* **134,** 139–51.

——, FABER, S., JACOB, A. W. B., KAMINSKI, W., NUNN, K., PRODEHL, C., FUCHS, K., KING, R. & WILLMORE, P. L. 1976. A lithospheric seismic profile in Britain—I. Preliminary results. *Geophysical Journal of the Royal Astronomical Society,* **44,** 145–60.

——, NUNN, K., PRODEHL, C. & JACOB, A. W. B. 1978. LISPB-IV in crustal structure of northern Britain. *Geophysical Journal of the Royal Astronomical Society,* **54,** 43–60.

BARTON, P. & WOOD, R. 1984. Tectonic evolution of the North Sea basin: crustal stretching and subsidence. *Geophysical Journal of the Royal Astronomical Society,* **79,** 987–1022.

——, MATTHEWS, D., HALL, J. & WARNER, M. 1984. Moho beneath the North Sea compared on normal incidence and wide angle seismic records. *Nature, London,* **308,** 55–6.

BERRY, M. & FUCHS, K. 1973. Crustal structure of the Superior and Grenville provinces of the northeastern Canadian Shield. *Bulletin of the Seismological Society of America,* **63,** 1393–432.

BOLLINGER, G., CHAPMAN, M. & MOORE, T. 1980. Central Virginia regional seismic network: crustal velocity structure in central and southwestern Virginia. *Nuclear Regulatory Commission Report No. 1217,* 187 pp.

BOTT, M. H. P., ARMOUR, A., HIMSWORTH, E., MURPHY, T. & WYLLIE, G. 1979. An explosion seismology investigation of the continental margin west of the Hebrides, Scotland, at 58 degrees North. *Tectonophysics,* **59,** 217–31.

——, GREEN, A., LONG, R. & STEVENSON, D. 1983. Preliminary deep structure beneath northern England from CSSP. *Geophysical Journal of the Royal Astronomical Society,* **73,** 285.

BREWER, J. & SMYTHE, D. 1984. MOIST and the continuity of crustal reflector geometry along the Caledonian–Appalachian orogen. *Journal of the Geological Society, London,* **141,** 105–20.

——, MATTHEWS, D., WARNER, M., HALL, J., SMYTHE, D. & WHITTINGTON, R. 1983. BIRPS deep seismic reflection studies of the British Caledonides. *Nature, London,* **305,** 206–10.

BRIDEN, J., WHITCOMBE, D., STUART, G., FAIRHEAD, J., DORBATH, C. & DORBATH, L. 1981. Depth of geological contrast across the West African craton margin. *Nature, London,* **292,** 123–8.

BROWN, L., ANDO, C., KLEMPERER, S., OLIVER, J., KAUFMAN, S., CZUCHRA, B., WALSH, T. & ISACHSEN, Y. 1983. Adirondack–Appalachian crustal structure: the COCORP northeast traverse. *Geological Society of America Bulletin,* **94,** 1173–84.

BUTLER, R. & COWARD, M. 1984. Geological constraints, structural evolution and deep geology of the Scottish Caledonide. *Tectonics,* **3,** 347–65.

CHRISTIE, P. & SCLATER, J. 1980. An extensional origin for the Witchground Graben in the North Sea. *Nature, London,* **283,** 729–32.

CLARKE, H., COSTAIN, J. & GLOVER, L., III. 1978. Structure and seismic reflection studies on the Brevard ductile deformation zone near Rosman, North Carolina. *American Journal of Science,* **278,** 419–41.

COOK, F. 1984a. Geophysical anomalies along strike of the southern Appalachian Piedmont. *Tectonics,* **3,** 45–61.

——1984b. Harmonic distortion on a seismic reflection profile across the Quebec Appalachians: relation to Bouguer gravity and implications for crustal structure. *Canadian Journal of Earth Sciences,* **21,** 346–53.

—— & OLIVER, J. 1981. The late Precambrian–early Paleozoic continental edge in the Appalachian orogen. *American Journal of Science,* **281,** 983–1008.

——, ALBAUGH, D., BROWN, L., KAUFMAN, S., OLIVER, J. & HATCHER, R., JR 1979. Thin-skinned tectonics in the crystalline southern Appalachians: COCORP seismic reflection profiling of the Blue Ridge and Piedmont. *Geology,* **7,** 563–7.

——, BROWN, L., KAUFMAN, S. & OLIVER, J. 1983. The COCORP seismic reflection traverse across the southern Appalachians. *American Association of Petroleum Geologists Studies in Geology No. 14,* 61 pp.

——, ——, —— & PETERSEN, T. 1981. COCORP seismic reflection profiling of the Appalachian orogen beneath the Coastal Plain of Georgia. *Geological Society of America Bulletin,* **92,** 738–48.

COSTAIN, J., GLOVER, L., III & CORUH, C. 1984. Seismic reflection and geology of the central Virginia Blue Ridge and Piedmont. *International Symposium on Deep Structure of the Continental Crust: Results from Reflection Seismology (Abstracts),* pp. 18–19, Cornell University, Ithaca, NY.

DAINTY, A., KEEN, C., KEEN, M. & BLANCHARD, J. 1966. Review of geophysical evidence on crust and upper mantle structure on the eastern seaboard of Canada. *In:* STEINHARDT, J. & SMITH, T. (eds) *The Earth Beneath the Continents. American Geophysical Union Monograph No. 10,* pp. 349–69.

DORBATH, C., DORBATH, L., LePAGE, A. & GAVLON, R. 1983. The West-African craton margin in eastern Senegal: a seismological study. *Annals of Geophysics,* **1,** 25–36.

GREEN, A. & BERRY, M. 1984. The third dimension of geology from seismic reflection studies in Canada. *International Symposium on Deep Structure of the Continental Crust: Results from Reflection Seismology (Abstracts),* pp. 35–6, Cornell University, Ithaca, NY.

HALES, A., HELSLEY, C. & NATION, J. 1970. Crustal structure study on Gulf coast of Texas. *Bulletin of the American Association of Petroleum Geologists,* **54,** 2045–57.

HALL, J. & AL-HADDAD, F. 1976. Seismic velocities in the Lewisian metamorphic complex, northwest Britain—*in situ* measurements. *Scottish Journal of Geology,* **12,** 305–14.

——, POWELL, D., WARNER, M., EL-ISA, Z., ADESANYA, O. & BLUCK, B. 1983. Seismological evidence for shallow crystalline basement in the Southern Uplands of Scotland. *Nature, London,* **305,** 418–20.

HARRIS, L., HARRIS, A., DE WITT, W. & BAYER, K. 1981. Evaluation of the southern eastern overthrust belt beneath Blue Ridge—Piedmont thrust. *Bulletin of the American Association of Petroleum Geologists*, **65**, 2497–505.

——, DE WITT, W., JR & BAYER, K. 1983. Interpretive seismic profile along Interstate I-64 from the Valley and Ridge to the Coastal Plain in central Virginia. *United States Geological Survey Oil and Gas Investigation Chart No. OC-123*.

HATCHER, R., JR & ZIETZ, I. 1980. Tectonic implications of regional aeromagnetic and gravity data from the southern Appalachians. *In*: WONES, D. (ed.) *The Caledonides in the USA: Proceedings of the International Geological Correlation Program— Caledonide Orogen Project 27, Blacksburg, VA. Department of Geological Sciences, Virginia Polytechnic Institute and State University, Memoir No. 2*, pp. 235–44.

HIRSCHLEBER, H., LUND, C., MEISSNER, R., VOGEL, A. & WEINREBE, W. 1975. Seismic investigations along the Scandinavian 'Blue Road' traverse. *Journal of Geophysics*, **41**, 135–48.

HUTCHINSON, D., GROW, J., KLITGORD, K. & SWIFT, B. 1983. Deep structure and evolution of the Carolina trough. *In*: WATKINS, J. & DRAKE, C. (eds) *Studies in Continental Margin Geology. American Association of Petroleum Geologists Memoir No. 34*, pp. 129–52.

JACOB, A. W. B. & BOOTH, D. 1977. Observations of PS reflections from the Moho. *Journal of Geophysics*, **43**, 687–92.

——, KAMINSKI, W., MURPHY, T., PHILLIPS, W. F. A & PRODEHL, C. 1985. A crustal model for a NE/SW profile through Ireland. *Tectonophysics*, **113**, 75–103.

KANESTROM, R. & HAUGHLAND, K. 1971. Crustal structure in southeastern Norway from seismic refraction measurements. *Scientific Report No. 5, ARPA Contract F61052-68-0019*, Seismic Observatory, University of Bergen, 73 pp.

KENT, P. 1980. The structural framework and history of subsidence in North Sea basin. *In*: COGNÉ, J. & SLANSKY, M. (eds) *Geology of Europe*, pp. 281–8, Société Géologique du Nord.

LAROCHE, P. 1983. Appalachians of southern Quebec seen through seismic line No. 2001. *In*: BALLY, A. (ed.) *Seismic Expression of Structural Styles. American Association of Petroleum Geologists Studies in Geology No. 15*, Vol. 3, pp. 7–22.

LEE, C. 1980. A study of the crustal structure of north central Georgia and South Carolina by analysis of synthetic seismograms. *M.S. Thesis*, Georgia Institute of Technology, Athens, GA, 121 pp.

—— & DAINTY, A. 1982. Seismic structure of the Charlotte and Carolina slate belts of south Carolina and Georgia. *Earthquake Notes*, **53**, 23–37.

LEEDER, M. 1983. Lithospheric stretching and North Sea Jurassic clastic sourcelands. *Nature, London*, **305**, 510–14.

LEPICHON, X., SIBUET, J. & FRANCHETEAU, J. 1977. The fit of the continents around the North Atlantic. *Tectonophysics*, **38**, 169–209.

LILLIE, R., NELSON, L., DE VOOGD, B., BREWER, J.,

OLIVER, J., BROWN, L., KAUFMAN, S. & VIELE, G. 1983. Crustal structure of Ouachita mountains, Arkansas: a model based on integration of COCORP reflection profiles and regional geophysical data. *Bulletin of the American Association of Petroleum Geologists*, **67**, 907–31.

MCCAMY, K. & MEYER, R. 1966. Crustal results of fixed multiple shots in the Mississippi Embayment. *In*: STEINHARDT, J. & SMITH, T. (eds) *The Earth Beneath the Continents. American Geophysical Union Monograph No. 10*, pp. 370–81.

MEISSNER, R. 1984. The continental crust in central Europe as based on reflection seismology. *International Symposium on the Deep Structure of the Continental Crust: Results from Reflection Seismology (Abstracts)*, pp. 57–8, Cornell University, Ithaca, NY.

NELSON, K., LILLIE, R., DE VOOGD, B., BREWER, J., OLIVER, J., KAUFMAN, S., BROWN, L. & VIELE, G. 1982. COCORP seismic reflection profiling in the Ouachita mountains in western Arkansas: geometry and geological interpretation. *Tectonics*, **1**, 413–30.

PETERSEN, T., BROWN, L., COOK, F., KAUFMAN, S. & OLIVER, J. 1984. Structure of the Riddleville basin from COCORP seismic data and implications for reactivation tectonics. *Journal of Geology*, **9**, 261–71.

PHILLIPS, W., STILLMAN, C. & MURPHY, T. 1976. A Caledonian plate tectonic model. *Journal of the Geological Society, London*, **132**, 579–609.

PHINNEY, R., CHOWDHURY, K. & LEVEN, J. 1984. Accretional architecture of the continental crust. *International Symposium on the Deep Structure of the Continental Crust: Results from Reflection Seismology (Abstracts)*, pp. 71–2, Cornell University, Ithaca, NY.

PRODEHL, C., SCHLITTENHARDT, J. & STEWART, S. 1984. Crustal structure of the Appalachian highlands in Tennessee. *Tectonophysics*, **109**, 61–76.

ST JULIEN, P., SLIVITSKY, A. & FEININGER, T. 1983. A deep structural profile across the Appalachians of southern Quebec. *In*: HATCHER, R., JR, WILLIAMS, H. & ZIETZ, I. (eds) *Contributions to the Tectonics and Geophysics of Mountain Chains. Geological Society of America Memoir No. 158*, pp. 103–12.

SEGUIN, M. 1982. Geophysics of the Quebec Appalachians. *Tectonophysics*, **81**, 1–50.

SELLEVOLL, M. 1973. Mohorovičić discontinuity beneath Fennoscandian and adjacent parts of the Norwegian Sea and North Sea. *Tectonophysics*, **20**, 359–66.

—— & WARWICK, R. 1971. A refraction study of the crustal structure in southern Norway. *Bulletin of the Seismological Society of America*, **61**, 457–71.

SMITH, P. & BOTT, M. H. P. 1975. Structure of the crust beneath the Caledonian foreland and the Caledonian belt of the North Scottish shelf region. *Geophysical Journal of the Royal Astronomical Society*, **40**, 187–205.

SMYTHE, D., DOBINSON, A., MCQUILLIN, R., BREWER, J., MATTHEWS, D., BLUNDELL, D. & KELK, B. 1982. Deep structure of the Scottish Caledonides revealed by the MOIST reflection profile. *Nature, London*, **299**, 338–40.

STEWART, D. 1984. The Quebec–Western Maine profile: first year results. *International Symposium on Deep Structure of the Continental Crust: Results from Reflection Seismology (Abstracts)*, pp. 84–5, Cornell University, Ithaca, NY.

TAYLOR, S. & TOKSOZ, M. 1982. Crust and upper mantle velocity structure in the Appalachian orogenic belt: implications for tectonic evolution. *Geological Society of America Bulletin*, **93**, 315–29.

——, —— & CHAPLIN, M. 1980. Crustal structure of the northeastern United States: contrasts between Grenville and Appalachian provinces. *Science*, **208**, 595–7.

VOGEL, W. & LUND, C. 1970. A combined interpretation of the trans-Scandinavian seismic profile, section 2–3. *Department of Solid Earth Physics, University of Uppsala, Report No. 4*, 22 pp.

WARNER, M., HIPKIN, R. & BROWITT, C. 1982. Southern Uplands seismic refraction profile—preliminary results. *Geophysical Journal of the Royal Astronomical Society*, **69**, 279.

WARREN, D. 1968. Transcontinental geophysical survey (35°–39° N)—seismic refraction profiles of the crust and upper mantle from 74° to 87° W longitude. *United States Geological Survey Geophysical Investigation Map No. I-535D*.

——, HEALY, J. & JACKSON, W. 1966. Crustal seismic measurements in southern Mississippi. *Journal of Geophysical Research*, **71**, 3437–58.

WOOD, R. & BARTON, P. 1983. Crustal thinning and subsidence in the North Sea. *Nature, London*, **302**, 134–6.

ZWART, H. & DORNSIEPEN, U. 1980. The Variscan and pre-Variscan tectonic evolution of central and western Europe: a tentative model. *In*: COGNÉ, J. & SLANSKY, M. (eds) *Geology of Europe*, pp. 281–8, Société Géologique du Nord.

F. A. COOK, Department of Geology and Geophysics, University of Calgary, Calgary, Alberta T2N 1N4, Canada.

D. H. MATTHEWS, Department of Earth Sciences, University of Cambridge, Madingley Road, Cambridge CB3 0EZ, UK.

A. W. B. JACOB, School of Cosmic Physics, Dublin Institute for Advanced Studies, 5 Merrion Square, Dublin 2, Ireland.

Palaeomagnetic constraints on the evolution of the Caledonian–Appalachian orogen

J. C. Briden, D. V. Kent, P. L. Lapointe, R. A. Livermore, J. L. Roy, M. K. Seguin, A. G. Smith, R. Van der Voo & D. R. Watts

SUMMARY: Late Proterozoic and Palaeozoic (pre-Permian) palaeomagnetic data from all regions involved in, or adjacent to, the Caledonian–Appalachian orogenic belt are reviewed. Between about 1100 and about 800 Ma the Laurentian and Baltic shields were close together, prior to the opening phase of the Caledonian–Appalachian Wilson cycle. The problems of tectonic interpretation of Palaeozoic palaeomagnetic data from within and around the belt derive mostly from differences of typically 10°–20° between the pole positions. These can variously be interpreted in terms of (i) relative displacements between different continents or terranes, (ii) differences in ages of remanence and (iii) aberrations due to inadequacy of data or geomagnetic complexity, and it is not always easy to discriminate between these alternatives. If the Pangaea A2 reassembly of continents around the northern and central Atlantic is taken as the end-product of Caledonian–Appalachian orogenesis, the following conclusions can be drawn.

1 Lower Palaeozoic palaeolatitude differences between the N American and British–Scandinavian margins of the Caledonides are small; hence any convergence must have been mainly E–W.
2 There are additional differences which could be due to major pre-Carboniferous strike-slip (more than 1000 km), although later strike-slip on this scale is no longer considered likely.
3 The Lower Palaeozoic apparent polar wander paths for Northern Scotland and N America disagree on face value, but must be reconciled if their conventionally assumed geographic relation is correct.
4 Lower Old Red Sandstone data from Britain and Norway disagree, but this is more likely to be due to magnetic overprinting in the Norwegian rocks than to remnant oceans between the regions of Old Red Sandstone facies.
5 Armorica seems to have been far to the S, adjacent to Gondwana, in Ordovician time. The latest view is that it collided with Euramerica in early Devonian time to form the Old Red Continent.
6 The timing of Gondwana's collision with the Old Red Continent is controversial; it is within either the late Devonian or the Carboniferous. If it occurred early in that time range, much of Hercynian–Alleghanian orogeny post-dated it.

Palaeomagnetic data from the continental crust were crucial in the recognition of Wegenerian continental drift which consists principally of the fragmentation and dispersal of Pangaea from Mesozoic times onward. However, limitations of precision and the indeterminacy of longitude which arises from the axial symmetry of the time-averaged palaeomagnetic field prevented the deduction of adequate and unique maps of the sequence of events. Simpler and more precise palaeomagnetic and tectonic data from the oceanic crust were required to achieve precise reassembly of relative positions and, once these were available, the principal role of continental data was to place those reassemblies into a latitude–longitude framework.

The application of continental palaeomagnetism to Palaeozoic continent distribution is even more hazardous than is the case for Mesozoic and younger periods for a number of reasons.

1 There is no additional constraint from contemporary oceanic crust, since none is preserved other than as ophiolite fragments.
2 The definition of Palaeozoic lithospheric fragments—plates and terranes—is not always clear.
3 There are insufficient data to chart the progress of all these fragments relative to the pole.
4 In general, older rocks are palaeomagnetically more complex. Whether by involvement in orogeny or by long-term exposure to geomorphological processes, older rocks are more likely to have been at least partially remagnetized. The dissection of the various magnetizations coexisting in such rocks is never straightforward and is sometimes impossible.
5 Problems of dating magnetizations are severe. Not only are there problems of dating the rocks themselves and of relating biostratigraphic and

From HARRIS, A. L. & FETTES, D. J. (eds), 1988, *The Caledonian–Appalachian Orogen,*
Geological Society Special Publication No. 38, pp. 35–48.

radiometric ages into an internally consistent scale, but there are also problems in relating magnetization components to datable events in the formation and subsequent history of those rocks, e.g. in red beds.

It follows that useful palaeomagnetic constraints on the evolution of an orogenic belt are best derived from sequences of precise dated palaeomagnetic field estimates from individual lithospheric fragments. Precision is vital because relative movements of the order of hundreds of kilometres or less are of key interest to students of the geology of orogeny. Sequences of data are necessary because the required order of precision is rarely attained in single rock formations. Dating is vital because relative ages of events are a key element in the pattern of tectonic evolution.

In the case of the Appalachian–Caledonian orogen the definition of terranes within the belt is still a matter of debate, the identity and character of much of the SE margin is uncertain and the geological record on the cratons available for palaeomagnetic sampling is far from adequate; it also emerges that much of the apparent polar wander (APW) that is found corresponds to a change in palaeo-orientation rather than palaeolatitude.

Hence the approach we take here is to assume that the major fragments of continental lithosphere in the lower Palaeozoic were Baltica, Gondwanaland, Laurentia and Siberia, which would progressively be sutured along the Caledonian, Appalachian, Hercynian and Uralian orogenic belts to form a Pangaea at least by late Palaeozoic times. We shall consider the motion of each of these blocks in so far as they are relevant to the Appalachian–Caledonian orogen, and we shall also consider marginal regions of those 'continents' within the orogen, and those possible microcontinental fragments caught up within the belt, for which there are any palaeomagnetic data.

The palaeomagnetic expression of plate convergence related to the Caledonides was first illustrated schematically as differences between 'European' and 'N American' Palaeozoic polar wander paths relative to the geometrical fits of Bullard *et al.* (1965) and of Smith & Hallam (1970) now called Pangaea A, by Briden *et al.* (1973) and McElhinny (1973). The obvious place to try to measure the amount of separation was the British Isles, which is the only place where the whole width of the belt is exposed on land, but early attempts (Briden *et al.* 1973, Piper 1979) were rather inconclusive owing to scatter in the data. A direct comparison of poles from two contemporaneous volcanic suites in Ireland

(Deutsch 1980) and a more generalized estimate based on sequences of data, some of it more refined than hitherto, by Briden *et al.* (1984) are more satisfactory. Van der Voo and co-workers (Van der Voo 1979, Hagstrum *et al.* 1980, Perroud *et al.* 1984) have extended the comparisons to embrace 'Armorica', which is hypothetically an Armorica plate consisting not only of the Armorican massif but of most of Hercynian Europe, probably the Avalonian terranes of northeastern N America and possibly southern England and Wales.

Morris (1976) pointed out that the long-known discrepancy between European and N American Ordovician–Devonian data on the base map of Bullard *et al.* (1965) was consistent with major transcurrent movement roughly along the present Atlantic margin.

Features such as these have been incorporated into palaeocontinental world maps on a variety of scales and generalizations (Smith *et al.* 1973, 1981, Zonenshayn & Gorodnitskiy 1977a, b, Kanasewich *et al.* 1978, Morel & Irving 1978, Scotese *et al.* 1979, Bambach *et al.* 1980, Turner & Tarling 1982, Scotese 1984, Livermore *et al.* 1985).

We have endeavoured to confine our considerations to data which can be considered reliable in terms of their sampling, magnetic cleaning and dating. We have not applied stringent numerical criteria for rejection. This would lead to the elimination of a large proportion of the data (*cf.* the small number of grade A poles listed by Briden & Duff (1981)). Moreover, rigid criteria are not favoured because it is unclear what number of samples is required to eliminate bias; samples may not actually be independent in the statistical sense, and small confidence limits may indicate high quality or simply failure to sample secular variation adequately. Further, the methods and standards of analysis vary between laboratories, e.g. in the averaging of palaeomagnetic directions or VGPs and in the calculation of error limits. Rather, those poles considered most reliable by palaeomagnetists familiar with the results from each continent or continental fragment have been sought. The poles used all conform to the minimum rejection criteria set out by McElhinny (1973).

Laurentia

Laurentia comprises N America, Greenland, W Spitzbergen, Rockall and NW Scotland. Its reassembly in the configuration of Bullard *et al.* (1965) is generally consistent with geological constraints, most importantly the continuity of

Archaean ('Lewisian') and Proterozoic ('Grenville') basement and lower Palaeozoic cover (Durness and Beekmantown sequences) across the Atlantic. Of course, in Lower Palaeozoic time Laurentia would have presented a somewhat different outline from now, since its margins have subsequently been much modified.

The polar wander path for the interval between 1150 and 820 Ma is documented by a comparatively high density of pole positions comprising the Keweenawan track and the Grenville track. The Keweenawan track is determined by poles from Keweenawan volcanics, intrusives and sediments, and is supported by data from the Proterozoic Grand Canyon sequence. The later Grenville track is derived almost entirely from intrusions which cooled slowly in the Grenville Province after the peak metamorphic event, often resulting in complex multi-vector palaeomagnetic records. The Grenville poles are now regarded as representative of Laurentia because similar poles have been identified outside the Grenville Province. The precise connection of the Grenville track with the Keweenawan track is equivocal. The continuous joined paths shown in Fig. 1 are from recent reviews (Buchan *et al.* 1983, Roy 1983), with the two tracks connected near the equator and the Grenville poles forming a counterclockwise loop (S poles) in the eastern hemisphere. The age calibration of the Keweenawan track is uncertain by ± 50 Ma (Roy 1983), and the Grenville track is perhaps better dated by ^{40}Ar/^{39}Ar dating of mineral separates (Buchan *et al.* 1983). The poles in the highest latitudes on the Keweenawan track may be the result of asymmetry between mean directions of palaeo-magnetic fields of opposite polarity during Keweenawan time (Nevanlinna & Pesonen 1983).

Palaeomagnetic poles from the Stoer Group and the Torridon Group of the NW Highlands of Scotland fall on the Keweenawan track when rotated into the N American frame of reference using a reconstruction (Smith *et al.* 1983) in the style of Bullard *et al.* (1965). This implies that the age of magnetization of these sediments is between 1100 and 1050 Ma, contrasting with the Rb–Sr closure ages of 968 Ma for the Stoer Group and 777 Ma for the Torridon Group. This discrepancy is open to a number of interpretations.

The polar wander track for Laurentia between 820 Ma ago and early Palaeozoic time is highly problematical because of the low density of pole determinations for this interval. Published interpretations have been criticized because they are based mainly on undated secondary magnetizations (McCabe & Van der Voo 1983, Roy 1983). A substantially larger data base is required for this interval before any consensus on the nature of the Laurentia polar wander path for this interval is reached.

Notwithstanding increasingly intensive study over the past 30 years, the Palaeozoic APW path for N America remains controversial. Almost all pole positions from upper Ordovician and younger rocks lie within 20° of the Permo-Carboniferous poles suggesting *either* that N America moved less relative to the poles in that time than any other fragment that has been palaeomagnetically studied *or* that the remanence of these rocks is dominated by Permo-Carboniferous overprints so that the mid-Palaeozoic APW of America is not yet fully discovered. Such a conclusion is implicit in the interpretation of Seguin & Gahé (1985). The remagnetization hypothesis was first proposed by Creer (1968) and has been convincingly documented in several specific cases (e.g. Roy *et al.* 1967, French & Van der Voo 1977, Irving & Strong 1984a, Kent & Opdyke 1985). More generally, it is suggested by the observations that Cambrian poles are spread along a line from the equatorial W Pacific to the vicinity of Permo-Carboniferous poles (Roy *et al.* 1983).

Those poles from Ordovician, Silurian and Devonian rocks which do not group close to Permo-Carboniferous poles are instead scattered roughly along the 30°N latitude line between about 160°E and 80°E with no clear chronological order to them (Roy *et al.* 1983), suggesting that overprinting was not restricted to Permo-Carboniferous time. Seguin & Michaud (1985) reached this conclusion in the case of sediments from the St Lawrence Lowlands.

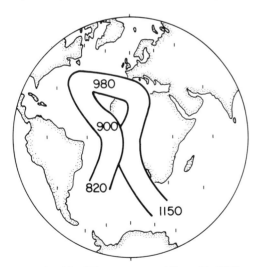

FIG. 1. Combined Keweenawan and Grenville APW paths (ages in Ma) (Redrawn after Buchan *et al.* 1983.)

Although more elaborate paths which imply extremely rapid and complex APW have been proposed (Dankers 1982), the path drawn by Van der Voo *et al.* (1980) (see also Van der Voo 1981) which is updated in Fig. 2 has been widely accepted as the best available estimate of the motion of the craton.

On this basis divergent data from lower Carboniferous and older rocks from the Appalachians have been interpreted as evidence for large-scale sinistral transcurrent motion (Kent & Opdyke 1979, Van der Voo *et al.* 1979, Kent 1982) and/or rotation (Spariosu & Kent 1983) of terranes within the Appalachians. However, this interpretation has been disputed (Roy 1982), and not all data from the belt conflict with that from the craton (Roy *et al.* 1983, Seguin *et al.* 1985). Moreover, Irving & Strong (1984b) have recently argued that what was originally interpreted as a pole position divergent from that applicable to the craton may instead be typical of the craton, while in other cases the presumed primary NRMs of cratonic rocks are now realized to be late Palaeozoic overprints (Kent & Opdyke 1985). Hence the notion of large-scale transcurrent motion in Carboniferous and later time is now discounted and hence, paradoxically, many of the best estimates of the N American APW path may have been derived from its deformed margin rather than its stable interior. If so, this may be because the rocks from the orogenic belt were

indurated and thus protected from the promotion of diagenesis by circulating groundwater, while the cratonic rocks were vulnerable to the effects of such processes (Irving & Strong 1984b, Seguin & Michaud 1985).

The lower Palaeozoic and Devonian APW paths for Scotland N of the Iapetus suture (Fig. 3A, B) are updated from Briden *et al.* (1984) and are extended into the lower Carboniferous. The data are entirely from igneous rocks, which are mostly intrusive, and high-grade metamorphic rocks. Although only a minority of the poles are dated directly, correlation is generally fairly well constrained by stratigraphic control and petrological affinity. As in N America red sediments appear to have been totally remagnetized in Permo-Carboniferous times (Tarling *et al.* 1976), and these data are omitted. Briden *et al.* (1984) sought to demonstrate that within these parts of Scotland there was no significant difference between the data from N and S of the Great Glen (compare Figs 3A and 3B), contrary to the conclusions of Van der Voo & Scotese (1981).

In Fig. 4 the N American data (Fig. 2) are rotated to Europe after Bullard *et al.* (1965). Comparison with Fig. 3 shows that on this reassembly the *bulk* of N American poles lie in systematically higher latitudes than is the case for the Scottish poles. This is consistent with a configuration like that proposed by Kent & Keppie (1987, Fig. 1) and subsequent sinistral shear. However, the most reliable of the critical N American data do not show this discrepancy; in particular, the Silurian data from the Rose Hill and Wabash Formations (9 and W in Fig. 4) are not significantly different from the poles from some of the Newer Granites in Scotland (HG, R and SG in Fig. 3A). Also, the paths from both regions backtrack together in the Lower Carboniferous. Thus it is possible that there may be a common APW path for Laurentia from Ordovician times to the end of the Palaeozoic; if this is so, it has the advantages of (a) not violating the widely accepted geometrical and geological reassembly, (b) not requiring transcurrent displacements younger than Caledonian age and (c) not requiring displacements of areas usually regarded as essentially part of the craton (Spariosu & Kent 1983).

FIG. 2. Palaeozoic APW path for N America according to Van der Voo *et al.* (1980) where most of the data are listed. Additional data are as follows: pole 9 revised after French & Van der Voo (1979); W, Wabash limestone (McCabe *et al.* 1985); T, Terenceville Formation (Kent 1982); D, Deer Lake Group (Irving & Strong 1984a).

Baltica

We refer to Baltica as the region bounded by the Caledonian, Uralian and Hercynian belts, and therefore consisting principally of Scandinavia and the Russian–central European platform, with Britain (S of the Iapetus suture) possibly at its

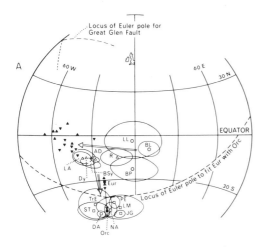

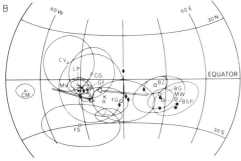

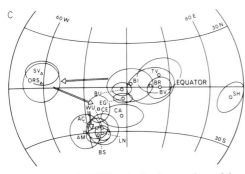

FIG. 3. Palaeozoic APW paths for three regions of the British Isles (A) N of the Great Glen fault, (B) between the Great Glen fault and the Solway line, and (C) S of the Solway line, with mean poles from other relevant areas: O, poles from Ordovician formations; Δ, Silurian–early Devonian; □, mid-Devonian and younger Palaeozoic. The 95% confidence limits are shown in all cases. Full symbols denote data from single sites. The data are from Briden *et al.* (1984), where the notation and sources are given, with additions as follows: FG, Foyers granite revised after Torsvik (1984); HG, Helmsdale granite (Torsvik *et al.* 1983); SG, Strontian grantie (Torsvik 1984); K, Kinghorn lavas (Everitt & Belshé 1960); CE, mean Carboniferous of England and Wales (Irving 1964).

western extremity, and central and eastern Spitzbergen and Novaya Zemlya on its northern flank. However, it is not clear for what period of time Baltica, as thus defined, was a tectonic entity, and the palaeomagnetic data base is so uneven, mainly because of the partiality of the stratigraphic record, that relative motions between parts of the region cannot be well defined at present.

A high density of pole determinations for the interval from 1040 to 840 Ma is available for Baltica, mainly from the Sveconorwegian fold belt which probably correlates with the Grenville province. This polar wander path is shown in Fig. 5. The palaeomagnetic poles span the same interval as the Grenville track, but the interpretation depicted in Fig. 5 shows the Baltic poles describing a clockwise path in the eastern hemisphere, opposite to the sense of movement depicted for the Grenville track as interpreted by various N American workers. Imprecision in the dating and location of the poles may be a factor in this ambiguity, and the Baltica polar wander path requires more precise calibration by ^{40}Ar/^{39}Ar age determinations as has been done for the Grenville track. Peripheral parts of Baltica may have been accreted during Proterozoic time, but there are no palaeomagnetic data to delimit this.

In the Palaeozoic the palaeomagnetic data distribution within Baltica is reversed and is concentrated in the peripheral regions such as Britain. Hence the data are again inadequate to determine when the present relative configuration was attained. In particular, the position of Scandinavia relative to southern Britain is not

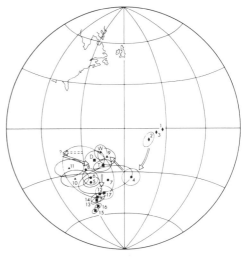

FIG. 4. N American data of Fig. 2 rotated to Europe after Bullard *et al.* (1965), plotted as South APW path and annotated for comparison with Fig. 3.

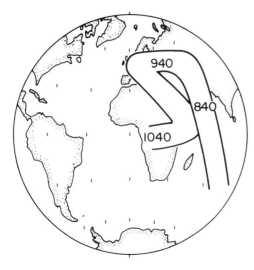

FIG. 5. APW path for Baltica for the interval 1040–840 Ma. (After Stearn & Piper 1984.)

determined. Hence, most unfortunately, data are inadequate to throw light on the possible evolution of the 'third arm' of the Caledonides through central Europe except to indicate that the Russian Cambro-Ordovician and British Ordovician palaeolatitudes were similar but that their orientations were very different from the present; this may imply substantial closure and relative rotation in later Lower Palaeozoic time.

All Cambrian sediments from Britain that have been studied (Briden et al. 1971, 1973, Claesson & Turner 1980) seem to have been remagnetized. Southern Britain, however, does provide a number of reasonably constrained Ordovician and Silurian data. Although the Lower Devonian is only represented by the pole from the Anglo-Welsh Old Red Sandstone (Chamalaun & Creer 1964), McClelland Brown (1983) has confirmed this and demonstrated that the primary remanence has been distinguished from the strong Permo-Carboniferous overprint. Hence the APW path for southern Britain (Fig. 3C) heads westward as does the path for Scotland (Fig. 3A, B), although in the former case it may be exaggerated by about 20° of fairly local clockwise rotation which deflects the regional Caledonoid trend in the Old Red Sandstone of W Wales. As with Laurentia, the path then backtracks in the Lower Carboniferous before heading to higher latitudes (about 30°) in later Carboniferous times.

Scandinavia provides fragmentary data including only four of Lower Palaeozoic age. The three possibly Cambrian poles, from the Alnö and Fen complexes and the Nexø sandstone, differ greatly

and it is premature to suggest an APW path (Piper 1981). That from the Ordovician Sulitjelma gabbro is of uncertain regional significance because of its allochthonous tectonic situation. There are three poles from the Norwegian Old Red Sandstone, all located approximately 20°S, 345°E and thus differing from the results from Britain and seeming to imply a 'Tornquist's Sea' up to 1000 km wide at this time (Kent & Keppie 1987, Fig. 1). However, this interpretation involves major separations between components of the Old Red Sandstone continent when the Old Red facies was already widely developed. Since the British data are corroborated by evidence from contemporaneous extrusive and intrusive igneous rocks while the Russian and Norwegian data are all from sediments and fall on later Palaeozoic parts of the British APW path, an alternative explanation of this difference is that the original NRM in the sediments has been overprinted.

For the Russian platform (Khramov et al. 1981) there are Cambro-Ordovician data which are regarded as reliable, but Ordovician, Silurian and early Devonian data are believed to have been affected by partial or total overprinting in the late Palaeozoic. Thus although Khramov et al. (1981) elicited some control on the position of the Russian platform in the Ordovician and Silurian using data from the Urals, these are insufficient to provide a reliable APW path (Fig. 6A).

Armorica

Van der Voo (1979) and Hagstrum et al. (1980) suggested, largely on palaeomagnetic grounds but augmented by geological argument, that the Armorican massif, together with the Bohemian massif, England and Wales and the Avalonian terranes of NE America, was part of a somewhat larger lithospheric plate 'Armorica' throughout much of Palaeozoic time. They argued that Armorica was still in high southerly latitudes in the early Ordovician (see the end of the APW path in Fig. 6(B) and Fig. 8(A)) but moved northwards to collide with N America in the Taconic orogeny. Perroud et al. (1984) have revised the estimate of collision to coincide with the Acadian orogeny and also pointed out that Armorica could have been a 'mosaic of tectonic elements . . . more or less at the same latitude' rather than a single plate.

The incorporation of Central Britain between the Hercynian front and the Iapetus suture into Armorica rests upon inconclusive late Proterozoic and Cambrian palaeomagnetic data and upon

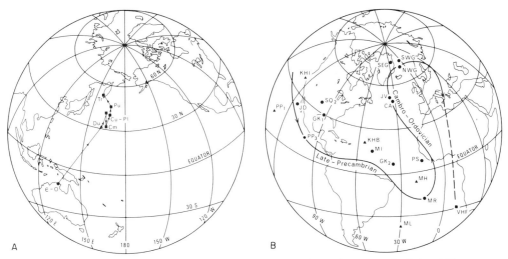

FIG. 6. Palaeozoic APW path for (A) the Russian platform (redrawn from Khramov *et al.* 1981) and (B) Armorica (Hagstrum *et al.* (1980) updated by Perigo *et al.* (1983) from where this map was redrawn). (Approximate stratigraphic ages and the middle Devonian to lower Carboniferous pole (VHF) from the Vosges, Harz and Franconian Forest (Bachtadse *et al.* 1983) have been added.)

uncharacteristically high inclinations (e.g. Thomas & Briden 1976) among a large body of Ordovician data which indicate lower latitudes (30°–43°S) than those of the Armorican massif (46°–76°S). Hence we regard central Britain as marginal to Baltica and not Armorica, and have discussed it in the previous section. This is contrary to the geologically based inferences of Ziegler (1984) that the London platform and Irish Sea horst belong to the same block as the Armorican and Bohemian massifs, unless we have been misled by the palaeomagnetic results from the latter regions. It should also be pointed out that the affinity of Avalonia and other marginal terranes of N America to Armorica is equivocal. However, the role of Armorica, even if it embraces no more than the stretch of Hercynian Europe from the Armorican to the Bohemian massif, is important to the tectonic evolution of the region as will be shown in the next section.

Relative positions of the crustal blocks

The palaeomagnetic data summarized in the foregoing sections provide control on the palaeolatitude and orientation of each crustal fragment, with uncertainties which amount to several degrees of arc (i.e. at least several hundred

kilometres) at the 95% confidence level. The relative longitude remains indeterminate so that formal estimates of the separation of fragments will always be minima and will be measured by differences in palaeolatitude only; it is for this reason that compilers of Palaeozoic world 'maps' (e.g. Smith *et al.* 1973) often refer to them as 'composites' rather than true maps. Control on actual palaeolongitudinal separation relies on rather generalized geological constraints, such as the timing of the eventual suturing of two margins, together with the assumption that plate velocities have not been an order of magnitude larger than the present maximum. In particular, the need to assemble Pangaea by the end of the Palaeozoic is a major constraint.

The arrangement of Pangaea that is usually considered is the least-squares continental fit (Bullard *et al.* 1965, Smith & Hallam 1970), now often called Pangaea A, which fits a great deal of continental geological evidence as well as sea-floor spreading data. However, as has been realized for many years (van Hilten 1964), Permian and early Triassic palaeomagnetic data from Laurasia and Gondwanaland do not conform to this reconstruction but are better fitted with the northern continents displaced westward (anticlockwise) relative to Gondwana (Van der Voo & French 1974, Van der Voo *et al.* 1976, Van der Voo *et al.* 1984) in the arrangement called Pangaea A2 by Morel & Irving (1981). This route has been followed by Livermore *et al.* (1985).

Precambrian

Fragments of a late Proterozoic reconstruction can be glimpsed in the available palaeomagnetic data. If the correlation of the Stoer and Torridonian poles with the Keweenawan poles is correct, i.e. older than their Rb–Sr closure ages, the fragment of Precambrian crust in the NW Highlands of Scotland must be placed near the position proposed by Bullard *et al.* (1965). However, this conclusion remains uncertain in the absence of direct confirmation of the age of remanence.

Grenville poles and contemporaneous poles from Baltica are consistent with a reconstruction in which Baltica lies against Laurentia and the Grenville Province is continuous with the Sveconorwegian belt (Stearn & Piper 1984). Baltica is 15°–20° S of the Bullard *et al.* (1965) fit in a position similar to some suggested Devonian reconstructions (e.g. Kent & Keppie 1988).

Cambrian and Ordovician

As the discussion of the palaeomagnetic data shows, maps of Cambrian and Lower Ordovician time are necessarily very speculative, at least as far as the continents bounding the Caledonides are concerned. Smith *et al.* (1973, 1981), Scotese *et al.* (1979) and Morel & Irving (1978) have all produced tentative versions, and while they differ greatly they have in common the placement of most major fragments in low latitude. Likewise, maps for later Ordovician time show Laurentia and Baltica in low latitudes, with Iapetus lying at 0–30°S.

In Fig. 7(A) (Livermore *et al.* 1985), which relates to late Ordovician–early Silurian times, Baltica is positioned on the basis of data mostly from England and Wales. Interpolation of the APW path from the Russian platform would put Baltica in a different orientation but a similar latitude. Laurentia is positioned on the basis of N American data; the difference between Laurentia and Baltica data implies a latitudinal width of about 2000 km for the Iapetus ocean, which is twice as wide as that estimated from the difference between data from England–Wales and Scotland alone (Briden *et al.* 1984). Thus, taken at face value, the palaeomagnetic data would place Scotland in Fig. 7(A) in the middle of the Iapetus ocean which would pose major geological problems. Figure 7(A) is a cartographic expression of the discrepancies between the Scottish and N American data discussed at the end of the section on Laurentia. Some regions of the Appalachians are positioned on the S side of Iapetus in this map, in conformity with some palaeomagnetic data (Lapointe 1979, Rao & Van der Voo 1979). This emphasizes that early or middle Palaeozoic closure and transcurrent movement within the Appalachians remain a distinct likelihood notwithstanding doubts about the reality of *late* Palaeozoic transcurrent displacement. Armorica and the southern Appalachians are both shown at about 60°S.

The Ordovician sketch map due to Perroud *et al.* (1984) (Fig. 8A) is essentially the same as Fig. 7(A) except in its treatment of central Britain as part of Armorica rather than Baltica. That association is not well supported by the palaeomagnetic evidence which indicates that Britain was in a significantly lower palaeolatitude. Duff (1980) associated both regions with the Baltic shield and drew a common APW path, but this depended heavily on similarity between data from the Fen complex (Norway) and results of a bare reconnaissance nature from igneous rocks in Leicestershire and slates from N Wales.

Silurian and Devonian

In the first of their alternative maps for the Siluro-Devonian boundary (Fig. 7B) Livermore *et al.* (1985) show Iapetus still up to 1000 km wide or more. On this map Baltica is shown in a position indicated by poles from the Norwegian Old Red Sandstone and from Avalonia. Cratonic N America is positioned separately, using the poles from the Peel Sound Formation and the Bloomsburg Formation. These choices of data imply that Baltica was offset dextrally from its Bullard *et al.* (1965) position relative to Laurentia, i.e. prior to sinistral displacements along the Caledonian–Appalachian belt (*cf.* Van der Voo & Scotese 1981).

If, instead, Laurasia were oriented as a single unit based on British and N American data from the Caledonian–Appalachian belt, the southern margin of the N American craton would be at nearly 60°S. This raises difficulties in relation to the Gondwana data (Kent *et al.* 1984, Livermore *et al.* 1985) as well as indicating that a version of Pangaea was already assembled as early as end-Silurian time.

For the early Devonian, Perroud *et al.* (1984) (Fig. 8B) show Laurentia and Baltica in positions not unlike those shown in Fig. 7(B), but with Armorica already adjacent.

Carboniferous

Figure 7(C) shows a map proposed by Livermore *et al.* (1985) for Eifelian–Tournasian time. It is based on various assumptions about the palaeomagnetic data, faunal provinciality and the

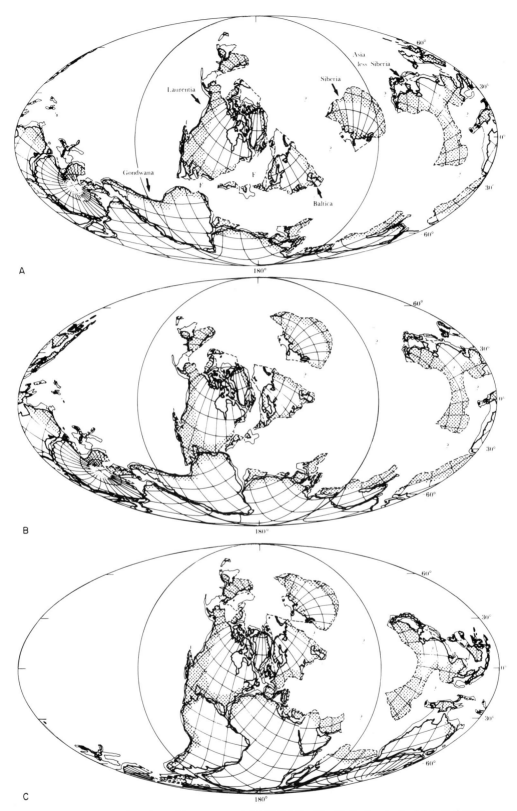

FIG. 7. Global reconstructions due to Livermore *et al.* (1985) (Mollweide elliptical projection) (stippled areas denote an approximate extent of orogenic deformation of the same age as the map or younger; F indicates that longitude separation is based on fossil evidence; ? in oceanic regions indicates uncertain longitudinal separation; ? in continental regions indicates that no palaeomagnetic data are available): (A) Caradoc–Wenlock time; (B) Ludlow–Emsian time; (C) Eifelian–Tournaisian time.

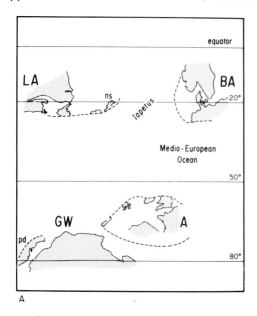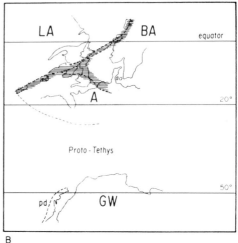

FIG. 8. Sketch maps of the palaeocontinental positions proposed by Perroud *et al.* (1984) (A, Armorica; GW, Gondwana; BA, Baltica; LA, Laurentia; ns, northern Scotland; pd, Delaware Piedmont); shaded zones in (B) are areas of collision between plates: (A) Ordovician; (B) Devonian.

subsequent configuration of Pangaea, and depicts most of the continents already in one reassembly with Siberia arbitrarily not far removed from Russia and with eastern Asia arbitrarily positioned. Laurentia–Baltica is positioned on this map using data from Britain, Avalonia, central Europe and Iberia. This places it in a very similar position to that indicated by the revised data from the Mauch Chunk Formation (Kent & Opdyke 1985) and the data from the Canadian Maritimes (Roy & Morris 1983). Watts (1985) has shown that data from Spitzbergen are consistent with the position in Fig. 7(C).

Palaeomagnetic overprints

In this paper we have emphasized primary magnetizations and the difficulty of distinguishing them when secondary overprinting has occurred. However, the overprints themselves are of considerable importance as indicators of the diagenesis or metamorphism which causes them, and when the secondary remanence can be dated they are as useful as any other data for palaeomagnetic purposes.

For example, among the British data (Fig. 3B) is a sequence from the Aberdeenshire gabbros (Watts & Briden 1984) in which palaeomagnetic direction changes systematically with cooling age as determined independently by K–Ar studies

(Dewey & Pankhurst 1970). It seems that the NRM is either viscous PTRM acquired during cooling to about 500°C, as the original investigators suggested, or CRM acquired during the last stages of cooling, i.e. significantly later but still related to the post-orogenic cooling and still indicative of its progression in time and space. Thus the data can be used, as here, to contribute to the local APW path, although the absolute age of remanence may not be unambiguously known. Conversely, if the magnetization process were clear the data could also be used to refine the post-orogenic cooling pattern for this terrane and to provide temperature–time points for elucidation of its history of uplift and unroofing.

Late Palaeozoic overprinting of older rocks has been a major phenomenon and is of interest in its own right. It is likely to be related to diagenetic redeposition of iron oxides owing to groundwater circulation in the widespread arid climates of the Permo-Carboniferous (French & Van der Voo 1977, Scotese *et al.* 1982, McCabe *et al.* 1983, Irving & Strong 1984a, Seguin & Michaud 1985). In many rocks, particularly permeable sediments, overprinting amounts to total remagnetization. However, even massive igneous and metamorphic rocks from well outside the Hercynian–Alleghanian belt, where cooling effects would have been operative, have been affected (Roy *et al.* 1983, Briden & Mullen 1984). The data are useful additions to the late Palaeozoic data base where precise ages can be attached to them, and the phenomenon is worthy of much magnetic and micro-mineralogical study of the processes that are involved.

Discussion

The maps in Figs 7 and 8 are extremely speculative because of the sparse data set and its uneven quality. The data amount to only a fraction of what is required for optimum palaeomagnetic control on evolution of the orogen. Nevertheless, limited but useful palaeomagnetic constraints upon the evolution of the belt can be deduced from the present data.

1   The Baltic and Laurentian shields may have been adjacent in the late Proterozoic before the opening phase of the Caledonian–Appalachian Wilson cycle.

2   In the Ordovician, Laurentia and Baltica were in similar palaeolatitudes and the convergence which caused the Scandinavian and British Caledonides must therefore have been principally along the lines of palaeolatitude.

3   The Armorican and Bohemian massifs comprised an 'Armorica' plate which was in high southerly latitudes in the early Palaeozoic but contiguous with Laurentia–Baltica by Devonian time; its convergence could coincide with and

partially account for Acadian–Caledonian orogenic phases and perhaps for the 'third arm' of the Caledonides through central Europe.

4   Gondwanaland began to collide with the northern supercontinent in the late Devonian or early Carboniferous. Repercussions of this collision constituted Carboniferous orogeny in the southern Appalachians–Hercynides.

However, the data are neither sufficiently complete nor sufficiently refined to assist greatly in resolving such vital questions as (a) the nature of the central European Caledonides (Ordovician data from the Baltic shield and Russian platform, and Cambrian data from England are required for this purpose) and (b) the relative roles of dextral and sinistral displacements during orogenesis. To remedy this we require many more data, particularly from the cratonic and platform regions in which primary magnetizations are resolved from secondary overprints. This is a task requiring the highest standards of analysis—standards which have not always been attained even in some recent studies—and will need to be integrated with tectonic and mineralogical study. Such work may contribute to knowledge of the metamorphic and diagenetic history of the region as well as to its evolving reassembly.

ACKNOWLEDGMENT: We acknowledge useful discussion and preprints of papers by E. Irving.

References

BACHTADSE, V., HELLER, F. & KRÖNER, A. 1983. Palaeomagnetic investigations in the Hercynian mountain belt of central Europe. *Tectonophysics*, **91**, 285–99.

BAMBACH, R. K., SCOTESE, C. R. & ZIEGLER, A. M. 1980. Before Pangaea: the geographies of the Palaeozoic world. *American Scientist*, **68**, 26–38.

BRIDEN, J. C. & DUFF, B. A. 1981. Pre-Carboniferous paleomagnetism of Europe north of the Alpine orogenic belt. *In*: MCELHINNY, M. W. & VALENCIO, D. A. (eds) *Paleoreconstruction of the Continents, Geodynamics Series*, Vol. 2, pp. 137–49, American Geophysical Union and Geological Society of America, Washington, DC.

—— & MULLEN, A. J. 1984. Superimposed Recent, Permo-Carboniferous and Ordovician palaeomagnetic remanence in the Builth Volcanic Series, Wales. *Earth and Planetary Science Letters*, **69**, 413–34.

——, TURNELL, H. B. & WATTS, D. R. 1984. British palaeomagnetism, Iapetus Ocean and the Great Glen fault. *Geology*, **12**, 428–31.

——, IRONS, J. & JOHNSON, P. A. 1971. Palaeomagnetic studies of the Caerfai Series and the Skomer

Volcanic Group (Lower Palaeozoic, Wales). *Geophysical Journal of the Royal Astronomical Society*, **22**, 1–16.

——, MORRIS, W. A. & PIPER, J. D. A. 1973. Palaeomagnetic studies in the British Caledonides—VI. Regional and global implications. *Geophysical Journal of the Royal Astronomical Society*, **34**, 107–34.

BUCHAN, K. L., FAHRIG, W. F., FREDA, G. N. & FRITH, R. A. 1983. Paleomagnetism of the Lac St. Jean anorthosite and related rocks, Grenville province, Quebec. *Canadian Journal of Earth Sciences*, **20**, 246–58.

BULLARD, E. C., EVERETT, J. & SMITH, A. G. 1965. The fit of the continents around the Atlantic. *Philosophical Transactions of the Royal Society of London, Series A*, **258**, 41–51.

CHAMALAUN, F. H. & CREER, K. M. 1964. Thermal demagnetization studies on the Old Red Sandstone of the Anglo-Welsh cuvette. *Journal of Geophysical Research*, **69**, 1607–16.

CLAESSON, K. C. & TURNER, P. 1980. Diagenetic magnetization of the Caerfai Bay Shales (Cambrian), South Wales. *Geophysical Journal of the Royal Astronomical Society*, **60**, 95–106.

CREER, K. M. 1968. Palaeozoic palaeomagnetism. *Nature, London,* **219**, 246–50.

DANKERS, P. 1982. Implications of Early Devonian poles from the Canadian Arctic Archipelago for the North American apparent polar wander path. *Canadian Journal of Earth Sciences,* **19**, 1802–9.

DEUTSCH, E. R. 1980. Magnetism of the Mid-Ordovician Tramore volcanics, SE Ireland, and the question of a wide Proto-Atlantic ocean. *Advances in Earth and Planetary Sciences,* **10**, 77–98.

DEWEY, J. F. & PANKHURST, R. J. 1970. The evolution of the Scottish Caledonides in relation to their isotopic age pattern. *Transactions of the Royal Society of Edinburgh,* **68**, 361–89.

DUFF, B. A. 1980. The palaeomagnetism of Jersey volcanics and dykes, and the Lower Palaeozoic apparent polar wander path for Europe. *Geophysical Journal of the Royal Astronomical Society,* **60**, 355–75.

EVERITT, C. W. F. & BELSHÉ, J. C. 1960. Palaeomagnetism of the British Carboniferous system. *Philosophical Magazine,* **5**, 675–85.

FRENCH, A. N. & VAN DER VOO, R. 1979. The magnetization of the Rose Hill Formation at the classical site of Graham's fold test. *Journal of Geophysical Research,* **84**, 7688–96.

FRENCH, R. B. & VAN DER VOO, R. 1977. Remagnetization problems with the palaeomagnetism of the Middle Silurian Rose Hill Formation of the Central Appalachians. *Journal of Geophysical Research,* **82**, 5803–6.

HAGSTRUM, J. T., VAN DER VOO, R., AUVRAY, B. & BONHOMMET, N. 1980. Eocambrian–Cambrian palaeomagnetism of the Armorican Massif, France. *Geophysical Journal of the Royal Astronomical Society,* **61**, 489–517.

VAN HILTEN, D. 1964. Evaluation of some tectonic hypotheses by paleomagnetism. *Tectonophysics,* **1**, 1–71.

IRVING, E. 1964. *Paleomagnetism and its Application to Geological and Geophysical Problems,* Wiley, New York.

—— & STRONG, D. F. 1984a. Paleomagnetism of the early Carboniferous Deer Lake Group western Newfoundland: no evidence for Carboniferous displacement of 'Acadia'. *Earth and Planetary Science Letters,* **69**, 374–91.

—— & —— 1984b. Evidence against large-scale Carboniferous strike-slip faulting in the Appalachian–Caledonian orogen. *Nature, London,* **310**, 762–4.

KANASEWICH, E. R., HAVSKOV, J. & EVANS, M. E. 1978. Plate tectonics in the Phanerozoic. *Canadian Journal of Earth Sciences,* **15**, 919–55.

KENT, D. V. 1982. Palaeomagnetic evidence for post-Devonian displacement of the Avalon platform (Newfoundland). *Journal of Geophysical Research,* **87**, 4441–50.

—— & KEPPIE, J. D. 1988. Silurian–Permian palaeocontinental reconstructions and circum-Atlantic tectonics. *This volume.*

—— & OPDYKE, N. D. 1979. The early Carboniferous palaeomagnetic field of North America and its bearing on tectonics of the northern Appalachians. *Earth and Planetary Science Letters,* **44**, 565–72.

—— & —— 1985. Multicomponent magnetizations from the Mississippian Mauch Chunk Formation of the central Appalachians and their tectonic implications. *Journal of Geophysical Research,* **90**, 5371–83.

——, DIA, O. & SOUGY, J. M. A. 1984. Paleomagnetism of Lower-Middle Devonian and upper Proterozoic–Cambrian (?) rocks from Mejeria (Mauritania, West Africa). *In:* VAN DER VOO, R., SCOTESE, C. R. & BONHOMMET, N. (eds) *Plate Reconstruction from Paleozoic Paleomagnetism, Geodynamics Series,* Vol. 12, pp. 99–115, American Geophysical Union, Washington, DC.

KHRAMOV, A. N., PETROVA, G. N. & PECHERSKY, D. M. 1981. Paleomagnetism of the Soviet Union. *In:* MCELHINNY, M. W. & VALENCIO, D. A. (eds) *Paleoreconstruction of the Continents, Geodynamics Series,* Vol. 2, pp. 177–94, American Geophysical Union and Geological Society of America, Washington, DC.

LAPOINTE, P. L. 1979. Paleomagnetism and orogenic history of the Botwood Group and Mount Peyton Batholith, Central Mobile Belt, Newfoundland. *Canadian Journal of Earth Sciences,* **16**, 866–76.

LIVERMORE, R. A., SMITH, A. G. & BRIDEN, J. C. 1985. Palaeomagnetic constraints on the distribution of continents in the late Silurian and early Devonian. *Philosophical Transactions of the Royal Society of London,* Series B, **309**, 29–56.

MCCABE, C. & VAN DER VOO, R. 1983. Paleomagnetic results of the Late Keweenawan Chequamegon Sandstone and implications for red bed diagenesis and Late Precambrian apparent polar wander of North America. *Canadian Journal of Earth Sciences,* **20**, 105–12.

——, ——, PEACOR, D. R., SCOTESE, C. R. & FREEMAN, R. 1983. Diagenetic magnetite carries ancient yet secondary remanence in some Paleozoic sedimentary carbonates. *Geology,* **11**, 221–3.

——, ——, WILKINSON, B. H. & DEVANEY, K. 1985. A middle/late Silurian palaeomagnetic pole from limestone reefs of the Wabash Formation (Indiana, USA). *Journal of Geophysical Research,* **90**, 2959–65.

MCCLELLAND BROWN, E. 1983. Palaeomagnetic studies of fold development in the Pembrokeshire Old Red Sandstone. *Tectonophysics,* **98**, 131–49.

MCELHINNY, M. W. 1973. *Palaeomagnetism and Plate Tectonics,* Cambridge University Press, Cambridge.

MOREL, P. & IRVING, E. 1978. Tentative palaeocontinental maps for the early Phanerozoic and Proterozoic. *Journal of Geology,* **86**, 536–61.

—— & —— 1981. Paleomagnetism and the evolution of Pangea. *Journal of Geophysical Research,* **86**, 1858–72.

MORRIS, W. A. 1976. Transcurrent motion determined palaeomagnetically in the Northern Appalachians and Caledonides and the Acadian Orogeny. *Canadian Journal of Earth Sciences,* **13**, 1236–43.

NEVANLINNA, H. & PESONEN, L. J. 1983. Late Precambrian Keweenawan asymmetric polarities as analyzed by axial offset dipole geomagnetic models. *Journal of Geophysical Research,* **88**, 645–58.

PERIGO, R., VAN DER VOO, R., AUVRAY, B. & BONHOMMET, N. 1983. Palaeomagnetism of late Precambrian–Cambrian volcanics and intrusives from the Armorican massif, France. *Geophysical Journal of the Royal Astronomical Society,* **75**, 235–60.

PERROUD, H., VAN DER VOO, R. & BONHOMMET, N. 1984. Palaeozoic evolution of the Armorica plate on the basis of palaeomagnetic data. *Geology,* **12**, 579–82.

PIPER, J. D. A. 1979. Aspects of Caledonian palaeomagnetism and their tectonic implications. *Earth and Planetary Science Letters,* **44**, 176–92.

—— 1981. Magnetic properties of the Alnön complex. *Geologiska Föreningens i Stockholm Förhandlingar,* **103**, 9–15.

RAO, K. V. & VAN DER VOO, R. 1979. Paleomagnetism of a Paleozoic anorthosite from the Appalachian Piedmont, Northern Delaware: possible tectonic implications. *Earth and Planetary Science Letters,* **47**, 113–20.

ROY, J. L. 1982. Paleomagnetism of Siluro-Devonian rocks from eastern Maine: discussion. *Canadian Journal of Earth Sciences,* **19**, 225–32.

—— 1983. Paleomagnetism of the North American Precambrian: a look at the data base. *Precambrian Research,* **19**, 319–48.

—— & MORRIS, W. A. 1983. A review of paleomagnetic results from the Carboniferous of North America; the concept of Carboniferous geomagnetic field horizon markers. *Earth and Planetary Science Letters,* **65**, 167–81.

——, OPDYKE, N. D. & IRVING, E. 1967. Further paleomagnetic results from the Bloomsburg Formation. *Journal of Geophysical Research,* **72**, 5075–86.

——, TANCZYK, E. & LAPOINTE, P. 1983. The paleomagnetic record of the Appalachians. *In*: SCHENK, P. W. (ed.) *Regional Trends in the Geology of the Appalachian–Caledonian–Hercynian–Mauritanide Orogen*, pp. 11–26, Reidel, Dordrecht.

SCOTESE, C. R. 1984. Palaeozoic palaeomagnetism and the assembly of Pangaea. *In*: VAN DER VOO, R., SCOTESE, C. R. & BONHOMMET, N. (eds) *Plate Reconstruction from Paleozoic Paleomagnetism, Geodynamics Series*, Vol. 12, pp. 1–10, American Geophysical Union, Washington, DC.

——, BAMBACH, R. K., BARTON, C., VAN DER VOO, R. & ZIEGLER, A. M. 1979. Palaeozoic base maps. *Journal of Geology,* **87**, 217–77.

——, VAN DER VOO, R. & McCABE, C. 1982. Paleomagnetism of the Upper Silurian and Lower Devonian carbonates of New York State: evidence for secondary magnetizations residing in magnetite. *Physics of the Earth and Planetary Interiors,* **30**, 385–95.

SEGUIN, M. K. & GAHÉ 1985. Paleomagnetism of Lower Devonian volcanics and Devonian dykes from north central New Brunswick, Canada. *Physics of the Earth and Planetary Interiors,* **38**, 262–76.

—— & MICHAUD, C. 1985. The Bécancour–Yamaska,

Quebec: a palaeomagnetic study. *Journal of Geomagnetism and Geoelectricity,* **37**, 895–912.

——, SINGH, A. & FYFFE, L. 1985. New paleomagnetic data from Carboniferous volcanics and red beds from Central New Brunswick. *Geophysical Research Letters,* **12**, 81–4.

SMITH, A. G. & HALLAM, A. 1970. The fit of the southern continents. *Nature, London,* **225**, 139–44.

——, BRIDEN, J. C. & DREWRY, G. E. 1973. Phanerozoic world maps. *Organisms and Continents through Time, Special Paper of the Palaeontological Association No. 12*, pp. 1–42.

——, HURLEY, A. M. & BRIDEN, J. C. 1981. *Phanerozoic Palaeocontinental World Maps*, Cambridge University Press, Cambridge, 102 pp.

SMITH, R. L., STEARN, J. E. F. & PIPER J. D. A. 1983. Palaeomagnetic studies of the Torridonian sediments, NW Scotland. *Scottish Journal of Geology,* **19**, 29–45.

SPARIOSU, D. J. & KENT, D. V. 1983. Palaeomagnetism of the Lower Devonian Traveler Felsite and the Acadian orogeny in the New England Appalachians. *Bulletin of the Geological Society of America,* **94**, 1319–28.

STEARN, J. E. F. & PIPER, J. D. A. 1984. Palaeomagnetism of the Sveconorwegian mobile belt of the Fennoscandian shield. *Precambrian Research,* **23**, 201–46.

TARLING, D. H., DONOVAN, R. N., ABOU-DEEB, S. M. & EL-BATROUK, S. I. 1976. Palaeomagnetic dating of hematite genesis in Orcadian basin sediments. *Scottish Journal of Geology,* **12**, 125–34.

THOMAS, C. & BRIDEN, J. C. 1976. Anomalous geomagnetic field during the late Ordovician. *Nature, London,* **259**, 380–2.

TORSVIK, T. H. 1984. Palaeomagnetism of the Foyers and Strontian Granites, Scotland. *Physics of the Earth and Planetary Interiors,* **36**, 163–77.

——, LØVLIE, R. & STORETVEDT, K. M. 1983. Multicomponent magnetization in the Helmsdale granite, North Scotland; geotectonic implication. *Tectonophysics,* **98**, 111–29.

TURNER, S. & TARLING, D. H. 1982. Thelodont and other agnathan distributions as tests of Lower Palaeozoic continental reconstructions. *Palaeogeography, Palaeoclimatology, Palaeoecology,* **39**, 295–311.

VAN DER VOO, R. 1979. Palaeozoic assembly of Pangaea: a new plate tectonic model for the Taconic, Caledonian and Hercynian orogenies. *EOS, Transactions of the American Geophysical Union,* **60**, 241 (abstract).

—— 1981. Paleomagnetism of North America: a brief review. *In*: McELHINNY, M. W. & VALENCIO, D. A. (eds) *Paleoreconstruction of the Continents, Geodynamics Series*, Vol. 2, pp. 159–76, American Geophysical Union and Geological Society of America, Washington, DC.

—— & FRENCH, R. B. 1974. Apparent polar wandering for the Atlantic-bordering continents: Late Carboniferous to Eocene. *Earth-Science Reviews,* **10**, 99–119.

—— & SCOTESE, C. R. 1981. Paleomagnetic evidence for a large (2,000 km) sinistral offset along the

Great Glen fault during Carboniferous time. *Geology*, **9**, 583–9.

——, FRENCH, A. N. & FRENCH, R. B. 1979. A paleomagnetic pole position from the folded Upper Devonian Catskill redbeds, and its tectonic implications. *Geology*, **7**, 345–8.

——, FRENCH, R. B. & WILLIAMS, D. W. 1976. Paleomagnetism of the Wilberns Formation (Texas) and the Late Cambrian paleomagnetic field for North America. *Journal of Geophysical Research*, **81**, 5633–8.

——, JONES, M., GROMME, C. S., EBERLEIN, G. C. & CHURKIN, M. JR 1980. Paleozoic paleomagnetism and northward drift of the Alexander Terrane, Southeastern Alaska. *Journal of Geophysical Research*, **85**, 5281–96.

——, PEINADO, J. & SCOTESE, C. R. 1984. A paleomagnetic reevaluation of Pangaea reconstructions. *In*: VAN DER VOO, R., SCOTESE, C. R. & BONHOMMET, N. (eds) *Plate Reconstruction from Paleozoic Paleomagnetism, Geodynamics Series*, Vol. 12, pp. 11–16, American Geophysical Union, Washington, DC.

WATTS, D. R. 1985. Palaeomagnetism of the Lower Carboniferous Billefjorden Group, Spitsbergen. *Geological Magazine*, **122,** 383–8.

—— & BRIDEN, J. C. 1984. Palaeomagnetic signature of slow post-orogenic cooling of the northeast Highlands of Scotland recorded in the Newer Gabbros of Aberdeenshire. *Geophysical Journal of the Royal Astronomical Society*, **77,** 775–88.

ZIEGLER, P. A. 1984. Caledonian and Hercynian crustal consolidation of western and central Europe—a working hypothesis. *Geologie en Mijnbouw*, **63**, 93–108.

ZONENSHAYN, L. P. & GORODNITSKIY, A. M. 1977a. Paleozoic and Mesozoic reconstructions of the continents and oceans. Article 1. Early and Middle Paleozoic reconstructions. *Geotectonics*, **11**, 83–94.

—— & —— 1977b. Paleozoic and Mesozoic reconstructions of the continents and oceans. Article 2. Late Paleozoic and Mesozoic reconstructions. *Geotectonics*, **11**, 159–72.

J. C. BRIDEN, Department of Earth Sciences, University of Leeds, Leeds LS2 9JT, UK. *Now at* Natural Environment Research Council, Swindon SN2 1EU, UK.

D. V. KENT, Lamont–Doherty Geological Observatory, Palisades, New York, NY 10964, USA.

P. L. LAPOINTE & J. L. ROY, Earth Physics Branch, Energy Mines and Resources, 1 Observatory Crescent, Ottawa K1A OY3, Canada.

R. A. LIVERMORE & A. G. SMITH, Department of Earth Sciences, University of Cambridge, Downing Street, Cambridge CB2 3EQ, UK. R.A.L. *now at* British Geological Survey, Keyworth, Nottingham NG12 5GG, UK.

M. K. SEGUIN, Department of Geology, Université Laval, Quebec City, Quebec G1K 7P4, Canada.

R. VAN DER VOO, Department of Geological Sciences, University of Michigan, Ann Arbor, MI 48109, USA.

D. R. WATTS, Department of Geology, University of Glasgow, Glasgow G12 8QQ, UK.

Geophysical evidence for the location of the NW boundary of Gondwanaland and its relationship with two older satellite sutures

J. P. Lefort, M. D. Max & J. Roussel

SUMMARY: The boundary between Gondwanaland and Laurussia can be traced from Portugal to southern New England using gravity and magnetic data. Further positional control using geochemistry and palaeomagnetism on rocks near the geophysical suture confirms its position. From Long Island to Florida the suture lies beneath the Coastal Plain and our interpretation relies only on geophysical data. This suture is marked by rift-associated rocks, back-arc intrusives, volcanic-arc rocks or remnants of oceanic crust. On-shore, between Cape Ann (near Boston) and Long Island Sound (near New York), the suture possibly follows the Clinton–Newbury fault. The arc-like swing to the W of the Chesapeake Bay region is probably the result of an indentation of the older Appalachian belts by the Mauritanian Reguibat prong during Carboniferous time. There are two major transform faults associated with the suture zone: N of Florida and W of Spain.

Two satellite sutures can be identified on the eastern side of the Atlantic. In northeastern Senegal and Mauritania the major gravity high which parallels the Mauritanian orogenic belt is interpreted as locating the Taconic? collision between Gondwanaland and a western microplate. S of Brittany the Spanish microplate collided with Laurussia during Acadian time. These two satellite sutures were rejuvenated during the main late Palaeozoic compression between Gondwanaland and Laurussia.

A long orogenic zone stretching from eastern Europe to the Ouachitas marks the collisional plate boundary between Laurussia and Gondwanaland. Identifying the location of this boundary and the deformational style along it is essential in trying to understand the middle and late Palaeozoic kinematics. The geophysical signature of such a boundary is distinctive between Spain and New England, but the superposition of several Palaeozoic collision events has left a complex record of sutures along the Appalachian belt. Subsequent rifting and formation of the Atlantic fragmented this record. Reconstruction of the pre-Mesozoic continental positions must be established before identifying and interpreting this old plate boundary.

Late Palaeozoic continental reconstruction

Since the pioneering reconstruction of Wegener (1929), important modifications have been made to the transatlantic 'fit' proposed by him. There have been revised closure reconstructions based on Mesozoic sea-floor spreading data or on continental geophysical markers. Although new reconstructions are similar on the small scale, differences become apparent on larger scales. The fits based on oceanic markers, which lead to a Jurassic or Triassic closure reconstruction, and those based on continental markers, which allow for older reconstructions, are different. This

difference may be due to the shear decoupling between America and Africa during Permian–Triassic time (Swanson 1982). Because the suture between Gondwanaland and Laurussia is middle Devonian to Carboniferous in age and because the youngest reliable correlatable markers known in the peri-Atlantic crust are late Hercynian in age, a later Hercynian fit is used here (Lefort & Van der Voo 1981) in preference to a Mesozoic reconstruction.

The late Palaeozoic suture between southern Spain and Florida

Three sections have been distinguished in the suture, the first based on geological and geophysical data, the second based only on geology and the third based only on geophysics.

The suture between Aracena (Spain) and Cape Ann (Massachusetts)

Delineation of this section of the suture is partly based on a magnetic and gravity compilation undertaken for the northern part of the N Atlantic area. The interpretation of the data has been simplified in its representation in Fig. 1 as two independent sets of anomalies. One set trends roughly E–W and crosses the other set which is oriented roughly N–S or N50°E to N60°E. Most of the gravity and magnetic highs are coincident and probably related to mafic bodies within the

From HARRIS, A. L. & FETTES, D. J. (eds), 1988, *The Caledonian–Appalachian Orogen*,
Geological Society Special Publication No. 38, pp. 49–60.

49

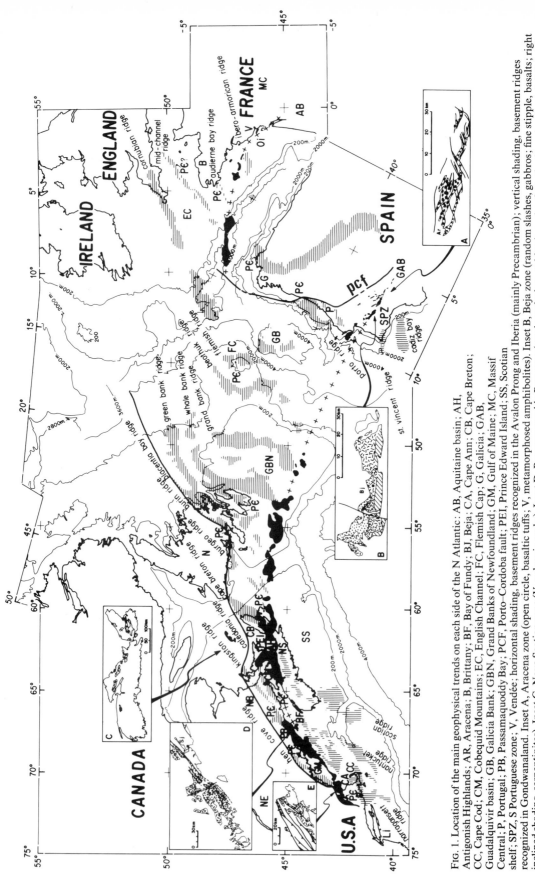

Fig. 1. Location of the main geophysical trends on each side of the N Atlantic: AB, Aquitaine basin; AH, Antigonish Highlands; AR, Aracena; B. Brittany; BF, Bay of Fundy; BJ, Beja; CA, Cape Ann; CB, Cape Breton; CC, Cape Cod; CM, Cobequid Mountains; EC, English Channel; FC, Flemish Cap; G, Galicia; GAB, Guadalquivir basin; GB, Galicia Bank; GBN, Grand Banks of Newfoundland; GM, Gulf of Maine; MC, Massif Central; P, Portugal; PB, Passamaquoddy Bay; PCF, Porto–Cordoba fault; PEI, Prince Edward Island; SS, Scotian shelf; SPZ, S Portuguese zone; V, Vendée; horizontal shading, basement ridges recognized in the Avalon Prong and Iberia (mainly Precambrian); vertical shading, basement ridges recognized in Gondwanaland. Inset A, Aracena zone (open circle, basaltic tuffs; V, metamorphosed amphibolites). Inset B, Beja zone (random slashes, gabbros; fine stipple, basalts; right inclined shading, serpentinites). Inset C, Nova Scotian zone (V, volcanic rocks). Inset D, Passamaquoddy Bay zone (random slashes, gabbroic rocks; fine stipple, volcanic rocks). Inset E, Cape Ann Zone (random slashes, gabbroic rocks). Black, sutures; crosses, extension of the Gondwanian suture; PE, Precambrian outcrops. (After Lefort 1983.)

crust or to the morphology of the top of the basement (Lefort 1983). Despite the gap observed between the Tail of the Grand Banks and the S Portuguese zone, it is possible to link some of the Canadian and European features.

In Spain and Portugal the Iberian mafic belt is marked in the W by the Devonian gabbro-dioritic zone of Beja (Fig. 1, inset B) which contains gabbro, basalt and serpentinite with ophiolitic composition (Andrade 1979). In Aracena (Fig. 1, inset A) felsic and mafic tuffs of pre-Silurian age are associated with layered amphibolites identical with abyssal tholeiites (Bard 1977). S of these zones, Devonian gabbros are known. Both areas are restricted to a narrow belt which has been interpreted as a geosuture (Lefort 1983). This mafic belt can be linked, beneath the Gualdalqui-vir basin, with the southern end of the Petite Sole–Porto–Cordoba fault. Although none of these rocks is considered part of an ophiolite suite, the entire S Portuguese zone has been interpreted as the location of a NE-dipping subduction zone (Bard *et al.* 1973). Recent geochemical data (Munha 1979) indicate that this Iberian mafic belt probably formed behind a volcanic arc; thus the true suture probably lies to the S, hidden beneath the Carboniferous cover of the S Portuguese zone.

The E–W linear magnetic anomaly on the southern Grand Banks of Newfoundland (the Collector anomaly of Haworth & McIntyre (1975)) projects eastwards into the Portuguese mafic belt and can be traced into Nova Scotia where it is regarded as a suture (Poole 1976). The mafic body causing this anomaly never crops out except perhaps in the Cobequid Mountains and the Antigonish Highlands, where Ordovician, Silurian and Devonian volcanics are intruded by Devonian diorites (Keppie 1979) (Fig. 1, inset C). Westwards, in the Bay of Fundy, the line of the Collector anomaly becomes indistinct, per-haps because of the thick blanket of sediments. Keppie (1977) regards the Fundy graben as the location of an ancient subduction zone which consumed the oceanic crust between the Avalon and Meguma zones. Near Passamaquoddy Bay (Fig. 1, inset D) mafic rocks are again exposed. Further S towards Cape Ann, coincident mag-netic and gravity highs (Kane *et al.* 1982) parallel the Bay of Maine igneous complex (Chapman 1962) which is composed of early Silurian to early Devonian andesitic and rhyolitic volcanics and Devonian gabbroic rocks (Gates 1969). The Bay of Maine mafic complex is probably structurally adjacent to a suture (Osberg 1978) and the geochemistry suggests in one area an oceanic crustal origin (Gaudette 1980).

Thus geological markers which cause similar positive geophysical anomalies can be followed from southern Iberia to S of the Maritimes.

We interpret the Massachusetts–S Portuguese mafic body as a middle to upper Palaeozoic plate boundary for the following reasons.

1 The Precambrian ridges of the Avalon zone to the N abut the inferred suture (Haworth & Lefort 1979).
2 Some of the mafic bodies show oceanic affinities and a volcanic or a back-arc basin is developed widely.
3 Volcanic and intrusive rocks range between late Ordovician and Devonian in age.
4 S of this line in Atlantic Canada, deep-sea fan facies of Cambro-Ordovician age—the Meguma Group—are known (Schenk 1971, Haworth & Keen 1979). It is possible that Meguma Group equivalents occur in the S Portuguese zone, where a thick series of schists characterized by a velocity of 5.3 km s^{-1} (Sousa Moreira *et al.* 1977) under-lies Carboniferous thrusts (the velocity of the Meguma Group in Nova Scotia is 5.4 km s^{-1} (Dainty *et al.* 1966)).

In the S Portuguese zone and in Nova Scotia, S of the suture, quasi-oceanic crust is suspected at depth on the basis of gravity and magnetotel-luric data (Gaibar-Puertas 1976, Cochrane & Wright 1977).

The suture between Cape Ann and Long Island Sound

Delineation of this short section of the suture (not illustrated here) is based primarily on geological data supplemented by geophysical data (Alvord *et al.* 1976). The Nashoba thrust zone (Clinton–Newbury–Bloody Bluff–Lake Char faults) sepa-rates the Gander zone in the NW from the Avalon zone in the SE. Each of these three zones has distinctive suites of granites with specific age, composition and metamorphic grade. On the basis of these data Zartman & Naylor (1984) concluded that the Nashoba zone was active after the Acadian orogeny, making it a likely location of Alleghanian transitional motion.

These conclusions suggest that part of the late Palaeozoic suture zone is a reactivation of the Devonian suture postulated by Osberg (1978) and Robinson & Hall (1980) at the same place. Palaeomagnetic poles of middle Devonian rocks in southern New England differ from those of N America (Schutts *et al.* 1976), and eastern Massachusetts appears to have been close to N Africa at that time.

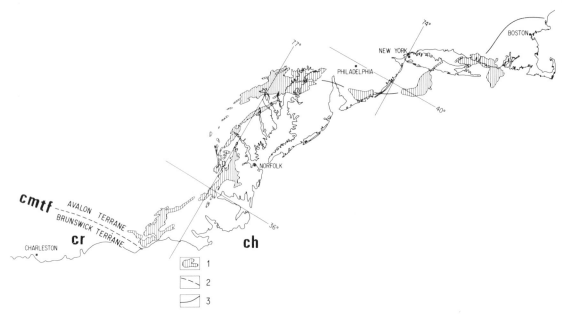

FIG. 2. The gravity magnetic 'suture' beneath the Coastal Plain: 1, magnetic high; 2, main magnetic boundary; 3, coast line; CH, Cape Hatteras; CMTF, Carolina–Mississippi transform fault; CR, Charleston region. (Magnetic data after Zietz *et al.* (1980) and Zietz & Gilbert (1980).)

The suture between Long Island Sound and northern Florida

S of Long Island Sound the suture is buried beneath the Coastal Plain. It is marked by a discontinuous line of magnetic highs linking southern Massachusetts to the Charleston area (Klitgord & Popenoe 1983) (Fig. 2). Gravity highs of up to 40 mGal are coincident with narrow magnetic highs. Unfortunately, between Long Island Sound and Philadelphia these anomalies tend to merge with the anomalies regarded as marking the suture of the older Iapetus Ocean (Hutchinson *et al.* 1983). However, S of the Chesapeake Bay the Appalachian trends can be separated from those associated with the Gondwanaland suture. The American features can only be understood fully if they are considered along with those of Mauritania (Lefort & Klitgord 1983). The details of the gravity and magnetic data used for this comparison can be found in Roussel & Liger (1983), Klitgord *et al.* (1983) and Lefort (1984).

S of Long Island, geophysical markers of the N American and African margins pass into one another. Gravity and magnetic lineaments beneath the Appalachians, the Coastal Plain, the eastern American shelf, the western African shelf and Mauritania can be separated into two major trends. In the W the geophysical lineations are parallel to the Appalachians, while in the E (Fig.

3) there is a westward-bending arc which is not related to the general Appalachian axis. In the Chesapeake region (Salisbury embayment) the gravity and magnetic highs of the Carolina slate belt and the magnetic highs and gravity lows of the Raleigh and Eastern slate belts are cross-cut at their northern end by this arc. S of the Reguibat uplift and beneath the Senegal basin the geophysical lineaments are parallel to the American belts and the Mauritanides. On the Long Island platform, S of New England, the N–S magnetic highs and gravity lows abut the same geophysical arc. Other features, such as the gravity high and magnetic low extension of the Waterbury dome in the N or the ridges running between Cape Look-out and Chesapeake Bay in the S, rotate westward when they reach the arc.

This westward arc in the geophysical trends is related to a structural arc with a radius of 250 km centred on Nouadhibou in Mauritania. It affects all the terranes located on the margin between New York and Cape Hatteras and is more or less concentric with the suggested course of the Mauritanides between the Senegal and Aaiun basins (Lecorche 1980). This arc has to be clearly distinguished from the offset shown by the Appalachians W of Philadelphia (Rankin 1976) which is inherited from the initial shape of the grenvillian craton.

Because the Mauritanian and eastern Appala-

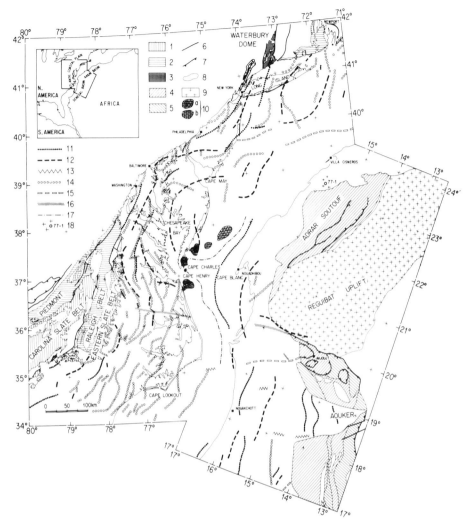

FIG. 3. Gravity and magnetic lineations in Senegal, Mauritania and the Coastal Plain of the USA: 1, island volcanic arc and sedimentary rocks; 2, quartz feldspar schists of amphibolite facies; 3, mainly tholeitic to calc-alkaline volcanic assemblages; 4, internal zone of the Mauritanides; 5, external zone of the Mauritanides; 6, faults; 7, thrusts; 8, contours of granites; 9, Reguibat uplift; 10a, magnetic intrusions; 10b, heavy intrusions; 11, gravity high; 12, gravity low; 13, gravity disruption; 14, magnetic high; 15, magnetic low; 16, magnetic disruption; 17, possible boundary between oceanic and continental crust; 18, drill hole. (After Lefort 1984.)

chian features seem to be deflected, the Reguibat uplift has been considered as an indenter (Lefort 1984). The indenting process probably accompanied the major Carboniferous thrusting seen on both sides of the N Atlantic but affected only a restricted area on the American plate (Lefort & Klitgord 1983). The mafic body along the arc lies at a depth of 6 km, whereas the top of the basement is at a depth of less than 0.5 km (Bayley & Muehlberger 1968), which suggests that the westernmost Mauritanian-like swing is of an intra-basement body.

All the terranes located beneath the Coastal Plain area may be autochthonous and the mafic rocks may be part of the now buried suture zone between Africa and American. Alternatively, if thin-skinned tectonics were operative in the area (Cook *et al.* 1979), the mafic body could be the root of a suture whose upper part has been removed. In either case the suture of Gondwanaland is probably buried beneath the Coastal Plain (Hatcher 1978, Zen 1981) where it would follow this magnetic–gravity lineament (Fig. 2).

S of Cape Hatteras, the suture is a narrow

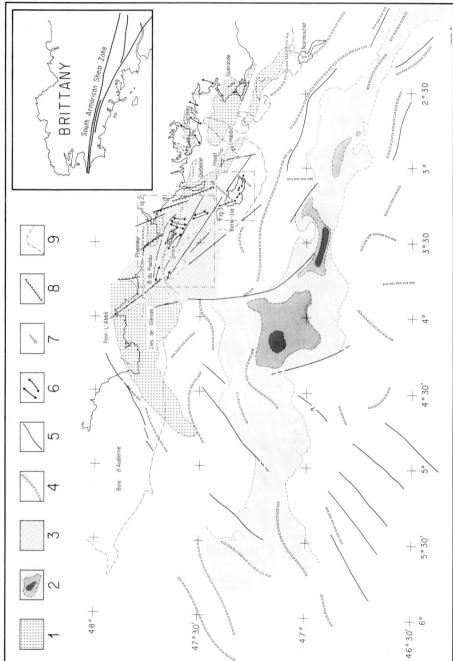

FIG. 4. Distribution of basement structures N of the S Armorican shelf: 1, 300 Ma granites; 2, high susceptibility bodies at depth (the higher susceptibilities are darker); 3, Ile de Groix graben; 4, axis of magnetic bodies based on the first derivative map reduced to the actual pole; 5, faults (inferred from offshore magnetic data); 6, offshore axial plane traces of major folds; 7, shear orientation in granites; 8, normal faults; 9, boundary between basement and cover. (After Lefort *et al.* 1982.)

feature located near the coast line until it reaches the Charleston region (Fig. 2).

The suture and its transform faults

Transform faults occur at both ends of the suture: between western Iberia and France, and N of Florida.

The Petite Sole–Porto–Cordoba transform fault

The S Armorican suture, which will be discussed later, is interrupted in the W by the Petite Sole lineament which is a northern extension of the Porto–Cordoba lineament (Lefort & Riberoi 1980) (Fig. 1). This fault is an important boundary for early Palaeozoic faunas (Paris & Robardet 1977) and was active throughout the Palaeozoic. It separates the Centro-Iberian domain from the W Iberian domain.

S Armorican subduction and major shear movements along the Iberian lineament took place at the same time (Lefort & Riberoi 1980). In Brittany, convergence probably began in the late Ordovician and ceased in Siluro-Devonian time; the S Armorican ocean was open before late Ordovician time. Dextral movement on the Cordoba lineament during the opening of the S Armorican Ocean reversed when the subduction began. The Petite Sole–Cordoba lineament thus occupies the geometrical position of a fossil transform fault. This lineament was probably not the only fracture involved in the inferred transform movement. Limited spreading may have taken place between the Avalon domain (e.g. Grand Banks of Newfoundland, Galicia Bank and W Portuguese zone) and the centre of Spain.

The relationships between the Petite Sole–Porto–Cordoba transform fault and the suture of Gondwanaland are less clear. There is only a strong geometrical correlation between these structures beneath the Tertiary Guadalquivir basin (Fig. 1).

The Carolina–Mississippi transform? fault

The aeromagnetic map of the southern part of the Coastal Plain allows interpretation of the deep basement of this region (Higgins & Zietz 1983, Klitgord *et al.* 1983, 1984). One of the most striking features of this map is a linear disruption (the Carolina–Mississippi transform? fault (Fig. 2)) which extends N of Charleston for more than 1000 km across the southeastern United States, marking the boundaries between the Brunswick and Appalachians terranes.

It is not exactly known whether the Brunswick terrane is Gondwanian because of the low gradients in its magnetic and gravity fields. Another possible boundary between the Appalachians and Gondwanaland is discussed by Klitgord *et al.* (1984), but the broad extent of the Brunswick terrane permits a variety of geometries. Popenoe & Zietz (1977) and Daniels *et al.* (1983) suggested that the suture lies more to the S, whereas Higgins & Zietz (1983) favoured the suture boundary along the Carolina–Mississippi fault.

The bordering sutures

The NW suture of Gondwanaland is flanked by two older sutures which rejuvenated during the collision between Gondwanaland and Laurussia.

The S Armorican suture and its Carboniferous reworking

In Brittany, Hercynian mountain building should be separated into two cycles (Cogné 1977). An earlier cycle from Silurian to middle Devonian time was probably the result of northward subduction beneath S Armorica (southern Brittany), whereas a later cycle, from Dinantian to Westphalian time, involved an ensialic evolution of the whole area.

Some Acadian events are seen onshore in Brittany (Armorican massif), and in the Massif Central (France). Marine geophysical and geological data (Audren & Lefort 1977, Lefort 1979, Lefort *et al.* 1982) also contribute significantly to a more accurate positioning of the suture. The suture probably occurs about 60 km to the S of Groix, where gravity and magnetic discontinuities lie in an arcuate belt which parallels the present coast line beneath the Mesozoic and Cenozoic cover (Figs 1 and 4). This belt separates two different structural domains. The southwestern zone is characterized by E–W gravity and magnetic trends which reflect a remnant of the Ibero-Armorican arc. These link with the Galician arc of Spain when the Bay of Biscay is closed. To the N and E are structures which are parallel to the S Armorican orogen (Lefort & Haworth 1979). In general, the inferred suture is characterized by a small volume of magnetic rocks, except SW of Groix where it is marked by a string of magnetic bodies (Fig. 4). Oriented specimens from Groix and the adjacent sea floor (Lefort *et al.* 1982) show that the axial traces of the main Hercynian folds follow a sigmoidal shape over 70 km which is probably controlled by a single large-scale structure.

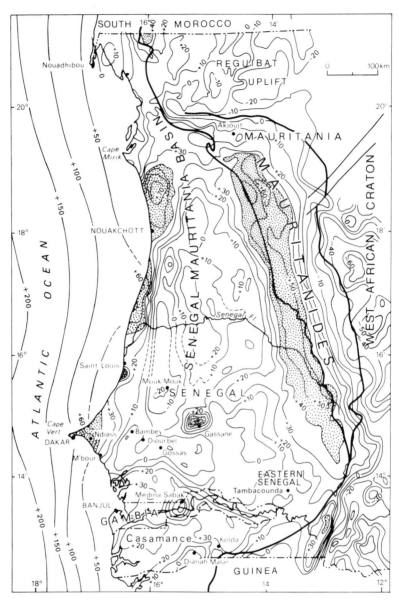

FIG. 5. Simplified Bouguer anomaly map (contour interval, 10 mGal) of Mauritania and Senegal. (After Crenn & Rechemann (1965) and Uchupi *et al.* (1976) in Lecorche *et al.* (1983).)

Leucogranites 300 Ma old form a broken arc of related intrusions which follow the coast line. Geophysical interpretation suggests that these granites are tabular and never thicker than 1 km (Vigneresse 1978). In the E their emplacement was confined between flat-lying shear zones in which movement was oriented in a N–S or WNW–ESE direction with a dextral component. In the W, other flat-lying shear planes were related to NE–SW displacements but with a sinistral component. In the Groix area the folding is probably related to a dextral shear strain in the E (4°–2°W) and sinistral shear in the W (4°–6°W) in a similar strain framework to that associated with emplacement of the granites. If the elongate magnetic bodies lying about 50 km off the coast represent pre-Hercynian relic oceanic material in an incomplete suture (Lefort 1979), the above structures are a result of a later compression across this suture.

Hercynian reworking of the Mauritanides suture

The Mauritanides fold belt, lying opposite the Appalachians across the present Atlantic, evolved along the margin of the W African Precambrian craton in Senegal, Mauritania and southern Morocco (Fig. 5). It is interrupted only by the old basement continuation of the Reguibat uplift. The belt is mainly characterized by roughly N–S structural trends and eastward thrusting. It has been shown (Lecorche 1980) that there were initially two distinct belts brought together in post-Frasnian times to produce the current polyphase Mauritanides. The first of these belts is represented by the external nappes which are well developed from eastern Senegal to the southern margin of the Reguibat uplift. The material of these nappes is primarily affected by a phase of folding related to an Ordovician event. This 'Taconic' deformation probably took place in a domain W of the area now occupied by the external nappes. The second belt is represented by the internal nappes which are located mainly in the Akjoujt region and in southern Morocco on both sides of the Reguibat uplift. The age of emplacement of these nappes is post-Devonian (Lecorche *et al.* 1983). The presence within the nappes of basement comparable with that of the Reguibat uplift suggests a source far to the W in the region of the Atlantic coast or even farther W (Lecorche *et al.* 1983).

A relationship at depth between the two main belts can be inferred from gravity data (Liger 1979, Guetat 1981). The so-called Mauritanides anomaly (Fig. 5) is a NNW–SSE-striking elongate feature which extends approximately 700 km from S of the Reguibat uplift to eastern Senegal. It probably marks a major crustal suture in the ancient W African cratonic margin and separates two crustal provinces: the W African craton and the Mauritania–Senegal coastal basin. Although the anomaly axis is displaced to the W of the

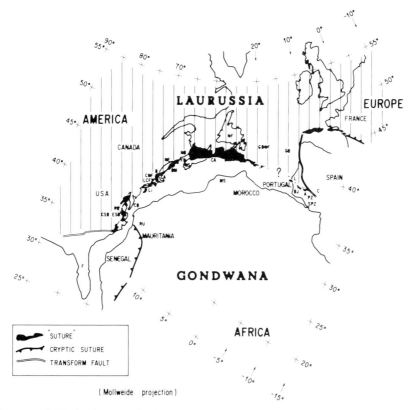

FIG. 6. The suture of NW Gondwanaland and related structures: A, Aracena; B, Boston; BJ, Beja; BM, Bay of Maine; C, Cordoba; CA, Cape Ann; CB, Chesapeake Bay; CNF, Clinton–Newbury fault; CSB, Carolina slate belt; ESB, Eastern slate belt; FB, Fundy Bay; CB, Galicia Bank; GBNF, Grand Banks of Newfoundland; L, Lisboa; Li, Long Island; M, Massachusetts; MS, Morocco; NB, New Brunswick; NE, New England; NF, Newfoundland; NS, Nova Scotia; RB, Raleigh belt; RU, Reguibat uplift; SPZ, S Portuguese zone. (After Lefort 1984.)

exposed Mauritanides belt, it remains parallel to the trend of the belt. The principal source of this anomaly must be a deep, dense and widespread body. Interpretation of gravimetric traverses across the anomaly shows that the major dense unit is deeply rooted and that the body is situated at a depth between 15 and 30 km and dips westward. This suggests an asymmetric eastward bulge in the mantle or an eastward thrusting of a western crustal block over the craton. According to Lecorche *et al.* (1983) the Mauritanides anomaly reflects the suture zone resulting from E–W compression during the Ordovician.

Conclusion

The closure of the Theic Ocean between Gond-

wanaland and Laurussia during middle Devonian and Carboniferous time was preceded by three earlier collisions which developed close to its boundaries. These collisions first accreted Senegal and western Mauritania to Gondwanaland in middle Ordovician time (Lecorche 1980). The Avalon plate (or Armorican plate) then collided with N America by Ordovician to Silurian time. Finally, Iberia (Spain and Portugal), which detached from Africa by late Ordovician time, collided with the Armorican plate between Silurian and lower Devonian time (Lefort 1983). The sutures resulting from these collisions rejuvenated when Gondwanaland collided with Laurussia and were responsible for the development of the Alleghanian–Hercynian orogenic belts along the contacts (Fig. 6).

References

ALVORD, D. C., BELL, K. G., PEASE, M. H., JR. & BAROSH, P. J. 1976. The aeromagnetic expression of bedrock geology between the Clinton–Newbury and Bloody Bluff fault zones, north-eastern Massachusetts. *United States Geological Survey Bulletin,* **4** (5), 601–4.

ANDRADE, A. A. S. 1979. Aspectos geoquimicos do Ofiolitoide de Beja. *Communicacoes Da Commissao dos Servicos Geologicos de Portugal, No. 64,* pp. 39–48.

AUDREN, C. & LEFORT, J. P. 1977. Géologie du plateau continental sud-armoricain entre les îles de Glenan et de Noirmoutier. Implications géodynamiques. *Bulletin de la Société Géologique de France,* **19,** 395–404.

BARD, J. P. 1977. Signification tectonique des métatholéites d'affinité abyssale de la ceinture métamorphique de basse pression d'Aracena (Huelva, Espagne). *Bulletin de la Société Géologique de France,* **19,** 385–93.

——, CAPDEVILA, R., MATTE, P. & RIBEIRO, A. 1973. Geotectonic model for the Iberian Variscan orogen. *Nature, London, Physical Science,* **241,** 50–2.

BAYLEY, R. W. & MUEHLBERGER, W. R. 1968. *Basement Rock Map of the United States,* United States Geological Survey.

CHAPMAN, C. A. 1962. Bays-of-Maine igneous complex. *Geological Society of America Bulletin,* **73,** 883–8.

COCHRANE, N. A. & WRIGHT, J. A. 1977. Geomagnetic sounding near the northern termination of the Appalachian system. *Canadian Journal of Earth Sciences,* **14,** 2858–64.

COGNÉ, J. 1977. La chaîne hercynienne ouest-européenne correspond-elle à un orogène par collision? Propositions pour une interprétation géodynamique globale. *CNRS International Symposium,* **268,** 111–29.

COOK, F. A., ALBAUGH, D. S., BROWN, L. D., KAUFMAN, S., OLIVER, J. E. & HATCHER, R. D., JR 1979. Thin-skinned tectonics in the crystalline southern Appalachians: COCORP seismic refle

ing of the Blue Ridge and Piedmont. *Geology,* **7** 563–7.

CRENN, Y. & RECHEMANN, J. 1965. Mesures gravimétriques et magnétiques au Sénégal et en Mauritanie occidentale. *Cahiers ORSTOM,* **176,** 1–59.

DAINTY, A. M., KEEN, C. E., KEEN, M. J. & BLANCHARD, J. E. 1966. Review of geophysical evidence on crust and upper mantle structure on the eastern seaboard of Canada. *The Earth Beneath the Continents. American Geophysical Union Monograph No. 10,* pp. 349–69.

DANIELS, D. L., ZIETZ, I. & POPENOE, P. 1983. Distribution of subsurface lower Mesozoic rocks in the south-eastern United States, as interpreted from regional aeromagnetic and gravity maps. *In:* GOHN, G. S. (ed.) *Studies Related to the Charleston, South Carolina Earthquake of 1886—Tectonics and Seismicity. United States Geological Survey Professional Paper No. 1313,* pp. K1–K24.

GAIBAR-PUERTAS, C. 1976. Variaciones del espesor crustal y grado de equilibro isostatico associables a las anomalias de Bouguer en la Espana Peninsular. *Boletin Geologico y Minero,* **87/84,** 371–401.

GATES, O. 1969. Lower Silurian–lower Devonian volcanic rocks of New England coast and southern New Brunswick. *In:* KAY, M. (ed.) *North Atlantic— Geology and Continental Drift. American Association of Petroleum Geologists Memoir No. 12,* pp. 484–503.

GAUDETTE, H. E. 1980. Zircon isotopic age from the Union ultramafic complex, Maine. *Canadian Journal of Earth Sciences,* **18,** 405–9.

GUETAT, Z. 1981. Etude gravimétrique de la bordure occidentale du craton ouest-africain. *Thèse de 3eme Cycle,* Université de Montpellier, 185 pp.

HATCHER, R. D. JR 1978. Tectonics of the western Piedmont and Blue Ridge, Southern Appalachians: review and speculation. *American Journal of Science,* **278,** 276–304.

HAWORTH, R. T. & KEEN, C. E. 1979. The Canadian

Atlantic margin: a passive continental margin encompassing an active past. *Tectonophysics*, **59**, 83–126.

—— & LEFORT, J. P. 1979. Geophysical evidence for the extent of the Avalon zone, in Atlantic Canada. *Canadian Journal of Earth Sciences*, **16**, 552–67.

—— & McINTYRE, J. B. 1975. The gravity and magnetic field of Atlantic Offshore Canada. *Geological Survey of Canada Paper No. 75–9*, 22 pp.

HIGGINS, M. W. & ZIETZ, I. 1983. Geologic interpretation of geophysical maps of the pre-Cretaceous 'basement' beneath the Coastal Plain of the Southeastern United States. *In*: HATCHER, R. D. JR, WILLIAMS, H. & ZIETZ, I. (eds) *Tectonics and Geophysics of Mountain Chains. Geological Society of America Memoir No. 158*, pp. 125–30.

HUTCHINSON, D. R., GROW, J. A. & KLITGORD, K. D. 1983. Crustal structure beneath the southern Appalachians: nonuniqueness of gravity modelling. *Geology*, **11**, 611–15.

KANE, M. F., YELLIN, M. J., BELL, K. G. & ZIETZ, I. 1982. Gravity and magnetic evidence of lithology and structures in the Gulf of Maine region. *United States Geological Survey Professional Paper No. 726B*, pp. 1–22.

KEPPIE, J. D. 1977. Tectonics of southern Nova Scotia. *Nova Scotia Department of Mines Paper No. 77–1*, pp. 1–34.

—— 1979. *Geological Map of the Province of Nova Scotia*. Department of Mines and Energy, Nova Scotia (Scale, 1:5 000 000).

KLITGORD, K. D. & POPENOE, P. 1983. Geophysical tectonic studies of the United States Atlantic Coastal Plain and Continental Margin. *In*: HAYES, W. W. & GORI, P. L. (eds) *Proceedings of Conference 20: A Workshop on 'The 1886 Charleston, South Carolina, Earthquake and its Implications for Today'. United States Geological Survey Open File Report No. 83–843*, pp. 185–99.

——, DILLON, W. P. & POPENOE, P. 1983. Mesozoic tectonics of the south-eastern United States Coastal Plain and Continental Margin. *In*: GOHN, G. S. (ed.) *Studies Related to the Charleston, South Carolina, Earthquake of 1886—Tectonics and Seismicity. United States Geological Survey Professional Paper No. 1313*, pp. P1–P15.

——, POPENOE, P. & SCHOUTEN, H. 1984. Florida: a Jurassic transform plate boundary. *Journal of Geophysical Research*, **89**, 7753–72.

LECORCHE, J. P. 1980. Les Mauritanides face au craton ouest-africain. Structure d'un secteur-clé: la région d'Ijibiten (Est d'Akjoujt, R.I. de Mauritanie). *Thesis*, University of Aix-Marseille III, 446 pp.

——, ROUSSEL, J., SOUGY, J. & GUETAT, Z. 1983. An interpretation of the geology of the Mauritanides orogenic belt (West Africa) in the light of geophysical data. *In*: HATCHER, R. D., JR, WILLIAMS, H. & ZIETZ, I. (eds) *Tectonics and Geophysics of Mountain Chains. Geological Society of America Memoir No. 158*, pp. 131–47.

LEFORT, J. P. 1979. Iberian–Armorican arc and Hercynian orogeny in Western Europe. *Geology*, **7**, 384–8.

—— 1983. A new geophysical criterion to correlate the Acadian and Hercynian orogenies of Western Europe and Eastern America. *In*: HATCHER, R. D., JR, WILLIAMS, H. & ZIETZ, I. (eds) *Tectonics and Geophysics of Mountain Chains. Geological Society of America Memoir No. 158*, pp. 3–18.

—— 1984. Mise en évidence d'une virgation carbonifère induite par la dorsale Reguibat (Mauritanie) dans les Appalaches du Sud (U.S.A.). Arguments géophysiques. *Bulletin de la Société Géologique de France*, **XXVI**, 1293–1303.

—— & HAWORTH, R. T. 1979. The age and origin of the deepest correlative structures recognised off Canada and Europe. *Tectonophysics*, **59**, 139–50.

—— & KLITGORD, K. D. 1983. Geophysical evidence for the existence of Mauritanian structures beneath the U.S. Atlantic coastal Plain. *In*: SCHENK, P. E. (ed.) *Regional Trends in the Geology of the Appalachian–Caledonian–Hercynian–Mauritanide Orogen*, p. 78, Reidel, Dordrecht.

—— & RIBEIRO, A. 1980. La faille Porto–Bajajoz–Cordoue a-t-elle contrôle l'évolution de l'océan paléozoique sud-armoricain? *Bulletin de la Société Géologique de France*, **22** (3), 455–62.

—— & VAN DER VOO, R. 1981. A kinematic model for the collision and complete suturing between Gondwanaland and Laurussia in the Carboniferous. *Journal of Geology*, **89** (5), 537–50.

——, AUDREN, C. & MAX, M. D. 1982. The southernmost zone of the Armorican orogenic belt: the result of crustal shortening related to reactivation of a Devonian paleosuture during Carboniferous time. *Tectonophysics*, **89**, 359–77.

LIGER, J. L. 1979. Structure profonde du Bassin cotier senegalo-mauritanien, interprétation de données gravimétriques et magnétiques. *Thesis*, University of Marseilles, 155 pp.

MUNHA, J. 1979. Blue amphiboles, metamorphic regime and plate tectonic modelling in the Iberian pyrite belt. *Contributions to Mineralogy and Petrology*, **69**, 279–89.

OSBERG, P. H. 1978. Synthesis of the geology of the north-eastern Appalachians, USA. *In*: TOZER, E. T. & SCHENK, P. E. (eds) *Caledonian–Appalachian Orogen of the North Atlantic Region. Geological Survey of Canada Paper No. 78–13*, pp. 137–48.

PARIS, F. & ROBARDET, M. 1977. Paléogéographie et relations ibero-armoricaines au Paléozoique anté-carbonifère. *Bulletin de la Société Géologique de France*, **19** (5), 1121–6.

POPENOE, P. & ZIETZ, I. 1977. The nature of the geophysical basement beneath the Coastal Plain of South Carolina and north-eastern Georgia. *In*: RANKIN, D. W. (ed.) *Studies Related to the Charleston, South Carolina, Earthquake of 1886—a Preliminary Report. United States Geological Survey Professional Paper No. 1028-I*, pp. 119–37.

POOLE, W. H. 1976. Plate tectonic evolution of the Canadian Appalachian Region. *Geological Survey of Canada Paper No. 76–18*, pp. 11–126.

RANKIN, D. W. 1976. Appalachian salients and recesses: late-Precambrian continental break up and the opening of the Iapetus Ocean. *Journal of Geophysical Research*, **81** (32), 5605–19.

ROBINSON, P. & HALL, L. M. 1980. Tectonic synthesis

of southern New England. *In*: WONES, D. R. (ed.) *The Caledonides in the USA: Proceedings of the International Geological Correlation Program—Caledonide Orogen Project 27, Blacksburg, VA. Department of Geological Sciences, Virginia Polytechnic Institute and State University, Memoir No. 2*, pp. 73–90.

ROUSSEL, J. & LIGER, J. L. 1983. A review of deep structures and ocean–continent transition in the Senegal basin (West Africa). *Tectonophysics*, **91**, 183–211.

SCHENK, P. E. 1971. South-eastern Atlantic Canada, north-western Africa and continental drift. *Canadian Journal of Earth Sciences*, **8**, 1218–51.

SCHUTTS, L. D., BRECHER, A., HURLEY, P. M. & MONTGOMERY, C. W. 1976. A case study of the time and nature of paleomagnetic resetting in a mafic complex in New England. *Canadian Journal of Earth Sciences*, **13**, 898–907.

SOUSA MOREIRA, J., MUELLER, S. T., MENDES, A. S. & PRODEHL, C. L. 1977. Crustal structure of Southern Portugal. *Publications of the Institute of Geophysics, ETH Zurich, No. A4 (115)*, pp. 413–26.

SWANSON, M. T. 1982. Preliminary model for an early transform history in central Atlantic rifting. *Geology*, **10**, 317–20.

UCHUPI, E., EMERY, K. D., BOWIN, C. D. & PHILLIPS, J. D. 1976. Continental margin of Western Africa: Senegal to Portugal. *Bulletin of the American Association of Petroleum Geologists*, **60**, 809–78.

VIGNERESSE, J. L. 1978. Gravimétrie et granites armoricains: structure et mise en place des granites hercyniens. *Thesis*, University of Rennes, 95 pp.

WEGENER, A. 1929. *Die Entstehung der Kontinente und Ozeane*, Veiweg, Braunschweig.

ZARTMAN, R. E. & NAYLOR, R. S. 1984. Structural implications of some radiometric ages of igneous rocks in south-eastern New England. *Geological Society of America Bulletin*, **95**, 522–39.

ZEN, E-AN 1981. An alternative model for the development of the allochthonous Southern Appalachian Piedmont. *American Journal of Science*, **281**, 1153–63.

ZIETZ, I. & GILBERT, F. P. 1980. Aeromagnetic map of part of the south-eastern United States. *United States Geological Survey, Geophysical Investigation Map GP936* (Scale, 1:2 000 000).

——, HAWORTH, R. T., WILLIAMS, H. & DANIELS, D. L. 1980. Magnetic anomaly map of the Appalachian orogen. *Memorial University of Newfoundland Map No. 2*.

J. P. LEFORT, Centre Armoricain d'Etude Structurale des Socles, LP CNRS, Institut de Géologie, Campus de Beaulieu, 35042 Rennes Cédex, France.

M. D. MAX, Geological Survey of Ireland, Beggars Bush, Haddington Road, Dublin 2, Ireland. *Present address*: Office of Naval Research, Washington, DC, USA.

J. ROUSSEL, Laboratoire associé au CNRS 132, Etudes Géologiques Ouest-Africaines, Université d'Aix-Marseille III, 13397 Marseille Cédex 13, France.

Pre-Arenig Activity in the Caledonian–Appalachian Orogen

CONVENOR
J. W. SKEHAN SJ
Weston Observatory
Boston

The age and distribution of basement rocks in the Caledonide orogen of the N Atlantic

Derek Powell, T. B. Andersen, A. A. Drake, Jr, Leo Hall & J. D. Keppie

SUMMARY: Available isotopic data suggest that the Precambrian basement elements of the northern parts of the Caledonide orogen in N America, Britain, Ireland, Greenland and Scandinavia comprise largely Grenvillian and Svecofennian continental crust. Archaean precursors have been identified in Greenland, Norway and Britain, but not positively in the Appalachians. Early Caledonian (Grampian–Finnmarkian) orogenic activity gave rise, in the Scandinavian and British–Irish sectors, to an early Palaeozoic basement which, in Norway, is overlain by Ordovician to Silurian supracrustal sequences. In contrast, a late Precambrian–early Cambrian (Cadomian–Avalonian and older) basement is present in southern parts of the orogen.

The distribution of these basement elements constrains any plate-tectonic reconstructions of the N Atlantic Caledonide orogen and suggests that the orogen was tripartite during its early development. Further, it suggests that transcurrent movements as well as obduction may have been important tectonic processes during Grampian–Finnmarkian tectonism.

The occurrence of Precambrian crystalline rocks within many fragments of the Caledonide orogen, as either autochthonous–parautochthonous massifs or components of nappe complexes, shows that the major part of the orogen is floored by Precambrian continental crust. Whereas in many places isotopic data indicate the age of this material in terms of its Precambrian history, there are insufficient data to permit the precise location of Precambrian age province boundaries within the orogen (Fig. 1). Archaean materials may be present in the Chain Lakes Massif of the N Appalachians (Fig. 2). They also occur as allochthonous inliers in the N Highlands of Scotland (Fig. 3), in the southern part of the E Greenland Caledonides (Fig. 4), the Lofoten Islands of Norway (Fig. 5) and the Channel Islands (Fig. 3). However, the original extent of such rocks is masked by subsequent reworking.

A southeastern limit of Grenvillian elements (1200–900 Ma) can be broadly identified in the Appalachians and the British Isles, but its extension to the E through northern Europe is not well constrained (Fig. 1). An Avalonian–Cadomian basement in the southern parts of the orogen is recognized in the Bohemian–Moldanubian Massif, southern Britain and Ireland, parts of the Armorican Massif, Nova Scotia, southeastern Newfoundland and southeastern New England (Fig. 1). Late Precambrian supracrustal rocks of Avalonian aspect form much of the Carolina slate belt in the southern Appalachians and the Caledonian Highlands of New Brunswick, and they also occur in Morocco and Iberia (Fig. 1) but here their status as basement is unclear. As with the southern limit of Grenvillian

elements, the northern limit of the Avalonian–Cadomian basement can only be broadly defined on the basis of isotopic evidence (Fig. 1).

In northern E Greenland the ages of Precambrian basement elements are not well constrained, but those in central E Greenland appear to reflect largely Grenvillian and Svecofennian activity, with possible relics of older material (Fig. 4). In the Scandinavian Caledonides isotopic evidence for Grenvillian (Sveconorwegian) and Svecofennian elements is substantial and there is some evidence of Archaean components in northern areas (Fig. 5). Within the southern Norwegian Caledonides the location of the Sveconorwegian (Dalslandian) front, which is clearly traceable through the southwestern part of the Baltic craton, is not well defined (Fig. 1). However, close similarities between the Sveconorwegian Province and rocks of the Grenville belt in Labrador (Gower & Owen 1984) suggest its continuation across the orogen (Fig. 6).

More positive and widespread evidence of the age of Precambrian basement rocks and the location of Precambrian province boundaries within the orogen would assist in constraining not only the positions of possible Caledonian sutures but also the configuration of continental crustal blocks during the late Proterozoic and the subsequent development of the Caledonide orogen (Fig. 6).

Whereas there is no international agreement as to the division of much of Precambrian time into eras and sub-eras the use of time-stratigraphic terms herein follows that given by Harland et al. (1982): late Proterozoic (Pt$_3$), 590–900 Ma; middle Proterozoic (Pt$_2$), 900–1600 Ma; early Proterozoic (Pt$_1$), 1600–2500 Ma.

From HARRIS, A. L. & FETTES, D. J. (eds), 1988, *The Caledonian–Appalachian Orogen,*
Geological Society Special Publication No. 38, pp. 63–74.

MIDDLE TO LATE PROTEROZOIC AGE PROVINCES
OF THE NORTH ATLANTIC CALEDONIDE & HERCYNIDE OROGENS

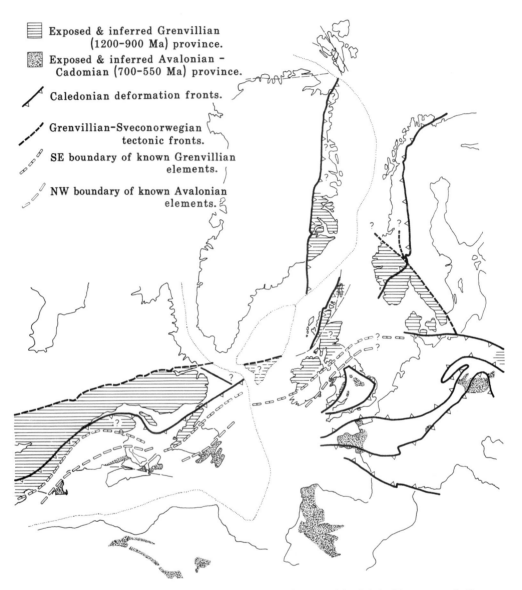

FIG. 1. Pre-Atlantic configuration of middle to late Proterozoic elements of the Caledonide orogen and adjacent regions. The deformation fronts in S Britain and Europe are based on the proposals of Ziegler (1984).

Legend:

Exposed & inferred Grenvillian (1200–900 Ma) province.

Exposed & inferred Avalonian – Cadomian (700–550 Ma) province.

Caledonian deformation fronts.

Grenvillian-Sveconorwegian tectonic fronts.

SE boundary of known Grenvillian elements.

NW boundary of known Avalonian elements.

Grenvillian and older basement elements

The Appalachians

Orthogneisses and paragneisses, lithologically comparable with the rocks of the Grenville Province of the Laurentian Shield, occur in much of the northwestern tract of the Appalachians along the Blue Ridge–Green Mountain axis, in the Indian Head–Long Ranges of Newfoundland and in the Western Gneiss Domes of the southern and central Appalachians (Fig. 2). U–Pb and Rb–Sr isotopic data, which suggest ages of

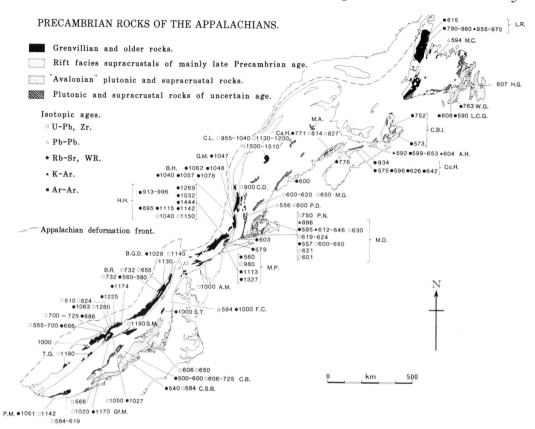

FIG. 2. Distribution of Precambrian elements of the Appalachians: AH, Antigonish Highlands; BR, Blue Ridge; Ca.H, Caledonian Highlands; CBI, Cape Breton Island; CL, Chain Lakes Massif; COH, Cobequid Highlands; CS, Carolina slate belt; GM, Green Mountains; LR, Long Range mountains; MD, Milford–Dedham zone; MP, Manhattan Prong. Based in part on Schenk (1978), Williams (1978), Rankin *et al.* (1983), Keppie (1985) and Drake *et al.* (in press).

between 1150 and 900 Ma (summarized by Rankin *et al.* 1983, Drake *et al.*, in press), confirm the lithological correlations and may also provide evidence for the occurrence in places (e.g. the Manhattan Prong and the Chain Lakes Massif) of older middle Proterozoic (Pt_2) relics. Thus the Pb^{206}–Pb^{206}, U^{235}–Pb^{207} and U^{238}–Pb^{206} minimum ages of 1500–1510 Ma, 1130–1200 Ma and 955–1040 Ma respectively from the Chain Lakes Massif (Fig. 2) (Naylor *et al.* 1973) may indicate Grenvillian reworking of older Proterozoic material, and the older ages could identify the Chain Lakes terrane as exotic (Osberg 1978, Keppie 1985).

Gneisses and metasediments form a Precambrian basement in the Caledonian Highlands of New Brunswick, the Cobequid Highlands and Cape Breton Island of Nova Scotia. Isotopic data for the former (Olszewski & Gaudette 1982) is equivocal, but suggests a minimum age of about

810 Ma. The gneisses and metasediments of the Cobequid Highlands would appear to be older than about 640 Ma, and the gneisses may be as old as, or older than, about 930 Ma (Gaudette *et al.* 1983). The basement gneisses and metasediments of Cape Breton Island are older than about 750 Ma (Jamieson & Craw 1983). Thus the age of these basement elements is poorly constrained; they may be Grenvillian, but equally they may constitute a late Proterozoic basement to the Avalonian–Cadomian province (see below).

The British Isles

On an early Permian continental reassembly map of the N Atlantic area, both the northwestern Caledonian deformation front of the N Appalachians and the Grenville front of the Laurentian Shield should run through the British Isles (Fig. 1). The Caledonian front probably runs just

N of the Irish mainland and thence northwards up the W coast of the Northern Highlands of Scotland as the Moine thrust zone (Fig. 3). In Scotland, W of the Moine thrust zone, narrow zones of Caledonian reworking, such as the Outer Isles thrust and possibly the Flannan thrust (Blundell 1984), traverse Archaean and early Proterozoic gneisses (the Lewisian) and middle to late Proterozoic cover sediments (the Torridonian) of the Caledonian foreland. These Precambrian basement gneisses and supracrustal rocks otherwise show no indications of either Grenvillian or Caledonian reworking. They thus formed a stable cratonic block during these episodes of orogenic activity.

Orthogneisses and paragneisses of middle Proterozoic (Grenvillian) age are present in the Belmullet peninsula of western Ireland (van Breemen *et al.* 1978), but the age of the high-grade metasediments of the NE Ox Mountain and Lough Derg inliers is uncertain (Fig. 3) (Long & Yardley 1979, Max & Long 1985). In the N Highlands of Scotland, the Moine schists which are lithologically similar to the Lough Derg rocks, comprise an extensive group of middle Proterozoic metasediments (Brook *et al.* 1976, 1977, Brewer *et al.* 1979) that contain allochthonous to parautochthonous inliers of early Proterozoic and Archaean basement (Tanner *et al.* 1970, Rathbone *et al.* 1983). Lithologically, the Moine schists do not resemble type Grenville material, but isotopic evidence is interpreted as demonstrating regional metamorphism and plutonism at about 1000 Ma (Brewer *et al.* 1979). The regional, though sparse, development of a suite of granitic pegmatites at 820–770 Ma (Piasecki & van Breemen 1983, Powell *et al.* 1983), may relate to later ductile crustal extension. Lithologically similar rocks to the Moine schists appear to underlie tectonically the Dalradian Supergroup to the SE of the Great Glen fault (Fig. 3) (Piasecki & van Breemen 1979). Although these rocks are older than about 750 Ma, there is no unequivocal isotopic evidence for their sedimentary age nor for their early metamorphism.

Further evidence for the possible southward extent of Grenvillian elements is provided by the presence of gneissic xenoliths in Carboniferous diatremes in the Midland Valley of Scotland and in central Ireland which lithologically do not resemble Lewisian material and give model ages of about 1000–1180 Ma (Fig. 3) (Strogen 1974, Aftalion *et al.* 1984, Upton *et al.* 1984).

Greenland

The Greenland fragment of the Caledonide orogen displays marked similarities to N Scotland in its middle Proterozoic history. In central E Greenland isotopic data suggest the presence of an older basement of early Proterozoic gneisses and plutonic rocks of Svecofennian age, together with relics of older Archaean material (Fig. 4). However, isotopic ages derived from intrusive rocks and the Krummedal metasedimentary sequence indicate deposition, regional metamorphism and plutonism between about 1250 and 950 Ma (Higgins 1976, Higgins *et al.* 1978, Henriksen 1985). This, together with the subsequent history, is remarkably similar to that of the Moine schists. As in Scotland, however, the Grenvillian elements are dissimilar to the type area, and together these may represent an atypical northern arm to the Grenville orogen (Fig. 1).

Scandinavia

In contrast with Scotland and Greenland, the basement of the Scandinavian Caledonides appears to comprise for the most part early Proterozoic materials together with plutonic rocks. Isotopic data, which give ages in the 1900–1600 Ma range, reflects this activity, as in the adjacent Svecofennian province of the Baltic craton (Fig. 5) (Wilson & Nicholson 1973, Scharer 1980, Skjernaa & Pedersen 1982). Likewise, older ages of 1750–1600 Ma in both the southern Norwegian Caledonides and the Gothides probably relate to early Proterozoic Svecofennian precursors (Fig. 5).

Isotopic data from autochthonous and allochthonous basement gneisses and plutonic rocks of the central and northern Norwegian area predominantly reflect Svecofennian events (Wilson & Nicholson 1973, Griffin *et al.* 1978), suggesting the continuation of the Svecofennian Province of the adjacent craton through the Caledonian nappes of the orogen (Fig. 5) (Pharaoh 1985). The isotopic evidence for Grenvillian activity in these areas (Heier & Compston 1969, Griffin *et al.* 1978, Reymer *et al.* 1980) is scant and equivocal. However, in the southern Norwegian Caledonides middle Proterozoic ages are widespread (Fig. 5) and, although much more isotopic data is required, a direct continuation of the Sveconorwegian (Dalslandian) front of the southern Baltic craton northwestward through the Norwegian Caledonides (Fig. 5) cannot be dismissed (Reymer *et al.* 1980, Ziegler 1984), particularly in view of the close temporal and spatial similarities between the lithotectonic regions of eastern Labrador and the Gothides of southern Sweden (Gower & Owen 1984).

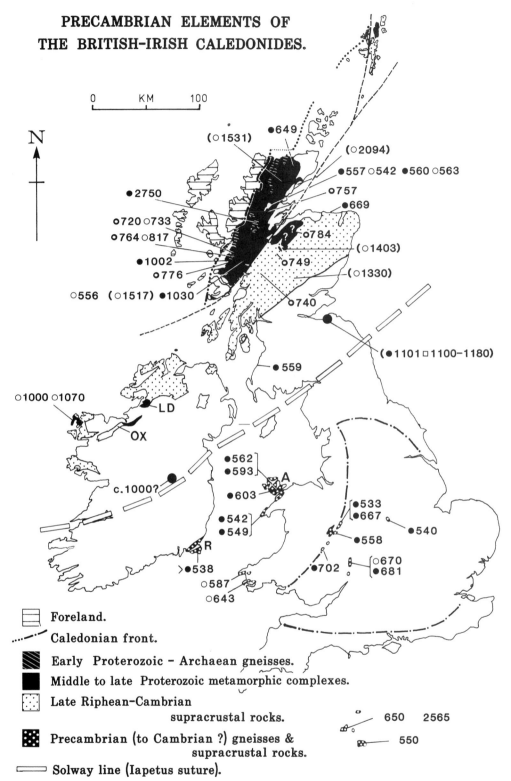

PRECAMBRIAN ELEMENTS OF
THE BRITISH-IRISH CALEDONIES.

Fig. 3. Basement elements in the British–Irish Caledonides: A, Anglesey; LD, Lough Derg inlier; OX, Ox Mountains; R, Rosslare. The symbols for isotopic data are as in Fig. 2 except for the following: o, Rb–Sr mineral age. The ages in parentheses are upper intercepts on condordia derived from Caledonian granites.

Foreland.

Caledonian front.

Early Proterozoic – Archaean gneisses.

Middle to late Proterozoic metamorphic complexes.

Late Riphean-Cambrian
           supracrustal rocks.

Precambrian (to Cambrian ?) gneisses &
           supracrustal rocks.

Solway line (Iapetus suture).

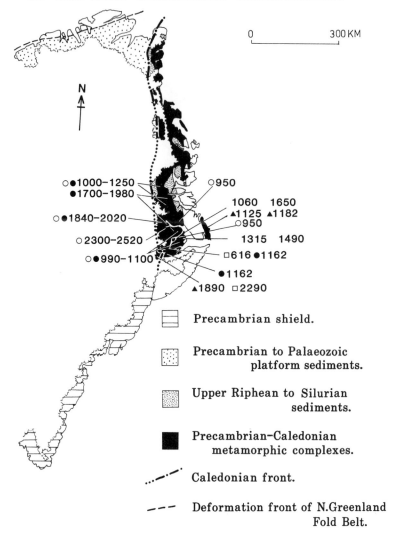

FIG. 4. Precambrian to lower Palaeozoic elements of the E Greenland Caledonides.

Avalonian–Cadomian elements

The late Proterozoic history of parts of the eastern Appalachians, NW Africa, Iberia, southern Britain and northern Europe differs markedly from that of the areas described above in as much as late Precambrian supracrustal sequences have in many places undergone late Proterozoic to early Cambrian deformation, metamorphism and/or plutonism between 800 and 540 Ma (Fig. 1).

Gneisses that may constitute a basement to these supracrustal sequences are present in Anglesey and the Welsh Borderland, Rosslare, the Channel Islands and Brittany, the Caledonian and Cobequid Highlands, and Cape Breton Island (Figs 2 and 3). The gneisses of Anglesey, however, give ages of 593 and 562 Ma and the associated granite has an age of 603 Ma (Beckinsale & Thorpe 1979), but similar gneisses in the Rosslare Complex of SE Ireland are certainly older than 538 Ma and may be as old as 2400–

PRECAMBRIAN AND "FINNMARKIAN"
ELEMENTS OF THE SCANDINAVIAN CALEDONIDES.

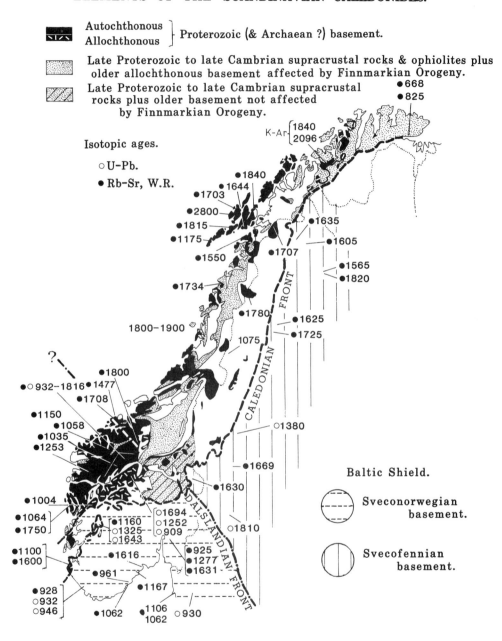

FIG. 5. Basement elements of the Scandinavian Caledonides. Isotopic data from Wilson & Nicholson (1973), Griffin *et al.* (1978), Reymer *et al.* (1980), Scharer (1980), Pharaoh *et al.* (1982), Skjernaa & Pedersen (1982) and Harvey (1983). Note that details of the geology are not given for Sweden.

1600 Ma (Max & Long 1985). Analyses of the orthogneisses of the Malvern Complex and the Rushton schists of the Welsh Borders (Fig. 3) yield isotopic ages of 680 Ma and 670 Ma respectively (Thorpe *et al.* 1984). In contrast, isotopic data from gneisses of the Channel Islands and Brittany give evidence for metamorphic activity at 1200–900 Ma (Leutwein 1968) and 2600–2300 Ma (Leutwein *et al.* 1973). However, plutonic activity in these areas, in part overlapping late Proterozoic (Cadomian) tectonism, is bracketed between 650 and 550 Ma (Bishop *et al.* 1975).

The age of basement gneisses in the Caledonian and Cobequid Highlands and Cape Breton Island in Canada (Fig. 2) is not well constrained, but they are possibly older than about 810 Ma, about 640 Ma and 750 Ma respectively (Olszewski & Gaudette 1982, Gaudette *et al.* 1983). These gneisses are overlain by metasediments and

metavolcanic rocks intruded by plutonic rocks with intrusive ages of 526 and 530 Ma (Caledonian Highlands), 575 and 642 Ma (Cobequid Highlands), 604 and 653 Ma (Antigonish Highlands), 574 Ma (Cape Breton Island) and 621–580 Ma (SE Newfoundland) (Benson 1974, Dallmeyer *et al.* 1981, Krogh & Papezik 1983, Wanless, personal communication). In many places these Precambrian rocks are overlain by Cambrian strata.

Plutonism in the Milford–Dedham zone of SE New England at 630–550 Ma is isotopically well constrained (Zartman & Naylor 1984), and syn- to post-tectonic events in the Carolina slate belt are dated at 650–564 Ma (Rankin *et al.* 1983). These, together with similar events recorded in Nova Scotia, Newfoundland, the British Isles and Brittany, suggest broad contemporaneity of orogenic and plutonic (Cadomain–Avalonian) activity along the southeasten tract of the Cale-

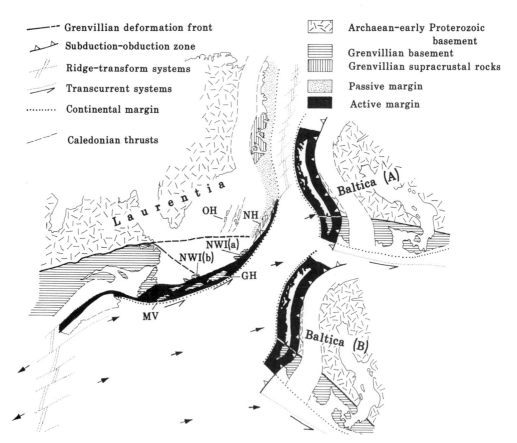

FIG. 6. Hypothetical configuration of the N Atlantic Caledonides at the onset of the Grampian–Finnmarkian orogeny: GH, Grampian Highlands; MV, Midland Valley; NWIa and NWIb, alternative positions for northwestern Ireland; NH, Northern Highlands of Scotland; OH, Outer Hebrides. For further explanation see text.

donides (Fig. 1). However, the age and distribution of older Precambrian basement materials in this zone is not clear.

The Grampian–Finnmarkian basement

There is substantial isotopic and some biostratigraphic evidence of pervasive polyphasal deformation, metamorphism and plutonism in the late Cambrian–early Ordovician interval (520–480 Ma) in parts of the N British–Irish Caledonides (the Grampian orogeny), throughout the upper Allochthon of the orogen in Norway and Sweden (the Finnmarkian orogeny), and perhaps in N Germany and Poland (Lambert & Mc-Kerrow 1976, Sturt 1984, Ziegler 1984). The Penobscotian deformation in the northern Appalachians is a correlative of this Grampian–Finnmarkian orogeny. In the Appalachians it involved the initial emplacement of ophiolite between 508 and 490 Ma, and is recognized in the Burlington Peninsula of Newfoundland through to southern Quebec, along the southern side of the Chain Lakes Massif and in N central Maine (Keppie *et al.* 1983, Keppie 1985). It is uncertain, however, whether the Penobscot event represents an early phase of the Taconic orogeny or was distinct.

No time equivalent of the Grampian–Finnmarkian Orogeny has yet been recognized in the E Greenland Caledonides.

A post-Finnmarkian pre-Scandian unconformity is recognized in many places in nappes of the upper Allochthon of the Norwegian Caledonides (Brekke *et al.* 1984 and personal communication, Sturt 1984, Sturt *et al.* 1984, Ramsay *et al.* 1985). Although such Ordovician and younger cover rocks are absent in the Scottish sector, in places rapid uplift occurred between 460 and 440 Ma (Dempster 1984). In Ireland Grampian deformation was essentially complete by about 460 Ma (Powell & Phillips 1984). Thus, through these areas the Grampian–Finnmarkian orogen formed a basement to later Palaeozoic sedimentation and could have provided a source for sedimentary detritus.

Isotopic evidence for Grampian orogenic activity in Scotland is limited to the Dalradian zone of the Grampian Highlands and Shetland, and possibly the Ballantrae ophiolite complex (Bradbury *et al.* 1976, Flinn & Pringle 1976, Bluck *et al.* 1980). There is no evidence for tectonometamorphic activity in the Northern Highlands in the 555–480 Ma interval (Powell & Phillips 1984). Indeed, peak Caledonian metamorphic conditions were achieved at about 470–450 Ma (van Breemen *et al.* 1974, Brewer *et al.* 1979).

Despite arguments to the contrary (van Breemen *et al.* 1979, Coward 1983), there is no evidence for diachroneity of activity or structural continuity across the Great Glen other than differences in the isotopic ages of events; no progressive changes in age *within* the two zones are apparent. It is therefore possible to consider that the northwestern and southeastern Highlands of Scotland behaved as separate entities during much of the evolution of the Grampian–Caledonian orogeny (Powell & Phillips 1984). The boundary between these zones may lie along the Ossian steep belt–Loch Awe syncline–Ox Mountains line rather than the Great Glen fault zone.

Conclusions

A hypothetical plate-tectonic configuration that might explain the distribution of Grenvillian elements in Laurentia and Baltica and the location of the tectonically passive and active margins to Iapetus during the Grampian–Finnmarkian orogeny is illustrated in Fig. 6. The reconstruction is based on regarding the 'Grenvillian' rocks and events of N Scotland and Greenland as relating to an atypical northern arm of the Grenville–Gothides belt, on the occurrence of Grenville-type rocks in western Ireland (van Breemen *et al.* 1978) and on the match of the Grenville front with its counterpart in Baltica. The alternative positions for Baltica arise from (a) the extension of the Grenville Front through the Rockall plateau (supported by Piper (1976)) and (b) the match of rocks in eastern Labrador with those of southern Sweden (Gower & Owen 1984).

Justification for considering a transcurrent model for the Grampian orogeny in the British–Irish sector (*cf.* Dewey & Shackleton 1984) lies in the known large transcurrent movements associated with the Highland Boundary fault zone (Bluck 1983), the possibility that the 'fountain of nappes' structure of the Dalradian (Thomas 1979) represents a deeper crustal analogue of a major 'flower structure', and the differences between the late Precambrian and/or early Palaeozoic history of the N Highland block, the Dalradian zone and the Highland Border (Powell & Phillips 1984). The obliquity of major structures in the Dalradian zone not only to the Highland Boundary fault but also to the trend of the Ossian steep belt (Thomas 1979) is also of note.

ACKNOWLEDGMENTS: DP acknowledges the financial assistance of the Natural Environment and Research Council (Grant GR3/3998). During the preparation of this paper the untimely death of Leo Hall occurred. The authors wish to acknowledge his contribution, his help and his enthusiasm; he will be sadly missed.

References

AFTALION, M., VAN BREEMEN, O. & BOWES, D. R. 1984. Age constraints on basement of the Midland Valley of Scotland. *Transactions of the Royal Society of Edinburgh, Earth Science*, **75**, 51–62.

BECKINSALE, R. D. & THORPE, R. S. 1979. Rubidium–strontium whole-rock isochron evidence for the age of metamorphism and magmatism in the Mona Complex of Anglesey. *Journal of the Geological Society, London*, **136**, 433–40.

BENSON, D. G. 1974. Geology of the Antigonish Highlands, Nova Scotia. *Geological Survey of Canada Memoir No. 376*, pp. 1–92.

BISHOP, A. C., ROACH, R. A. & ADAMS, C. J. D. 1975. Precambrian rocks within the Hercynides. *In*: HARRIS, A. L., SHACKLETON, R. M., WATSON, J., DOWNIE, C., HARLAND, W. B. & MOORBATH, S. (eds) *A correlation of Precambrian Rocks in the British Isles. Special Report of the Geological Society of London No. 6*, pp. 102–7.

BLUCK, B. J. 1983. Role of the Midland Valley of Scotland in the Caledonian orogeny. *Transactions of the Royal Society of Edinburgh, Earth Science*, **74**, 119–36.

——, HALLIDAY, A. N., AFTALION, M. & MACINTYRE, R. M. 1980. Age and origin of Ballantrae ophiolite and its significance to the Caledonian orogeny and Ordovician time scale. *Geology*, **8**, 492–5.

BLUNDELL, D. J. 1984. Deformation of the Caledonide lithosphere of Northwest Scotland. *Tectonophysics*, **109**, 137–45.

BRADBURY, H. J., SMITH, R. A. & HARRIS, A. L. 1976. Older granites as time markers in Dalradian evolution. *Journal of the Geological Society, London*, **132**, 677–84.

VAN BREEMEN, O., AFTALION, M., PANKHURST, R. J. & RICHARDSON, S. W. 1979. Age of the Glen Dessary syenite, Inverness-shire: diachronous Palaeozoic metamorphism across the Great Glen. *Scottish Journal of Geology*, **15**, 49–62.

——, HALLIDAY, A. N., JOHNSON, M. R. W. & BOWES, D. R. 1978. Crustal additions in late Precambrian times. *In*: BOWES, D. R. & LEAKE, B. E. (eds) *Crustal Evolution in Northwestern Britain and Adjacent Regions. Geological Journal Special Issue*, **10**, 82–106.

——, PIDGEON, R. T. & JOHNSON, M. R. W. 1974. Precambrian and Palaeozoic pegmatites in the Moines of northern Scotland. *Journal of the Geological Society, London*, **130**, 493–508.

BREKKE, H., FURNES, H., NORDÅS, J. & HERTOGEN, J. 1984. Lower Palaeozoic convergent plate margin volcanism on Bulo, SW Norway, and its bearing on the tectonic environments of the Norwegian Caledonides. *Journal of the Geological Society, London*, **141**, 1015–32.

BREWER, M. S., BROOK, M. & POWELL, D. 1979. Dating of the tectono-metamorphic history of the south-western Moine, Scotland. *In*: HARRIS, A. L., HOLLAND, C. H. & LEAKE, B. E. (eds) *The Caledonides of the British Isles Reviewed. Special Publication of the Geological Society of London No. 8*, pp. 129–37.

BROOK, M., POWELL, D. & BREWER, M. S. 1976. Grenville age for rocks in the Moine of north-western Scotland. *Nature, London*, **260**, 515–17.

——, —— & —— 1977. Grenville events in Moine rocks of the Northern Highlands, Scotland. *Journal of the Geological Society, London*, **133**, 489–96.

COWARD, M. P. 1983. The thrust and shear zones of the Moine Thrust Zone and the NW Caledonides. *Journal of the Geological Society, London*, **140**, 745–812.

DALLMEYER, R. D. ODHAM, A. L., O'DRISCOLL, C. F. & HUSEY, E. M. 1981. Geochronology of the Swift Current granite and host volcanic rocks of the Love Cove Group, SW Avalon Zone, Newfoundland. *Canadian Journal of Earth Sciences*, **18**, 699–707.

DEMPSTER, T. J. 1984. Localized uplift in the Scottish Dalradian. *Nature, London*, **307**, 156–9.

DEWEY, J. F. & SHACKLETON, R. M. 1984. A model for the evolution of the Grampian tract in the early Caledonides and Appalachians. *Nature, London*, **312**, 115–21.

DRAKE, A. A. JR, HALL, L. & NELSON, A. E. Basement and basement-cover relation map of the Appalachian orogen in the United States. *United States Geological Survey Paper No. XX*, in press.

FLINN, D. & PRINGLE, I. R. 1976. Age of migmatisation in the Dalradian of Shetland. *Nature, London*, **259**, 299–300.

GAUDETTE, H. E., OLSZEWSKI, W. J. & DONOHOE, H. V. 1983. Age and origin of the basement rocks, Cobequid Highlands, Nova Scotia. *Geological Society of America Abstracts with Programs*, **15**, 136.

GOWER, C. F. & OWEN, V. 1984. Pre-Grenvillian and Grenvillian lithotectonic regions in eastern Labrador—correlations with the Sveconorwegian Orogenic Belt in Sweden. *Canadian Journal of Earth Sciences*, **21** (6), 678–93.

GRIFFIN, W. L., TAYLOR, P. N., HAKKINEN, J. W., HEIER, K. S., IDEN, I. K., KROGH, E. J., MALM, O., OLSEN, K. I., ORMAASEN, D. E. & TVETEN, E. 1978. Archaean and Proterozoic crustal evolution in Lofoten–Vesteralen, N Norway. *Journal of the Geological Society, London*, **135**, 629–48.

HARLAND, W. B., COX, A. V., LLEWELLYN, P. G., PICKTON, C. A. G., SMITH, A. G. & WALTERS, R. 1982. *A Geologic Time Scale*, Cambridge University Press, Cambridge.

HARVEY, M. A. 1983. A geochemical and Rb–Sr study of the Proterozoic augen orthogneiss on Molde peninsula, west Norway. *Lithos*, **16**, 325–38.

HEIER, K. & COMPSTON, W. 1969. Interpretation of Rb–Sr age patterns in high grade metamorphic rocks, north Norway. *Norsk Geologisk Tidsskrift*, **49**, 257–83.

HENRIKSEN, N. 1985. The Caledonides of central East Greenland 70°–76°N. *In*: GEE, D. G. & STURT, B. A. (eds) *The Caledonide Orogen—Scandinavia and Related Areas*, pp. 1095–113, Wiley, Chichester.

HIGGINS, A. K. 1976. Pre-Caledonian metamorphic

complexes within the southern part of the East Greenland Caledonides. *Journal of the Geological Society, London,* **132,** 289–305.

——, FREDERICKSEN, J. D., REX, D. C. & GLEDHILL, A. R. 1978. Early Proterozoic isotopic ages in the East Greenland Caledonian Fold Belt. *Contributions to Mineralogy and Petrology,* **67,** 87–94.

JAMIESON, R. A. & CRAW, D. 1983. Reconnaissance mapping of the southern Cape Breton Highlands— a preliminary report. *Geological Survey of Canada Paper No. 83-1A,* pp. 263–8.

KEPPIE, J. D. 1985. The Appalachian College. *In:* GEE, D. G. & STURT, B. A. (eds) *The Caledonide Orogen—Scandinavia and Related Areas,* pp. 1217–26, Wiley, Chichester.

——, ST JULIEN, P., AUBERT, C., BELAND, J., SKIDMORE, B., FYFFE, L. R., RUITENBERG, A. A., MC-CUTCHEON, S. R., WILLIAMS, H. & BURSNALL, J. 1983. Times of deformation in the Canadian Appalachians. *NATO Advanced Study Institute, Series C, Mathematical and Physical Sciences,* **116,** 307–14.

KROGH, T. E. & PAPEZIK, D. F. 1983. Precise U–Pb ages of zircons from volcanic and plutonic units in the Avalon Peninsula. *Geological Society of America, Abstracts with Programs,* **15,** 135.

LAMBERT, R. ST J. & MCKERROW, W. S. 1976. The Grampian orogeny. *Scottish Journal of Geology,* **12,** 271–92.

LEUTWEIN, F. 1968. Contribution à la connaissance du précambrian récent en Europe Occidentale et développement géochronologique du Briovérien en Bretagne (France). *Canadian Journal of Earth Sciences,* **5,** 673–82.

——, POWER, G., ROACH, R. & SONET, J. 1973. Quelques résultats géochronologiques obtenus sur des roches d'âges précambrien du Cotentin. *Comptes Rendus Hebdomadaires des Séances de l'Academie des Sciences, Série D,* **276,** 2121–4.

LONG, C. B. & YARDLEY, B. W. D. 1979. The distribution of pre-Caledonian basement in the Ox mountains inlier, Ireland. *In:* HARRIS, A. L., HOLLAND, C. H. & LEAKE, B. E. (eds) *The British Caledonides Reviewed. Special Publication of the Geological Society of London No. 8,* pp. 153–6.

MAX, M. D. & LONG, C. B. 1985. Pre-Caledonian basement in Ireland and its cover relationships. *Geological Journal,* **20,** 341–66.

NAYLOR, R. S., BOONE, G. M. & BOUDETTE, E. L. 1973. Pre-Ordovician rocks in the Bronson Hill and Boundary Mountain Anticlinoria, New England, USA. *Eos, Transactions of the American Geophysical Union,* **54,** 495 (abstract).

OLSZEWSKI, W. J. & GAUDETTE, H. E. 1982. Age of the Brookville Gneiss and associated rocks, Southeastern New Brunswick. *Canadian Journal of Earth Sciences,* **19,** 2158–66.

OSBERG, P. H. 1978. Synthesis of the geology of the northeastern Appalachians, U.S.A. *In:* TOZER, E. T. & SCHENK, P. E. (eds) *Caledonian–Appalachian Orogen of the North Atlantic Region. Geological Survey of Canada Paper No. 78-13,* pp. 137–48.

PHARAOH, T. 1985. Volcanic and geochemical stratigraphy of the Nussir Group of Arctic Norway—an early Proterozoic greenstone suite. *Journal of the Geological Society, London,* **142,** 259–78.

PHARAOH, T. C., MACINTYRE, R. M. & RAMSAY, D. M. 1982. K–Ar determinations on the Raipas suite in the Komagfjord Window, northern Norway. *Norsk Geologisk Tidsskrift,* **62,** 51–7.

PIASECKI, M. A. J. & VAN BREEMEN, O. 1979. The 'Central Highland Granulites': cover–basement tectonics in the Moine. *In:* HARRIS, A. L., HOLLAND, C. H. & LEAKE, B. E. (eds) *The British Caledonides Reviewed. Special Publication of the Geological Society of London No. 8,* pp. 139–44.

—— & —— 1983. Field and isotopic evidence for a *c.* 750 Ma tectonic event in Moine rocks in the Central Highland region of the Scottish Caledonides. *Transactions of the Royal Society of Edinburgh, Earth Science,* **73,** 119–34.

PIPER, J. D. A. 1976. Palaeomagnetic evidence for a Proterozoic supercontinent. *Philosophical Transactions of the Royal Society of London, Series A,* **280,** 469–90.

POWELL, D. & PHILLIPS, W. E. A. 1984. Time of deformation in the British and Irish Caledonides. *In:* HARRIS, A. L. (ed.) *The Nature and Timing of Orogenic Activity in the Caledonian and Hercynian Rocks of the British Isles. Memoir of the Geological Society of London No. 9,* pp. 17–39.

——, BROOK, M. & BAIRD, A. W. 1983. Structural dating of a Precambrian pegmatite in Moine rocks of N Scotland and its bearing on the status of the 'Morarian Orogeny'. *Journal of the Geological Society, London,* **140,** 813–23.

RAMSAY, D. M., STURT, B. A., ROBERTS, D. & ZWAAN, K. B. 1985. Caledonides of northernmost Norway. *In:* GEE, D. G. & STURT, B. A. (eds) *The Caledonide Orogen—Scandinavia and Related Areas,* pp. 163–84, Wiley, Chichester.

RANKIN, D. W., STERN, T. W., MCLELLAND, J., ZARTMAN, R. E. & ODOM, A. L. 1983. Correlation chart for Precambrian rocks of the eastern United States. *United States Geological Survey Professional Paper No. 1241-E,* pp. 1–18.

RATHBONE, P. A., COWARD, M. P. & HARRIS, A. L. 1983. Cover and basement: A contrast in style and fabrics. *Geological Society of America Memoir No. 158,* pp. 213–23.

REYMER, A. P. S., BOELRIJK, N. A. I. M., HEBEDA, E. H., PRIEM, H. N. A., VERDURMEN, E. A. TH. & VERSCHURE, R. H. 1980. A note on Rb–Sr whole-rock ages in the Seve Nappe of the central Scandinavian Caledonides. *Norsk Geologisk Tidsskrift,* **60,** 139–47.

SCHARER, U. 1980. U–Pb and Rb–Sr dating of a polymetamorphic nappe terrain: The Caledonian Jotun Nappe, S Norway. *Earth and Planetary Science Letters,* **49,** 205–18.

SCHENK, P. E. 1978. Synthesis of the Canadian Appalachians. *In:* TOZER, E. T. & SCHENK, P. E. (eds) *Caledonian–Appalachian Orogen of the North Atlantic Region. Geological Survey of Canada Paper No. 78-13,* pp. 111–36.

SKJERNAA, L. & PEDERSEN, S. 1982. The effects of penetrative Sveconorwegian deformations on Rb–Sr Isotope systems in the Romskog-Aurskog-

Holland area, SE Norway. *Precambrian Research,* **17**, 215–43.

STROGEN, P. 1974. The sub-Palaeozoic basement in central Ireland. *Nature, London,* **250**, 562–3.

STURT, B. A. 1984. The accretion of ophiolite terranes in the Scandinavian Caledonides. *Geologie en Mijnbouw,* **63**, 201–12.

——, ROBERTS, D. & FURNES, H. 1984. A conspectus of Scandinavian ophiolites. *In*: GASS, I. G., LIPPARD, S. & SHELTON, A. (eds) *Ophiolites and Oceanic Lithosphere. Special Publication of the Geological Society of London No. 13,* pp. 381–91.

TANNER, P. W. G., JOHNSTONE, G. S., SMITH, D. I. & HARRIS, A. L. 1970. Moinian stratigraphy and the problem of the Central Ross-shire inliers. *Geological Society of America Bulletin,* **81**, 299–306.

THOMAS, P. R. 1979. New evidence for a Central Highland root zone. *In*: HARRIS, A. L., HOLLAND, C. H. & LEAKE, B. E. (eds) *The Caledonides of the British Isles Reviewed. Special Publication of the Geological Society of London No. 8,* pp. 205–12.

THORPE, R. S., BECKINSALE, R. D., PATCHETT, P. J., PIPER, J. D. A., DAVIES, G. R. & EVANS, J. A. 1984. Crustal growth and late Precambrian-early Palaeozoic plate tectonic evolution of England and Wales. *Journal of the Geological Society, London,* **141**, 521–36.

UPTON, B. G. J., ASPEN, P. & HUNTER, R. H. 1984. Xenoliths and their implications for the deep geology of the Midland Valley of Scotland and adjacent regions. *Transactions of the Royal Society of Edinburgh, Earth Sciences,* **75**, 65–70.

WILLIAMS, H. 1978. Tectonic-lithofacies map of the Appalachian orogen. *Memorial University of Newfoundland Map No. 1.*

WILSON, M. R. & NICHOLSON, R. 1973. The structural setting and geochronology of basal granitic gneisses in the Caledonides of part of Nordland, Norway. *Journal of the Geological Society, London,* **129**, 365–88.

ZARTMAN, R. E. & NAYLOR, R. S. 1984. Structural implications of some radiometric ages of igneous rocks in southeastern New England. *Geological Society of America Bulletin,* **95**, 522–39.

ZIEGLER, P. A. 1984. Caledonian and Hercynian crustal consolidation of Western and Central Europe—a working hypothesis. *Geologie en Mijnbouw,* **63**, 93–108.

D. POWELL, Department of Geology, Royal Holloway & Bedford New College, University of London, Egham, Surrey TW20 0EX, UK.

T. B. ANDERSEN, Geologisk Institutt Avd. A, Universitetet i Bergen, 5000 Bergen, Norway.

A. A. DRAKE, JR, United States Geological Survey, Reston, VA 22092, USA.

L. HALL, Department of Geology, University of Massachusetts, Amherst, MA 01003, USA.

J. D. KEPPIE, Department of Mines and Energy, PO Box 1087, Halifax, Nova Scotia, Canada.

Pre-Arenig evolution of the Appalachian–Caledonide orogen: sedimentation and stratigraphy

Frederic L. Schwab, Johan P. Nystuen & Linda Gunderson

SUMMARY: The Vendian and Cambrian–Tremadoc stratigraphic record documents the initial plate-tectonic evolution of the Appalachian–Caledonide (Iapetus) orogen. On the western margin several stratigraphic units indicate an episode of late Precambrian continental rifting. Triassic-like intra-cratonic basins were developed within the continental interior. Aulacogens and marginal ensialic shelf basins were located along a subsiding zigzagging continental edge marked by high scarp-bounded mountainous relief. The early Palaeozoic Atlantic-type margin that followed consisted of a landward easterly-thickening continental shelf wedge (basal quartz sandstone and an overlying carbonate bank blanket), bank-edge breccia and, oceanward, a continental rise prism.

The eastern margin, at least in Scandinavia, is very similar in lithology and depositional setting to the western margin. However, S of Scandinavia, in continental Europe and across the British Isles, and farther S and W in N America, lay the Avalon terrane. This regionally extensive strip of apparently sialic crust was criss-crossed in late Precambrian time by a series of grabens that filled with rift-basin deposits (coarse clastic sedimentary rocks interbedded with basic to alkalic volcanic rocks, all deformed by Pan-African-type orogeny). In the early Palaeozoic this Avalon 'microcontinent' was a platform (transgressive quartzite, sandstone and mudrock) bordered to the NW by a continental rise. Farther E and S lay the western margin of France–Iberia–Africa with a late Precambrian history of rifting, followed by the early Palaeozoic development of an Atlantic-type continental shelf-rise margin.

The physical aspects of the sedimentary and stratigraphic framework of the Appalachian–Caledonide orogen during its initial stages of development, essentially following the Grenville–Sveconorwegian–Carolinidian orogenies (950–1100 Ma) through earliest Ordovician time (up to Arenig (c. 495 Ma)), are summarized in this paper. There is no review of the palaeontological evidence for Iapetus during this time interval (but see, e.g. Poole et al. 1983 and Conway Morris & Rushton 1988). Stratigraphic ages and correlations are based on a variety of criteria including (1) age dates on underlying basement rocks and interbedded volcanic units, (2) direct age estimates of sedimentary rock diagenesis, (3) metamorphic age dates, (4) the position within sequences of glacial tillites presumed to be Varangerian (c. 653 ± 7 Ma) and (5) fossil content, in particular acritarchs, stromatolites and advanced metazoa.

To ensure that the review is relatively easy to follow it is necessary to subdivide the time-span into an *earlier* late Proterozoic (very late Riphean and Vendian) interval and a *later* Cambrian to Tremadoc interval. The orogen and its precursor, the Iapetus Ocean basin, are simplistically divided into an uncomplicated *western* ('American–NW Britain–Greenland') margin (Figs 1A and 1B) and a more complex *eastern* ('Avalon–African–European–Baltic') margin (Figs 1C and

1D). Each margin is separately described in geographical segments (running S to N for the western margin and N to S for the eastern margin). Critical stratigraphic units referred to in the text are numerically keyed to the appropriate diagrams that comprise Fig. 1. Figure 1 deliberately omits inferred positions for palaeo-poles and the palaeo-equator because considerable disagreement exists as to their precise locations during the relevant time intervals.

A narrative description was intentionally chosen in preference to a tabular outline of the units described in the interest of clarity and cohesion of discussion. Excellent tabular summaries of the stratigraphic relations during this episode of initial development and evolution of the Appalachian–Caledonide orogen include those of Bond et al. (1984) and Barker & Gayer (1985).

Western margin (S–N)

Overview

The western margin shows a late Proterozoic history of rifting. Thick tillite-bearing clastic wedges accumulated in a series of Triassic-like intra-cratonic rift basins and adjacent to scarps developed along a zigzagging continental edge.

From HARRIS, A. L. & FETTES, D. J. (eds), 1988, *The Caledonian–Appalachian Orogen,*
Geological Society Special Publication No. 38, pp. 75–91.

A. late Precambrian

B. Early Paleozoic

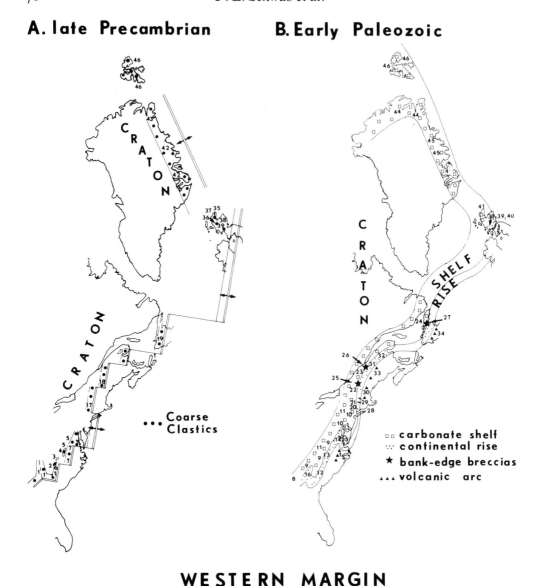

WESTERN MARGIN

FIG. 1. Principal settings for sedimentation with numbered stratigraphic assemblages indexed in the text. The base map used is that of LePichon *et al.* (1977).

In early Palaeozoic time, a passive Atlantic-type margin developed with an eastwardly-thickening prism of continental shelf deposits (basal transgressive sandstone overlain by neritic carbonate). This miogeoclinal succession is characterized by a widespread late lower Cambrian regression. The continental shelf passed eastward across a bank edge, locally marked with breccias, into thicker offshore continental rise–slope–apron deposits. An island-arc–trench complex lay still farther E in late lower Ordovician time.

Central and southern Appalachians

Late Proterozoic

Within and adjacent to the Blue Ridge, stratified sequences range in thickness from a few metres

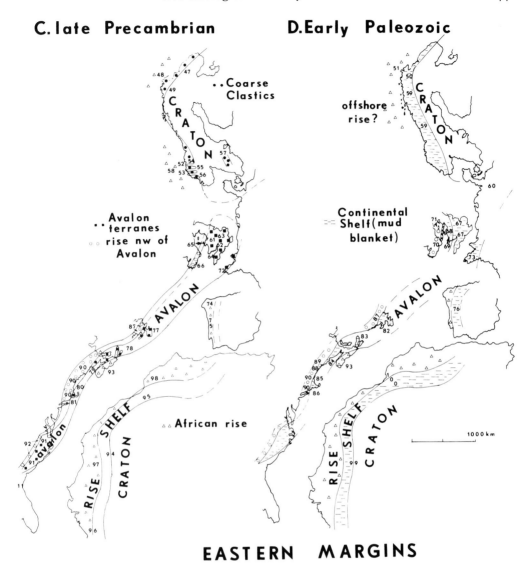

C. late Precambrian

..Coarse
Clastics

..Avalon
..terranes
o o rise nw of
Avalon

.. African rise

D. Early Paleozoic

offshore
rise?

Continental
Shelf(mud
blanket)

1000 km

EASTERN   MARGINS

to more than 8 km (Ocoee Supergroup, Tennes-see, and the Carolinas (unit 1)). Several units are localized rift-valley deposits which are arkosic in composition, rich in conglomerate and show centripetal dispersal (Grandfather Mountain Formation, N Carolina (unit 2); the tillite-bearing Mount Rogers Formation, SW Virginia (unit 3); Mechum River Formation, central Virginia (unit 4)). Several units are intimately interbedded with peralkaline volcanics (such as the Catoctin

Formation (unit 5)). Other late Precambrian units are regionally-extensive graded greywacke-shale turbidite sequences that contain scarp-related breccias (Rockfish conglomerate of the Lynch-burg Formation) derived from a mountainous continental edge almost coincident with the Blue Ridge (Ashe and Tallulah Falls Formations, Carolinas and Tennessee (unit 6); Lynchburg Formation, Virginia (unit 7); portions of the Ocoee Supergroup (unit 1)). Fine-grained pelagic deposits of possible late Proterozoic age farther E in the western Piedmont (Chauga and Poor Mountain Formations and parts of the Smith River allochthon) may be the initial deposits of a developing continental slope–apron and abyssal plain (Schwab 1985, Wehr & Glover 1985). Portions of the Ocoee Supergroup appear to be inland-sea continental shelf and rise deposits derived from continental blocks located to both the E and W, perhaps in an aulacogen or graben isolated from the main continental margin by basement horsts (Rast 1984).

Overall, the margin resembled the eastern margin of N America during Triassic and Jurassic time, with a series of interior rift valleys like the Newark basin parallel to the major zigzagging continental edge farther E. Some of the basins may have been aulacogens (failed arms developed at triple bends of rift axes). Others may have been generated as embayments into the continental margin created where transform faults connected separate laterally-offset rift axes (Thomas 1977, Fisher *et al.* 1979).

Cambrian–Tremadoc

A simple passive Atlantic-type margin can be defined. Near-shore, shallow-marine basal quartz-rich sandstones (Weisner quartzite, Georgia and Alabama (unit 8); the Chilhowee Group, Tennessee through Virginia to Maryland (unit 9); Hardyston–Chickies–Poughquag quartzites of Pennsylvania, New Jersey and New York (unit 10)) and finer-grained near-shore (brief regressive) shales are overlain by Cambrian–Ordovician carbonates (Conasauga Group, Elbrook Formation (unit 11); Leithville–Copper Ridge–Allentown–Conococheague Formations; Knox–Beekmantown Group) (Palmer 1971). This eastward-thickening (1000–3000 m) continental shelf wedge was bordered along its southeastern edge by an abrupt submarine escarpment marked by carbonate breccias (Kinzers Formation, Virginia; Frederick Valley carbonates, Maryland; Conestoga Ls., Pennsylvania) (Rodgers 1968; Reinhardt 1974).

To the E of this bank edge lay an eastward-thinning continental rise prism of turbidite sandstone, pelagic shale and interbedded volcanic rocks (Alligator Back Formation, Carolinas (unit 12); Evington Group, Virginia (unit 13)). In eastern Maryland and Pennsylvania an embayment extended northward into the carbonate bank, almost completely isolating a tongue-like sliver of continent farther E, analogous to Korea or the Kamchatka Peninsula in the present NW Pacific. The various units of the Glenarm Supergroup (unit 14)—the basal clastic Setters and Sugarloaf Mountain quartzites, the overlying carbonate bank deposits of the Frederick Valley and Cockeysville marble, and the interbedded wacke and mudrock of the Wissahickon Formation—accumulated within the resulting inland sea (analogous to the modern Sea of Okhotsk and Yellow Sea). Late Cambrian thrusting towards the W (obduction?) generated eastwardly derived boulder gneisses and diamictites (Sykesville facies of the Glenarm Supergroup) that were deposited contemporaneously with the development of an offshore volcanic island-arc–trench system (unit 15, James Run and Chopawamsic Formation of Maryland and Virginia). This portion of the western margin was therefore transformed into a back-arc setting like that seen today in the Ryukyu Islands S of Korea or the Kuril Islands S of Kamchatka (Conley 1978, Schwab 1985, Wehr & Glover 1985). In Tennessee and Georgia, a similar embayment straddling the core of the Blue Ridge was perhaps inherited from the Ocoee graben or aulacogen (shallow- to deep-water clastics and carbonates of the Murphy belt and the Coweeta Group (unit 16)).

New England and Canadian Appalachians

Late Proterozoic

No clear-cut evidence exists of a series of interior tensionally produced Triassic-like basins or aulacogens similar to the Grandfather Mountain and analogous basins to the S. However, typical eugeoclinal 'offshore' continental rise prisms several kilometres thick and of predominantly early Palaeozoic age may contain at their base late Proterozoic continental edge non-marine conglomeratic fill (parts of the Pinnacle, Hoosac, Underhill and Cavendish Formations, western New England (unit 17); Anse Miranda Formation and the Charny, Armagh, Oak Hill, Rosaire and Caldwell Groups, Quebec, and the basal portion of the Shickshock Group, Gaspé (unit 18)) (Cady 1969, Bird & Dewey 1970, St Julien & Hubert 1975).

The 10 km thick Fleur de Lys Supergroup of western Newfoundland (unit 19) contains a possible tillite near its base interbedded with fluviatile clastic sedimentary rocks, although the bulk of the unit is early Palaeozoic turbidite sandstone and shale interbedded with mafic volcanic pillow lavas (Williams & Stevens 1974, Williams *et al.* 1974, de Wit 1981).

Cambrian–Tremadoc

The western margin across western New England and eastern Canada resembled that of the Central and Southern Appalachians. A 500–3000 m thick eastward-thickening wedge of shallow-water carbonate bank deposits (Inwood marble, New York (unit 20); Stockbridge Ls., Massachusetts (unit 21); various carbonates of the Champlain Valley, Vermont and New York (unit 22); Rock River–Saxe Brook and Beekmantown carbonates, Quebec (unit 23); upper Labrador Group and St George Limestone, Newfoundland (unit 24)) overlies a 100–1000 m thick sheet of basal Cambrian quartz-rich sandstone (Potsdam Formation and Lowerre quartzite, New York and Quebec; Cheshire and Dalton Formations, Vermont; Beaver Brook, Kippens and Cloud Mountains Formations, Newfoundland). As is the case farther S, the escarpment marking the carbonate bank edge is commonly delineated by carbonate breccias (Rugg Brook Dolomite, Vermont (unit 25); Levis Formation, Quebec (unit 26); Cow Head breccia–Cooks Brook Formation, Newfoundland (unit 27)) (Rodgers 1968, Cady 1969, Bird & Dewey 1970, Palmer 1971).

Farther E lay an eastward-thinning? wedge of continental rise and slope–apron clastics (Manhattan schist and Waramaug Formation, New York and Connecticut (unit 28); Nassau, Bull and Rennselaer Formations, Taconic region, western New England (unit 29); Pinney Hollow, Ottaquechee, Sweetsburg and Stowe Formations, Vermont (unit 30); Levis and St Daniel Formations, Quebec (unit 31); Mansonville and Kamouraska Formations, Schickshock Group, Gaspé (unit 32); upper portions of the Fleur de Lys Group, Newfoundland (unit 19)). The early Palaeozoic sequences in the Taconics are allochthonous and appear to be fine-grained slope–apron deposits. The latest Cambrian–earliest Ordovician sequences farther E contain interbedded volcanic rocks (parts of the Ottaqueechee and Stowe Formations, Vermont; Ascot and Weedon Formations, Quebec (unit 33); Rambler and Cape St John Formations, Newfoundland (unit 34)) and suggest the incipient development of offshore island-arc–trench complexes (Bird & Dewey 1970, Zen 1972, 1983).

NW British Isles (Scotland and NW Ireland)

Four separate, though not invariably distinct, sequences must be considered: (1) the Moine metamorphic rocks, (2) the 'Torridonian', (3) the Dalradian Supergroup and (4) the Durness sequence. The Torridonian and Durness successions occur only in Scotland; Dalradian and possibly Moine rocks occur in both Ireland and Scotland.

Late Proterozoic

The Moine succession (unit 35) is a thick assemblage of Proterozoic metamorphic rocks whose exact age and regional relationships are uncertain. Much of the Moine succession appears to be metamorphosed from shallow-water high-energy marine-shelf and shore-line sandstones and shales derived from source areas S? of the exposure belt. The Moine sequences occur in a band occupying much of the Scottish Highlands between the Moine thrust and the Great Glen fault. Although much of the Moine succession is believed to be aged between 1050 and 1300 Ma, the oldest Grampian Group of the Dalradian Supergroup S of the Great Glen fault is considered to be 'young' Moine by many and is tentatively correlated with the Torridon Group (Harris *et al.* 1978, Anderton *et al.* 1979, Johnson 1983a, b).

The thick sequence of unmetamorphosed redbed clastics known collectively as the 'Torridonian' actually consists of two similar but distinct units, an older unit (*c.* 1000 Ma)—the Stoer Group—and a younger unit (*c.* 800 Ma)—the Torridon Group, which in this paper includes the Sleat Group. The Stoer Group (unit 36) (300–2000 m) defines the narrow westernmost belt of Torridonian rocks and consists of a lower 'marginal' facies (breccias, conglomerates, coarse sandstone), interpreted as fanglomerate deposits, and an upper 'exotic' facies (mainly red sandstone and shale), interpreted by Williams (1969) as alluvium derived from the NW. The Stoer Group is similar in lithology, distribution and basin setting to late Proterozoic units elsewhere, e.g. the Grandfather Mountain Formation of the southern Appalachians, and may represent the fill of a small fault-bounded tensional 'Newark-type' basin developed within the continental crust prior to the opening of the Iapetus Ocean basin farther SE (Stewart 1982, Johnson 1983a). The Torridon Group (unit 37) reflects crustal upwarping, tilting of the Stoer 'graben' and subsequent subsidence producing marine transgression from the S and/or SE (deltaic and shallow-marine sediments of the Sleat Group (2000–3500 m thick) and the overlying Diabaig Group (0–2000 m thick)). This transgressive blanket was subsequently buried beneath thicker (1000–7000 m) coarser alluvial-fan, fluvial–deltaic and continental-margin deposits of the upper Torridonian Aultbea, Applecross and Cailleach Head Formations (Stewart 1982, Johnson 1983a). Although these younger clastic-wedge accumulations indicate block faulting, crustal extension and the uplift of topographically-high sources compositionally reminiscent of rock types in Greenland (Williams 1969, Allen *et al.* 1974), the Torridonian basin developed upon continental crust and was exterior to any true continental edge (Bamford *et al.* 1977).

Farther S, across the orthotectonic Caledonides in the Grampian Highlands of Scotland and in Antrim, Derry, Mayo, Donegal and Connemara, Ireland, lies the 'young' Moine succession (i.e. the 1000–4000 m thick Grampian Group of the Dalradian) and the 2000–7000 m thick Lower Dalradian or Appin Group (collectively shown as unit 38). These sequences consist of blanket-shaped sandstone and shale units derived from low-lying northwesterly source areas and are believed to have been deposited by rivers flowing across flood-plain and deltaic complexes onto a broad marine shelf and/or littoral basin. A probable glacigenic deposit, the Kinlochlaggen boulder bed, occurs within the Appin Group in Inverness-shire, Scotland (Anderton 1979, 1982, Treagus 1981, Johnson 1983b). The 'young' Moine–lower Dalradian basin, like the Torridonian basin farther N and perhaps contiguous with it, lay entirely within the continental block that formed the western margin of Iapetus rather than at the continental edge itself.

Latest Precambrian (Vendian) and early Palaeozoic

For this time interval the western margin is represented by the remainder of the Dalradian, the 5000–8000 m thick Argyll Group or middle Dalradian and the 4000–5000 m thick Southern Highland Group or upper Dalradian. The base of the middle Dalradian (unit 39) is marked by a series of tillites (Cleggan boulder bed and Doogort boulder bed, Ireland; Port Askaig tillite and Schiehallion boulder bed, Scotland) which are assumed to be Varangerian. These tillites are in turn overlain by presumably latest Proterozoic stable-margin dolomites and quartzites (Bon-haven dolomite, and Jura, Islay and Durnhill quartzites) which pass up into heterogeneous lithologies that differ markedly from one another in thickness and composition. Mass-flow and turbidite deposits as well as bank-edge breccias (Scarba conglomerate) are interleaved with deeper-water basinal mudstone (Easdale slate). This fragmentation of the Dalradian basin into a series of more rapidly subsiding deep-water basins separated by quasi-stable, locally-emer-gent platforms occurred roughly at the Pre-cambrian–Cambrian boundary (Knill 1963, Anderton 1979). In the early Palaeozoic Southern Highland or upper Dalradian Group (unit 40) platformal limestones are interleaved with bank-edge breccias and deeper-water turbiditic carbon-ates and shale (Tayvallich limestone). Deep-sea

fan sandstones (Ben Levy Formation, Ireland; Crinan and Loch Avich grits, Scotland) are intimately associated with pillow basalts (Tay-vallich and Loch Avich volcanics) (Dhonau & Holland 1974, Phillips 1981a, b, Johnson 1983b).

Significantly, most of this immature early Palaeozoic late Dalradian detritus appears to be derived from proximal tectonically-active *sialic* source terranes located SE of the present High-land Boundary fault, perhaps somewhere in the Midland Valley, further supporting the conten-tion that the Dalradian accumulated *within* the northern continental block bordering Iapetus rather than along the ocean margin itself. Al-though that sialic block was distended and fragmented into a series of subsiding sialic blocks, the continental edge must have lain farther S, presumably S of the Southern Uplands (a small intervening 'Ballantrae basin' is also possible) (Harris *et al.* 1976, Smith 1976, Watson & Dunning 1979). Contemporaneous early Cam-brian to early Ordovician units of the Durness sequence of northwestern Scotland (unit 41) represent a thinned continental shelf succession of this interior Dalradian basin, with a basal transgressive sheet of quartzose sandstone and siltstone (the 200 m thick Eriboll sandstone and An-t-Sron Formation) overlain by 1200–1400 m of shallow-water carbonates (the Durness For-mation), most of which are either lower Cambrian or early Ordovician (Swett 1969, Walton 1983).

Greenland

Although belts of late Proterozoic and early Palaeozoic rocks occur along the northern as well as northeastern–eastern margin of Greenland, only the latter part—the E Greenland Caledon-ides—is discussed in detail because the former is largely unrelated to the Appalachian–Caledonide orogen.

Late Proterozoic

Two thick dominantly-clastic late Proterozoic sequences reflect an episode of crustal distension and marginal subsidence with the development of an ensialic basin, or series of basins, along the eastern and northeastern margins of Greenland. These two units are the Eleonore Bay Group (unit 42) of the E Greenland Caledonides proper and the Hagen Fjord Group and its equivalent (unit 43) of northeastern Greenland.

The Eleonore Bay Group was deposited on the eroded roots of the Carolinidian mobile belt. This unit thickens dramatically from 6300 m in the nunatak zone to more than 16 000 m in the fjord zone along the E coast. Basal portions may be from source areas located offshore to the E, but the bulk of the unit comprises clastic marine deposits derived from the interior of Greenland to the W. The upper Eleonore Bay Group is a transgressive sedimentary succession composed of quartz-arenite, limestone and dolomite; oolites, mudcracks and other shallow-water structures are common (Haller 1971, Henriksen 1978). A thin (200–1000 m) sequence of glacial tillites, which may be equivalent to the Varangerian tillite group, overlies the upper Eleonore Bay Group and is in turn overlain by 250–350 m of shallow-water mudstone, dolomite and carbonate which are presumably latest Proterozoic or Vendian (Canyon and Spiral Creek Formations) (Henriksen & Higgins 1976, Higgins 1981). No trace of a continental rise prism, which is presumably located farther E, has been described. The entire late Proterozoic succession of E Greenland is essentially a typical miogeoclinal neritic-shelf assemblage (Birkelund *et al.* 1974).

The late Proterozoic sequences of NE Greenland are collectively referred to as the Hagen Fjord Group. An autochthonous 2000 m thick foreland succession of fluvial, glacial and neritic sedimentary rocks exposed in Hagen Fjord is considered to be equivalent to the thicker allochthonous marginal trough and neritic miogeoclinal units exposed in the Hekla Sound area (basal Stenørken phyllite, Tågefjeldene greywacke, Rivieradal sandstone). This tremendous volume of clastic sediments, like the Eleonore Bay Group farther S, was deposited essentially in an ensialic basin. Varangerian? tillites cap the sequence (Ulvebjerg Formation) (Henriksen & Higgins 1976).

Cambrian–Tremadoc

These sequences of eastern and northeastern Greenland imply a shallow shelf setting reminiscent of that documented for contemporaneous units in northwestern Britain and throughout the Appalachians. A series of basal quartzose transgressive sandstones (Kløftelv and Bastion Formations, eastern Greenland (unit 44); portions of the Campanuladal and Kap Holbæk Formations, northeastern Greenland (unit 45)) pass up into shallow-water continental shelf–epicontinental sea carbonates (Ella Island, Hyolithus Creek, Dolomite Point and Cass Fjord Formations, eastern Greenland; Campanuladal, Fyn Sø and Amdrup Formations, northeastern Greenland). As elsewhere along the western margin in Britain and the Appalachians, evidence exists for a late lower Cambrian episode of regression with early Cambrian and early Ordovician time much better represented than the intervening interval (Palmer

& James 1980). Finally, no carbonate bank-edge breccias have been described nor can continental rise sequences be found, which is additional evidence that the true continental edge lay E of Greenland (Cowie 1971, Dawes 1976, Henriksen & Higgins 1976).

The northern Greenland succession is a rather thin homoclinal sequence of epicontinental shelf–platform carbonates interbedded with quartz-rich transgressive sandstone. These Palaeozoic units have a regionally developed unconformity. A tillite unit (Moraenesø Formation) and older Proterozoic clastic sequences occur locally immediately beneath the regional unconformity (Dawes 1976, Clemmensen 1981, Dawes & Peel 1981).

Svalbard Archipelago (Spitsbergen and related areas)

The Caledonides of at least western Svalbard have more in common with the E Greenland Caledonides than with the Scandinavian Caledonides; their close proximity to the latter is presumably the result of strike-slip faulting (Birkenmajer 1975). Harland (1978) and Hambrey (1982, 1983) suggest that Svalbard should be subdivided into western and eastern provinces brought together by mid-Palaeozoic sinistral transcurrent faulting. If Svalbard is in fact a composite assemblage of far-travelled terranes, the several thousand metres of late Proterozoic shelf and slope deposits (western province) now located N of Greenland may represent the original western margin deposits. Conversely, the thin shelf sequences of the eastern province (Ny Friesland, Nordaustlandet and Kvitøya) conceivably belong to the eastern margin. It is even possible that *both* Svalbardian provinces may have been loated at the *same* margin, either the western or eastern. These various possibilities should be kept in mind in light of the rather simplistic discussion below which lumps the relevant Svalbardian sequences together.

These late Proterozoic–lower Ordovician stratigraphic units are commonly referred to collectively as the Hecla Hoek Succession (unit 46), although the use of this term for the units of the eastern province seems inappropriate in view of the possibility that they were originally physically separated from the western province. The stratigraphic thickness can exceed 20 km, but regional unconformities permit definition of distinct 'basinal assemblages' (based on Harland 1969, 1978, Roberts & Gale 1978, Birkenmajer 1981, Hambrey *et al.* 1981).

Late Proterozoic

Sedimentary rocks of the lower Hecla Hoek (9–
11.5 km) comprise the Torellian basin complex,
which is a series of basins filled with interbedded
volcanic and clastic rocks. Both the eastern and
western margins of this basin complex were
deformed by the Torellian (Carolinidian–Grenville) orogeny. The middle Hecla Hoek (1.5–
7 km) consists of mainly shallow-marine miogeoclinal (i.e. continental shelf and platform) deposits capped with Vendian tillites (Sveanor and
Polarisbreen Tillite Formations) which filled the
so-called Jarlsberg basin, the axis of which lay
somewhat W of the earlier Torellian basin. This
basin was deformed by the Jarlsbergian orogeny
(*c.* 600 Ma; essentially Cadomian–Avalonian).

Early Palaeozoic

The upper Hecla Hoek (0.8–2.3 km) consists of
intermixed early Cambrian quartz-rich sandstone
and shallow-marine platformal carbonates that
are deformed by a middle to end Cambrian
(Hornsundian) orogeny and unconformably overlain by early Ordovician quartz-arenites and
carbonates.

In summary, the stratigraphic record in Svalbard resembles that of nearby northeastern
Greenland with a series of broadly-subsiding
evidently ensialic basins, perhaps in part distal
equivalents of the Eleonore Bay–Hagen Fjord
basins of the western margin proper further W.
Equivalent sequences of the eastern province of
Svalbard may have straddled the future axis of
continental separation or may mark the incipient
continental edge.

Eastern margins (N–S)

Overview

The eastern margin, at least in Scandinavia,
mirrors the western margin, except that the
Cambrian–Tremadoc continental shelf cover is a
thin blanket of black shale and that a better
record of a paired continental rise prism exists. S
of Scandinavia, however, lies the Avalon terrane
of southern Britain, Brittany, eastern Newfoundland, the Maritime Provinces and New England,
with a presumed southern continuation in the
Carolina slate belt. This strip of possibly sialic
crust was repeatedly stretched and ruptured in
the late Proterozoic. Sub-aerial and submarine
volcanicity accompanied the development of
numerous grabens and perhaps small ocean
basins that filled with clastic sediments and were

repeatedly deformed by Pan-African-style orogeny. In the early Palaeozoic, the Avalon terranes
(an Avalon 'microcontinent'?) acted as a stable
platform, which is covered by transgressive
quartzites overlain by a thin mudstone blanket or
locally with thicker basinal sequences, bordered
to the NW by a continental rise (Gander Lake
terranes). E of Avalon lay the western margin of
France–Iberia–Africa with a late Precambrian
history of rupture and orogeny and an early
Palaeozoic sequence of paired continental shelf–
continental rise sedimentary rocks (Mauritanides–Moroccan Anti-Atlas and perhaps the displaced Meguma terrane of Nova Scotia).

Finnmark (northern Scandinavia)

Late Proterozoic

A series of nappes thrust from the N transported
several thick clastic sequences originally deposited N of the present coast of Finnmark.
Sequences several kilometres thick are also
present beyond the Caledonian nappe front on
the Varanger Peninsula, NW of the major
Trollfjord–Komagelv fault. The 14 km thick
Barents Sea and the overlying Løkvikfjell Groups
(collectively unit 47) consist of marine and non-
marine fluvial–deltaic sandstone and shale deposited across a broad ensialic basin. This basin
appears to have been separated by a sialic horst
from an offshore deeper-water trough in which
the various units of the Kalak Nappe Complex
(unit 48) were deposited—a paired shelf–rise
ensemble that may constitute the fill of the so-
called Timanian aulacogen running sharply E off
the general northerly-trending Caledonian belt.
Immediately S of the Barents Sea–Løkvikfjell
belt lie thinner (3 km) autochthonous shallow-
marine, tidal-flat and braided fluvial clastic
sediments of equivalent age (Vadsø, Tanafjord
and lower Vestertana Groups (unit 49)) (Føyn
1985). Varanger tillites (Nyborg Formation,
Mortenses tillite) cap this succession.

Late Vendian–early Ordovician

Immediately above the Varangerian tillites is a
thin (1–2 km) marine transgressive sequence
(collectively unit 50): quartz-rich sandstone of
the upper Vestertana, Breivik and Stappogiedde
Formations and the Duolbasgaissa quartzite, a
lower Cambrian–middle Cambrian hiatus and
the latest Cambrian–Tremadoc black shales
(Digermul Group) (Bergström 1980). Allochthonous units in the Kalak Nappe Complex transported from areas further N off the coast
(Hellefjord schist (unit 51) and associated units)

may be deeper-water continental shelf and rise equivalents (Sturt & Roberts 1978).

Central and southern Scandinavian Caledonides

Late Proterozoic

Kumpulainen & Nystuen (1985) recognize four stages of sedimentation in the autochthonous to allochthonous sequences.

1 During late Riphean time (800–750 Ma) the Baltic shield was domed, eroded and initially distended, producing embryonic fault basins in which the initial sediments of the Tossåsfjallet, Valdres, Hedmark, Risbäck and Vättern basins were deposited.
2 Crustal stretching continued during late Riphean–early Vendian time (700–650 Ma). Broad ensialic exterior basins developed and filled with braided-stream, sheet-flood, lacustrine, fanglomerate and carbonate deposits (Tossåsfjallet (unit 52) and Engerdalen Groups (unit 53)). To the E, basins which were interior relative to the developing continental margin accumulated thick alluvial-fan deposits, turbidites, carbonates and black shales, and even shallow lacustrine deposits (Risbäck Group (unit 54); Hedmark Group (unit 55); Valdres Group (unit 56)). Local tholeiitic basalts formed by fissure eruption. Still farther E and well within the continental interior was the Triassic-like graben of the Vättern basin (Visingö Group (unit 57)).
3 These various basin sequences, each several kilometres thick, were mantled by tills deposited during the Varanger ice age (*c.* 650 Ma) (Moelv–Långmarkberg tillites).
4 As the ice retreated, a westward-thickening sequence of late Vendian shallow-marine and deltaic deposits accumulated (Ekre shale and Vangsås–Vemdal Formations).

Various units of the Western Complex (unit 58), now transported in nappes like the Seve and Kolï Nappes, may in part be late Proterozoic in age (Trondheim Supergroup, Gula and Støren Groups) and be portions of a developing ocean-basin–island-arc–back-arc basin complex farther offshore (Gee 1975, 1978).

Early Palaeozoic

Simple marine transgression deposited a blanket of quartz-rich sandstone (Ringsaker quartzite, Vemdal sandstone, Balka sandstone) that is overlain by upper Cambrian and Tremadoc (Alum) shales (Strand & Kulling 1972, Martinsson 1974, Bergström & Gee 1985). Various units

of the Western Complex are presumably equivalent in age and represent continental rise, island-arc and back-arc deposits.

A branch or offshoot of the Iapetus Ocean basin may have extended into the continental interior (the German–Polish Caledonides (unit 60)) separating the Baltic–Scandinavian craton from the W German–SE Britain craton, but this area will not be discussed at length.

Southern Britain (Wales, English Midlands and SE Ireland)

Late Precambrian

Several thick sequences of late (900–590 Ma) Proterozoic volcanic-rich sedimentary rock units that rest unconformably on somewhat older, generally Proterozoic, metasedimentary terranes have been described (Harris *et al.* 1975). These sequences include the following.

1 The Wrekin, Shropshire (unit 61): the 1500 m Uriconian (632 ± 32 Ma) rhyolite and andesite lavas and pyroclastics and probably younger 8000 m Longmyndian succession (*c.* 600 Ma) (the lower dominantly-shaly Stretton series and the upper mainly-sandy conglomeratic Wentnorian series), which are collectively interpreted as a regressive sequence upwards from marginal marine to fluvial–deltaic deposits.
2 Malvern Hills, Worcestershire–Herefordshire border (unit 62): rhyolites, spilites and tuffs of the Warren House volcanic series (unknown thickness) (*c.* 635–600 Ma?).
3 The eastern English Midlands (unit 63): the 2600 m Charnian with basal rhyolitic and andesitic tuffs and lavas overlain by conglomerate, sandstone and slate (*c.* 600–700 Ma).
4 S Wales (unit 64): Pebidian Complex (1400 m) of acid and intermediate tuffs, lavas and interbedded coarse clastics (*c.* 600–650 Ma).
5 N Wales: the Mona or Monian Supergroup (unit 65) (minimum age 620 Ma) and a thick succession of (i) deep-water turbidite sandstone and shale interbedded with pillowed volcanic rocks (New Harbour Group (2000 m)), (ii) overlying argillaceous sediments, cherts and pillowed volcanic rocks (Skerries Group (500 m)) and (iii) at the top, quartz-arenite, oolitic and stromatolitic limestone, pillowed volcanic rock, bedded chert and a 900 m melange (Gwna Group (3000 m)). The Monian is unconformably overlain by latest Proterozoic–earliest Cambrian rocks of the Arvonian succession (mainly acid inigbrites 1–2 km thick).

6 Southeastern Ireland: Cullenstown Formation, County Wexford (unit 66) which is a sequence of greywacke, shale and quartzites of unknown thickness and uncertain age.

The depositional environment, tectonic setting and specific correlation among these sequences, and with comparable sequences elsewhere in the Appalachians (see below), is uncertain owing to deformation and metamorphism. Nevertheless, any model must satisfactorily explain the unusual combination of events suggested by such rock assemblages: late Proterozoic crustal tension, extensive sub-aerial and submarine volcanism, the development of local basins that fill with both marine and non-marine sediment, a stage of terminal Precambrian deformation (Avalonian–Cadomian–Pan-African orogeny) and behaviour in the early Palaeozoic (see below) as a stable cratonic platform (Anderton *et al.* 1979). Such terranes, which are also widespread in eastern Newfoundland, the eastern Maritime Provinces of Canada, eastern New England and the Carolina slate belts, are collectively referred to as *Avalonian* terranes.

Dewey (1969) believed that the late Precambrian sequences of southern Britain, at least, accumulated along the southern margin of the newly opened Iapetus Ocean basin. He showed the Monian as continental rise and slope deposits straddling the ocean–continent crustal boundary which became a detachment zone for southerly subduction right at the end of the Precambrian. However, Baker (1973) argued that the Monian included shallow-water as well as deep-water deposits and showed it accumulating along the southern flank of an offshore microcontinental landmass located in N Wales. His hypothetical narrow 'Monian marginal ocean basin' was floored with ocean crust, with the major southern or European continental block located just to the S in S Wales and the English Midlands.

Rast *et al.* (1976) believed that the late Proterozoic–early Palaeozoic history suggested by these various sequences for southern Britain could also best be related to a sliver of sialic crust (Avalon). Avalon was shown as separated from the African continent by a closing Cadomian ocean basin and from the N American–NW Britain continent by a small opening back-arc ocean basin, which in Palaeozoic time grew into Iapetus. Wedges of continental shelf and rise sediment were shown not only along the northern edges of Avalon (Monian Supergroup) but also along the southern margin (Brioverian of Normandy and Brittany in France (see below)).

More recent studies do indeed support the existence of Avalon as a strip of continental crust extending across southern Britain into the Appalachian system, and its evolution will be discussed further within that context below (Rast 1980, O'Brien *et al.* 1983).

Early Palaeozoic

Southern Britain constitutes the NW-facing continental margin of Iapetus during this time interval. This margin can be subdivided into two components: (a) a southeastern (landward) platform (Midland platform of Shropshire, the Malvern area and the English Midlands) and (b) a northwestern (oceanward) zone within which a series of structural basins developed (Welsh and Leinster basins) (Rushton 1974, Dhonau & Holland 1974, Anderton *et al.* 1979).

Thin (500–1500 m) and generally fine clastic sediments accumulated across the Midland platform (sequences shown collectively as unit 67): basal early Cambrian (Comley) transgressive quartz-rich sandstones (Wrekin, Malvern and Hartshill quartzites) overlying lower and middle (St David's) Cambrian shallow-water sandstone, shale and limestone (Comley and Hollybush sandstones), and finally a late Cambrian (Merioneth)–early Ordovician (Tremadoc) blanket of potassium-rich mudstone comparable in age and lithology with the Alum shales of Scandinavia.

N of the Midland platform lay the Welsh basin, an ensialic intra-shelf basin filled with alternating shallow- and deep-water clastics (Caerfai and Solva Groups and the Harlech grits (unit 68)) derived from sources located both to the N (Irish Sea platform separating the Welsh and Leinster basins) and to the S (material crossing the Midland platform). The Welsh basin separated the Midland platform from the Arvonian volcanic arc, and conceivably was a back-arc basin similar to portions of the Avalon terranes elsewhere outside the British Isles. Just as in the Midland platform, late Cambrian and early Ordovician time was characterized by thin, possibly shallow-water mudstone and siltstone (Lingula Flags, Maentwrog and Ffestinog beds (unit 69)) that in Tremadoc time were tilted and eroded as a sea transgressed from S to N across the Irish Sea platform.

The Leinster–Wexford–Cumbria basin lay along the northwestern flank of the Irish Sea platform. Within this basin are interbedded shale and turbidite sandstone derived from source areas located both to the N (Southern Uplands?) and to the S (Bray Group of Ireland's Eye and Bray Head (unit 70); Ribband and Cahore Group, Wexford; possibly portions of the Manx and Skiddaw slates, Isle of Man and Lake District (unit 71)).

Brittany and Normandy, France

Late Proterozoic

This area constitutes the southern flank of Avalon as well as the northwestern margin of the Cadomian Ocean, which finally closed as Avalon converged with the Africa–northern France–SE Britain continental block producing the Cadomian orogeny (early or Domnonean phase, pre-600 Ma; later or Ligerian phase, *c.* 570 Ma). The late Proterozoic sequence is referred to as the Brioverian (unit 72), and is a 10–15 km thick succession composed mainly of clastic sedimentary rocks. Middle Brioverian shales were deformed into a series of rising eroding cordillera during the earlier phase of the Cadomian orogeny. The lower portion of the upper Brioverian sequence is a thick clastic wedge of deltaic sandstone and conglomerate derived from this uplift (Granville, Gourin and Plusquellec Formations). This is in turn overlain by rhythmically interbedded greywacke and shale—flysch-like material signalling the resumption of subsidence (Binic and Laize Series, Neant Flags). The second (Ligurian) phase of the Cadomian orogeny marks the Precambrian–Cambrian boundary and the final closure of the Cadomian Ocean (Durand 1977, Pomerol 1980).

Early Palaeozoic

Earliest Palaeozoic uplift and erosion of the Cadomian belt preceded general submergence and transgression (the blanket of generally reddish sandstone and shale immediately beneath the Arenig Amorican sandstone (unit 73) is probably middle Cambrian to Tremadoc).

Atlantic France and the Iberian Peninsula

The age, thickness, regional trend and depositional setting for late Proterozoic and early Palaeozoic sequences across this area are obscured by the effects of later, principally Hercynian, overprinting. Late Proterozoic sequences around Coruna in Galicia (La Coruna (unit 74)) and farther S in western Spain and Portugal (Extremadura (unit 75)) resemble the Brioverian rocks of Brittany—the thick mica schist and quartzite successions that were deposited apparently along both the northwestern (Avalonian) and southeastern (African) margins of the Cadomian Ocean.

The exact trend of the Cadomian mountain system is also obscure, but it apparently rimmed the northern and western margin of the Iberian Peninsula. Cambrian and early Ordovician sequences (unit 76) thicken to the N and W, and generally suggest paired shelf and rise sediment prisms (Ager 1980).

Avalon terrane: Maritime Provinces of Canada and the New England Appalachians

The stratigraphic record for the Avalon terrane in eastern Newfoundland has been extremely well documented (Brückner 1969, McCartney 1969, Rast *et al.* 1976, Strong 1979, King 1980, O'Brien *et al.* 1983). General patterns established there can be extrapolated southward (Rast 1980, Skehan & Murray 1980, Skehan & Rast 1983).

Late Precambrian

The Avalon zone of Newfoundland may have been contiguous with similar terranes in Britain. In any event, in eastern Canada and the USA it appears to be an elongated strip of continental crust (Skehan & Rast 1983) which perhaps was torn from either the N American or the African–European continents or conceivably was accreted as an ensialic island arc developed above a consuming plate margin.

The late Proterozoic stratigraphy of the Avalon Peninsula and the Burin Peninsula of eastern Newfoundland suggests generally limited, although variable, crustal thinning and separation. Prolonged continental extension, perhaps accompanied by the development of small ocean basins, i.e. the Burin Group, and local rupturing, generated basin and range topography with a series of ensialic grabens. Several kilometres of dominantly sub-aerial volcanic flows and pyroclastic deposits accumulated (Long Harbour, Connaigne Bay, Marystown, Love Cove and Harbour Main Groups (unit 77); Bull Arm Formation of the Musgravetown Group). Analogous broadly-contemporaneous volcanic-rich sequences elsewhere in easternmost Canada include the Forchu Group, Cape Breton (unit 78), the Coldbrook Group, New Brunswick (unit 79), the Mattapan–Eastern Massachusetts volcanic complex (unit 80) and portions of the Newport and Price's Neck Formations, Rhode Island (unit 81).

The above volcaniclastic sequences (750–570 Ma) intertongue and pass up into thick (3–5 km) marine turbidites and shales (Connecting Point and Conception Bay Groups, Avalon Peninsula, Newfoundland; the latter contains interbedded tillite horizons referred to as the Gaskiers Formation). These mainly deep-water deposits are in turn conformably overlain by 8–10 km of shallow-marine, deltaic, fluvial and alluvial-fan clastic sediments (Hodgewater, St

John's, Signal Hill and Inlet Groups, Newfoundland). Comparable molasse units elsewhere include the Morrison River Formation, Cape Breton, the Ratcliffe Brook Formation, New Brunswick, and the Boston Bay Group, Massachusetts.

Early Palaeozoic

The end Precambrian Avalonian (Cadomian) orogeny (deformation, metamorphism, intrusion) consolidated the various blocks and basins of the Avalon terranes. Erosional bevelling followed. During the early Palaeozoic, the Avalon terranes of N America, as in Britain, were relatively stable. Basal transgressive quartzites (Random Formation, Newfoundland (unit 82); quartzites at the top of the Morrison River Formation, Cape Breton (unit 83); Glens Falls Formation, New Brunswick (unit 84)) are overlain by thin dominantly-shaly Cambrian and early Ordovician units (Bonavista, Brigus, Elliott Cove and Clarenville Formations; Wabana and Bell Island Groups, Newfoundland; Navy Island and Suspension Bridge Formations, S Nova Scotia; Weymouth and Braintree Formations, Massachusetts (unit 85); Newport and Jamestown Formations, Rhode Island (unit 86)).

Gander zone: Maritime Provinces, Canada and New England Appalachians

The Gander zone is a clastic apron of continental shelf, rise, slope and abyssal-plain sediments several kilometres thick that accumulated along the northwestern margin of the Avalon microcontinent in both late Proterozoic and early Palaeozoic time. These deposits either faced an opening Iapetus to the NW or were components of a back-arc basin located above a subduction zone descending beneath Avalon. Deformation and metamorphism make identification and definite correlation difficult, but sequences that should be included are the Gander Lake Group, Newfoundland (unit 87), the lower Tetagouche sequence, New Brunswick (unit 88), the Grand Pitch Formation, Maine (unit 89) and perhaps some of the gneisses and associated metasedimentary rocks that core various anticlinoria and domes throughout eastern New England (Bronson Hill and Boundary Mountains anticlinoria, the Pelham and various eastern Connecticut domes, the Massabesic gneiss, New Hampshire, the Nashoba terrane, Massachusetts, and the Blackstone Series, Rhode Island) (Schenk 1978, Robinson & Hall 1980, Williams & Hatcher 1983, Zen 1983). Comparable units in southern Britain are the Cullenstown Formation, Ireland (unit 66), the

Bray Series, Ireland (unit 70), and perhaps portions of the Manx and Skiddaw slates, Lake District and Isle of Man (unit 71).

Central and Southern Appalachians (Avalon and Gander? terranes)

The Carolina slate belt and, farther E, the eastern slate belt adjacent to the coastal plain of Georgia and the Carolinas together with the Belair belt, a detached segment in S Carolina and Georgia, form a dominantly low-grade terrane (unit 91) of volcaniclastic sedimentary rocks and mafic to felsic volcanics more than 13 km thick. The northern third of the terrane is generally late Proterozoic, and the southern and central parts are Cambrian or latest Precambrian.

A wide variety of ideas exists about the origin and sedimentary development of the belt (Bearce *et al.* 1982), but many workers now favour the interpretation that the belt is a calc-alkaline island arc generated on either oceanic or thin continental crust. Late Proterozoic crustal stretching generated a series of shallow- and deep-water basins, with some Cambrian platform deposits, a scenario reminiscent of Avalonia elsewhere in N America and Britain.

The high-grade zone W of the Carolina slate belt—the Charlotte belt (unit 92)—is considered by some as a southern continuation of the Gander zone, i.e. a continental shelf–rise embankment flanking the northwestern margin of Avalon.

Meguma zone, southern Nova Scotia

The Meguma Group (unit 93) comprises over 14 km of turbidite sandstone and black slate of possibly the latest Proterozoic, Cambrian and early Ordovician. These rocks constitute a coalescing submarine fan complex deposited near the toe of a continental embankment as well as younger Ordovician continental rise deposits of the embankment itself. Deep erosion of a metasedimentary–continental crustal terrane located somewhere to the SE is required; this is most probably the Guiana or Brazilian shield of northwestern S America, the Moroccan area of northwestern Africa or possibly portions of the Iberian Peninsula and Western Europe (Schenk 1978, 1981).

NW and W Africa

A thin blanket of epicontinental and continental shelf deposits is exposed along the western margin of the W African craton in the Taoudeni basin (Mauritania) and in the Tindouf basin and Anti-Atlas region of Morocco, Mauritania, Algeria and the Spanish Sahara. Thicker, commonly deeper-water, volcanic-rich clastic sequences occur in the overthrust fold belts of W Africa (the Rokelides and Mauritanides, and the High Atlas and Anti-Atlas of Morocco). The more internal parts of these belts are covered by Mesozoic–Cenozoic sedimentary rocks (Mauritania–Senegal, Bové and Aaiun basins), leaving the stratigraphic framework uncertain (Dillon & Sougy 1974).

Late Precambrian

Thin flat-lying or gently folded continental shelf marine and non-marine sandstone, shale and limestone units occur in the Mauritanian Adrar (the 1500 m Unit I, Supergroup 1 or Taoudeni Supergroup (unit 94)). Equivalent quartzites and limestones in the Anti-Atlas region of Morocco (unit 95) may be folded Precambrian II$_2$, the Eocambrian or Vendian Adoudou Supergroup (or Adoudounian System) or even the Precambrian III (750–1000 Ma) mixed red beds, rhyolitic-andesitic and basaltic volcanics, and lacustrine deposits of the Ouarzazate Group or System. In any case, these shallow-water sedimentary rocks have been interpreted as grading westward into volcanic-rich slope–rise–back-arc successions of the Rokelides (unit 96), internal Mauritanides (unit 97) and Moroccan High Atlas (unit 98) (Schenk 1971, Grant 1973).

Latest Proterozoic and early Palaeozoic

In the Mauritanian Adrar a 1200 m thick sequence of platform sandstone, shale and stromatolitic-bearing carbonates interbedded with (Pan-African?) molasse-like red beds (collectively Unit 2 or Supergroup 2 or the Kayes and Kiffa Groups (unit 99)) rests unconformably upon Supergroup 1. The base of this unit is marked with a glacial tillite (Jbeliat Group) and capped with Tremadocian sandstone (Deynoux & Trompette 1981, Tucker & Reid 1981). Units of similar age in the Anti-Atlas belt of Morocco occur within the upper part of the Adoudou Supergroup (Adoudounian System) (unit 100), which is a succession of marine limestone, dolomite, shale and continental clastics 3–4 km thick ('Lie de vin series') (Salop 1983). Parts of the continental rise–slope–island-arc sequences farther W are of equivalent age (the High Atlas of Morocco, the Bou Regreg Formation of the Rabat–Tiflet zone and the internal Mauritanides).

The rather straightforward Atlantic-type margin described above was affected by the Pan-African movements near the end of the Precambrian around the margins of all African cratonic blocks. This orogeny, which was presumably due to repeated attempts of jostling sialic blocks to break apart, resulted in crustal thinning, minor rifting and limited subduction and obduction. Many of the Pan-African belts surrounding the W African craton (Pharusian belt, Dahomeyan belt) appear to have developed from ensialic basins or upper crustal grabens. The various slope, arc, rise and shelf deposits of the Rokelides–Mauritanides–Atlas belt may have developed within a series of intra-continental basins that straddled the ocean–continent boundary (O'Brien *et al.* 1983). Lécorché *et al.* (1983) suggest that the so-called Mauritanides anomaly beneath the Mauritania–Senegal basin marks a major crustal suture and/or mantle ridge separating the W African craton from an offshore coastal sialic block that collided with W Africa near the end of the Precambrian.

References

AGER, D. V. 1980. *The Geology of Europe*, Wiley, New York, 535 pp.

ALLEN, P., SUTTON, J. & WATSON, J. V. 1974. Torridonian tourmaline-quartz pebbles and the Precambrian crust northwest of Britain. *Journal of the Geological Society, London*, **130**, 85–91.

ANDERTON, R. 1979. Slopes, submarine fans, and syndepositional faults: sedimentology of parts of the Middle and Upper Dalradian in the SW Highlands of Scotland. *In*: HARRIS, A. L., HOLLAND, C. H. & LEAKE, B. E. (eds) *The Caledonides of the British Isles Reviewed. Geological Society of London Special Publication No. 8*, pp. 483–8.

—— 1982. Dalradian deposition and the late Precambrian–Cambrian history of the North Atlantic region: a review of the early evolution of the Iapetus Ocean. *Journal of the Geological Society, London*, **139**, 421–31.

——, BRIDGE, P. H., LEEDER, M. R. & SELLWOOD, B. W. 1979. *A Dynamic Stratigraphy of the British Isles*, George Allen & Unwin, London, 301 pp.

BAKER, J. W. 1973. A marginal late Proterozoic ocean basin in the Welsh region. *Geological Magazine*, **110**, 447–55.

BAMFORD, D., NUNN, K., PRODEHL, C. & JACOB, B. 1977. LISPB-III upper crustal structure of northern Britain. *Journal of the Geological Society, London*, **133**, 481–8.

BARKER, A. J. & GAYER, R. A. 1985. Caledonide-Appalachian tectonic analysis and evolution of related oceans. *In*: GAYER, R. A. (ed.) *The Tectonic Evolution of the Caledonian–Appalachian Orogen*, pp. 126–65, Vieweg, Braunschweig.

BEARCE, D. N., BLACK, W. W., KISH, S. A. & TULL, T. F. (eds) 1982. *Tectonic Studies in the Talladega and Carolina Slate Belts, Southern Appalachian Orogen. Geological Society of America Special Paper No. 191*, 164 pp.

BERGSTRÖM, J. 1980. The Caledonian margin of the Fennoscandinavian shield during the Cambrian. *In*: WONES, D. R. (ed.) *The Caledonides in the USA: Proceedings of the International Geological Correlation Program—Caledonide Orogen Project 27, Blacksburg, VA. Department of Geological Sciences, Virginia Polytechnic Institute and State University, Memoir No. 2*, pp. 9–13.

—— & GEE, D. G. 1985. The Cambrian in Scandinavia. *In*: GEE, D. G. & STURT, B. A. (eds) *The Caledonide Orogen—Scandinavia and Related Areas*, Wiley, Chichester.

BIRD, J. M. & DEWEY, J. F. 1970. Lithosphere plate–continental margin tectonics and the evolution of the Appalachian orogen. *Geological Society of America Bulletin*, **81**, 1031–60.

BIRKELUND, T., PERCH-NILSEN, K., BRIDGEWATER, D. & HIGGINS, A. K. 1974. An outline of the geology of the Atlantic coast of Greenland. *In*: NAIRN, A. E. M. & STEHLI, F. G. (eds) *The Ocean Basins and Margins*, Vol. 2, *The North Atlantic*, pp. 125–59, Plenum, New York.

BIRKENMAJER, K. 1975. Caledonides of Svalbard and plate tectonics. *Bulletin of the Geological Society of Denmark*, **23**, 1–19.

—— 1981. The geology of Svalbard, the western part of the Barents Sea and the continental margin of Scandinavia. *In*: NAIRN, A. E. M., CHURKIN, M., JR, & STEHLI, F. G. (eds) *The Ocean Basins and Margins*, Vol. 5, *The Arctic Ocean*, pp. 265–329, Plenum, New York.

BOND, G. C., NICKESON, P. A. & KIMINZ, M. A. 1984. Breakup of a supercontinent between 625 Ma and 555 Ma: new evidence and implications for continental histories. *Earth and Planetary Science Letters*, **70**, 325–45.

BRÜCKNER, W. D. 1969. Geology of eastern part of Avalon Peninsula, Newfoundland—a summary. *In*: KAY, M. (ed.) *North Atlantic—Geology and Continental Drift. American Association of Petroleum Geologists Memoir No. 12*, pp. 130–8.

CADY, W. 1969. *Regional Tectonic Synthesis of Northwestern New England and Adjacent Quebec. Geological Society of America Memoir No. 120*, 181 pp.

CLEMMENSEN, L. B. 1981. Late Precambrian tilloids of Peary Land, north Greenland. *In*: HAMBREY, M. J. & HARLAND, W. B. (eds) *Earth's Pre-Pleistocene Glacial Record*, pp. 782–6, Cambridge University Press, Cambridge.

CONLEY, J. F. 1978. Geology of the Piedmont of Virginia—interpretations and problems. *Contributions to Virginia Geology III. Virginia Division of Mineral Resources Publication No. 7*, pp. 115–49.

CONWAY MORRIS, S. & RUSHTON, A. W. A. 1988. Precambrian to Tremadoc biotas in the Caledonides. *This volume*.

COWIE, J. W. 1971. The Cambrian of the North American Arctic regions. *In*: HOLLAND, C. H. (ed.) *Lower Paleozoic Rocks of the World*, Vol. 1, *Cambrian of the New World*, pp. 325–83, Wiley-Interscience, New York.

DAWES, P. R. 1976. Precambrian to Tertiary of northern Greenland. *In*: ESCHER, A. & WATT, W. S. (eds) *Geology of Greenland*, pp. 248–303, Geological Survey of Greenland.

—— & PEEL, J. S. 1981. The northern margin of Greenland from Baffin Bay to the Greenland Sea. *In*: NAIRN, A. E. M., CHURKIN, M., JR, & STEHLI, F. G. (eds) *The Ocean Basins and Margins*, Vol. 5, *The Arctic Ocean*, pp. 201–64, Plenum, New York.

DEWEY, J. F. 1969. Evolution of the Appalachian–Caledonian orogen. *Nature, London*, **222**, 124–8.

DEYNOUX, M. & TROMPETTE, R. 1981. Late Precambrian tillites of the Taoudeni basin, west Africa. *In*: HAMBREY, M. J. & HARLAND, W. B. (eds) *Earth's Pre-Pleistocene Glacial Record*, pp. 123–131, Cambridge University Press, Cambridge.

DHONAU, N. B. & HOLLAND, C. H. 1974. The Cambrian of Ireland. *In*: HOLLAND, C. H. (ed.) *Cambrian of the British Isles, Norden, and Spitzbergen*, pp. 157–76, Wiley, New York.

DILLON, W. P. & SOUGY, J. M. A. 1974. Geology of West Africa and Canary and Cape Verde Islands. *In*: NAIRN, A. E. M. & STEHLI, F. G. (eds) *The Ocean Basins and Margins*, Vol. 2, *The North Atlantic*, pp. 315–90, Plenum, New York.

DURAND, S. 1977. *Bretagne, Guides Géologiques Régionaux*, Masson, Paris, 208 pp.

FISHER, G. W., HIGGINS, M. W. & ZIETZ, I. 1979. Geological interpretations of aeromagnetic maps of the crystalline rocks in the Appalachians, northern Virginia to New Jersey. *Maryland Geological Survey Report of Investigations No. 32*, 43 pp.

FØYN, S. 1985. The late Precambrian in northern Scandinavia. *In*: GEE, D. G. & STURT, B. A. (eds) *The Caledonide Orogen—Scandinavia and Related Areas*, Wiley, Chichester.

GEE, D. G. 1975. A tectonic model for the central part of the Scandinavian Caledonides. *American Journal of Science*, **275A**, 468–515.

—— 1978. Nappe displacement in the Scandinavian Caledonides. *Tectonophysics*, **47**, 383–515.

GRANT, N. M. 1973. Orogeny and reactivation to the west and southeast of the West African craton. *In*: NAIRN, A. E. M. & STEHLI, F. G. (eds) *The Ocean Basins and Margins*, Vol. 1, *The South Atlantic*, pp. 447–92, Plenum, New York.

HALLER, J. 1971. *Geology of the East Greenland Caledonides*, Wiley-Interscience, New York, 413 pp.

HAMBREY, M. J. 1982. Late Precambrian diamictites of northeastern Svalbard. *Geological Magazine*, **119**, 527–51.

—— 1983. Correlation of Late Proterozoic tillites in the North Atlantic region and Europe. *Geological Magazine*, **120**, 209–30.

——, HARLAND, W. B. & WADDAMS, P. 1981. Late Precambrian tillites of Svalbard. *In*: HAMBREY, M. J. & HARLAND, W. B. (eds) *Earth's Pre-

Pleistocene Glacial Record, pp. 592–600, Cambridge University Press, Cambridge.

HARLAND, W. B. 1969. Contribution of Spitsbergen to understanding of tectonic evolution of North Atlantic region. *In*: KAY, M. (ed.) *North Atlantic— Geology and Continental Drift. American Association of Petroleum Geologists Memoir No. 12*, pp. 817–51.

—— 1978. The Caledonides of Svalbard. *In*: TOZER, E. T. & SCHENK, P. E. (eds) *Caledonian–Appalachian Orogen of the North Atlantic Region. Geological Survey of Canada Paper No. 78–13*, pp. 3–11.

HARRIS, A. L., BALDWIN, C. T., BRADBURY, H. J., JOHNSON, H. D. & SMITH, R. A. 1976. Ensialic basin sedimentation: the Dalradian Supergroup. *In*: BOWES, D. R. & LEAKE, B. E. (eds) *Crustal Evolution in Northwestern Britain and Adjacent Regions. Special Publication of the Geological Society of London No. 10*, pp. 115–38.

——, JOHNSON, M. R. W. & POWELL, D. 1978. The orthotectonic Caledonides (Moines and Dalradians) of Scotland. *In*: TOZER, E. T. & SCHENK, P. E. (eds) *Caledonian–Appalachian Orogen of the North Atlantic Region. Geological Survey of Canada Paper No. 78–13*, pp. 79–85.

——, SHACKLETON, R. M., WATSON, J., DOWNIE, C., HARLAND, W. B. & MOORBATH, S. 1975. *A Correlation of the Precambrian Rocks in the British Isles. Geological Society of London Special Report No. 6*, 135 pp.

HENRIKSEN, N. 1978. East Greenland Caledonian fold belt. *In*: TOZER, E. T. & SCHENK, P. E. (eds) *Caledonian–Appalachian Orogen of the North Atlantic Region. Geological Survey of Canada Paper No. 78–13*, pp. 105–9.

—— & HIGGINS, A. K. 1976. East Greenland Caledonian fold belt. *In*: ESCHER, A. & WATT, W. S. (eds) *Geology of Greenland*, pp. 182–246. The Geological Survey of Greenland, Copenhagen.

HIGGINS, A. K. 1981. The late Precambrian Tillite Group of the Kong Oscars Fjord and Kejser Franz Josefs Fjord region of East Greenland. *In*: HAMBREY, M. J. & HARLAND, W. B. (eds) *Earth's Pre-Pleistocene Glacial Record*, pp. 778–81, Cambridge University Press, Cambridge.

JOHNSON, M. R. W. 1983a. Torridonian–Moine. *In*: CRAIG, G. Y. (ed.) *Geology of Scotland*, 2nd edn, pp. 49–75, Wiley, New York.

—— 1983b. Dalradian. *In*: CRAIG, G. Y. (ed.) *Geology of Scotland*, 2nd edn, pp. 77–104, Wiley, New York.

KING, A. F. 1980. The birth of the Caledonides: late Precambrian rocks of the Avalon Peninsula, Newfoundland, and their correlatives in the Appalachian orogen. *In*: WONES, D. R. (ed.) *The Caledonides in the USA: Proceedings of the International Geological Correlation Program—Caledonide Orogen Project 27, Blacksburg, VA. Department of Geological Sciences, Virginia Polytechnic Institute and State University, Memoir No. 2*, pp. 3–8.

KNILL, J. L. 1963. A sedimentary history of the Dalradian Series. *In*: JOHNSON, M. R. W. & STEWART, F. H. (eds) *The British Caledonides*, pp. 99–121, Oliver and Boyd, Edinburgh.

KUMPULAINEN, R. & NYSTUEN, J. P. 1985. Late

Proterozoic basin evolution and sedimentation in the westernmost part of Baltoscandia. *In*: GEE, D. G. & STURT, B. A. (eds) *The Caledonian Orogen—Scandinavia and Related Areas*, Wiley, Chichester.

LÉCORCHÉ, J. P., ROUSSEL, J., SOUGY, J. & GUETAT, Z. 1983. An interpretation of the Mauritanides orogenic belt (West Africa) in light of geophysical data. *In*: HATCHER, R. D., JR, WILLIAMS, H. & ZIETZ, I. (eds) *Contributions to the Tectonics and Geophysics of Mountain Chains. Geological Society of America Memoir No. 158*, pp. 131–47.

LE PICHON, X., SUBUET, J. C. & FRANCHTEAU, J. 1977. The fit of the continents around the North Atlantic. *Tectonophysics, 38*, 169–209.

MARTINSSON, A. 1974. The Cambrian of Norden. *In*: HOLLAND, C. H. (ed.) *Cambrian of the British Isles, Norden, and Spitzbergen*, pp. 185–283, Wiley, New York.

MCCARTNEY, W. D. 1969. Geology of Avalon Peninsula, southeast Newfoundland. *In*: KAY, M. (ed.) *North Atlantic—Geology and Continental Drift. American Association of Petroleum Geologists Memoir No. 12*, pp. 115–38.

O'BRIEN, S. J., WARDLE, R. J. & KING, A. F. 1983. The Avalon zone: a Pan-African terrane in the Appalachian orogen of Canada. *Geological Journal, 18*, 195–222.

PALMER, A. R. 1971. The Cambrian of the Appalachian and eastern New England regions, eastern United States. *In*: HOLLAND, C. H. (ed.) *Cambrian of the New World*, pp. 169–217, Wiley-Interscience, New York.

—— & JAMES, N. P. 1980. The Hawke Bay event: a circum-Iapetus regression near the lower Middle Cambrian boundary. *In*: WONES, D. R. (ed.) *The Caledonides in the USA: Proceedings of the International Geological Correlation Program—Caledonide Orogen Project 27, Blacksburg, VA. Department of Geological Sciences, Virginia Polytechnic Institute and State University, Memoir No. 2*, pp. 15–26.

PHILLIPS, W. E. A. 1981a. The orthotectonic Caledonides. *In*: HOLLAND, C. H. (ed.) *A Geology of Ireland*, pp. 17–39, Wiley, New York.

—— 1981b. The pre-Caledonian basement. *In*: HOLLAND, C. H. (ed.) *A Geology of Ireland*, pp. 7–16, Wiley, New York.

POMEROL, C. 1980. *Geology of France with Twelve Itineraries*, Masson, Paris, 256 pp.

POOLE, W. H., MCKERROW, W. S., KELLING, G. & SCHENK, P. E. 1983. A stratigraphic sketch of the Caledonide–Appalachian–Hercynian orogen. *In*: SCHENK, P. E. (ed.) *Regional Trends in the Geology of the Appalachian–Caledonian–Hercynian–Mauritanide Orogen*, pp. 75–111, Reidel, Dordrecht.

RAST, N. 1980. The Avalonian plate in the northern Appalachians and Caledonides. *In*: WONES, D. R. (ed.) *The Caledonides in the USA: Proceedings of the International Geological Correlation Program—Caledonide Orogen Project 27, Blacksburg, VA. Department of Geological Sciences, Virginia Polytechnic Institute and State University, Memoir No. 2*, pp. 63–6.

—— 1984. The late Precambrian sediments at the

eastern margin of the Laurentian shield in the southern Appalachians. *Geological Society of America Abstracts with Programs*, **16**, 188.

——, O'BRIEN, B. H. & WARDLE, R. J. 1976. Relationships between Precambrian and Lower Paleozoic rocks of the 'Avalon Platform' in New Brunswick, the northeast Appalachians and the British isles. *Tectonophysics*, **30**, 315–38.

REINHARDT, J. 1974. Stratigraphy, sedimentology, and Cambrian–Ordovician paleogeography of the Frederick Valley, Maryland. *Maryland Geological Survey Report of Investigations No. 23*, 74 pp.

ROBERTS, D. & GALE, G. H. 1978. The Caledonian–Appalachian Iapetus Ocean. *In*: TARLING, D. H. (ed.) *Evolution of the Earth's Crust*, pp. 255–342, Academic Press, London.

ROBINSON, P. & HALL, L. M. 1980. Tectonic synthesis of southern New England. *In*: WONES, D. R. *The Caledonides in the USA: Proceedings of the International Geological Correlation Program—Caledonide Orogen Project 27, Blacksburg, VA. Department of Geological Sciences, Virginia Polytechnic Institute and State University, Memoir No. 2*, pp. 73–82.

RODGERS, J. 1968. The eastern edge of the North American continent during the Cambrian and early Ordovician. *In*: ZEN, E-AN, WHITE, W. S., HADLEY, J. B. & THOMPSON, J. B., JR (eds) *Studies of Appalachian Geology: Northern and Maritime*, pp. 141–9, Wiley-Interscience, New York.

RUSHTON, A. W. A. 1974. The Cambrian of Wales and England. *In*: HOLLAND, C. H. (ed.) *Cambrian of the British Isles, Norden, and Spitzbergen*, pp. 43–123, Wiley, New York.

SALOP, L. J. 1983. *Geological Evolution of the Earth During the Precambrian*, Springer, Berlin, 459 pp.

SCHENK, P. E. 1971. Southeastern Atlantic Canada, northwestern Africa, and continental drift. *Canadian Journal of Earth Sciences*, **8**, 1218–51.

—— 1978. Synthesis of the Canadian Appalachians. *In*: TOZER, E. T. & SCHENK, P. E. (eds) *Caledonian–Appalachian Orogen of the North Atlantic Region. Geological Survey of Canada Paper No. 78–13*, pp. 111–36.

—— 1981. The Meguma zone of Nova Scotia—a remnant of western Europe, South America, or Africa? *In*: KERR, J. W. & FERGUSSON, A. J. (eds) *Geology of the North Atlantic Borderlands. Canadian Society of Petroleum Geologists Memoir No. 7*, pp. 119–48.

SCHWAB, F. L. 1985. Latest Precambrian–earliest Paleozoic sedimentation, Appalachian Blue Ridge and adjacent areas: review and speculation. *In*: GLOVER, L. & McDOWELL, R. (eds) *Department of Geological Sciences, Virginia Polytechnic Institute and State University, Memoir No. 3*, 115–37.

SKEHAN, J. W., S. J. & MURRAY, D. P. 1980. A model for the evolution of the eastern margin (EM) of the northern Appalachians. *In*: WONES, D. R. (ed.) *The Caledonides in the USA: Proceedings of the International Geological Correlation Program—Caledonide Orogen Project 27, Blacksburg, VA. Department of Geological Sciences, Virginia Polytechnic Institute and State University, Memoir No. 2*, pp. 67–72.

—— & RAST, N. 1983. Relationship between Precambrian and lower Paleozoic rocks of southeastern New England and other North Atlantic Avalonia terranes. *In*: SCHENK, P. E. (ed.) *Regional Trends in the Geology of the Appalachian–Caledonian–Hercynian–Mauritanide Orogen*, pp. 131–62, Reidel, Dordrecht.

SMITH, A. G. 1976. Plate tectonics and orogeny: a review. *Tectonophysics*, **33**, 215–85.

STEWART, A. D. 1982. Late Proterozoic rifting in NW Scotland: the genesis of the Torridonian. *Journal of the Geological Society, London*, **139**, 413–20.

ST JULIEN, P. & HUBERT, C. 1975. Evolution of the Taconian orogen in the Quebec Appalachians. *American Journal of Science*, **275A**, 337–62.

STRAND, T. & KULLING, O. 1972. *Scandinavian Caledonides*. Wiley-Interscience, New York, 302 pp.

STRONG, D. F. 1979. Proterozoic tectonics of northwestern Gondwanaland: new evidence from eastern Newfoundland. *Tectonophysics*, **54**, 81–101.

STURT, B. A. & ROBERTS, D. 1978. Caledonides of northernmost Norway (Finnmark). *In*: TOZER, E. T. & SCHENK, P. E. (eds) *Caledonian–Appalachian Orogen of the North Atlantic Region. Geological Survey of Canada Paper No. 78–13*, pp. 17–24.

SWETT, K. 1969. Interpretation of depositional and diagenetic history of Cambrian–Ordovician succession of northwest Scotland. *In*: KAY, M. (ed.) *North Atlantic—Geology and Continental Drift. American Association of Petroleum Geologists Memoir No. 12*, pp. 630–646.

THOMAS, W. A. 1977. Evolution of Appalachian–Ouachita salients and recesses from reentrants and promontories in the continental margin. *American Journal of Science*, **277**, 1233–78.

TREAGUS, J. P. 1981. The lower Dalradian Kinlochlaggan boulder bed, central Scotland. *In*: HAMBREY, M. J. & HARLAND, W. B. (eds) *Earth's Pre-Pleistocene Glacial Record*, pp. 637–9, Cambridge University Press, Cambridge.

TUCKER, M. E. & REID, P. C. 1981. Late Precambrian glacial sediments, Sierra Leone. *In*: HAMBREY, M. J. & HARLAND, W. B. (eds) *Earth's Pre-Pleistocene Glacial Record*, pp. 132–9, Cambridge University Press, Cambridge.

WALTON, E. K. 1983. Lower Paleozoic stratigraphy. *In*: CRAIG, G. Y. (ed.) *Geology of Scotland*, 2nd edn, pp. 105–37, Wiley, New York.

WATSON, J. & DUNNING, F. W. 1979. Basement–cover relations in the British Caledonides. *In*: HARRIS, A. L., HOLLAND, C. H. & LEAKE, B. E. (eds) *The Caledonides of the British Isles Reviewed. Special Publication of the Geological Society of London No. 8*, pp. 67–91.

WEHR, F. & GLOVER, L., III 1985. Stratigraphy and tectonics of the Virginia–North Carolina Blue Ridge: evolution of a late Proterozoic–early Paleozoic hinge zone. *Geological-Society of America Bulletin*, **96**, 285–95.

WILLIAMS, G. E. 1969. Petrography and origin of pebbles from Torridonian strata (late Precambrian), northwest Scotland. *In*: KAY, M. (ed.) *North Atlantic—Geology and Continental Drift. American*

Association of Petroleum Geologists Memoir No. 12, pp. 609–29.

WILLIAMS, H. & HATCHER, R. D., JR 1983. Appalachian suspect terranes. *In*: HATCHER, R. D., JR, WILLIAMS, H. & ZIETZ, I. (eds) *Contributions to the Tectonics and Geophysics of Mountain Chains. Geological Society of America Memoir No. 158,* pp. 33–53.

—— & STEVENS, R. K. 1974. The ancient continental margin of eastern North America. *In*: BURK, C. A. & DRAKE, C. L. (eds) *The Geology of Continental Margins,* pp. 781–96, Springer, Berlin.

——, KENNEDY, M. J. & NEALE, E. R. W. 1974. The northeastward termination of the Appalachian orogen. *In*: NAIRN, A. E. M. & STEHLI, F. G. (eds) *The Ocean Basins and Margins*, Vol. 2, *The North Atlantic*, pp. 79–123, Plenum, New York.

DE WIT, M. 1981. Late Precambrian metaconglomerate, Burlington Peninsula, Newfoundland. *In*: HAMBREY, M. J. & HARLAND, W. B. (eds) *Earth's Pre-Pleistocene Glacial Record*, pp. 768–70, Cambridge University Press, Cambridge.

ZEN, E-AN, 1972. *The Taconide Zone and the Taconic Orogeny in the Western part of the Northern Appalachian Orogen. Geological Society of America Special Paper No. 135,* 72 pp.

—— 1983. Exotic terranes in the New England Appalachians—limits, candidates, and ages: a speculative essay. *In*: HATCHER, R. D., JR, WILLIAMS, H. & ZIETZ, I. (eds) *Contributions to the Tectonics and Geophysics of Mountain Chains. Geological Society of America Memoir No. 158,* pp. 55–81.

F. L. SCHWAB, Department of Geology, Washington and Lee University, Lexington, VA 24450, USA.

J. P. NYSTUEN, Institut for Geologi, Norges Lanbrukshøgskole, Boks 21, 1432 Ås-NLH, Norway.

L. GUNDERSON, United States Geological Survey, Federal Center, Denver, CO 80225, USA.

Precambrian to Tremadoc biotas in the Caledonides

S. Conway Morris & A. W. A. Rushton

SUMMARY: The early Phanerozoic faunas of the Caledonides (late Precambrian to Tremadoc) are reviewed; they reflect the early history of the Iapetus Ocean. The long-established distinction between 'Pacific' and 'Atlantic' faunas is justified, but the latter are divisible into Avalonian and Baltic sub-faunas. Putative deep-water faunas have a more cosmopolitan distribution. Five time segments are considered: late Precambrian (Vendian), early, middle and late Cambrian, and Tremadoc. In the late Precambrian, consideration is given to the distribution of soft-bodied Ediacaran faunas. In the Cambrian and Tremadoc, interpretations are based primarily on trilobite distributions, although other fossils have biogeographical importance. Supposed transgressive–regressive cycles, which are connected with eustatic sea-level changes, influence faunal distributions. The perturbations giving rise to the biomeres recognized around the N American craton also appear to be recognizable elsewhere in the Caledonides; they may reflect eustatic changes of sea level.

Ever since Wilson (1966) used fossil distributions as a major criterion in his classic paper arguing for the existence of a precursor to the Atlantic, such information has played an invaluable part in elucidating the history of the Iapetus Ocean. A trend of increasing biotic similarity between N America and Europe during the Ordovician and Silurian has been interpreted as reflecting the progressive closure of Iapetus and the elimination of faunal barriers. The exchange by migration of various faunal elements across given distances has been linked to mode of life, especially the time available for larval migration (McKerrow & Cocks 1976, Fortey & Cocks 1988). According to this scheme Iapetus must have been even wider in the Cambrian, although not necessarily earlier in the late Precambrian, and classic studies of the distribution of Cambrian trilobites into Acado-Baltic ('Atlantic') and N American ('Pacific') provinces (Palmer 1969, 1972, Cowie 1971, 1974, Jell 1974), supported by other lines of evidence (Swett 1981), provide ample confirmation of this. Earlier suggestions that these provincial distinctions reflected environmental or facies controls (Lochman-Balk & Wilson 1958) were overshadowed by the incorporation of this biogeographical pattern into the context of plate tectonics. In particular, the postulate of a vanished Iapetus explained disjunct distributions. For example, the transposed locations on opposite sides of the Atlantic of N American faunas in Scotland and Acado-Baltic faunas in SE Newfoundland resulted from its opening along a line that did not coincide exactly with the Iapetus suture.

Invocation of a substantial faunal barrier in the Cambrian, sometimes equated with a wide and deep Iapetus ocean (Jell 1974), has been so generally accepted that it may be asked if any new insights can be added. Cambrian provinces are recognized almost solely on trilobites. Although the role of other organisms in elucidating biogeographical patterns has been touched upon in previous reviews (Spjeldnaes 1978, Holland & Hughes 1979, Poole *et al.* 1983), new information is accumulating and such data are of special relevance for geological periods prior to the appearance of the trilobites during the lower Cambrian. Only a broad overview can be provided here, and our discussion revolves around five divisions: late Precambrian (Vendian), lower, middle and upper Cambrian, and Tremadocian. The many uncertainties in assessing biotic distributions are compounded by problems of stratigraphic correlation and radiometric dating, and these are most severe for the Vendian and lower Cambrian. Before the biogeographical information is discussed four more general factors require consideration.

General factors

Environment and palaeo-oceanography

With regard to the Precambrian the meagre fossil record prejudices firm conclusions on palaeo-environment or palaeo-oceanography. Evidence for major changes in ocean chemistry close to the Precambrian–Cambrian boundary (Holser 1977, 1984, Cook & Shergold 1984) does not appear to have received detailed consideration in the context of the early growth of Iapetus, although the narrow rift zone of an incipient Iapetus would be a possible location for the storage of isotopically-heavy brines that upwelled during the Yudomski event (Holser 1977).

With regard to the Cambrian, speculation on the palaeo-environment and palaeo-oceogra-

From HARRIS, A. L. & FETTES, D. J. (eds), 1988, *The Caledonian–Appalachian Orogen,*
Geological Society Special Publication No. 38, pp. 93–109.

phy is more constrained by a better fossil record. In general, the use of marine fossil distributions has concentrated on palaeobiogeographic analysis, and the relevant criteria have been discussed by Cocks & Fortey (1982). Here we wish to stress that contrasts between Cambrian faunas in Iapetus primarily reflect an environmental gradient that appears to have been largely temperature controlled. Such differences of temperature are primarily controlled by latitude, but the actual extent of geographic separation is probably more reliably calculated on palaeomagnetic criteria. Thus, while Iapetus may have been a wide and deep ocean, the faunal barriers were probably controlled more by the steepness of environmental gradients and by oceanic circulation than by distance *per se* (see also Taylor & Forester 1979). Such environmental controls will be more clearly understood when Cambrian palaeo-oceanography is better documented; at present the subject is in its infancy (Ross 1975, Leggett *et al*. 1981, Spjeldnaes 1981, Parrish 1982, Theokritoff 1985).

Persuasive evidence for the existence of a thermocline in some Cambrian oceans (Taylor 1977) and its inferred existence in Iapetus (Fig. 1) during at least the lower Cambrian (Theokritoff 1979) seems to have considerable palaeo-oceanographic significance (Taylor & Forester 1979). If Iapetus was a bilayered thermally stratified ocean for much of the Cambrian it may have been more like present-day oceans than, say, those of the Cretaceous, which appear to have been dominated by salinity rather than temperature (see also Theokritoff 1985). Thus steep latitudinal temperature gradients together with the generation of cold-water masses in the polar regions (Ziegler *et al*. 1981) promoted a vigorous circulation of cold oxygenated water masses in the deep oceans. Cryophilic faunas that occupied shallow-water habitats at high latitudes existed in deeper cold water at lower latitudes, a feature also seen in Recent groups such as malacostracan crustaceans (Taylor 1977). The inferred presence of cryophilic faunas appears to explain a number of aspects of faunal distributions in Iapetus, but it is admitted that little is known of deep-sea Cambrian faunas. In view of the almost complete obliteration during plate collision of sediments deposited on oceanic crust and the frequent tectonic mangling of slope deposits, the possible distribution of a deep-sea Cambrian biota is difficult to assess. On the basis of trace fossils Crimes (1974) suggested that 'Significant colonisation of the deep ocean floor does not . . . seem to have taken place before the close of the Cambrian period'. However, the widespread distribution of sub-thermocline trilobites in the upper Cambrian (Taylor 1977) and the evidence

of lower Cambrian slope faunas in Iapetus (Theokritoff 1979, 1981) suggests that habitats at least as deep as the lower continental slope were colonized (Fig. 1).

By the late middle Cambrian and more particularly the upper Cambrian the widespread distribution of black shales in the Iapetus region, often with a low-diversity fauna adapted to dysaerobic conditions, may reflect diminished latitudinal temperature gradients. This may correspond to a phase of oceanic stagnation arising from more limited and sluggish circulation (see also Thickpenny 1984) coinciding with eustacy and the maximum extent of the Cambrian transgression (Spjeldnaes 1978, 1981, Leggett *et al*. 1981). Other workers, however, have argued for a continuation of a bilayered ocean state during the upper Cambrian (Taylor 1977, Taylor & Forester 1979). The possibility that there was a shift in ocean state during the Cambrian was hinted at by Spjeldnaes (1981), and should be investigated further. In particular, the distribution of the continents and circulatory patterns in the Cambrian ocean, especially the ease of access of deep polar currents to low latitudes, is of critical importance (Parrish 1982).

Cambrian transgressions

The major Cambrian transgressions must influence our understanding of the palaeobiogeography. In particular, the restricted area of shelf sedimentation resulting from the narrowing of facies belts during the early stages of a transgression and the predominance of poorly-fossiliferous quartzite sands and conglomerates limits the available biotic diversity and renders biogeographical comparisons more hazardous (see also Brasier 1979). The detailed patterns of the Cambrian transgressions are not well known (Matthews & Cowie 1979), but if more recent sea-level curves are any guide it is most unlikely to have been an inexorable drowning of the cratons. Bjørlykke's (1982) preliminary attempt to identify phases of regression and transgression in the Baltic region may eventually be applied to circum-Iapetus sites so that a clear differentiation can be made between sedimentary and eustatic factors. Anderton (1982) linked the main early Cambrian transgression in the Iapetus region to the displacive activity of the spreading ridges and regional subsidence of the passive margins, but other tectonic factors no doubt contributed. Evidence for a major regression (Hawke Bay Event) near the lower–middle Cambrian boundary has been identified on both Laurentian (Palmer & James 1980, Peel 1982) and Scandian (Bergström & Ahlberg 1981) margins, although

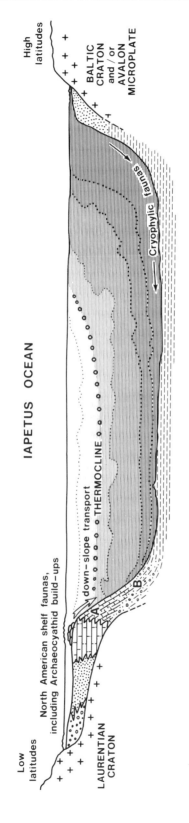

FIG. 1. Hypothetical cross-section of the Iapetus Ocean during the late lower Cambrian (schematic and not to scale), based on the work of Taylor (1977) and Taylor & Forester (1979), showing suggested isotherms (denser shading indicates colder water) and the thermocline. The belts of sedimentation around the cratons include detrital matter and, in low latitudes, carbonates. A and B denote the sites of *Pagetides* faunules and *Elliptocephala asaphoides* fauna respectively.

in the latter case it may have begun somewhat earlier. In any event this regression may represent a temporary cessation of spreading activity. Major hiatuses in late Precambrian sequences in Scandinavia and Greenland (Vidal 1981) could have a similar explanation. In more recent faunas, such as those of the Cretaceous on each side of the newly-opening Atlantic (Coates 1973, Skelton 1982), correlations have been made between the degree of endemicity and regression, although the extent to which such examples might be recognizable in the Iapetus region or are artefacts of the record (Jablonski 1980) remains uncertain. We comment below on other possible sea-level changes of middle Cambrian to Tremadoc ages.

The Cambrian metazoan evolutionary explosion

Our ability to decipher biotic distributions in the early Phanerozoic must be set in the context of early metazoan evolution. In effect, biogeographical patterns come increasingly into 'focus' during the Cambrian with the onset of a skeletal fossil record and increasing diversity. The latter element included the evolution of supposedly pelagic animals, e.g. agnostoids and graptolites. Prior to their appearance stratigraphic correlation, especially intercontinentally, is not secure (Robison et al. 1977) and accordingly biogeographical comparisons must be more suspect. The paucity of an effective fossil record in most Precambrian sections means that biotic distributions can play little effective part in determining the extent or even existence of Iapetus (see below). For much of the Cambrian the primary source of biogeographical data is the relatively diverse trilobite assemblages. Trilobite distributions most probably were controlled by such ecological factors as temperature, substrate and salinity, but ignorance of palaeo-ecology makes analyses more speculative. However, other Cambrian groups (especially in the 'non-trilobite zone') and Precambrian biotas may ultimately provide additional biogeographical insights, but with the exception of archaeocyathids information is still limited (see below).

Palaeocontinental reconstructions

The early history of Iapetus, the disposition of the surrounding continents and the possible locations of microcontinents, island arcs or continental archipelagoes are still speculative (Scotese et al. 1979). There is evidence that southern Britain, SE Newfoundland, New Brunswick and parts of New England formed a unit, possibly a separate Avalonian microplate (Ava-lonia) sundered by oceanic crust from both the Baltic and Laurentian areas (Rast 1980, Anderton 1982, Poole et al. 1983, Thorpe et al. 1984). Piqué (1981) treated Morocco and parts of Europe as an extension of this microplate, although its degree of separation from Africa is uncertain. Faunal evidence bearing on this is touched on below. Many of the classic comparisons of the N American and European trilobite provinces reflect the existence of faunal barriers between Avalonia and Laurentia. It seems unlikely that Avalonia was the only microplate. Identification of the Carolina slate belt as another example by Secor et al. (1983) is especially relevant because of the occurrence of late Precambrian and middle Cambrian faunas (see below), while Williams & Hatcher (1983) argue for even more examples of exotic terranes now welded onto the Appalachian belt.

In conclusion, the present consensus suggests that contiguity between the large cratonic areas of Laurentia and Baltica persisted until the very late Precambrian or early Cambrian (Anderton 1982) when the rapidly-widening Iapetus separated them. However, the disposition of the microplates is still poorly constrained. The postulated Avalonia may have included an island-arc component adjacent to a major craton comprising part of the Precambrian supercontinent (Thorpe et al. 1984), but its detailed history of involvement with the developing Iapetus is largely unknown.

Precambrian (Vendian)

Our discussion is limited to the Vendian biotas, of which the principal sources of evidence are the soft-bodied Ediacaran faunas and the organic-walled acritarchs; as far as we are aware no biogeographical patterns relevant to Iapetus have been noted amongst the late Precambrian stromatolites. By far the most profuse Ediacaran faunas in the Iapetus region are from the Conception Group and the lower part of the St John's Group, Newfoundland (Anderson 1978, Anderson & Conway Morris 1982). Approximately 30 species are known, including both benthic and pelagic organisms. The fauna appears to have inhabited relatively deep water and largely owes its preservation to catastrophic burial by ash-falls. In comparison with other Ediacaran localities (reviewed by Glaessner 1984), many of which represent shallow-water deposits, the great majority of Newfoundland species appear as endemics, although this may be as much due to facies contrast as to biogeographical isolation. A notable exception is the frond-like fossil *Charnia*, first described from the Woodhouse Beds (Maplewell Group) of Charnwood Forest. In addition to its occurrence in Newfoundland this genus occurs in the White Sea localities of the northern USSR (Fedonkin 1981) and possibly further afield. *Glaessnerina* is related to *Charnia* and may occur in Newfoundland (Anderson & Conway Morris 1982). A similar medusoid-like organism with prominent concentric annulations occurs in both Newfoundland and Charnwood (Williams & King 1979, S. Conway Morris, personal observations). There are, however, a number of poorly preserved undescribed specimens in Charnwood (H. Boynton & T. Ford, personal communication) that seem to resemble certain elements of the Newfoundland assemblage. Williams & King (1979) and King (1980) have suggested correlations between units in SE Newfoundland and Charnwood. The extent of faunal and other similarities between the two areas must await more detailed documentation, but the known resemblances are consistent with a shared location on Avalonia.

Establishing similarities with other areas is less easy. An Ediacaran fauna in the Carolina slate belt includes problematic traces (*Vermiforma antiqua*) that appear to have been preserved in a deep-water facies (Cloud *et al.* 1976) sedimentologically comparable with the Conception Group. More recently this fauna has been augmented by the discovery farther S of material identified as *Pteridinium* (Gibson *et al.* 1984), a widespread Ediacaran genus (Glaessner 1984). The available evidence is consistent with suggestions that the Carolina slate belt was a separate terrane and not linked directly to the postulated Avalon microplate (Secor *et al.* 1983).

The Ediacaran assemblages discussed above may have inhabited a deep-water slope facies but, as noted, the proximity of these associated terranes or microplates to the major cratons is uncertain. Examples from shallow-water shelf deposits of the latter regions are meagre. The medusoid-like *Kullingia concentrica* occurs in late Precambrian sandstones in northern Sweden (Føyn & Glaessner 1979), but a closely comparable form occurs in central Australia (Glaessner 1984). More prolific faunas occur on the edges of the White Sea (Fedonkin 1981), and in terms of late Precambrian palaeogeography presumably would have been close to the Swedish locality and any incipient opening of Iapetus in the area. The White Sea Ediacaran faunas show striking similarities, although by no means complete identity, with the classic S Australian localities (Glaessner 1984). Some palaeogeographic reconstructions (e.g. Scotese *et al.* 1979) place the

White Sea and Australian localities in opposite hemispheres and apparently separated by oceanic barriers. Nothing definite is known about the dispersal phase in the life cycle of Ediacaran organisms. The existence of widely distributed Ediacaran species that appear to have been benthic as adults argues either for great larval longevity and/or relative indifference to faunal barriers, or alternatively and more plausibly a greater proximity of Vendian continents in agreement with other workers (Piper 1982, Thorpe *et al.* 1984). In terms of recognizing a Vendian Iapetus on faunal criteria, the lack of evidence thus far for Laurentian Ediacaran faunas in the vicinity of Iapetus makes comparisons impossible, although sequences such as the Fleur de Lys (Kennedy 1975) and Dalradian (Anderton 1982) appear to have sequences of appropriate age that may warrant restudy. McMenamin (1982) has offered some preliminary thoughts on the distribution of Ediacaran organisms, but apart from suggesting that certain benthic elements were unable to reach Laurentia because of oceanic barriers his analysis has little direct bearing on the possible existence of Iapetus during the Vendian.

Biogeographical information on other Vendian biotas is still meagre, despite the increasing attention being paid to microbiotas. These include acritarchs as well as relatively-diverse permineralized microbiotas. The biostratigraphical emphasis given to many reports (e.g. Vidal 1981) suggests a cosmopolitan distribution, hardly unexpected given the wide variety of planktonic forms (Vidal & Knoll 1983). Even when more specific affinities are noted, such as those that appear to exist between late Precambrian microbiotas in SE Newfoundland and those in northern France (Brioverian) and Scotland (Dalradian) (Hofmann *et al.* 1979), this information is still difficult to put in a comprehensible biogeographical context. Although there is a growing understanding of facies control, especially with respect to onshore–offshore gradients and the recognition of stressed environments with opportunistic forms such as *Bavlinella* (Vidal & Knoll 1983), there appears to be no definite information yet on provinciality. Knoll (1982) has provided some preliminary remarks concerning the opening of Iapetus, noting the probable existence of a passive continental margin in Nordauslandet, Svalbard, and stratigraphic and palaeontological correlations with eastern Greenland. More tentative evidence based on the Ocoee basin sequence also led Knoll (1982) to suggest that the opening of Iapetus was diachronous, spreading S in terms of present-day geography, although Rankin (1975) has suggested that the

Ocoee basin was remote from the spreading centre of Iapetus.

In conclusion, there seems to be little faunal evidence to support the existence of an Iapetus Ocean between the Baltic and Laurentian cratons before the latest Precambrian, a view consistent with other lines of evidence (Bjørlykke *et al.* 1976, Anderton 1982, Nystuen 1982, Coish *et al.* 1985). The northern region (present coordinates) may have been a passive margin bordering some yet larger ocean, and as noted above the supposed Avalonian microplate could have been far removed from this area.

Lower Cambrian

Analysis of lower Cambrian biogeographical patterns across Iapetus, and indeed for the remainder of the period, is based almost entirely on the distribution of trilobites, and it is appropriate to begin by reviewing present understanding. The classic distinction within the olenellid realm of 'Pacific–N American' and 'Atlantic–northern European' provinces has been modified by Theokritoff (1979). In brief, he suggested that within the 'Atlantic' area a distinction be made between a Scandian province (Norway and the circum-Baltic region) and an Avalonian province (eastern Massachusetts, southern New Brunswick, Cape Breton Island, SE Newfoundland, England and Wales). Such a distinction is consistent with the proposed separation (see above) of an Avalonian microplate which may have been largely surrounded by deep water, although a record of *Myopsolenus* from N Wales (Bassett *et al.* 1976) illustrates the possible connection with the trilobite faunas of Morocco. The concept of a distinct Scandian faunal province seems to be acceptable to Scandinavian trilobite workers who refer to it as the Baltoscandian province and draw closest comparisons with Polish faunas (Bergström 1976, Ahlberg 1984a). The N American province includes shelf faunas in eastern New York, Vermont, NW Newfoundland and adjacent Labrador, NW Scotland, E Greenland and possibly Ny Friesland, Spitsbergen (Theokritoff 1979, 1985).

The major faunal divisions (N American, Avalonian and Scandian) thus appear to be discrete and recognizable, and were presumably separated by faunal barriers. The Avalonian and Scandian provinces both appear to have been located in cool waters of relatively high latitudes, and their mutual distinctiveness may reflect separation by a deep ocean, unfavourable ocean currents or some other barrier (see below). In the case of the lower-latitude N American province,

however, a temperature gradient, conceivably augmented by schizohaline (Swett 1981) or slightly hypersaline conditions in the shelf areas owing to enhanced evaporation, may have provided a barrier as effective as any major expanse of deep ocean. Within this pattern interest resides in the so-called 'intermediate' faunas (Theokritoff 1968, 1979, 1981, 1985). The best documented is the *Elliptocephala asaphoides* fauna from the Taconics of New York and Vermont, which Theokritoff (1985) now believes has somewhat greater affinities with the Laurentian faunas than previously thought (Theokritoff 1979, 1981). Of the five other faunas originally listed by Theokritoff from New York, Quebec, Vespitsbergen, E Greenland and Newfoundland, he now regards the last two as also being Laurentian (Theokritoff 1985).

Notwithstanding their name, the remaining 'intermediate' faunas are not simple mixtures of N American and Avalonian and/or Scandian elements. The degree of affinity is dependent on the taxonomic level chosen, but in general the 'intermediate' faunas show a greater affinity with the Avalonian province, suggesting that a biogeographical filter operated in that direction as against a barrier towards the N American province (Theokritoff 1968, 1979).

Much of the similarity between the 'intermediate' and Avalonian faunas is based on the shared presence of species of the eodiscids *Serrodiscus* and *Calodiscus*; the latter are also recorded from the Scandian province (Ahlberg 1984b). The palaeo-ecology of eodiscids is not well known, although they may have been pelagic (Jell 1975). Such a mode of life would facilitate dispersal, but eodiscid distribution was more probably controlled by water depth and temperature. Thus at least some of these faunas appeared to have inhabited deep-water slope environments, possibly beneath the thermocline, with little or no post-mortem input from shallow-shelf faunas, although the *Pagetides* fauna may have been exceptional in residing above the thermocline (Theokritoff 1979) (Fig. 1).

The late lower Cambrian Leny limestone (Stubblefield, cited by Brown *et al.* 1965) has attracted particular attention because of the reliability of its date (based on the trilobite *Pagetides*) in the context of the age of the upper part of the Dalradian Supergroup, while the presence of a corynexochid and possibly *Antagmus* (Thomas *et al.* 1984) suggests a comparison with the faunas of the shelf-edge carbonates which occur as pebbles in the conglomerates of Quebec.

The general similarity between the Avalonian and 'intermediate' faunas may represent a deep-water equator-ward extension adjacent to the N American platform (Fig. 1) and possibly even further afield (Poulsen 1969) of cryophilic forms that lived in shallow water at higher latitudes (e.g. the Comley Limestone faunas). Extension of these cryophilic species onto the shallow-water Laurentian platforms would be barred by the thermocline, except possibly during a biomere extinction event (see below).

The concept of a thermally stratified Iapetus may also explain other aspects of biogeography. For example Kay & Eldredge (1968) reported a middle Cambrian 'intermediate' fauna from Dunnage Island in the Central Belt of Newfoundland, with the occurrence of the conocoryphid trilobite *Bailiella* indicating a similarity to Avalonian faunas. It is significant that this genus is homeomorphic with *Atops*, a lower Cambrian trilobite known from the 'intermediate' *Elliptocephala asaphoides* fauna and the Avalonia province. It seems possible that the ecological requirements of *Atops* and *Bailiella* were comparable—conceivably both inhabited deep cool water—and *Bailiella* is also known to have migrated to China and India (Jell 1974). Kay & Eldredge (1968) regarded this record as representing a shoal facies, but if comparisons with the lower Cambrian 'intermediate' faunas discussed above are valid an alternative explanation is that the Dunnage Island locality is a slope fauna, possibly part of an island-arc complex to the E of the Laurentian platform (Williams & Hatcher 1983). A similar mixture of deeper-water slope faunas with European affinities and shallow-water elements derived from the N American shelf was recognized in the middle and upper Cambrian of western Newfoundland (Whittington & Kindle 1969, Kindle 1982). Comparable features have also been observed amongst Ordovician faunas with evidence for widespread deep-water assemblages (Fortey 1975, Fortey & Barnes 1977), although Bruton & Bockelie (1980) argued that the N American faunas in the Hölonda area, Trondheim, were originally on the opposite side of Iapetus and owe their present location to obduction onto the Baltic plate.

To what extent do the biogeographical patterns amongst trilobites find parallels in other Cambrian groups? This question is particularly relevant to the non-trilobite sequences, approximately equivalent to part of the classic Atdabanian and Tommotian stages of the Siberian platform, which contain a distinctive assemblage of small shelly fossils. Various workers (e.g. Matthews & Missarzhevsky 1975, Brasier 1984) have indicated that some forms had a wide distribution with no clear biogeographical pattern. Assemblages of small shelly fossils are

known from Avalonia, especially SE Newfoundland (Bengtson & Fletcher 1983), areas of the American Maritimes (Landing *et al.* 1980, Landing & Brett 1982) and the English Midlands (Brasier 1984). Bengtson & Fletcher (1983) commented on various faunal affinities within the Avalonian province and also with Baltoscandinavian localities and Poland.

In contrast, the distribution of the enigmatic conoidal shells *Salterella* and *Volborthella* (Yochelson 1977, 1981) appears to be more or less explicable in terms of the lower Cambrian biogeography outlined above (*cf.* Theokritoff 1985). Thus *Salterella* is confined to the N American province with examples from NW Scotland, Ny Friesland (Spitsbergen), Greenland, Labrador, NW Newfoundland and elsewhere in eastern Canada and the USA as well as localities in the western Cordillera. *Volborthella*, however, has a somewhat less clear-cut distribution in that, although most examples occur in the Baltic region (Scandian province) (Yochelson 1981), records exist from New Brunswick (Avalonian province) and California.

The distribution of the lower Cambrian archaeocyathids provides a generally coherent pattern that probably reflects a preference for warmer waters (Spjeldnaes 1978). The absence of archaeocyathids in the Scandian and Avalonian provinces (Spjeldnaes 1978, Theokritoff 1979) contrasts with a broad distribution along the opposite side of Iapetus with superb examples known from Labrador (Debrenne & James 1981) as well as from New Jersey (Palmer & Rozanov 1976) and farther S (Palmer 1971b). All the assemblages evidently belong to one archaeocyathid province (Debrenne & Rozanov 1983). Comminuted archaeocyathid fragments found in some deep-water 'intermediate' faunas are evidently derived by post-mortem transport from shallow water and provide indirect evidence for outer-shelf occurrences now obliterated by tectonism (Theokritoff 1981). Comparable evidence for carbonate build-ups on the N American margin of Iapetus is known from younger Cambrian rocks (James 1981). This clear distribution would appear to support arguments given above for faunal differences on each side of Iapetus being strongly temperature controlled. It also casts doubt (see also Debrenne 1984) on reports of archaeocyathids from Sørøy in Norway (Holland & Sturt 1970) unless, unlike other terranes (Bruton & Bockelie 1980), the allochthonous unit (Kalak Nappe) ultimately originated from the opposite side of Iapetus, for which there seems to be no other convincing evidence (Robins & Gardner 1975, Sturt *et al.* 1978).

Other occurrences of archaeocyathids in areas

now geographically adjacent, or believed to have been so during the lower Cambrian, are open to conflicting explanations. Present proximity may reflect tectonic juxtaposition, but uncertainties regarding the tolerances of archaeocyathids mean that certain distributions could be explained as reflecting preferences for specific facies. The inclusion of Morocco in the apparently high-latitude Avalonia was mooted above, but seems difficult to reconcile with the occurrence there of archaeocyathids (Rozanov & Debrenne 1974, Debrenne & Rozanov 1983). If the association between Avalonia and Morocco receives further support it may be necessary to invoke impingement of warm currents derived from low latitudes. Theokritoff (1979) discussed this, and noted palaeomagnetic evidence that Morocco came under progressively stronger polar influence during the course of the Cambrian. Similar problems surround the present proximity of the Avalonian and Scandian provinces to archaeocyathid-bearing units in Europe, especially Normandy and Germany (Rozanov & Debrenne 1974, Freyer *et al.* 1982, Theokritoff 1985).

Other groups provide little further insight into the biogeography of Iapetus, although in principle invertebrates such as sponges (Rushton & Phillips 1973), echinoderms (Paul 1979), brachiopods and molluscs should ultimately play a role. In the case of molluscs Runnegar (1981) has offered some preliminary ideas, and his choice of N America and Europe–Avalonia as regions for discussion indicated that trans-Iapetus patterns may emerge despite the apparent widespread distribution of some genera. In addition Pojeta (1979) has documented the distribution of Cambrian rostroconchs around Iapetus, but data are meagre.

Although at first sight trace fossils might seem an improbable source of biogeographical information Seilacher & Crimes (1969) documented 'European' trilobite burrows (upper Cambrian and lower Ordovician) in SE Newfoundland, noting that this distribution was consistent with other faunal evidence regarding separation of the N American and Avalonian–Scandian provinces. A comparable viewpoint was expressed by Bergström (1976), but otherwise little new information on Cambrian trace fossil distributions seems to have emerged. Hofmann & Cecile (1981) reviewed the distribution of the lower Cambrian trace fossil *Oldhamia*. This trace has a wide distribution, but within the Iapetus region, if highly dubious and refuted observations are excluded, is reported almost exclusively from the 'European' side of Iapetus except for an occurrence in Rensselaer County, where one of the 'intermediate' faunas occurs in slightly younger rocks (see above). It may be significant that

Hofmann & Cecile (1981) drew attention to the possible preference of *Oldhamia* for deep oceanic sediments.

In the case of lower Cambrian microbiotas (Downie *et al.* 1971, Downie 1982, Martin & Dean 1983), recent work confirms that despite their greater diversity they are similar to Vendian assemblages in that many taxa appear to be widespread and, although invaluable for regional correlation, they provide few biogeographical insights as yet. Less appears to be known about younger pre-Tremadoc microbiotas (Potter 1974), but preliminary information indicates that they follow a similar pattern; Downie *et al.* (1979) demonstrated a greater diversity in the Tremadoc floras, but their results are nearly all from the European side of Iapetus.

In conclusion, the faunal distributions in the lower Cambrian are consistent with the existence of Iapetus. If evidence from the late Precambrian biotas is accepted (see above), this suggests that widening of Iapetus was rapid although faunal differences would have been accentuated by any steepening of latitudinal gradients. Separation of Baltica and Laurentia, together with recognition of Avalonia as a separate entity, provides a framework of discussion but should not be used to mask problems of faunal distribution such as that which appears to be set by the archaeocyathids.

Middle Cambrian

The generalized facies belts of detrital and carbonate sedimentation surrounding the edge of the N American craton, as described in western N America (Palmer 1972), can be identified in a fragmentary way in the Appalachian belt (summary in Palmer 1971b) and includes consideration of material from boulder conglomerates in Quebec and NW Newfoundland (Kindle 1982). The widespread 'northern European' faunal elements on the craton edge such as northern Greenland (Poulsen 1969, Peel 1982), NW Newfoundland and the Carolina slate belt (Secor *et al.* 1983) can be seen as a further example of the wide dispersal of cool-water faunas beneath the thermocline. Furthermore, the faunal links between Avalonia and the Gondwanan margin in southern Europe are maintained and extend to Turkey (Dean 1972) during the middle Cambrian.

Improved correlation is possible in the middle Cambrian because of the widespread occurrence of certain agnostoid faunas, especially those of the *Ptychagnostus gibbus–Ptychagnostus atavus* zones and the *Lejopyge laevigata* zone. Rowell *et al.* (1982, p. 176) tentatively suggested that the facies changes associated with the spread of these *Ptychagnostus* species onto the craton might have been caused by a eustatic sea-level rise (*cf.* Palmer 1981, especially fig. 1, columns E–H), which could therefore have introduced cold-water elements. Similar changes are recorded in northern Greenland (Peel 1982), and facies changes introducing dark shales are known in other areas including those where the particular *Ptychagnostus* species are rare or absent, e.g. in the Abbey Shales of central England (Taylor & Rushton 1972).

It has been suggested that agnostoids were pelagic (Robison 1972), but Jago's (1973) documentation of agnostid biofacies points towards some type of benthic control. Their wide distribution could reflect a preference for transoceanic deep cool waters, as against a life position near the top of the water column. The distribution of selected agnostid groups is shown in Fig. 2. Their regional provinciality probably reflects temperature variations and may be compared with the manner in which eodiscid faunas were controlled. Although a number of polymerid trilobites (e.g. *Paradoxides* species) were also widespread, most polymerids and other benthos were endemic to their local cratonic margins. Thus there are few polymerid species in common between Avalonia and Baltica, and, presuming they had benthic habitats, this favours separation of those areas across the Tornquist Sea (Cocks & Fortey 1982, Poole *et al.* 1983). The patterns of distribution are comparable with those shown by Cocks & Fortey (1982) for the lower Ordovician and in some details seem more coherent on their palaeogeographical reconstruction than on that proposed by Scotese *et al.* (1979).

Near the end of the middle Cambrian a regressive interval caused a pause in deposition in Avalonia (Rushton 1978), and the same regression brought about a change in the otherwise uniform conditions on parts of the Baltic platform: in Scania and on Bornholm the monotonous deposition of Alum shales (Thick-

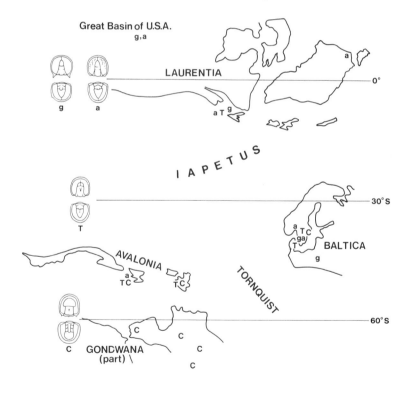

FIG. 2. Distribution of selected agnostoid taxa superimposed on a suggested palaeogeography around Iapetus during the middle Cambrian epoch. *Ptychagnostus gibbus* (g) (Linnarsson) and *Ptychagnostus atavus* (Tullberg) (a) predominate at low latitudes. *Tomagnostus fissus* (Linnarsson) (T) and other *Tomagnostus* abound in Avalonia. High latitudes are characterized by Condylopygidae such as *Condylopyge rex* (Barrande) (C), together with *Phalacroma, Phalagnostus* and *Peronopsella*. Species of the agnostoid *Peronopsis* occur at almost all sites, but each platform area has endemic benthic polymerids.

penny 1984) gave way temporarily to the formation of the Andrarum limestone which is
remarkable for its fauna of trilobites (e.g.
Dorypyge, Dolichometopus and *Anomocare*) typical
of families that otherwise characterize circum-
cratonic sites in, for example, N America and
Australia. In other areas of Sweden the interval
is represented by the Exporrecta conglomerate,
whereas in the ocean-facing areas Alum shale
deposition continued without interruption. It is
not yet known whether this regression can be
correlated with events in N America such as the
development of more massive limestones in the
Great Basin of the USA and the deposition of
the '50-foot conglomerate' at Broom Point,
Newfoundland (zone 4 of Kindle 1982).

Upper Cambrian

The upper Cambrian areas of deposition around
Iapetus were tectonically stable and allow a
clearer view of evolving biotas than is possible
for earlier epochs. The SW European platform
area has yielded few upper Cambrian faunas, but
those that are recorded have a distinctively E
Asian affinity (Shergold *et al.* 1983, Feist &
Courtessole 1984); they presumably migrated
along the Gondwanan cratonic margin and may
owe their distribution to the impingement of a
current originating from low latitudes.

The Baltic platform preserves a thin succession
of Alum shales deposited in conditions of generally low oxygenation (Thickpenny 1984) and
inhabited by olenid trilobites, the biostratigraphy
of which is well documented (Henningsmoen
1957a). Outer-shelf environments of Avalonia
and the Scandes yield similar, but not always
identical, olenid faunas, also generally living in
oxygen-deficient environments, but in some instances with a sparing admixture of non-olenid
trilobite 'invaders' (Henningsmoen 1957b, Rushton 1978, 1983). Some of the 'invaders' are of E
Asian affinity (*Drepanura, Cycloroenzella* and
possibly *Maladioidella*, following Shergold &
Sdzuy (1984)), but the occurrence of N American
'invaders' suggests the operation of various
factors. *Parabolinoides*, which is present in N
Wales, may primarily have inhabited cool water
and colonized the N American shelf seas only
when the thermocline extended onto the craton.
In contrast *Irvingella* evolved on the N American
craton (Palmer 1965) and migrated, presumably
in warmer waters above the thermocline, to all
areas in low or middle latitudes but not, as far as
is known, to circum-polar sites. The dikeloce-
phalid *Briscoia*(?) occurs in N Wales and although

species of this genus are known from the seaward
edge of the middle carbonate belt in Alaska
(Palmer 1968) most dikelocephalids occur in
inner detrital environments. The relationships of
these to the Welsh form is at present problematical. Several other genera typical of the middle
carbonate belt are represented in a supposed
shelf-margin or slope fauna in New York State
(Theokritoff 1984), but none is known to range as
far as Baltica or Avalonia.

Apart from trilobites the fauna of these oxygen-
deficient environments is restricted to sponges,
brachiopods, thin-shelled ostracodes and conodonts. The last, like the olenids, are represented
by species known on the Baltic platform and are
also found in deep-water slope deposits on the
opposite side of Iapetus, e.g. in western Newfoundland (Fåhraeus & Nowlan 1978).

The N American shelf faunas have higher
diversity, consistent with a low latitudinal position (Palmer 1972). The trilobite faunas show a
series of evolutionary developments, known as
biomeres, separated by extinction events (Palmer
1984). The causes of these extinctions are debated,
but may have been the spreading of cold water
across the platform, with the demise of indigenous
trilobites, which allowed the introduction of
trilobites otherwise restricted to cooler and
usually deeper water (Stitt 1977). Ludvigsen &
Westrop (1983) have shown that one of the
'extinction' events is a rapid biofacies shift, with
consequent shifting rather than extinction of the
fauna, but extinction could follow from the
concomitant narrowing of the inhabitable biofacies belts (Ludvigsen 1982). If Palmer's (1979)
revision of the biomere boundaries is adopted,
the trilobite extinction events are matched by
changes in the brachiopod and conodont faunas
(Rowell & Brady 1976).

At or near the horizon of the biomere boundaries there is evidence of a transgressive phase of
deposition, with sediments of the outer detrital
belt (e.g. the Dunderberg shale of the Great
Basin) encroaching towards the craton interior,
although the facies patterns are complicated in
detail (Palmer 1971a, Ludvigsen 1982).

If biomere bases were determined only by
incursions of cool water onto the shelves, their
effects would be muted in high latitudes. If,
however, they were accompanied by eustatic sea-
level changes, there is a prospect of recognizing
them on the Baltic platform if not in the deeper
waters off Avalonia. On the Scandinavian platform, where average sedimentation rates were
very low, the faunal record is interrupted at
intervals. Aside from local diastems of uncertain
significance there are, in the most complete
sections in Scania (Martinsson 1974), non-fossi-

liferous thicknesses of rock (1) below the *Olenus* zone, (2) below the *Parabolina spinulosa* zone, (3) below the *Acerocare* zone and (4) below the base of the Dictyonema shales (Tremadoc). These barren intervals seem to be significant events; collectively they occupy on average nearly a quarter of the total thickness of the upper Cambrian in Scania (Westergård 1944, pp. 28–9). The lower three of the barren intervals correspond exactly, within the resolving power of the available biostratigraphy, to biomere bases (Fig. 3), and the fourth corresponds to the basal Tremadoc transgression. The cause of these barren intervals is unknown. It seems unlikely to be a regression like that associated with the formation of the Andrarum limestone and the Exporrecta conglomerate. A cooling event is unlikely to have affected the olenid fauna, which was already adapted to cool conditions, unless the water had some unfavourable property such as an altered salinity or reduced oxygen content. However, a short-lived eustatic rise of sea level could have brought oxygen-minimum conditions onto the Scandinavian platform, so that the olenids, adapted though they were to dysaerobic conditions, were displaced shorewards. If this possibility were critically examined it might have an important bearing on theories of the origin of biomeres.

In the Anglo-Welsh region there is little or no indication of these environmental perturbations, as is expected in such basinal or shelf-edge sites. The fossil record is nearly, although sparsely, continuous, and the deposition of thick sandy beds (Ffestiniog Flags Formation) at about the base of the Ptychaspid biomere may be of only local significance.

Tremadoc

Interest in the Cambrian–Ordovician boundary problem has led to the publication of much information on Tremadoc faunal distributions (Bassett & Dean 1982). Compared with the Cambrian, the faunas around Iapetus changed significantly during the Tremadoc, and these changes are related to such factors as the evolutionary radiations of the epoch and to supposed changes in oceanography. Nevertheless, the influences of the thermocline and of sea-level changes continued to be important.

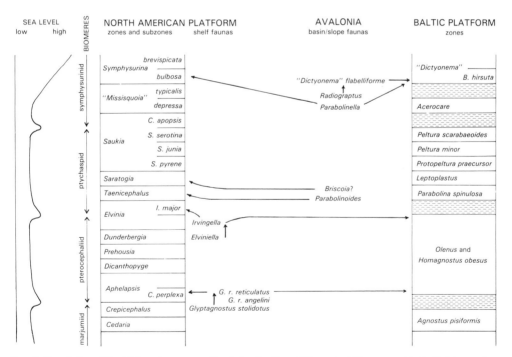

FIG. 3. Correlation of the N American upper Cambrian (and basal Tremadoc) biomeres with the Baltic zonal succession. The N American column is based on Palmer (1984) and Stitt (1977). The Baltic zones are from Henningsmoen (1957a, b): B, *Boeckaspis*. Shading represents barren intervals in the succession in Scania. Shelf-edge and slope faunas migrate onto the platform areas, especially during times of transgression. The speculative sea-level curve is shown on the left.

The early Ordovician radiations are most conspicuous among the shallow-shelf faunas of N America and of other cratons lying at low latitudes. They represent the emergence of Sepkoski's (1981) 'Palaeozoic fauna' which established new benthic community structures that persisted to the end of the Permian. The regression just below the base of the Tremadoc was followed by a eustatic sea-level rise which reached a maximum near the middle of the epoch (Fortey 1984), and it was perhaps this transgressive phase that helped to trigger the Tremadoc radiations. The subsequent regressive phase in the late Tremadoc led to a eustatic minimum near the base of the Arenig. Compared with the perturbations in the upper Cambrian, these eustatic changes seem to have been large-scale fluctuations. At the same time, the stagnant oceanic conditions of the upper Cambrian appear gradually to have given way to conditions with improved oxygenation, at least around parts of Avalonia (Henningsmoen 1957a) and Baltica. This is evinced by the less pyritic and carbonaceous mudstones of the Tremadoc, the presence of extensive bioturbation and the more varied benthos. None the less, the distribution of graptoloids indicates that the oceans continued to be thermally layered, with cool water playing an important part in biogeography (Erdtmann 1984).

Siculate graptoloids probably evolved in Iapetus, in deep water off N America (Fortey & Skevington 1980). During the Tremadoc they presumably inhabited cool water at some depth below turbulent surface waters, as discussed by Erdtmann (1982) who stressed the association of *Dictyonema* with anoxic black shales. *Dictyonema*, however, occurs regularly in grey and green, sometimes bioturbated, argillites and was not primarily influenced by anoxic waters; we prefer Erdtmann's (1984) later suggestion that water depth and temperature were more significant influences in their distribution.

The early Tremadoc transgression flooded the N American platform, providing an impetus to the radiation of such groups as brachiopods, conodonts and various molluscs, notably cephalopods. Trilobites had passed their upper Cambrian peak of diversity but the Tremadoc saw a large generic turnover. Whittington & Hughes (1974) analysed Tremadoc trilobite distributions and, although part of their data came from records of pre-Tremadoc faunas, the congruence of Trempealeauan and Tremadoc distribution makes their general conclusions on faunal affinities acceptable. They isolate the N American shelf faunas from the 'European' olenid or ceratopygid faunas which represent the deepwater faunas of the epoch, and it seems that few elements crossed Iapetus. The rare ellesmerocerid nautiloids in the Tremadoc slate of N Wales have not been shown to be of N American rather than, say, E Asian descent, but the gastropods from the Askingarran Formation of Wexford, Ireland, resemble N American Helicotomidae (Crimes & Crossley 1968).

Around Baltica and Avalonia the prevailing conditions during the earliest Tremadoc resembled those of the latest upper Cambrian. *Dictyonema*, representing Cooper's (1979) graptolite 'Assemblages 1 and 2', entered the areas with the transgression, the earliest forms occurring at sites that lay in the Welsh Trough and nearest to the Tornquist Sea (Oslo and Scania). In England, the Shineton shales basin, perhaps representing the infilling of the E Midlands aulacogen (Evans 1979), received great thicknesses of detritus deposited in oxygenated waters. Here *Dictyonema* abounded and brachiopods were common, but olenids were rarer than in Baltica. Graptolites representative of Cooper's 'Assemblage 3' are widespread at the height of the transgression and reached the N American craton (Erdtmann & Comeau 1980).

With the late Tremadoc regression the graptolites left the shelf seas, presumably as water below the thermocline retreated. Graptolites of Cooper's 'Assemblage 4' are absent in Baltica and Avalonia, except in the ocean-facing sites of the Oslo area (Monsen 1925) and the English Lake District (Rushton 1985). On the Baltic platform and in the Welsh Trough and England the late Tremadoc was characterized by oxygenated environments with a comparatively diverse shelly fauna. Although it has been suggested that the non-olenid trilobites and associated forms were derived from N American stocks, Whittington & Hughes (1974) showed that they were more closely related to 'Ceratopyge province' faunas of predominantly shelf-edge environments in Asia and S America, and several forms were recruited from slope faunas already present around Avalonia in the latest upper Cambrian (Rushton 1982).

ACKNOWLEDGMENTS: We thank Dr R. A. Fortey for discussion, and acknowledge helpful comments by M. D. Brasier and D. L. Bruton. M. Askham and S. Last typed the manuscript, and H. Foxwell and J. Proctor prepared Figs 1 and 2. AWAR publishes by permission of the Director, British Geological Survey (Natural Environment Research Council). This is Cambridge Earth Sciences Publication No. 531.

References

AHLBERG, P. 1984a. Lower Cambrian trilobites and biostratigraphy of Scandinavia. *Lund Publs geol.* **22**, 1–37.

—— 1984b. A Lower Cambrian trilobite fauna from Jämtland, central Scandinavian Caledonides. *Geologiska Föreningens i Stockholm Förhandlingar,* **105**, 349–61.

ANDERSON, M. M. 1978. Ediacaran fauna. *In: McGraw-Hill Yearbook of Science and Technology, 1978*, pp. 146–9, McGraw-Hill, New York.

—— & CONWAY MORRIS, S. 1982. A review, with descriptions of four unusual forms, of the soft-bodied fauna of the Conception and St John's Groups (late-Precambrian), Avalon Peninsula, Newfoundland. *Proceedings of the 3rd North American Paleontological Convention*, Vol. 1, pp. 1–8.

ANDERTON, R. 1982. Dalradian deposition and the late Precambrian–Cambrian history of the N. Atlantic region: a review of the early evolution of the Iapetus Ocean. *Journal of the Geological Society, London,* **139**, 421–31.

BASSETT, M. G. & DEAN, W. T. (eds) 1982. *The Cambrian–Ordovician Boundary: Sections, Fossil Distributions, and Correlations. National Museum of Wales Geological Series No. 3*, 227 pp.

——, OWENS, R. M. & RUSHTON, A. W. A. 1976. Lower Cambrian fossils from the Hell's Mouth Grits, St Tudwal's peninsula, North Wales. *Journal of the Geological Society, London,* **132**, 623–44.

BENGTSON, S. & FLETCHER, T. P. 1983. The oldest sequence of skeletal fossils in the lower Cambrian of southeastern Newfoundland. *Canadian Journal of Earth Sciences,* **20**, 525–36.

BERGSTRÖM, J. 1976. Lower Palaeozoic trace fossils from eastern Newfoundland. *Canadian Journal of Earth Sciences,* **13**, 1613–33.

—— & AHLBERG, P. 1981. Uppermost lower Cambrian biostratigraphy in Scania, Sweden. *Geologiska Föreningens i Stockholm Förhandlingar,* **103**, 193–214.

BJØRLYKKE, K. 1982. Correlation of late Precambrian and early Palaeozoic sequences by eustatic sea-level changes and the selection of the Precambrian–Cambrian boundary. *Precambrian Research,* **17**, 99–104.

——, ELVSBORG, A. & HØY, T. 1976. Late Precambrian sedimentation in the central Sparagmite basin of south Norway. *Norsk Geologisk Tidsskrift,* **56**, 233–90.

BRASIER, M. D. 1979. The Cambrian radiation event. *Systematics Association Special Volume,* **12**, 103–59.

—— 1984. Microfossils and small shelly fossils from the lower Cambrian *Hyolithes* limestone at Nuneaton, English Midlands. *Geological Magazine,* **121**, 229–53.

BROWN, P. E., MILLER, J. A., SOPER, N. J. & YORK, D. 1965. Potassium–argon age pattern of the British Caledonides. *Proceedings of the Yorkshire Geological Society,* **35**, 103–38.

BRUTON, D. L. & BOCKELIE, J. F. 1980. Geology and paleontology of the Hölonda area, western Nor-

way—a fragment of North America? *In:* WONES, D. R. (ed.) *The Caledonides in the USA: Proceedings of the International Geological Correlation Program—Caledonide Orogen Project 27, Blacksburg, VA. Department of Geological Sciences, Virginia Polytechnic Institute and State University, Memoir No. 2*, pp. 41–7.

CLOUD, P., WRIGHT, J. & GLOVER, L. 1976. Traces of animal life from 620-million-year-old rocks in North Carolina. *American Scientist,* **64**, 396–406.

COATES, A. G. 1973. Cretaceous Tethyan coral-rudist biogeography related to the evolution of the Atlantic. *Palaeontological Association Special Papers in Palaeontology No. 12*, pp. 169–74.

COCKS, L. R. M. & FORTEY, R. A. 1982. Faunal evidence for oceanic separation in the Palaeozoic of Britain. *Journal of the Geological Society, London,* **139**, 465–78.

COISH, R. A., FLEMING, F. S., LARSEN, M., POYNER, R. & SEIBERT, J. 1985. Early rift history of the proto-Atlantic ocean: geochemical evidence from meta-volcanic rocks in Vermont. *American Journal of Science,* **285**, 351–78.

COOK, P. J. & SHERGOLD, J. H. 1984. Phosphorus, phosphorites and skeletal evolution at the Precambrian–Cambrian boundary. *Nature, London,* **308**, 231–6.

COOPER, R. A. 1979. Sequence and correlation of Tremadoc graptolite assemblages. *Alcheringa,* **3**, 7–19.

COWIE, J. W. 1971. Lower Cambrian faunal provinces. *In:* MIDDLEMISS, F. A., RAWSON, P. F. & NEWALL, G. (eds) *Faunal Provinces in Space and Time. Special Publication of the Geological Society of London No. 4*, pp. 31–46.

—— 1974. The Cambrian of Spitsbergen and Scotland. *In:* HOLLAND, C. H. (ed.) *Lower Palaeozoic Rocks of the World*, Vol. 2, *Cambrian of the British Isles, Norden and Spitsbergen*, pp. 125–55.

CRIMES, T. P. 1974. Colonisation of the early ocean floor. *Nature, London,* **248**, 328–30.

—— & CROSSLEY, J. D. 1968. The stratigraphy, sedimentology, ichnology and structure of the Lower Palaeozoic rocks of part of north-eastern Co. Wexford. *Proceedings of the Royal Irish Academy, Section B,* **67**, 185–215.

DEAN, W. T. 1972. The trilobite genus *Holasaphus* Matthew, 1895 in the Middle Cambrian rocks of Nova Scotia and Eastern Turkey. *Canadian Journal of Earth Sciences,* **9**, 266–79.

DEBRENNE, F. 1984. Archaeocyatha from the Caledonian rocks of Sørøy, North Norway—a doubtful record. *Norsk Geologisk Tidsskrift,* **64**, 153–4.

—— & JAMES, N. P. 1981. Reef-associated archaeocyathans, lower Cambrian of southern Labrador and western Newfoundland. *Palaeontology,* **24**, 343–78.

—— & ROZANOV, A. 1983. Paleogeographic and stratigraphic distribution of regular Archaeocyatha (lower Cambrian fossils). *Geobios,* **16**, 727–36.

DOWNIE, C. 1982. Lower Cambrian acritarchs from Scotland, Norway, Greenland and Canada. *Transactions of the Royal Society of Edinburgh*, **72**, 257–85.

——, BOOTH, G., RASUL, S. & POTTER, T. 1979. Changes in the acritarch assemblages at the Tremadoc boundaries in the United Kingdom. *4th International Palynology Conference, Lucknow, 1976–77*, Vol. 2, pp. 78–83.

——, LISTER, T. R., HARRIS, A. L. & FETTES, D. J. 1971. A palynological investigation of the Dalradian rocks of Scotland. *Reports of the Institute of Geological Sciences*, **71** (9), 1–29.

ERDTMANN, B-D. 1982. Palaeobiogeography and environments of planktic dictyonemid graptolites during the earliest Ordovician. *In*: BASSETT, M. G. & DEAN, W. T. (eds) *The Cambrian–Ordovician Boundary: Sections, Fossil distributions, and Correlations*. National Museum of Wales Geological Series No. 3, pp. 9–27.

—— 1984. Outline ecostratigraphic analysis of the Ordovician graptolite zones in Scandinavia in relation to the paleogeographic disposition of the Iapetus. *Geologica et Palaeontologica*, **18**, 9–15.

—— & COMEAU, D. J. 1980. A new *Anisograptus* fauna from the Goodwin Formation (Tremadoc, early Ordovician) of central Nevada and the Cambrian–Ordovician boundary. *Journal of Paleontology*, **54**, 719–27.

EVANS, A. M. 1979. The East Midlands aulacogen of Caledonian age. *Mercian Geologist*, **7**, 31–42.

FÅHRAEUS, L. E. & NOWLAN, G. S. 1978. Franconian (late Cambrian) to early Champlainian (middle Ordovician) conodonts from the Cow Head Group, western Newfoundland. *Journal of Paleontology*, **52**, 444–71.

FEDONKIN, M. A. 1981. White Sea biota of Vendian (Precambrian non-skeletal fauna of the north Russian platform). *Trudy Akademii Nauk SSSR*, **342**, 1–100 (in Russian).

FEIST, R. & COURTESSOLE, R. 1984. Découverte de Cambrian supérieur à trilobites de type estasiatique dans la Montagne Noire (France méridionale). *Comptes Rendus Hebdomadaires des Séances de l'Academie des Sciences*, **298** (II), 177–82.

FORTEY, R. A. 1975. Early Ordovician trilobite communities. *Fossils and Strata*, **4**, 339–60.

—— 1984. Global earlier Ordovician transgressions and regressions and their biological implications. *In*: BRUTON, D. L. (ed.) *Aspects of the Ordovician System*, pp. 37–50, Oslo.

—— & BARNES, C. R. 1977. Early Ordovician conodont and trilobite communities of Spitsbergen: influence on biogeography. *Alcheringa*, **1**, 297–309.

—— & COCKS, L. R. M. 1988. Arenig to Llandovery faunal distributions in the Caledonides. *This volume.*

—— & SKEVINGTON, D. 1980. Correlation of Cambrian–Ordovician boundary between Europe and North America: new data from western Newfoundland. *Canadian Journal of Earth Sciences*, **17**, 382–8.

FØYN, S. & GLAESSNER, M. F. 1979. *Platysolenites*, other animal fossils, and the Precambrian–Cambrian transition in Norway. *Norsk Geologisk Tidsskrift*, **59**, 25–46.

FREYER, G., GEISSLER, E., HOTH, K. & NHUAN, T. T. 1982. Die Bedeutung der Fossilfunde im Schaubergwerk Rabenstein bei Karl-Marx-Stadt. *Zeitschrift für Geologische Wissenschaften*, **10**, 265–6.

GIBSON, G. G., TEETER, S. A. & FEDONKIN, M. A. 1984. Ediacarian fossils from the Carolina slate belt, Stanley County, North Carolina. *Geology*, **12**, 387–90.

GLAESSNER, M. F. 1984. *The Dawn of Animal Life. A Biohistorical Study*. Cambridge University Press, Cambridge, 244 pp.

HENNINGSMOEN, G. 1957a. The trilobite family Olenidae with descriptions of Norwegian material and remarks on the Olenid and Tremadocian Series. *Skrifter Utgitt av det Norske Videnskaps-Akademi i Oslo 1957. I. Malematisk-Naturvidenskapelig Klasse* **1**, pp. 1–303.

—— 1957b. A trilobite with North American affinities from the Upper Cambrian of Sweden. *Bulletin of the Geological Institution of the University of Uppsala*, **37**, 167–72.

HOFMANN, H. J. & CECILE, M. P. 1981. Occurrence of *Oldhamia* and other trace fossils in lower (?) Cambrian argillites, Niddery Lake map area, Selwyn Mountains, Yukon Territory. *Current Research A, Geological Survey of Canada Paper No. 81–1A*, pp. 281–90.

——, HILL, J. & KING, A. F. 1979. Late Precambrian microfossils, southeastern Newfoundland. *Current Research B, Geological Survey of Canada Paper No. 79–1B*, pp. 83–98.

HOLLAND, C. H. & HUGHES, C. P. 1979. Evolving life of the developing Caledonides. *In*: HARRIS, A. L., HOLLAND, C. H. & LEAKE, B. E. (eds) *The Caledonides of the British Isles—Reviewed. Special Publication of the Geological Society of London No. 8*, pp. 387–403.

—— & STURT, B. A. 1970. On the occurrence of archaeocyathids in the Caledonian metamorphic rocks of Sørøy and their stratigraphic significance. *Norsk Geologisk Tidsskrift*, **50**, 341–55.

HOLSER, W. T. 1977. Catastrophic chemical events in the history of the ocean. *Nature, London*, **267**, 403–8.

—— 1984. Gradual and abrupt shifts in ocean chemistry during Phanerozoic time. *In*: HOLLAND, H. D. & TRENDALL, A. F. (eds) *Patterns of Change in Earth Evolution*, pp. 123–43, Dahlem Konferenzen.

JABLONSKI, D. 1980. Apparent versus real biotic effects of transgressions and regressions. *Paleobiology*, **6**, 397–407.

JAGO, J. B. 1973. Cambrian agnostid communities in Tasmania. *Lethaia*, **6**, 405–21.

JAMES, N. P. 1981. Megablocks of calcified algae in the Cow Head Breccia, western Newfoundland: vestiges of a Cambro-Ordovician platform margin. *Geological Society of America Bulletin*, **92**, 799–811.

JELL, P. A. 1974. Faunal provinces and possible planetary reconstruction of the Middle Cambrian. *Journal of Geology*, **82**, 319–50.

—— 1975. Australian Middle Cambrian eodiscoids with a review of the superfamily. *Palaeontographica, Abteilung A*, **150**, 1–97.

KAY, M. & ELDREDGE, N. 1968. Cambrian trilobites in central Newfoundland volcanic belt. *Geological Magazine*, **105**, 372–7.

KENNEDY, M. J. 1975. The Fleur de Lys Supergroup: stratigraphic comparison of Moine and Dalradian equivalents in Newfoundland with the British Caledonides. *Journal of the Geological Society, London*, **131**, 305–10.

KINDLE, C. H. 1982. The C. H. Kindle collection: Middle Cambrian to Lower Ordovician trilobites from the Cow Head Group, western Newfoundland. *Current Research B, Geological Survey of Canada Paper No. 82–1C*, pp. 1–17.

KING, A. F. 1980. The birth of the Caledonides: late Precambrian rocks of the Avalon peninsula, Newfoundland, and their correlations in the Appalachian orogen. *In*: WONES, D. R. (ed.) *The Caledonides in the USA: Proceedings of the International Geological Correlation Program—Caledonide Orogen Project 27, Blacksburg, VA. Department of Geological Sciences, Virginia Polytechnic Institute and State University, Memoir No. 2*, pp. 3–8.

KNOLL, A. H. 1982. Microfossil-based biostratigraphy of the Precambrian Hecla Hoek sequence, Nordaustlandet, Svalbard. *Geological Magazine*, **119**, 269–79.

LANDING, E. & BRETT, C. E. 1982. Lower Cambrian of eastern Massachusetts: microfaunal sequence and the oldest known borings. *Geological Society of America Abstracts with Programs*, **14**, 33.

LANDING, E., NOWLAN, G. S. & FLETCHER, T. P. 1980. A microfauna associated with Early Cambrian trilobites of the *Callavia* Zone, northern Antigonish Highlands, Nova Scotia. *Canadian Journal of Earth Sciences*, **17**, 400–18.

LEGGETT, J. K., MCKERROW, W. S., COCKS, L. R. M. & RICKARDS, R. B. 1981. Periodicity in the early Palaeozoic marine realm. *Journal of the Geological Society, London*, **138**, 167–76.

LOCHMAN-BALK, C. & WILSON, J. L. 1958. Cambrian biostratigraphy in North America. *Journal of Paleontology*, **32**, 312–50.

LUDVIGSEN, R. 1982. Upper Cambrian and Lower Ordovician trilobite biostratigraphy of the Rabbitkettle Formation, western District of Mackenzie. *Contributions to Life Sciences, Royal Ontario Museum*, **134**, 1–188.

—— & WESTROP, S. R. 1983. Trilobite biofacies of the Cambrian–Ordovician boundary interval in northern North America. *Alcheringa*, **7**, 301–19.

MARTIN, F. & DEAN, W. T. 1983. Late Early Cambrian and early Middle Cambrian acritarchs from Manuels River, eastern Newfoundland. *Current Research B, Geological Survey of Canada Paper No. 83–1B*, pp. 353–63.

MARTINSSON, A. 1974. The Cambrian of Norden. *In*: HOLLAND, C. H. (ed.) *Lower Palaeozoic Rocks of the World*, Vol. 2, *Cambrian of the British Isles, Norden, and Spitsbergen*, pp. 185–283.

MATTHEWS, S. C. & COWIE, J. W. 1979. Early Cambrian transgression. *Journal of the Geological Society, London*, **136**, 133–5.

—— & MISSARZHEVSKY, V. V. 1975. Small shelly fossils of late Precambrian and early Cambrian age: a review of recent work. *Journal of the Geological Society, London*, **131**, 289–304.

MCKERROW, W. S. & COCKS, L. R. M. 1976. Progressive faunal migration across the Iapetus Ocean. *Nature, London*, **263**, 304–6.

MCMENAMIN, M. A. S. 1982. A case for two late Proterozoic–earliest Cambrian faunal province loci. *Geology*, **10**, 290–2.

MONSEN, A. 1925. Über eine neue Ordovicische graptolithenfauna. *Norsk Geologisk Tidsskrift*, **8**, 147–87.

NYSTUEN, J. P. 1982. Late Proterozoic basin evolution in the Baltoscandian craton: the Hedmark Group, southern Norway. *Norges Geologiske Undersøkelse*, **375**, 1–74.

PALMER, A. R. 1965. Trilobites of the late Cambrian Pterocephaliid biomere in the Great Basin, United States. *United States Geological Survey Professional Paper No. 493*, pp. 1–105.

—— 1968. Trilobites of east-central Alaska. *United States Geological Survey Professional Paper No. 559B*, pp. 1–115.

—— 1969. Cambrian trilobite distributions in North America and their bearing on Cambrian paleogeography in Newfoundland. *In*: KAY, M. (ed.) *North Atlantic—Geology and Continental Drift. American Association of Petroleum Geologists Memoir No. 12*, pp. 139–48.

—— 1971a. The Cambrian of the Great Basin and adjacent area, western United States. *In*: HOLLAND, C. H. (ed.) *Lower Palaeozoic Rocks of the World*, Vol. 1, *Cambrian of the New World*, pp. 1–78.

—— 1971b. The Cambrian of the Appalachian and eastern New England regions, eastern United States. *In*: HOLLAND, C. H. (ed.) *Lower Palaeozoic Rocks of the World*, Vol. 1, *Cambrian of the New World*, pp. 169–217.

—— 1972. Problems of Cambrian biogeography. *24th International Geology Congress*, Section 7, pp. 310–15.

—— 1979. Biomere boundaries re-examined. *Alcheringa*, **3**, 33–41.

—— 1981. On the correlatability of grand cycle tops. *United States Geological Survey Open-File Report No. 81–743*, pp. 156–9.

—— 1984. The biomere problem: evolution of an idea. *Journal of Paleontology*, **58**, 599–611.

—— & JAMES, N. P. 1980. The Hawke Bay Event: a circum-Iapetus regression near the Lower Middle Cambrian boundary. *In*: WONES, D. R. (ed.) *The Caledonides in the USA: Proceedings of the International Geological Correlation Program—Caledonide Orogen Project 27, Blacksburg, VA. Department of Geological Sciences, Virginia Polytechnic Institute and State University, Memoir No. 2*, pp. 15–18.

—— & ROZANOV, A. YU. 1976. Archaeocyatha from New Jersey: evidence of an intra-Cambrian unconformity in the north-central Appalachians. *Geology*, **4**, 773–4.

PARRISH, J. T. 1982. Upwelling and petroleum source beds, with reference to Palaeozoic. *American Association of Petroleum Geologists Bulletin*, **66**, 750–74.

PAUL, C. R. C. 1979. Caledonian echinoderms of the British Isles. *In*: HARRIS, A. L., HOLLAND, C. H. & LEAKE, B. E. (eds) *The Caledonides of the British Isles—Reviewed. Special Publication of the Geological Society of London No. 8*, pp. 435–56.

PEEL, J. S. 1982. The lower Paleozoic of Greenland. *Memoirs of the Canadian Society of Petroleum Geologists*, **8**, 309–30.

PIPER, J. D. A. 1982. The Precambrian palaeomagnetic record: the case for the Proterozoic supercontinent. *Earth and Planetary Science Letters*, **59**, 61–89.

PIQUÉ, A. 1981. Northwestern Africa and the Avalonian plate: relations during late Precambrian and late Paleozoic time. *Geology*, **9**, 319–22.

POJETA, J. 1979. Geographic distribution of Cambrian and Ordovician rostroconch molluscs. *In*: GRAY, J. & BOUCOT, A. J. (eds) *Historical Biogeography, Plate Tectonics, and the Changing Environment*, pp. 27–36.

POOLE, W. H., MCKERROW, W. S., KELLING, G. & SCHENK, P. E. 1983. A stratigraphic sketch of the Caledonide–Appalachian–Hercynian orogen. *In*: SCHENK, P. E. (ed.) *Regional Trends in the Geology of the Appalachian–Hercynian–Mauritanide Orogen*, pp. 75–111, Reidel, Dordrecht.

POTTER, T. L. 1974. British Cambrian acritarchs—a preliminary account. *Review of Palaeobotany and Palynology*, **18**, 61–2.

POULSEN, V. 1969. An Atlantic middle Cambrian fauna from North Greenland. *Lethaia*, **2**, 1–14.

RANKIN, D. W. 1975. The continental margin of eastern North America in the southern Appalachians. The opening and closing of the proto-Atlantic ocean. *American Journal of Science*, **275A**, 298–336.

RAST, N. 1980. The Avalonian plate in the northern Appalachians and Caledonides. *In*: WONES, D. R. (ed.) *The Caledonides in the USA. Proceedings of the International Geological Correlation Program—Caledonide Orogen Project 27, Blacksburg, VA. Department of Geological Sciences, Virginia Polytechnic Institute and State University, Memoir No. 2*, pp. 63–6.

ROBINS, E. & GARDNER, P. M. 1975. The magmatic evolution of the Seiland Province, and Caledonian plate boundaries in northern Norway. *Earth and Planetary Science Letters*, **26**, 167–78.

ROBISON, R. A. 1972. Mode of life of agnostoid trilobites. *24th International Geological Congress*, Section 7, pp. 33–40.

——, ROSOVA, A. V., ROWELL, A. J. & FLETCHER, T. P. 1977. Cambrian boundaries and divisions. *Lethaia*, **10**, 257–62.

ROSS, R. J. 1975. Early Paleozoic trilobites, sedimentary facies, lithospheric plates, and ocean currents. *Fossils and Strata*, **4**, 307–29.

ROWELL, A. J. & BRADY, M. J. 1976. Brachiopods and biomeres. *Brigham Young University Geological Studies*, **23**, 165–80.

——, ROBISON, R. A. & STRICKLAND, D. K. 1982. Aspects of Cambrian agnostoid phylogeny and chronocorrelation. *Journal of Paleontology*, **56**, 161–82.

ROZANOV, A. YU. & DEBRENNE, F. 1974. Age of archaeocyathid assemblages. *American Journal of Science*, **274**, 833–48.

RUNNEGAR, B. 1981. Biostratigraphy of Cambrian molluscs. *United States Geological Survey Open-File Report No. 81–743*, pp. 198–202.

RUSHTON, A. W. A. 1978. Fossils from the Middle–Upper Cambrian transition in the Nuneaton district. *Palaeontology*, **21**, 245–83.

—— 1982. The biostratigraphy and correlation of the Merioneth–Tremadoc series boundary in North Wales. *In*: BASSETT, M. G. & DEAN, W. T. (eds) *The Cambrian–Ordovician Boundary: Sections, Fossil Distributions, and Correlations. National Museum of Wales Geological Series No. 3*, pp. 41–59.

—— 1983. Trilobites from the Upper Cambrian *Olenus* zone in central England. *Palaeontological Association Special Papers in Palaeontology No. 30*, pp. 107–39.

—— 1985. A Lancefieldian graptolite from the Lake District. *Geological Magazine*, **122**, 329–33.

—— & PHILLIPS, W. E. A. 1973. A *Protospongia* from the Dalradian of Clare Island, Co. Mayo, Ireland. *Palaeontology*, **16**, 231–7.

SCOTESE, C. R., BAMBACH, R. K., BARTON, C., VAN DER VOO, R. & ZIEGLER, A. M. 1979. Paleozoic base maps. *Journal of Geology*, **87**, 217–77.

SECOR, D. T., SAMSON, S. L., SNOKE, A. W. & PALMER, A. R. 1983. Confirmation of the Carolina Slate Belt as an exotic terrane. *Science*, **221**, 649–51.

SEILACHER, A. & CRIMES, T. P. 1969. 'European' species of trilobite burrows in eastern Newfoundland. *In*: KAY, M. (ed.) *North Atlantic—Geology and Continental Drift. American Association of Petroleum Geologists Memoir No. 12*, pp. 145–8.

SEPKOSKI, J. J. 1981. A factor analytic description of the Phanerozoic marine fossil record. *Paleobiology*, **7**, 36–53.

SHERGOLD, J. H. & SDZUY, K. 1984. Cambrian and early Tremadocian trilobites from Sultan Dağ, central Turkey. *Senckenbergiana Lethaea*, **65**, 51–135.

——, LIÑAN, E. & PALACIOS, T. 1983. Late Cambrian trilobites from the Najerilla Formation, north-eastern Spain. *Palaeontology*, **26**, 71–92.

SKELTON, P. 1982. Aptian and Barremian rudist bivalves of the New World: some Old World similarities. *Cretaceous Research*, **3**, 145–53.

SPJELDNAES, N. 1978. Faunal provinces in the Proto-Atlantic. *In*: BOWES, D. R. & LEAKE, B. E. (eds) *Crustal Evolution in Northwestern Britain and Adjacent Regions. Special Publication of the Geological Society of London No. 10*, pp. 139–50.

—— 1981. Lower Palaeozoic palaeoclimatology. *In*: HOLLAND, C. H. (ed.) *Lower Palaeozoic Rocks of the World*, vol. 3, *Lower Palaeozoic of the Middle East, Eastern and Southern Africa, and Antarctica*, pp. 199–256.

STITT, J. H. 1977. Late Cambrian and earliest Ordovician trilobites Wichita Mountains area, Oklahoma. *Oklahoma Geological Survey Bulletin*, **124**, 1–79.

STURT, B. A., PRINGLE, I. R. & RAMSAY, D. M. 1978. The Finnmarkian phase of the Caledonian orogeny. *Journal of the Geological Society, London*, **135**, 597–610.

SWETT, K. 1981. Cambro-Ordovician strata in Ny Friesland, Spitsbergen and their palaeotectonic significance. *Geological Magazine*, **118**, 225–50.

TAYLOR, K. & RUSHTON, A. W. A. 1972 [1971]. The pre-Westphalian geology of the Warwickshire Coalfield. *Bulletin of the Geological Survey of Great Britain*, **35**, 1–150.

TAYLOR, M. E. 1977. Late Cambrian of western North America: trilobite biofacies, environmental significance, and biostratigraphic implications. *In*: KAUFFMAN, E. G. & HAZEL, J. E. (eds) *Concepts and Methods in Biostratigraphy*, pp. 397–425.

—— & FORESTER, R. M. 1979. Distributional model for marine isopod crustaceans and its bearing on early Paleozoic paleo-zoogeography and continental drift. *Geological Society of America Bulletin*, **90**, 405–13.

THEOKRITOFF, G. 1968. Cambrian biogeography and biostratigraphy in New England. *In*: ZEN, E-AN, WALTER, S. W., HADLEY, J. B. & THOMPSON, J. B. (eds) *Studies in Appalachian Geology: Northern and Maritime*, pp. 9–22, Wiley-Interscience, New York.

—— 1979. Early Cambrian provincialism and biogeographic boundaries in the North Atlantic region. *Lethaia*, **12**, 281–95.

—— 1981. Early Cambrian faunas of eastern New York State—taphonomy and ecology. *United States Geological Survey Open-File Report No. 81-743*, pp. 228–30.

—— 1984. Dresbachian trilobites from the Taconic sequence, eastern New York State. *Journal of Paleontology*, **58**, 834–42.

—— 1985. Early Cambrian biogeography in the North Atlantic region. *Lethaia*, **18**, 283–93.

THICKPENNY, A. 1984. The sedimentology of the Swedish Alum shale. *In*: STOW, D. A. V. & PIPER, D. J. W. (eds) *Fine-grained Sediments: Deep-water Processes and Facies. Special Publication of the Geological Society of London No. 15*, pp. 511–25.

THOMAS, A. T., OWENS, R. M. & RUSHTON, A. W. A. 1984. Trilobites in British stratigraphy. *Special Publication of the Geological Society of London No. 16*, pp. 1–78.

THORPE, R. S., BECKINSALE, R. D., PATCHETT, P. J., PIPER, J. D. A., DAVIES, G. R. & EVANS, J. A. 1984. Crustal growth and late Precambrian–early Palaeozoic plate tectonic evolution of England and Wales. *Journal of the Geological Society, London*, **141**, 521–36.

VIDAL, G. 1981. Aspects of problematic acid-resistant, organic-walled microfossils (acritarchs) in the Upper Proterozoic of the North Atlantic region. *Precambrian Research*, **15**, 9–23.

—— & KNOLL, A. H. 1983. Proterozoic plankton. *Geological Society of America Memoir No. 161*, pp. 265–77.

WESTERGÅRD, A. H. 1944. Borrningar genom Skånes alunskiffer 1941–42. *Sveriges Geologiska Undersökning, Serie C*, **459**, 1–45.

WHITTINGTON, H. B. & HUGHES, C. P. 1974. Geography and faunal provinces in the Tremadoc epoch. *Society of Economic Paleontologists and Mineralogists Special Publication*, **21**, 203–18.

—— & KINDLE, C. H. 1969. Cambrian and Ordovician stratigraphy of western Newfoundland. *In*: KAY, M. (ed.) *North Atlantic—Geology and Continental Drift. American Association of Petroleum Geologists Memoir No. 12*, pp. 655–64.

WILLIAMS, H. & HATCHER, R. D. 1983. Appalachian suspect terranes. *In*: HATCHER, R. D., JR., WILLIAMS, H. & ZIETZ, I. (eds) *Tectonics and Geophysics of Mountain Chains. Geological Society of America Memoir No. 158*, pp. 33–53.

—— & KING, A. E. 1979. Trespassey map area, Newfoundland. *Geological Survey of Canada Memoir No. 389*, pp. 1–24.

WILSON, J. T. 1966. Did the Atlantic close and then re-open? *Nature, London*, **211**, 676–81.

YOCHELSON, E. L. 1977. Agmata, a proposed extinct phylum of early Cambrian age. *Journal of Paleontology*, **51**, 437–54.

—— 1981. A survey of *Salterella* (Phylum Agmata). *United States Geological Survey Open-File Report No. 81-743*, pp. 244–8.

ZIEGLER, A. M., PARRISH, J. T. & SCOTESE, C. R. 1981. Cambrian world paleogeography, biogeography and climatology. *United States Geological Survey Open-File Report No. 81-743*, p. 252.

S. CONWAY MORRIS, Department of Earth Sciences, University of Cambridge, Downing Street, Cambridge CB2 3EQ, UK.

A. W. A. RUSHTON, British Geological Survey, Keyworth, Nottingham NG12 5GG, UK.

Early deformation in the Caledonian–Appalachian orogen

Nicholas Rast, B. A. Sturt & A. L. Harris

S U M M A R Y: Deformation isotopically dated at 1100–1000 Ma has been recorded in the Moine rocks of N Scotland and may be related to the latest stages of Grenville orogenesis of N America. Late Precambrian orogenesis is widely recorded in the dispersed fragments of Avalonia particularly in the eastern Appalachians, eastern Newfoundland and southern Britain. Localized evidence for late Cambrian–early Ordovician orogenesis is forthcoming in the Appalachians (Penobscot) in Scandinavia (Finnmarkian) and in Scotland and Ireland (Grampian).

The geographically isolated segments of the Caledonian–Appalachian orogen (Fig. 1) are as follows: 1, Scandinavia and Svalbard (1 and 1′ on Fig. 1); 2, British Isles (2 on Fig. 1); 3, Greenland (3 on Fig. 1); 4, northern and south-central Appalachians (4 on Fig. 1); 5, NW European mainland (5 on Fig. 1); 6, Spain and W Africa (6 on Fig. 1).

Most of the evidence presented here in discussing pre-Arenig deformation is gained from segments 1, 2 and 4. E Greenland, NW Scotland, NW Newfoundland and the western part of the Appalachians which represent one fragmented former edge of the orogen, while Scandinavia, S British Isles and the eastern parts of the N and S Appalachians represent the other edge.

The Scandinavian Caledonides—Finnmarkian

The Scandinavian Caledonides (Fig. 2) are characterized by far-transported thrust nappes involving late Proterozoic to Silurian cover sequences and basement elements comprising both ancient continental and oceanic crust. Traditionally Scandinavia was viewed in terms of an eastern miogeosynclinal and a western eugeosynclinal facies (Stormer 1967, Strand & Kulling 1972). Subsequently, it has been interpreted in terms of the Wilson cycle (Gee 1975, Roberts & Gale 1978), involving a late Precambrian ocean opening followed by Cambrian sea-floor spreading, subduction in the Ordovician and a collisional orogeny (Scandinavian orogeny) in late Silurian to earliest Devonian times. Gee (1975) and Roberts & Gale (1978) considered this evolution as essentially a *continuum* with one major episode of mid-Palaeozoic orogenic deformation. The alternative explanation of separate episodes put forward by Sturt (1984) is supported by deformation patterns, geochronology and the emplace-ment of major ophiolites at an early stage of Caledonian orogenesis (Sturt *et al.* 1978, 1984, Furnes *et al.* 1979, 1983, 1985, Roberts & Sturt 1980, Gee & Sturt 1983, Dallmeyer *et al.* 1985, Ramsay *et al.* 1985, Ryan & Sturt 1985). This late Cambrian–early Ordovician *Finnmarkian* orogeny involved obduction of major ophiolite complexes onto the continental margin of Baltica. The type area and the most complete development of the Finnmarkian orogeny is in the northern-most part of Norway where the following sequence of events has been recognized.

1 During late Riphean–early Vendian times the Baltic Shield was the site of continental sedimentation of Sparagmite clastic sediments in a series of initially separated grabens and half-grabens. In the southern section only the western-most or Tossofjallet Basin opened westward and received partly shallow marine deposits; in the furthest N the late Riphean and Vendian strata are essentially characterized by shallow marine deposits in a basin open to the W (Johnson *et al.* 1978, Sturt 1984, Kumplaninen & Nystuen 1985). This marked the beginning of marine sedimen-tation and occurred prior to the opening of Iapetus.

2 In Vendian times a 650 Ma diabase dyke-swarm with mid-ocean ridge basalt (MORB) geochemistry was emplaced into rocks now in the middle allochthon (Gee 1975, Solymon *et al.* 1978, Gayer *et al.* 1985). This is consistent with incipient opening of Iapetus Ocean (Gee 1975, Solymon *et al.* 1978, Claesson & Roddick 1983, Sturt *et al.* 1984).

3 After the emplacement of the dykes Cam-brian sea-floor spreading occurred. In W Norway ensimatic island-arc volcanics of the Gutung Farm, Bomlø, unconformably overlie ophiolites (Lykling) and keratophyres of the arc sequence and have yielded a 535 ± 46 Ma Rb–Sr isochron (Amaliksen 1982, Furnes *et al.* 1983, Nordas *et al.* 1985). The oceanic crust represented by the

From HARRIS, A. L. & FETTES, D. J. (eds), 1988, *The Caledonian–Appalachian Orogen,* Geological Society Special Publication No. 38, pp. 111–122.

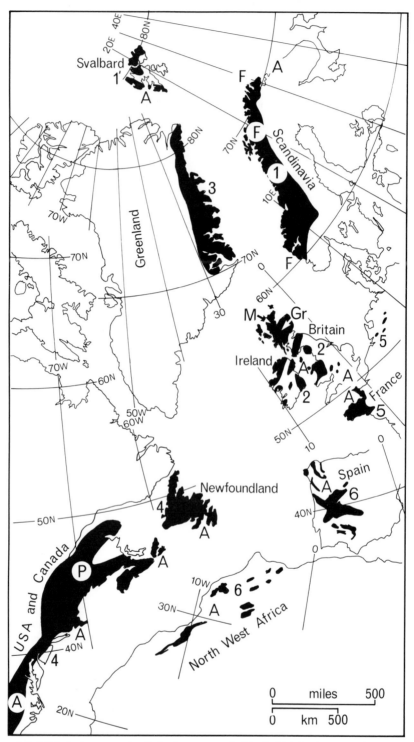

Fig. 1. Fragmented Caledonian orogen (on Bullard reconstruction) in the N Atlantic area: 1, Scandinavia, 1′, Svalbard; 2, British Isles; 3, E Greenland; 4, USA and Canada; 5, NW Europe; 6, Spain and NW Africa; A, Avalonian; P, Penobscot; F, Finnmarkian; Gr, Grampian; M, Moine.

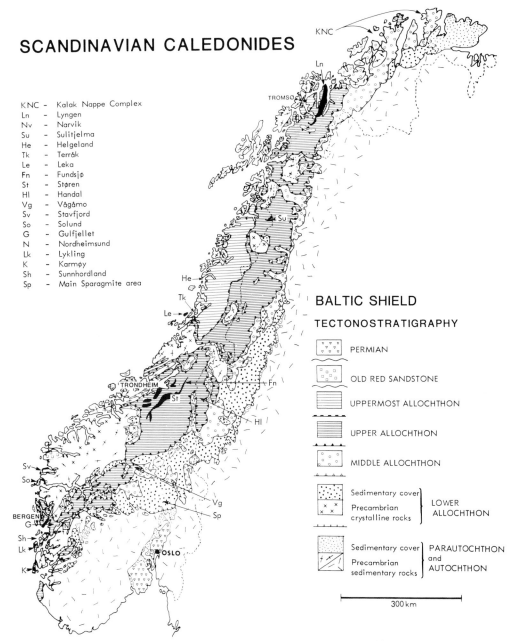

SCANDINAVIAN CALEDONIDES

KNC – Kalak Nappe Complex
Ln – Lyngen
Nv – Narvik
Su – Sulitjelma
He – Helgeland
Tk – Terråk
Le – Leka
Fn – Fundsjø
St – Støren
Hl – Handal
Vg – Vågåmo
Sv – Stavfjord
So – Solund
G – Gulfjellet
N – Nordheimsund
Lk – Lykling
K – Karmøy
Sh – Sunnhordland
Sp – Main Sparagmite area

BALTIC SHIELD

TECTONOSTRATIGRAPHY

PERMIAN

OLD RED SANDSTONE

UPPERMOST ALLOCHTHON

UPPER ALLOCHTHON

MIDDLE ALLOCHTHON

Sedimentary cover ⎱
Precambrian   ⎰ LOWER ALLOCHTHON
crystalline rocks

Sedimentary cover ⎱ PARAUTOCHTHON
Precambrian   ⎰ and
sedimentary rocks   AUTOCHTHON

300 km

FIG. 2. Tectonostratigraphy of the Scandinavian Caledonides.

Lykling ophiolites is thus older than the kerato-phyres. This is consistent with the pre-Tremadoc age of the Funsjø Group volcanics in the Trondheim region. By the end of the Cambrian a clear distinction could be drawn between the miogeoclinal prism and the oceanic crust of the expanding Iapetus Ocean (Gee 1975, D. Roberts et al. 1984, Sturt 1984). The most complete section through the prism is found in the Kalak Nappe Complex (Sturt et al. 1975, 1978, Ramsay et al. 1985) where each nappe involves a continental basement with Riphean–Cambrian cover rocks. The cover sediments are of a continental shelf assemblage. Ramsay et al. (1985) estimated the width of this shelf as more than 500 km (Kjøde et al. 1978).

4   In late Cambrian times subduction was initiated to produce an ensimatic island arc(s) identified on Romlø in Sunnhordland and Funsjø in the Trondheim area. In addition some of the ophiolites (e.g. Karmøy, Lykling and Gullfiellet) have been associated with late-stage ensimatic arc magmatism (Pederson 1982, Furnes *et al.* 1985). It has been suggested that rocks in the Kruttfjellet Unit in the central Caledonides represent deposits of a fore-arc basin which occupied a position offshore to the Baltic continental margin and which received sediment from that margin and from the western arc. Dallmeyer *et al.* (1985), using evidence from the upper Köli nappes, implied that these had suffered Finnmarkian deformation and metamorphism. Ramsay (1973) and Robins & Gardner (1975) proposed an eastward-dipping subduction zone, but Sturt *et al.* (1984) believe that it has a westward dip. If deformation and metamorphism accompanied subduction they have been obliterated by the Finnmarkian and Scandian orogenies. Finnmarkian deformation was initiated in late Cambrian time in the wake of the subduction (Sturt *et al.* 1978, Sturt 1984). The Finnmarkian orogeny destroyed the miogeoclinal prism resulting in a cratonward movement of basement-cover nappes. Two periods of deformation (D1 and D2) have been identified (Sturt *et al.* 1978). In the W Finnmark region the rocks of the Seiland Igneous Province (Barth 1927, Sturt & Ramsay 1965, Robins & Gardner 1975) were syntectonic. The mafic–ultramafic plutons, including alkaline types, were emplaced successively during deformation and metamorphism. Thus the plutons and their associated minor intrusions make almost ideal relative time-markers during the Finnmarkian orogeny. Dating of this plutonic sequence implies a time-span of 535–485 Ma and the age of its later stages is supported by K–Ar nepheline ages of 495–480 Ma (Sturt *et al.* 1967, 1978). During Finnmarkian D1 (Sturt 1984) continental crust of the prism underwent subduction, and D1 blastomylonites and kyanite-grade metamorphism were formed. The D2 folds of the Finnmark region show an ESE sense of movement and relate to cratonward movement of nappes. Slates varying from mid-Proterozoic to Vendian in the adjacent autochthon and parautochthon yield Finnmarkian D2 ages in the general range 505–480 Ma (Sturt *et al.* 1978, Taylor & Pickering 1981). Recent [39]Ar–[40]Ar studies of shear zones in the western basement of Senja have hornblende plateau ages of about 510 Ma (Dallmeyer *et al.* 1985). Thus the Finnmarkian orogeny affected the northernmost part of Baltica in earliest Ordovician times. Evidence for Finnmarkian deformation outside the type area is sparse.

Blastomylonites underlying the Sarv Nappe yielded an Rb–Sr isochron age of 485 Ma (Claesson 1980). Dallmeyer *et al.* (1985) obtained [39]Ar–[40]Ar mineral plateau ages for hornblende in the range 485–450 Ma from the Seve nappes and in the range 510–480 Ma for the older parts of the Köli nappes.

5   During the Finnmarkian orogeny slabs of Iapetus crust and parts of ensimatic island arcs were incorporated into the deforming prism. An earliest Ordovician age is inferred. In the northern section both the Finnmarkian metamorphic complex of the Vaddas Nappe and the ophiolitic rocks of the Lyngen Nappe are unconformably overlain by an Upper Ordovician–Lower Silurian sequence (Ramsay *et al.* 1985). In the Trondheim region, however, the Støren ophiolite is unconformably overlain by top mid-Arenig clastic sediments (Roberts *et al.* 1984), thus attesting to the earliest Ordovician obduction of the ophiolite. In the southern section the Lykling ophiolite is unconformably overlain by the Middle Ordovician continental volcanics (Furnes *et al.* 1983). The Karmøy ophiolite is penetrated by a series of dioritic and granitoid plutons of the W Karmøy Igneous Complex (Sturt & Thon 1978, Sturt *et al.* 1979, Ledru 1980). The latter contains, in addition to ophiolitic fragments, xenoliths derived from underlying continental basement indicating that this ophiolite had overthrust the continental margin by early Ordovician times. The ophiolites were involved in deformation and metamorphism, probably during the Finnmarkian orogeny. The metamorphic effects are unambiguous in the cap-rock sequences of the Karmøy, Norheimsund and Gullfjellet ophiolites where there is a metamorphic hiatus at the base of the Middle–Upper Ordovician unconformity (Sturt *et al.* 1984). Sjøstrom & Gee (1984) showed that the amphibolite-facies metamorphism of the Handal ophiolite is coeval with that in the underlying Seve metasediments.

6   A major belt-length unconformity in the middle, upper and uppermost allochthons cuts deeply into both the ophiolites and the metamorphosed continental prism (Sturt 1984). It is impossible to place a precise age on this unconformity as in many areas the only datable part of the overlying succession is Ashgillian. However, in the Trondheim area it predates upper Middle Arenig clastic sediments and, on Bomlø, Middle Ordovician continental volcanics (Furnes *et al.* 1983, Roberts *et al.* 1984). The unconformable deposits form a thick clastic wedge, in part continental and in part shallow marine. During this morphogenic stage uplift and erosion exposed amphibolite-facies rocks of the prism and levels in ophiolites varying from pelagic cap-rocks to

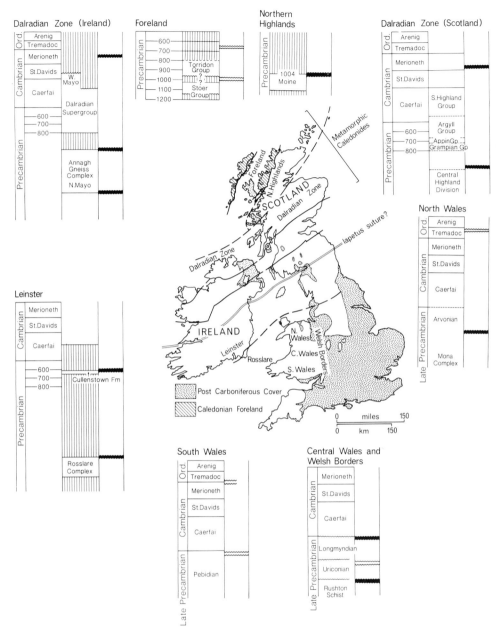

FIG. 3. Timing of early deformation in the British Isles (in part after Powell & Phillips 1985). Solid black undulations in the columns indicate severe deformation; open undulations indicate mild deformation.

foliated harzburgites. Thus the early stages of the Scandinavian Caledonides involved a probably late Precambrian phase of ocean opening, Lower and Middle Cambrian sea-floor spreading and a destructive orogenic cycle were initiated in the late Cambrian culminating in the morphogenic stage in Lower and Middle Ordovician times.

Britain and Ireland (Fig. 3)

NW foreland

The Moine Thrust defines the NW limit of the metamorphic Caledonides in Scotland beyond which late Archaean rocks (Lewisian) form the

Hebridean craton, the Caledonian foreland. Here they are overlain by Torridonian (late Proterozoic) clastic deposits and by Cambro-Ordovician siliceous sandstones and carbonates. Pre-Arenig deformation in the foreland comprises open folding and tilting responsible for the break in deposition and slight unconformity between the Stoer (lower) and Torridonian (upper) Groups of the Torridonian and the unconformity between the Torridonian and the Cambrian. Localized faulting (Stewart 1982) influenced the deposition and facies of both the Stoer and Torridon Groups.

Metamorphic Caledonides

To the SE of the Moine thrust the Moine and Dalradian Supergroups comprising the metamorphic Caledonides are traced from Scotland to Ireland, the Dalradian possibly corresponding in part to the Fleur de Lys Group of Newfoundland (Kennedy 1979).

Moine

To the NW of the Great Glen Fault in Scotland the Moine comprises three divisions—the Morar, Glenfinnan and Locheil. To the SE of the Great Glen Fault, the Central Highland Division resembles the gneisses and amphibolites of the Glenfinnan Division. The Grampian Division, which also occurs SE of the Great Glen, is essentially the same as the Grampian Group of the Dalradian as defined by Harris *et al.* (1978) and should be included with the Dalradian Supergroup.

Isotopic age dating on pelitic paragneisses (Brewer *et al.* 1979) and granitic orthogneisses (Brook *et al.* 1976) has shown that the Moine of the N Highlands suffered polyphase deformation and regional metamorphism of Barrovian type between 1050 and 1000 Ma ago. It was subsequently deformed by thrusting and related polyphase folding between about 460 and 420 Ma ago (A. M. Roberts *et al.* 1984, Barr *et al.* 1986). Cores of Lewisian (Archaean) basement gneiss possibly rooting to the W form the core of major E-facing folds of the episode which took place about 1000 Ma ago. Intrusions of basic dykes or sheets and the emplacement of a major sheet-like body of adamellitic Ardgour orthogneiss preceded or coincided with this late Proterozoic orogenesis and its accompanying amphibolite-facies metamorphism.

Dalradian

Four groups—Grampian, Appin, Argyll and Southern Highland—comprise the Dalradian

Supergroup. The youngest Dalradian rocks are probably middle Cambrian in age and the whole Supergroup has been affected in Scotland and Ireland by Grampian orogenesis (Lambert & McKerrow 1976). The age of Grampian orogenesis is constrained by the age of emplacement of the 514^{+6}_{-7} Ma Ben Vuirich granite (Bradbury *et al.* 1976). This granite cuts fabrics related to the first two episodes of deformation in the Dalradian rocks of the Pitlochry area of the Central Highlands and is cut by a third set of structures which are approximately coeval with the emplacement of the 491 ± 15 Ma Dunfallandy Hill granite of the same area.

In NE Scotland the metamorphism related to the Grampian deformation is constrained by the broadly synorogenic Newer Gabbros (489 ± 17 Ma) (Pankhurst 1970) and is of the Buchan type.

Precambrian of England and Wales

The Precambrian rocks of England and Wales form part of the SE Marginal Zone of the Caledonide–Appalachian Belt (Rast & Skehan 1983b). Four sets of rocks can be distinguished including the Pentevrian of the Channel Islands, gneisses and schists of the Midlands and Welsh Borders, and gneisses and schists of Wales.

The Pentevrian of the Channel Islands consists of ancient Archaean–early Proterozoic gneisses (1750 Ma), possibly of age and origin comparable with the Rosslare gneisses of SE Ireland. Elsewhere in England and Wales strong evidence for ancient continental basement gneisses is lacking, although some gneisses in N Wales are interpreted as ancient basement by Barber & Max (1979).

The uncertainty about the ages of the gneisses of Wales and the evidence of the Lithosphere Seismic Profile in Britain (LISPB), which indicates lower crustal seismic velocities of only 6.3 km s^{-1}, led Bamford *et al.* (1976) to infer the absence of a continuous dense continental basement below S Britain. The petrology and geochemistry of the Precambrian rocks of England and Wales are believed by Thorpe (1979) to indicate late Precambrian island-arc magmatism and related sedimentation and metamorphism. The deeply-penetrating and long-lived structures such as the Malvern and Church Stretton faults largely control their present-day outcrop.

N Wales

Greenly (1919) recognized two divisions in the Precambrian of N Wales—the Mona Complex (Avalonian?) and the Arvonian (volcanic) series.

The former consists of gneisses and the bedded succession (Monian Supergroup of Shackleton (1975)), comprising metasedimentary and basic metavolcanic rocks of greenschist to amphibolite facies, deformed and metamorphosed in the late Precambrian or earliest Cambrian. The Arvonian succession is probably unconformable on the Monian and includes dominantly felsic ignimbrites and volcanigenic sediments. The Mona Complex was intruded by late Precambrian or early Cambrian granitoids.

Greenly (1919) considered that the Monian Supergroup must be a continuous sequence some 6000 m thick.

Structural facing (*sensu* Shackleton 1958) shows that the upright to overturned major folds of the Mona Complex on Holy Island (Anglesey) consistently face upwards and to the SE (Shackleton 1975). The diamictite within the Gwna Group of the Monian known as the Gwna Melange contains blocks of thicknesses ranging from millimetres to kilometres and is regarded as an olistostrome (Shackleton 1969, pp. 9–10, Wood 1974), largely because it is of regional extent and has sharp concordant contacts with undisturbed formations above and below and because the clasts, although mainly chaotic, show a ghost stratigraphy in places. Wood (1974) has interpreted the association of olistostrome melange, ophiolites (serpentine, gabbro and pillow basalts) and deep-water sediments together with the glaucophane schist-facies metamorphism of SE Anglesey as indicating late Precambrian deposition and deformation in a subduction-related trench.

Greenly (1919) thought that the gneisses in Anglesey form a basement to the bedded succession, but Shackleton (1969, p. 14) pointed out that the gneisses are not adjacent to the *oldest* parts of the Monian Supergroup and that the highest grades of metamorphism are not related to stratigraphic level. Shackleton's interpretation has been supported by Beckinsale & Thorpe (1979) who showed that Rb–Sr whole-rock isochrons from orthogneisses and paragneisses indicate a metamorphic event at 595 ± 12 Ma while a low initial $^{87}Sr/^{86}Sr$ ratio shows that a long crustal history for the gneisses is improbable. Nb–Sm investigations by Thorpe *et al.* (1984) indicate that the gneisses are post-1300 Ma and pre-890 Ma in age.

The Mona Complex was intruded by two late Precambrian–Cambrian granites—the Coedana granite of Anglesey and the Sarn granite of Lleyn. These are regarded as closely related to the formation of gneisses and schists.

England, Welsh Borderland and S Wales

A large part of central and eastern England is underlain by upper Proterozoic volcanic rocks which have been encountered in virtually all the boreholes which have passed through the Phanerozoic cover and which crop out as small structurally controlled inliers such as that of Charnwood Forest, Leicestershire. More diverse Precambrian lithological units outcrop sporadically along an arcuate tectonically controlled zone continuous through the Welsh Borderland into SW Wales. Much of this zone has a complex history of displacements and probably marked the SE margin of the Welsh Lower Palaeozoic basin.

Malvernian rocks consist largely of dioritic plutonic rocks (Calloway 1893, Lambert & Holland 1971). These range from mafic diorites to leucocratic tonalites cut by veins of syenite and granite. The whole of the Malvernian is probably a somewhat gneissic plutonic complex of variable composition, possibly regionally metamorphosed during the Precambrian at high grade (Fitch *et al.* 1969). Brittle deformation which affected the Malvernian (Fitch *et al.* 1969, p. 44) also affected the post-Malvernian but Precambrian Warren House volcanic rocks and may coincide with the last major isotopic event (590 ± 20 Ma) in the Malvernian (Lambert & Rex 1966). Thorpe (1979) suggested that it is most likely that the Malvernian is a plutonic complex closely related to the calc-alkaline late-Precambrian volcanics.

The late Precambrian *Longmyndian* sedimentary rocks of the Welsh Borderland (less than 8000 m thick) are thought to rest unconformably on the *Uriconian* calc-alkaline volcanics and intrusions, occurring as a number of fault-bounded lenticular outcrops. Some Longmyndian units are tuffaceous and there may be a broad overlap in time between Uriconian and Longmyndian facies. The main evidence for the Precambrian deformation of the Longmyndian derives from its strong large-scale folding into a large isoclinal syncline that is overturned and faces up towards the W; evidence for this deformation is completely lacking in adjacent Cambrian rocks occurring in the Church Stretton fault zone. Folding of the Longmyndian may coincide with the brittle retrogressive reworking of the Malvernian rocks.

In S Wales (Dyfed) two main complexes—the volcanic Pebidian and the intrusive Dimetian—have been recognized. The slightly metamorphosed volcanic Pebidian sequence thins from W to E.

Thomas & Jones (1912) demonstrated that the Lower Cambrian Caerfai Group basal conglomerates (Cowie *et al.* 1972) post-date all the intrusive rocks grouped with the Dimetian and are younger than the penetrative deformation which affected the Pebidian rocks. Green (1908) showed that the Dimetian St Davids granophyre is overlain by the basal Cambrian conglomerate. The implied lapse of time between Pebidian and Lower Cambrian is in marked contrast with the Arvonian–Lower Cambrian which seem almost stratigraphically continuous and imply that the Precambrian volcanics of N and S Wales are probably of somewhat different age.

The *Charnian* rocks of Leicestershire consist of about 2600 m of Precambrian volcanics and sediments overlain by Triassic sandstone. Similar rocks are found at Barnt Green and Nuneaton in the English Midlands. Charnian rocks carry a penetrative cleavage that does not exist in adjacent Cambrian strata. Sedimentary structures and probable coelenteratal algae *Charnia masoni* and *Charnodiscus concentricus* (Ford 1958) are found and suggest a Vendian age (Downie 1975). The cleavage-generating deformation is thus late Vendian or lowermost Cambrian.

N America

The following Precambrian successions are recognized in the Appalachians (Fig. 4): 1, Grenville and pre-Grenville crystalline massifs intruded in the S Appalachians by about 700 Ma granitoids (Fig. 5); 2, late Proterozoic sediments including carbonates and clastics; 3, late Proterozoic Avalonian clastics and associated volcanics, both mafic and felsic but predominantly felsic, associated with or resting on late Precambrian granites.

All the above sequences are generally unconformably overlain by Cambrian strata that consist of coarse clastics (earlier) and carbonates (later) with occasional shales forming part of the carbonate bank of the Laurentian craton (Rodgers 1970).

Grenville crystalline rocks forming the massifs are generally granites, high-grade gneisses and granulites. They have lithologies found in cratonic Grenville rocks such as charnockite and anorthosite (Fig. 5). There are also blocks of older units such as the Chain Lakes massif in the N Appalachians (Boone 1973, Naylor 1975, Osberg 1983, p. 317), which Boudette (1981) suggested is an allochthonous fragment. Zen (1983) considered this massif and fragments of Avalonian terranes as non-American and inserted a separating suture in the N Appalachians (a on Fig. 4), although Williams (1979) proposed a different line (b on Fig. 4). Either suture is considered by Zen as mid-Ordovician (Taconian) in age. However, in the N Appalachians an earlier (late Cambrian, late Ordovician) Penobscot suture is also present (Boone & Boudette 1985). A similar situation is perceived in the S Appalachians (Pavlides 1985) where well-developed melanges are associated with ophiolitic rocks. This work strongly supports that of Neuman (1967) who first recognized that in central Maine (3 on Fig. 4) strongly deformed Cambrian strata are unconformably overlain by much less deformed Arenig rocks, indicating an orogenic event.

Signs of another orogenic episode can be detected among the fragments of the Avalon terrane (Williams & Hatcher 1983) (SE of the broken line c on Fig. 4). Despite the fragmentary nature of this terrane (Rast & Skehan 1983b, Keppie 1985), the general similarity of their constituent rocks (about 620 Ma granites, 600 Ma volcanics and terrigenous or shallow marine sediments) indicates that the fragments were parts of an originally continuous volcanigenic terrane, such as an island arc, partly lying on continental basement. The continental masses underlying this terrane are similar to the W African craton and yield isotopic ages of 1500–2000 Ma. The arc had a prolonged history and may have been part of the Pan-African orogenic belt. In several localities such as Newfoundland, New England and the Carolina slate belt there is evidence for a late Precambrian orogenic episode known as the Avalonian (for references see Rast & Skehan 1983a) which is equated with the timing of the closure of the Cadomian Ocean. The event appears to have been collisional. Therefore the arc probably collided with America prior to the opening of the Iapetus Ocean; it was then fragmented during the Palaeozoic opening of the ocean, but parts of it and its basement (Chain Lakes massif) were involved in the Penobscot collision.

Discussion

This brief review of the nature and timing of pre-Arenig deformation in the Caledonian–Appalachian orogen is concerned with events whose relationships are largely obscured by subsequent deformation and metamorphism.

A generally coherent history emerges from studies of the Avalonian terranes which record widespread late Proterozoic volcanism and related plutonism and sedimentation throughout the eastern Appalachians, southern Britian, western Europe and NW Africa (Fig. 1). These rocks were affected by late Precambrian orogenesis about 600 Ma ago. More precise studies of the Avalonian rocks may reveal a more complex

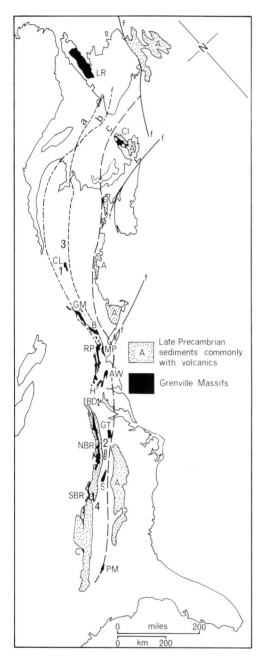

Late Precambrian
sediments commonly
with volcanics

Grenville Massifs

story; work in Britain (e.g. Gibbons 1983) is already suggesting a collage of small terranes and major late Precambrian strike-slip displacements. The presence of possible Avalonian rocks in Svalbard (Fig. 1) suggests considerable strike-slip displacement.

Precise correlatives are lacking for the orogenic history of the Moine rocks of the northern Scottish Highlands which appear as a small terrane of unknown affinity which suffered mid-upper amphibolite-facies metamorphism during intense deformation between 1050 and 1000 Ma ago. These rocks were subsequently caught up in

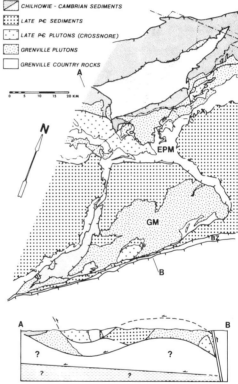

CHILHOWIE - CAMBRIAN SEDIMENTS

LATE PЄ SEDIMENTS

LATE PЄ PLUTONS (CROSSNORE)

GRENVILLE PLUTONS

GRENVILLE COUNTRY ROCKS

FIG. 5. Grandfather Mountain area showing relationships between Precambrian and Cambrian rocks: GM, Grandfather Mountain; EPM, Elk Park Grenville Massif; BZ, Brevard Zone. Granitoids are about 700 Ma old.

FIG. 4. Distribution of Grenville massifs and late Precambrian sediments and volcanics in the Appalachians. The localities mentioned in the text and located on this map are as follows: 1, Hurricane Mountain melange and ultramafics; 2, Maryland—Smith River melange and volcanics; 3, Shin-Pond in central Maine; 4, Grandfather Mountain. Main Grenville massifs from N to S: LR, Long Ridge; CI, Cape Breton Island; CL, Chain Lakes; GM, Green Mountain; B, Barkshire; RP, Reading Prong; MP, Manhattan Prong; AW, Wilmington; H, Honey Brook Upland; BD, Baltimore Domes; GT, Goochland Terrane; NBR, Northern Blue Ridge; S, Sauratown Mountains; SBR, Southern Blue Ridge; C, Corbin; PM, Pine Mountain. (a) Taconian suture according to Zen (1983); (b) Taconian suture according to Williams (1979); (c) line marking westward extent of Avalonian fragments; f–f, major fault.

the WNW-directed late Caledonian (about 460–430 Ma ago) thrusting typical of the NW flank of the orogen and are now adjacent, across the Great Glen fault, to the Dalradian rocks. The structure of the latter is dominated by the SSE-directed Tay (Grampian) Nappe. Although this nappe has been interpreted as part of a NW-foreland-propagating diachronous thrust sequence (Watson 1984) its age and sense of transport are comparable with the E-directed Finnmarkian nappes of Scandinavia, while it appears to be some tens of millions of years older than the Caledonian thrust nappes of the Moine terrane.

A further problem concerns the extent and distribution of the rocks affected by Penobscot orogenesis in N America and their relationship, if any, to rocks caught up in Grampian and Finnmarkian events in N Europe.

References

AMALIKSEN, K. G. 1982. *Cand. Real Thesis* (unpublished), University of Bergen.

BAMFORD, D., FABER, S., JACOB, B., KAMINSKI, W., NUNN, K., PRODEHL, C., FUCHS, K., KING, R. & WILLMORE, P. 1976. A lithosphere seismic profile in Britain—1. Preliminary results. *Geophysical Journal of the Royal Astronomical Society*, **44**, 145–60.

BARBER, A. J. & MAX, M. D. 1979. A new look at the Moine Complex (Anglesey, North Wales). *Journal of the Geological Society, London*, **136**, 407–32.

BARR, D., HOLDSWORTH, R. E. & ROBERTS, A. M. 1986. Caledonian ductile thrusting in a Precambrian metamorphic complex: the Moine of northwestern Scotland. *Bulletin of the Geological Society of America*, **97**, 754–64.

BARTH, T. F. W. 1927. Die Pegmatitgange des Kaledonischen Intrusivegesteine im Seiland–Gebeite. *Norske Videnskaps-Akademi Skrifte I*, **8**.

BECKINSALE, R. D. & THORPE, R. S. 1979. Rubidium–strontium whole-rock isochron evidence for the age of metamorphism and magmatism in the Mona Complex of Anglesey. *Journal of the Geological Society, London*, **136**, 433–9.

BOONE, G. McG. 1973. Metamorphic stratigraphy, petrology and structural geology of the Little Bigelow Mountain map area, western Maine. *Maine Geological Survey Bulletin*, **24**, 136 pp.

—— & BOUDETTE, E. L. 1985. Hurricane Mountain formation melange: history of Cambro–Ordovician accretion of the Boundary Mountains terrane within the Northern Appalachian orthotectonic zone. *Abstracts with Programs of the Geological Society of America*, **17**, 528.

BOUDETTE, E. L. 1981. Ophiolite assemblage of early Palaeozoic age in central western Maine. *Geological Association of Canada Special Paper No. 24*, pp. 209–30.

BRADBURY, H. J., SMITH, R. A. & HARRIS, A. L. 1976. 'Older' granites as time markers in Dalradian evolution. *Journal of the Geological Society, London*, **132**, 677–84.

BREWER, M. S., BROOK, M. & POWELL, D. 1979. Dating the tectono-metamorphic history of the southwestern Moine, Scotland. *In:* HARRIS, A. L. *et al.* (eds) *The Caledonides of the British Isles—Reviewed. Special Publication of the Geological Society of London No. 8*, pp. 129–37.

BROOK, M., POWELL, D. & BREWER, M. S. 1976. Grenville age for rocks in the Moine of northwestern Scotland. *Nature, London*, **260**, 515–17.

CALLOWAY, C. 1893. On the origin of the crystalline schists of the Malvern Hills. *Quarterly Journal of the Geological Society of London*, **49**, 398–425.

CLAESSON, S. 1980. A Rb–Sr isotope study of granitoids and related mylonites in the Tannas Augen Gneiss Nappe, southern Swedish Caledonides. *Geologiska Föreningens i Stockholm Förhandlingar*, **102**, 403–20.

—— & RODDICK, J. C. 1983. $^{40}Ar/^{39}Ar$ data on the age and metamorphism of the Ottafjället dolerites, Särv Nappe, Swedish Caledonides. *Lithos*, **16**, 61–73.

COWIE, J. W., RUSHTON, A. W. A. & STUBBLEFIELD, C. J. 1972. A correlation of Cambrian rocks in the British Isles. *Special Report of the Geological Society of London No. 1*, 42 pp.

DALLMEYER, R. D., GEE, D. G. & BECKHOLMEN, M. 1985. $^{40}Ar/^{39}Ar$ mineral age record of Early Caledonian tectonothermal activity in the Baltoscandian Miogeocline, Central Scandinavia. *American Journal of Science*, **285**, 532–68.

DOWNIE, C. 1975. Precambrian of the British Isles––palaeontology. *In:* HARRIS, A. L. *et al.* (eds) *A Correlation of Precambrian Rocks in the British Isles. Special Report of the Geological Society of London No. 6*, pp. 113–5.

FITCH, F. J., MILLER, J. A., EVANS, A. L., GRASTY, R. L. & MENEISY, M. Y. 1969. Isotopic age determinations on rocks from Wales and the Welsh Borders. *In:* WOOD, A. (ed.) *The Precambrian and Lower Palaeozoic Rocks of Wales*, pp. 23–45, University of Wales Press, Cardiff.

FORD, T. D. 1958. Pre-Cambrian fossils from Charnwood Forest. *Proceedings of the Yorkshire Geological Society*, **31**, 211–7.

FURNES, H., AUSTRHEIM, H., AMALIKSEN, K. G. & NORDAS, J. 1983. Evidence for an incipient early Caledonian (Cambrian) Orogenic phase in southwestern Norway. *Geological Magazine*, **120**, 607–12.

——, ROBERTS, D., STURT, B. A., THON, A. & GALE, G. H. (1979). Ophiolite fragments in the Scandinavian Caledonides. *Proceedings of the International Ophiolite Symposium, Cyprus*, pp. 582–600.

——, RYAN, P. D., GRENNE, T., ROBERTS, D., STURT,

B. A. & PRESTVIK, T. 1985. Geological and geochemical classification of the ophiolite fragments in the Scandinavian Caledonides. *In:* GEE, D. G. & STURT, B. A. (eds) *The Caledonide Orogen—Scandinavia and Related Areas.* Wiley, Chichester.

GAYER, R. A., HUMPHREYS, R. J., BINNS, R. E. & CHAPMAN, T. J. 1985. Tectonic modelling of the Finnmark and Troms Caledonides based on high level igneous rock geochemistry. *In:* GEE, D. G. & STURT, B. A. (eds) *The Caledonide Orogen—Scandinavia and Related Areas,* pp. 931–52, Wiley, Chichester.

GEE, D. G. 1975. A tectonic model for the central part of the Scandinavian Caledonides. *American Journal of Science,* **275A,** 468–515.

—— & STURT, B. A. 1983. Sequential development of the Scandinavian Caledonides. *In:* SCHENK, P. E. (ed.) *Regional Trends in the Geology of the Appalachian–Caledonian–Hercynian–Mauritanide Orogen,* pp. 163–7, Reidel, Dordrecht.

GIBBONS, W. 1983. Stratigraphy, subduction and strike-slip faulting in the Mona Complex of North Wales—a review. *Proceedings of the Geological Association of London,* **94,** 147–63.

GREEN, J. F. N. 1908. The geological structure of the St. Davids area. *Quarterly Journal of the Geological Society of London,* **64,** 363–83.

GREENLY, E. 1919. The geology of Anglesey. *Memoir of the Geological Survey of the United Kingdom.*

HARRIS, A. L., BALDWIN, C. T., BRADBURY, H. J., JOHNSON, H. D. & SMITH, R. A. 1978. Ensialic basin sedimentation: the Dalradian Supergroup. *In:* BOWES, D. R. & LEAKE, B. E. (eds) *Crustal Evolution of NW Britain and Adjacent Regions, Geological Journal Special Issue No. 10.*

JOHNSON, H. D., LOVELL, B. K. & SIEDLECKI, S. 1978. Late Precambrian sedimentary rocks in East Finnmark, north Norway, and their relationship to the Trollfjord–Komagelv Fault. *Journal of the Geological Society, London,* **135,** 517–34.

KENNEDY, M. J. 1979. The Fleur de Lys Supergroup. Stratigraphic comparison of Moine and Dalradian equivalents in Newfoundland with the British Caledonides. *Journal of the Geological Society, London,* **131,** 305–10.

KEPPIE, J. D. 1985. The Appalachian collage. *In:* STURT, B. A. & GEE, D. G. (eds) *The Caledonian Orogen—Scandinavia and Related Areas,* pp. 422–37, Wiley, Chichester.

KJØDE, J., STORETVEDT, K. M., ROBERTS, D. & GISKEHAUG, A. 1978. Palaeomagnetic evidence for large scale dextral movement along the Trollfjord–Komagelv Fault, Finnmark, north Norway. *Physics of the Earth and Planetary Interiors,* **161,** 132–44.

KUMPLANINEN, R. & NYSTUEN, J. P. 1985. Late Proterozoic basin evolution and sedimentation in the western part of Baltoscanida. *In:* GEE, D. G. & STURT, B. A. (eds) *The Caledonide Orogen—Scandinavia and Related Areas,* pp. 213–32, Wiley, Chichester.

LAMBERT, R. St. J. & HOLLAND, J. G. 1971. The petrography and chemistry of the igneous complex

of the Malvern Hills, England. *Proceedings of the Geological Association of London,* **82,** 323–51.

—— & McKERROW, W. S. 1976. The Grampian orogeny. *Scottish Journal of Geology,* **12,** 271–92.

—— & REX, D. C. 1966. Isotopic ages of minerals from the Precambrian complex of the Malverns. *Nature, London,* **209,** 605–6.

LEDRU, P. 1980. Evolution structurale et magmatique du complexe plutonique de Karmoy. *Bullétin de la Societé de Géologie et Minérale Bretagne,* **12,** 1–106.

NAYLOR, R. S. 1975. Age provinces in the Northern Appalachians. *Annual Reviews of the Earth and Planetary Sciences,* **3,** 387–400.

NEUMAN, R. B. 1967. Bedrock geology of the Skin-pond and Stacyville quadrangles, Penobscot County, Maine. *U.S. Geological Survey Professional Paper No. 524-1,* 37 pp.

NORDAS, J., AMALIKSEN, K. G., BREKKE, H., SUTHREN, R. J., FURNES, H., STURT, B. A. & ROBINS, B. 1985. Lithostratigraphy and petrochemistry of Caledonian rocks on Boml, southwest Norway. *In:* GEE, D. G. & STURT, B. A. (eds) *The Caledonide Orogen—Scandinavia and Related Areas,* pp. 679–92, Wiley, Chichester.

OSBERG, P. H. 1983. Timing of orogenic events in the U.S. Appalachians. *In:* SCHENK, P. E. (ed.) *Regional Trends in the Geology of the Appalachian–Caledonian–Hercynian–Mauritanide Orogen,* pp. 315–37, Reidel, Dordrecht.

PANKHURST, R. J. 1970. The geochronology of the basic igneous complexes. *Scottish Journal of Geology,* **6,** 83–107.

PAVLIDES, L. 1985. Early Paleozoic composite melange in the central Appalachian Piedmont, Virginia and Maryland. *Abstracts with Programs of the Geological Society of America,* **17,** 686.

PEDERSEN, R. B. 1982. *Cand. Real. Thesis* (unpublished), University of Bergen.

POWELL, D. & PHILLIPS, W. E. A. 1985. Time of deformation in the Caledonide Orogen of Britain and Ireland. *In:* HARRIS, A. L. (ed.) The nature and timing of orogenic activity in the Caledonian rocks of the British Isles. *Memoir of the Geological Society of London,* **9,** 17–39 and Pl. 2.

RAMSAY, D. M. 1973. Possible existence of a stillborn marginal ocean in the Caledonian Orogenic Belt of North-West Norway. *Nature, London, Physical Science,* **245,** 107–9.

——, STURT, B. A., ZWANN, K. B. & ROBERTS, D. 1985. Caledonides of northern Norway. *In:* GEE, D. G. & STURT, B. A. (eds) *The Caledonide Orogen—Scandinavia and Related Areas,* pp. 163–84, Wiley, Chichester.

RAST, N. & SKEHAN, J. W. 1983a. The evolution of the Avalonian plate. *Tectonophysics,* **100,** 251–86.

—— & —— 1983b. Assembly of the Avalonian terrane of North America and the British Isles. *Abstracts with Programs of the Geological Society of America,* **15,** 196.

ROBERTS, A. M., SMITH, D. I. & HARRIS, A. L. 1984. The structural setting and tectonic significance of the Glen Dessary syenite, Inverness-shire. *Journal of the Geological Society, London,* **141,** 1033–42.

ROBERTS, D. & GALE, G. 1978. The Caledonian–

Appalachian Iapetus Ocean. *In:* TARLING, D. H. (ed.) *Evolution of the Earth's Crust*, pp. 255–342, Academic Press, New York.

—— & STURT, B. A. 1980. Caledonian deformation in Norway. *Journal of the Geological Society, London*, **137**, 241–50.

——, GRENNE, T. & RYAN, P. D. 1984. Ordovician marginal basin development in the central Norwegian Caledonides. *Special Publication of the Geological Society of London No. 12*, pp. 233–44.

ROBINS, B. & GARDNER, P. M. 1975. The magmatic evolution of the Sieland province and Caledonian plate boundaries in Northern Norway. *Earth and Planetary Science Letters*, **26**, 167–78.

RODGERS, J. 1970. *The Tectonics of the Appalachians*, Wiley-Interscience, New York, 271 pp.

RYAN, P. D. & STURT, B. A. 1985. Early Caledonian orogenesis in northwestern Europe. *In:* GEE, D. G. & STURT, B. A. (eds) *The Caledonide Orogen—Scandinavia and Related Areas*, pp. 1227–40, Wiley, Chichester.

SHACKLETON, R. M. 1958. Downward-facing structures of the Highland Border. *Quarterly Journal of the Geological Society of London*, **113**, 361–93.

—— 1969. The Precambrian of North Wales. *In:* WOOD, A. (ed.) *The Precambrian and Lower Palaeozoic Rocks of Wales*, pp. 1–22, University of Wales Press, Cardiff.

—— 1975. Precambrian rocks of Wales. *In:* HARRIS, A. L. *et al.* (eds) *A correlation of Precambrian rocks in the British Isles. Special Report of the Geological Society of London No. 6*, pp. 76–82.

SJØSTROM, H, & GEE, D. G. 1984. Early Caledonian obduction of the Handol Ophiolite (Abs.). *Medd. Stockh. Univ. Geol. Inst.*, **255**, 72.

SOLYMON, Z., GORBATSCHEV, R. & JOHANSSON, I. 1978. The Ottfjallet Dolerites, geochemistry of the dyke swarm in relation to the geodynamics of the Caledonide orogen in central Scandinavia. *Sveriges Geologiska Undersökrung*, **756**, 1–38.

STEWART, A. D. 1982. Late Proterozoic rifting in NW Scotland; genesis of the Torridonian. *Journal of the Geological Society, London*, **139**, 413–20.

STORMER, L. 1967. Some aspects of the Caledonian geosyncline and foreland west of the Baltic Shield. *Quarterly Journal of the Geological Society of London*, **123**, 183–214.

STRAND, T. & KULLING, O. 1972. *Scandinavian Caledonides*, Wiley, New York.

STURT, B. A. 1984. The accretion of ophiolitic terrains in the Scandinavian Caledonides. *Geologie en Mijnbouw*, **46**, 201–12.

—— & RAMSAY, D. M. 1965. The alkaline complex of the Breivikbotn area, Soroy, northern Norway. *Norges Geologiske Undersökelse*, **231**, 1–142.

—— & THON, A. 1978. An ophiolite complex of probable early Caledonian age, discovered on Karmoy. *Nature, London*, **275**, 538–9.

——, FURNES, H. & THON, A. 1979. The Karmøy Ophiolite, southwest Norway. *Geology*, **7**, 316–20.

——, MILLER, J. A. & FITCH, F. J. 1967. The age of alkaline rocks from west Finnmark, northern Norway, and their bearing on the dating of the Caledonian orogeny. *Norsk Geologisk Tidsskrift*, **47**, 255–73.

——, PRINGLE, I. R. & RAMSAY, D. M. 1978. The Finnmarkian phase of the Caledonian orogeny. *Journal of the Geological Society, London*, **135**, 597–610.

——, —— & ROBERTS, D. 1975. Caledonian nappe sequence of Finnmark, northern Norway, and the timing of orogenic deformation and metamorphism. *Bulletin of the Geological Society of America*, **86**, 710–8.

——, ROBERTS, D. & FURNES, H. 1984. A conspectus of Scandinavian Caledonian ophiolites. *Journal of the Geological Society, London, Special Publication No. 13*, pp. 381–91.

TAYLOR, P. H. & PICKERING, K. T. 1981. Rb–Sr isotopic age determination of the late Precambrian Kongsfjord Formation and the timing of deformation in the Barents Sea Group, East Finnmark. *Norges Geologiske Undersökelse*, **367**, 105–10.

THOMAS, H. H. & JONES, O. T. 1912. The Precambrian and Cambrian of Pembrokeshire. *Quarterly Journal of the Geological Society of London*, **68**, 374–400.

THORPE, R. S. 1979. Late Precambrian igneous activity in southern Britain. *In:* HARRIS, A. L. *et al.* (eds) *The Caledonides of the British Isles—Reviewed. Special Publication of the Geological Society of London No. 8*, pp. 579–84.

——, BECKINSALE, R. D., PATCHETT, P. J., PIPER, J. D. A., DAVIES, G. R. & EVANS, J. R. 1984. Crustal growth and late Precambrian–early Palaeozoic plate tectonic evolution of England and Wales. *Journal of the Geological Society, London*, **141**, 521–36.

WATSON, J. V. 1984. The ending of the Caledonian orogeny in Scotland. *Journal of the Geological Society, London*, **141**, 193–220.

WILLIAMS, H. 1979. Appalachian orogen in Canada. *Canadian Journal of Earth Sciences*, **16**, 792–807.

—— & HATCHER, R. D., Jr., 1983. Appalachian suspect terranes. *Geological Society of America, Memoir*, **158**, 33–53.

WOOD, D. S. 1974. Ophiolites, melanges, blueschists and ignimbrites: early Caledonian subduction in Wales? *In:* DOTT, R. H. & SHAVER, R. H. (eds) *Modern and Ancient Geosynclinal Sedimentation. Special Publication of the Society of Economic Paleontology and Mineralogy No. 12*, pp. 334–44.

ZEN, E-AN 1983. Exotic terranes in the New England Appalachians—limits, candidates and ages: a speculative study. *Geological Society of America, Memoir*, **158**, 55–81.

N. RAST, Department of Geological Sciences, University of Kentucky, Lexington, KY 40506, USA.

B. A. STURT, Department of Geology, University of Bergen, Bergen, Norway.

A. L. HARRIS, Department of Geological Sciences, University of Liverpool, Liverpool L69 3BX, UK.

Lower Palaeozoic metamorphism in the Moine–Dalradian belt of the British Isles

Ben Harte

SUMMARY: Greenschist- to amphibolite-facies mineral assemblages occur which are of Proterozoic as well as lower Palaeozoic age in the Moine rocks but are only Lower Palaeozoic in the Dalradian rocks. The widespread age of high-grade metamorphism in the Dalradian is 520–490 Ma (Grampian), whilst in the Moines N of the Great Glen high-grade Lower Palaeozoic metamorphism is dated at 460–440 Ma. In Moine rocks, Grampian deformation and metamorphism may be absent N of the Great Glen but present S of the Great Glen, and this may indicate substantial movement on the Great Glen Fault between about 500 and 450 Ma. In addition to Moine metamorphism and deformation, the 460–440 Ma period appears to encompass diverse and extensive tectonic activity near the southern margin of the belt: thrusting in Connemara, Highland Border Downbend formation in Scotland and ophiolite emplacement in the Shetland Isles. A set of probably basement-controlled tectono-metamorphic domains in the Scottish Dalradian is suggested.

The northwestern part of the Caledonide tract in Scotland and Ireland is formed of metamorphic rocks, essentially belonging to the greenschist, epidote–amphibolite and amphibolite facies, which have been assigned to the Moine succession and Dalradian Supergroup (Harris & Pitcher 1975, Johnstone 1975, Johnson 1983a). The zone containing these rocks has recently been referred to as the orthotectonic zone or northern belt of the British Caledonides (Johnson et al. 1979, Fettes 1983). In Scotland (Fig. 1) this zone is transected by the Great Glen Fault to the N of which occurs the major outcrop of Moine rocks whose NW margin is the Moine Thrust. NW of the Moine Thrust lies a foreland of Precambrian gneisses belonging to the Lewisian Complex, overlain by Torridonian (Proterozoic) and Cambro-Ordovician sediments. S of the Great Glen Fault in Scotland, rocks referred to the Moine succession are overlain to the S by the Dalradian Supergroup which is truncated by the Highland Boundary Fault (Johnson et al. 1979, Piasecki et al. 1981). Considerable strike-slip movement along the zone marked by the Highland Boundary Fault has been suggested (Bluck 1984, Dewey & Shackleton 1984, Harte et al. 1984).

In Ireland the boundaries of the orthotectonic zone are less clearly marked (Johnson et al. 1979, Long & Yardley 1979), and extensive outcrops of Dalradian rocks occur to the S of the possible extensions of the Highland Boundary Fault (Leake et al. 1984).

In the Shetland Isles, NE of Scotland, there occur a series of metamorphic rocks which are probably equivalent to much of the Dalradian and Moine successions of Scotland. On the W of these rocks is a possible Caledonian orogenic front against Lewisian-like gneisses, whilst to the E the Dalradian–Moine rocks are overlain by ophiolite nappes (Flinn et al. 1979).

Metamorphism of both Proterozoic and lower Palaeozoic age is recognized within the Moine successions of the British Isles. However, the time of deposition of the sediments giving rise to the Dalradian rocks appears to span the Precambrian–Cambrian boundary, and the Dalradian rocks only yield evidence of Lower Palaeozoic metamorphism. The principal concern of the work reported in this paper is the timing of Lower Palaeozoic metamorphic events, and both the ages of peak (highest-grade) metamorphism and radiometric cooling ages are documented. The data are summarized in Table 1. Relationships of metamorphism to tectonic and igneous events are noted, and the possibility of significant strike-slip movement along the Great Glen Fault during the time-span of metamorphism is raised. Relatively little attention is paid to the spatial distribution of different grades or facies of metamorphism because excellent compilations of this information have recently been given by Fettes (1983), Long et al. (1983) and Fettes et al. (1984). An exception to this is made in the case of the Dalradian belt in Scotland for which many new data are available.

Since the lower Palaeozoic metamorphic events in the Moine–Dalradian rocks of the British Isles spread continuously through the age range 520–390 Ma, no attempt has been made to separate pre-Arenig from post-Arenig events in accordance with the general sub-divisions adopted in this volume.

From HARRIS, A. L. & FETTES, D. J. (eds), 1988, The Caledonian–Appalachian Orogen, Geological Society Special Publication No. 38, pp. 123–134.

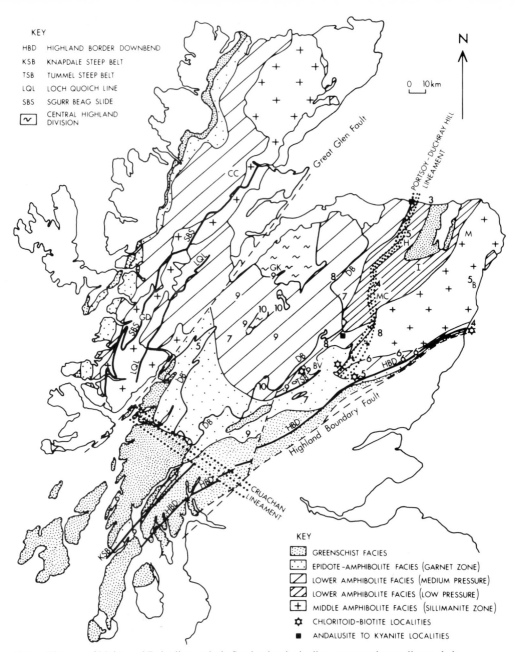

KEY

HBD   HIGHLAND BORDER DOWNBEND
KSB   KNAPDALE STEEP BELT
TSB   TUMMEL STEEP BELT
LQL   LOCH QUOICH LINE
SBS   SGURR BEAG SLIDE
⟨~⟩   CENTRAL HIGHLAND
       DIVISION

0   10 km

KEY

▨   GREENSCHIST FACIES
▨   EPIDOTE-AMPHIBOLITE FACIES (GARNET ZONE)
▨   LOWER AMPHIBOLITE FACIES (MEDIUM PRESSURE)
▨   LOWER AMPHIBOLITE FACIES (LOW PRESSURE)
⊞   MIDDLE AMPHIBOLITE FACIES (SILLIMANITE ZONE)
✿   CHLORITOID-BIOTITE LOCALITIES
■   ANDALUSITE TO KYANITE LOCALITIES

FIG. 1. The area of Moine and Dalradian rocks in Scotland, principally ornamented according to their metamorphic facies. Approximate pressures in kilobars of peak-temperature metamorphic conditions are indicated by numbers and are based on the following work: Baker (1985), Booth (1984), Dempster (1983, 1985), Droop & Charnley (1985), Graham *et al.* (1983), Harte (unpublished), Hudson (1985), Moles (1985), Richardson & Powell (1976), Wells (1979) and Watkins (1983). Facies boundaries are after Fettes *et al.* (1984) with some modifications after the workers cited above and Harte & Hudson (1979). The lines labelled KSB and TSB refer to the southern margins of the Knapdale Steep Belt and the Tummel Steep Belt respectively. The DB line largely marks the base of the Appin Group of the Dalradian Supergroup and roughly corresponds to the old boundary between the Dalradian and Moine assemblages (see text). The boundary of the Central Highland Division corresponds to the Grampian Slide (Piasecki & van Breemen 1983). Igneous intrusions are omitted but letters indicate the position of intrusions of particular significance for dating events: CC, Carn Chuinneag granite; GD, Glen Dessary syenite; GK, Glen Kyllachy granite; BV, Ben Vuroch granite; H, I, M, B, MC, the newer gabbro intrusions of Huntly, Insch, Maud, Bethelvie and Morven-Cabrach in NE Scotland. The two 'lineaments' marked correspond to 'zones of discontinuity' in metamorphic and other features (see text); the Portsoy–Duchray Hill 'lineament' extends from the position marked to the western edge of the low-pressure (Buchan) metamorphic facies.

TABLE 1. *Ages of metamorphic and related events in the Dalradian and Moine rocks of Ireland, Scotland and the Shetland Isles*

Age(Ma)	(a) Irish Dalradian Connemara	(b) Scottish Dalradian Eastern & south-central Highlands	(c) Central Highlands (Scotland) Central Highland & Grampian Divisions	(d) Northern Highlands (Scotland) Morar-Glenfinnan – Glen Dessary	(e) Shetland Isles	Age(Ma)
550			Early deformation & metam.	c. 1000-1050 Ma Grenvillian orogeny	>860 Ma metam. in Walls Metamorphic series	550
–	D1	D1 and D2 major nappe structures	c. 750 Ma Grampian STide & pegmatites	c. 800-750 Ma Morarian pegmatites		–
–				(Carn Chuinneag granite)	Migmatisation & metam. ? in Dalradian (?) rocks	–
–	D2 major folds Basic intrusions Gt. Metam.	D3 folding, peak metam. (Grampian age) in Barrovian & Buchan terranes (Ben Vuroch & Newer Gabbro intrusions)	Deformation & metam. (Grampian age?)			–
500	St, Ky metam.					500
–	D3 nappes, Sillim, Cord, Andal metam. Acid intrusions	(Granitic intrusions)				–
–						–
–	Mannin thrust	K/Ar mica cooling ages and uplift with D4 structures and Highland Border Downbend formation (460-440Ma)	Deformation & metam. (G. Kyllachy granite)	Deformation & metam. (Glen Dessary syenite)	Ophiolite nappe emplacement.	–
450						450
–	D4 Connemara antiform and steep zone		K/Ar mica cooling ages, low pressure contact metam about granitoid intrusions	Moine Thrust K/Ar mica cooling ages		–
–		Low pressure contact metam. about granitoid intrusions		Low pressure contact metam. about granitoid intrusions	K/Ar mica cooling ages, low pressure contact metam. about granitoid intrusions	–
–	Low pressure contact metam. about granitoid intrusions					–
400						400
–						–

D prefixes refer to deformation phases; metam. refers to metamorphism. Where listed events in 550-400 Ma. period are accompanied by a vertical line (continuous or dashed) then definite radiometric age evidence exists. A dashed vertical line indicates the major range of ages by K/Ar method on muscovite and biotite of metamorphism; such ages are interpreted as cooling ages following peak metamorphism (unless the metamorphism is very low grade), and they overlap with ages of igneous intrusions in columns (c), (d), (e). References giving sources of all data: van Breemen & Piasecki 1983; Dempster 1983, 1985; Dewey & Pankhurst 1970; Flinn et al. 1979; Harte et al. 1984; Leake et al. 1984; Pankhurst 1982; Piasecki & van Breemen 1983; Powell et al. 1983; Yardley 1980.

The Dalradian Supergroup

General features and time relations

The Dalradian Supergroup of Ireland, Scotland and probably the Shetland Isles shows widespread late Cambrian and early Ordovician tectonic and greenschist–amphibolite-facies metamorphic events. Since these events are well documented in the Grampian Highlands of Scotland they are commonly referred to as *Grampian*, and in this paper this term is used only to imply an age of events rather than broader connotations of tectonic regime or areal distribution (*cf.* Lambert & McKerrow 1976, Dewey & Shackleton 1984). The highest-grade metamorphic assemblages found in Dalradian rocks usually appear to be Grampian in age. The Grampian events are followed by retrograde metamorphism and a variety of tectonic events and major phases of igneous intrusion which take the history of the Dalradian belt through to the early Devonian.

A summary of the timing of these events is given in Table 1, columns (a), (b) and (e). The ages given in column (a) for Connemara are strongly constrained by the ages of about 500 Ma for a Connemara basic intrusion (Pidgeon 1969) and about 460 Ma for the Mannin Thrust (Leake *et al.* 1984). The basic intrusion is part of an ultrabasic–acid igneous suite which is dominantly intermediate in composition but became more acidic with time (Table 1). The data of Table 1 are slightly simplified because in detail the metamorphism is diachronous across Connemara (Yardley, personal communication).

N of Connemara in Ireland a syn-metamorphic ultrabasic–acid igneous suite is absent, and in these areas of Ireland only the D_1–D_2 events and the post-D_2 Barrovian metamorphic event of Table 1, column (a), clearly apply (Yardley 1980). Outside Connemara there are also few constraints on the age of the Barrovian metamorphism. However, the view that the Ox Mountains granodiorite of Mayo was intruded at about 480 Ma shortly after the regional metamorphic peak (Long & Max 1977, Long & Yardley 1979; *cf.* Andrews *et al.* 1978) has recently been supported by new radiometric data (Long *et al.* 1984), and this strengthens the evidence of a Grampian age for the peak Barrovian regional metamorphism well to the N of Connemara in Ireland. In these more northerly areas of Mayo and Donegal retrograde metamorphism may be widespread (Long *et al.* 1983), but its age other than pre-dating contact metamorphism around 420–390 Ma igneous intrusions is not well known.

The ages of metamorphic and other events in both Barrovian and Buchan (see below) meta-

morphic areas of the eastern and S central Scottish Highlands (Table 1, column (b)) are firmly based on ages from both igneous intrusives and metamorphic rocks. The ages presented refer particularly to the tectonometamorphic domains 1, 2 and 4 of the discussion in the next section. In the SW Scottish Highlands the age of major prograde metamorphism is not so clear, but the structural sequence is very similar to that of Table 1, column (b), and localized secondary metamorphism involving the formation of albite porphyroblast schists (Graham *et al.* 1983, Watkins 1983) is associated with structures of apparent D_4 age, like the Highland Border Downbend and the Tarbert Monoform, which give rise to Highland Border and Knapdale Steep Belts (Fig. 1).

Time relations in the remainder of the Dalradian of the Scottish mainland are often less clearly known, and will be further discussed as appropriate in later sections. In the Shetland Isles (Table 1, column (e)) there are many K–Ar data for the probable Dalradian–Moine? succession but relatively few radiometric ages which give definite ages of intrusion or metamorphism rather than cooling ages.

The metamorphic minerals above greenschist facies in most of the Dalradian across the British Isles include garnet and kyanite, and the metamorphism is therefore largely Barrovian in the broad sense (different facies series exist in detail (Harte & Hudson 1979)). An early blueschist is found at one locality in Ireland (Gray & Yardley 1979). The main departures from Barrovian metamorphic conditions are seen in the low-pressure (andalusite–cordierite) assemblages found in Connemara and Buchan (NE Scotland). The association of these low-pressure assemblages with basic intrusions in both Connemara and Buchan has been noted by several workers (e.g. Yardley 1980), and a volcanic-arc setting has been proposed for both areas (e.g. Yardley *et al.* 1982). However, the overall characters of the igneous rocks show some marked differences between the two areas, and there are some clear differences in their metamorphic and structural histories. Whilst the Buchan amphibolite-facies metamorphism appears to have a reasonably clear peak and, despite spatial variations in pressure, little evidence of temporal variations in pressure (Harte & Hudson 1979), the Connemara metamorphism involves a marked temporal evolution from Barrovian amphibolite facies at pressures of at least 7 kbar (Yardley *et al.* 1980) through to the crystallization of andalusite-bearing migmatites at about 2.5 kbar (Barber & Yardley 1985). Both nappe formation and uplift accompany this metamorphism in Connemara

(Yardley 1980). In NE Scotland, Ashcroft *et al.* (1984) argue for a relatively unthickened crustal block affected by sub-vertical shear zones. Kneller (1985) associates the Buchan metamorphism with lithospheric stretching rather than compression.

It is conspicuous that throughout much of the Dalradian and Moine zone of the British Isles the period 460–440 Ma was one of both considerable and diverse activity. Leake *et al.* (1984) record the extensive occurrence of probably SSE-directed thrusting, as particularly demonstrated by the Mannin Thrust at about 460 Ma. In the Buchan area upright shear zones of possibly similar age are described by Ashcroft *et al.* (1984). In the Southern Scottish Highlands Harte *et al.* (1984) suggest 460–440 Ma as the age of formation of the major Highland Border Downbend and that this structure involved major uplift. At the same time, major regional deformation and metamorphism affected the Moine rocks (see below), whilst in Shetland this appears to be the approximate time of major ophiolite emplacement (Flinn *et al.* 1979).

Variations in peak metamorphic conditions in the Scottish Dalradian

In recent years a considerable amount of information concerning temperature–pressure conditions of metamorphism over much of the Scottish Dalradian has been obtained (see in particular the thematic set of papers introduced by Graham & Harte (1985)). A synopsis of the more recent pressure estimates is superimposed on the map of Scottish metamorphic zones and facies in Fig. 1. Apart from its historical importance (Atherton 1977) the Dalradian is a particularly interesting terrane in which to seek evidence of the causes of metamorphism. Not only its metamorphic zones but also its stratigraphy and structure are well defined. Furthermore, it consists predominantly of metasediments which generally appear to have been affected by only one major regional metamorphic event; thus it should be comparatively free from the problems associated with the sluggish kinetics of transformation of already crystalline rocks and poly-orogenic metamorphism.

The zonal pattern of Fig. 1 largely reflects the temperature variation at peak metamorphism (Grampian age for the Dalradian) with most temperatures falling between 400 and 700 °C (somewhat higher in some southeastern parts of the Dalradian sillimanite zone according to Baker (1985)). The zonal pattern suggests much of the broad simplicity that led Kennedy (1948) to postulate a thermal anticline model, but a more complex situation is suggested by evidence both of steep and abrupt thermal gradients (e.g. to the S and SW of the sillimanite zone in the Eastern Highlands (Harte & Hudson 1979, Baker & Droop 1983, Baker 1985, McLellan 1985)) and of possibly inverted zones (Chinner 1978, Watkins 1983). Similarly these data strongly indicate the operation of more factors than a simple depth-controlled model of metamorphism, whether it be that of Kennedy (1948) or the one-dimensional quantitative pressure–temperature–time path models of England & Richardson (1977) or England & Thompson (1984).

Examination of the pressure estimates (numbers in kilobars in Fig. 1) in comparison with the temperature ranges implied by the metamorphic zones or facies in Fig. 1 further shows the absence of a simple depth control of the zone distribution. There is manifestly an absence of correlation of temperature with pressure (depth). The extreme SW and SE areas show this very clearly: in the SW widespread relatively low-grade assemblages are associated with pressures of 8–10 kbar, whereas in the SE relatively high-grade rocks and strong temperature gradients occur at pressures of 4–7 kbar. In the Central Highlands N of the Tummel Steep Belt (Fig. 1) there is clear evidence of a comparatively late (post-D_3) phase of peak metamorphism in which higher-pressure assemblages replace lower-pressure assemblages (Harte *et al.* 1985, Dempster & Harte 1986). Pseudomorphs of kyanite after andalusite in Glen Clunie and Portsoy (the andalusite to kyanite localities of Fig. 1) similarly indicate increasing pressure during metamorphism and thereby depart from the thickening–heating–erosion controls of the common England–Thompson pressure–temperature–time paths. These features argue for the strong influence of tectonic controls on a scale much smaller than that of the area occupied by the whole Dalradian outcrop; this has been indicated by Harte & Hudson (1979, p. 333) and has already been shown by Dempster's (1984, 1985) combined radiometric and metamorphic work.

By considering the whole of the Scottish Dalradian (Fig. 1) and the relations between pressure, temperature and time which are known for different areas, the following major tectono-metamorphic domains or provinces can be distinguished.

1 A SE province, including Barrow's type area, in which very strong temperature gradients occur adjacent to the Highland Boundary Fault (Harte & Hudson 1979) and from which there is some evidence of a distinctive uplift history (Dempster 1984, 1985): this province is E of the Portsoy–

Duchray Hill lineament in Fig. 1 and extends from the southern part of the sillimanite zone to the Highland Boundary Fault.

2 A NE province containing the area of Buchan (low-pressure amphibolite-facies) metamorphism (Fig. 1) which partly corresponds to the area Ashcroft *et al.* (1984) have argued to be a 'distinctive crustal segment'.

3 A SW domain in which the grade is generally of greenschist facies, although it includes a 'spine' of garnet-grade rocks whose distribution may also be tectonically controlled (Borradaile 1976, Atherton 1977, Chinner 1978). On present information the obvious eastern boundary to this southwestern domain is the Cruachan lineament (Fig. 1), where a major change in gravity approximately coincides not only with the limit of the late granite intrusions and the boundary of the Moine outcrops (Hall 1985), but also with a marked deflection of the isograds (Fig. 1) and the northeastern limit of very extensive basic extrusives and intrusives in the sedimentary pile (Graham & Harte 1985, Graham, in press).

4 A southern Central Highland area S of the Tummel Steep Belt and respectively W and E of domains 1 and 3 and dominated by the Perthshire Flat Belt of the Tay Nappe and the Highland Border Steep Belt (these are separated by the Highland Border Downbend structure of Fig. 1 and may form subdivisions of this domain).

5 The area in the Central Highlands N of the Tummel Steep Belt (Fig. 1) showing increasing pressure during peak metamorphism (Dempster & Harte 1986).

6 The rest of the Dalradian region, and adjacent Moine or Grampian Group rocks, N of areas 3 and 5 and W of area 2: there is insufficient information to be sure that this should be treated as a single domain and it merely constitutes the remainder after domains 1–5 have been separated.

The boundaries to the above domains usually appear to be tectonic and stratigraphic as well as metamorphic, although their origin is often not clear and major features such as the Tay Nappe (D_1) may cross the boundaries. The Cruachan lineament may be a potentially long-standing boundary transverse to the Caledonoid trend whose influence may extend back into the Dalradian sedimentary and volcanic history. The Portsoy–Duchray Hill lineament (Fig. 1), although less clear cut and perhaps corresponding to a series of lineaments or 'zones of discontinuities', also appears to have had a long-standing influence on Dalradian development. As drawn on Fig. 1 its southern part marks a zone of fault movements (Barrow 1893, Barrow *et al.* 1912)

and uncertain stratigraphic correlation (Read 1928), whereas its northern part follows the line of major shear zones delineated by Ashcroft *et al.* (1984). Serpentine bodies which are both pre- and post-metamorphic in origin (D. J. Fettes, personal communication 1984) also occur along and adjacent to this zone. In the S the general NE–SW orientation of Barrow's metamorphic zones in the southeastern province is interrupted along the trend of the Portsoy–Duchray lineament (Chinner 1980, Baker & Droop 1983, Baker 1985, McLellan 1985). Further N the 'lineament' partly corresponds to the boundary of the low-pressure (andalusite-bearing) Buchan metamorphism, and can readily be envisaged as extending westwards from the restricted zone marked on Fig. 1 to include the whole of this boundary and the locations where kyanite is found replacing andalusite.

The Cruachan and Portsoy–Duchray Hill lineaments therefore appear to have influenced pre-metamorphic sedimentation and tectonics as well as the metamorphic and subsequent orogenic history. (Subsequent to the writing of this paper further aspects of the definition and importance of such lineaments have been presented in a paper by Fettes *et al.* (1986).) The features suggest a relation to some fundamental basement structures which have been periodically activated but also frequently transgressed (as in the formation of the Tay Nappe and gross aspects of stratigraphy). It is to be emphasized that the operation of such basement tectonic controls on the metamorphism takes place in several ways. Thus they may not only cause local variations in uplift rate and timing whilst metamorphism is in progress, but their influence on pre-metamorphic sedimentation, magmatism and structure may also create variations in the thickness, conductivity and heat production of the pre-metamorphic pile. These variations will then generate a different pressure–temperature–time path (England & Thompson 1984) for each of the basement-controlled domains (Harte & Dempster, in press).

Moine rocks of the Scottish Highlands

The traditional distinction of the Moine and Dalradian successions in the Scottish Highlands was based on the change from the diverse lithostratigraphic units of the Dalradian to dominantly psammitic rocks, as occurs essentially along the line DB in Fig. 1. More recent work (Harris *et al.* 1978, Treagus & King 1978) has shown that the psammitic rocks just N of this line are often in continuity with the Dalradian succession. Accordingly these psammites have been assigned to a *Grampian Group* lithostratigraphic unit below the Appin Group within the Dalradian Supergroup (Harris *et al.* 1978). Other work S of the Great Glen Fault (summarized by Piasecki & van Breemen 1983) has led to the separation of an older Moine unit (the Central Highland Division shown on Fig. 1) from a younger Moine unit (Grampian Division) across a tectonic boundary (the Grampian Slide). No discontinuity separating the Grampian Division from the aforementioned Grampian Group has been recognized, and they thus appear to be part of the same lithostratigraphic unit. In the present instance we shall use the word Moine in its old connotation to include the Central Highland and Grampian Divisions as well as the widely recognized Moinian rocks N of the Great Glen. Some rocks of Moinian affinities have been recognized in Ireland and Shetland, but their lower Palaeozoic metamorphic histories generally have not been separated from those of their accompanying Dalradian as summarized in the previous section.

Moine rocks N of the Great Glen Fault

Abundant radiometric age determinations have been made on rocks from the more southerly part of this region of Moine rocks, and these data are summarized in Table 1, column (d). In this area three tectonostratigraphic units are recognized: going from W to E these are the Morar, Glenfinnan and Loch Eil Divisions. The Morar and Glenfinnan Divisions are separated from each other by the Sgurr Beag Slide (Fig. 1), and the Loch Eil Division for the most part lies E of the Loch Quoich Line (Fig. 1). Table 1, column (d), shows a multiple orogenic history spanning about 600 Ma, and it should be emphasized that the conditions of metamorphism shown in Fig. 1 for N of the Great Glen represent a composite of Precambrian and Caledonian metamorphisms. Some investigators (Winchester 1974) have made distinctions between earlier and later events within the same area, and in the SW it appears that roughly similar grade and zones were established in both Precambrian and Caledonian metamorphisms (Powell *et al.* 1981). Generally speaking the age of particular metamorphic assemblages in the Moine outcrop is often uncertain (Fettes 1983).

The age of the Grenville metamorphism (see also Powell *et al.* 1988) in Table 1 comes from whole-rock Rb–Sr data (Brook *et al.* 1976, Brewer *et al.* 1979), of which that on the Ardgour Granitic Gneiss (within the Glenfinnan Division) is

probably most definitive. The age of the Morarian pegmatites is based largely on the work of Powell *et al.* (1983) and van Breemen *et al.* (1974) and references cited therein.

The Morarian pegmatites have usually been assumed to mark a major tectothermal event (van Breemen *et al.* 1974, Lambert *et al.* 1979, Piasecki *et al.* 1981), but Powell *et al.* (1983) question this identification of a 'Morarian orogeny' and attribute Precambrian metamorphism only to the Grenvillian event. Piasecki *et al.* (1981) and Piasecki & van Breemen (1979, 1983) have suggested that the Morar and Loch Eil Divisions may be younger than Grenvillian in age with the Sgurr Beag Slide and Loch Quoich Line being analogous to the Grampian Slide approximately 750 Ma ago in the Moine S of the Great Glen (see below). Lambert *et al.* (1979) also suggest that the Loch Eil Division was deposited unconformably on metamorphosed Glenfinnan Division. Aspects of these suggestions conflict with the data of Brewer *et al.* (1979) and Powell *et al.* (1983) on the Morar Division which suggest a Grenvillian age. The recent work of Roberts & Harris (1983) and Roberts *et al.* (1984) argues strongly that the Loch Quoich Line represents a limit of Caledonian tectonic reworking and that there is no evidence of a discontinuity between the Glenfinnan and Loch Eil Divisions whose contact crosses the Line locally. Furthermore, granitic gneisses of supposed Grenvillian age occur in the Loch Eil Division as well as the Glenfinnan Division (Barr *et al.* 1985). Thus Roberts *et al.* (1984) and Powell *et al.* (1981, 1983) emphasize the Caledonian nature of the Sgurr Beag Slide and Loch Quoich Line boundaries, whilst Lambert *et al.* (1979) and Piasecki & van Breemen (1983) emphasize a Precambrian origin.

The 460–430 Ma age of major Caledonian deformation and metamorphism in Table 1, column (d), is based primarily on the structural investigations of Roberts *et al.* (1984) in the Glen Dessary area (Fig. 1) in conjunction with radiometric age determinations on the Glen Dessary syenite and associated pegmatites by van Breemen *et al.* (1979). This age is one of major vertical structural reworking in the Glen Dessary area and may coincide with the deformation and metamorphism associated with formation of the Sgurr Beag slide (Roberts *et al.* 1984, Powell *et al.* 1981, 1983; *cf.* discussion in Baird *et al.* 1985). Possibly coincident Rb–Sr whole-rock ages are given by Brewer *et al.* (1979). Ages of about 450–440 Ma for Caledonian pegmatites and migmatites in the Glenfinnan area (van Breemen *et al.* 1974, 1979) also fall in the same bracket. Thus there is overall strong evidence for a 460–430 Ma period of major Caledonian metamorphism and deformation. The development of the Moine Thrust zone at 430–425 Ma occurs at the close of this period and is believed to have generated widespread mica K–Ar cooling ages with similar ages to the thrusting (Johnson *et al.* 1985).

Radiometric data for metamorphism before 460 Ma and subsequent to the Morarian pegmatite event is haphazard, and in view of the evidence of previous Precambrian metamorphism must be considered extremely suspect. Caledonian (in the broad sense of lower Palaeozoic) metamorphism N of the Great Glen therefore seems to be essentially confined to the 460–430 Ma event and the earlier Grampian metamorphism at about 500 Ma seen in the Dalradian appears to be absent. At the same time it must be noted that the polymetamorphic nature of these Moine rocks may mean that a given metamorphic event is restricted in its effects for kinetic reasons and is hard to detect.

Moine rocks S of the Great Glen Fault

Age relationships in the Moine of the Central Highlands of Scotland are summarized in Table 1, column (c). An important set of dates are those of about 750 Ma obtained from pegmatites associated with a slide contact (the Grampian Slide) which commonly replaces a presumed unconformable contact between Central Highland Division basement (see earlier and Fig. 1) and Grampian Division cover (van Breemen & Piasecki 1983, Piasecki & van Breemen 1983). The age of these pegmatites is clearly similar to that of the Morarian pegmatites (Table 1, column (d)) N of the Great Glen, and Piasecki & van Breemen (1983) associate them with an important tectonothermal event, although this is doubted by Soper & Anderton (1984). Piasecki & van Breemen (1983) further suggest close similarities S and N of the Great Glen, with the Central Highland Division being broadly correlated with the Glenfinnan Division and of presumed Grenvillian age. Precise radiometric evidence for Grenvillian age metamorphism in the Central Highlands is lacking, but the existence of a Precambrian basement is supported by Harris *et al.* (1983) even though they do not support the views of Piasecki & van Breemen (1983, pp. 123, 132) over similarities between the Grampian Slide (S of the Great Glen) and the Sgurr Beag Slide and Loch Quoich Line (N of the Great Glen) (see also discussion in previous subsection).

A strongly emphasized date in the Central Highland calendar (Table 1, column (c)) is that of about 440 Ma for the phase of metamorphism and deformation closely associated with the intrusion time of the Glen Kyllachy (Fig. 1) granite and pegmatites (van Breemen & Piasecki 1983). Here again there is a marked similarity to the age of Caledonian metamorphism and deformation N of the Great Glen (Table 1, column (d)). This similarity is strengthened by the abundance of K–Ar mica ages (presumed to relate to cooling following peak metamorphism conditions) in the 430–400 Ma bracket from both sides of the Great Glen (Dewey & Pankhurst 1970) which are relatively young compared with the Scottish Dalradian K–Ar ages of 470–430 Ma (Table 1).

A key question in the similarity of orogenic events N and S of the Great Glen therefore becomes that of the distribution of the Grampian (upper Cambrian and lower Ordovician) tectonothermal events which are so important in the Dalradian. We have noted the absence of clear evidence for these events in the Moine N of the Great Glen. To the S of the Great Glen there is also no specific dated evidence from the Moine outcrop area, but Grampian tectonometamorphic events are advocated for both metamorphic and most particularly structural reasons. Van Breemen & Piasecki (1983, p. 49) note that metamorphism associated with the event at about 750 Ma is restricted and emphasize the regional importance of Grampian metamorphism (about 500 Ma), although Piasecki & Temperley (personal communication 1985) now believe that the importance of Grampian metamorphic and structural events may have been over-emphasized. Thomas (1979, 1980) has documented the involvement of Grampian Division rocks in the Grampian tectonic events and has interpreted a steep belt in the Grampian Division as a 'root zone' of early Grampian nappe structures affecting the whole Dalradian succession. Piasecki & van Breemen (1983, p. 124) trace this steep belt over a considerable distance in both Grampian and Central Highland Division rocks. It seems possible that some of the steepness of this belt results from fairly late Caledonoid deformation (Bradbury 1985), but this does not negate the presence of early Grampian age structures (Thomas 1979, 1980).

Although there is evident uncertainty, available information suggests that S of the Great Glen both Moine and Dalradian rocks have been affected by both Grampian (about 500 Ma) and later Caledonoid (460–440 Ma) tectonothermal events (Table 1). Whilst the later metamorphic events are largely markedly retrograde and associated with uplift in the main Dalradian outcrop (Harte *et al.* 1984, Dempster 1985), they appear to be of somewhat higher grade in the Central Highland Moine (van Breemen & Piasecki 1983). Van Breemen & Piasecki (1983, pp. 57–9) link this change with a 'tectonic diachronism' across the Central Highland block between the Great Glen and Highland Boundary Faults and regard uplift events in the S as distinctly different from tectonothermal events in the N. Dempster (1985) points out that the metamorphic differences between these events may be simply related to depth and that episodes of rapid uplift may create provinces showing quite sharp transitions in metamorphic conditions for a given time period.

Clearly Table 1 (see also discussion in the section on the Dalradian Supergroup) provides evidence of a wide variety of tectonic and metamorphic activity throughout the whole Irish–Scottish Dalradian and Moine outcrop at 460–440 Ma. From the viewpoint of the orthotectonic British Isles it is this period around 450 Ma for which the name Caledonian orogeny might be used in the restricted sense.

Ordovician movement on the Great Glen Fault

From the viewpoint of the distribution of major events, a most striking feature is the absence of evidence of Grampian (about 500 Ma) events in the Moine rocks N of the Great Glen (given their presence throughout both Dalradian and Moine rocks in the block between the Great Glen Fault and the Highland Boundary Fault). Published information suggests that this change occurs sharply at the Great Glen Fault. Thus in the sense of Williams & Hatcher (1983) the Northern Highlands (N of the Great Glen) and the Central Highlands (S of the Great Glen and extending to the Highland Boundary Fault) may represent different terranes which were divided by transcurrent motion on the Great Glen Fault and only became closely united after the Grampian orogenic events. Other features distinguish these two terranes.

1   The absence of definite Dalradian rocks N of the Great Glen Fault.
2   The absence of definite Lewisian rocks S of the Great Glen Fault. Certainly there are *possible* Lewisian and Dalradian rocks S and N respectively of the Great Glen (Smith & Watson 1983), but the correlations are tenuous (*cf.* Rock *et al.* 1984).
3   The uncertainty of correlations of the Moine rocks S and N of the Great Glen.
4   The development of a stable shelf Cambro-Ordovician sequence in the NW Highlands at the same time as the Dalradian of the Central Southern Highlands was following a tectonically-active sedimentological, volcanic and metamorphic history.
5   The distinct step in the height of the basement in the LISPB seismic profile at the Great Glen Fault (Bamford *et al.* 1977) and the fact that seismic correlations of this basement are only broad petrological indicators and not precise identifications of the same rock unit.

This suggestion of separate 'terranes' N and S of the Great Glen implies that they were brought into close proximity by major strike-slip motion along the Great Glen Fault between the Grampian (about 500 Ma) and late Caledonian (about 450 Ma) tectonothermal events. More limited transcurrent motion may well have continued into the Devonian period in accordance with features recorded by Johnson & Frost (1977) so that movement was substantially complete before the end of the Devonian (Smith & Watson 1983, Briden *et al.* 1984 and references cited therein). Unfortunately there are insufficient palaeomagnetic data (Briden *et al.* 1984) for comparison of the terranes N and S of the Great Glen in the period preceding about 430 Ma.

Given that the Moines of the Northern Highlands contain definite evidence of the Grenvillian orogeny and have a spatially associated Lewisian basement and platform carbonate (Cambro-Ordovician) succession, it is clear that the Northern Moines relate closely to the NW Foreland of the Caledonide orogen. It is the Dalradian block between the Great Glen and Highland Boundary Faults, which appears as the more suspect or 'exotic' terrane, whose initial relative position is most obscure. This postulate is reinforced by the lack of any clear stratigraphic correlatives in either America or Scandinavia of the varied and distinctive Dalradian Supergroup rocks (particularly the Appin and Argyll Groups) which are so easily correlated across the whole of Ireland and Scotland. It is also supported by the lack of geological connections between the Dalradian and Midland Valley blocks of Scotland (Bluck 1984). It is therefore speculated that the Dalradian Supergroup occurs in a relatively small block or terrane which had a restricted development in a major zone dominated by large strike-slip movements.

ACKNOWLEDGMENTS: I wish to thank many people for helpful discussions and am particularly indebted to D. Barr, T. J. Dempster, D. J. Fettes, C. M. Graham, M. R. W. Johnson, C. B. Long, J. R. Mendum, D. R. Watts and B. W. D. Yardley. Patricia Stewart is thanked for typing the manuscript and Diane Baty for drafting the figure.

References

ANDREWS, J. R., PHILLIPS, W. E. A. & MOLLOY, M. A. 1978. The metamorphic rocks of part of the north central Ox Mountains inlier of counties Sligo and Mayo. *Journal of Earth Sciences, Royal Dublin Society*, **1**, 173–94.

ASHCROFT, W. A., KNELLER, B. C., LESLIE, A. G. & MUNRO, M. 1984. Major shear zones and autochthonous Dalradian in the NE Scottish Caledonides. *Nature, London*, **310**, 760–2.

ATHERTON, M. P. 1977. The metamorphism of the Dalradian rocks of Scotland. *Scottish Journal of Geology*, **13**, 331–70.

BAIRD, A. W., ROBERTS, A. M., SMITH, D. I., HARRIS, A. L., HOLDSWORTH, R. E., STRACHAN, R. A., BARR, D. & TOBISCH, O. T. 1985. Discussion of the structural setting and tectonic significance of the Glen Dessary Syenite, Inverness-shire. *Journal of the Geological Society, London*, **142**, 713–18.

BAKER, A. J. 1985. Pressures and temperatures of metamorphism in the eastern Dalradian. *Journal of the Geological Society, London*, **142**, 137–48.

—— & DROOP, G. T. R. 1983. Grampian metamorphic conditions deduced from mafic granulites and sillimanite–K-feldspar gneisses in the Dalradian of Glen Muick, Scotland. *Journal of the Geological Society, London*, **140**, 489–98.

BAMFORD, D., NUNN, K., PRODEHL, C. & JACOB, B. 1977. LISPB—III. Upper crustal structure of northern Britain. *Journal of the Geological Society, London*, **133**, 481–8.

BARBER, J. P. & YARDLEY, B. W. D. 1985. Conditions of high grade metamorphism in the Dalradian of Connemara, Ireland. *Journal of the Geological Society, London*, **142**, 87–96.

BARR, D., ROBERTS, A. M., HIGHTON, A. J., PARSON, L. M. & HARRIS, A. L. 1985. Structural setting and geochronological significance of the West Highland Granitic Gneiss, a deformed early granite with Proterozoic, Moine rocks of NW Scotland. *Journal of the Geological Society, London*, **142**, 643–61.

BARROW, G. 1893. On an intrusion of muscovite–biotite gneiss in the southeast Highlands of Scotland and its accompanying metamorphism. *Quarterly Journal of the Geological Society of London*, **19**, 33–58.

——, CUNNINGHAM CRAIG, H. H. & HINXMAN, L. W. 1912. The geology of Braemar, Ballater and Glen Clova. *Memoirs of the Geological Survey of Scotland*, **65**.

BLUCK, B. J. 1984. Pre-Carboniferous history of the Midland Valley of Scotland. *Transactions of the Royal Society of Edinburgh, Earth Sciences*, **75**, 275–95.

BOOTH, J. E. 1984. Structural, stratigraphic and metamorphic studies in the SE Scottish Dalradian Highlands. *Ph.D. Thesis* (unpublished), University of Edinburgh.

BORRADAILE, G. J. 1976. Thermal anisotropy—a factor contributing to the distribution of Caledonian metamorphic zones in the southwest Scottish Highlands. *Geologie en Mijnbouw*, **42**, 121–42.

BRADBURY, H. J. 1985. The Caledonian metamorphic core: an Alpine model. *Journal of the Geological Society, London*, **142**, 129–36.

VAN BREEMEN, O. & PIASECKI, M. A. J. 1983. The Glen Kyllachy Granite and its bearing on the nature of the Caledonian orogeny in Scotland. *Journal of the Geological Society, London*, **140**, 47–62.

——, PIDGEON, R. T. & JOHNSON, M. R. W. 1974. Precambrian and Palaeozoic pegmatites in the Moines of northern Scotland. *Journal of the Geological Society, London*, **130**, 493–507.

——, AFTALION, M., PANKHURST, R. J. & RICHARDSON, S. W. 1979. Age of the Glen Dessary Syenite, Inverness-shire: diachronous Palaeozoic metamorphism across the Great Glen. *Scottish Journal of Geology*, **15**, 49–62.

BREWER, M. S., BROOK, M. & POWELL, D. 1979. Dating of the tectono-metamorphic history of the southwestern Moine, Scotland. *In:* HARRIS, A. L., HOLLAND, C. J. & LEAKE, B. E. (eds) *The Caledonides of the British Isles Reviewed. Special Publication of the Geological Society of London No. 8*, pp. 129–37.

BRIDEN, J. C., TURNELL, H. B. & WATTS, D. R. 1984. British palaeomagnetism, Iapetus Ocean, and the Great Glen fault. *Geology*, **12**, 428–31.

BROOK, M., BREWER, M. S. & POWELL, D. 1976. Grenville ages for rocks in the Moine of northwestern Scotland. *Nature, London*, **260**, 515–17.

CHINNER, G. A. 1978. Metamorphic zones and fault displacement in the Scottish Highlands. *Geological Magazine*, **115**, 37–45.

—— 1980. Kyanite isograds of Grampian metamorphism. *Journal of the Geological Society, London*, **137**, 35–9.

DEMPSTER, T. J. 1983. Studies of orogenic evolution in the Scottish Dalradian. *Ph.D. Thesis* (unpublished), University of Edinburgh.

—— 1984. Localised uplift in the Scottish Dalradian. *Nature, London*, **307**, 156–9.

—— 1985. Uplift patterns and orogenic evolution in the Scottish Dalradian. *Journal of the Geological Society, London*, **142**, 111–28.

—— & HARTE, B. 1986. Polymetamorphism in the Dalradian of the Central Scottish Highlands. *Geological Magazine*, **123**, 95–104.

DEWEY, J. F. & PANKHURST, R. J. 1970. The evolution of the Scottish Caledonides in relation to their radiometric age pattern. *Transactions of the Royal Society of Edinburgh*, **68**, 361–89.

—— & SHACKLETON, R. M. 1984. A model for the evolution of the Grampian tract in the early Caledonides and Appalachians. *Nature, London*, **312**, 115–21.

DROOP, G. T. R. & CHARNLEY, N. 1985. Comparative geobarometry of pelitic hornfelses associated with the newer gabbros: a preliminary study. *Journal of the Geological Society, London*, **142**, 53–62.

ENGLAND, P. C. & RICHARDSON, S. W. 1977. The influence of erosion upon the mineral facies of rocks from different metamorphic environments. *Journal of the Geological Society, London*, **134**, 201–13.

—— & THOMPSON, A. B. 1984. Pressure–temperature–time paths of regional metamorphism. I. Heat transfer during the evolution of regions of thickened continental crust. *Journal of Petrology*, **25**, 894–928.

FETTES, D. J. 1983. Metamorphism in the British Caledonides. *In:* SCHENK, P. E. (ed.) *Regional Trends in the Geology of the Appalachian–Caledonian–Hercynian–Mauritanide Orogen*, pp. 205–19, Reidel, Dordrecht.

——, GRAHAM, C. M., HARTE, B. & PLANT, J. A. 1986. Lineaments and basement domains: an alternative view of Dalradian evolution. *Journal of the Geological Society, London*, **143**, 453–64.

——, LONG, C. B., MAX, M. D. & YARDLEY, B. W. D. 1984. *Grade and Time of Metamorphism in the Caledonide Orogen of Britain and Ireland. Geological Society of London Memoir No. 9*, Plate 3.

FLINN, D., FRANK, P. L., BROOK, M. & PRINGLE I. R. 1979. Basement-cover relations in Shetland. *In:* HARRIS, A. L., HOLLAND, C. H. & LEAKE, B. E. (eds) *The Caledonides of the British Isles Reviewed. Special Publication of the Geological Society of London No. 8*, pp. 109–15, Blackwell Scientific Publications, Oxford.

GRAHAM, C. M. The role of the Cruachan lineament during Dalradian evolution. *Scottish Journal of Geology*, in press.

—— & HARTE, B. 1985. Conditions of Dalradian metamorphism. *Journal of the Geological Society, London*, **142**, 1–3.

——, GREIG, K. M., SHEPPARD, S. M. F. & TURI, B. 1983. Genesis and mobility of the H_2O–CO_2 fluid phase during regional greenschist and epidote amphibolite facies metamorphism: a petrological and stable isotope study in the Scottish Dalradian. *Journal of the Geological Society, London*, **140**, 577–99.

GRAY, J. R. & YARDLEY, B. W. D. 1979. A Caledonian blueschist from the Irish Dalradian. *Nature, London*, **278**, 736–7.

HALL, J. 1985. Geophysical constraints on crustal structure in the Dalradian region of Scotland. *Journal of the Geological Society, London*, **142**, 149–56.

HARRIS, A. L. & PITCHER, W. S. 1975. The Dalradian Supergroup. *In:* HARRIS, A. L. *et al.* (eds) *A Correlation of the Precambrian Rocks in the British Isles. Special Report of the Geological Society of London No. 6*, pp. 52–75.

——, BALDWIN, C. T., BRADBURY, H. J., JOHNSON, H. D. & SMITH, R. A. 1978. Ensialic basin sedimentation: the Dalradian Supergroup. *In:* BOWES, D. R. & LEAKE, B. E. (eds) *Crustal Evolution in Northwestern Britain and Adjacent Regions. Geological Journal Special Issue*, **10**, 115–38.

——, HIGHTON, A. M., ROBERTS, A. M. & STOKER, M. S. 1983. Discussion on the nature of the Glen Kyllachy Granite and its bearing on the nature of the Caledonian orogeny in Scotland. *Journal of the Geological Society, London*, **140**, 961–3.

HARTE, B. & DEMPSTER, T. J. Regional metamorphic zones: tectonic controls. *Philosophical Transactions of the Royal Society, Series A*, in press.

—— & HUDSON, N. F. C. 1979. Pelite facies series and the temperatures and pressures of Dalradian metamorphism. *In:* HARRIS, A. L., HOLLAND, C. H. & LEAKE, B. E. (eds) *The Caledonides of the British Isles Reviewed. Special Publication of the Geological Society of London No. 8*, pp. 323–37.

——, BOOTH, J. E., DEMPSTER, T. J., FETTES, D. J., MENDUM, J. R. & WATTS, D. 1984. Aspects of the post-depositional evolution of Dalradian and Highland Border Complex rocks in the Southern Highlands of Scotland. *Transactions of the Royal Society of Edinburgh, Earth Sciences*, **75**, 151–63.

——, DEMPSTER, T. J. & BOOTH, J. E. 1985. *P–T* estimates and mineral facies variations in space and time in the central and SE Scottish Highlands. *Journal of the Geological Society, London*, **142**, 4 (abstract).

HUDSON, N. F. C. 1985. Conditions of Dalradian metamorphism in the Buchan area. *Journal of the Geological Society, London*, **142**, 63–76.

JOHNSON, M. R. W. 1983a. Torridonian–Moine. *In:* Craig, G. Y. (ed.) *The Geology of Scotland*, pp. 49–75, Scottish Academic Press, Edinburgh.

—— 1983b. Dalradian. *In:* CRAIG, G. Y. (ed.) *The Geology of Scotland*, pp. 77–104, Scottish Academic Press, Edinburgh.

—— & FROST, R. T. C. 1977. Fault and lineament patterns in the southern Highlands of Scotland. *Geologie en Mijnbouw*, **56**, 287–94.

——, KELLEY, S. P., OLIVER, G. J. H. & WINTER, D. A. 1985. Thermal effects and timing of thrusting in the Moine Thrust zone. *Journal of the Geological Society, London*, **142**, 863–73.

——, SANDERSON, D. J. & SOPER, N. J. 1979. Deformation in the Caledonides of England, Ireland and Scotland. *In:* HARRIS, A. L., HOLLAND, C. H. & LEAKE, B. E. (eds) *The Caledonides of the British Isles Reviewed. Special Publication of the Geological Society of London No. 8*, pp. 165–86.

JOHNSTONE, G. S. 1975. The Moine succession. *In:* HARRIS, A. L. *et al.* (eds) *A Correlation of the Precambrian rocks of the British Isles. Special Report of the Geological Society of London No. 6*, pp. 30–42.

KENNEDY, W. Q. 1948. On the significance of thermal structure in the Scottish Highlands. *Geological Magazine*, **85**, 229–34.

KNELLER, B. C. 1985. Dalradian basin evolution and metamorphism. *Journal of the Geological Society, London*, **142**, 4 (abstract).

LAMBERT, R. ST. J. & MCKERROW, W. S. 1976. The Grampian orogeny. *Scottish Journal of Geology*, **12**, 271–92.

——, WINCHESTER, J. A. & HOLLAND, J. G. 1979. Time, space and intensity relationships of the Precambrian and Lower Palaeozoic metamorphisms of the Scottish Highlands. *In:* HARRIS, A. L., HOLLAND, C. H. & LEAKE, B. E. (eds) *The Caledonides of the British Isles Reviewed. Special Publication of the Geological Society of London No. 8*, pp. 363–7.

LEAKE, B. E., TANNER, P. W. G., MacINTYRE, R. M. & ELIAS, E. 1984. The tectonic position of the Dalradian rocks of Connemara: the Connemara nappe and the Midland Valley of Scotland. *Transactions of the Royal Society of Edinburgh, Earth Sciences*, **75**, 165–71.

LONG, C. B. & MAX, M. D. 1977. Metamorphic rocks in the SW Ox Mountains inlier, Ireland; their structural compartmentation and place in the Caledonian orogen. *Journal of the Geological Society, London*, **133**, 413–32.

—— & YARDLEY, B. W. D. 1979. The distribution of pre-Caledonian basement in the Ox Mountains inlier, Ireland. *In:* HARRIS, A. L., HOLLAND, C. H. & LEAKE, B. E. (eds) *The Caledonides of the British Isles Reviewed, Special Publication of the Geological Society of London No. 8*, pp. 153–6.

——, MAX, M. D. & O'CONNOR, P. J. 1984. Age of the Lough Talt and Easky adamellites in the central Ox Mountains, NW Ireland, and their structural significance. *Geological Journal*, **19**, 389–97.

——, —— & YARDLEY, B. W. D. 1983. Compilation Caledonian metamorphic map of Ireland. *In:* SCHENK, P. E. (ed.) *Regional Trends in the Geology of the Appalachian–Caledonian–Hercynian–Mauritanide Orogen*, pp. 221–33, Reidel, Dordrecht.

MCLELLAN, E. L. 1985. Metamorphic reactions in the kyanite and sillimanite zones of the Barrovian type area. *Journal of Petrology*, **26**, 789–818.

MOLES, N. R. 1985. Metamorphic conditions and uplift history in central Perthshire: evidence from mineral equilibria in the Foss celsian–barite–sulphide deposit. *Journal of the Geological Society, London*, **142**, 39–52.

PANKHURST, R. J. 1982. Geochronological tables from British igneous rocks. *In:* SUTHERLAND, D. S. (ed.) *Igneous Rocks of the British Isles*, pp. 575–81. Wiley, London.

PIASECKI, M. A. J. & VAN BREEMEN, O. 1979. The 'Central Highland Granulites': cover-basement tectonics in the Moine. *In:* HARRIS, A. L., HOLLAND, C. H. & LEAKE, B. E. (eds) *The Caledonides of the British Isles Reviewed. Special Publication of the Geological Society of London No. 8*, pp. 139–44.

—— & —— 1983. Field and isotopic evidence for a c. 750 Ma tectonothermal event in Moine rocks in the Central Highland Region of the Scottish Caledonides. *Transactions of the Royal Society of Edinburgh, Earth Sciences*, **75**, 151–63.

——, —— & WRIGHT, A. E. 1981. The Late Precambrian Geology of Scotland, England and Wales. *In:* KERR, J. W. & FERGUSSON, A. J. (eds) *Geology of the North Atlantic Borderlands. Canadian Society of Petroleum Geologists Memoir No. 7*, pp. 57–94.

PIDGEON, R. T. 1969. Zircon U-Pb ages from the Galway Granite and the Dalradian, Connemara, Ireland. *Scottish Journal of Geology*, **5**, 375–92.

POWELL, D., ANDERSEN, T. B., DRAKE, A. A. JR, HALL, L. & KEPPIE, J. D. 1988. The age and distribution of basement rocks in the Caledonide Orogen of the N Atlantic. *This volume*.

——, BAIRD, A. W., CHARNLEY, N. R. & JORDAN, P. J. 1981. The metamorphic environment of the Sgurr Beag Slide: a major crustal displacement zone in Proterozoic Moine rocks of Scotland. *Journal of the Geological Society, London*, **138**, 661–73.

——, BROOK, M. & BAIRD, A. W. 1983. Structural dating of a Precambrian pegmatite in Moine rocks of northern Scotland and its bearing on the status

of the 'Morarian Orogeny'. *Journal of the Geological Society, London*, **140**, 813–23.

READ, H. H. 1928. The Highland Schists of middle Deeside and east Glen Muick. *Transactions of the Royal Society of Edinburgh*, **55**, 755–72.

RICHARDSON, S. W. & POWELL, R. 1976. Thermal causes of the Dalradian metamorphism in the Central Highlands of Scotland. *Scottish Journal of Geology*, **12**, 237–68.

ROBERTS, A. M. & HARRIS, A. L. 1983. The Loch Quoich Line—a limit of early Palaeozoic crustal reworking in the Moine of the Northern Highlands of Scotland. *Journal of the Geological Society, London*, **140**, 883–92.

——, SMITH, D. I. & HARRIS, A. L. 1984. The structural setting and tectonic significance of the Glen Dessary syenite, Inverness-shire. *Journal of the Geological Society, London*, **141**, 1044–52.

ROCK, N. M. S., JEFFREYS, L. A. & MACDONALD, R. 1984. The problem of local anomalous limestone-pelite successions within the Moine outcrop. I. Limestones of the Great Glen area, from Ardgour to Nigg. *Scottish Journal of Geology*, **20**, 283–306.

SMITH, D. I. & WATSON, J. 1983. Scale and timing of movements on the Great Glen Fault, Scotland. *Geology*, **11**, 523–6.

SOPER, N. J. & ANDERTON, R. 1984. Did the Dalradian slides originate as extensional faults? *Nature, London*, **307**, 357–60.

THOMAS, P. R. 1979. New evidence for a Central Highland Root zone. *In:* HARRIS, A. L., HOLLAND, C. H. & LEAKE, B. E. (eds) *The Caledonides of the British Isles Reviewed. Special Publication of the Geological Society of London No. 8*, pp. 205–12.

—— 1980. The stratigraphy and structure of the Moine rocks N of the Schiehallion complex, Scotland. *Journal of the Geological Society, London*, **137**, 469–82.

TREAGUS, J. E. & KING, G. 1978. A complete Lower Dalradian succession in the Schiehallion district, Central Perthshire. *Scottish Journal of Geology*, **4**, 157–66.

WATKINS, K. P. 1983. Petrogenesis of Dalradian albite porphyroblast schists. *Journal of the Geological Society, London*, **140**, 601–18.

WELLS, P. R. A. 1979. *P–T* conditions in the Moines of the Central Highlands, Scotland. *Journal of the Geological Society, London*, **136**, 663–71.

WILLIAMS, H. & HATCHER, R. D., JR 1983. Appalachian suspect terranes. *In:* HATCHER, R. D., JR, WILLIAMS, H. & ZEITZ, I. (eds) *Contributions to the Tectonics and Geophysics of Mountain Chains. Geological Society of America Memoir No. 158*, pp. 33–53.

WINCHESTER, J. A. 1974. The zonal pattern of regional metamorphism in the Scottish Caledonides. *Journal of the Geological Society, London*, **130**, 509–24.

YARDLEY, B. W. D. 1980. Metamorphism and orogeny in the Irish Dalradian. *Journal of the Geological Society, London*, **137**, 303–9.

——, LEAKE, B. E. & FARROW, C. M. 1980. The metamorphism of Fe-rich pelites from Connemara, Ireland. *Journal of Petrology*, **21**, 365–99.

——, VINE, F. J. & BALDWIN, C. T. 1982. The plate tectonic setting of NW Britain and Ireland in late Cambrian and early Ordovician times. *Journal of the Geological Society, London*, **139**, 455–63.

B. HARTE, Grant Institute of Geology, University of Edinburgh, West Mains Road, Edinburgh EH9 3JW, UK.

Early Palaeozoic metamorphism in the Scandinavian Caledonides

Inge Bryhni

S U M M A R Y : Early Palaeozoic metamorphism is represented in several of the nappes of the Scandinavian Caledonides, although it is often severely overprinted by late Silurian–early Devonian events. It is defined particularly in N Norway where the Finnmarkian phase probably reached peak conditions at about 535 Ma with extensive cooling and uplift at about 485 Ma. On Spitsbergen there was a phase of low- to high-grade metamorphism of jadeite–glaucophane type prior to the late Ordovician–Silurian.

In 1920 Olaf Holtedahl was able to demonstrate that the Appalachian–European–Arctic geosynclinal belt had evolved through various successive events. For Norway he distinguished a major orogenic phase called the Trondheim Disturbance, characterized by upheaval, deep intrusions and deep denudation, prior to a later Ordovician and an end-Silurian event.

The ideas on the climactic development of the Scandinavian Caledonides were developed further by Vogt (1929, 1945) and Størmer (1967) who made elaborate time–disturbance charts based on fossil dating and breaks in deposition. Thus Vogt stated that the Trondheim Disturbance seemed to have been of considerable regional significance throughout the Scandinavian Caledonides with a metamorphic break beneath conglomerate horizons. Near Trondheim, the oldest strata above the unconformity have now been dated by graptolites to upper middle Arenig (Ryan et al. 1980). On the foreland a corresponding 'Trysil phase' was recognizable from arkosic sandstone deposited during the lower Arenig.

Outside the Trondheim region and the foreland belt of low-grade sediments, however, there are no fossils to prove a period of metamorphic development in the early Ordovician or earlier. What can be demonstrated is the presence of conglomerates overlain by sequences bearing Ashgill–Llandovery fossils and containing clasts with predepositional metamorphic fabrics and mineral assemblages. The conglomerates overlie an unconformity which transects major lithologies and serves as an important time-marker for at least a two-stage metamorphic development of the Scandinavian Caledonides (Kvale 1960, Naterstad 1976, Sturt & Thon 1976, Bryhni 1983, Gee & Roberts 1983, Sturt 1984).

Radiometric dating has now made possible a more precise understanding of the development, although the available dates are still few and in some cases equivocal. Thus the early Caledonian phase in northernmost Norway is dated between 535 and 490 Ma and a later phase is dated between 420 and 400 Ma (Sturt et al. 1978). The early phase, termed Finnmarkian, involved destruction of a continental geosyncline/rise prism by continentward thrusting, polyphasal folding, metamorphism and accretion of an early group of ophiolitic assemblages onto the Baltic Shield (Furnes et al. 1980, Sturt 1984).

The term Finnmarkian is now commonly used for orogenic events dated within the range 535–490 Ma also outside the type N Norway area, and has replaced the older term Trondheim Disturbance and the contemporaneous Trysil phase for regional rather than local usage. The late Silurian–early Devonian event has been termed the Scandian or Scandinavian phase (Gee 1975). Metamorphic events whose ages are uncertain by virtue of being constrained either by radiometric cooling ages or, more commonly, by being prior to the unconformities with a minimum Ashgill age will be included in the present review.

Finnmarkian of the type area

Ramsey & Sturt (1976) proposed the term Finnmarkian phase for the orogenic development of the Kalak Nappe Complex and its substrate in N Norway. Previously it had been referred to as the Sørøyan event by Gee & Wilson (1974). In the Kalak Nappe Complex the Finnmarkian involved polyphase deformation, metamorphism and plutonism during late Cambrian to early Ordovician time. The essential features are given in a review article by Sturt et al. (1978):

1 The plutonic rocks (e.g. the Seiland Province) include ultramafic, mafic and alkaline types and thus represent unusual elements in Caledonian geology.

2 Two major cycles of deformation, D_1 and D_2, occurred before and after the metamorphic peak which reached amphibolite facies with formation of local migmatite complexes. Deformation during D_2 led to initial emplacement of the Kalak Nappe Complex and tectonically underlying units onto the Baltic Shield.

From HARRIS, A. L. & FETTES, D. J. (eds), 1988, *The Caledonian–Appalachian Orogen,* Geological Society Special Publication No. 38, pp. 135–140.

3 A lower age bracket was initially given by structures presumed to be archaeodecyatides of lower to middle Cambrian age. These fossil-like structures have recently (Debrenne 1984) been shown to be of anorganic origin, however, and there is thus no clear stratigraphic evidence to give a lower age bracket for the phase. Radiometric dating by the Rb–Sr whole-rock method has given dates in the interval 535–490 Ma (see Sturt *et al.* 1978 for references) while K–Ar nepheline dates from the D_2 alkaline rocks fall in the range 480–491 Ma, which could presumably represent cooling ages attained during the uplift and erosion of the Finnmarkian mountain belt. Recently, it has been proposed that the evidence for Finnmarkian orogenesis should be re-examined in the type area (Krill & Zwaan, in press). It is here maintained that the folding and metamorphism attributed to Finnmarkian orogenesis may rather be Scandian phenomena.

Metamorphism in each of the major tectonostratigraphic units

The Scandinavian Caledonides are essentially a succession of nappes with separate metamorphic histories. In the following, metamorphism will be related to the sub-division given in the tectonostratigraphic map by Gee & Roberts (1983) which recognizes five major units: uppermost allochthon, upper allochthon, middle allochthon, lower allochthon and parautochthon–autochthon (Figs 1 and 2). It can be shown that the pre-Arenig (pre-Ashgill) evolution is of major importance in the uppermost and upper allochthons which represent the most distal elements in the geosynclinal belt. In N Norway the Finnmarkian influence can also be distinguished in the lower units where it is marked by progressive metamorphism through the ascending nappe sequence, i.e. generally northwestwards through the original geosyncline.

For the *uppermost allochthon* there is an important element of Precambrian crystalline rocks which have been re-metamorphosed to an unknown extent during the Caledonian orogeny (Cribb 1981, Riis & Ramberg 1981). It is not yet clear how much lower Palaeozoic cover, if any, is present. The widely distributed supracrustal rocks are metamorphosed in the staurolite–kyanite and sillimanite grade. The youngest ages for this metamorphism are given by Rb–Sr whole-rock dates on igneous intrusions at 447 ± 7 Ma (Claesson 1979), 459 ± 35 Ma (Reymer 1979) and 464 ± 22 Ma (Råheim & Ramberg, personal communication 1984) for the Rødingsfjället

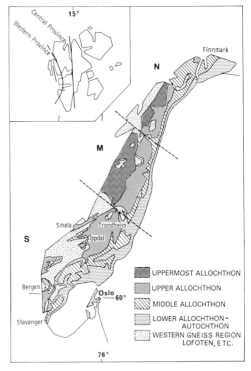

FIG. 1. Major tectonostratigraphic elements of Spitsbergen (inset) and the northern (N), middle (M) and southern (S) parts of the Scandinavian Caledonides. (From Harland *et al.* 1979, Gee & Roberts 1983, Gee *et al.* 1985.)

Nappe Complex, 457 ± 14 Ma for the Helgeland Nappe Complex (Tørudbakken, personal communication 1984) and 495 ± 14 Ma for the Beiarn Nappe (Cribb 1981). All these dates are recorded for intrusions which cut the main schistosity of the rocks in the area, and must indicate significant plutonic activity during the lower and middle Ordovician.

The *upper allochthon* probably also contains original Precambrian rocks in places, but its most characteristic constituents are ophiolites and associated eugeosynclinal sequences. There is some evidence to suggest that the ophiolites experienced low-grade ocean-floor metamorphism prior to obduction (Brekke & Pedersen, personal communication 1984). This early phase of metamorphism is marked by epidotization and the formation of chlorite, actinolite and albite prior to intrusion of sheeted dykes. The time of obduction of the Lykling ophiolite is bracketed within the interval 533–464 Ma (Furnes *et al.* 1983) and the Karmøy ophiolite may have been emplaced before 445 Ma (Råheim, personal communication 1978; cited by Furnes *et al.* 1980). The obduction was associated with greenschist-

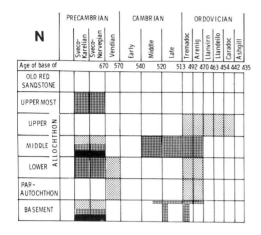

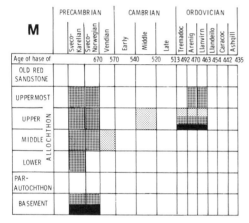

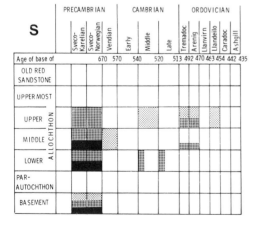

FIG. 2. Recorded early Palaeozoic (pre-Ashgill) metamorphism in the tectonostratigraphic sequence for the northern (N), middle (M) and southern (S) parts of the Scandinavian Caledonides: black, granulite facies; dark shade, amphibolite facies; light shade, greenschist facies or lower.

facies metamorphism in south-western Norway, possibly increasing to lower amphibolite facies at Bergen and further northwards along the coast. Thus there is a facies contrast in the northern part of the Major Bergen Arc where the rocks below the pre-Ashgill unconformity give evidence of amphibolite-facies metamorphism before the onset of erosion while the rocks above are only affected under middle greenschist-facies conditions (Henriksen 1981). In the Trondheim area there are indications of two low-grade metamorphic events, one pre-dating upper middle Arenig (Ryan *et al.* 1980) and another in the Llandeilo-Caradoc (Vogt 1945, Roberts 1980, Ryan *et al.* 1980). At Smøla the later phase is bracketed by diorites 436 ± 7 Ma old which cut limestones bearing late Arenig–early Llanvirn fossils (Bruton & Bockelie 1979, Roberts 1980).

In Sweden there is evidence that the Seve unit and the uppermost parts of the Köli unit were metamorphosed in the interval 510–450 Ma but at different times in the two units (Dallmeyer *et al.* 1983). Rb–Sr and U–Pb zircon dates around 490 Ma led Claesson *et al.* (1983) to suggest that an outboard arc was active for the Köli terrane during the early Ordovician into Middle Ordovician. Eclogites and glaucophane-bearing rocks are present in the Seve (van Roermund 1984, Stephens & van Roermund 1984), and $^{40}\text{Ar}/^{39}\text{Ar}$ dating of hornblendes from such rocks indicates a 491 ± 8 Ma age for the uplift/cooling following high-pressure metamorphism and retrogression while phengitic muscovite indicates temperatures around 440°C for post-metamorphic cooling (Dallmeyer & Gee 1986). Subsequent lower-grade metamorphism took place in this area during the late Silurian orogenesis when the whole Seve–Köli Nappe Complex and the underlying units were emplaced upon the Balto-Scandian Platform (Gee & Sjøstrøm 1984).

For the *middle allochthon*, great differences can be documented between the southern and the northern part of the belt. In the SE there was mainly movement of huge crystalline Precambrian blocks with Caledonian metamorphism confined to the thrust zones. Eclogites probably formed in shear zones in western parts of Norway (e.g. near Bergen and Stavanger). Sm–Nd dating on minerals from an eclogite near Bergen fixes this age to around 517 Ma (Griffin & Austrheim, personal communication 1984). Mylonites separating the Särv Nappe from the underlying Tännäs Augen Gneiss in Sweden have yielded an age of 485 ± 50 Ma (Claesson 1979) which indicates that, at least in the thrust zones, the metamorphism was related to the Finnmarkian. In the type area in Finnmark there was penetrative metamorphism during two deformational events, extensive migmatization and igneous activity. The orogeny occurred in this area at an earlier date and reached a more advanced stage of development than in the southern parts of the Scandinavian Caledonides (Sturt *et al.* 1978). The presence of Ashgill and Llandovery fossils indicates, however, that part of the Kalak Nappe Complex was metamorphosed only during the Scandian phase (Binns & Gayer 1980) and Krill & Zwaan (in press) have recently suggested that evidence for the Finnmarkian orogenesis should be reconsidered even in the type area.

In the *lower allochthon* there is only evidence of pre-Arenig metamorphism in the Laksefjord Nappe where the formation of cleavage is dated at 493 ± 45 Ma (Sturt *et al.* 1978). The Western Gneiss Region may have experienced a profound tectonometamorphic disturbance during a Caledonian phase prior to the late Silurian. Evidence in favour of this is the $^{40}Ar/^{39}Ar$ plateau date of 524 ± 6 Ma for hornblende and 488 ± 2 Ma for biotite (Bryhni *et al.* 1971) and the recent discovery that the pre-Ashgillian unconformity in W Norway extends into previously deformed/metamorphosed quartzites of the Dalsfjord Nappe (Brekke, personal communication 1984). Such an early tectonic phase may have produced the tectonic stacking of orthogneisses and psammitic rocks recorded from other parts of the Western Gneiss Region like that of the Fjordane Complex (Bryhni & Grimstad 1970) and Oppdal (Krill 1980). In the latter area, units of the thrust sequence were already emplaced before completion of the main Caledonian deformation and metamorphism with local formation of eclogites at the end of the Silurian (Krill 1981).

The *parautochthon–autochthon* has only suffered mild metamorphism of greenschist–subgreenschist facies. Minerals in the uppermost part of the Precambrian crystalline basement have locally been reset in terms of their $^{40}Ar/^{39}Ar$ ratio. Thus Dallmeyer & Andresen (1984) report both Finnmarkian (about 500 Ma) and Scandian (about 385 Ma) events and have also found local evidence for a 700–650 Ma thermal resetting of hornblende. The late Precambrian–Tremadoc sedimentary cover has locally a distinct cleavage, which in northernmost Norway appears to be dated by Rb–Sr whole-rock isochrons at 504 ± 7 Ma (Sturt *et al.* 1978). Thus for the fossiliferous slates in the upper part of the succession there is a very short time interval available for the admittedly slight metamorphism and regional-scale open folding.

A very complete sedimentary succession from middle Cambrian to Pridoli is present in the Oslo region. A break is locally present at the base of the Ordovician beds, but is not present everywhere since Upper Cambrian black shales continue uninterrupted into Tremadocian graptolite shales near Oslo. In this area, at least, there is no evidence for any early Finnmarkian event. During the late Arenig–early Llanvirn, however, a regional shallowing took place, resulting in transition from graptolite shale environment to *Orthoceras* limestone. Evidence of contemporaneous volcanism is given by extensive beds of bentonite in the interval from upper Llanvirn to early Caradoc.

Bjørlykke (1974) demonstrated that chlorite is first introduced to the sediments in Arenig and increases in relative importance through the middle Ordovician. At the same time there is an increase in the magnesium, iron, nickel and chromium in the shales and detrital chromite even occurs in the middle Ordovician sediments. Such changes have been related to the influence of Caledonian orogenic activity further W involving emplacement of crystalline nappes (e.g. Jotun and Trondheim Nappe Complexes) and the development of island-arc systems (Bjørlykke 1974).

Spitsbergen

The island group of Spitsbergen (Fig. 1) forms a northward continuation of the Caledonide belt to the Arctic. Its pre-Carboniferous position may have been connected in part with NE Greenland rather than with Scandinavia. Spitsbergen can be divided into three or more provinces which in the 'palaeomobilistic' model of Harland & Wright (1979) were formed when far apart but became juxtaposed by late Devonian sinistral transcurrent faulting. Possible early Palaeozoic metamorphism has been recorded from two of these provinces.

The Western Province contains thick flyschoid sequences with intercalated volcanics indicative of tectonic mobility almost throughout the Riphean to the Wenlock or Ludlow time (Harland *et al.* 1979). A phase of progressive low- to high-grade metamorphism of jadeite–glaucophane type has been identified (Horsfield 1972, Ohta 1979, 1984). The metamorphic products include blueschists, jadeite–quartz–albite assemblages and eclogites which are definitely older than an unconformably-overlying flyschoid succession of late Ordovician?–Silurian age. The latter contains basal conglomerate with pebbles of the underlying high-pressure metamorphic rocks and fossils in the matrix (Ohta 1984). An apparent K–Ar age on separated muscovite suggests that this mineral cooled at around 470 Ma (Horsfield 1972) which may not have been much later than the high-pressure metamorphism.

The Central Province contains metamorphic supracrustals and gneisses, the latter sometimes with sillimanite occurring with cordierite–garnet–biotite. Hjelle (1979) reported an 'early Caledonian' phase of regional metamorphism reaching upper amphibolite facies which took place prior to a probably Silurian event of recrystallization, migmatitization and syntectonic emplacement of granitic intrusives. The true age and characteristics of the early phase has not yet been clearly distinguished from the dominating later effects, but a Middle Cambrian hiatus on S Spitsbergen may correspond to such an early event of Caledonian diastrophism further N in the same province.

According to work recently reviewed by Ohta (1984), the early Caledonian metamorphism on western Spitsbergen can be related to a change in tectonic domain from that of a continental shelf to an active plate-boundary environment.

Conclusions

Later research has only served to strengthen the hypotheses, advanced by Holtedahl and Vogt in the 1920s, concerning the sequence of Caledonian events in the northern areas. Early Caledonian, early Paleozoic events can be identified in most of the allochthonous units constituting the Scandinavian Caledonides and Spitsbergen, although they are in some cases essentially plutonic and have in some places been obscured by the Scandian phase in the late Silurian. The various allochthons were, however, once separated by considerable expanses of the Iapetus Sea and certain events may have been of only local significance. It would therefore be advisable to use the term 'early Caledonian' as the general designation for movements within this period and restrict the use of 'Finnmarkian', 'Trondheim Disturbance', 'Trysil phase' etc. to the tectonic units or terranes where evidence of these movements was originally found.

ACKNOWLEDGMENTS: The author wishes to thank many colleagues for helpful discussions and assistance, in particular P. G. Andreasson, D. L. Bruton, W. L. Griffin, B. Harte, H. van Roermund and B. Torudbakken.

References

BINNS, R. E. & GAYER, R. A. 1980. Silurian and Upper Ordovician fossils at Guolasjav'ri, Troms, Norway. *Nature, London*, **284**, 53–5.

BJØRLYKKE, K. 1974. Geochemical and mineralogical influence of Ordovician island arcs on epicontinental clastic sedimentation. A study of lower palaeozoic sedimentation in the Oslo Region, Norway. *Sedimentology*, **21**, 251–72.

BRUTON, D. L. & BOCKELIE, J. F. 1979. The Ordovician sedimentary sequence on Smøla, west central Norway. *Norges Geologiske Undersøkelse*, **348**, 21–51.

BRYHNI, I. 1983. Regional overview of metamorphism in the Scandinavian Caledonides. *In:* SCHENK, P. E. (ed.) *Regional Trends in the Geology of the Appalachian–Caledonian–Hercynian–Mauritanide Orogen*, pp. 193–204, Reidel, Dordrecht.

—— & GRIMSTAD, E. 1970. Supracrustal and infracrustal rocks in the Gneiss region west of Brimsvatn. *Norges Geologiske Undersøkelse*, **266**, 105–40.

——, FITCH, F. J. & MILLER, J. A. 1971. $^{40}Ar/^{39}Ar$ dates from recycled Precambrian rocks in the Gneiss region of the Norwegian Caledonides. *Norsk Geologisk Tidsskrift*, **51**, 391–406.

CLAESSON, S. 1979. Pre-Silurian orogenic deformation in the north-central Scandinavian Caledonides. *Geologiska Föreningens i Stockholm Förhandlingar*, **101**, 353–56.

——, KLINGSPOR, I. & STEPHENS, M. B. 1983. U-Pb and Rb-Sr isotopic data on an Ordovician volcanic-subvolcanic complex from the Tiopasi Group, Köli Nappes, Swedish Caledonides. *Geologiska Föreningens i Stockholm Förhandingar*, **105**, 9–15.

CRIBB, S. J. 1981. Rb/Sr geochronological evidence suggesting a reinterpretation of part of the north Norwegian Caledonides. *Norsk Geologisk Tidsskrift*, **61**, 97–110.

DALLMEYER, R. D. & ANDRESEN, A. 1984. Tectonothermal evolution of the Precambrian basement terrane of western Troms and northern Nordland: evidence from preliminary $^{40}Ar/^{39}Ar$ incremental release mineral ages. *Stockholm University Geological Institute Meddelelser*, **255**, 50.

——, GEE, D. G. & BECKHOLMEN, M. 1983. $^{40}Ar/^{39}Ar$ evidence of superposed metamorphism in the central Scandinavian Caledonides, Jämtland, Sweden. *Geological Society of America Abstract No. 31796*, p. 553.

—— & GEE, D. G. 1986. $^{40}Ar/^{39}Ar$ mineral ages from retrogressed eclogites within the Baltoscandian miocline: Implications for a polyphase Caledonian orogenic evolution. *Geological Society of America Bulletin*, **97**, 26–34.

DEBRENNE, F. 1984. Archaeocyatha from the Caledonian rocks of Sørøy, North Norway—a doubtful record. *Norst Geologisk Tidsskrift*, **64**, 153–4.

FURNES, H., AUSTRHEIM, H., AMALIKSEN, K. G. & NORDÅS, J. 1983. Evidence for an incipient early Caledonian (Cambrian) orogenic phase in southwestern Norway. *Geological Magazine*, **120**, 607–12.

——, ROBERTS, D., STURT, B. A., THON, A. & GALE, G. H. 1980. Ophiolite fragment in the Scandinavian Caledonides. *In*: PANAYIOTOU, A. (ed.) *Ophiolites—Proceedings of the International Ophiolite Symposium, Cyprus, 1979*, pp. 582–600.

GEE, D. G. 1975. A geotraverse through the Scandinavian Caledonides—Østersund to Trondheim. *Sveriges Geologiska Undersøkning, Serie C*, **717**, 1–66.

—— & ROBERTS, D. 1983. Timing of deformation in the Scandinavian Caledonides. *In*: SCHENK, P. E. (ed.) *Regional Trends in the Geology of the Appalachian–Caledonian–Hercynian–Mauritanide Orogen*, pp. 193–204, Reidel, Dordrecht.

——, KÜMPÄLAINEN, R., ROBERTS, D., STEPHENS, M. B., THON, A. & ZACHRISSON, E. 1985. Tectonostratigraphic map of the Scandinavian Caledonides. *In*: GEE, D. G. & STURT, B. A. (eds) *The Caledonide Orogen—Scandinavia and Related Areas*, Wiley, Chichester.

—— & SJØSTRØM, H. 1984. Early Caledonian obduction of the Handöl ophiolite. *Stockholm University Geological Institute, Middelelser*, **255**, 72.

—— & WILSON M. R. 1974. The age of orogenic deformation in the Swedish Caledonides. *American Journal of Science*, **274**, 1–9.

HARLAND, W. B., HORSFIELD, W. T., MANBY, G. M. & MORRIS, A. P. 1979. *Norsk Polarinstitutt, Skrifter*, **167**, 119–44.

—— & WRIGHT, N. J. R. 1979. Alternative hypothesis for the pre-Carboniferous evolution of Svalbard. *Norsk Polarinstitutt, Skrifter*, **167**, 89–117.

HJELLE, A. 1979. Aspects of the geology of northwest Spitsbergen. *Norsk Polarinstitutt, Skrifter*, **167**, 37–62.

HENRIKSEN, H. 1981. A major unconformity within the metamorphic lower Palaeozoic sequence of the Major Bergen Arc, Osterøy, western Norway. *Norges Geologiske Undersøkelse*, **367**, 65–73.

HOLTEDAHL, O. 1920. Paleography and diastrophism in the Atlantic–Arctic region during Paleozoic time. *American Journal of Science*, **49**, 1–25.

HORSFIELD, W. T. 1972. Glaucophane schists of Caledonian age from Spitsbergen. *Geological Magazine*, **109**, 29–36.

KRILL, A. G. 1980. Tectonics of the Oppdal area, central Norway. *Geologiska Föreningens i Stockholm Förhandlingar*, **102**, 523–30.

—— 1981. 'Stockwerk' tectonic relationships between the Trondheim synclinorium and the Western Gneiss Region of Norway. *Terra Cognita*, **1**, 56.

—— & ZWAAN, K. B. Reinterpretation of Finnmarkian deformation on western Sørøy, northern Norway. *Norsk Geologisk Tidsskrift*, **67**, in press.

KVALE, A. 1960. The nappe area of the Caledonides in western Norway. Excursion guide. *Norges Geologiske Undersøkelse*, **212**, 1–43.

NATERSTAD, J. 1976. Comments on the lower Paleozoic unconformity in west Norway. *American Journal of Science*, **276**, 394–7.

OHTA, Y. 1979. Blue schists from Motalafjella, western Spitsbergen. *Norsk Polarinstitutt, Skrifter*, **167**, 171–217.

—— 1984. Timing of Caledonian high-P metamorphism in Spitsbergen, based on geological data. *Abstracts, Tectonic and Structural Study Group, 2nd Annual Meeting, Bergen 1984*, 2 pp.

RAMSEY, D. M. & STURT, B. A. 1976. The synmetamorphic emplacement of the Magerøy Nappe. *Norsk Geologisk Tidsskrift*, **56**, 291–308.

REYMER, A. P. S. 1979. Investigations into the metamorphic nappes of the central Scandinavian Caledonides on the basis of Rb–Sr and K–Ar age determinations. *Thesis*, University of Leiden, 123 pp.

RIIS, F. & RAMBERG, I. B. 1981. The uppermost allochthon—the Rødingsfjället and the Helgeland Complex in a segment south of Ranafjorden, *Terra Cognita*, **1**, 69.

ROBERTS, D. 1980. Petrochemistry and palaeographic setting of the Ordovician Volcanic rocks of Smøla, Central Norway. *Norges Geologiske Undersøkelse*, **359**, 43–60.

VAN ROERMUND, H. 1984. Eclogites of the Seve Nappe, Central Scandinavian Caledonides. *In*: GEE, D. G. & STURT, B. A. (eds) *The Caledonide Orogen: Scandinavia and Related Areas*, pp. 873–86. Wiley, Chichester.

RYAN, P. D., WILLIAMS, D. M. & SKEVINGTON, D. 1980. A revised interpretation of the Ordovician stratigraphy of Sør-trøndelag and its implications for the evolution of the Scandinavian Caledonides. *In*: WONES, D. R. (ed.) *The Caledonides in the USA: Proceedings of the International Geological Correlation Program—Caledonide Orogen Project 27, Blacksburg, VA. Department of Geological Sciences, Virginia Polytechnic Institute and State University, Memoir No. 2*, pp. 99–103.

STEPHENS, M. B. & VAN ROERMUND, H. 1984. Occurrence of glaucophane in association with eclogites in the upper part of the Seve Nappes, southern Norrbotten Caledonides, Sweden. *Stockholm University Geological Institute Meddelelser*, **255**, 212.

STØRMER, L. 1967. Some aspects of the Caledonian geosyncline and foreland west of the Baltic Shield. *Quarterly Journal of the Geological Society of London*, **123**, 103–214.

STURT, B. A. 1984. The accretion of ophiolitic terrains in the Scandinavian Caledonides. *Geologie en Mijnbouw*, **63**, 201–12.

—— & THON, A. 1976. Discussion. The age of orogenic deformation in the Scandinavian Caledonides. *American Journal of Science*, **276**, 385–90.

——, PRINGLE, I. R. & RAMSEY, D. M. 1978. The Finnmarkian phase of the Caledonian orogeny. *Geological Society of Canada, Journal*, **135**, 576–610.

VOGT, TH. 1929. Den norske fjellkjedes revolusjonshistorie. *Norsk Geologisk Tidsskrift*, **10**, 97–115.

—— 1945. The geology of part of the Hólolanda–Horg district, a type area in the Trondheim region. *Norsk Geologisk Tidsskrift*, **23**, 449–528.

I. BRYHNI, Mineralogisk-Geologisk Museum, Sars'gt. 1, N–0562 Oslo 5, Norway.

Pre-Arenig metamorphism in the Appalachians

Jo Laird

SUMMARY: Our understanding of the distribution of pre-Arenig metamorphism in the Appalachians is rudimentary because of polymetamorphism, complex structure and the need for further combined field, structural, isotopic and petrological studies. Available data indicate that in the northern Appalachians pre-Arenig metamorphism is preserved in distinct terranes often collectively referred to as Avalonia. In Maritime Canada 800–700 Ma dates on amphibolite-facies gneisses are interpreted as metamorphic ages. Amphibolite- to greenschist-facies metamorphism is older than 600 Ma granitic rocks. Several areas in eastern New England may record late Proterozoic to early Ordovician amphibolite- to greenschist- facies metamorphism. In the central Appalachians metamorphism older than about 500 Ma is granulite facies in southeastern Pennsylvania and amphibolite to greenschist facies in northern Virginia. Except in the Grenville basement, metamorphism in the southern Appalachians is generally inferred to be Arenig or younger.

Because the distribution of pre-Arenig metamorphism in the Appalachians is not well understood, the main purpose of this paper is to summarize data indicating pre-Arenig ages of metamorphism rather than to try to interpret the causes and relationships of that metamorphism. Tables 1–3 summarize the data, and Fig. 1 shows the locations discussed below.

Northern Appalachians—Maritime Canada

Olszewski et al. (1981) and Gaudette et al. (1985) interpreted their 701 and 686 Ma Rb–Sr ages on biotite gneiss from location 1 as metamorphic ages, arguing that the upper amphibolite-facies metamorphism observed probably reset the primary protolith age. Jamieson (1984) estimated the pressure and temperature of metamorphism at 1–3.5 kbar and 580–700 °C on the basis of mineral equilibria within biotite gneiss, cordierite + biotite gneiss, and migmatitic cordierite + sillimanite and/or andalusite gneiss. She suggested that the low-pressure facies series metamorphism may have been caused by intrusion of diorite closely associated with the gneiss complex. However, Gaudette et al. (1985) reported a younger age for the diorite than the probable metamorphic age of the gneiss complex (Table 1).

The timing of pre-Arenig metamorphism at location 2 is unclear. A 595 Ma granite intrudes deformed and metamorphosed basement and felsic and mafic schists, giving a minimum age of metamorphism. Gaudette et al. (1983) interpret a 930 Ma Rb–Sr whole-rock date on granitic gneisses and 810 and 740 Ma dates on other

granite gneisses that intrude felsic and mafic schists as deformation ages.

Major regional metamorphism at location 3 has been dated by Olszewski & Gaudette (1982) at about 800 ± 30 Ma. Euhedral overgrowths on detrital zircon from quartz + feldspar + biotite and hornblende + quartz + feldspar + biotite gneisses show two lead-loss events, one at 783 Ma and the other at 369 Ma. Zircons in quartz diorite gneiss intruding low-grade (dolomite + quartz in calcareous rocks) platform metasedimentary rocks have similar upper and lower intercepts on a concordia diagram (827 Ma and 333 Ma respectively). The gneisses give a combined Rb–Sr whole-rock isochron age of 771 Ma. The lower intercept ages are interpreted as a time of retrograde metamorphism, intrusion and deformation.

Northern Appalachians—USA

Much debate exists concerning the possible presence of pre-Arenig regional metamorphism in eastern New England. Stewart (1974) suggested that Precambrian medium-grade metamorphism is preserved in a fault-bounded block in Penobscot Bay (location 4). The age assignment is based on the 600 Ma age of a pegmatite which is interpreted as being older than the metamorphism. Boucot et al. (1972) have identified Caradocian fossils on the W side of Penobscot Bay. On the E side, Stewart & Wones (1974) reported that greenschist-facies metavolcanics were metamorphosed before the middle Silurian. Does the 520 Ma whole-rock Rb–Sr isochron age (Brookins 1976) on these metavolcanics date the volcanism or the metamorphism?

From HARRIS, A. L. & FETTES, D. J. (eds), 1988, *The Caledonian–Appalachian Orogen*, Geological Society Special Publication No. 38, pp. 141–147.

TABLE 1. *Pre-Arenig metamorphism in the northern Appalachians—Maritime Canada*

Location	Rock type	Metamorphic facies/grade	Age (Ma)	Comment	Reference
1 Cape Breton Island, Nova Scotia	Migmatitic paragneiss, very minor amphibolite	Upper amphibolite (cordierite + andalusite + sillimanite)	701 ± 33, 686 ± 30 (Rb–Sr whole-rock isochron, biotite gneiss)	Associated with diorite giving 636 ± 69 Ma Rb–Sr whole-rock isochron age	Olszewski et al. 1981, Jamieson 1984, Gaudette et al. 1985
SE Cape Breton Highland, N of 1	Metasedimentary–metavolcanic complex	Lower greenschist to upper amphibolite	≳614	Zircon age of tonalite that intrudes metamorphic rocks; metamorphic grade increases to N	R. A. Jamieson 1986, personal communication
2 Cobequid Highlands, Nova Scotia	Granitoid gneisses Basement and cover of felsic and mafic schists	Amphibolite Amphibolite	930 (Rb–Sr whole-rock) >595 (Rb–Sr whole-rock)	Rocks occur in fault-bounded blocks; age of deformation Based on age of intrusive granite	Gaudette et al. 1983 Gaudette et al. 1983
3 St John, New Brunswick	Felsic and mafic gneiss	Upper amphibolite	783 ± 40 (U–Pb zircon, older lower intercept, two lead-loss event model)	No isotopic evidence for the Ordovician metamorphic event suggested by others	Olszewski & Gaudette 1982
	Pelitic, calcareous and felsic metasedimentary rocks	Generally low grade; low-pressure amphibolite facies near gneiss	827 ± 40 (U–Pb zircon, concordant at ≈814)	Age of gneiss which probably intruded at the time of metamorphism	Olszewski & Gaudette 1982

TABLE 2. *Pre-Arenig metamorphism in the northern Appalachians—USA**

Location	Rock type	Metamorphic facies/grade	Age (Ma)	Comment	Reference
4 Penobscot Bay (700 acre and smaller islands), Maine	Pelitic schist, amphibolite, quartzite, marble	Garnet + andalusite	>600 ± 15 (Rb–Sr mineral isochron, cross-cutting pegmatite)	May correlate with low-grade rocks at location 3; fault-bounded block	Stewart 1974, Brookins 1976, 1982
5 Passagassawakeag Formation, Maine	Felsic gneiss, amphibolite, calc-silicate rocks	Upper amphibolite, sillimanite + muscovite + K-feldspar	>430 ± 10 (tentative $^{207}Pb/^{206}Pb$ age on youngest migmatite from cross-cutting granitic dykes)	Three deformation events pre-430 Ma, but relation to metamorphism?	Stewart & Wones 1974, Wones 1974, Bickel 1976
6 Casco Bay, Maine	Mafic and felsic schist and gneiss, metapelite, calc-silicate rocks	Greenschist to amphibolite (sillimanite + muscovite)	481 to 539 ± 30 (Rb–Sr whole-rock isochron)	Are these metamorphic ages?	Brookins & Hussey 1978, Brookins 1982

7 SE New Hampshire and adjacent Maine and Massachusetts	Felsic, calcareous and pelitic metasedimentary rocks	Greenschist to amphibolite	>473±37 (Rb–Sr whole-rock isochron, cross-cutting pluton); probably ≥671±21 (Rb–Sr whole rock), 681±147 to 619±11 (U–Pb zircon, upper intercept)	P∈ age is from a migmatitic gneiss complex which is gradational with the metasediments	Kelly *et al.* 1980, Lyons *et al.* 1982, Bothner *et al.* 1984, Gaudette *et al.* 1984, Olszewski *et al.* 1984
8 Milford–Dedham zone, eastern Massachusetts	Felsic and mafic volcanics, quartzite, gneiss, pelitic schist, amphibolite	Weakly metamorphosed to lower amphibolite (staurolite–kyanite)	>622±7 (U–Pb zircon, <10% discordant)	Crystalline age of granite which intrudes the metamorphic unit and contact metamorphoses volcanics	Skehan & Murray 1980, Naylor 1981, Skehan 1983, Zen 1983, Smith & Hon 1984, Zartman & Naylor 1984
	Micaceous schist and gneiss	Amphibolite	>591±50 (Rb–Sr whole-rock isochron); 619±5, 624±5. (^{207}Pb/^{206}Pb zircon)	Age of granite which intrudes metamorphic rocks	
9 Esmond–Dedham zone, northwestern Rhode Island, to Hope Valley shear zone	Mafic flows and volcaniclastics, gabbro, serpentinite?, metasedimentary rocks	Greenschist to lower amphibolite	>621±8, 648±27 (U–Pb zircon)	Age of granitic rocks which include xenoliths and roof pendants of metasedimentary rocks; highest grade probably Alleghanian	Dreier & Mosher 1981, Hermes *et al.* 1981, Dreier 1983, Skehan 1983, O'Hara & Gromet 1985
10 Eastern Connecticut and adjacent Rhode Island E of Lake Char fault to Hope Valley shear zone	Felsic, pelitic and mafic schist and gneiss	Greenschist to lower amphibolite	>625 (U–Pb zircon)	Age of granitic rocks with sparse screens of metamorphic rock; highest grade probably Alleghanian	Hermes *et al.* 1981, Skehan 1983, Danforth & Owens 1984, O'Hara & Gromet 1985
11 Newport, Rhode Island	Sandstone, slate, siltstone overlain by volcaniclastic rocks	Weakly metamorphosed to low greenschist, later contact metamorphism (andalusite + cordierite)	603±14 (Rb–Sr whole-rock)	Age of granite that caused the contact metamorphism	Smith & Giletti 1978, Rast & Skehan 1981, 1983, Skehan 1983

* The overprint of Alleghanian metamorphism in Rhode Island, Connecticut and Massachusetts is very strong, and it is difficult to separate out earlier metamorphism. Metamorphism in locations 5–7 is variously assigned to Precambrian to Devonian, and further study is needed here.

TABLE 3. *Pre-Arenig metamorphism in the central Appalachians*

Location	Rock type	Metamorphic facies/grade	Age (Ma)	Comment	Reference
12 SE Pennsylvania and N Delaware, Wilmington complex (WC) and N and E of WC	Pelitic schist and migmatite	Granulite, sillimanite + orthoclase, low-pressure facies series	502 ± 20 (Rb–Sr whole-rock, poor isochron); age of Arden pluton in WC, 441 (U–Pb lower intercept, zircon; nearly concordant, WC)	M2 metamorphism of Crawford & Crawford (1980), Crawford & Mark (1982); Arden pluton deforms foliation of WC; pre-Arenig to as young as Ashgillian	Foland & Muessig 1978, Crawford & Crawford 1980, Crawford & Mark 1982, Srogi *et al.* 1983
13 S of Potomac River, Fairfax County, Virginia	Pelitic schist, mafic–ultramafic rocks, migmatite	Greenschist to medium amphibolite (chlorite to sillimanite+muscovite) $P \sim Al_2SiO_5$ triple point	$>494 \pm 14$ (Rb–Sr whole-rock isochron), ≈ 560 (U–Pb zircon, upper intercept, concordant at 558)	Ages reported and much debated for batholith which intrudes into and contact metamorphoses the regionally metamorphosed rocks	Seiders *et al.* 1975, Higgins *et al.* 1977, Mose & Nagel 1982, Drake 1984, 1985

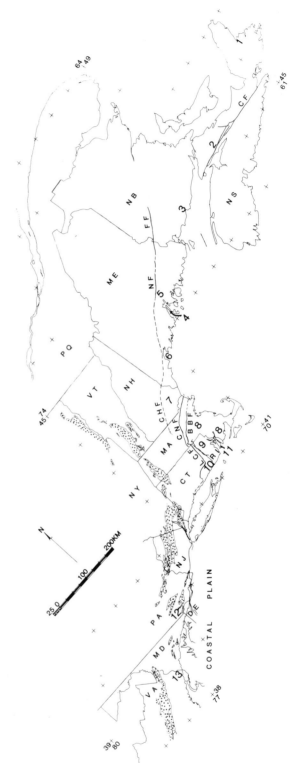

FIG. 1. Map of the northern and central Appalachians (after Williams 1978) showing the locations of pre-Arenig metamorphism (indicated by numbers 1–13 defined in Tables 1–3). In the northern Appalachians, this metamorphism occurs E of the Lake Char (LCF), Bloody Bluff (BBF) or Clinton–Newbury (CNF), Campbell Hill (CHF), Norumbega (NF) and Fredericton (FF) faults and N of the Chedabucto fault (CF) in distinct terranes often collectively referred to as Avalonian. The fault at the Rhode Island–Connecticut border is the Hope Valley shear zone. Grenvillian basement exposed farther W is shown by the stippled areas.

Two other areas in coastal Maine may preserve pre-Arenig metamorphism, but additional data are needed to test this hypothesis. Locality 5 is a high-grade gneiss terrane that shows three periods of deformation before the intrusion of a pluton that is at least as old as Ordovician, but it is not clear when metamorphism occurred relative to deformation (Stewart & Wones 1974). Bickel (1976) favours Precambrian age metamorphism. Brookins & Hussey (1978) and Brookins (1982) reported ages of about 500 Ma for locality 6 (Table 2) but did not speculate as to whether or not these were metamorphic ages. Metamorphism here is indicated as Devonian on the Maine state map (Osberg *et al.* 1984).

Evidence for pre-Arenig metamorphism in southeastern New Hampshire (location 7) includes field and petrographic data indicating a progressive increase in metamorphism (greenschist to middle and possibly upper amphibolite) towards a late Proterozoic migmatitic gneiss with no structural break (Bothner *et al.* 1984, Gaudette *et al.* 1984, Olszewski *et al.* 1984). Regional metamorphism must be older than a cross-cutting 473 Ma pluton that contact metamorphoses the country rock (Gaudette *et al.* 1984). In view of the continuity of metamorphic units, structure and metamorphic grade, this metamorphism may also continue into adjacent Massachusetts and Maine. However, many geologists working in these states would disagree with this interpretation and are not convinced that the contact relationships with the migmatitic gneiss are interpreted correctly.

Zen (1983) and Robinson (1983) mapped pre-Arenig age greenschist- to amphibolite-facies regional metamorphism in eastern Massachusetts, Rhode Island and eastern Connecticut (Fig. 1 and Table 2, locations 8–10). Ordovician metamorphism occurs between the Bloody Bluff and Clinton–Newbury faults (Fig. 1), as discussed by Laird (1987), but pre-Arenig metamorphism may also be preserved here (Skehan 1983, W. J. Olszewski 1985, personal communication). However, Alleghanian metamorphism is widespread and it is difficult to distinguish older events. Understanding of pre-Arenig metamorphism hinges on determination of the state of sedimentary and igneous xenoliths and roof pendants in the 650–500 Ma granitic rocks prior to emplacement.

Zartman & Naylor (1984) argued that the late Precambrian granitic rocks at location 8 show little evidence of being metamorphosed except along faults, implying that regional metamorphism is pre-Arenig. Intrusion of a 622 Ma granite has resulted in contact metamorphism (Smith & Hon 1984). Some, but not all, xenoliths in 648–621 Ma granitic rocks at location 9 are rotated relative to the foliation within the granitic rocks (O. D. Hermes 1984, personal communication), and pre-Arenig and later metamorphism may have occurred. However, O'Hara & Gromet (1985) have shown that a Devonian granite and the late Precambrian granitic rocks share the same microscopic and macroscopic structural elements related to a syn-metamorphic fault zone E of the Lake Char fault (Fig. 1). They conclude that the amphibolite-facies or higher-grade metamorphism in western Rhode Island and adjacent Connecticut and Massachusetts is Alleghanian (locations 9 and 10). An earlier, presumably lower-grade, metamorphism at locality 10 is implied by the presence of metamorphosed rock included as screens within late Precambrian granitic rocks (Table 2).

Perhaps the least controversial evidence for pre-Arenig metamorphism in the United States Appalachians is the presence of contact metamorphism associated with the 603 Ma granite at location 11 (Rast & Skehan 1981). These sedimentary and volcanic–volcaniclastic rocks were deformed and weakly metamorphosed before the intrusion of the granite (Rast & Skehan 1983).

Central Appalachians

In the central Appalachians two periods of metamorphism are identified in southeastern Pennsylvania (location 12) by Crawford & Crawford (1980), Crawford & Mark (1982) and Srogi *et al.* (1983). The latter is Ordovician in age; the earlier may be pre-Arenig (but not Precambrian) to Ashgillian. Details concerning the metamorphic history of this area are discussed by Laird (1988).

Detailed mapping and structural studies by Drake (1984, 1985) indicate that much of the greenschist- to amphibolite-facies metamorphism in northern Virginia S of the Potomac River (location 13) took place prior to emplacement of a series of allochthons and the intrusion of the Occoquan batholith. This metamorphism is pre-Arenig if the 494 and 560 Ma ages on the batholith are accurate (but see Higgins *et al.* (1977) for a discussion of this age).

Conclusion

In our quest to understand pre-Arenig metamorphism in the Appalachians we are far from being able to see through younger metamorphism and deformation. Our present understanding is based to a large extent on detailed isotopic studies in the northern Appalachians, detailed petrological studies in southeastern Pennsylvania (central Appalachians) and detailed structural studies in northern Virginia (central Appalachians). We need to combine all three kinds of studies before we will be able to map the distribution of pressure, temperature and time for pre-Arenig metamorphism.

References

BICKEL, C. E. 1976. Stratigraphy of the Belfast quadrangle, Maine. *In*: PAGE, L. R. (ed.) *Contributions to the Stratigraphy of New England. Geological Society of America Memoir No. 148*, pp. 97–128.

BOTHNER, W. A., BOUDETTE, E. L., FAGAN, T. J., GAUDETTE, H. E., LAIRD, J. & OLSZEWSKI, W. J. 1984. Geologic framework of the Massabesic Anticlinorium and the Merrimack Trough, southeastern New Hampshire. *In*: HANSON, L. S. (ed.) *Geology of the Coastal Lowlands, Boston to Kennebunk, Maine. New England Intercollegiate Geologic Conference, 76th Annual Meeting*, pp. 186–206, Salem State College, Salem, MA.

BOUCOT, A. J., BROOKINS, D. G., FORBES, W. & GUIDOTTI, C. V. 1972. Staurolite zone Caradoc (middle–late Ordovician) age, Old World Province brachiopods from Penobscot Bay, Maine. *Geological Society of America Bulletin*, **83**, 1953–60.

BROOKINS, D. G. 1976. Geochronologic contributions to stratigraphic interpretation and correlation in the Penobscot Bay area, eastern Maine. *In*: PAGE, L. R. (ed.) *Contributions to the Stratigraphy of New England. Geological Society of America Memoir No. 148*, pp. 129–45.

—— 1982. Geochronologic studies in Maine—Part 1: Preliminary Rb–Sr study of the Casco Bay Group, Maine. *Isochron West No. 34*, pp. 9–15.

—— & HUSSEY, A. M., II. 1978. Rb–Sr ages for the Casco Bay Group and other rocks from the Portland–Orrs Island area, Maine. *Geological Society of America Abstracts with Programs*, **10**, 34.

CRAWFORD, M. L. & CRAWFORD, W. A. 1980. Metamorphism and tectonic history of the Pennsylvania Piedmont. *Journal of the Geological Society, London*, **137**, 311–20.

—— & MARK, L. E. 1982. Evidence from metamorphic rocks for overthrusting, Pennsylvania Piedmont, U.S.A. *Canadian Mineralogist*, **20**, 333–47.

DANFORTH, W. & OWENS, J. P. 1984. A characterization of the western margin of the Avalonian terrane of SE New England. *Geological Society of America Abstracts with Programs*, **16**, 11.

DRAKE, A. A., JR 1984. Pre-Taconian deformation in the Potomac Valley of northern Virginia—Penobscotian, Cadomian, or both? *In*: BIRD, S. O. (ed.) *Tectonics and Stratigraphy of Virginia, Harris Volume*, Virginia Division of Mineral Resources, Richmond, VA.

—— 1985. Tectonic implications of the Indian Run Formation, a newly recognized sedimentary melange in the northern Virginia Piedmont. *U.S. Geological Survey Professional Paper No. 1324*.

DREIER, R. B. 1983. The Blackstone series: evidence for Avalonian tectonics in northern Rhode Island. *Geological Society of America Abstracts with Programs*, **15**, 129.

—— & MOSHER, S. 1981. The Blackstone Series: evidence for an Avalonian Plate margin in northern Rhode Island. *In*: BOOTHROYD, J. C. & HERMES, O. D. (eds) *Guidebook to Geologic Field Studies in Rhode Island and Adjacent Areas. New England Intercollegiate Geologic Conference, 73rd Annual Meeting*, pp. 93–102, University of Rhode Island, Kingston, RI.

FOLAND, K. A. & MUESSIG, K. W. 1978. A Paleozoic age for some charnocktic–anorthositic rock. *Geology*, **6**, 143–6.

GAUDETTE, H. E., BOTHNER, W. A., LAIRD, J., OLSZEWSKI, W. J., JR & CHEATHAM, M. M. 1984. Late Precambrian/early Paleozoic deformation and metamorphism in southeastern New Hampshire—confirmation of an exotic terrane. *Geological Society of America Abstracts with Programs*, **16**, 516.

——, OLSZEWSKI, W. J., JR & DONOHOE, H. V., JR 1983. Age and origin of the basement rocks. Cobequid Highlands, Nova Scotia. *Geological Society of America Abstracts with Programs*, **15**, 136.

——, —— & JAMIESON, R. A. 1985. Rb–Sr ages of some basement rocks, Cape Breton Highlands, Nova Scotia. *Geological Association of Canada and Mineralogical Association of Canada, Abstracts*, **10**, A20.

HERMES, O. D., GROMET, L. P. & ZARTMAN, R. E. 1981. Zircon geochronology and petrology of plutonic rocks in Rhode Island. *In*: BOOTHROYD, J. C. & HERMES, O. D. (eds) *Guidebook to Geologic Field Studies in Rhode Island and Adjacent Areas. New England Intercollegiate Geologic Conference, 73rd Annual Meeting*, pp. 315–38, University of Rhode Island, Kingston, RI.

HIGGINS, M. W., SINHA, A. K., ZARTMAN, R. E. & KIRK, W. S. 1977. U–Pb zircon dates from the central Appalachian Piedmont. A possible case of inherited radiogenic lead. *Bulletin of the Geological Society of America*, **88**, 125–32.

JAMIESON, R. A. 1984. Low pressure cordierite-bearing migmatites from Kelly's Mountain Nova Scotia. *Contributions to Mineralogy and Petrology*, **86**, 309–20.

KELLY, W. J., OLSZEWSKI, W. J., JR & GAUDETTE, H. E. 1980. The Massabesic orthogneiss, southern New Hampshire. *Geological Society of America Abstracts with Programs*, **12**, 45.

LAIRD, J. 1988. Arenig to Wenlock age metamorphism in the Appalachians. *This volume*.

LYONS, J. B., BOUDETTE, E. L. & ALEINIKOFF, J. N. 1982. The Avalonian and Gander zones in central eastern New England. *In*: ST JULIEN, P. & BELAND,

J. (eds) *Major Structural Zones and Faults of the Northern Appalachians. Geological Association of Canada Special Paper No. 24*, pp. 43–66.

MOSE, D. G. & NAGEL, M. S. 1982. Plutonic events in the Piedmont of Virginia. *Southeastern Geology*, **23**, 25–39.

NAYLOR, R. S. 1981. Felsic volcanic units in the Boston area, Massachusetts. *In*: BOOTHROYD, J. C. & HERMES, O. D. (eds) *Guidebook to Geologic Field Studies in Rhode Island and Adjacent Areas. New England Intercollegiate Geologic Conference, 73rd Annual Meeting*, pp. 303–14, University of Rhode Island, Kingston, RI.

O'HARA, K. & GROMET, L. P. 1985. Two distinct late Precambrian (Avalonian) terranes in southeastern New England and their late Paleozoic juxtaposition. *American Journal of Science*, **285**, 673–709.

OLSZEWSKI, W. J., JR & GAUDETTE, H. E. 1982. Age of the Brookville Gneiss and associated rocks, southeastern New Brunswick. *Canadian Journal of Earth Sciences*, **19**, 2158–66.

——, ——, BOTHNER, W. A., LAIRD, J. & CHEATHAM, M. M. 1984. The Precambrian(?) rocks of southeastern New Hampshire—a forgotten land. *Geological Society of America Abstracts with Programs*, **16**, 54.

——, ——, KEPPIE, J. D. & DONOHOE, H. V. 1981. Rb–Sr whole-rock age of the Kelly's Mountain basement complex, Cape Breton Island. *Geological Society of America Abstracts with Programs*, **13**, 169.

OSBERG, P. H., HUSSEY, A. M. & BOONE, G. M. 1984. Bedrock geologic map of Maine. *Maine Geological Survey Open-File Map No. 84–1*.

RAST, N. & SKEHAN, J. W., S. J. 1981. Possible correlation of Precambrian rocks of Newport, Rhode Island, with those of Anglesey, Wales. *Geology*, **9**, 596–601.

—— & —— 1983. The evolution of the Avalonian plate. *Tectonophysics*, **100**, 257–86.

ROBINSON, P. 1983. Realms of regional metamorphism in southern New England, with emphasis on the eastern Acadian metamorphic high. *In*: SCHENK, P. E. (ed.) *Regional Trends in the Geology of the Appalachian–Caledonian–Hercynian–Mauritanide Orogen*, pp. 249–58, Reidel, Dordrecht.

SEIDERS, V. M., MIXON, R. B., STERN, T. W., NEWELL, M. F. & THOMAS, C. B., JR 1975. Age of plutonism and tectonism and a new minimum age limit on the Glenarm Series in the northeast Virginia Piedmont near Occoquan. *American Journal of Science*, **275**, 481–511.

SKEHAN, J. W., S. J. 1983. Geological profiles through the Avalonian terrain of southeastern Massachu-

setts, Rhode Island, and eastern Connecticut, U.S.A. *Profiles of Orogenic Belts. Geodynamic Series*, Vol. 10, pp. 275–300, American Geophysical Union, Washington, DC.

—— & MURRAY, D. P. 1980. Geologic profile across southeastern New England. *Tectonophysics*, **69**, 285–319.

SMITH, B. M. & GILETTI, B. J. 1978. Rb–Sr whole rock study of the deformed porphyritic granitic rocks of Aquidneck and Conanicut Islands, Rhode Island. *Geological Society of America Abstracts with Programs*, **10**, 86.

SMITH, C. J. & HON, R. 1984. Geology, petrology and origin of the Precambrian igneous rocks located in the area north of Boston. *In*: HANSON, L. S. (ed.) *Geology of the Coastal Lowland, Boston to Kennebunk, Maine. New England Intercollegiate Geologic Conference, 76th Annual Meeting*, pp. 292–309, Salem State College, MA.

SROGI, L., WAGNER, M. E., LUTZ, T. M. & HAMRE, J. 1983. Metamorphic and tectonic history of a Paleozoic granulite facies terrane, Delaware–Pennsylvania Piedmont. *Geological Society of America Abstracts with Programs*, **15**, 694.

STEWART, D. B. 1974. Precambrian rocks of Seven Hundred Acre Island and development of cleavage in the Isleboro Formation. *In*: OSBERG, P. H. (ed.) *Guidebook for Field Trips in East-central and North-central Maine. New England Intercollegiate Geological Conference, 66th Annual Meeting, Orono, ME*, pp. 86–98.

—— & WONES, D. B. 1974. Bedrock geology of northern Penobscot Bay area. *In*: OSBERG, P. H. (ed.) *Guidebook for Field Trips in East-central and North-central Maine. New England Intercollegiate Geological Conference, 66th Annual Meeting, Orono, ME*, pp. 223–39.

WILLIAMS, H. 1978. Tectonic lithofacies map of the Appalachian orogen. *Memorial University of Newfoundland Map No. 1a*.

WONES, D. R. 1974. Igneous petrology of some plutons in the northern part of the Penobscot Bay area. *In*: OSBERG, P. H. (ed.) *Guidebook for Field Trips in East-central and North-central Maine. New England Intercollegiate Geological Conference, 66th Annual Meeting, Orono, ME*, pp. 99–125.

ZARTMAN, R. E. & NAYLOR, R. S. 1984. Structural implications of some radiometric ages of igneous rocks in southeastern New England. *Geological Society of America Bulletin*, **95**, 522–39.

ZEN, E-AN (ed.) 1983. Bedrock geologic map of Massachusetts. *United States Geological Survey Map* (Scale 1:250 000).

J. LAIRD, Department of Earth Sciences, University of New Hampshire, Durham, NH 03824, USA.

Plutonism and volcanism related to the pre-Arenig evolution of the Caledonide–Appalachian orogen

D. W. Rankin, Harald Furnes, A. C. Bishop, B. Cabanis, D. J. Milton, S. J. O'Brien & R. S. Thorpe

SUMMARY: Igneous activity younger than 1 Ga related to crustal extension characterizes the western part of the orogen from N America to Scotland in the Laurentian plate and the eastern part of the orogen in Scandinavia in the Baltic plate. Sub-aerial tholeiites, locally with alkalic rhyolites at embayments, and accompanying mafic dyke-swarms indicate late Proterozoic continental rifting; oceanic tholeiites followed. Iapetus oceanic crust is preserved in ophiolites obducted to the W in Laurentia and to the E in Baltica. Ensimatic island arcs developed locally in late Cambrian and early Ordovician in Scandinavia were broadly coeval with plutonic rocks intruding continental-shelf sediments during the late Finnmarkian deformation in northern Norway. E of the Iapetus suture in N America, southern Britain and northern France many of the accreted igneous rocks underwent or were generated during a late Proterozoic orogeny (Avalonian or Cadomian). Locally fossiliferous lower Cambrian strata rest unconformably on calc-alkaline Avalonian or Cadomian granites.

Type I, or cratonal, terranes formed the rifted margins of the Iapetus Ocean. Type II, or accreted, terranes appear not to have been part of the Iapetus rifting cycle and are not now tied stratigraphically to any large cratonal masses. Type II terranes terminate northward against the projection of Tornquist's line which may have originated in the late Proterozoic as the southern rifted margin of Baltica.

Igneous activity younger than the Precambrian basement is focussed on in this paper. For this purpose basement is defined as rocks separated in time from overlying rocks by orogenesis severe enough to cause the older rocks to react differently from younger cover rocks during subsequent orogenic activity. In the Caledonide–Appalachian orogen to the NW of the Iapetus suture this basement had experienced high-grade mid-Proterozoic (Grenvillian) or, in the case of NW Scotland, late Archaean metamorphism. Along the eastern margin of the orogen in Scandinavia the high-grade metamorphism of the basement was largely early Proterozoic, but includes a middle Proterozoic event in the SW.

Within the accreted terranes SE of the Iapetus suture in N America, the British Isles and northern France, where many of the igneous rocks underwent or were generated during a late Proterozoic orogeny, it is not clear whether any of the pre-Arenig rocks are related to the Iapetan rifting cycle and the concept of a Precambrian basement is different from that for the Laurentian and Baltic margins of Iapetus. In some accreted terranes SE of the Iapetus suture, such as much of the Carolina slate belt, pre-Arenig igneous rocks were first deformed in the Palaeozoic. All pre-Arenig igneous activity of the accreted terranes SE of the Iapetan suture are covered, at least briefly, in this paper.

For maps showing the distribution of these rocks in the context of the Appalachian–Caledon-ide orogen the reader is referred to the national maps generated by IGCP Project 27 (e.g. Brown *et al.* 1985).

The contributions of individual authors are indicated by initials at the end of each section.

Cratonic margins: western margin—the Laurentian plate

The western part of the orogen on the Laurentian plate in N America and the British Isles is characterized by late Proterozoic to early Palaeozoic igneous activity related to continental crustal extension, rifting and subsequent sea-floor spreading.

N America (Table 1)

The columns in Table 1 portray the generalized W–E zones of the western crystalline Appalachians. Except for W Newfoundland, all rocks are probably allochthonous; transport direction was to the W or NW and most rocks are polydeformed. Palaeozoic metamorphism imposed a W–E metamorphic gradient or gradients from little metamorphosed platform rocks to, locally, at least sillimanite from Massachusetts southward. The age of most rocks is poorly constrained. Many of the volcanic rocks are in metamorphosed stratified sequences having no palaeontological control

From HARRIS, A. L. & FETTES, D. J. (eds), 1988, *The Caledonian–Appalachian Orogen,* Geological Society Special Publication No. 38, pp. 149–183.

TABLE 1. *Pre-Arenig volcanic and plutonic rocks of the Appalachian orogen of the Laurentian plate in N America*

Column No.	1	2	3	4	5	6	7
			Blue-Green-Long (BGL) axis				
			All rocks, except those in Newfoundland, probably transported from the east				
Location	Platform		West of Northwest flank	Zone of external massifs (basement not necessarily exposed)	East or southeast flank (a tectonic stratigraphy in most places)	Internal massifs	Baie Verte–Brompton line in Canada; Eastern allochthons in United States
Newfoundland Canada Belle Isle	Subaerial tholeiites (Lighthouse Cove Fm., LÉ–LÉ[1] Tholeiitic dikes cutting crystalline basement of Grenville Province (Strong, 1974a)						
Western Newfoundland	Ocean ridge ophiolite (Bay of Islands Com.),[1,2] (Malpas, 1977; Suenn et al., 1979; Jacobsen & Wasserburg, 1979) (Hare Bay allochthon, Williams, 1975) Oceanic fracture zone ophiolite (Coastal Complex, Karson & Dewey, 1978) Off-axis seamount: ankaramite-trachyte (Skinner Cove Gp., LO-UÉ)[a] (Strong, 1974b)			Thoeiitic dikes cutting crystalline basement of long Range (Strong, 1974a)	Fragmented ophiolite (Birchy Complex) tectonically inter-layered with Fleur de Lys Supergroup (É-LÉ) which contains minor mafic volcanic rock (Williams & St-Julien, 1982)		Fragmented ophiolite (Advocate Complex) (Williams & St-Julien, 1982)
Quebec, Canada Gaspé Peninsula				Mafic volcanic rocks (Shickshock Gp., É) Fragmented ophiolite (Mt. Albert peridotite, tectonically above Shick-shock (Laurent, 1977; St-Julien & Hubert, 1975)			Mafic volc. rocks, incl. pillow lavas (Maquereau Gp., Fragmented ophiolite as blocks in an olistostromal melange (North Port-Daniel River Complex) (Williams & St-Julien, 1982)
Eastern Townships Sutton Mountains embayment				Mafic volc. rocks and minor alkalic rhyolite, probably submarine. (Tibbet Hill Volcanic Mbr. of Pinnacle Fm., LÉ-LP[1] (St-Julies & Hubert, 1975; Rankin, 1976)	Submarine tholeiites (Caldwell Gp., UÉ-MÇ(?) (St-Julien et al., 1983)		Oceanic ridge ophiolite (Thetford Mines Ophiolite Complex and others) (Williams and St-Julien, 1982)
Northeastern U.S. Northern Vermont				Oceanic tholeiites (Tibbet Hill Volcanic Mbr. of Pinnacle Fm.) (Pierratt, 1976)	Oceanic tholeiites and frag-mented ophiolites in an accretionary wedge. (A tectonic stratigraphy incl. from W to E, Hazens Notch, Ottauquechee, Stowe and western part of Moretown Fms., LÇ-É) (Doolan et al., 1982; Stanley et al., 1984)		
Eastern New York and western Massachusetts	Submarine tholeiites (basal Nassau Fm. associated with Rensselaer Graywacke Mbr., LÉ-LÉ[1], (Balk, 1953; Zen, 1983)			Sparse mafic dikes cutting crystalline basement of Berkshire massif (Zen, 1983)	Submarine mafic volcanic rocks and fragmented ophiolites in an accretionary wedge. (A tectonic stratigraphy in Rowe-Hawley zone including Chester Amphibolite Mbr. of Rowe Fm., LÇ-É) (Zen, 1983). Sparse submarine mafic volc. rocks (Moosac Fm., LÇ-LP) (Norton, 1976; Zen, 1983)		
Middle Atlantic U.S. Lower Hudson River Valley (N.Y. promontory)				High-Ti continental tholeiite dikes cutting crystalline basement of Hudson Highlands, LP. (Ratcliffe, 1983)		Granite (Yonkers and Pound Ridge Granite Gneisses, LÉ-LÉ in the Fordham Prong)[5] (Hall & Robinson, 1983)	Fragmented ophiolite (Serpentinite of Staten Island) (see Fisher et al., 1970)
Southeastern Pennsylvania	Submarine calc-alkaline and oceanic tholeiite basalt lavas and intrusives, possibly trench-related, in Hamburg klippe. (Jonestown volcanic rocks, LO)[a] (Lash, 1984)			Serpentinite of unknown age in crystalline basement of Honey Brook upland (Berg) 1980) Mafic dikes cutting crystal-line basement of Honey Brook upland (Berg, 1980)		Serpentinite of unknown age in crystalline basement of West Chester-Avondale massif) (Berg, 1980) Mafic dikes cutting crystalline basement of West Chester-Avondale massif) (Berg, 1980)	

Region				
Southcentral Pennsylvania and Maryland (South Mountain embayment)		Alkalic rhyolite lavas and ash flow tuffs and continental tholeiites (Catoctin Fm., LP)[1,6] (Berg, 1980; Blackburn & Brown, 1967; Rankin, 1976)		Fragmented ophiolite in several thrust sheets and melanges (Central Appalachian ophiolite including Baltimore and Piney Branch Complex, Morgan, 1977; Drake & Morgan, 1981). Parts of complex now lie NW of internal massifs. The Baltimore gneiss domes. Nd-Sm systematics of Bel Air belt, Baltimore complex suggest continental contamination (Shaw & Wasserburg, 1984)
Central Virginia	Subaerial continental alkalic and tholeiitic basalt lavas (Catoctin Fm., LP)[1] (Reed & Morgan, 1971)	Tholeiitic dikes cutting crystalline basement of the Blue Ridge (Reed & Morgan, 1971; Reed, 1955; Espenshade, 1986) Alkalic and peralkaline granite (Robertson River Pluton)[3] (Lukert & Banks, 1984; Rankin, 1975)	Fragmented ophiolites (Small ultramafic bodies either as olistoliths or fault slivers in the Lynchburg Fm., LP)(See Brown, 1970) Mafic volcanic rocks Subaerial continental tholeiite lavas and breccias in north (Catoctin Fm., LP) (Espenshade, 1986) Submarine lavas and dikes in south (Catoctin Fm., LP) (Lynchburg Fm., LP) (Brown, 1970)	Felsic (some peralkaline) and mafic dikes in crystalline basement of the Sauratown Mountains anticlinorium Alkalic granite (Crossnore Plutonic-Volcanic Complex, 1975) (Espenshade and others, 1975)
Southeastern U.S. Northwestern North Carolina and adjacent Tennessee (Mt. Rogers embayment)	Thin, subaerial, continental tholeiite lavas (Unicoi Fm. LE(?)-LP)[10] (Rankin, 1976)	Alkalic rhyolite and ash flow tuff (subaerial) and alkalic to tholeiitic basalt extrusives and dikes (Mt. Rogers Fm. of Crossnore Plutonic Complex, LP)[4,6,9] (Rankin, 1975 & 1976; Novak & Rankin, 1980) Subvolcanic alkalic rhyolite plutons (Crossnore Plutonic-Volcanic Complex, LP)[9]	Alkalic basalt and minor rhy. (Grandfather Mountain Fm., LP)[2] Alkalic diabase in Grandfather Mountain Fm., LP (Linville Metadiabase)[4] (Bryant & Reed, 1970) Alkalic granite, gabbro, mafic and felsic dikes in crystalline basement of Blue Ridge thrust sheets and Grandfather Mn. window. (Numerous plutons of Crossnore Plutonic-Volcanic Complex, LP)[9,10,12] (Rankin, 1975; Bryant & Reed, 1970)	Minor submarine tholeiites (Alligator Back Fm., LO-LP) LO-LP)[9] (Rankin, 1975) Fragmented ophiolites (Ultramafic bodies either as olistoliths or fault slivers in the Ashe Fm., LP (See Scotford & Williams, 1983) Submarine tholeiites (Ashe Fm., LP)[9] (Rankin, 1975)
Southern North Carolina and adjacent Georgia and South Carolina				Fragmented oceanic ridge ophiolite (Ultramafic bodies in Tallulah Falls Fm., LP. At least one body emplaced along a pre- to syn-metamorphic thrust) Hatcher et al., 1984; Shaw & Wasserburg, 1984) Submarine mafic volcanic rocks, some with continental affinity. (Tallulah Falls Fm., LP) (Hatcher et al., 1984)
Alabama				Submarine oceanic tholeiites, Tallapoosa block [Emuckfaw Fm., €-LP] Coosa block [Asland Supergroup, U-LP, includes pyroxenite pods within amphibolites] (Tull, 1978; Stowe et al., 1984)

*Fossil control of age.
1. Overlain by fossiliferous Lower Cambrian.
2. U-Pb ages of zircons from Trondhjemite of 504±10 and 508±5 Ma (Mattinson, 1976). Sm-Nd internal isochrons for pyroxene gabbros, 508±6 and 501±13 Ma (Jacobsen & Wasserburg, 1979).
3. $^{40}Ar/^{39}Ar$ age of 605±10 Ma (Stukas and Reynolds, 1974).
4. Analyses normalized Volatile-free and reduced (total iron as FeO).
5. Rb-Sr ages of 528±82, 563±35, and 583±25 Ma, recalculated data of others (Rankin et al., 1983).
6. Discordant U-Pb age of zircons from rhyolite of this and two other formations of 810 Ma interpreted to be igneous crystallization age (Shaw & Wasserburg, 1984).
7. Sm-Nd mineral isochrons for Bel Air belt, Baltimore Complex yield an age of 490-20 Ma interpreted to be the igneous crystallization age (Shaw & Wasserburg, 1984).
8. Discordant U-Pb age of zircons, 730 Ma (Lukert & Banks, 1984).
9. Rankin, Arth, Novak, Lopez and Frey in various combinations, unpublished data.
10. Rb-Sr ages of three granite plutons suggest crystallization between 680 and 710 Ma (Odom & Fullagar, 1984). U-Pb ages of zircons from granites of 824 Ma (Rankin et al., 1983) probably reflect inherited zircon as also pointed out by Odom and Fullagar (1984) who present additional U-Pb data.
11. Pb-Pb ages of zircons of 854 and 720 Ma (Rankin et al., 1983) probably reflect inherited zircons.
12. Rb-Sr age of 734-26 Ma for the Bakersville Metadiabase swarm (Goldberg et al., 1985).

and commonly are distant from or faulted against middle Proterozoic basement.

Most of the igneous activity was related to continental rifting and subsequent opening of the Iapetus Ocean. The early episode of continental rifting was marked by sub-aerial flood basalts of alkalic to continental tholeiitic composition W of the Blue–Green–Long (BGL) axis in Newfoundland and Virginia (Table 1, columns 1 and 3). Alkalic rhyolite accompanied the mafic volcanic rocks at three major embayments—Sutton Mountains, Quebec, South Mountain, Pennsylvania, and Mount Rogers, Virginia. Rhyolites are rare in the Sutton Mountains, but form major rock bodies at South Mountain and Mount Rogers where three volcanic centres probably erupted about 500–1000 km^3 of rhyolite.

Mafic dyke-swarms intrude continental basement rocks of the external massifs from Newfoundland to N Carolina (Table 1, column 4). The dykes are probably mostly of late Proterozoic age, but some may be early Cambrian. Dyke compositions are alkalic and high-titanium continental tholeiitic. In places in the Blue Ridge of northwestern North Carolina mafic dykes and sills make up as much as 50% of the basement terrane over areas as large as 8 km^2 (Rankin 1976). In such areas the volume of dyke implies large amounts of crustal extension. Such extensively dyked continental crust could be passive-margin transitional crust.

In some areas the external massifs contain mafic to felsic plutons, mostly late Proterozoic but including early Cambrian rocks in the Manhattan prong. These plutons are particularly abundant in the area of the Mount Rogers embayment which locally also contains abundant rhyolite dykes in Grenvillian basement. The felsic plutonic rocks have the same alkalic to peralkaline character as the rhyolites.

In summary, late Proterozoic to early Cambrian igneous activity along the BGL axis was bimodal with a composition gap between 53% and 68% SiO$_2$ (Rankin 1976). Rhyolites are restricted to the embayments.

Possibly the external massifs along the BGL axis reflect a late Proterozoic shoreline or hinge zone (Rankin 1975, Wehr & Glover 1985). Volcanic rocks, which are almost exclusively mafic SE of the axis, are typically associated with thick sequences of sub-aqueous sandstone and shale (Table 1, column 5). Sparse chemical data suggest that these basalts are oceanic tholeiites. In N Vermont, where the Palaeozoic metamorphic grade is low, much of the sequence thought to be late Proterozoic and early Palaeozoic E of the BGL axis is a 'tectonic stratigraphy', possibly a subduction-related accretionary wedge of slope–rise sedimentary rocks (Stanley et al. 1984). In W central Vermont the structurally-lowest unit of the eastern stratified sequence, the Pinnacle Formation, and its correlative to the S, the Hoosac Formation, unconformably overlie Laurentian basement. The proposed accretionary wedge overrides the basal units from the E, and ultramafic rocks interpreted as fragments of oceanic crust occur as slivers along imbricate faults within the wedge (Stanley et al. 1984, Stanley & Ratcliffe 1985). Thus, in Vermont, the eastern pre-Arenig stratified sequence consists of (i) a western package tied stratigraphically to Laurentian basement and lacking ultramafic rock bodies (represented by the Pinnacle and Hoosac) and (ii) an overriding thrust package that contains ultramafic rock bodies but is tied stratigraphically to neither Laurentian nor fossiliferous rocks (Hazens Notch Formation and the Rowe–lower Moretown interval). Doolan et al. (1982) have concluded that the assemblages containing ultramafic bodies are probably pre-middle Ordovician.

A comparable interpretation probably applies to the E flank of the BGL axis in the S Appalachians where the cover sequence is locally tied stratigraphically to Laurentia (the Lynchburg, Ashe and possibly Tallulah Falls Formations), but structurally-higher parts of these sequences to the SE contain ultramafic bodies. The sequence which contains the ultramafic bodies has been interpreted as late Proterozoic–early Palaeozoic (Rankin et al. 1983), but they are only known to be post-Grenvillian and pre-Arenig. By analogy with New England a fault may separate the ultramafic-bearing parts of the Lynchburg and Ashe Formations from those parts stratigraphically tied to Laurentia. Hatcher (1978) and Abbott & Raymond (1984) argued that the presence of ultramafic bodies in the Ashe and Tallulah Falls Formations suggests that they were deposited, at least in part, on oceanic crust.

Of the internal massifs (Table 1, column 6), the Manhattan prong, the West Chester–Avondale massifs and the Sauratown Mountains anticlinorium, at least, include various combinations of mafic dykes, peralkaline granitic dykes and granite, some of which is peralkaline, which are all interpreted as late Proterozoic and intruding Grenvillian basement. Rankin (1976) suggested that the massifs initially formed as horsts on the eastern side of a late Proterozoic rift system. W. A. Thomas (1977) suggested that the internal massifs originated as microcontinents that drifted from the Laurentian plate during early stages of the opening of Iapetus and returned to collide with that plate during closure. If significant oceanic crust formed in the opening rift,

Thomas's interpretation is preferable. The main Iapetus Ocean opened E of the internal massifs but, since the sedimentary packages containing the ultramafic rock bodies are not tied stratigraphically to Laurentia, the presence of oceanic crust inboard of the internal massifs does not settle the problem.

The ultramafic bodies in the W Appalachians are generally rootless pods commonly associated with metamorphosed gabbro and basalt. They occur as large far-travelled allochthons (Bay of Islands Complex), slivers along imbricate thrust faults (McElhaney & McSween 1983, Hatcher *et al.* 1984, Stanley *et al.* 1984) or olistoliths in ophiolitic melange (Drake & Morgan 1981). Many workers have argued that these ultramafic bodies are fragments of ophiolites derived from the obduction of Iapetus oceanic crust. This is supported by a considerable body of chemical data (Hatcher *et al.* 1984, Lipin 1984). Shaw & Wasserburg (1984), however, used neodymium and Rb–Sr analyses to show that mafic–ultramafic complexes in the western ultramafic belt of the Appalachians probably have more than one origin.

On the Maine–Quebec border, nearly 100 km SE of the Baie Verte–Brompton line, lies the Chain Lakes massif of Precambrian basement, which is unlike the Grenvillian basement of the nearby Canadian shield and may be an accreted terrane (Zen 1983). An ophiolite of Cambrian? to early Ordovician? age is obducted onto the S flank of the massif (Boudette 1981), and consists of ultramafic and other plutonic rocks (Boil Mountain Complex) and the overlying Jim Pond Formation—pillowed basalt, dacite and associated sedimentary rocks interpreted as oceanic crust.

Mafic plutonic rock including gabbro, norite and diorite—the Rich Acres Formation—crops out in the Smith River allochthon in S central Virginia (Conley & Henika 1973). The Smith River allochthon also includes stratified metamorphic units containing mafic volcanic rocks as well as altered metapyroxenite and talc schist, all of uncertain age. They are not shown in Table 1 but have a setting much like the Baltimore Complex of column 7, i.e. they are both in thrust sheets that have overridden internal massifs. The Rich Acres Formation is associated with gneissic diamictites similar to the sedimentary melange that constitutes the Sykesville Formation of N Virginia and Maryland (Rankin 1975).

The age of Iapetan rifting is poorly constrained. Stukas & Reynolds (1974) report a ^{40}Ar/^{39}Ar age of 605 ± 10 Ma for diabase dykes thought to be feeders for the Lighthouse Cove basalts of Newfoundland, in agreement with the strati-graphic position of these basalts beneath fossiliferous lower Cambrian shales.

Goldberg *et al.* (1985) determined an Rb–Sr whole-rock isochron of 734 ± 26 Ma on eight dykes of the Bakersville metadiabase swarm in western N Carolina and adjacent Tennessee. A discordant U–Pb age of 810 Ma, based upon five zircon samples from the rhyolitic Catoctin, Mount Rogers and Grandfather Mountain Formations (Rankin *et al.* 1983), may be too old in that a gap of nearly 250 Ma between Iapetan rifting (rhyolites) and drifting (basal Cambrian clastic rocks of the Chilhowee Group) seems too great.

Late Proterozoic alkalic granites which have been dated (Pb–U or Rb–Sr) appear significantly younger than rhyolite zircon ages. Odom & Fullagar (1984) report Rb–Sr whole-rock ages of between 680 and 710 Ma on three granites of the Crossnore Plutonic–Volcanic Complex, arguing that the older U–Pb ages reflect zircons inherited from the Grenvillian basement. Lukert & Banks (1984) determined a discordant U–Pb age of 730 Ma for zircons from the Robertson River pluton of central Virginia. Farther N in the New York promontory somewhat younger Rb–Sr whole-rock ages were obtained for the Yonkers Gneiss (528 ± 82 and 563 ± 35 Ma) and Pound Ridge Granite Gneiss (583 ± 25 Ma) (Rankin *et al.* 1983). Williams *et al.* (1985) reported a Pb–U zircon age of 602 ± 10 Ma for the newly recognized late Proterozoic Round Pond granite in W Newfoundland, an age similar to that of Long Range diabase dykes. Williams *et al.* (1985) argued for diachronous Iapetus rifting—older in the S (about 730 Ma) and younger in the N.

Minor early Cambrian basaltic volcanism recorded in the Unicoi Formation at the base of the Chilhowee persists for 160 km along strike in the Mount Rogers embayment. These continental tholeiites indicate that the magma-forming process (crustal extension?) in the Mount Rogers embayment may have spanned as much as 150 Ma.

The only direct evidence for the age of the oceanic crust is isotopic ages of 510–500 Ma from the Bay of Islands Complex, Newfoundland (Mattinson 1976, Jacobson & Wasserburg 1979), but the first oceanic crust could have formed much earlier than that. On general geological grounds the earliest oceanic crust probably coincided with the basal Cambrian clastic sequence which was succeeded by a shelf sequence.

Rankin (1976) and W. A. Thomas (1977) discussed the mechanism by which the rifting originated. The present salients and recesses in Appalachian structural trends may be inherited from the embayments and promontories of the late Proterozoic continental margin of the Laurentian plate formed by initial Iapetan rifting. The jagged nature could have originated from an oceanic ridge (R) offset by transform faults (T) or RT (W. A. Thomas 1977) or from the intersection of continental rifts (R) at a triple junction or RRR (Rankin 1976). Either model must explain the restriction of rhyolites to Appalachian embayments, but it is clear that the BGL axis coincides with continental rifts and not with an oceanic ridge–transform system. The Mesozoic opening of the present Atlantic Ocean implies that continental rifting pre-dated the drifting phases. A consequence of the RRR model is that one of the rifts at a triple junction could fail, i.e. not produce continental separation and oceanic crust. This failed arm or aulacogen should point into the continent at the embayments. In the Appalachians the Ottawa–Bonnechere graben, trending WNW from the Sutton Mountains embayment, is the best candidate for an Iapetan failed arm (Rankin 1976). Documentation that promontories evolved from RRR triple junctions is difficult because the failed arm would be carried off with the departing continent during the drifting phase. Promontories would probably experience greater strain than embayments during ocean closing.

Once the crustal fracture pattern has been established it is entirely reasonable that one of the remaining two sets of rift systems could evolve into transform faults, leaving the other set to become the oceanic ridges. Certainly the Iapetan crustal fracture pattern influenced the location and geometry of the Mesozoic rift system of eastern N America (Rankin 1976) and even the locus of N Atlantic transform faults such as the Oceanographer fracture zone. Possibly an earlier Grenville rifting and RT system influenced the Iapetan system but at present we have no evidence for this. As Williams (1984) pointed out, however, the Appalachian miogeocline does crudely parallel Grenvillian deformed zones.

D.W.R.

British Isles

Thorpe *et al.* (1984) have drawn attention to the contrast in late Precambrian to early Palaeozoic times between the basement characteristics of the British Isles N and S of the Iapetus suture. Archaean–Proterozoic crystalline basement is present in Scotland and is overlain unconformably by Precambrian Torridonian sedimentary rocks deposited after *c.* 1140 Ma. The Stoer Group at the base of the Torridonian succession contains a unique volcanic marker horizon, the Stac Fada Member, which is a sedimentary unit containing abundant fragments of pumice, shards

and devitrified glass and is interpreted as an ash or pyroclastic flow deposited in shallow water (Lawson 1974, Stewart 1975).

The Dalradian Supergroup is lithologically diverse and was deposited over about 200 Ma in a complex trough aligned NE–SW. Dunning (1972) has suggested an age of *c.* 700 Ma for the Moine–Dalradian transition. The trough lay to the SW of the foreland and is tectonically broken away from it. The Dalradian has been reviewed by Harris & Pitcher (1975) and the associated igneous rocks have been described by Leake (1982).

Igneous rocks in the Dalradian of Scotland and Ireland are almost entirely mafic and occur principally in the Argyll (middle) and Southern Highlands (upper) Dalradian where extrusive pillow lavas, crystal tuffs and originally mafic glassy material occur interbedded with sedimentary rocks in the Loch Awe–Knapdale region of Scotland. Metamorphosed pillow lavas also occur in Banffshire, the Highland Border zone, and in Ireland. There has been debate as to whether the original magma was notably sodic or whether the spilitization was a later event. Opinion generally favours an origin by metasomatic segregation.

Intrusive rocks, principally mafic sills and fewer dykes, are associated with and related to the lavas. Some dykes fed the volcanic rocks. Caledonian granitic rocks were emplaced over a considerable time-span. The 'older granites' of Scotland are igneous rocks which, on structural or radiometric evidence, pre-date the main Caledonian (Grampian) metamorphism; Pankhurst & Sutherland (1982) have reviewed these rocks. Pidgeon & Aftalion (1978) describe the U–Pb systems in zircons from Scottish and English granites and have drawn attention to the influence of older inherited zircons in producing discordant U–Pb zircon patterns. The principle older granites are listed in Table 2. The information is based largely on Appendix C of Sutherland (1982). The range of radiometric ages among the older granites shows that they were not emplaced during a single episode. Pidgeon & Aftalion (1978) discuss the age and origin of the Ardgour granite gneiss, which has a zircon U–Pb age similar to that of the Inchbae rock of the Carn Chuinneag Complex, and are of the view that it post-dates the regional migmatites; however, Barr *et al.* (1986) believe that this granitic gneiss was emplaced during high-grade metamorphism and deformation at *c.* 1030 Ma. The foliated Slieve Gamph Complex in western Ireland, although yielding an Ordovician date, is probably synchronous with or earlier than the metamorphism. The young age (405 ± 11 Ma) of the Vagastie Bridge granite in northern Scotland is unex-

TABLE 2. *Older granites of Scotland and Ireland*

Rock type	Age (Ma)	Method	Reference
Portsoy granite gneiss (Scotland)	655 ± 17	Rb–Sr WR	Pankhurst 1974
Carn Chuinneag granite (Scotland)	550 ± 10	Rb–Sr WR	Long & Lambert 1963
	555 ± 10	U–Pb zircon	Pidgeon & Johnson 1974
Ben Vuirich granite (Scotland)	514 ± 7	U–Pb zircon	Pankhurst & Pidgeon 1976
Dunfallandy Hill granite (Scotland)	481 ± 15	Rb–Sr WR	Pankhurst & Pidgeon 1976
Slieve Gamph complex (Ireland)	477 ± 6	Rb–Sr WR	Pankhurst *et al.* 1976
Vagastie Bridge granite (Scotland)	405 ± 11	U–Pb zircon	Pidgeon & Aftalion 1978

WR, whole rock.

plained, as there is no evidence of Caledonian deformation later than this date. Although dates of about 480–500 Ma have been obtained from the mafic plutons of NE Scotland and W Ireland, these plutons are not discussed here because they were emplaced synchronously with Caledonian metamorphism and deformation and are later than the time-span considered in this paper.

Dewey (1971) and Bird *et al.* (1971) argued that the rocks of the Highland Border fracture zone, which separates Caledonian metamorphic rocks to the N from the non-metamorphosed upper Palaeozoic sedimentary rocks of the Midland Valley, formed part of an ophiolite complex. The rocks within this zone are known as the Highland Boundary (or Border) Complex (Ikin 1983) and comprise pillow lavas, serpentinized mafic and ultramafic rocks, jaspers, cherts and black shales, limestones, breccias, conglomerates and arenites. They have been reviewed by Bloxam (1982) and Curry *et al.* (1984). Faunal evidence indicates that the sediments in the Highland Boundary Complex range in age from Cambrian to upper Ordovician (Jehu & Campbell 1917, Downie *et al.* 1971, Curry *et al.* 1984), which precludes the correlation of the pillow lavas with those of the Dalradian as had been suggested on structural grounds by Johnson & Harris (1967) and Henderson & Robertson (1982). The rocks of the Highland Boundary Series cannot have undergone Grampian deformation as did the Dalradian.

There is general agreement that the Dalradian sediments were deposited at a continental margin, probably in a marginal basin or ensialic trough which may have been caused by back-arc spreading (Phillips *et al.* 1976, Wright 1976). The basaltic volcanism seems to have been related to extension at the continental margin and the magma was of tholeiitic type; attempts to characterize the tholeiite further in relation to the basaltic environment have not been conclusive (Leake 1982).

The Highland Boundary Complex has been interpreted as the relics of a NW-dipping subduc-

tion zone, but opinion has moved in favour of it being an ophiolite remnant either of the main Iapetus Ocean (Lambert & McKerrow 1976) or of a marginal basin to the N (Henderson & Robertson 1982, Ikin 1983, Curry *et al.* 1984) transported southwards as a slab of ocean floor obducted onto the southern continental margin.

A.C.B.

Cratonic margins: eastern margin—the Baltic plate

Pre-Arenig magmatic rocks in the Scandinavian Caledonides occur within a number of nappe units (Fig. 1) divided into four major complexes, the lower, middle, upper and uppermost Allochthons (Roberts & Gee 1985). Most of the magmatic sequences occur in the upper Allochthon. Products of late Proterozoic crustal rifting occur in the lower and middle Allochthons and the lower part of the upper Allochthon. Finnmarkian syn-orogenic mafic–ultramafic intrusions occur in the middle Allochthon. Evidence of the spreading stages of the Iapetus Ocean is preserved in obducted ophiolite fragments found in the higher parts of the upper and uppermost? Allochthons as are convergent plate margin products, representing early ensimatic island-arc activity. The sequence indicates broadly that successive segments of the Iapetan oceanic crust and its Scandinavian supra-subduction margin have been brought eastward and stacked by a combination of obduction and tectonism in a succession of events which span the early history of ocean closure. A more comprehensive picture of the overall magmatic evolution of Scandinavian Caledonian magmatism was presented by Stephens *et al.* (1985).

Stratigraphic packages are bounded in the nappes by tectonic junctions; thus a systematic description of the volcanic rocks must be based on the tectonostratigraphy. Hence the following sections are arranged according to nappe succession.

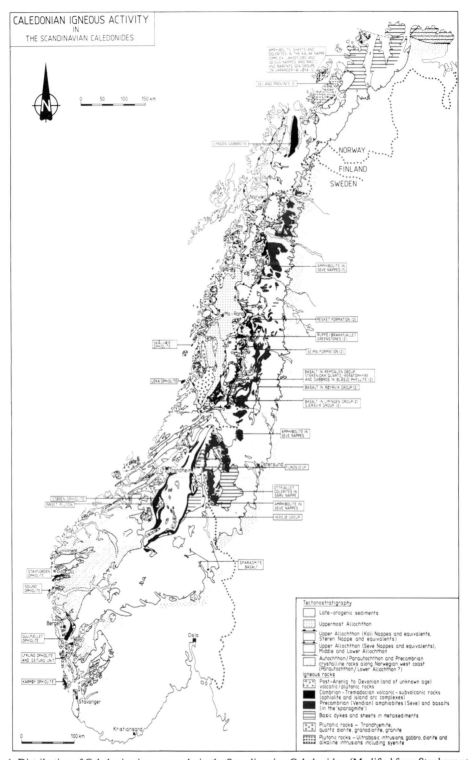

Fig. 1. Distribution of Caledonian igneous rocks in the Scandinavian Caledonides. (Modified from Stephens *et al.* 1985.)

Rift-related ensialic igneous activity in the lower, middle and upper Allochthons

Within the 'sparagmites' of the Hedmark Group in the SE part of the lower Allochthon (Fig. 1) minor basalt lavas and dykes, which are probably upper Riphean or Vendian (late Proterozoic), occur beneath the Moelv tillite (e.g. Saether & Nystuen 1981). Of typical continental tholeiitic composition, they may have formed in an aulacogen related to the central rift zone of the Iapetus Ocean (Furnes *et al.* 1983a).

The Ottfjället dolerites of the Särv Nappe (middle Allochthon), cutting a non-fossiliferous sequence of alluvial and shallow-marine felds-pathic sandstone, dolomite and glaciogenic sedimentary rocks (Röshoff 1975, Kumpalainen 1980), have been dated ($^{40}Ar/^{39}Ar$) at $665 \pm$ 10 Ma (Claesson & Roddick 1983). They are of mid-ocean ridge basalt (MORB) affinity (Fig. 2A) and may relate to the continental break-up and initial development stage of the Iapetus Ocean (Gee 1975, Solyom *et al.* 1979b). In the upper part of the Leksdal Nappe (middle Allochthon in the Tommerås area, NE of Trondheim), equivalent to the Särv Nappe, metabasalt dykes with MORB–WPB affinities (WPB, within-plate basalt) may represent the same dyke generation as the Ottfjället dolerites (Andreasson *et al.* 1979). The Kalak Nappe Complex (Sturt *et al.* 1978) of the middle Allochthon in northern Norway

contains amphibolite-facies mafic dykes with MORB to transitional continental WPB affinities (Gayer & Humphreys 1981).

Within the Seve Nappe, comprising the lower part of the upper Allochthon (Zachrisson 1973), amphibolites associated with quartzo-felds-pathic, garnet-mica and calcareous schists and with local migmatic gneisses (Trouw 1973) show MORB affinity (Fig. 2B) (Solyom *et al.* 1979a, b, Hill 1980); although their emplacement age is not established, Solyom *et al.* (1979a) favour a late Proterozoic age.

Arc-related (probably ensimatic) igneous activity in the Køli Nappes and equivalents of the upper Allochthon

Lower Palaeozoic fossil-bearing successions, generally metamorphosed in the greenschist facies, occur in a number of thrust nappes and overlie the Seve Nappes and related units of the upper Allochthon (Stephens *et al.* 1985). In the central Caledonides these are the Køli Nappes, subdivided into the lower, middle and upper Køli; each nappe complex contains several volcanic–sub-volcanic associations at different tectonostratigraphic and lithostratigraphic levels (Stephens 1980). Only the upper part of the upper Køli Nappe may be at the same tectonostratigraphic level as the Støren Nappe which contains ophio-

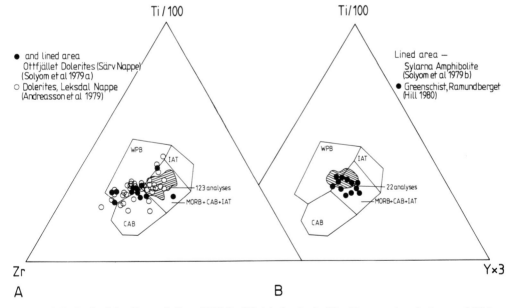

FIG. 2. Ti–Zr–Y plot (after Pearce & Cann 1973) for (A) dolerites in the Särv Nappe and equivalents and (B) for the metamafic rock in the Seve Nappe: MORB, mid-ocean ridge basalts; CAB, calc-alkaline basalts; IAT, island-arc tholeiite; WPB, within-plate basalts.

lite fragments. Hence, even though these arc-related volcanics are certainly younger than the oldest ophiolites (Group I), logically they will be described before the ophiolites because of their lower tectonostratigraphic position.

In the lower Køli Nappes volcanic rocks occur at two stratigraphic positions, the oldest of pre-Ashgill age and the youngest of Llandovery age. The pre-Ashgill Tjopasi Group (Seima Formation), directly overlying schists and amphibolites of the Seve Nappe (Stephens *et al.* 1985), contains volcanic rocks of a mixed mafic and felsic assemblage associated with phyllites. The meta-basalts are transitional tholeiitic–alkaline of WPB and MORB affinities (Fig. 3). The age is uncertain, but some of the rocks lying stratigraph-ically above the Seima Formation contain fossils of mid-Ordovician age (Kulling cited by Strand & Kulling 1972).

The middle Køli Nappes consist of several Ordovician? volcanic–sub-volcanic complexes and calcareous flysch-like sediments (Zachrisson 1964, 1969, Halls *et al.* 1977, Sjøstrand 1978, Kollung 1979, Lutro 1979). The tectonostrati-graphically-lowest volcanic rocks of the Remda-len and Røyrvik Groups consist of tholeiitic to alkaline pillow lavas and hyaloclastites of MORB to WPB character (Fig. 3), in association with phyllites and recrystallized ribbon cherts (Zach-risson 1966, Olsen 1980, Stephens *et al.* 1985). The Remdalen Group is stratigraphically over-lain by a bimodal, felsic-dominated volcanic–sub-volcanic complex (Stekenjokk quartz kera-tophyre) in which pyroclastic and high-level intrusive rocks dominate. Altered basalts, basal-tic andesites and low-potassium dacite–rhyolite are believed to be represented, and three separate fractionation series involving basalts and basaltic andesites have been suggested (Stephens 1982) (Fig. 3): (i) a mildly-tholeiitic series of basalts and basaltic andesites which are highly depleted in titanium, zirconium, yttrium and phosphorus relative to MORB (1A series), (ii) a tholeiitic series showing MORB affinity (1B and 2A series) and (iii) fractionated alkaline basalts (2B series). The tectonostratigraphically-highest volcanics within the middle Køli, the Gjersvik Nappe, consist of bimodal mafic and felsic volcanic rocks, of which the lowest basalts and basaltic andesites have trace-element abundances similar to island-arc tholeiite (IAT) which are succeeded by tholeiitic MORB-like basalts, again overlain by alkaline basalts (Fig. 3). This would point to a probably ensimatic island-arc to tensional envi-ronment related to arc splitting (Stephens 1977, 1981). The Fundsjø and Hersjø Groups further to the S (S of the Grong–Olden culmination) in the Meråker Nappe (Wolff & Roberts 1980) contain

volcanic and high-level intrusive rocks, and have been correlated with the Gjersvik Group (Grenne & Reinsbakken 1981). The mafic rocks in the otherwise bimodal mafic–felsic Fundsjø Group show IAT as well as MORB character (Grenne & Lagerblad 1985).

The upper Køli Nappes contain volcanic rocks at three tectonostratigraphic levels, of which two may be pre-Arenig (Stephens *et al.* 1985). The tectonostratigraphically-lowest unit, the Krutfjel-let Nappe, contains mafic volcanic and sub-volcanic rocks at apparently three separate tectonostratigraphic levels, of which the two lowest show island-arc tholeiitic affinity and the highest shows alkaline affinity (Stephens & Senior 1981). Two conspicuous units of mafic volcanic rocks, the Ruffe and Brackfjallet greenstones, occur at the highest tectonostratigraphic level in the upper Køli Nappes. The Ruffe greenstone is tholeiitic and shows mixed MORB–WPB affini-ties, while the tectonically-overlying Brackfjallet greenstone is alkaline and shows WPB affinity (Stephens *et al.* 1985).

Ophiolite fragments and associated island-arc magmatism in the upper and uppermost Allochthons

From Karmøy to Lyngen in the Norwegian Caledonides a number of rock sequences in the upper Allochthon (Fig. 1) may be ophiolitic. The geochemical composition of the pillow lavas and dyke complexes is predominantly MORB. Those recognized in the Støren Nappe, in the Trond-heim region, probably lie either at the same tectonostratigraphic level (Roberts *et al.* 1970, Wolff & Roberts 1980) or above (Gee & Zachris-son 1974) the arc-related succession of the Køli Nappe Complex as described above.

Known Norwegian ophiolites range from prob-able Vendian (late Proterozoic) to middle Ordo-vician. An important bipartite grouping can be discerned from the combined criteria of field relationships, faunal constraints, radiometric dating and comprehensive geochemical studies. The two groups, I and II (Furnes *et al.* 1985), equate in broad terms with Vendian?–Cambrian and Ordovician ocean-floor assemblages respec-tively, and the late Cambrian–earliest Ordovician Finnmarkian orogenic event (Sturt *et al.* 1978) provides a natural and convenient line of separa-tion between the two. The most complete ophio-lite fragment in the Scandinavian Caledonides is the Leka ophiolite (Fig. 1).

The other ophiolite fragments contain only minor serpentinite bodies, although layered and high-level gabbros, sheeted dyke complexes and non-vesicular locally-variolitic pillow lavas are

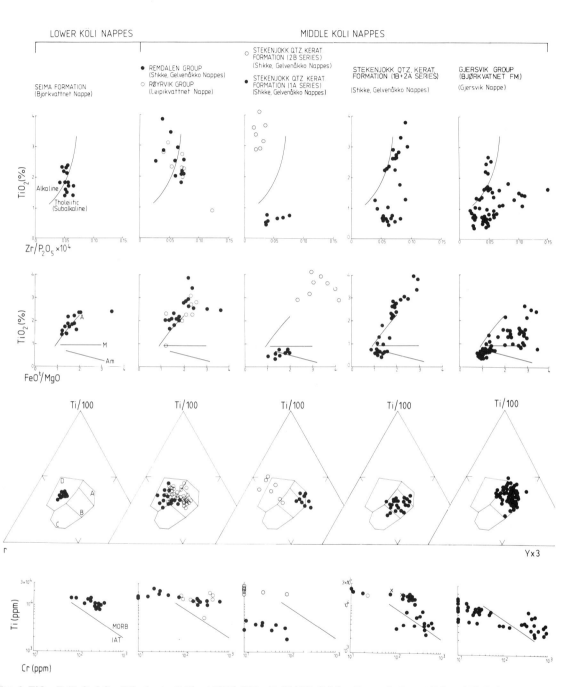

IG. 3. TiO₂–Zr/P₂O₅ (after Winchester & Floyd 1976), TiO₂–FeO(t)/MgO (after Pearce & Cann 1973) and Ti–Cr (Pearce 975) plots for basaltic rocks and basaltic andesites in the lower and middle Køli Nappes (upper Allochthon). A, M and Am on ιe TiO₂–FeO(t)/MgO diagram refer to trend lines for abyssal tholeiite, Macauley Island tholeiitic island arc series and the ₋magi calc-alkaline series. A, B, C and D on the Ti–Zr–Y diagram refer to the fields of IAT, MORB + IAT, CAB and WPB respectively (abbreviations as in Fig. 2). (Modified from Stephens *et al.* 1985.)

common. Plagiogranites are typically present in the upper part of the gabbroic zone or the sheeted intrusive complex. Detailed descriptions of each individual ophiolite fragment and their geochemical development have been summarized by Furnes et al. (1980a,b, 1982, 1985), Prestvik (1980), Sturt et al. (1984) and Roberts et al. (1985).

Group I ophiolite complexes (Fig. 1) may be derived from either a major ocean or a marginal basin, and evidence points to their Finnmarkian eastward obduction and internal deformation.

In western Norway there is also evidence for the existence of an upper Cambrian primitive island arc (Furnes et al. 1983b). This sequence, the Geitung unit, comprising a mixed extrusive–sedimentary sequence, rests unconformably upon the Lykling ophiolite (Fig. 1). The volcanic rocks are predominantly low-potassium tholeiitic metabasalts and felsic hyaloclastites as well as massive flow units associated with cherts, minor conglomerates and sandstones (Nordås et al. 1985). Keratophyres 535 ± 46 Ma old (Furnes et al. 1983b) occur in this unit. These island-arc products were obducted together with the subjacent oceanic crust during Finnmarkian orogenesis. The Group I ophiolites and associated island-arc developments were further dissected and deformed during Scandian mid-to-late Silurian orogenesis.

The syn-orogenic intrusive Seiland Province in the Kalak Nappe Complex (middle Allochthon)

The Scandinavian Caledonides contain several isolated mafic, ultramafic and alkaline complexes of widely-variable petrographic character as well as the single large Seiland Province of N Norway, in which numerous intrusions were emplaced at different times during early Caledonian orogenesis. No related volcanic rocks are known to be associated with these complexes.

Mafic complexes

Gabbroic complexes were emplaced during inter-kinematic episodes within the two phases of Finnmarkian deformation as well as during the intervening main phase of porphyroblastesis (Sturt et al. 1978). The gabbro complexes intrude a metamorphosed sedimentary sequence of probable late Precambrian age (Sturt et al. 1978) as well as the Precambrian gneissic basement to this sequence (Ramsay & Sturt 1977, Ramsay et al. 1979, Akselsen 1980). The mafic magmatic activity appears to have been protracted but episodic. Rb–Sr whole-rock isochron ages suggest repeated emplacement of magmas from 540 ± 17 ma to 490 ± 27 Ma (Sturt et al. 1978). Cumulate

structures and textures are variably preserved in all the major bodies and some exhibit extensive cryptic variation (Robins & Gardner 1974, Gardner 1980, Robins 1982). The largest of the intrusions contains cumulate sequences 1–8 km thick.

Plutons emplaced before the second phase of deformation are uniformly tholeiitic, whereas the later intrusions in the eastern part of the province were of alkaline olivine basalt (Robins & Gardner 1975, Robins 1982). An exception to this pattern is the tholeiitic Lille Kufjord gabbro, the lower part of which contains repeated cyclic units in which peridotites grade upwards into leucogabbros (Oosterom 1955, Robins & Gardner 1975). According to Robins & Gardner (1975), the magmatic activity was related to upwelling of mantle diapir above a progressively steepening Benioff zone.

Ultramafic complexes

The high-temperature intrusive peridotites present in the Seiland Province appear to be unique in the Scandinavian Caledonides. They show certain similarities, however, to the syn-orogenic ultramafic intrusions of Alaska and the Ural Mountains (Taylor 1967, Irvine 1974). The peridotites of the Seiland Province were emplaced late in the second major phase of Finnmarkian deformation. However, they are locally deformed and cut by alkaline dykes probably intruded at 490 ± 27 Ma (Sturt et al. 1978).

In all the complexes the ultramafic rocks are cut by ultramafic dykes, swarms of veins of highly-variable composition and regionally-developed picritic to olivine basaltic dykes (Robins & Takla 1979).

Alkaline intrusions and carbonatites

In the Seiland Province alkaline rocks, carbonatites and fenites form three major complexes emplaced into syn-orogenic gabbros or their metasedimentary host during the closing stages of the Finnmarkian tectonothermal event. These are the Breivikbotn Complex (490 ± 27 Ma) (Sturt et al. 1978) on Sørøy (Sturt & Ramsay 1965), the Lillebukt Alkaline Complex (Heier 1961, Robins 1980) and the Pollen carbonatite (Robins & Tysseland 1983). Dykes of carbonatite, alkaline pyroxenite and both feldspathoidal and nepheline-free syenite pegmatites are also widely developed in the province (Sturt & Ramsay 1965, Robins & Tysseland 1979, Robins 1982). Several rock types in the province are not known from other orogenic terranes.

Syn-orogenic trondhjemite and granite in the Trondheim Nappe Complex and equivalents (upper Allochthon)

Intrusive rocks of trondhjemitic affinity in the Trondheim Nappe Complex (Wolff & Roberts 1980) show a range in composition from trondhjemite (*s.s.*) through tonalite to occasional granodiorite. They occur as widespread relatively small bodies, the largest being the Innset Pluton (Fig. 1). Most are found in the Gula Nappe, but they cut earliest Ordovician and/or pre-Ordovician volcanic units (the Støren, Fundsjø and Hersjø Groups) and overlying sedimentary rocks in the Støren and Meråker Nappes. Rb–Sr whole-rock isochron ages range from 509 to 451 Ma and a zircon U–Pb age from the Vakkerlien trondhjemite gave 509^{+5}_{-4} Ma (Klingspor & Gee 1985). They generally cut fabrics and folds in the host rocks although, in the Gula Nappe, some are apparently affected by the earliest deformation.

Summarizing comments

Pre-Arenig magmatic activity within the Scandinavian Caledonides may represent the following sequence of events.

1 An upper Riphean–Vendian rifting stage represented by (a) typical continental tholeiites in the lower Allochthon, probably formed in an aulacogen relative to the central rift zone of the Iapetus Ocean, and (b) metabasalt dykes of MORB to WPB type in the middle and upper Allochthons related to the first development of the Iapetus Ocean.
2 Vendian?–Cambrian ocean development represented by the many ophiolite fragments along the Norwegian coast and in central Norway within the upper and perhaps uppermost Allochthons.
3 Development of ensimatic island arcs around upper Cambrian–lower Ordovician times in S to central Norway and northern Sweden. These appear at different tectonostratigraphic levels within the upper Allochthon, suggesting a complex island-arc development at this stage.

During approximately the same time period, in northern Norway, the Seiland Province of plutonic rocks intruded the continental-shelf sediments during the late Cambrian–early Ordovician Finnmarkian deformation.

H.F.

Accreted terranes: USA

Two outboard N American areas ('Avalonia') which have escaped severe metamorphism and deformation record igneous activity in the latest Proterozoic: these areas are the Carolina slate belt in the S and the Milford–Dedham zone in the N.

In the southern part of the Carolina slate belt a thick felsic volcaniclastic sequence, the Uwharrie Formation, is succeeded by the Albemarle Group, a sedimentary sequence with subsidiary volcanics which are predominantly basaltic and andesitic. A near-concordia zircon date of 586 ± 10 Ma for the uppermost Uwharrie (Wright & Seiders 1980) and the presence of Vendian or Ediacaran (late Proterozoic) macrofossils in the upper Albemarle (Gibson *et al.* 1984) fix the age. Stratigraphic similarities suggest correlation of the Uwharrie–Albemarle sequence with sequences elsewhere in the Carolina slate belt which are less securely dated. On the Georgia–S Carolina border, the Lincolnton Metadacite with a discordant zircon date of 568 Ma (Carpenter *et al.* 1982) and a felsic pyroclastic sequence may be equivalent to the Uwharrie, and an overlying argillite sequence with some greywacke and thin interbedded mafic volcanics may be equivalent to the Albemarle. In the Virgilina area on the N Carolina–Virginia border, gross similarities suggest that the Hyco Quartz Porphyry with the comagmatic sub-volcanic Flat River Complex of McConnell & Glover (1982) may be the equivalent of the Uwharrie, and the overlying Aaron Slate and Virgilina Greenstone may be the equivalent of the Albemarle. This speculative correlation, suggested although not favoured by Wright & Seiders (1980), requires rejection of a discordant zircon date of 650 ± 30 Ma for the Flat River Complex (McConnell & Glover 1982) and the opinion of recent workers that the entire sequence is unconformable beneath the Uwharrie and is separated in time by the Virgilina deformation (Harris & Glover 1983). The Kings Mountain belt, across strike to the W, has some resemblances to the Carolina slate belt. The Battleground Formation, with dacitic-to-andesitic volcanics, and the Blacksburg Formation, which is predominantly metasedimentary but with metabasaltic amphibolites (Horton 1984), may match the Uwharrie and the Albemarle respectively. Zircons from a metatonalite which is presumably consanguineous with the volcanic rocks of the Battleground Formation yield a late Proterozoic age (Horton 1984). Plutonic rocks of pre-Arenig age are sparse in the Carolina slate belt. However, undated metaplutonic rocks that make up much of the Charlotte belt apparently grade through hypabyssal types into metavolcanics that are probably equivalent to the metavolcanics of the Carolina slate belt to the E and the Kings Mountain belt to the W. Palaeontological evidence shows that the sedimentary history of the Carolina slate belt in S Carolina extended into the middle Cambrian (Secor *et al.* 1983), but apparently no volcanic units occur in the younger sequences.

The Carolina slate belt is generally regarded as representing an island arc, but geochemical interpretations of the environment of volcanism are based only on major-element and very limited trace-element chemistry. Seiders (1978) emphasizes the bimodal and calc-alkalic nature of the Uwharrie–Albemarle volcanics. Whitney *et al.* (1978) consider the Georgia–Carolina segment to be a primitive oceanic island arc. In a recent summary, Feiss (1982) is justifiably inconclusive but suggests that the Carolina slate belt formed in a subduction-related orogenic environment analogous to the modern Lesser Antilles and characterized by a bimodal suite of calc-alkaline to tholeiitic rocks. All such conclusions may be vitiated by the limited data and the lumping together of rocks that formed over an extended period of time. For example, the bimodality may largely be an artefact arising from telescoping an earlier felsic and a later mafic group.

The Milford–Dedham zone of eastern Massachusetts, Rhode Island and easternmost Connecticut shows some striking similarities to the Carolina slate belt. Here an older mafic plutonic and volcanic assemblage in eastern Massachusetts, which includes among other units the Salem Gabbro-diorite, the Middlesex Falls Volcanic Complex and the metabasalts of the Blackstone Group (Goldsmith in press), is essentially undated and may be either an early manifestation of the Caledonide cycle or unrelated basement. Extensive batholithic granites, the metaluminous Dedham Granite, the peraluminous Milford Granite and numerous units of lesser areal extent (Wones & Goldsmith in press) are younger than these. Zartman & Naylor (1984) find zircon ages from 645 to 590 Ma for members of this complex. The Mattapan Volcanic Complex, S of the Boston Basin, and the Lynn Volcanic Complex, N of the basin, are felsic suites consisting of rhyolite and rhyodacite flows, welded ash flows, flow breccias and tuffs. Both the Mattapan and the Lynn Volcanic Complexes overlie the Dedham Granite but locally grade through hypabyssal bodies into late phases of the plutonic complex. A concordia date of 602 ± 3 Ma for zircons from the Mattapan (Kaye & Zartman 1980) is supported by the occurrence of Proterozoic acritarchs in the overlying Boston Bay Group (Lenk *et al.* 1982). Within the lower Boston Bay Group there is one volcanic unit, the Brighton melaphyre, consisting dominantly of quartz keratophyre, keratophyre and spilite. Fossiliferous lower and middle Cam-

brian strata occur in the Milford–Dedham zone, and at Hoppin Hill, MA, lower Cambrian strata unconformably overlie Dedham-like granite, but there is no evidence of igneous activity in Cambrian or early Ordovician time.

On the basis of bulk composition and lithology Goldsmith (in press) considers the mafic plutonic-volcanic complex in E Massachusetts to be an 'island arc–continental margin(?) association in a compressional tectonic regime', although its relation to a Caledonide cycle has not been established and is doubted by Goldsmith. He regards the younger Dedham (Milford) and related Granites and the Mattapan and Lynn Volcanic Complexes as products of subduction-related tectonics in a compressional–extensional regime preceding the opening of Iapetus, whereas the Brighton Melaphyre reflects post-rifting extensional tectonics. Neodymium values (Hon *et al.* 1984) indicate mantle and crustal sources for rocks of the Milford–Dedham zone and the Lynn volcanics. Model ages for both sources are 10^3 Ma or younger, indicating the absence of ancient crust beneath.

Further NE small areas of pre-Arenig schist, quartzite, marble and amphibolite of volcanic origin crop out in the vicinity of Penobscot Bay, ME (Stewart 1974). These rocks are in tectonic contact with the surrounding rocks, but since they have been through one additional metamorphism they are interpreted as older (D. B. Stewart 1984, personal communication). A younger sequence of chlorite-grade rocks includes pelite, carbonate, quartzite and a strongly bimodal suite of volcanic rocks consistent with a continental-margin environment (D. B. Stewart 1974, and 1984, personal communication). These rocks include the Ellsworth, Islesboro and North Haven Formations, which may be as old as late Proterozoic but are interpreted by Stewart as Cambrian and/or Ordovician.

A palaeotectonic interpretation of the central Virginia volcanic–plutonic belt, which is more deformed and metamorphosed than the Milford–Dedham zone and the Carolina slate belt, is based on rare-earth patterns as well as major- and trace-element chemistry (Pavlides 1981, Pavlides *et al.* 1982). The age of the units is uncertain, but according to Pavlides (1981), who interprets the entire belt as an island-arc sequence, discordant zircon ages suggest a Cambrian, perhaps an early Cambrian age. The Chopawamsic Formation, on the western side of the belt, consists of varied but dominantly felsic and intermediate volcanics of tholeiitic and calc-alkaline geochemical affinities intruded by plagiogranitic and trondhjemitic plutons. The Ta River Metamorphic Suite to the E is more mafic and is dominated by tholeiitic amphibolites, suggesting a more oceanward environment. These fit the model of an island arc off an eastern continental margin, apparently ensimatic but perhaps on a thin continental crust. A melange NW of the Chopawamsic Formation which includes blocks of serpentinite, metagabbro, metavolcanic rocks and some metagreywacke may be the remnant of a back-arc basin. The James Run Formation of NE Maryland is a suite similar to and probably correlatable with the central Virginia volcanic-plutonic belt.

The Chopawamsic Formation was intruded by granitic plutons during the latest stages of the island-arc magmatism. The Occoquan pluton yields an Rb–Sr date of 494 ± 14 Ma (Mose & Nagel 1982), and the Dale City pluton is clearly unconformably overlain by the fossiliferous late? Ordovician Quantico Formation (Pavlides *et al.* 1980).

Other presumably pre-Arenig igneous rocks exist outside these fairly well-defined areas but are so obscured by later metamorphism and deformation that they are difficult to define. The recently described Halifax County Complex (Kite & Stoddard 1984) in NC appears similar to the Baltimore Complex but has not been dated. It is interpreted as oceanic lithosphere probably formed in the early stages of development of an intra-oceanic island arc.

Inland from the Avalonian terranes but outboard of clearly cratonic N America are some suspect terranes, the affinities of which are obscure in part because of repeated orogeny through the Palaeozoic. In the S, one such zone is the very extensive Inner Piedmont belt, which lies between the Avalonian Carolina slate belt–Charlotte belt–Kings Mountain belt terrane and the clearly N American Blue Ridge belt. Apparently metavolcanic gneisses, both felsic and mafic, are abundant but undated. The Henderson Gneiss—535 Ma according to Odom & Fullagar (1973) and 593 Ma according to Sinha & Glover (1978)—may be a pre-Arenig probably metaplutonic unit. In the N, the Nashoba zone lies adjacent to the Milford–Dedham zone and contrasts with it by the absence of major late Proterozoic granite as well as by the stronger metamorphism and deformation (Hepburn & Munn 1984). The predominantly leucocratic Fishbrook Gneiss is inferred to have a tuffaceous protolith. Zircons of igneous morphology yield an age of 730 ± 26 Ma, which is taken as the date of eruption (Olszewski 1980). A thicker unit, the Marlboro Formation, consists predominantly of amphibolites—originally mildly-alkaline to high-alumina basalts that have rare-earth and trace-element patterns characteristic of basalts erupted at convergent plate boundaries or in marginal basins (DiNitto *et al.* 1984). Neodymium isotopic studies indicate an age greater than 450 Ma. It is possible that the Marlboro is contemporaneous with the mafic volcanic-plutonic complex of the Milford–Dedham zone in E Massachusetts. The Passagassawakeag terrane in SE Maine, which includes the metavolcanics of the Casco Bay Group—'Cambro-Ordovician or older?' (Brookins & Hussey 1978)—is similar to the Nashoba zone.

D.J.M.

Accreted terranes: Atlantic Canada

Variably tectonized late Proterozoic? to Cambrian igneous rocks are the major component of much of the eastern margin of the Appalachians of Atlantic Canada. They comprise significant portions of the Avalon zone and its equivalents in Newfoundland, Nova Scotia and New Brunswick. Igneous rocks of this age have not been recognized in the adjacent Meguma zone to the S.

Newfoundland

Late Proterozoic igneous rocks are disposed in five NE-trending fault-bounded massifs. The easternmost is underlain by the Harbour Main Group, a lithologically diverse bimodal volcanic sequence several kilometres thick which underlies fossiliferous Cambrian strata and has yielded zircons dated at 618^{+8}_{-6} Ma (Krogh *et al.* 1983). The group has mildly-alkaline to tholeiitic affinities, and is interpreted as forming in an extensional intra-plate environment (Nixon & Papezik 1979).

W of and stratigraphically above the Harbour Main Group is the Musgravetown Group, a mainly clastic succession which contains near its base a sub-aerial to submarine bimodal basalt–rhyolite unit of highly variable thickness. Although the volcanics are extensively metasomatized (Hughes & Malpas 1971), they display peralkaline affinities locally (Hussey 1980).

The Musgravetown Group is locally overthrust by the Burin Group, a succession 5 km thick of submarine flows, hyaloclastites, gabbro sills and associated carbonate and clastic sedimentary rocks. Dated at 760 ± 2 Ma (Krogh 1982), it is the oldest stratigraphic unit in the Newfoundland Avalon zone. The group displays a chemical variation upwards from alkali basalt to more primitive oceanic tholeiite (Strong *et al.* 1978), and is thought to have formed in a small oceanic basin (Strong *et al.* 1978, O'Brien *et al.* 1983).

The Burin Group is faulted against mainly sub-aerial flows and pyroclastic rocks and associated shallow marine epiclastic rocks of the Love Cove Group and its correlative, the Marystown Group. These groups are both more than 10 km thick and are unconformably overlain by fossiliferous lower Cambrian clastic rocks; the Love Cove Group has been dated at 570 ± 20 Ma (Dallmeyer et al. 1981) and the Marystown Group at 608 ± 25 and c. 607 Ma (Dallmeyer 1980, Krogh 1980, personal communication). The stratigraphic relationships of these groups to volcanics to the E are uncertain. Both are essentially bimodal alkaline suites, but they contain significant amounts of mafic to intermediate rocks of mildly-tholeiitic affinity in their lowest stratigraphic formations. The groups are chemically similar to volcanic rocks of rift-related Basin and Range style tectonic–volcanic environments.

The westernmost massif comprises the Long Harbour Group and the stratigraphically-equivalent Connaigne Bay Group. Both contain a lower felsic pyroclastic succession, which is lithically and in places chemically similar to the Marystown and Love Cove Groups, overlain by an intermediate marine clastic unit and an upper bimodal suite of commenditic felsic pyroclastic and mafic hypabyssal rocks. The peralkaline rocks are unconformably overlain by terrigenous clastic rocks which pass conformably upwards into fossiliferous lower Cambrian strata.

Pre-Arenig plutonic rocks are mainly hornblende–biotite granites, with variable volumes of associated gabbro, diorite and alkali granite. Age determinations on these rocks vary from 580 to 620 Ma (Dallmeyer et al. 1981, Krogh et al. 1983). The granites are mainly calc-alkaline, I type and locally co-magmatic with surrounding volcanic rocks (O'Driscoll & Strong 1979, Dallmeyer et al. 1981).

In Newfoundland, middle Cambrian volcanic rocks form thin intra-formational members comprising mafic pillow lava, aquagene breccia and tuff within black shaley successions. A number of gabbro sills are associated with the lavas, and these intrude the middle Cambrian strata.

The lavas are continental-rift-facies alkali basalts of alkaline chemical affinities and are thought to have formed in response to limited crustal stretching in an anorogenic environment (Greenough 1984, personal communication).

Nova Scotia

Pre-Arenig igneous rocks occur in three main areas within the Avalon zone of the Nova Scotia Appalachians: Cape Breton Island, the Antigonish Highlands and the Cobequid Mountains.

The Precambrian of northern Cape Breton Island includes gneissic rocks of unknown age overlain by the mainly metaclastic George River Group, which contains volcanic rocks in its upper parts (Keppie 1982). The southern Cape Breton Highlands are underlain by a basal succession of migmatitic paragneiss surrounded by an unnamed meta-igneous–metasedimentary complex and its gneissic equivalents together with variably-deformed diorite, gabbro and granitoid plutons. One of these has been dated at 750 ± 65 Ma (Jamieson & Craw 1983). Many of the late Proterozoic plutons are lithically alike and contain early diorite, granodiorite and quartz monzonite phases intruded by pink leucogranites.

Late Proterozoic stratified rocks of the Antigonish Highlands comprise two distinctive units, the Georgeville Group and the Keppoch Formation (Murphy 1982). The Georgeville Group is dominantly clastic but contains inter-stratified submarine basalts. In contrast, the Keppoch Formation is characterized by intercalated rhyolitic volcaniclastic rocks (Murphy 1982). The contrasting volcanic styles are interpreted as the result of differences in basement lithology, i.e. a continental basement to the Keppoch Formation and an oceanic crustal substrate to the Georgeville Group (Murphy 1982). Plutonic rocks of the Antigonish Highlands include Proterozoic appinitic gabbros and granites; the latter are regarded as co-genetic with the Keppoch Formation. The main Proterozoic unit of southeastern Cape Breton Island is the dominantly-volcanic Forchu Group (Weeks 1954). It is a sub-aerial to submarine dominantly-felsic pyroclastic sequence with subordinate felsic, intermediate and mafic tuffs and flows and co-magmatic calc-alkaline felsic to mafic intrusive sheets (Murphy 1977). The volcanics have calc-alkaline affinities and are interpreted as part of a late Precambrian ensialic arc (Keppie et al. 1979).

The Proterozoic of the Cobequid Mountains comprises mainly crystalline rocks, the oldest of which are amphibolite, paragneiss and granitic gneiss (c. 980 Ma) (Donahoe 1983). These are overlain by later Proterozoic volcanics, quartzites, iron formation and carbonates and latest Proterozoic volcanic rocks; all are intruded by a suite of quartz diorite, gabbro and syenodiorite, and subsequently by hornblende–biotite granites and syenites (Clarke et al. 1980).

In Nova Scotia the main exposure of Cambrian volcanic rocks occurs within the Bourinot Group, a middle Cambrian bimodal suite of tholeiitic basalt and minor rhyolite that is interbedded with shallow-marine sedimentary rocks (Keppie & Dostal 1980). Other Cambrian volcanic rocks occur in the Gillis Brook Formation, an early middle Cambrian suite of basalt and rhyolite interbedded with fossiliferous sandstone, siltstone and conglomerate. The lavas are chemically similar to those of the Bourinot Group. A third Cambrian unit, the Arbuckle Brook Formation, is a Cambrian dominantly-volcanic bimodal sequence with chemical affinities transitional between those of alkaline and tholeiitic intraplate lavas (Keppie & Dostal 1980).

New Brunswick

Pre-Arenig igneous rocks are essentially restricted to the area S of the Belle Isle fault where they form a significant part of the Avalon zone of the Caledonian Highlands. Apart from metaigneous rocks in the remobilized basement gneiss domes (Wardle 1978, Currie *et al.* 1981, O'Brien *et al.* 1983), most pre-Arenig igneous rocks occur within either the late Proterozoic Coldbrook Group (Alcock 1938) or spatially-associated plutons. Minor felsic volcanic rocks occur in the Cambrian St John Group. The Coldbrook Group is disposed in three broad lithically-distinctive belts separated by areas underlain mainly by plutonic rock. The eastern belt is characterized by shallow-marine pyroclastic and epiclastic rocks, the central belt by ash-flow and air-fall tuffs, and the western belt by mainly felsic volcanic rocks (Ruitenberg *et al.* 1979). Published chemical data are sparse; Ruitenberg *et al.* (1979) stated that the group is bimodal, containing basalts of tholeiitic affinities. On the basis of regional relationships, Rast *et al.* (1976) suggested that the Coldbrook Group volcanic rocks formed part of a late Proterozoic ensialic arc. The late Proterozoic plutons of southern New Brunswick, mainly hornblende-biotite tonalities and granodiorites, have been dated at *c.* 615 Ma (Poole 1980). They are I-type calc-alkaline plutons thought to be formed by partial melting of the lower crust above a late Proterozoic subduction zone (Dickson 1984).

S.J.O'B.

Accreted terranes: Caledonides of the British Isles

In contrast with the Archaean–Proterozoic gneisses and schists (*c.* 2900–400 Ma) which form the basement to the N of the Iapetus suture, the basement to the S of the suture comprises late Proterozoic low-grade metamorphic rock together with intrusive and extrusive igneous rock and penecontemporaneously derived sedimentary rock. Such basement forms much of central England and Wales, but older (early and middle

Proterozoic) basement may occur in southeastern Ireland and forms the basement of the Channel Islands and northern France. Little or no geological evidence supports the presence of basement older than *c.* 900 Ma in central England and Wales, and basement here is considered to have formed between *c.* 700 and 450 Ma ago. The features of late Precambrian igneous rocks and their role in crustal evolution have been summarized by Thorpe (1982) and Thorpe *et al.* (1984) and are reviewed below. Most of the localities discussed are shown in Fig. 4.

Southeastern Ireland

The Precambrian rocks of southeastern Ireland comprise the Rosslare Complex and the Cullenstown Group. The Rosslare Complex is composed of paragneisses with mafic and felsic orthogneisses which have experienced a complex metamorphic history, possibly dating from the early Proterozoic (Max 1975) but more likely to be of late Proterozoic age, experiencing cooling from amphibolite-facies conditions at *c.* 650 Ma (Winchester & Max 1982). The Rosslare Complex is adjacent to the less-deformed and metamorphosed Cullenstown Group which is correlated with the Mona Complex of Anglesey. The Rosslare Complex was intruded by the Carnsore granodiorite at 520 ± 6 Ma (Leutwein *et al.* 1972).

Anglesey–Lleyn, N Wales

This area forms the largest outcrop of Precambrian rock within southern Britain (Shackleton 1969, 1975), and comprises a thick succession (over 7000 m) of flysch-type sedimentary rocks (the 'Bedded Succession') of late Precambrian and, according to Barber & Max (1979), lower Palaeozoic age. The succession contains chert and manganiferous shale, mafic and ultramafic intrusive rocks (gabbro and serpentinite) and pillow basalts which chemically resemble the components of oceanic crust and can be interpreted as fragments of a disrupted ophiolite complex (Thorpe 1978). The youngest part of the succession is the Gwna Group, a melange of regional extent interpreted as an olistostrome, which contains blocks of limestone, quartzite and pillow basalt, locally metamorphosed in the lawsonite–glaucophane facies.

These rocks were folded, metamorphosed and intruded by igneous rocks during the late Precambrian–lower Palaeozoic, although Barber & Max (1979) argue that much of the deformation is Caledonian. The complex includes sillimanite–almandine-facies gneisses which have yielded an Rb–Sr whole-rock isochron age of 595 ± 12 Ma

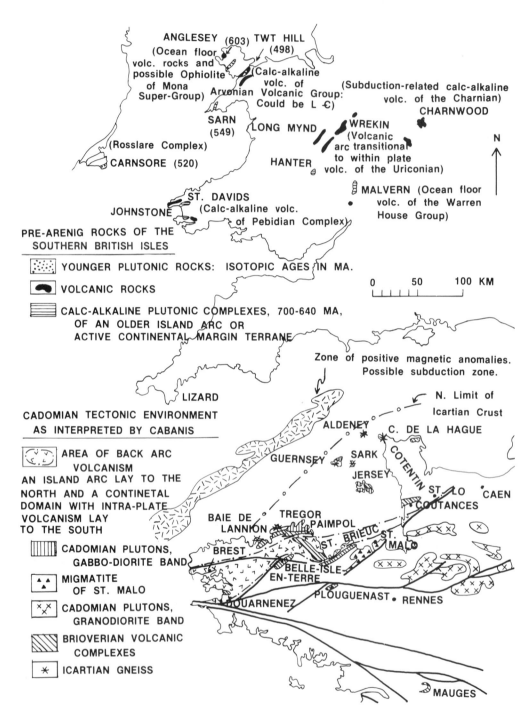

FIG. 4. Pre-Arenig igneous rock of the southern British Isles and northern France. Compiled by Rankin from data given by Bishop, Cabanis and Thorpe in this paper and from Cabanis *et al.* (1984), Peucat *et al.* (1981) and Piasecki *et al.* (1981).

(Beckinsale & Thorpe 1979). Although it has been suggested that these gneisses represent a 'gneissose continental basement' (Barber & Max 1979), the field evidence (Shackleton 1969, 1975) and Rb–Sr and Sm–Nd dating (Thorpe *et al.* 1984) are consistent with derivation of the gneisses by metamorphism of part of the Bedded Succession. The gneisses are associated with igneous rocks dated at 562 ± 31 Ma, and the Carnsore granite was emplaced into the Mona Complex at 603 ± 34 Ma (Beckinsale & Thorpe 1979). In the Lleyn Peninsula, analogous almandine–amphibolite-facies metamorphic rocks (Parwyd) have been dated at 542 ± 17 Ma and the pre-Arenig Sarn Complex (diorite, tonalite and adamellite) was emplaced at 549 ± 19 Ma and experienced a resetting event at 458 ± 16 Ma (Beckinsale *et al.* 1984).

In N Wales, the Arvonian volcanic group (Arfon Group: basalt, andesite, dacite and rhyolite) occurs within the lowermost Cambrian (or late Precambrian). Outcrops tentatively correlated with the Arvonian overlie the Mona Complex and may indicate a pre-'Cambrian' age for the metamorphism. The pre-Arenig 'Twt Hill' granite at Carnarvon is emplaced within the Arvonian and has been dated at 498 ± 7 Ma (Beckinsale *et al.*, personal communication).

S Wales–Stanner–Hanter–Malvern

These areas include a variety of volcanic and plutonic rocks. Intrusive complexes (Johnston Complex of S Wales) are of hornblende-bearing calc-alkaline gabbro associated with diorite–tonalite–granite dated between *c.* 700 and 640 Ma which might represent the earliest igneous activity in southern Britain. The Johnston and Malvernian Complexes are cut by high-level dolerite–diorite intrusions of late Precambrian–lower Palaeozoic age. The Malvern Complex is in tectonic contact with a tholeiitic basalt–andesite–rhyolite association (the Warren House Group) which has chemical characteristics appropriate to ocean-floor basalt.

Welsh borderlands–central England

In Shropshire, the (almandine–amphibolite-facies) Rushton Schist has yielded an Rb–Sr whole-rock isochron age of 667 ± 20 Ma (Beckinsale *et al.*, personal communication) and forms the basement for the Uriconian (basalt–andesite–rhyolite) volcanic association (558 ± 16 Ma (Patchett *et al.* 1980)) and the overlying Longmyndian sedimentary sequence (younger than *c.* 600 Ma (Bath 1974)). The Uriconian rocks have chemical characteristics transitional between those of volcanic-arc and within-plate lavas, and such a transitional character is consistent with eruption within the extensional environment which culminated in deposition of the overlying Longmyndian sediments within a fault-bounded depression upon the surface of the volcanic rocks. The Uriconian and Longmyndian rock units were folded probably prior to the local Cambrian but certainly before the Caradocian (Greig *et al.* 1968). The Ercall granophyre (533 ± 12 Ma (Patchett *et al.* 1980, Thorpe *et al.* 1984)) was emplaced through the Rushton schist and Uriconian and probably Cambrian rocks of Shropshire, and may be of early Cambrian age. (Dr Alan Wright (pers. comm.) has reported that the Cambrian rocks rest unconformably on, and are partly derived from, the Ercall Granophyre and that its age is more likely to be 560–570 Ma. A.L.H.)

Within central England, the Charnian rocks of Charnwood Forest comprise a sequence of volcaniclastic sedimentary rocks and lavas associated with diorite intrusions. The lavas form a basaltic andesite–andesite–dacite association of late Precambrian age, and the Charnian rocks were intruded by diorites at 540 ± 57 Ma (Cribb 1975, *cf.* Thorpe *et al.* 1984).

Tectonic setting

The Rb–Sr and Sm–Nd isotopic data are consistent with the occurrence of a spectrum of igneous and metamorphic events resulting in the formation of most of the basement of southern Britain between *c.* 700 and 450 Ma (Thorpe *et al.* 1984). The older plutonic complexes (Johnston, Stanner–Hanter and Malvernian Complexes) are calc-alkaline and have chemical characteristics indicating formation within island arcs or at active continental margins. The (younger?) volcanic and hypabyssal associations are varied and include ocean-floor volcanic rocks (e.g. Gwna Group, Mona Complex and Warren House Group), subduction-related calc-alkaline rocks (e.g. Charnian) and transitional calc-alkaline–alkaline lavas formed within environments transitional between island-arc–active-continental-margin and within-plate environments (e.g. Uriconian). These characteristics are interpreted in terms of crustal growth by plate-tectonic processes near the SE margin of the Iapetus Ocean between *c.* 700 and 450 Ma.

This may have involved SE-directed subduction of oceanic lithosphere below southern Britain (*cf.* section on the Laurentian plate in Britain). The earliest products of the subduction were the Johnston, Stanner–Hanter and Malvernian Complexes (*c.* 700–640 Ma) which may have been coeval with the deposition of the Mona Complex (including emplacement of 'ophiolitic' ultramafic and mafic rocks) within the Iapetus Ocean, which was deformed, metamorphosed and experienced intrusive activity at *c.* 600–550 Ma. This was broadly contemporaneous with late Precambrian–lower Palaeozoic emplacement of hypabyssal and volcanic rocks of mildly-alkaline composition (intrusions in the Johnston and Malvernian Complexes, Uriconian volcanic association) associated with local late-tectonic–extensional regimes within the orogenic belt. However, continued magmatism between *c.* 550 and 400 Ma (i.e. Arenig–Silurian) represented continued subduction below the juvenile late Precambrian crust. This activity was allied with migration of the subduction zone to the NW and was responsible for continued magmatism throughout the Ordovician in Wales and central and NW England (Fitton *et al.* 1982).

The pre-Arenig basement zones of the British Isles can therefore be broadly correlated with the tectonic zones of the Appalachians. The crustal zone to the N of the Iapetus suture with ancient crustal basement corresponds to the Humber zone, while the late Precambrian basement of southern Britain, S of the Iapetus suture, can be compared with the Avalon zone of Newfoundland (Rast *et al.* 1976, O'Brien *et al.* 1983).

However, in contrast with southern Britain, the Avalon zone appears to have formed upon mid-Proterozoic sialic basement (older than *c.* 800 Ma) and involved crustal rifting associated with bimodal volcanism prior to the Avalonian orogeny at *c.* 650–600 Ma. The Avalonian may therefore reflect an earlier stage of crustal evolution, involving rifting during opening of an early ocean, in contrast to the late Precambrian of southern Britain which formed by accretion of island arcs within such an oceanic area.

R.S.T.

Accreted terranes: Hercynides of the Channel Islands and northern France

Two syntheses of the accreted terranes of the Channel Islands and northern France, which have both been deformed by Hercynian events, are presented in this section. The first, by A. C. Bishop, is written from the perspective of a geologist working in the Channel Islands, and the second, by B. Cabanis, is written from the perspective of a geologist working in Brittany and is based upon very recent work, some of it unpublished. Most of the localities discussed are shown in Fig. 4.

Pentevrian complex: basement

The term Pentevrian was applied by Cogné (1959) to metamorphic rocks near St Brieuc, Brittany, which later yielded dates of 1200–900 Ma (Leutwein & Sonet 1965, Leutwein 1968) and which are overlain unconformably by Brioverian rocks. Further occurrences of Pentevrian basement were later recognized in the Channel Islands (southern Guernsey, western Alderney and, most probably, Sark) and near Cap de la Hague in the Cotentin. These rocks (also called Icartian, after the Icart orthogneiss of Guernsey) are principally gneisses, amphibolites and schists which have yielded early Proterozoic dates of *c.* 2000 Ma (Bishop *et al.* 1975).

Brioverian succession: volcanic and hypabyssal rocks

French workers have ascribed to lower and middle Brioverian a variably metamorphosed sequence of volcanic and sedimentary rocks in Brittany. Basal mica schists give place upwards to spilitic pillow basalts and tuffs which are succeeded by greywacke-type sedimentary rocks, followed by a thick sequence of pelites and black cherts of low metamorphic grade. This sequence, it is claimed, was folded during the Cadomian I episode of the Cadomian orogeny before the deposition of the upper Brioverian sequence of sandstones, quartzites, greywackes and pelites. Cadomian II movements folded the upper Brioverian rocks which were metamorphosed to low (typically greenschist-facies) grade. The assignment of certain high-grade migmatitic gneisses around St Malo to the lower Brioverian has been challenged by Brown and co-workers (Brown *et al.* 1971, Brown 1978), who regard as Pentevrian the rocks ascribed by French workers to the lower and middle Brioverian. Brioverian (upper Brioverian) rocks also occur in Normandy, and Graindor (1957) correlated the Jersey Shale Formation with the upper Brioverian of Normandy. NW of St Brieuc, the upper Brioverian Paimpol spilites and Tréguier tuffs have yielded a reliable Rb–Sr whole-rock isochron age of 640 Ma (Auvray 1979, Vidal *et al.* 1981). The Tréguier tuffs are keratophyric and the overlying Paimpol spilites comprise, in addition to pillow lavas, massive lavas and pyroclastic rocks. The pillow lavas are thought to have been erupted at relatively shallow depth (Auvray 1979). Dykes of similar composition intrude the Perros–Guirec granodiorite (see below) and are considered to be related to the volcanic rocks.

The Brioverian Jersey Shale Formation is overlain by calc-alkaline andesites and rhyolites. The andesites are sub-aerial lavas, tuffs and agglomerates which include some basalts. An angular discordance separates these from the overlying rhyolites but probably represents no great temporal break (G. M. Thomas 1977). The earliest felsic volcanic rocks are massive ignimbrites and are succeeded by rhyolite flows with thin ignimbrites and air-fall pyroclastic rocks. The volcanism followed closely on the Brioverian sedimentation and terminated the Precambrian history of northern Armorica. Similar late Brioverian felsic volcanic rocks occur at St Germain de Gaillard in the Cotentin (Boyer 1970) and in the Trégor (Lézardrieux volcanics), where Cambrian ignimbrites have been described by Auvray (1975, 1979). Duff (1978) obtained a Cambrian age (533 Ma) for the Jersey andesites, but this is difficult to reconcile with the geological evidence and may reflect the age of a nearby granite (Bishop & Mourant 1979). The Jersey Shale Formation and the volcanic rocks of Jersey (andesites and the overlying rhyolites) have undergone Cadomian folding and the whole sequence has been called Brioverian. An alternative view is given by Cabanis later in this section.

The Erquy spilites in Brittany, once considered to be of 'lower Brioverian' age, have yielded an age of 482 Ma (Vidal *et al.* 1971), which is confirmed by the associated microfauna (Deunff *et al.* 1973).

Plutonic rocks

A group of older Cadomian plutonic rocks was emplaced at about 690–630 Ma before the Cadomian (Cadomian II) deformation. These plutons are typically foliated and include the Gneiss de Brest granodiorite in western Brittany (Bishop *et al.* 1969), the L'Erée adamellite in Guernsey, the foliated 'granites' of Sark, Les Ecréhous and Les Minquiers in the Channel Islands (Bishop *et al.* 1975) and the Perros–Guirec–Bréhat granodiorite of the Trégor (Auvray 1979). Gabbro and diorite were subsequently emplaced about 600–580 Ma after the Cadomian (Cadomian II) deformation and include masses in the Channel Islands, Normandy and Brittany. In the Channel Islands these mafic rocks were followed by and intimately associated with the younger granites emplaced between *c.* 570 and 500 Ma. The Mancellian granites of Normandy are part of this group, although they were emplaced somewhat earlier than those of the Channel Islands. The Vire granite (617 Ma (Vidal 1976)) is overlain unconformably by Cambrian sedimentary rocks. Auvray (1979) has depicted these relationships as two parallel bands oriented ENE–WSW, each about 100 km wide. The northern 'basic band'

extends from N of Alderney to the estuary of the Rance and Granville and includes most of the Brioverian mafic volcanic rocks as well as the plutonic rocks; S of this, the 'granodiorite band' includes the Mancellian granites. Vidal *et al.* (1981) conclude from the isotopic composition of the granites and the Pentevrian basement rocks that the latter played only a limited part in the origin of the Cadomian and Hercynian magmatism.

Tectonic setting

Relating late Precambrian events in the Armorican area (NW France and the Channel Islands) to those of Britain is not simple. Magmatism in Wales and the English Midlands (the Midland block) can be explained by SE-dipping subduction in the region of Anglesey, and French workers (e.g. Auvray 1979, Cogné & Wright 1980) have similarly interpreted the Armorican area, invoking a late Proterozoic SE-dipping subduction zone in the English Channel and citing the line of high magnetic anomalies as evidence for the presence of an ancient subduction zone. Two periods of subduction, corresponding to Cadomian I and Cadomian II, are envisaged by French workers.

Leaving aside the disputed Cadomian I deformation, it has been suggested that either the Channel subduction zone is the same as that in Anglesey, but displaced eastwards by E–W transcurrent faults (Vidal 1976), or that the Midland block was separated from Armorica by a branch of Iapetus—the Manche Ocean (Auvray 1979). Thorpe *et al.* (1984) have shown that it is unlikely that basement older than *c.* 900 Ma underlies the Midland block and, since Pentevrian basement is present in Armorica, it seems unlikely that these are parts of the same area that have been separated by faulting. Brioverian sedimentary rocks in Armorica were deposited on continental basement and it is possible that the rocks of the Midland block were deposited in a marginal basin to the N of this continental edge.

Palaeomagnetic data indicate distinct apparent polar wander paths for the Midland and Armorican blocks until the Ordovician, indicating that the two were probably loosely coupled but not closely adjacent in the late Proterozoic (Piper 1982). Further, the magnetic highs in the Channel may be interpreted other than as a relict subduction zone. The anomaly is situated too close to the Channel Islands to be reconciled readily with a subduction model, and the K_2O content of the Jersey andesites suggests a trench much further to the N (G. M. Thomas 1977).

The thrust mass of the Lizard has been cited in support of the late Proterozoic subduction zone, but recent work shows it to have the characteristics of a spreading ridge and to be of Palaeozoic age. This accords well with the scenario of Cocks & Fortey (1982) who, on faunal grounds, argue for a widening Rheic Ocean in Silurian and Devonian times, separating England and Wales from Armorica and Iberia. The Lizard could represent part of this spreading ridge thrust to the N (Styles & Kirby 1980), and the magnetic highs could equally well relate to this episode as to the late Proterozoic.

A.C.B.

Icartian basement

Icartian or Pentevrian basement relicts are recognized in northwestern Brittany (Trégor), the Channel Islands (Guernsey, Sark and Alderney) and Cotentin (Cap de la Hague) (Calvez & Vidal 1978, Auvray *et al.* 1980). These rocks lie along a NE–SW trend and consist mainly of mica schist, gneiss and calc-alkaline granodiorite with associated volcanic rocks (amphibolite and leptynite).

Brioverian supracrustal rocks

A new coherent geodynamical model of the Cadomian orogeny based on work on different parts of the Brioverian sequence in the Armorican massif is summarized here.

In the Baie de Lannion area in the western part of Trégor (northern Brittany) the Brioverian succession starts with a transgressive sequence of conglomerate, arkose and felsic tuff (Tréguier tuff) unconformably above orthogneiss of the Icartian basement (Locquirec area). The gradual passage upward from the felsic tuff to a spilitic group (Paimpol spilite) and subsequently a detrital group indicates the existence in the Baie de Lannion area of a continuous sequence that includes volcanic rocks which show a progressive evolution from the base to the top during the late Proterozoic (Autran *et al.* 1979). Structural analysis shows the absence of the Cadomian deformation; greenschist metamorphism and folds in the Baie de Lannion must be related to Hercynian events well known around the Morlaix basin (Cabanis *et al.* 1979). A similar geological history has been deduced in the pre-Arenig units of the Pays de Leon where Brioverian rocks became mica schist, gneiss and anatexite during mesozonal metamorphism and two phases of folding in the Hercynian orogeny (Cabanis 1975). The Brest orthogneiss in the southern part of Leon, considered by Bishop *et al.* (1969) to be Brioverian in age (*c.* 690 Ma), is now well dated

by U–Pb on zircons at about 460 Ma (Ordovician) (Cabanis *et al.* 1977, Cabanis 1983). A similar Ordovician age has been obtained for the Douarnenez orthogneiss.

In the Baie de Lannion–Trégor area volcanic rocks are common and reflect a change with time from felsic (keratophyric) to mafic (spilitic) volcanism. They include the older felsic tuff (Locquirec, Locquémeau, Tréguier) and the younger mafic lava flows (pillow lavas and breccias) (Pointe Armorique, Cote de Tredrez, Pointe Guilben). These volcanic rocks are calc-alkaline in character (Cabanis *et al.* 1984), and the basal felsic units of the Paimpol volcanic sequence (Tréguier tuff) have yielded an Rb–Sr whole-rock isochron of about 640 Ma (Auvray 1979). Calc-alkaline plutonism followed the volcanism in Trégor and has been dated at 615 Ma (Graviou 1984).

In the St Brieuc Bay (SW part of Trégor) recent work has refined the stratigraphy and structure of the Precambrian rocks. Several units succeed one another in a unique sedimentary cycle which includes an important episode of volcanism (Rabu *et al.* 1983). Volcanic rocks are present on both sides of the St Brieuc Bay (Lanvollon to the W and Hillion to the E) and are composed of thick lava flows which are locally pillowed (Pointe Roselier). A geochemical study of trace elements shows that the rocks have characteristics of a back-arc tholeiite association (Cabanis *et al.* 1984). One Cadomian orogenic cycle has been identified (Rabu *et al.* 1983) and has been dated by the associated plutonism (granodiorite of St Quay Portrieux) between 585 and 595 Ma (Vidal *et al.* 1972).

A major conclusion of the recent work reported here is that the Brioverian supracrustal rocks experienced only one Precambrian (Cadomian) orogenic event. The identification of two orogenic events, i.e. Cadomian I and Cadomian II (Cogné 1959, 1970), is incorrect and the concept must be abandoned.

In the eastern part of St Brieuc Bay, in the St Malo area, crustal anatexis is locally developed and dated at about 540 Ma.

The Douarnenez Bay area at the western end of central Brittany is characterized by feldspathic sedimentary rocks similar to those of central Brittany. The volcanic rocks, however, are different. Mafic pillow lavas that are exposed in the Telgruc area show the geochemical characteristics of back-arc tholeiites (Cabanis & Darboux 1984).

The Brioverian succession is different in central Brittany. An intra-plate basin is filled with feldspathic sedimentary rocks (flysch); volcanic rocks are sparse. Two units—'phtanites' (cherts) and 'post-phtanites'—are distinguished, but recent work indicates no structural discontinuity and little lithic difference between the two units. The volcanic rocks that are present indicate typical continental intra-plate volcanism related to extension. Mafic alkaline volcanic rocks, including pillow lavas, are present in the Baie de la Fresnaye region, and further S primitive tholeiites occur in the Plouguenast series which is younger than the cherts (Cabanis *et al.* 1984).

To the S in the Vendée (Massif des Mauges), the Brioverian succession and subsequent geological history have much in common with those in central Brittany (Cabanis *et al.* 1984). Intra-plate volcanic rocks have been recognized and have undergone polyphase deformation.

In Normandy two provinces of sedimentary rocks are recognized. In the N the Cotentin basin contains shale, siltstone and mafic volcanic rocks (Montsurvent spilite). The arc-tholeiitic character of the volcanic rocks suggests that the Cotentin basin is similar to the Trégor area (Dupret *et al.* 1984).

S of Coutance–St Lo, the Mancellian basin contains feldspathic sedimentary rocks but no volcanic rocks and is similar to central Brittany. This area, called Mancellian, is the type area for the Cadomian orogeny (Cadomus is Latin for Caen). Structural and metamorphic effects of the Cadomian are only moderate in Mancellian, but an important plutonic event has been dated between 540 and 520 Ma. Odin *et al.* (1983) suggests that this be defined as the Proterozoic–Cambrian boundary. The aluminous and potassic granitoids are thought to have been generated in the deep crust by anatexis at the end of the Cadomian orogeny. In the Caen area, at 'Rocreux rock' in the Laize Valley, an unconformity is well exposed between late Proterozoic stratified rocks and Cambrian basal conglomerate. In other places Cambrian basal conglomerate overlies Mancellian granitoids; at Roche d'Oetre, for example, the conglomerate is unconformable on Athis granite.

Cambrian time

Cambrian sedimentary rocks in the Armorican massif are only well developed in the Mancellia area where the basal conglomerate is successively overlain by a carbonate unit, psammite and pelite. Elsewhere Cambrian deposits are not preserved and Tremadocian conglomerate directly overlies the Brioverian with angular discordance, such as in the Douarnenez Bay area near Telgruc.

In the northwestern part of the Armorican massif an episode of felsic volcanism followed shortly after the Cadomian orogeny and took place along a NE–SW Cadomian trend from Cotentin (St Germain-le-Gaillard series) through Jersey to Trégor (Leza Drieux series). The felsic volcanic rocks are mainly massive ignimbritic rhyolites with rhyolite flows and felsic tuffs. In the Trégor area ignimbrites overlie with angular discordance the Brioverian Treguier tuff and are dated about 540 Ma; small microgranitoids of the same age are intrusive into the Brioverian. The low $^{87}Sr/^{86}Sr$ isotopic ratio (0.706 for rhyolites and 0.709 for associated granitoids) is interpreted to mean that these rocks represent the latest magmatic event in the subduction cycle (Auvray 1979).

Two volcanic episodes are distinguished on the island of Jersey: basal andesites and rhyolites, dated at 533 Ma (Duff 1978), are overlain by ignimbritic rhyolites associated with tuffs and breccias (Boyer 1974). The same succession is described near St Germain-le-Gaillard in Cotentin, at the base of the Cambrian strata.

In the eastern part of Mancellia, Normandy–Maine, which is outside the Cadomian orogenic domain, an important episode of felsic volcanism spanned the time from early lower Cambrian to upper Cambrian (Boyer 1974). Ignimbritic units of about the same age are known in the Vendée (Cholet, Haut Bocage).

In summary, and in contrast with the views of Bishop given above, all these are Cambrian rocks, consisting predominantly of ignimbritic rhyolite with tuff and breccia, and are thought to represent sub-aerial explosive volcanism. Locally, lesser amounts of andesite, dacite and rhyolite lavas with calc-alkaline characteristics crop out (Le Gall & Cabanis 1984). As in northwestern Brittany, this calc-alkaline andesitic volcanism is related to post-orogenic intra-plate distention situated on the border of the Cadomian zone. The ignimbrites are interpreted as the latest differentiates, as in Trégor, or as crustal melting products (Boyer 1974, Auvray 1979, Le Gall & Cabanis 1984).

Tectonic setting

About 640 Ma ago calc-alkaline volcanism was well developed on the border of the Icartian craton and is interpreted as island-arc volcanism. Only the Lannion Bay and Paimpol Bay sequences belong to this calc-alkaline volcanism (Cabanis *et al.* 1984). The island arc lay along a NE–SW trend and must be related to a SE-dipping subduction zone located in the English Channel. Positive magnetic anomalies in the Channel are interpreted as marking the subduction zone in the northern edge of the Icartian basement (Le Fort 1975, Auvray 1979, Cogné & Wright 1980, Cabanis *et al.* 1984). A Celtic oceanic plate situated to the N of the Channel was being subducted under the Armorican continental plate represented by remnants of Icartian craton (Trégor, Channel Islands, Cotentin).

This model agrees with recent geochemical studies on the St Brieuc Bay volcanic series which show back-arc tholeiite characteristics and are thought to be related to back-arc basin opening.

The beginning of the collision is well dated by calc-alkaline plutonism in Trégor at 615 Ma (Graviou 1984) and followed the termination of the calc-alkaline volcanism. The major tectonometamorphic event is dated by syn-tectonic granodiorite (St Quay–La Latte) dated between 595 and 585 Ma.

The last tectonometamorphic Cadomian event in this area was the thrusting of the Icartian basement over the upper Brioverian chert sequence (Balé & Brun 1983). This thrusting produced crustal thickening responsible locally for crustal anatexis in the St Malo area dated at about 540 Ma. The zone of thrusting now separates a volcanic orogenic domain to the N from a continental domain to the S.

This tectonic model agrees well with the presence of a mafic–ultramafic complex near Belle-Isle-en-Terre in N central Brittany. The complex has been dated at 602 Ma by the U–Pb zircon method and is interpreted as an ophiolite complex related to a back-arc orogenic setting (Peucat *et al.* 1981).

The collision in the southern part of the Cadomian orogen induced important crustal anatexis and the intrusion of the Mancellian batholith composed of aluminous granodiorites, monzogranites and leucogranites between 540 and 520 Ma. The plutonism marks the end of the Cadomian orogeny in the Armorican massif.

During the Cambrian, beginning at 540 Ma and following the end of compression, an episode of felsic volcanism took place represented mainly by sub-aerial ignimbrites and minor calc-alkaline andesites and rhyolites. This Cambrian volcanism reflects a later tectonic event during which crustal melting occurred along a zone of intraplate distention situated around the Cadomian zone (Cabanis 1983).

B.C.

Conclusions

The Caledonide–Appalachian orogen, now distributed on both sides of the N Atlantic, is a composite orogen formed by several non-parallel compressive events during the Palaeozoic. Attempts to synthesize the pre-Arenig igneous activity of the orogen reveal an overall pattern. The various parts of the orogen can be grouped into two types of terranes referred to here as type I or cratonal, which formed the rifted margins of the Iapetus Ocean, and type II or accreted, which appear not to have been part of the Iapetus rifting cycle (Rankin 1985).

Type I terranes are stratigraphically tied to large cratonal masses or fragments thereof and include Laurentia (in N America, Greenland and the British Isles), Baltica and possibly the W African Shield. Continental rifting, which led to the opening of Iapetus, began in the late Proterozoic. Mafic dyke-swarms related to this rifting cut older crystalline basement in N America and Scandinavia but are absent in E Greenland and eastern N Greenland and in the Lewisian of Scotland. The absence of late Proterozoic dykes in the crystalline basement of the latter two areas suggests that the zone of Iapetan opening was located farther from those basement terranes than areas in which late Proterozoic dykes are common. In both these areas the Iapetus Ocean lay E of the basement terranes. Interestingly, another feature shared by these areas is that neither E Greenland nor eastern N Greenland nor Scotland NW of the Moine thrust have been affected by Grenville metamorphism. Furthermore, these areas contain thick sequences of Proterozoic supracrustal rocks that at least span the age of Grenville metamorphism. The Stac Fada Member (Torridonian) of Scotland and the Zig-Zag Dal Basalt Formation of N Greenland are the igneous representatives of these sequences. Stewart (1982) discussed the rift environment of the Torridonian and argued that the rifting was not genetically related to Grenville metamorphism. The Zig-Zag Dal Basalt has been interpreted as a typical tholeiitic flood basalt (Jepsen *et al.* 1980) that conformably overlies the Independence Fjord Group, a sequence of thick homogeneous sandstones, some of which are red, and some red siltstone interpreted to have been deposited in an intra-cratonal lake (Collinson 1979, 1980). Whether these rocks of Scotland and Greenland, which have ages of more than 1 Ga, are precursors of Iapetus rifting or extensions of a N American Keweenawan rift system is not known. If, however, this episode of crustal extension is called Iapetan, it pushes the initiation of Iapetan rifting back about 300 Ma. The Keweenawan interpretation is preferred. Thus Greenland and northwestern Scotland represent anomalies within the type I or cratonal terranes of the Caledonide–Appalachian orogen.

Other parts of the Appalachian–Caledonide orogen have different characteristics. They are not tied stratigraphically to any large cratonal mass. For some, such as the Carolina terrane of Secor *et al.* (1983), no unequivocal (pre-Appalachian basement) has been identified. These non-cratonal terranes underwent a compressional episode at the end of the late Proterozoic (the Avalonian or Cadomian) which produced calc-alkaline plutonic rocks and a volcanic suite commonly described as island arc. As a group, these terranes are those previously identified as accreted or exotic in part on the basis of faunal differences in comparison with adjacent cratonal terranes. The type II or accreted terranes are SW of the Iapetus suture. Basement rocks of the two types of terranes do not match across the suture. The early histories of the exotic accreted terranes are so different from those of the cratonal terranes that it is suggested that they did not originate as margins of Iapetus but came from somewhere else yet to be determined.

Some areas in Norway E of the Iapetus suture may constitute exotic terranes, e.g. the Hölonda area of western Norway (Neuman 1984, and references cited therein), but for the most part the accreted exotic terranes are S of Scandinavia as well as E of the Iapetus suture. Tornquist's line or the Teisseyre–Tornquist zone is a major geological boundary in Europe, extending from the area of Koszalin, Poland, to the Black Sea. It separates the stable E European craton to the NE from the fragmented W European platform to the SW (Brochwicz-Lewiński *et al.* 1984). Cocks & Fortey (1982) noted faunal differences for the Arenig between Baltica and a Gondwanan continent which included Armorica, Iberia, eastern Newfoundland and the southern part of the British Isles. They inferred the existence of an ocean that they named Tornquist's Sea which separated Baltica and the Gondwanan continent in the early Ordovician but which closed in the late Ordovician. Perhaps Tornquist's line originated in the late Proterozoic as the southern rifted margin of Baltica—the E European craton. Guterch (1984) has also pointed out that, in terms of crustal structure and geological setting, Tornquist's line is similar to palaeo-rifts in other areas. If Caledonide structural trends from central Britain (the Iapetus suture for example) and Norway are projected into the North Sea they intersect at a pronounced angle more or less on the projection of Tornquist's line. The Tornquist 'rift' appears to have intersected the main Iapetus rift at a major triple junction in the Caledonide–Appalachian orogen.

The problem remains of how many accreted terranes make up the orogen S of Tornquist's line and E of the Iapetus suture and how they relate to one another. This is clearly beyond the scope of this paper. Some observations arise from this attempt to synthesize the pre-Arenig igneous activity. The local terranes of the Milford–Dedham zone in southeastern New England, Isleseboro in Penobscot Bay, ME, coastal New Brunswick, parts of Nova Scotia, the Burin and Avalon Peninsulas of Newfoundland and south-western Britain have in common a basement of similar age and/or lithology and an overlying late Proterozoic–early Palaeozoic stratified sequence containing similar volcanic rocks typically of low metamorphic grade. Basement rocks in these terranes are mostly in the age range 700–800 Ma and are an assemblage of quartzite, carbonate and mafic volcanic or intrusive rocks commonly interpreted to be oceanic. The basement of southern Britain, although of appropriate age, is interpreted to represent an island arc or active continental margin. In these same areas, the approximately 100 Ma from about 650 to 550 Ma (and in many areas the span was much shorter) were characterized by considerable and varied tectonic and igneous activity including continued rifting and subsequent closure of narrow ocean basins accompanied by widespread sub-aerial volcanism, block faulting and calc-alkaline I-type granitic plutonism (the compositions are best documented in Avalon). Block faulting probably produced considerable topographic relief in the Milford–Dedham zone, Avalon and Anglesey. Finally, in the Milford–Dedham zone and Avalon fossiliferous lower Cambrian strata rest uncomformably on granites probably as young as 590–610 Ma. The geological history of Brittany and the Channel Islands shares much in common with these areas except that basement rock there (Icartian gneiss) is considerably older. Brittany and the Channel Islands may not have been part of the same late Proterozoic terrane.

D.W.R.

References

Editors' note
Many references in this list are not cited in the text of the paper but are included to provide as complete a bibliography as possible in 1985.

ABBOT, R. N. & RAYMOND, L. A. 1984. The Ashe Metamorphic Suite, northwest North Carolina: metamorphism and observations on geologic history. *American Journal of Science*, **284**, 350–75.

AKSELSEN, J 1980. Tectonic and metamorphic development of the Pre-Cambrian and Caledonian rocks of north-eastern Seiland, Finnmark, *Thesis*, University of Bergen, 351 pp. (unpublished).

ANDREASSON, P. G., SOLYOM, Z. & ROBERTS, D. 1979. Petrochemistry and tectonic significance of basic and alkaline–ultrabasic dykes in the Leksdal Nappe, northern Trondheim Region, Norway. *Norges Geologiske Undersøkelse*, **348**, 47–72.

AUTRAN, A., CHANTRAINE, J. & RABU, D. 1979. Lithostratigraphie et déformation du Briovérien de la Baie de Lannion. Implication sur les relations entre les cycles cadomien et hercynien. *Bulletin du Bureau de Recherche Géologiques et Minières (France), Section 1*, **4**, 277–92.

AUVRAY, B. 1975. Relations entre plutonisme acide et volcanisme ignimbritique: example des manifestations magmatiques Cambriennes du Nord de la Bretagne. *Petrologie*, **1**, 125–37.

—— 1979. Génèse et évolution de la croûte continentale dans le nord du Massif Armoricain. *Thèse d'Etat*, Université de Rennes, 681 pp.

——, CHARLOT, R. & VIDAL, P. 1980. Données nouvelles sur le Protérozoïque inférieur du domaine nord-armoricain (France): âge et signification. *Canadian Journal of Earth Sciences*, **17**, 532–8.

BALÉ, P. & BRUN, J. P. 1983. Les chevauchements cadomiens de la baie de St. Brieuc (Massif Armoricain). *Comptes Rendus Hebdomadaires des Séances de l'Academie des Sciences*, **297**, 359–62.

BALK, R. 1953. Structure of the graywacke areas and Taconic Range, east of Troy, New York. *Geological Society of America Bulletin*, **64**, 811–64.

BARBER, A. J. & MAX, M. D. 1979. A new look at the Mona Complex (Anglesey, N. Wales). *Journal of the Geological Society, London*, **136**, 407–32.

BARR, D., HOLDSWORTH, R. E. & ROBERTS, A. M. 1986. Caledonian ductile thrusting in a Precambrian metamorphic complex: the Moine of northwestern Scotland. *Geological Society of America Bulletin*, **97**, 754–64.

BATH, A. H. 1974. New isotopic data on rocks from the Long Mynd, Shropshire. *Journal of the Geological Society, London*, **130**, 567–74.

BECKINSALE, R. D. & THORPE, R. S. 1979. Rubidium–strontium whole-rock isochron evidence for the age of metamorphism and magmatism in the Mona Complex of Anglesey. *Journal of the Geological Society, London*, **136**, 433–40.

——, EVANS, J. A., THORPE, R. S., GIBBONS, W. & HARMON, R. S. 1984. Rb–Sr whole-rock isochron ages, $\delta^{18}O$ values and geochemical data for the Sarn Igneous complex and the Parwyn gneisses of the Mona Complex of Llyn, N. Wales. *Journal of the Geological Society, London*, **142**, 701–9.

BERG, T. M. 1980. Geologic map of Pennsylvania. *Pennsylvania Geological Survey, 4th Series, Map 1*, scale 1:250000.

BIRD, J. M., DEWEY, J. F. & KIDD, W. S. F. 1971. Proto-Atlantic oceanic crust and mantle. Appalachian–Caledonian ophiolites. *Nature, London, Physical Science*, **231**, 28–31.

BISHOP, A. C. & MOURANT, A. E. 1979. Discussion on Rb–Sr whole-rock age determination of the Jersey Andesite Formation, Jersey, C. I. *Journal of the Geological Society, London*, **136**, 121–2.

——, BRADSHAW, J. D., RENOUF, J. T. & TAYLOR, R.

T. 1969. The stratigraphy and structure of part of west Finistère, France. *Quarterly Journal of the Geological Society of London*, **124**, 309–48.

——, ROACH, R. A. & ADAMS, C. J. D. 1975. Precambrian rocks within the Hercynides. *In:* HARRIS, A. L., SHACKLETON, R. M., WATSON, J., DOWNIE, C., HARLAND, W. B. & MOORBATH, S. (eds) *A Correlation of the Precambrian Rocks in the British Isles. Special Report of the Geological Society of London No. 6*, pp. 102–7.

BLACKBURN, W. H. & BROWN, W. R. 1976. Petrochemical evidence relating the Catoctin volcanic series to late Precambrian continental separation. *Geological Society of America Abstracts with Programs*, **8**(2), 136.

BLOXAM, T. W. 1982. Ordovician volcanism in Scotland. *In:* SUTHERLAND, D. S. (ed.) *Igneous Rocks of the British Isles*, pp. 51–63, Wiley, New York.

BOUDETTE, E. L. 1981. Ophiolite assemblage of early Paleozoic age in central western Maine. *Geological Association of Canada Special Paper No. 24*, pp. 209–30.

BOYER, C. 1970. Contribution à l'étude de volcanisme acide de Jersey (Îles anglo-normandes). *Bulletin de la Société Linnéenne de Normandie*, **101**, 20–5.

—— 1974. Volcanisme acide paléozoïque dans le Massif Armoricain. *Thèse d'Etat*, Orsay, 380 pp.

BROCHWICZ-LEWIŃSKI, W., POZARYSKI, W. &. TOMCZYK, H. 1984. Sinistral strike-slip movements in central Europe in the Paleozoic. *Publications of the Institute of Geophysics, Polish Academy of Sciences*, **A13**(160), 3–13.

BROOKINS, D. C. & HUSSEY, A. M. 1978. Rb–Sr ages for the Casco Bay Group and other rocks from the Portland–Orrs Islands area, Maine. *Geological Society of America Abstracts with Programs*, **10**(2), 34.

BROWN, G. C., FRANCIS, E. H., KENNAN, P. & STILLMAN, C. J. 1985. Caledonian igneous rocks of Britain and Ireland. *In:* HARRIS, A. L. (ed.) *The Nature and Timing of Orogenic Activity in the Caledonian rocks of the British Isles. Memoirs of the Geological Society of London No. 9*, pp. 1–15, Plate 1.

BROWN, M. 1978. The tectonic evolution of the Precambrian rocks of the St. Malo region, Armorican Massif, France. *Precambrian Research*, **6**, 1–21.

——, BARBER, A. J. & ROACH, R. A. 1971. Age of the St. Malo migmatite belt, northern Brittany. *London, Physical Science*, **234**, 77–9.

BROWN, W. R. 1970. Investigations of the sedimentary record in the Piedmont and Blue Ridge of Virginia. *In:* FISHER, G. W., PETTIJOHN, F. J., REED, J. C., JR., & WEAVER, K. N. (eds) *Studies of Appalachian geology: Central and Southern*, pp. 335–49, Wiley-Interscience, New York.

BRYANT, B. & REED, J. C., JR 1970. Geology of the Grandfather Mountain window and vicinity, North Carolina and Tennessee. *United States Geological Survey Professional Paper No. 615*, 190 pp.

CABANIS, B. 1975. L'orogénèse hercynienne, phénomène majeur dans la partie orientale du Pays de

Léon (Bretagne Nord Occidentale). *Comptes Rendus Hebdomadaires des Séances de l'Academie des Sciences, Série D,* **280**, 1769–72.

—— 1983. Main features of volcanism and plutonism in late Proterozoic and Dinantian times in France. *In*: SCHENK, P. E. (ed.) *Regional Trends in the Geology of the Appalachian–Caledonian–Hercynian–Mauritanide Orogen,* pp. 187–92, Reidel, Dordrecht.

—— & DARBOUX, J. R. 1984. Le volcanisme briovérien de la région de Telgruc (Baie de Douarnenez): étude géochimique et signification géodynamique. *R. C. P. 705—Géodynamique du Massif Armoricain. Colloque Journées du Mans, October 1–2, 1984, Hercynica.*

—— & WYNS, R. 1984. Le volcanisme précambrien des Mauges et ses caractères géochimiques. *R.C.P. 705—Géodynamique du Massif Armoricain. Colloque Journées du Mans, October 1–2, 1984, Hercynica.*

——, CHANTRAINE, J. & HERROUIN, Y. 1979. Le Bassin de Morlaix unité circonscrite et indépendant dans le contexte géologique régional. *Bulletin du Bureau de Recherche Géologiques et Minières (France), Section 1,* **4**, 269–76.

——, —— & RABU, D. Caractérisation géochimique de quelques volcanismes briovériens (protérozoique supérieur) dans le Nord du Massif Armoricain: implications sur l'évolution géodynamique cadomienne. *Bulletin de la Société Géologique de France,* in press.

——, MICHOT, J. & DEUTSCH, S. 1977. Remise en question de la datation géochronologique des gneiss de Brest. *Comptes Rendus Hebdomadaires des Séances de l'Academie des Sciences, Série D,* **284**, 883–6.

——, SAUNIER, J. F. & CHAUVEL, J. J. 1984. Etude géochimique (majeurs et traces) des amphibolites du dôme cristallophyllien de Plouguenast (Protérozoique supérieur du domaine Centre Armoricain). *R.C.P. 705—Géodynamique du Massif Armoricain. Colloque Journées du Mans, October 1–2, 1984, Hercynica.*

CALVEZ, J. Y. & VIDAL, P. 1978. Two billion year old relicts in the Hercynian belt of western Europe. *Contributions to Mineralogy and Petrology,* **65**, 395–9.

CARPENTER, R. H., ODOM, A. L. & HARTLEY, M. E., III 1982. Geochronological investigation of the Lincolnton metadacite, Georgia and South Carolina. *Geological Society of America Special Paper No. 191,* pp. 145–52.

CLAESSON, S. & RODDICK, J. C. 1983. ^{40}Ar/^{39}Ar data on the age and metamorphism of the Ottfjället dolerites, Särv Nappe, Swedish Caledonides. *Lithos,* **16**, 61–73.

CLARKE, D. B., BARR, S. M. & DONAHOE, H. V. 1980. Granitoid and other plutonic rocks of Nova Scotia. *In*: WONES, D. R. (ed.) *The Caledonides in the USA: Proceedings of the International Geological Correlation Program—Caledonide Orogen Project 27, Blacksburg, VA. Department of Geological Sciences, Virginia Polytechnic Institute and State University, Memoir No. 2,* pp. 107–16.

COCKS, L. R. M. & FORTEY, R. A. 1982. Faunal evidence for oceanic separations in the Palaeozoic of Britain. *Journal of the Geological Society, London,* **139**, 465–78.

COGNÉ, J. 1959. Données nouvelles sur l'Antécambrien dans l'Ouest de la France: Pentévrien et Briovérien en baie de Saint-Brieuc (Côtes du Nord). *Bulletin de la Sociéte Géologique de France, Série 7,* **1**, 112–18.

—— 1970. Le Briovérien et le cycle Cadomien dans le carde des orogènes fini-précambriens. *Notes et Memoires du Service Géologique du Maroc,* **236**, 193–218.

—— & WRIGHT, A. E. 1980. L'orogène Cadomien. *In: Géologie de l'Europe: Colloque C6, 26 Congrès Géologique International, Paris, 1980,* pp. 29–55.

COLLINSON, J. D. 1979. The Proterozoic sandstones between Heilprin Land and Mylius-Erichsen Land, eastern North Greenland. *Rapport Grønlands Geologiske Undersøgelse, No. 88,* pp. 5–10.

—— 1980. Stratigraphy of the Independence Fjord Group (Proterozoic) of Eastern North Greenland. *Rapport Grønlands Geologiske Undersøgelse No. 99,* pp. 7–23.

CONLEY, J. F. & HENIKA, W. S. 1973. Geology of the Snow Creek, Martinsville East, Price, and Spray quadrangles, Virginia. *Virginia Division of Mineral Resources Report of Investigations No. 33,* 71 pp.

CRIBB, S. J. 1975. Rubidium–strontium ages and strontium isotope ages from the igneous rocks of Leicestershire. *Journal of the Geological Society, London,* **131**, 203–12.

CURRIE, K. L., NANCE, R. D., PAJARI, G. E., JR & PICKERILL, R. K. 1981. Some aspects of the pre-Carboniferous geology of Saint John, New Brunswick. *Current Research, Part A. Geological Survey of Canada Paper No. 81–1A,* pp. 23–30.

CURRY, G. B., BLUCK, B. J., BURTON, C. J., INGHAM, J. K., SIVETER, D. J. & WILLIAMS, A. 1984. Age, evolution and tectonic history of the Highland Border Complex, Scotland. *Transactions of the Royal Society of Edinburgh, Earth Sciences,* **75**, 113–33.

DALLMEYER, D. 1980. Geochronology report. *Current Research, Mineral Development Division, Newfoundland Department of Mines and Energy, Report No. 80–1,* pp. 143–6.

——, ODOM, A. L., O'DRISCOLL, C. F. & HUSSEY, E. M. 1981. Geochronology of the Swift Current granite and host volcanic rocks of the Love Cove Group, southwestern Avalon Zone, Newfoundland. Evidence of a late Proterozoic volcanic-subvolcanic association. *Canadian Journal of Earth Sciences,* **18**, 699–707.

DEUNFF, J., AUVRAY, B., COGNÉ, J., HAMEURT, J., JEANETTE, D. & VIDAL, O. 1973. Confirmation micropaléontologique de l'âge radiométrique ordovicien inférieur de groupe spilitique d'Erquy (Cote-du-Nord). *Comptes Rendus Hebdomadaires des Séances de l'Academie des Sciences, Série D,* **276**, 935–7.

DEWEY, J. F. 1971. A model for the Lower Palaeozoic evolution of the southern margin of the early

Caledonides of Scotland and Ireland. *Scottish Journal of Geology*, **7**, 219–40.

DICKSON, W. L. 1984. Geology, geochemistry and petrology of the Precambrian igneous rocks and Carboniferous granitoid rock between St. John and Beaver Harbour, southern New Brunswick. *Ph.D. Thesis*, University of New Brunswick, 397 pp. (unpublished).

DiNITTO, R. G., HEPBURN, J. C., CARDOZA, K. D. & HILL, M. 1984. The Marlboro Formation in its type area and associated rocks just west of the Bloody Bluff fault zone, Marlborough area, Massachusetts. *In*: HANSON, L. S. (ed.) *Geology of the Coastal Lowlands, Boston to Kennebunk Maine. New England Intercollegiate Geological Conference 76th Annual Meeting*, pp. 271–91.

DONAHOE, H. V. 1983. Cobequid Highlands Project. *Report of Activities, Nova Scotia Department of Mines and Energy, Report, 83–1*, p. 327.

DOOLAN, B. L., GALE, M. H., GALE, P. N. & HOAR, R. S. 1982. Geology of the Quebec re-entrant: possible constraints from early rifts and the Vermont–Quebec serpentine belt. *In*: ST JULIEN, P. & BELAND, J. (eds) *Major Structural Zones and Faults of the Northern Appalachians. Geological Association of Canada Special Paper No. 24*, pp. 87–115.

DOWNIE, C., LISTER, T. R., HARRIS, A. L. & FETTES, D. J. 1971. A palynological investigation of the Dalradian rocks of Scotland, *Report of the Institute of Geological Sciences No. 71/9*, 30 pp.

DRAKE, A. A., JR & MORGAN, B. A. 1981. The Piney Branch Complex—a metamorphosed fragment of the Central Appalachian ophiolite in northern Virginia. *American Journal of Science*, **281**, 484–508.

DUFF, B. A. 1978. Rb–Sr whole-rock age determination of the Jersey Andesite Formation, Jersey, C. I. *Journal of the Geological Society, London*, **135**, 153–6.

DUNNING, F. W. 1972. Dating events in the Metamorphic Caledonides: impressions of the symposium held in Edinburgh, September 1971. *Scottish Journal of Geology*, **8**, 179–91.

DUPRET, L., CABANIS, B., LE GALL, J. & DORE, F. 1984. Caractères pétrographiques et géochimiques des volcanites briovériennes de Montsurvent (Manche): leur place dans l'évolution orogénique cadomiènne du Nord de l'Armorique. *R.C.P. 705—Géodynamique du Massif Armoricain. Colloque Journées du Mans October 1–2, 1984, Hercynica*.

ESPENSHADE, G. H. 1986. Geology of the Marshall Quadrangle, Fauquier County, Virginia. *United States Geological Survey Bulletin No. 1560*, 60 pp.

——, RANKIN, D. W., SHAW, K. W. & NEWMAN, R. B. 1975. Geologic map of the east half of the Winston Salem quadrangle, North Carolina, Virginia. *United States Geological Survey Miscellaneous Geological Investigations Map I–709B*, scale 1:250 000.

FEISS, P. G. 1982. Geochemistry and tectonic setting of the volcanics of the Carolina slate belt. *Economic Geology*, **77**, 273–93.

FISHER, D. W., ISACHSEN, Y. W. & RICKARD, L. V. 1970. Geologic map of New York. *New York State Museum and Science Service, Map and Chart Series No. 15*, scale 1:250 000.

FITTON, J. G., THIRLWALL, M. F. & HUGHES, D. J. 1982. Volcanism in the Caledonian belt of Britain. *In*: THORPE, R. S. (ed.) *Andesites: Orogenic Andesites and Related Rock*, pp. 611–36, Wiley, Chichester.

FURNES, H., AUSTRHEIM, H., AMALIKSEN, K. G. & NORDÅS, J. 1983a. Evidence for an incipient early Caledonian (Cambrian) orogenic phase in southwestern Norway. *Geological Magazine*, **120**, 607–12.

——, NYSTUEN, J. P., BRUNFELT, A. & SOLHEIM, S. 1983b. Geochemistry of upper Riphean–Vendian basalts associated with the 'sparagmites' of southern Norway. *Geological Magazine*, **120**, 349–61.

——, ROBERTS, D., STURT, B. A., THON, A. & GALE, G. H. 1980a. Ophiolite fragments in the Scandinavian Caledonides. *In*: PANAYIOTOU, A. (ed.) *Ophiolites: Proceedings of the International Ophiolite Symposium, Nicosia*, pp. 582–600, Geological Survey Department, Nicosia.

——, RYAN, P. D., GRENNE, T., ROBERTS, D., STURT, B. A. & PRESTVIK, T. 1985. Geological and geochemical classification of the ophiolite fragments in the Scandinavian Caledonides. *In*: GEE, D. G. & STURT, B. A. (eds) *The Caledonide Orogen–Scandinavia and Related Areas*, Wiley, Chichester.

——, STURT, B. A. & GRIFFIN, W. L. 1980b. Trace element geochemistry of metabasalts from the Karmoy ophiolite, southwest Norwegian Caledonides. *Earth and Planetary Science Letters*, **50**, 75–91.

——, THON, A., NORDÅS, J. & GARMANN, L. B. 1982. Geochemistry of Caledonian metabasalts from some Norwegian ophiolite fragments. *Contributions to Mineralogy and Petrology*, **79**, 295–307.

GARDNER, P. M. 1980. The geology and petrology of the Hasvik gabbro, Sørøy, Northern Norway. *Ph.D. Thesis*, University of London, 311 pp. (unpublished).

GAYER, R. A. & HUMPHREYS, J. R. 1981. Tectonic modelling of the Finnmark and Troms Caledonides based on high level igneous rock geochemistry. *Terra Cognita*, **1**, 44.

GEE, D. G. 1975. A tectonic model for the central part of the Scandinavian Caledonides. *American Journal of Science*, **275A**, 468–515.

—— & ZACHRISSON, E. 1974. Comments on stratigraphy, faunal provinces and structure of the metamorphic allochthon, central Scandinavian Caledonides. *Geologiska Föreningens i Stockholm Förhandlingar*, **96**, 61–6.

GIBSON, G. G., TEETER, S. A. & FEDONKIN, M. A. 1984. Ediacarian fossils from the Carolina Slate belt, Stanly County, North Carolina. *Geology*, **12**, 387–90.

GOLDBERG, S. A. & BUTLER, J. R. 1984. Characteristics of Bakersville metadiabase dikes. *Geological Society of America Abstracts with Programs*, **16** (3), 141.

——, —— & FULLAGAR, P. D. 1985. Age of the Bakersville Metadiabase dike swarm, North Carolina–Tennessee. *Geological Society of America Abstracts with Programs*, **17** (2), 93.

GOLDSMITH, R. in press. Structural and metamorphic history of Eastern Massachusetts. *In*: HATCH, N. L., Jr (ed.) *The bedrock geology of Massaachusetts, U.S. Geological Survey Professional Paper 1366.*

GRAINDOR, M. J. 1957. Le Brioverien dans le nord-est du Massif Armoricain. *Memoires du Service de la Carte Géologique de France No. 211.*

GRAVIOU, J. 1984. Pétrogénèse des magmas calco-alcalins: example des granitoides cadomiens du Nord du Massif Armoricain. *Thèse du 3e Cycle*, Université de Rennes, 220 pp.

GREIG, D. C., WRIGHT, J. E., HAINS, B. A. & MITCHELL, H. G. 1968. Geology of the county around Church Stretton, Craven Arms, Wenlock Edge and Brown Clee. *Memoirs of the Geological Survey of the United Kingdom.*

GRENNE, T. & LAGERBLAD, B. 1985. The Fundsjø Group, central Norway—a lower Palaeozoic island arc sequences: geochemistry and regional implications. *In*: GEE, D. G. & STURT, B. A. (eds) *The Caledonide Orogen—Scandinavia and Related Areas*, Wiley, Chichester.

—— & REINSBAKKEN, A. 1981. Possible correlation of island arc greenstone belts and related sulphide deposits from Grong and eastern Trondheim districts of the central Norwegian Caledonides. *Transactions of the Institute of Mining and Metallurgy, Section B*, **90**, B59.

GUTERCH, A. 1984. Deep structure of the earth's crust in the contact zone between Palaeozoic and Precambrian platforms in Poland. *Publications of the Institute of Geophysics, Polish Academy of Sciences*, **A13** (160), 63–4.

HALL, L. M. & ROBINSON, P. 1982. Stratigraphic-tectonic subdivisions of southern New England. *In*: ST JULIEN, P. & BELAND, J. (eds) *Major Structural Zones and Faults of the Northern Appalachians. Geological Association of Canada Special Paper No. 24*, pp. 15–41.

HALLS, C., REINSBAKKEN, A., FERRIDAY, I., HAUGEN, A. & RANKIN, A. 1977. Geological setting of the Skorovas orebody within the allochthonous volcanic stratigraphy of the Gjersvik Nappe, central Norway. *In*: *Volcanic Processes in Ore Genesis. Institute of Mining and Metallurgy and Geological Society of London Special Paper No. 7*, pp. 128–51.

HARRIS, A. L. & PITCHER, W. S. 1975. The Dalradian Supergroup. *In*: HARRIS, A. L., SHACKLETON, R. M., WATSON, J., DOWNIE, C., HARLAND, W. B. & MOORBATH, S. (eds) *A Correlation of the Precambrian Rocks in the British Isles. Special Report of the Geological Society of London No. 6*, pp. 52–75.

HARRIS, C. W. & GLOVER, L., III 1983. An unconformity in the Carolina slate belt of North Carolina: new evidence for the areal extent of the *ca.* 600 Ma Virgilina deformation. *Geological Society of America Abstracts with Programs*, **15**, 75.

HARRISON, J. E. & PETERMAN, Z. E. 1980. Note 52—a preliminary proposal for a chronometric time scale for the Precambrian of the United States and Mexico. *Geological Society of America Bulletin*, **91**, 377–80.

HATCHER, R. D., JR 1978. Tectonics of the western Piedmont and Blue Ridge, Southern Appalachians: review and speculation. *American Journal of Science*, **278**, 276–304.

——, HOOPER, R. T., PETTY, S. M. & WILLIS, J. D. 1984. Structure and chemical petrology of three Southern Appalachian mafic–ultramafic complexes and their bearing upon the tectonics of emplacement and origin of Appalachian ultramafic bodies. *American Journal of Science*, **284**, 484–506.

HEIER, K. S. 1961. Layered gabbro, hornblende, carbonatite and nepheline syenite on Stjernøy, North Norway. *Norsk Geologisk Tidsskrift*, **41**, 109–55.

HENDERSON, W. G. & ROBERTSON, A. H. F. 1982. The Highland Border rocks and their relation to marginal basin development in the Scottish Caledonides. *Journal of the Geological Society, London*, **139**, 433–50.

HEPBURN, J. C. & MUNN, B. 1984. A geologic traverse across the Nashoba Block, eastern Massachusetts. *In*: HANSON, L. S. (ed.) *Geology of the Coastal Lowlands, Boston to Kennebunk, Maine. New England Intercollegiate Geological Conference, 76th Annual Meeting*, pp. 103–23.

HILL, T. 1980. Geochemistry of the greenschists in relation to the Cu–Fe deposit in the Ramundberget area, central Swedish Caledonides. *Norges Geologiske Undersøkelse*, **360**, 195–210.

HON, R., HILL, M., HEPBURN, J. C. & SMITH, C. 1984. Composition and age of source materials for the late Proterozoic magmas in the Avalon terrane of eastern North America—evidence from the Boston Platform. *Geological Society of America Abstracts with Programs*, **16**, 543.

HORTON, J. W., JR 1984. Stratigraphic nomenclature in the Kings Mountain belt, North Carolina and South Carolina. *United States Geological Survey Bulletin No. 1537-A*, pp. 59–68.

HUGHES, C. J. & MALPAS, J. G. 1971. Metasomatism in the late Precambrian Bull Arm Formation in southeastern Newfoundland: recognition and implications. *Proceedings of the Geological Association of Canada*, **24**, 85–93.

HUSSEY, E. M. 1980. Geology of the Clode Sound area, Newfoundland, Canada. *Unpublished M.Sc. thesis*, Memorial University of Newfoundland, St John's, Newfoundland, Canada.

IKIN, N. P. 1983. Petrochemistry and tectonic significance of the Highland Border Suite mafic rocks. *Journal of the Geological Society, London*, **140**, 267–78.

IRVINE, T. N. 1974. Petrology of the Duke Island ultramafic complex, southeastern Alaska. *Geological Society of America Memoir No. 138*, 240 pp.

JACOBSON, S. R. & WASSERBURG, G. J. 1979. Nd and Sr isotopic study of the Bay of Islands Ophiolite Complex and the evolution of the source of midocean ridge basalts. *Journal of Geophysical Research*, **84**, 7429–45.

JAMIESON, R. A. & CRAW, D. 1983. Reconnaissance mapping of the southern Cape Breton Highlands—a preliminary report. *Current Research, Part A*,

Geological Survey of Canada Paper No. 83–1A, pp. 263–8.

JEHU, T. J. & CAMPBELL, R. 1917. The Highland Border rocks of the Aberfoyle district. Transactions of the Royal Society of Edinburgh, 52, 175–212.

JEPSEN, H. F. & KALSBEEK, F. 1979. Igneous rocks in the Proterozoic platform of eastern North Greenland. Rapport Grønlands Geologiske Undersøgelse No. 88, pp. 11–14.

——, —— & SUTHREN, R. J. 1980. The Zig-Zag Dal Basalt Formation, North Greenland. Rapport Grønlands Geologiske Undersøgelse No. 99, pp. 25–32.

JOHNSON, M. R. W. & HARRIS, A. L. 1967. Dalradian–?Arenig relations in part of the Highland Border, Scotland, and their significance in the chronology of the Caledonian orogeny. Scottish Journal of Geology, 3, 1–16.

KARSON, J. A. & DEWEY, J. F. 1978. Coastal complex, western Newfoundland: an early Ordovician oceanic fracture zone. Geological Society of America Bulletin, 89, 1037–49.

KAYE, C. A. & ZARTMAN, R. E. 1980. A late Proterozoic to Cambrian age for the stratified rocks of the Boston Basin, Mass., USA. In: WONES, D. R. (ed.) The Caledonides in the USA: Proceedings of the International Geological Correlation Program—Caledonide Orogen Project 27, Blacksburg, VA. Department of Geological Sciences, Virginia Polytechnic Institute and State University, Memoir No. 2, pp. 257–62.

KEPPIE, J. D. 1982. Geology and tectonics of Nova Scotia. Field Trip Guide for the Avalon and Meguma Zones. Memorial University of Newfoundland Report No. 9, pp. 125–39.

——, —— & MURPHY, J. B. 1979. Petrology of the late Precambrian Forchu Group in the Louisbourg area, Cape Breton Island. Nova Scotia Department of Mines Paper No. 79–1, 18 pp.

—— & DOSTAL, J. 1980. Paleozoic volcanic rocks of Nova Scotia. In: WONES, D. R. (ed.) The Caledonides in the USA: Proceedings of the International Geological Program—Caledonide Orogen Project 27, Blacksburg, VA. Department of Geological Sciences, Virginia Polytechnic Institute and State University, Memoir No. 2, pp. 249–56.

KITE, L. E. & STODDARD, E. F. 1984. The Halifax County complex: oceanic lithosphere in the eastern North Carolina Piedmont. Geological Society of America Bulletin, 95, 422–32.

KLINGSPOR, I. & GEE, D. G. 1985. The age of some Trøndelag trondhjemites. In: GEE, D. G. & STURT, B. A. (eds). The Caledonide Orogen—Scandinavia and Related Areas, Wiley, Chichester.

KOLLUNG, S. 1979. Stratigraphy and major structures of the Grong District, Nord-Trøndelag. Norges Geologiske Undersøkelse, 354, 1–51.

KROGH, T. E. 1982. Improved accuracy of U–Pb zircon ages by the creation of more concordant systems using an air abrasion technique. Geochimica et Cosmochimica Acta, 46, 637–50.

——, STRONG, D. F. & PAPEZIK, V. 1983. Precise U–Pb ages of zircons from volcanic and plutonic units in the Avalon Peninsula. Geological Society of America Abstracts with Programs, 15, 135.

KUMPALAINEN, R. 1980. Upper Proterozoic stratigraphy and depositional environments of the Tossåsfjallet Group, Särv Nappe, southern Swedish Caledonides. Geologiska Föreningens i Stockholm Förhandlingar, 102, 531–50.

LAMBERT, R. ST J. & McKERROW, W. S. 1976. The Grampian orogeny. Scottish Journal of Geology, 12, 271–92.

LASH, G. G. 1984. The Jonestown Volcanic rocks, eastern Pennsylvania—near trench volcanism in the Central Appalachians. Geological Society of America Abstracts with Programs, 16 (1), 46.

LAURENT, R. 1977. Ophiolites from the Northern Appalachians of Quebec. In: COLEMAN, R. G. & IRWIN, W. P. (eds) North America Ophiolites. Oregon Department of Geology and Mineral Industries Bulletin No. 95, pp. 25–40.

LAWSON, D. E. 1974. Torridonian volcanic sediments. Scottish Journal of Geology, 8, 345–62.

LEAKE, B. E. 1982. Volcanism in the Dalradian. In: SUTHERLAND, D. S. (ed.) Igneous Rocks of the British Isles, pp. 45–50, Wiley, New York.

LE FORT, J. P. 1975. Le socle peri-armoricain. Etude géologique et géophysique de socle submergé à l'Ouest de la France. Thèse d'Etat, Université de Rennes, 217 pp.

LE GALL, J. & CABANIS, B. 1984. Caractères chimico-minéralogiques des ignimbrites et laves cambriennes de l'Est du Massif Armoricain: implication pétrogénètiques. R.C.P. 705—Géodynamique du Massif Armoricain. Colloque Journées du Mans, October 1–2, 1984, Hercynica.

LENK, C., STROTHER, P. K., KAYE, C. A. & BARGHOORN, E. S. 1982. Precambrian age of the Boston Basin: new evidence from microfossils. Science, 216, 619–20.

LEUTWEIN, F. 1968. Contribution à la connaissance du précambrien récent en Europe occidentale et développement géochronologique du Briovérien en Bretagne (France). Canadian Journal of Earth Sciences, 5, 673–82.

—— & SONET, J. 1965. Contribution à la connaissance de l'évolution géochronologique de la partie nord-est du Massif Armoricain Français. Sciences de la Terre, 10, 345–67.

——, —— & MAX, M. D. 1972. The age of the Carnsore granodiorite. Geological Survey of Ireland Bulletin No. 1, pp. 303–9.

LIPIN, B. R. 1984. Chromite from the Blue Ridge province of North Carolina. American Journal of Science, 284, 507–29.

LONG, L. E. & LAMBERT, R. ST J. 1963. Rb-Sr isotopic ages from the Moine Series. In: JOHNSON, M. R. W. & STEWART, F. H. (eds) The British Caledonides, pp. 217–48, Oliver & Boyd, Edinburgh.

LUKERT, M. T. & BANKS, P. O. 1984. Geology and age of the Robertson River pluton. In: BARTHOLOMEW, M. J. (ed.) The Grenville Event in the Appalachians and Related Topics. Geological Society of America Special Paper No. 194, pp. 161–6.

LUTRO, O. 1979. The geology of the Gjersvik area, Nord-Trondelag. Norges Geologiske Undersøkelse, 354, 53–100.

MALPAS, J. 1977. Petrology and tectonic significance of

Newfoundland ophiolites, with examples from the Bay of Islands. *In*: COLEMAN, R. G. & IRWIN, W. P. (eds) *North America Ophiolites. Oregon Department of Geology and Mineral Industries Bulletin No. 95*, pp. 13–23.

MATTINSON, J. M. 1976. Ages of zircons from the Bay of Islands ophiolite complex, Western Newfoundland. *Geology*, **4**, 393–4.

MAX, M. D. 1975. Precambrian rocks of south-east Ireland. *In*: HARRIS, A. L., SHACKLETON, R. M., WATSON, J., DOWNIE, C., HARLAND, W. B. & MOORBATH, S. (eds) *A Correlation of Precambrian Rocks in the British Isles. Special Report of the Geological Society of London No. 6*, pp. 96–101.

MCCONNELL, K. I. & GLOVER, L., III 1982. Age and emplacement of the Flat River Complex, an Eocambrian sub-volcanic pluton near Durham, North Carolina. *Geological Society of America Special Paper No. 191*, pp. 133–43.

MCELHANEY, M. S. & MCSWEEN, H. Y., JR 1983. Petrology of the Chunky Gal Mountain mafic-ultramafic complex, North Carolina. *Geological Society of America Bulletin*, **94**, 855–74.

MIYASHIRO, A. 1975. Classification, characteristics and origin of ophiolites. *Journal of Geology*, **83**, 249–81.

MOSE, D. G. & NAGEL, M. S. 1982. Plutonic events in the Piedmont of Virginia. *Southeastern Geology*, **23**, 25–40.

MURPHY, J. B. 1977. The stratigraphic and geological history of the Forchu Group, southeastern Cape Breton, Nova Scotia. *M.Sc. Thesis*, Acadia University, Wolfville, Nova Scotia, 187 pp. (unpublished).

—— 1982. Tectonics and magmatism in the northern Antigonish Highlands, *PhD thesis*. Montreal, McGill University.

NEUMAN, R. B. 1984. Geology and paleobiology of islands in the Ordovician Iapetus Ocean: review and implications. *Geological Society of America Bulletin*, **95**, p 1188–201.

NIXON, G. T. & PAPEZIK, V. S. 1979. Late Precambrian ash-flow tuffs and associated rocks of the Harbour Main Group near Colliers, eastern Newfoundland: chemistry and magmatic affinities. *Canadian Journal of Earth Sciences*, **12**, 167–81.

NORDÅS, J., AMALIKSEN, K. G., BREKKE, H., SUTHREN, R., FURNES, H., STURT, B. A. & ROBINS, B. 1985. Lithostratigraphy and petrochemistry of Caledonian rocks on Bømlo, W. Norway. *In*: GEE, D. G. & STURT, B. A. (eds) *The Caledonide Orogen—Scandinavia and Related Areas*, Wiley, Chichester.

NORTON, S. A. 1976. Hoosac Formation (early Cambrian or older) on the east limb of the Berkshire massif, western Massachusetts. *In*: PAGE, L. R. (ed.) *Contributions to the Stratigraphy of New England. Geological Society of America Memoir No. 148*, pp. 357–71.

NOVAK, S. W. & RANKIN, D. W. 1980. Mineralogy and geochemistry of an ash-flow tuff of peralkaline affinity from the Mt. Rogers Formation, Grayson Co., Virginia. *Geological Society of America Abstracts with Programs*, **12** (4), 203–4.

O'BRIEN, S. J., WARDLE, R. J. & KING, A. F. 1983. The Avalon zone: a pan-African terrane in the Appalachian orogen of Canada. *Geological Journal*, **18**, 195–222.

ODIN, G. S., GALE, N. H., AUVRAY, B., BIELSKI, M., DORÉ, F., LANCELOT, S. R. & PASTEELS, P. 1983. Numerical dating of Precambrian–Cambrian boundary. *Nature, London*, **302**, 21–3.

ODOM, A. L. & FULLAGAR, P. D. 1973. Geochronologic and tectonic relationship between the Inner Piedmont, Brevard Zones, and Blue Ridge belts, North Carolina. *American Journal of Science*, **237A**, 1334–49.

—— & —— 1984. Rb–Sr whole-rock and inherited zircon ages of the plutonic suite of the Crossnore Complex, Southern Appalachians, and their implications regarding the time of opening of the Iapetus Ocean. *In*: BARTHOLOMEW, M. J. (ed.) *The Grenville Event in the Appalachians and Related Topics. Geological Society of America Special Paper No. 194*, pp. 255–61.

O'DRISCOLL, C. F. & STRONG, D. F. 1979. Geology and geochemistry of Late Precambrian volcanic and intrusive rocks of southwestern Avalon Zone in Newfoundland. *Precambrian Research*, **8**, 19–48.

OLSEN, J. 1980. Genesis of the Joma stratiform sulphide deposit, central Norwegian Caledonides. *Proceedings of the 5th IAGOD Symposium, Alta, UT, 1978*, Vol. 1, pp. 745–57.

OLSZEWSKI, W. J., JR 1980. The geochronology of some stratified metamorphic rocks in northeastern Massachusetts. *Canadian Journal of Earth Sciences*, **17**, 1407–16.

OOSTEROM, M. G. 1955. Some notes on the Lille Kufjord layered gabbro, Seiland, Finnmark, Northern Norway. *Norges Geologiske Undersøkelse*, **195**, 73–87.

PANKHURST, R. J. 1974. Rb-Sr whole-rock chronology of Caledonian events in Northeast Scotland, *Geological Society of America Bulletin*, **85**, 345–50.

—— & PIDGEON, R. T. 1976. Inherited isotope systems and the source region pre-history of early Caledonian granites in the Dalradian Series of Scotland, *Earth and Planetary Science Letters*, **31**, 55–68.

—— & SUTHERLAND, D. S. 1982. Caledonian granites and diorites of Scotland and Ireland. *In*: SUTHERLAND, D. S. (ed.) *Igneous Rocks of the British Isles*, pp. 149–90, Wiley, New York.

——, ANDREWS, J. R., PHILLIPS, W. E. A., SANDERS, I. S. & TAYLOR, W. E. G. 1976. Age and structural setting of the Slieve Gamph Igneous Complex, Co. Mayo, Eire. *Journal of the Geological Society of London*, **132**, 327–34.

PATCHETT, P. J., GALE, N. H., GOODWIN, R. & HUMM, M. J. 1980. Rb–Sr whole-rock isochron ages of late Precambrian to Cambrian igneous rocks from southern Britain. *Journal of the Geological Society, London*, **137**, 649–56.

PAVLIDES, L. 1981. The Central Virginia volcanic-plutonic belt: an island arc of Cambrian(?) age. *Geological Survey Professional Paper No. 1231-A*, 34 pp.

——, GAIR, J. E. & CRANFORD, L. 1982. Massive sulfide deposits of the Southern Appalachians. *Economic Geology*, **77**, 233–72.

——, POJETA, J., GORDON, M., PARSLEY, R. L. & BOBYARCHICK, A. R. 1980. New evidence for the age of the Quantico Formation of Virginia. *Geology,* **8**, 286–90.

PEARCE, J. A. 1975. Basalt geochemistry used to investigate past tectonic environments on Cyprus. *Tectonophysics,* **25**, 41–68.

—— & CANN, J. R. 1973. Tectonic setting of basic volcanic rocks determined using trace element analyses. *Earth and Planetary Science Letters,* **19**, 290–300.

PEUCAT, J. J., HIRBEC, Y., AUVRAY, B., COGNÉ, J. & CORNICHET, J. 1981. Late Proterozoic zircon ages from a basic-ultrabasic complex: a possible Cadomian orogenic complex in the hercynian belt of Western Europe. *Geology,* **9**, 169–73.

PHILLIPS, W. E. A., STILLMAN, C. J. & MURPHY, T. 1976. A Caledonian plate tectonic model. *Journal of the Geological Society, London,* **132**, 579–609.

PIASECKI, M. A. J., VAN BREEMEN, D. & WRIGHT, A. E. 1981. Late Precambrian geology of Scotland, England and Wales. *In:* KERR, J. W. & FERGUSSON, A. J. (eds) *Ecology of the North American Borderlands. Canadian Society of Petroleum Geologists, Memoir 7,* 57–94.

PIDGEON, R. T. & AFTALION, M. 1978. Cogenetic and inherited zircon U–Pb systems in granites: Paleozoic granites of Scotland and England. *In:* BOWES, D. R. & LEAKE, B. E. (eds) *Crustal Evolution in Northwestern Britain and Adjacent Regions, Special Publication of the Geological Society of London No. 10,* pp. 183–220.

—— & JOHNSON, M. R. W. 1974. A comparison of zircon U–Pb and whole-rock Rb–Sr systems in three phases of the Carn Chuinneag granite, northern Scotland, *Earth and Planetary Science Letters,* **24**, 105–12.

PIERATTI, D. D. 1976. The origin and tectonic significance of the Tibbet Hill metavolcanics northwestern Vermont. *Geological Society of America Abstracts with Programs,* **8** (2), 246.

PIPER, J. D. A. 1982. A palaeomagnetic investigation of the Malvernian and Old Radnor Precambrian, Welsh Borderlands. *Geological Journal,* **17**, 69–88.

POOLE, W. H. 1980. Rb–Sr age of some granitic rocks between Ludgate Lake and Negro Harbour, southwestern New Brunswick. *Rb–Sr and U–Pb Isotopic Age Studies. Current Research, Part C, Geological Survey of Canada Paper No. 80–1C,* pp. 170–3.

PRESTVIK, T. 1980. The Caledonian ophiolite complex of Leka, north central Norway. *In:* PANAYIOTOU, A. (ed.) *Ophiolites: Proceedings of the International Ophiolite Symposium, Nicosia, 1979,* pp. 555–66, Geological Survey Department, Nicosia.

—— & ROALDSET, E. 1978. Rare earth element abundances in Caledonian metavolcanics from the island of Leka, Norway. *Geochemistry International,* **12**, 89–100.

RABU, D., CHAUVEL, J. J. & CHANTRAINE, J. 1983. Nouvelles propositions pour la lithostratigraphie du Briovérien (Protérozoique supérieur) et pour l'évolution géodynamique cadomienne en baie de St Brieuc (Massif Armoricain). *Bulletin de la Société Géologique de France,* **24** (4), 615–21.

RAMSAY, D. M. & STURT, B. A. 1977. A sub-Caledonian unconformity within the Finnmarkian nappe sequence and its regional significance. *Norges Geologiske Undersøkelse,* **334**, 107–16.

——, —— & ANDERSEN, T. B. 1979. The sub-Caledonian unconformity on Hjelmsøy—new evidence of primary basement–cover relations in the Finnmarkian nappe sequence. *Norges Geologiske Undersøkelse,* **351**, 1–12.

RANKIN, D. W. 1975. The continental margin of eastern North America in the Southern Appalachians: the opening and closing of the proto-Atlantic Ocean. *American Journal of Science,* **275A** 298–336.

—— 1976. Appalachian salients and recesses: late Precambrian continental breakup and the opening of the Iapetus Ocean. *Journal of Geophysical Research,* **81**, 5605–19.

—— 1985. Pre-Arenig characteristics of terranes of the Appalachian–Caledonide orogen. *Geological Society of America Abstracts with Programs,* **16**, 59.

——, STERN, T. W., McLELLAND, J., ZARTMAN, R. E. & ODOM, A. L. 1983. Correlation chart for Precambrian rocks of the eastern United States. *United States Geological Survey Professional Paper No. 1241–E,* pp. E1–E18.

RAST, N., O'BRIEN, B. & WARDLE, R. J. 1976. Relationships between Precambrian and lower Paleozoic rocks of the 'Avalon Platform' in New Brunswick, the Northeast Appalachians and the British Isles. *Tectonophysics,* **30**, 315–38.

RATCLIFFE N. M. 1983. Possible Catoctin age diabase dikes in the Hudson Highlands of New York and New Jersey: geochemistry and tectonic significance. *Geological Society of America Abstracts with Programs,* **15**, 172.

REED, J. C., JR 1955. Catoctin Formation near Luray, Virginia. *Geological Society of America Bulletin,* **66**, 871–96.

—— & MORGAN, B. A. 1971. Chemical alteration and spilitization of the Catoctin greenstones, Shenandoah National Park, Virginia. *Journal of Geology,* **79**, 526–48.

ROBERTS, D. & GEE, D. G. 1985. Caledonian tectonics in Scandinavia. *In:* GEE, D. G. & STURT, B. A. (eds) *The Caledonide Orogen—Scandinavia and Related Areas,* Wiley, Chichester.

——, SPRINGER, J. & WOLFF, F. CHR. 1970. Evolution of the Caledonides in the northern Trondheim region, Central Norway: a review. *Geological Magazine,* **107**, 133–45.

——, STURT, B. A. & FURNES, H. 1985. Volcanite assemblages and environments in the Scandinavian Caledonides and the sequential development history of the Mountain belt. *In:* GEE, D. G. & STURT, B. A. (eds) *The Caledonide Orogen—Scandinavia and Related Areas,* Wiley, Chichester.

ROBINS, B. 1980. The evolution of the Lillebukt alkaline complex. Stjernøy, Norway. *Lithos,* **13**, 219–20 (abstract).

—— 1982. The geology and petrology of the Rognsund intrusion, West Finnmark, Northern Norway. *Norges Geologiske Undersøkelse,* **371**, 1–55.

—— & GARDNER, P. M. 1974. Synorogenic layered basic intrusions in the Seiland petrographic province, Finnmark. *Norges Geologiske Undersøkelse*, **312**, 91–130.

—— & —— 1975. The magmatic evolution of the Seiland province, and Caledonian plate boundaries in Northern Norway. *Earth and Planetary Science Letters*, **26**, 167–78.

—— & TAKLA, M. A. 1979. Geology and geochemistry of metamorphosed picrite–ankaramite dyke suite from the Seiland province, northern Norway. *Norsk Geologisk Tidsskrift*, **59**, 67–95.

—— & TYSSELAND, M. 1979. Fenitization of some mafic igneous rocks in the Seiland province, northern Norway. *Norsk Geologisk Tidsskrift*, **59**, 1–23.

—— & —— 1983. The geology, geochemistry, and origin of ultrabasic fenites associated with the Pollen carbonatite (Finnmark, Norway). *Chemical Geology*, **40**, 65–95.

RÖSHOFF, K. 1975. A probable glaciogenic sediment in the Särv Nappe, central Swedish Caledonides. *Geologiska Föreningens i Stockholm Förhandlingar*, **97**, 192–5.

RUITENBERG, A. A., GILES, P. S., VENUGOPAL, D. V., BUTTIMER, S. M., McCUTCHEON, S. R. & CHANDRA, J. 1979. Geology and mineral deposits of the Caledonia area. *New Brunswick Department of Natural Resources Memoir No. 1*, 213 pp.

SAETHER, T. & NYSTUEN, J. P. 1981. Tectonic framework, stratigraphy, sedimentation and volcanism of the Late Precambrian Hedmark Group, Østerdalen, South Norway. *Norsk Geologisk Tidsskrift*, **61**, 163–211.

ST JULIEN, P. & HUBERT, C. 1975. Evolution of the Taconian orogen in the Quebec Appalachians. *American Journal of Science*, **275A**, 337–62.

——, SLIVITSKY, A. & FEININGER, T. 1983. A deep structural profile across the Appalachians of southern Quebec. *In:* HATCHER, R. D., JR, WILLIAMS, H. & ZIETZ, I. (eds) *Contributions to the Tectonics and Geophysics of Mountain Chains. Geological Society of America Memoir No. 158*, pp. 103–11.

SCOTFORD, D. M. & WILLIAMS, J. R. 1983. Petrology and geochemistry of metamorposed ultramafic bodies in a portion of the Blue Ridge of North Carolina and Virginia. *American Mineralogist*, **68**, 78–94.

SECOR, D. T., JR, SAMSON, S. L., SNOKE, A. W. & PALMER, A. R. 1983. Confirmation of the Carolina slate belt as an exotic terrane. *Science*, **221**, 649–50.

SEIDERS, V. M. 1978. A chemically bimodal, calc-alkaline suite of volcanic rocks, Carolina volcanic slate belt, central North Carolina. *Southeastern Geology*, **19**, 241–65.

SHACKLETON, R. M. 1969. The Precambrian of North Wales. *In:* WOOD, A. (ed.) *The Precambrian and Lower Palaeozoic of Wales*, pp. 1–22, University of Wales Press, Cardiff.

—— 1975. Precambrian rocks of Wales. *In:* HARRIS, A. L., SHACKLETON, R. M., WATSON, J., DOWNIE, C., HARLAND, W. B. & MOORBATH, S. (eds) *A*

Correlation of Precambrian Rocks in the British Isles, Special Report of the Geological Society of London No. 6, pp. 76–82.

SHAW, H. F. & WASSERBURG, G. J. 1984. Isotopic constraints on the origin of Appalachian mafic complexes. *American Journal of Science*, **284**, 319–49.

SINHA, A. K. & GLOVER, L., III 1978. U–Pb systematics of zircons during dynamothermal metamorphism. *Contributions to Mineralogy and Petrology*, **66**, 304–10.

SJØSTRAND, T. 1978. Caledonian geology of the Kvarnbergsvattnet area, northern Jamtland, central Sweden. *Sveriges Geologiska Undersökning, Serie C, No. 735*, 107 pp.

SMITH, C. J. & HON, R. 1984. Geology, petrology, and origin of the Precambrian igneous rocks located in the area north of Boston. *In:* HANSON, L. S. (ed.) *Geology of the Coastal Lowlands, Boston to Kennebunk, Maine. New England Intercollegiate Geological Conference, 76th Annual Meeting*, pp. 292–309.

SOLYOM, Z., ANDREASSON, P. G. & JOHANSSON, I. 1979a. Geochemistry of amphibolites from Mt. Sylarna, Central Scandinavian Caledonides. *Geologiska Föreningens i Stockholm Förhandlingar*, **101**, 17–27.

——, GORBATCHEV, R. & JOHANSSON, I. 1979b. The Ottfjället Dolerites. Geochemistry of the dyke swarm in relation to the geodynamics of the Caledonide orogen in central Scandinavia. *Sveriges Geologiska Undersökning, Serie C, No. 756*, 38 pp.

STANLEY, R. S. & RATCLIFFE, N. M. 1985. Tectonic synthesis of the Taconian Orogeny in western New England. *Geological Society of America Bulletin*, **96**, 1227–50.

——, ROY, D. L., HATCH, N. L., JR & KNAPP, D. A. 1984. Evidence for tectonic emplacement of ultramafic and associated rocks in the pre-Silurian eugeoclinal belt of western New England— vestiges of an ancient accretionary wedge. *American Journal of Science*, **284**, 559–95.

STEPHENS, M. B. 1977. The Stekenjokk volcanites— segment of a lower Palaeozoic island arc complex. *In:* BJØRLYKKE, A., LINDAHL, I. & VOKES, F. M. (eds) *Kaledonske Malmforekomster*, pp. 24–36, BVLIS Tekniske Virksomhet, Trondheim.

—— 1980. Occurrence, nature and tectonic significance of volcanic and high-level intrusive rocks within the Swedish Caledonian. *In:* WONES, D. R. (ed.) *The Caledonides in the USA: Proceedings of the International Geological Correlation Program— Caledonide Orogen Project 27, Blacksbury, VA. Department of Geological Sciences, Virginia Polytechnic Institute and State University, Memoir No. 2*, pp. 289–98.

—— 1981. Evidence for Ordovician arc build-up and arc splitting in the upper Allochthon of central Scandinavia. *Terra Cognita*, **1**, 75.

—— 1982. Field relationships, petrochemistry and petrogenesis of the Stekenjokk volcanites, central Swedish Caledonides. *Sveriges Geologiska Undersökning, Serie C, No. 786*.

—— & SENIOR, A. 1981. The Norra Storfjället lens— an example of fore-arc basin sedimentation and volcanism in the Scandinavian Caledonides. *Terra Cognita,* **1**, 76–7.

——, FURNES, H., ROBINS, B. & STURT, B. A. 1985. Igneous activity within the Scandinavian Caledonides. *In:* GEE, D. G. & STURT, B. A. (eds) *The Caledonide Orogen—Scandinavia and Related Areas,* Wiley, Chichester.

STEWART, A. D. 1975. 'Torridonian' rocks of Western Scotland. *In:* HARRIS, A. L., SHACKLETON, R. M., WATSON, J., DOWNIE, C., HARLAND, W. B. & MOORBATH, S. (eds) *A Correlation of the Precambrian Rocks in the British Isles. Special Report of the Geological Society of London No. 6,* pp. 43–51.

—— 1982. Late Proterozoic rifting in NW Scotland: the genesis of the 'Torridonian'. *Journal of the Geological Society, London,* **139**, 413–20.

STEWART, D. B. 1974. Precambrian rocks of Seven Hundred Acre Island and development of cleavage in the Isleboro Formation. *In:* OSBERG, P. H. (ed.) *Guidebook for Field trips in East-central and North-central Maine. New England Intercollegiate Geological Conference, 66th Annual Meeting, October 12–13, 1974, Orono, ME,* pp. 86–98.

STOW, S. H., NEILSON, M. J. & NEATHERY, T. L. 1984. Petrography, geochemistry, and tectonic significance of the amphibolites of the Alabama Piedmont. *American Journal of Science,* **284**, 416–36.

STRAND, T. & KULLING, O. 1972. *Scandinavian Caledonides,* Wiley, New York, 302 pp.

STRONG, D. F. 1974a. Plateau lavas and diabase dikes of northwestern Newfoundland. *Geological Magazine,* **111**, 501–14.

—— 1974b. An 'off-axis' alkalic volcanic suite associated with the Bay of Islands Ophiolites, Newfoundland. *Earth and Planetary Science Letters,* **21**, 301–9.

——, O'BRIEN, S. J. & DOSTAL, J. 1984. Petrochemical evolution of Late Proterozoic rocks of the Avalon Zone type-area in Newfoundland. *Geological Society of America Abstracts with Programs,* **16**, 65.

——, ——, TAYLOR, S. W., STRONG, P. G. & WILTON, D. H. 1978. Aborted Proterozoic rifting in eastern Newfoundland. *Canadian Journal of Earth Sciences,* **15**, 117–31.

STUKAS, V. & REYNOLDS, P. H. 1974. ^{40}Ar/^{39}Ar dating of the Long Range dikes, Newfoundland. *Earth and Planetary Science Letters,* **22**, 256–66.

STURT, B. A. & RAMSAY, D. M. 1965. The alkaline complex of the Breivikbotn area, Sørøy, Northern Norway. *Norges Geologiske Undersøkelse,* **231**, 1–142.

——, PRINGLE, I. R. & RAMSAY, D. M. 1978. The Finnmarkian phase of the Caledonian Orogeny. *Journal of the Geological Society, London,* **135**, 597–610.

——, ROBERTS, D. & FURNES, H. 1984. A conspectus of Scandinavian Ophiolites. *In:* GASS, I. G., LIPPARD, S. J. & SHELTON, A. W. (eds) *Ophiolites and Oceanic Lithosphere. Special Publication of the Geological Society of London No. 13,* pp. 381–91.

STYLES, M. T. & KIRBY, G. A. 1980. New investigations of the Lizard complex, Cornwall, England and a discussion of an ophiolite model. *In:* PANAYIOTOU, A. (ed.) *Ophiolites: Proceedings of the International Ophiolite Symposium, Nicosia, 1979,* pp. 517–26, Geological Survey Department, Nicosia.

SUEN, C. J., FREY, F. A. & MALPAS, J. 1979. Bay of Islands ophiolite suite, Newfoundland: petrologic and geochemical characteristics with emphasis on rare earth elements geochemistry. *Earth and Planetary Science Letters,* **45**, 337–48.

SUTHERLAND, D. S. (ed.) 1982. *Igneous Rocks of the British Isles.* Wiley, London.

TAYLOR, H. P. 1967. The zoned ultramafic complexes of southeastern Alaska. *In:* WYLLIE, P. J. (ed.) *Ultramafic and Related Rocks,* pp. 96–118, Wiley, New York.

THOMAS, G. M. 1977. Volcanic rocks and their minor intrusives, eastern Jersey, Channel Islands. *Ph.D. Thesis,* University of London (unpublished).

THOMAS, W. A. 1977. Evolution of Appalachian–Ouachita salients and recesses from reentrants and promontories in the continental margin. *American Journal of Science,* **277**, 1233–78.

THORPE, R. S. 1978. Tectonic emplacement of ophiolitic rocks in the Precambrian Mona Complex of Anglesey. *Nature, London,* **275**, 57–8.

—— 1982. Precambrian igneous rock. *In:* SUTHERLAND, D. S. (ed.) *Igneous Rocks of the British Isles,* pp. 19–35, Wiley, New York.

——, BECKINSALE, R. D., PATCHETT, P. J., PIPER, J. D. A., DAVIES, G. R. & EVANS, J. A. 1984. Crustal growth and late Precambrian-early Palaeozoic plate tectonic evolution of England and Wales. *Journal of the Geological Society, London,* **141**, 521–36.

TROUW, R. A. J. 1973. Structural geology of the Marsfjällen area, Caledonides of Västerbotten, Sweden. *Sveriges Geologiska Undersökning, Serie C, No. 689,* 115 pp.

TULL, J. F. 1978. Structural development of the Alabama Piedmont northwest of the Brevard zone. *American Journal of Science,* **278**, 442–60.

VIDAL, P. 1976. L'évolution polyorogénique de massif Armoricaine—Apport de la géochronologie et de la géochimie isotopique de strontium. *Thèse,* Université de Rennes, 142 pp.

——, AUVRAY, B., CHARLOT, R. & COGNÉ, J. 1981. PreCadomian relicts in the Armorican Massif: their age and role in the evolution of the western and central European Cadomian–Hercynian belt. *Precambrian Research,* **14**, 1–20.

——, ——, CHAUVET, J. F. & COGNÉ, J. 1972. L'âge radiométrique de la diorite de Saint Quay Portrieux (Côtes du Nord): ses conséquences sur le Briovérien de la baie de St Brieuc. *Comptes Rendus Hebdomadaires des Séances de l'Academie des Sciences,* **275**, 1323–6.

——, ——, COGNÉ, J., HAMEURT, J. & JEANETTE, D. 1971. Données géochronologiques sur la série spilitique d'Erquy: problèmes noveaux à propos du Briovérien de Bretagne septentional. *Comptes Rendus Hebdomadaires des Séances de l'Academie des Sciences,* **273**, 132–5.

WARDLE, R. J. 1978. The stratigraphy and tectonics of the Green Head Group: its relationship to Hadrynian and Paleozoic rocks, southeastern New

Brunswick. *Ph.D. Thesis*, University of New Brunswick, 294 pp. (unpublished).

WATSON, J. 1975. The Precambrian rocks of the British Isles—a preliminary review. *In*: HARRIS, A. L., SHACKLETON, R. M., WATSON, J., DOWNIE, C., HARLAND, W. B. & MOORBATH, S. (eds) *A Correlation of Precambrian Rocks in the British Isles. Special Report of the Geological Society of London No. 6*, pp. 1–10.

WEEKS, L. J. 1954. Southeast Cape Breton Island, Nova Scotia. *Geological Survey of Canada Memoir No. 227*.

WEHR, F. & GLOVER, L., III 1985. Stratigraphy and tectonics of the Virginia–North Carolina Blue Ridge: Evolution of a late Proterozoic early Paleozoic hinge zone. *Geological Society of America Bulletin*, **96**, 285–95.

WHITNEY, J. A., PARIS, T. A., CARPENTER, R. H. & HARTLEY, M. E., III 1978. Volcanic evolution of the southern slate belt of Georgia and South Carolina: a primitive oceanic island arc. *Journal of Geology*, **86**, 173–92.

WILLIAMS, H. 1975. Structural succession, nomenclature, and interpretation of transported rocks in western Newfoundland. *Canadian Journal of Earth Sciences*, **12**, 1874–94.

—— 1984. Miogeoclines and suspect terranes of the Caledonian–Appalachian orogen: tectonic patterns in the North Atlantic region. *Canadian Journal of Earth Sciences*, **21**, 887–901.

—— & ST JULIEN, P. 1982. The Baie Verte–Brompton line: early Paleozoic continent–ocean interface in the Canadian Appalachians. *In*: ST JULIEN, P. & BELAND, J. (eds) *Major Structural Zones and Faults of the Northern Appalachians. Geological Association of Canada Special Paper No. 24*, pp. 277–307.

——, GILLESPIE, R. T. & VAN BREEMEN, O. 1985. A late Precambrian rift-related igneous suite in western Newfoundland. *Canadian Journal of Earth Sciences*, **22**, 1727–35.

WINCHESTER, J. A. & FLOYD, P. A. 1976. Geochemical magma type discrimination: application to altered and metamorphosed basic igneous rocks. *Earth and Planetary Science Letters*, **28**, 459–69.

—— & MAX, M. D. 1982. The geochemistry and origins of the Precambrian rocks of the Rosslare Complex, S.E. Ireland. *Journal of the Geological Society, London*, **139**, 309–19.

WOLFF, F. CHR. & ROBERTS, D. 1980. Geology of the Trondheim region. *Norges Geologiske Undersøkelse*, **356**, 117–28.

WONES, D. R. & GOLDSMITH, R. in press. Intrusive rocks of eastern Massachusetts. *In*: HATCH, N. L., Jr. (ed.) *The bedrock geology of Masachusetts. U.S. Geological Survey Professional Paper 1366*.

WRIGHT, A. E. 1976. Alternating subduction direction and the evolution of the Atlantic Caledonides. *Nature, London*, **264**, 156–60.

WRIGHT, J. E. & SEIDERS, V. M. 1980. Age of zircon from volcanic rocks of the central North Carolina Piedmont and tectonic implications for the Carolina volcanic slate belt. *Geological Society of America Bulletin*, **91**, 287–94.

ZACHRISSON, E. 1964. The Remdalen syncline. *Sveriges Geologiska Undersökning, Serie C, No. 596*, 53 pp.

—— 1966. A pillow lava locality in the Grong District, Norway. *Norsk Geologisk Tidsskrift*, **46**, 375–8.

—— 1969. Caledonian geology of Northern Jamtland—Southern Västerbotten. *Sveriges Geologiska Undersökning, Serie C, No. 644*, 33 pp.

—— 1973. The westerly extension of Seve rocks within the Seve–Køli Nappe Complex in the Scandinavian Caledonides. *Geologiska Föreningens i Stockholm Förhandlingar*, **95**, 243–51.

ZARTMAN, R. E. & NAYLOR, R. S. 1984. Structural implications of some radiometric ages of igneous rocks in southeastern New England. *Geological Society of America Bulletin*, **95**, 522–39.

ZEN, E-AN 1983. Exotic terranes in the New England Appalachians—limits, candidates, and ages: a speculative essay. *Geological Society of America Memoir No. 158*, pp. 55–82.

——, GOLDSMITH, R., RATCLIFFE, N. M., ROBINSON, P. & STANLEY, R. S. 1983. *Bedrock Geologic Map of Massachusetts*, United States Geological Survey and Commonwealth of Massachusetts, Department of Public Works (scale, 1:250000).

D. W. RANKIN, U.S. Geological Survey, Mail Stop 926, National Center, Reston, VA 22092, USA.

H. FURNES, Geologisk Institutt Avd. A, Allegaten 41, 5000 Bergen, Norway.

A. C. BISHOP, Keeper of Mineralogy, British Museum (Natural History), Cromwell Road, London SW7 5BD, UK.

B. CABANIS, Laboratoire de Géochimie Comparée et Systématique, Tour 16–26, 4 place Jussieu, 75230 Paris Cédex 05, France.

D. J. MILTON, U.S. Geological Survey, Mail Stop 928, National Center, Reston, VA 22092, USA.

S. J. O'BRIEN, Mineral Development Division, Department of Mines and Energy, PO Box 4750, St John's, Newfoundland A1C 5T7, Canada.

R. S. THORPE, Department of Earth Sciences, The Open University, Walton Hall, Milton Keynes MK7 6AA, UK.

Evolution of the Iapetus Ocean and its borders in pre-Arenig times: a synthesis

James W. Skehan, SJ

SUMMARY: On the margins of the Laurentian continent the interval *c*. 800–492 Ma was dominated by (1) rifting involving continental crust and (2) rift sedimentation with or without related volcanicity and plutonism, culminating in (3) the formation of the Iapetus Ocean and succeeded by (4) initial phases of compressional tectonics. The latter involved the approach of volcanic island-arc systems and the partial or complete obduction of ophiolites of the oceanic crust cutting through the slope–rise prism and, at least in some parts of the orogen, being thrust onto the continental-shelf deposits in the Cambrian and Tremadocian. These processes led to the closing of the ocean in the mid-Ordovician Taconian and the Silurian Caledonian orogenies. The earliest and most complete pre-Arenig orogenic movements are recorded in the Finnmarkian orogeny, including obduction of ophiolites in Scandinavia (520–480 Ma). Related sedimentation gaps, preceded by deformation and ophiolite obduction and/or uplift, were accompanied by tectonic melange development and/or volcanicity. These features are recorded widely from northern Britain and Ireland (Grampian orogeny), and from the Appalachians of Newfoundland (Burlington orogenic episode), Maine, USA, and Quebec, Canada (Penobscot orogeny). Movements interpreted as relating to the Penobscotian are now recognized as widespread in the US Appalachians. The Sardic orogenic phase in southern Europe (*c*. 510 Ma) is associated with plutonism and metamorphism and may be related to late Cadomian III orogenic movements.

In the southeastern landmasses of Gondwanaland (Avalonian–Cadomian–Pan-African) essentially the same time interval (*c*. 800–492 Ma) was also dominated initially by rifting of continental crust overlain by late Proterozoic shelf deposits and the obduction and folding of ophiolites (Cadomian I orogeny) and underlying rocks, followed by intrusion of late- to post-tectonic plutons (Bleida). Cadomian II resulted in the deposition of coarse clastics, volcanics and glacigenic sediments (Tiddiline), and folding, erosion and deposition of a thick wedge of late Proterozoic carbonate and clastic rocks with alkaline volcanics (Adoudounian) overlain conformably by lower and middle Cambrian that are overlain disconformably by Tremadocian clastic sediments. During the rifting phase continental fragments drifted away and/or became volcanic arcs with subduction zones and back-arc basins constituting the weakly orogenic Avalonian terrane to the W and the strongly orogenic but discontinuous belt forming a terrane characterized by Cadomian fragments between the Avalonian terrane of the British Isles and the W African craton. Stratigraphic columns and schematic time-slice stratigraphic profiles with interpreted tectonic environments from various parts of the orogen provide comparisons and contrasts in stratigraphic, faunal, structural, volcanic, plutonic and metamorphic evolution.

The pre-Arenig components of the now-composite Appalachian–Caledonide–Avalonian–Cadomian–Pan-African orogenic system (Fig. 1) circumscribe the N Atlantic region. Consideration of this orogenic complex is integral to discussion of the evolution of the Iapetus Ocean and its borders, and may be thought of in broad terms as consisting of a complex of at least two generally distinctive belts.

1 The first comprises the western and northern part of the main Appalachian–Caledonide (AC) belt of eastern N America, the N British Isles, E Greenland, Svalbard, Scandinavia and a restricted part of adjacent N central Europe. In terms of the rocks that are linked to the respective cratons and their oceanic margins, the western border of the AC belt consists of a basement of mainly middle Proterozoic Grenville rocks overlain unconformably by upper Proterozoic rift clastics and lower Palaeozoic shelf clastics, i.e. a continental slope–rise–abyssal prism (SRAP) of clastic and volcanic rocks which formed the eastern margin of the Laurentian–Greenland craton (Fig. 1) and the western and southern margin of the Fennoscandian–Baltic craton. The pre-Arenig part of this orogenic belt also consists of oceanic crust with a complex of associated ocean-floor igneous rocks—arc-volcanic and plutonic rocks, olistostromes and melanges which reflect increasing tectonic instability with time as they were transported by plate-tectonic mechanisms toward the respective cratons. Within this time frame the volcanic arcs collided diachronously and with varying degrees of intensity and completeness with the cratons and their sedimen-

From HARRIS, A. L. & FETTES, D. J. (eds), 1988, *The Caledonian–Appalachian Orogen,*
Geological Society Special Publication No. 38, pp. 185–229.

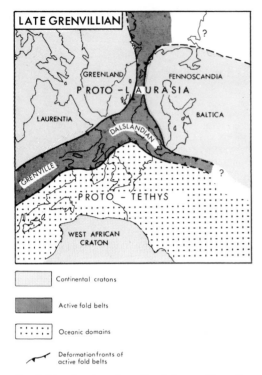

Continental cratons

Active fold belts

Oceanic domains

Deformation fronts of
active fold belts

Fig. 1. Map showing schematic relative positions of
the Laurentian–Greenland, Fennoscandian–Baltic
and W African cratons with respect to the
Grenvillian–Dalslandian basin of deposition and the
proto-Tethys Ocean. (Modified from Ziegler 1984.)

tary aprons. The result was deformation by
folding and thrusting, including ophiolite obduction and nappe formation, igneous activity,
metamorphism, uplift and erosion.

2 The Avalonian–Cadomian–Pan-African
(ACPA) belt, except in NW Africa proper, shows
only limited evidence of basement rocks but has
a substantial development of late Proterozoic
shelf clastics upon which are developed magmatic
arcs and a coarse volcaniclastic cover. These are
overlain in places conformably and elsewhere
unconformably by lower Palaeozoic clastic rocks
carrying an Acado-Baltic fauna. The ACPA belt
comprises the eastern N American seaboard, the
southern parts of Ireland and the British Isles,
NW Africa and parts of western and central
Europe and of the Iberian Peninsula. However,
western and central Europe and the Iberian
Peninsula are so strongly overprinted by Acadian
and Variscan orogenic movements that, with
some notable exceptions, an understanding of
their relationship to the Caledonide and Cadomian orogenic movements is still in early stages (N.
Rast 1986, personal communication).

This discussion of the early development of
both these belts, as well as interactions between
them and their relationships to other exotic
terranes possibly originating as part of either
belt, is basic to a consideration of the post-Arenig
evolutionary history of the AC and the ACPA
orogens.

Basement rocks

The part of the Laurentian–Greenland craton
relevant to this discussion, as well as a part of the
Baltic craton, was consolidated in pre-Grenville
time (>1100 Ma) (Fig. 1). The Hebridean craton
yields radiometric ages between 2700 and
1750 Ma (Watson & Dunning 1979). The continental crust underlying the Faeroes and at least
the northern parts of the Rockall–Hatton Bank
was consolidated during the Lewisian (Scourian–
Laxfordian) orogenic cycles (Roberts 1975). The
bulk of the Fennoscandian–Baltic craton was
consolidated in pre-Grenvillian time with isochron ages of metamorphic and intrusive rocks
ranging from 2000 to 1280 Ma (Karelian–Gothian).

Appalachian–Caledonide Belt

Riphean and Vendian stratigraphic sequences of
the western margin of the AC orogen (Schwab *et
al*. 1988) record late Precambrian distension
associated with the early evolution of the Iapetus
Ocean. Schwab *et al*. present stratigraphic arguments that sequences such as the Upper Precambrian of the southern Appalachians were
deposited in intra-cratonic grabens, small aulacogens and marginal ensialic shelf basins proximal to a subsiding topographically-abrupt,
zigzagging continental edge extending the length
of the Appalachians from Georgia to Newfoundland across NW Britain and through E Greenland, Svalbard and Scandinavia.

Figure 2 presents stratigraphic columns from
Greenland (A and B), Svalbard (C), and Norway
(D–G) whose sediments and volcanic rocks
represent such environments during Riphean and
Vendian time. Figure 3 suggests the general
character and distribution of sediments and
volcanics of the rifting environment associated
with the collapse of continental crust (Grenvillian
basement) in Vendian and Cambrian times.

By middle Cambrian to Tremadocian time a
rifting environment in the continental margins
had been replaced by a stable continental-shelf
environment in which quartz arenites and carbonates dominate where the underlying basement
is continental crust (Fig. 3). Beyond the edge of

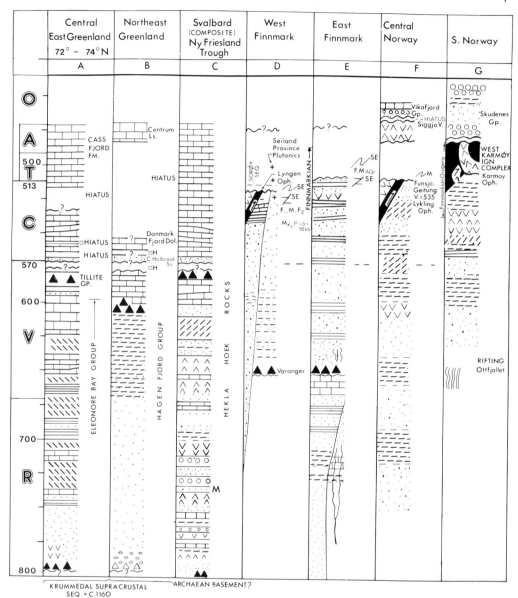

FIG. 2. Stratigraphic columns for eastern Greenland (A–B) and Svalbard (C) (after Haller 1971, Henriksen & Higgins 1976, Higgins & Phillips 1979) and Norway (D–G) (Sturt 1984 and 1985, personal communication).

the continental shelf, however, the SRAP sediments and volcanics rest on oceanic crust. The character of these deposits, which include olistostromes and melanges, indicates the progressive approach of a volcanic island arc. The sedimentary record indicates that in Scandinavia collision of a volcanic arc with the continental margin accompanied by thrusting of nappes, including

obduction of Group I ophiolite sequences (Fig. 2, columns D, F and G) onto shelf sediments, had been accomplished from middle Cambrian to Tremadocian time during the D_2 episode of the Finnmarkian orogeny (Fig. 4). Elsewhere in the AC orogen there is widespread but imprecise stratigraphic and tectonic evidence in the form of melanges and obducted ophiolites (Fig. 3,

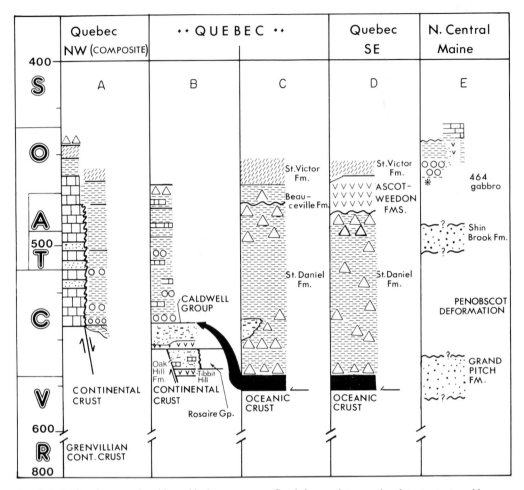

FIG. 3. A shelf environment is evidenced by lower to upper Cambrian sandstone and carbonate strata and by carbonate and sandstone breccias distinctive of the zone near the shelf-edge–continental-slope boundary; deposits of the slope–rise prism suggest the initial stages of compression signalling the approach of the volcanic arc from the E (Quebec area after St. Julien & Hubert (1975); Maine area after Osberg (1985)).

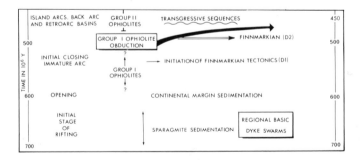

FIG. 4. Development of Scandinavian Caledonides (Sturt 1984, personal communication). The portion of this figure relevant to this synthesis includes crustal closing of an immature arc with obduction of Group I ophiolites in the D_1 and D_2 periods of Finnmarkian tectonics.

columns B and C) that the initial phases of similar orogenic activity took place in pre-Taconian time but somewhat later than in Scandinavia, mainly in late Cambrian to middle Ordovician times.

Avalonian–Cadomian–Pan-African belts

The record within ACPA orogenic belts indicates that they originated as volcanic arcs developed dominantly on a cratonal continental-basement margin as well as on isolated continental blocks separated by oceanic basins (Fig. 5) (Rast & Skehan 1983). This complex of orogenic belts developed in a tectonic environment character-ized by a complicated interaction of forces which produced both rifting and drifting. This situation is best illustrated in the Anti-Atlas of Morocco (Fig. 6) where several phases of rifting alternated with compressional phases (Fig. 7, column 21), the latter producing the main late Proterozoic–Cadomian I thrusting and ophiolite obduction, syn-tectonic and post-tectonic folding and asso-ciated foliations, plutonism, metamorphism, uplift and erosion. Tiddiline conglomerates, volcanics and glacigenic deposits were laid down on the erosion surface and deformed by Cadom-ian II orogenic movements. The Cadomian–Pan-African belt of Morocco and the Avalonian belts of Newfoundland, the Maritime Provinces of Canada and the Boston area appear to be volcanic arcs built on continental crust but closely associ-ated with a subduction zone producing back-arc ensimatic basins and calc-alkaline volcanic and plutonic rocks (Rast & Skehan 1983).

Continental basement involved in rifting—Laurentian–Greenland and Fennoscandian–Baltic shields

The crystalline basement of the N Atlantic region consists of a mosaic of crustal elements consoli-dated sequentially during the pre-Grenvillian (>1100 Ma), Grenville–Dalslandian (850–1100 Ma), Morarian or Knoydartian (690–780 Ma) and Cadomian (685–550 Ma) orogenic cycles (Ziegler 1984). The forelands of the region (Fig. 1) consist of (1) the Laurentian–Greenland Shield, of which the Rockall–Faeroe plateau and the Hebridean craton form a part, (2) the Fennoscandian or Baltoscandian shield and its extension beneath the Baltic depression and the Moscow platform and (3) the W African craton.

Appalachians

Rocks which were affected by the 'Grenville event' about 1000–1200 Ma formed the crystal-line basement of Laurentia–Greenland upon which late Proterozoic and Palaeozoic sedimen-tary-volcanic rock accumulated prior to the early to late Palaeozoic orogenic pulses which produced the Appalachian orogen as we know it.

Within the complex of orogenic belts, which together make up the present Appalachian orogen, basins containing great thicknesses of sedimentary rocks of late Proterozoic and early Palaeozoic age are separated by massifs of granites, gneisses and granulites that have been interpreted as Grenville massifs (Williams 1978, Glover *et al.* 1983) and form the true continental basement. The 'Grenville' massifs are so named because they yield age dates compatible with the Grenville orogenic dates of 1000–1200 Ma and have lithologies associated with cratonic Gren-ville rocks including charnockites and anorthos-ites. These external and internal massifs have been described by Hatcher (1984), and the external massifs have been reviewed by Bartho-lomew & Lewis (1984) and in part by Glover *et al.* (1983).

The external massifs make up some of the most important Precambrian anticlinoria and blocks of the Appalachian orogen. These include the Blue Ridge (Fig. 8) from Pennsylvania to Geor-gia, the Green Mountains of Vermont and the Long Range of Newfoundland (the Long–Green–Blue of Rankin (1975)) which comprise the most extensive exposures of basement rocks in the Appalachian margin of Laurentia. These com-plexes have been the subject of many investiga-tions (Brace 1953, Skehan 1961, Bartholomew *et*

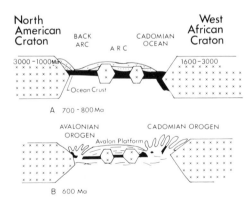

FIG. 5. (a) Schematic cross-section from the N American (Laurentian) craton to the W African (Gondwanan) craton through the Cadomian basins and microcontinent (*c.* 700–800 Ma) (Rast & Skehan 1983, p. 277); (b) schematic cross-section through the Avalonian orogen and platform and the Cadomian orogen (*c.* 600–650 Ma) (Rast & Skehan 1983, p. 277).

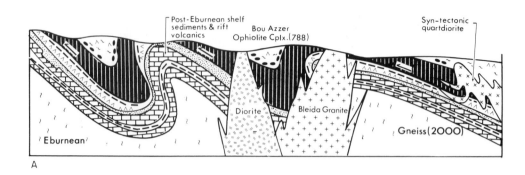

A

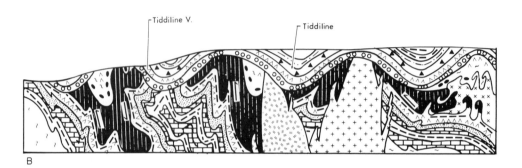

B

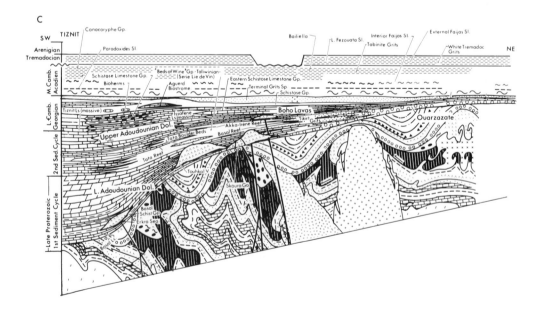

C

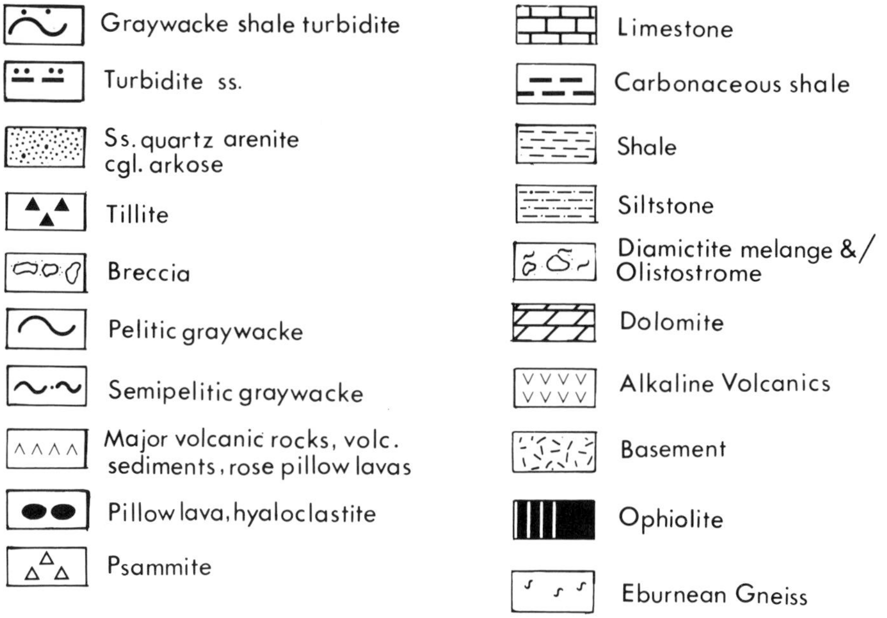

~	Graywacke shale turbidite	Limestone	Limestone
·· ··	Turbidite ss.	---	Carbonaceous shale
	Ss. quartz arenite cgl. arkose		Shale
▲▲	Tillite		Siltstone
⌒○·◌	Breccia	ō 𝒮⌐	Diamictite melange &/ Olistostrome
⌒~	Pelitic graywacke		Dolomite
~·~	Semipelitic graywacke	v v v v / v v v v	Alkaline Volcanics
∧∧∧∧	Major volcanic rocks, volc. sediments, rose pillow lavas		Basement
●●	Pillow lava, hyaloclastite	‖‖‖	Ophiolite
ᐃ ᐃ ᐃ	Psammite	ꜱ ꜱ ꜱ	Eburnean Gneiss

FIG. 6. Schematic restored profiles through the Anti-Atlas (and the Haut Atlas Occidental) of Morocco (based mainly on data from the publications cited below).

(a) Eburnean gneiss (*c.* 2000 Ma) forms the basement of the W African craton upon which Upper Proterozoic continental-shelf deposits of carbonates, quartz arenites, and glacigenic and volcanigenic sediments were laid down. The main episode of Cadomian I resulted in the obduction of the Bou Azzer ophiolite sequence (788 Ma) from the NE toward the SW (the age of the syn-tectonic quartz diorite is 685 Ma), folding, uplift and erosion. Late post-tectonic diorite (615 Ma) and the Bleida granite (623 Ma) are intrusive into the ophiolite sequence (Leblanc & Lancelot 1980).

(b) The Tiddiline Group was deposited with angular unconformity on the previous sequence. It consists dominantly of basal coarse clastics, volcanics and glacigenic sediments. These rocks were folded in Cadomian II or the D_2 phase of the Cadomian orogeny, which is later than 615 Ma, and were uplifted and eroded before the deposition of the lower Adoudounian (Michard 1976, Leblanc & Lancelot 1980).

(c) The lower and upper Adoudounian sequences consist of shelf clastics and carbonates that thicken toward the SW. They pass conformably up into the fossiliferous lower and middle Cambrian, Georgian and Acadien fine-grained clastics. Upper Cambrian rocks are absent; Tremadocian sediments are also fine-grained clastics (shales and siltstones) (Michard 1976, Leblanc & Lancelot 1980).

al. 1981, 1982, Dewey *et al.* 1983, Herz 1984, Herz & Force 1984, Sinha & Bartholomew 1984). These consist of granulitic and amphibolitic gneisses intruded by granites. Gneisses yield 1200–900 Ma ages and granites yield 550–720 Ma ages. The internal massifs commonly appear in windows and as domes, such as the Baltimore Dome of the central Appalachians and the Chester and Sadawga Pond Dome of the northern Appalachians.

The British Isles

The basement rocks of Northern Ireland and Scotland consist of Lewisian gneisses and granu-lites of Archaean age (*c.* 2700 Ma) of the Hebridean craton and adjacent parts of the Caledonides probably reworked down to early Proterozoic times (*c.* 1750 Ma) (Watson & Dunning 1979).

The Lewisian basement of the Hebridean craton is overlain unconformably by two Torri-donian groups dated respectively at *c.* 800 Ma and *c.* 1000 Ma (Moorbath 1969). In the meta-morphic Caledonides, the Lewisian basement is overlain unconformably by the polyphasally deformed and metamorphosed Moine which was deposited in a fluviatile or deltaic environment on an actively-subsiding block-faulted cratonal margin (Stewart 1975, Watson & Dunning 1979).

Shackleton (1979, p. 303), interpreting the seismic profiles of Bamford *et al.* (1978), inferred that the Moine from near the present location of the Great Glen fault is underlain by Grenvillian

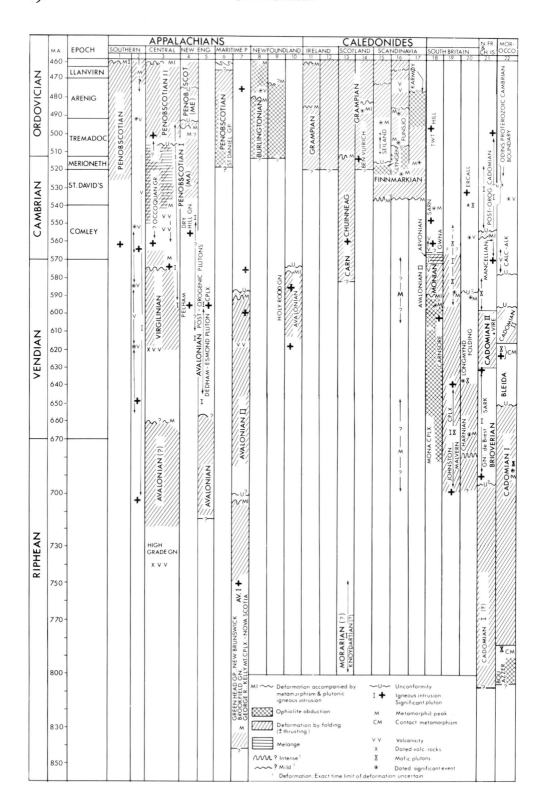

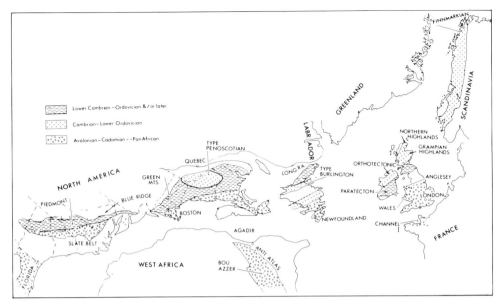

FIG. 8. Sketch map of the Appalachian–Caledonide–Avalonian–Cadomian–Pan-African orogens showing the location and approximate known or inferred extent of Grampian and Cadomian orogenesis of early Palaeozoic and late Proterozoic age (modified in part from Hall & Roberts (1988) and in part from Rast & Skehan (1983, Fig. 7).

granulites to at least as far S as the Highland Boundary fault and that these granulites continue to be present at least as far S as the Midland Valley and under central Ireland (Watson & Dunning 1979). There is now a strong possibility that the crust below the Midland Valley has no links to that of the Scottish Highlands, the Highland Boundary Fault being a major terrane boundary. Evidence for the existence of a Grenvillian–Dalslandian and a Morarian basement complex in Northern Ireland and Scotland is derived from areas overprinted by the Caledonian orogeny (van Breemen *et al.* 1978, Piasecki & van Breemen 1983, Piasecki *et al.* 1981).

Greenland

The major part of E Greenland consists of the Archaean Flyverfjord infracrustal complex (FIC)

FIG. 7. Timing of episodes of pre-middle Ordovician compressive deformation and related metamorphic and plutonic manifestations. Column numbers represent the following lithotectonic subdivisions: 1, S Appalachian Piedmont; 2, Carolina slate belt–Charlotte belt; 3, central Appalachian Piedmont–Chopawamsic belt; 4, New England central mobile belt; 5, southern New England Avalonian belt; 6, Maritime Provinces, Canada, central mobile belt; 7, Maritime Avalonian belt; 8, Newfoundland Fleur de Lys zone; 9, Botwood–Gander zone; 10, Avalon Peninsula; 11, Caledonides, Ireland (orthotectonic zone); 12, Ireland (paratectonic zone); 13, Scotland, N Highlands; 14, Grampian Highlands; 15, Scandinavia–Finnmark; 16, central Caledonides; 17, S Caledonides; 18, S Britain, Anglesey–Lleyn, N Wales; 19, S Wales–Stanner–Hanter–Malvern; 20, Welsh Borderlands–central England; 21, N France–Channel Islands; 22, Morocco, Anti-Atlas Mountains. The columns are based in part on Bryhni (1988), Hall & Roberts (1988), Harte (1988) and Rankin *et al.* (1988) and in part on the following: 1, Dallmeyer 1975, Hatcher 1978a, b, Pavlides 1981, Samson *et al.* 1982, Williams & Hatcher 1983; 2, Kish *et al.* 1979, Secor *et al.* 1983; 3, Glover & Sinha 1973, Drake & Lyttle 1981, Drake & Morgan 1981, Pavlides *et al.* 1982, Osberg 1983; 4, Neuman 1967, Robinson & Hall 1980, Boone 1983, Zartman & Naylor 1984; 5, Mosher & Rast 1984, Robinson 1983, Rast & Skehan 1983, Skehan & Rast 1983, Zen 1983; 6, St Julien & Hubert 1975, Williams & St Julien 1982; 7, Stewart 1974, Murray & Skehan 1979, Olszewski & Gaudette 1982, Keppie *et al.* 1983, Rast & Skehan 1983, Mosher & Rast 1984; 8, Kennedy 1980; Dewey *et al.* 1983; 9, Dewey *et al.* 1983; 10, Dallmeyer *et al.* 1981, Rast & Skehan 1983; 11, Rast & Crimes 1969, Yardley *et al.* 1980, Barber & Yardley 1985; 12, Rast & Crimes 1969, Dewey 1974; 13, Rast & Crimes 1969, Dewey 1974; 14, Rast & Crimes 1969, Dewey 1974; 15, Sturt *et al.* 1978; 16, Reading 1965, Bryhni *et al.* 1971, Gee 1975, Claesson & Roddick 1983, Furnes *et al.* 1983, Dallmeyer & Anderson 1984; 17, Furnes *et al.* 1983, Gee & Roberts 1983, Sturt 1984, and 1985, personal communication; 18, Bennison & Wright 1969, Rast & Skehan 1983; 19, Bennison & Wright 1969, Thorpe *et al.* 1974, Rast & Skehan 1983; 20, Bennison & Wright 1969, Beckinsale & Thorpe 1979; 20, Rast & Skehan 1983; 21, Clauer 1976, Ducrot & Lancelot 1977, 1978; 22, Michard 1976, Leblanc & Lancelot 1980, Leblanc 1981.

(*c.* 2300–3000 Ma), which mainly consists of biotite- and hornblende-bearing gneisses, amphibolites and ultramafic and granite bodies, overlain by supracrustal rock of middle Proterozoic age.

Supracrustal middle Proterozoic rocks overlie the FIC and both were first deformed and metamorphosed during the middle Proterozoic Carolinidian orogenesis. This movement affected rocks correlated with the Krummedal supracrustal sequence (Fig. 2, columns A and B). Zircon and Rb–Sr whole-rock studies suggest that the extensive migmatite zone was the site of a middle Proterozoic orogenic belt corresponding in time to the Grenville–Sveco–Norwegian events of N America and Europe. Late Proterozoic quartzites and shales, tillite sediments of the Eleonore Bay and Tillite Groups (Henriksen 1978, p. 105, 1985, p. 1095 *et seq.*) (Fig. 2, column A) were deposited on the cratonal margin during Riphean and Vendian time (Phillips *et al.* 1973, Higgins & Phillips 1979). Late Proterozoic deposits, well recorded in E Greenland, the British Isles, Spitzbergen and N Norway, are regarded as shelf sediments accumulated during the early evolution of the Iapetus Ocean (Harland & Gayer 1972, Higgins & Phillips 1979).

Norway and Sweden

Basement rocks of Scandinavia consist dominantly of autochthonous rocks of the Fennoscandian–Baltic craton. In Finnmark the autochthonous Vadsø Group (825 Ma—diagenesis) (Fig. 9) rests with angular unconformity on crystalline basement which in part consists of the orthogneiss and paragneiss complexes. Lower-grade supracrustals of Karelian age are also present (Sturt & Roberts 1978, p. 17). In the Kalak Nappe, however, two different types of basement are present (Fig. 9, rows A and B) the Raipas Suite (Fig. 9, row A) in parautochthonous nappes, and paragneisses and orthogneisses in thrust sheets internal to the Nappe Complex (Sturt & Roberts 1978, p. 18).

The autochthonous basement of N central Norway and Sweden consists of crystalline basement yielding mainly late Svecofennian ages (1700–1800 Ma, Rb–Sr) and dates for a younger thermal event of Grenvillian–Dalslandian age at 1100–1200 Ma. In the Lofoten–Vesteralen area of N Norway there is a wide range of ages from 3500 to 1100 Ma (Gustavson 1978, p. 25).

In S central Norway and Sweden autochthonous crystalline basement yields a range of ages

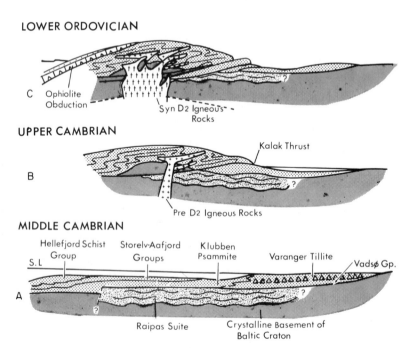

FIG. 9. Schematic cross-sectional restorations through Finnmark illustrating the pre-Arenig evolutionary model of Sturt & Roberts (1978) and Ramsey *et al.* (1985, p. 181).

representing Svecofennian (1700–1900 Ma), Gothian (1468 Ma) and Sveconorwegian (1000–1100 Ma) orogenic phases (Roberts 1978, p. 32). In S Norway (Fig. 1) the autochthonous basement and the Telemark supracrustal rocks yield mainly Sveconorwegian dates (900–1200 Ma), but some gneisses yield dates of approximately Svecofennian age (1600–1700 Ma). Allochthonous rocks of the Ulriken Gneiss Nappe and the overlying anorthosite complex also yield a similar age range (Sturt & Thon 1978, p. 43).

The crust of southern Sweden and Norway, consolidated during the Dalslandian–Grenvillian orogenic cycle, yields isochron ages between 1800 and 860 Ma (Berthelsen 1981, Ziegler 1984). The presence of a Morarian basement under large parts of Denmark is inferred from several age determinations on basement rocks in boreholes (Larsen 1971). However, it is difficult to map the extent of the areas affected by the Morarian diastrophism on the basis of available data or to assess the plate movements associated with it. Grenvillian age metamorphic rocks are reported in the Norwegian Caledonides and in the Scoresby Sound area of eastern Greenland (Zwart & Dornsiepen 1978). This suggests that the Grenvillian–Dalslandian fold belt extended through the Norwegian–Greenland Sea area (Fig. 1). Palaeomagnetic data suggest that, following the Grenvillian–Dalslandian orogenic cycle, Laurentia–Greenland and Fennoscandia–Baltica formed part of the same megacontinent (Patchett & Bylund 1977, Ziegler 1984). These now widely separated Grenvillian–Dalslandian fold belts probably marked the southern margin of Proto-Laurasia.

Avalonian, Cadomian and Pan-African (ACPA) domains

Avalonian and Cadomian stratigraphic sequences for the most part consist of late Proterozoic shelf sediments deposited on continental cratonal crust, as well as partly on rifted continental basement and partly on oceanic crust (Fig. 5). In W Africa (Fig. 6) these shelf sediments were deposited on Eburnean gneiss (*c.* 2000 Ma), a part of the W African craton. The craton is divided into (1) a western domain of Liberian age (*c.* 3000 Ma), which is almost unaffected by Eburnean reactivation (at *c.* 2000 Ma) and consists essentially of granulites (western Mauritania, Sierra Leone, Liberia, western Ivory Coast) but includes some Archaean low-grade greenstone belts in Sierra Leone, and (2) an eastern domain dominated by pre-Eburnean (2700 Ma) reactivated basement and NNE–SSW-trending Birrimian (lower Proterozoic) belts of metavol-

canic–sedimentary rocks with widespread syntectonic and late tectonic granites (2000 + 100 Ma). With some exceptions the middle Proterozoic (*c.* 2000–1000 Ma) is generally absent in the W African craton, which has remained notably stable for the last 1700 Ma (Caby *et al.* 1981).

In the Anti-Atlas Mountains of Morocco (Choubert 1947) the Precambrian basement comprises two major structural units: (1) the northern border of the W African Eburnean craton (2000 Ma) (Charlot 1978) to the SW and (2) a segment of the Pan-African orogenic belt (680–580 Ma) to the NE (Leblanc 1981, p. 436). The gneissic rocks of the Eburnean craton are overlain unconformably by shelf sediments, quartzites and stromatolitic limestones deformed during the Cadomian I phase of the Pan-African orogeny (Leblanc & Lancelot 1980, Leblanc 1981) (Fig. 6a).

Throughout the Cadomian and Avalonian domains and terranes of W Europe, S Britain and Ireland and along the eastern seaboard of N America, basement rocks are not well defined. Where such basement blocks have been identified they are of limited size and where dated they are younger than 900 Ma. Rast & Skehan (1983) and Skehan & Rast (1983) discussed basement–cover relationships and correlations throughout these terranes of the N Atlantic region.

Supracrustal rocks (late Proterozoic–Tremadocian)— Laurentian–Greenland and Fennoscandian margins

General statement

Late Proterozoic supracrustal sedimentary rocks mainly comprised great clastic wedges deposited upon the eastern margin of the respective basements discussed above. These clastic wedges throughout the orogen have many features in common throughout its component parts but there are also important differences. These contrasts may be significant in understanding certain variations in the character of the orogenic system during pre-Arenig time and may have an important bearing on effects produced in post-Arenig orogenic cycles.

Southern and central Appalachians

Throughout the Appalachian orogen, the late Proterozoic is chiefly represented by thick piles of interbedded metasedimentary and metavol-

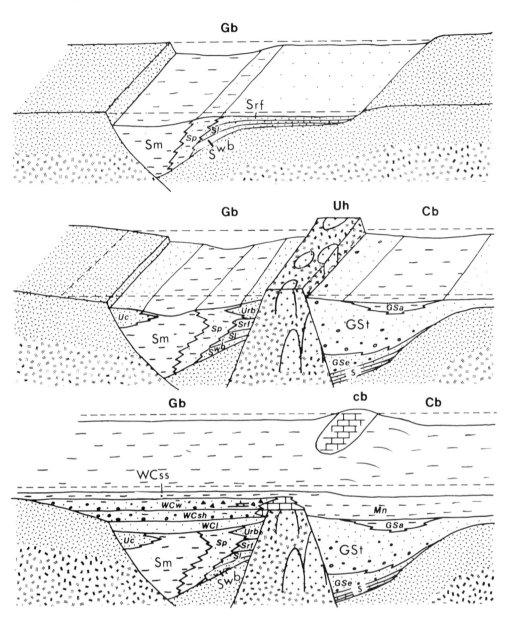

Fig. 10. Schematic representation of the depositional history and palaeogeography of the Ocoee Supergroup. Geographic features: cb—carbonate bank, Cb—Clingman basin, Gb—Gatlinburg basin, Uh—Unaka horst. Stratigraphic units: GSa—Anakeesta Formation (shales and minor sandstones), GSe—Elkmont Sandstone, GSt—Thunderhead Sandstone, Mn—Nantahala Slate (of Murphy Group), S—Snowbird Group (Wading Branch, Longarm, and Roaring Fork), Sl—Longarm Quartzite, Sm—Metcalf Phyllite, Sp—Pigeon Siltstone, Srf—Roaring Fork Sandstone, Swb—Wading Branch Formation (sandstones and conglomerates), Uc—Cades Sandstone, Urb—Rich Butt Sandstone, WCl—Licklog Formation (sandstones), WCsh—Shields Formation (conglomerates and sandstones), WCss—Sandsuck Formation (shales), WCw—Wilhite Formation (shales and sandstones with conglomerates and carbonate breccias). Patterns: bricks—limestone, crosses—granitoids, single cross-hatched—amphibolite-facies Grenville basement, double cross-hatched—granulite-facies Grenville basement (from Rast & Kohles, 1986, p. 598).

canic rocks overlying the basement complex with angular unconformity. These late Proterozoic stratified rocks include those exposed in the Blue Ridge anticlinorium (Fig. 8), e.g. the Catoctin, Lynchburg and Ashe Formations and their equivalents, the Ocoee Supergroup (Fig. 10 and Table 1) and its correlatives, such as the Tallulah Falls Formation, and rocks of the Ashland–Wedowee belt. The present Blue Ridge is at the site of the western margin of the rifted graben system of the late Proterozoic, but the major ocean basin—the Iapetus Ocean—eventually opened E of a line of gneiss domes of 1000 Ma continental crust in the Piedmont forming the eastern edge of the graben system (Rankin 1975, p. 298) and located near the boundary of continental with oceanic crust.

In the Blue Ridge the Ocoee Supergroup forms the base of the late Proterozoic basal clastic sequence (Fig. 10). The Ocoee Supergroup rocks are exposed over a length of 300 km and a breadth of 80 km from NE Tennessee to NW Georgia. Stratigraphic relations are best known in the vicinity of the Great Smoky Mountains. Here three groups of formations, the basal Snowbird Group, the Walden Creek Group and the Great Smoky Group total at least 12 000 m (Table 1) (King *et al.* 1958), thickening dramatically from NE to SW. Additionally, volcanic rocks decrease towards the SW with a pronounced increase of fine-grained to very-fine-grained clastic rocks (Fig. 10). The inter-relationships of these groups are not entirely clear. Hadley (1970) estimated a

total thickness for the Ocoee of 12 km. Rodgers (1972, p. 512) suggested that the great thickness and evidence of rapid deposition and poor sorting of some strata was a result of strong local uplift and subsidence of nearby basins where the deposits are now found. Rankin (1975) suggested that Precambrian block faulting was operative here as well as further NE. This conclusion was reinforced and extended by Rast & Kohles (1986) who developed models for provenance and environment of deposition of the component formations comprising the Ocoee Supergroup (Fig. 10 and Table 1).

The Ocoee Supergroup is anomalous because (1) it is a thick Precambrian marine deposit NW of the axis of the Blue Ridge anticlinorium, (2) this marine sequence is directly overlain by the Chilhowee and (3) volcanic rocks are absent. Rankin (1975) stated that the Ocoee Supergroup breaks the pattern of the late Precambrian shoreline which follows the trend of the axes of basement-cored anticlinoria and closely associated volcanism which holds from N Carolina to Newfoundland. Rankin (1975) suggested that the Ocoee Supergroup was deposited on the craton side of the main trend of westernmost late Precambrian basins and perhaps separated from that trend by a horst of basement. The basal Snowbird has a southeastern source area and thins to the SE in the Great Smoky Mountains. Hadley & Goldsmith (1963) and King (1964, p. 69) suggested that the thinning might be toward the SE of the basin of subsidence as a result of

TABLE 1. *Subdivisions of the Ocoee Supergroup, as well as underlying and overlying units, NW of and below the Greenbrier fault (Succession A) and their interpreted equivalents SE of and above the Greenbrier fault (Succession B). These successions can be cross-correlated only at the level of the Snowbird Group (Rast & Kohles 1986, modified from King et al. 1958)*

Age	Succession A:	Northwest of and below the Greenbrier fault		Succession B:	Southeast of and above the Greenbrier fault
Middle Cambrian through Middle Ordovician		Knox Group Conasauga Group Rome Formation			Murphy Group
Early Cambrian		Chilhowee Group			
Late Precambrian	Walden Creek Group	Sandsuck Formation Wilhite Formation Shields Formation Licklog Formation		Great Smoky Group	Anakeesta Formation / Thunderhead Sandstone
	Unclassified Formations	Cades Sandstone: Sandstones of Webb Mountain and Big Ridge / Rich Butt Sandstone			Elkmont Sandstone
	Snowbird Group	Metcalf Phyllite Pigeon Siltstone Roaring Fork Sandstone Longarm Quartzite Wading Branch Formation		Snowbird Group	Roaring Fork Sandstone Longarm Quartzite Wading Branch Formation
Earlier Precambrian		Grenville basement			

(Ocoee Supergroup label spans the Late Precambrian rows in both Succession A and Succession B.)

overlap. Rankin (1975) suggested that the extension which created the deep Ocoee basin did not come close to rifting the continental crust as occurred in the basins to the E and that the absence of volcanic rocks suggests remoteness from the hypothetical spreading centre of the proto-Atlantic. The basin of deposition of the Ocoee Supergroup, possibly fault bounded, lay W of the main graben system as now preserved. The Ocoee basin differs from the main graben system in that volcanic rocks are absent from the former but present in the latter. The Ocoee basin may thus have characteristics analogous to the Sparagmite basins of southern Scandinavia but differing from the latter which developed on the craton. The Ocoee, in contrast, is recorded in thrust slices.

Rankin *et al.* (1983, 1988) have summarized Proterozoic volcanicity in the Appalachians of the U.S.A. and indicated that tholeiitic basaltic lavas are found on both sides of the Blue–Green–Long basement axis and record a shoreline which is sub-aerial to the NW and submarine to the SE. Rhyolites are seen only at embayments such as Mount Rogers (peralkaline), South Mountain and Sutton Mountains. Moreover, Rankin related this volcanicity to Iapetus rifting with development of embayments and promontories, with the location of the volcanics being controlled by hot spots and triple junctions (Rankin *et al.* 1983, p. 174, 1987), or to transform faults according to Rodgers (1970) and Thomas (1979).

Early Palaeozoic metasedimentary sequences, mainly along the western edge of the Blue Ridge belt, include the Chilhowee Group (Table 1, column A), rocks of the Talladega belt and the Murphy synclinal belt (Table 1, column B). The western boundary of the Blue Ridge belt (Fig. 8) is marked by the Valley and Ridge belt which comprises dominantly carbonate strata (Fig. 11) (Colton 1970, Misra & McSween 1984, p. 297). Conformable mafic extrusive rocks are found in both late Proterozoic and early Palaeozoic strata. The mafic rocks form an integral component of most of the late Proterozoic stratified sequences and are only locally associated with large quantities of felsic volcanic rocks; exceptions are the Mount Rogers Formations and the Catoctin greenstone (Fig. 10). The Ocoee Supergroup (Fig. 10) contains no mafic rocks.

An understanding of these late Proterozoic clastic sequences has emerged from a painstaking study of several generations of complex folds and faults. From Philadelphia southward along the length of the Appalachian chain the late Proterozoic is represented by thick piles of metasedimentary and metavolcanic rocks which thicken to the SW and SE. These Proterozoic clastics, which rest with angular unconformity on the Grenville, are overstepped by lower Cambrian clastics along their western margin (Fig. 11). To the W the Cambrian rocks also rest with angular unconformity on Grenville gneisses. These relationships, typical of the Appalachians generally, are illustrated in Figs 10 and 11 in which the late Precambrian beds to the SE in Virginia rest with angular unconformity on Grenville basement. A short distance to the NW, near the West Virginia–Virginia boundary (Fig. 11), the basal Cambrian clastics overstep late Proterozoic sedimentary rocks and rest with angular unconformity on the Grenville. This overstep of the late Proterozoic by the basal Cambrian is located a very short distance NW of the thrust system that has transported the Blue Ridge anticlinorium onto the Palaeozoic continental-shelf sequence of cratonal Laurentia.

A similar situation to that in the central and southern Appalachians prevails in the northern Appalachians. At the southern end of the Green Mountain massif (Figs 8 and 12) there is a thickness of only about 30 m of unfossiliferous Moosalamoo phyllite (Mendon) below the lower Cambrian fossiliferous horizon and above the Grenvillian basement (Skehan 1961, Stanley & Ratcliffe 1985, fig. 3). Only a short distance to the W of the central Green Mountain core near the New York–Vermont border the fossiliferous upper Cambrian Potsdam sandstone rests with angular unconformity on the Grenville basement.

Continental platform—southern Appalachians

The stratigraphic succession of the southern Appalachians may serve as a starting point and a basis for comparison of the patterns of late Proterozoic and early Palaeozoic geology throughout the AC belt. Lower Palaeozoic rocks comprise a wedge of sediment from Cambrian to lower Ordovician, overlain unconformably by lower parts of the middle Ordovician Stones River Group and Chickamauga Group (Fig. 11). This Cambrian–lower Ordovician depositional unit is a westward transgressive sequence that gradually changes from a dominantly clastic to dominantly carbonate succession. These relationships are illustrated in Fig. 11. The initial deposits (Chilhowee Group) consist of near-shore shallow-marine sandstones interfingering with offshore relatively-deeper water shale and siltstone (Harris & Milici 1977). In general, the character of the basal conglomeratic and arkosic sediments changed upward to orthoquartzites with westward transgression. Clastic sedimentation was followed by the development of a shallow carbonate bank, the Shady dolomite, containing both

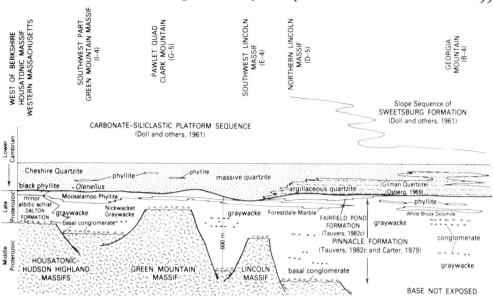

FIG. 12. S–N generalized stratigraphic relations of the upper Proterozoic to lower Cambrian section along the western side of the parautochthonous middle Proterozoic massifs showing suggested correlation of units that have been used in various ways by different workers. (From Stanley & Ratcliffe 1985, p. 1231.)

an early and a middle Cambrian fauna. The Rome Formation is interpreted as an inter-tidal and shallow sub-tidal environment W of the Shady carbonate bank. Following the deposition of the Rome Formation (lower and middle Cambrian) the basin gradually subsided so that offshore marine environments prevailed. During this period, when the source for clastic materials was to the W and N, a relatively deep-water lagoonal sequence of shale, siltstone and thin-bedded limestone (Conasauga Group) accumulated in the western part of the Valley and Ridge and the adjacent Appalachian plateau. During late Cambrian, the eastern carbonate shelf sequence (Knox Group) transgressed westward to cover the entire Appalachian basin. Sedimentation ended in early Ordovician time when uplift of much of the eastern Laurentian continent formed a carbonate lowland on which karst topography was widespread. Uplift and erosion, associated with the development of the regional unconformity during early Ordovician times, were greater in the Piedmont than in the Valley and Ridge. Lower Cambrian clastic and volcanic materials are found beneath the unconformity in the Piedmont (Harris & Milici 1977).

Northern Appalachians

The supracrustal clastic wedge of later Proterozoic age appears to thicken to the NE in the northern Appalachians in somewhat the same way that rocks of equivalent age in the central and southern Appalachians thicken both to the SW along strike and to the SE across strike from the craton. Figure 12 portrays such relationships from S to N from southeastern New York through to Quebec while St Julien & Hubert (1975) (Fig. 3) illustrate relationships from W to E across the trend of the late Proterozoic and early Palaeozoic shoreline.

A notable difference between the southern and central Appalachians and the northern Appalachians is that the Cambro-Ordovician shelf clastics and carbonates of the latter area have a restricted development in the Valley and Ridge Province, which is very narrow in the northern Appalachians, especially in eastern New York and western New England, perhaps largely as a result of tectonic shortening due to thrusting against the buttress of the Adirondack Mountains. Related shelf sediments are preserved, however, in thrust sheets transported onto the carbonate platform in Taconian orogenic phases. For example, the basal part of the autochthonous carbonate platform rests unconformably on middle Proterozoic Grenville rocks at the eastern margin of the Green Mountain massif (Skehan 1961, Thompson 1972). Additionally, thin carbonates and quartzites correlated with these shelf clastics are recorded in close association with Grenville basement correlatives (Wilmington gneiss) (Skehan 1961) derived from near the continental-oceanic crust boundary by thrusting (Stanley & Ratcliffe 1985).

The Green Mountain massif of Vermont (Fig. 8), which is itself allochthonous with a parautochthonous cover sequence, is tectonically in about the same position as the Blue Ridge anticlinorium. The Dalton conglomerate, Mendon Formation (black phyllite) and Cheshire quartzite lie unconformably on the Grenville core gneisses and are probably correlative with the Readsboro Formation (albite-mica schists) and the Heartwellville schist (black to green quartz-mica schists) (Skehan 1961). These in turn may be correlative with the Fleur de Lys Supergroup of Newfoundland and the Dalradian of Scotland. Higher thrust sheets containing sequences of schists and gneisses, and therefore transported from parts of the basin(s) lying farther E, differ in the fact that carbonate rocks of the lower sheets give way to mafic volcanic rocks and feeder dykes in the upper sheets (Stanley & Ratcliffe 1985).

Newfoundland

The Humber zone of western Newfoundland is characterized by a Grenvillian-age crystalline basement overlain unconformably by a Cambro-Ordovician clastic and carbonate sequence (Fig. 13) containing trilobite and graptolite faunas of the Pacific faunal province. The carbonates constitute the most northeasterly extension of the carbonate terrane forming the continental shelf of Laurentia from Newfoundland to Alabama. This autochthonous sequence is overlain by overthrust sheets of Cambro-Ordovician clastic and carbonate rocks, originally deposited E of the Humber zone. Latest Proterozoic clastic rocks may occur at the base of this sequence and in turn are structurally overlain by allochthonous ophiolite complexes and smaller slices of mafic volcanic and plutonic rocks. Final emplacement of these thrust sheets was in middle Ordovician time, but early stages of emplacement took place in the Arenig or earlier (Dallmeyer 1977). Deformation and metamorphism in the Humber zone is weak, but the rocks of the eastern parts of the zone are tightly folded and weakly metamorphosed. Higher-grade metamorphic rocks of the Fleur de Lys zone are thrust on the autochthonous–parautochthonous carbonates in the eastern parts of this zone (Dewey *et al.* 1983).

The Fleur de Lys zone is characterized by a thick mainly clastic complexly-deformed metasedimentary succession in upper greenschist to amphibolite facies. These rocks are considered to range from late Proterozoic to Cambro-

Ordovician in age and are assigned to the Fleur de Lys Supergroup. The boundary between continental and oceanic crust probably is present in this zone as the western part of the belt is underlain by an older gneissic basement whereas the eastern Fleur de Lys clastics, which are separated from the western clastics by a steep belt of dismembered ophiolite complexes and associated mafic volcanic rocks, are overlain by mafic and silicic metavolcanic rocks which are absent to the W. The Fleur de Lys rocks are probably underlain in the E by a mafic and ultramafic basement. Metamorphism of the Fleur de Lys is probably early Ordovician in age (Dewey *et al.* 1983).

Strong & Williams (1972) attributed lower Palaeozoic tholeiitic flood basalts of NW Newfoundland to crustal rifting and suggested that similar volcanics occur near the western margin of the crystalline belt of the Appalachians as far S as the Catoctin Formation of Virginia (Fig. 10).

The theory of late Precambrian–early Ordovician crustal extension evolved mainly in the northern Appalachians and Caledonides with many important contributions to the theory from more recent papers. In summary it can be said that in the southern Appalachians the foreland is broader, younger Precambrian stratified rocks are more abundant than in the northern Appalachians and a well-developed suite of anorogenic younger Proterozoic rocks is present (Rankin 1968).

British Isles

The northwestern marginal zone (Williams 1972, Dewey 1974) of the Caledonides of this region and Greenland consists of Precambrian basement overlain by Upper Proterozoic to Cambro–Ordovician sequences. This marginal belt is continuous along the length of the Appalachian chain in N America and thus the basic geological framework along the orogen in late Proterozoic time has a fundamental unity but with important differences.

The 'Torridonian' rocks of NW Scotland rest unconformably on an irregular Lewisian basement topography and have been divided into two groups (Stewart 1969). The Stoer Group red beds are dated at 995–935 Ma by Rb–Sr whole-rock isochrons (Moorbath 1969, Dewey 1974). They wedge out eastward under and are overlain unconformably by the regionally more extensive 7 km thick Torridon Group of red beds with marine intercalations dated at 810 Ma near its base (Moorbath 1969) and 751 ± 24 Ma (Dewey 1974). The latter sediments are W derived and their deposition in a block-faulted basin may be

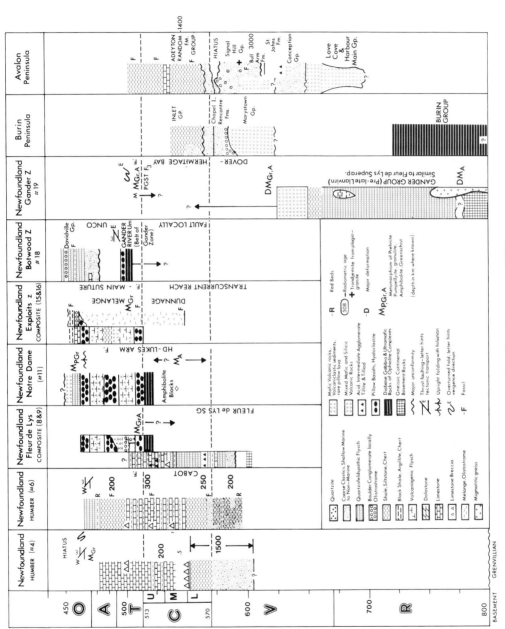

FIG. 13. Stratigraphic columns for Newfoundland. (Modified from Dewey *et al.* 1983.)

related to the opening of the Iapetus Ocean (Stewart 1975). No red-bed sequences of comparable thickness have been recognized in the northern Appalachians (Kennedy 1975, p. 36). The Stoer Group was derived from the E, and the Torridon Group, fining to the E, was deposited by E-flowing currents. The unconformity between these groups coincides with a palaeomagnetic break recorded by a 50° shift in the palaeomagnetic pole position (Irving & Runcorn 1957, Dewey 1974, p. 210).

During the late Proterozoic the Torridon Group was tilted westward and eroded before an early Cambrian marine transgression deposited the shallow-marine sandstone sequence of the Eriboll Formation. The overlying An t-Sron Formation consists of the Fucoid beds (dolomitic siltstone with *Olenellus*) and the Serpulite Grit (orthoquartzite). These in turn are succeeded by the dolostones, limestones and cherts of the Durness Formation. All these units record a progressive marine incursion and the establishment of a carbonate shelf environment (Dewey 1974, p. 210). The highest unit of the Durness is regarded by Skevington (1968) as Arenig (*Didymograptus nitidus* zone).

To the SE of the shelf sequence and lying between the Moine thrust and the Highland Boundary–Clew Bay fault zones is the Moine–Dalradian sequence whose composite thickness is probably greater than 20 000 m. The Moine consists of *c.* 8000 m of quartzofeldspathic psammite, semipelite, pelitic schist, calc-silicate and rare marble (Dewey 1974, p. 211). The Dalradian assemblage consists of separate successions. The Ballappel succession conformably overlies the young Moine (Grampian Division) and occurs along the northwestern part of the Grampian Highlands (Fig. 8). It consists of quartzite, pelite, limestone and dolostone. The Iltay succession also conformably overlies the young Moine but is tectonically juxtaposed against it, at least locally, by a major slide (Dewey 1974, p. 211). It is now recognized that the Ballappel succession stratigraphically underlies that of the Iltay Dalradian (Harris & Pitcher 1975, and references cited therein). The Iltay Dalradian is divided as follows (Dalradian terminology after Harris & Pitcher (1975)).

1 The Appin (Lower) and Argyll (middle) Dalradian Groups, consisting of *c.* 8000 m of quartzite, pelite and carbonate deposited in a shallow-marine environment. The base of the Argyll (middle Dalradian) Group is formed of the Portaskaig boulder bed lying between the Islay limestone below and the Islay quartzite above. This distinctive conglomerate, found in

Ireland as well as in Scotland, is probably of glacial origin (Kilburn *et al.* 1965).
2 The Southern Highland (upper Dalradian) Group of the Iltay succession is composed of *c.* 4000 m of mainly immature sediments, largely deposited by turbidity currents. Mafic volcanicity was important during the deposition of the Southern Highland and upper Argyll Groups.

The higher parts of the Dalradian sequence contain abundant evidence of its Cambrian age (Downie *et al.* 1971). The Precambrian–Cambrian boundary appears to be in a conformable sequence between the Easdale slate, carrying spheaeromorphs of probably latest Precambrian age, and the Tayvallich limestone, containing abundant acritarchs of probably early Cambrian age (Downie *et al.* 1971). The time of onset of Moine sedimentation on Lewisian basement and correlations between the foreland and the northern Highlands and Grampian Highlands (Fig. 8) are equivocal. Rb–Sr isotopic data indicate a maximum age of 1000 Ma for the onset of Moine sedimentation (Long & Lambert 1963). Lambert (1969) presents an age of 800 Ma for the western part of the Moine assemblage and suggests that it represents a distinct Precambrian metamorphic episode, the Morarian event. Supporting evidence is obtained from Rb–Sr ages of 765 $\pm$ 15 Ma from micas in a pegmatite near Knoydart (Giletti *et al.* 1961). On this basis the Stoer–Torridon Group unconformity may be an external foreland manifestation of the Morarian event (Fig. 7, column 13) (Dewey 1974).

Within the central Highlands of Scotland rocks which have been referred to the Moine (the Grampian Division of Piasecki 1980) pass up without significant stratigraphic break into the Dalradian. However, most UK geologists (Brook *et al.* 1977, Harris *et al.* 1978) now accept that the Moine can be divided into a cover–basement sequence. The older Moine rocks originally lay unconformably on the Lewisian (Archaean) basement and suffered (Grenville?) (*c.* 1000–1100 Ma) and Morarian (*c.* 750 Ma) orogenesis. The younger Moines which pass up into the Dalradian suffered only the Cambro–Ordovician Grampian orogenesis (Harte 1988). A putative unconformity between the two Moines is thought to exist in the central Highlands, while the Moine of the N Highlands, having experienced the Grenville? and Morarian events, was subsequently involved in Caledonian (*c.* 480–440 Ma) thrusting and related folding (Barr *et al.* 1986). The relationship of either of the Torridonian groups to the Moine (young or old) or the Dalradian is uncertain, although there is a strong possibility that the Torridon Group can be broadly correlated with the young Moine and that the upper part of the Dalradian Argyll Group may be equivalent to the lower part of the Eriboll–Durness sequence.

E central Greenland

Major developments of upper Proterozoic and lower Palaeozoic non-metamorphic to slightly metamorphic sedimentary rocks more than 17 000 m thick include arenaceous–argillaceous, calc-argillaceous, argillaceous–arenaceous, quartzite, multicoloured and limestone–dolomite sequences of the Eleonore Bay series and the Tillite series of late Proterozoic age (Fig. 2, columns A and B) (Henriksen 1978, 1985). Lower Cambrian to middle Ordovician sediments overlie the Tillite Group and comprise a uniformly developed 3000 m thick succession of mainly limestones and dolomites with sandstones at the base; there are several minor breaks in the sequence. Swett & Swit (1972) made detailed comparisons of the Cambro–Ordovician successions of western Newfoundland, NW Scotland (foreland) and the fold belt of E Greenland and conclude that the lower Palaeozoic successions of these regions developed contemporaneously on a contiguous broad marine shelf bordering the western margin of the Iapetus Ocean. The Cambro–Ordovician of E Greenland compares most closely with the Durness shelf facies of Scotland, and has no equivalent of the more basinal facies of the Argyll and southern High-land Dalradian Groups of Scotland and Ireland (Higgins & Phillips 1979).

Scandinavia

The late Precambrian sediments of N and S Norway show several strong contrasts (Fig. 2, columns D–G). Sediments of the sparagmite region in S Norway are characterized by rapid lateral facies variations (Table 2 and Fig. 14) and clastic wedges (fan deltas). However, in the N the broad features of the stratigraphy of Finnmark can be correlated over distances of 100–300 km along the depositional strike (Bjørlykke 1978). Table 2 summarizes a comparison of S Norway sparagmite basin sediments with the continental margin facies of Finnmark.

The presence of extensive supra-tidal dolomites in N Norway indicates sedimentation on a stable craton subsiding at variable rates, whereas the sparagmites formed in response to block faulting in rift valleys (Bjørlykke 1976) or an aulacogen (Roberts & Gale 1978) probably associated with volcanicity. Block faulting ended in early Cambrian times as the Baltic shield was inundated by an epicontinental sea (Bjørlykke 1978).

The glacial conglomerates of the Vestertana Group (Table 2) represent two distinct climatic episodes. At the top of this group is the Stappogiedde Formation, correlated with the Hyolithus zone through Sweden that correlates with the Ekre shale and Vangsas Formation of

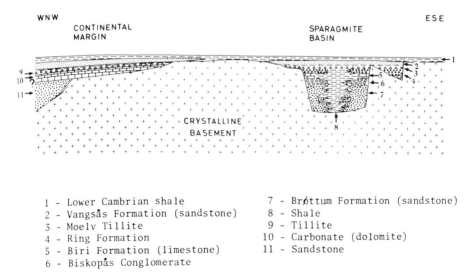

1 - Lower Cambrian shale
2 - Vangsås Formation (sandstone)
3 - Moelv Tillite
4 - Ring Formation
5 - Biri Formation (limestone)
6 - Biskopås Conglomerate
7 - Bróttum Formation (sandstone)
8 - Shale
9 - Tillite
10 - Carbonate (dolomite)
11 - Sandstone

FIG. 14. Reconstructed cross-section through Scandinavia showing a rift valley basin (sparagmite basin) and an onlapping continental margin sequence to the W corresponding to the Finnmark succession and possibly also to the Kvitvola sequence. (From Bjørlykke 1978, p. 53.)

TABLE 2. *Comparison of the Rift Valley basins of S Norway with the continental margin facies of N Norway*

	Sparagmite Region South Norway	Finnmark North Norway
Dimensions of the basin	50-60 km width	Hundreds of km
Thickness of latest Precambrian sediment	3000-4000 m	10-20 km ?
Lithostratigraphic Units	Hedmark Group	Vestertana Group Tanafjord Group Vadsø Group
Lithology		
Arkoses	common	rare
Coarse conglomerates exclusive of glacial conglomerates	common	some
Glacial conglomerates	One well-defined unit (Moelv Tillite)	Two well-defined tillite (Smalfjord and Mortensnes Tillite)
Carbonate rocks	Marginal limestone facies passing into basinal mud facies	Extensive dolomites, supratidal facies
Facies variation	Rapid lateral facies variation from margin to central basin	Persistent lithology over long distances
Turbidites	present in the basal part	common
Alluvial fan deposits	widespread along the basin margin	not reported
Type of basin subsidence	contemporaneous faulting	subsiding continental margin without clear evidence of contemporaneous faulting
Volcanic activity	Lavas of probable latest Precambrian age	No evidence of volcanic activity
Plate tectonic situation	Rift Valley	Passive margin

From Bjørlykke (1978, p. 53).

S Norway. The sediments overlying the Stappogiedde, the Breivik and Duolbasgaissa Formations contain early and middle Cambrian trace fossils (Bjørlykke 1978).

In late Precambrian time the passive continental-margin facies was represented by the Finnmark sequence and possibly by that in the Kvitvola Nappe of the middle Allochthon (Table 3) (Roberts & Gee 1985, p. 60). The sediments of the Kvitvola sequence of SE Norway have certain features in common with the sparagmites, but overall they have other features similar to those of Finnmark, suggesting that they were deposited along the western passive margin of the Baltic shield (Bjørlykke 1976, 1978). The basement rocks of the Kvitvola Nappe suggest that it may be part of the Jotun Nappe Complex (Table 3).

'Supracrustal' rocks (late Proterozoic–Tremadocian)–Avalonian–Cadomian–Pan-African (ACPA) orogens

General statement

'Supracrustal' rocks of the ACPA domains in large part have a different character and relationship to the rocks on which they rest than is the case in the AC orogen proper. The nature of the basement in these orogens has been discussed above. Relationships among various parts of the stratigraphic succession may best be understood in the Anti-Atlas Mountains of Morocco where an Upper Proterozoic sequence of dominantly

TABLE 3. *Correlation of the principal tectonostratigraphic units in the Scandinavian Caledonides*

REGIONS / Main tectonostrati-divisions	NORTHERN NORWAY (Ramsay et al.)	NORTH-CENTRAL NORWAY/SWEDEN (Stephens et al.)	SOUTH-CENTRAL NORWAY/SWEDEN (Gee et al.)	SOUTHEASTERN NORWAY/SWEDEN (Bockelie and Nystuen)	SOUTHWESTERN NORWAY (Bryhni and Sturt)
UPPERMOST ALLOCHTHON	Tromsø Nappe	Helgeland Nappe Cpx and Beiarn Nappe / Rødingsfjäll Nappe Cpx	Helgeland Nappe Complex		
UPPER ALLOCHTHON	Lyngen, Dyrøy, Magerøy, Kafkord, Senja and Vaddas Nappes	K Storfjället, Gasak, ö Stikke, Gjersvik l and Bjørkvattnet i Nappes / Seve Nappes	Støren Nappe, Gula Nappe, Meråker and other nappe units, Trond-heim Nappe Cpx. / Seve Nappes (incl. Essandsjø, Skjøtingen and Blahø Nappes)	Koli Nappes / Seve Nappes	Sunnhordland Nappe Complex / Eugeosynclinal rocks of western Sogn and Sunnfjord
MIDDLE ALLOCHTHON	Kalak Nappe Cpx. / Laksefjord Nappe	? Särv Nappes / Offerdal, Stalon and Abisko Nappes	Särv, Sætra and Leksdal Nappes / Offerdal, Tannäs, Risberget and Hærvola Nappes	Särv Nappes / Tannäs and Veman Ns. / Rondane Nappe / Kvitvola Nappe / Valdres Nappe	Hardangervidda-Ryfylke and Jotun Nappe Cpxs. / Bergen Anorthosite Cpx. (Lindås Nappe) / Dalsfjord Nappe / Valdres Nappe
LOWER ALLOCHTHON	Gaissa and Jerta Nappes	Jämtlandian, Blaik, Ström and Rautas Nappes	Jämtlandian Nappes / Osen-Røa Nappe Cpx.	Synnfjell Nappe / Osen-Røa, Hede and Vemdalen Nappes	Unnamed Nappes ('Phyllite Division') / Synnfjell Nappe / Aurdal Nappe (Osen-Røa Nappe Cpx.)
PARAUTOCHTHON	Minor thrust sheets	Minor thrust sheets	Various minor thrust sheets	Various minor thrust sheets	Autochthon and/or various minor thrust sheets
AUTOCHTHON	Precambrian crystalline basement	Precambrian crystalline basement	Precambrian crystalline basement	Precambrian crystalline basement	Precambrian crystalline basement

The regions and references are those of the regional review papers in Gee & Sturt (1985, p. 60).

continental-shelf deposits of carbonates, quartz arenites and glacigenic and volcanigenic deposits rest with angular unconformity on Eburnean gneiss (*c.* 2000 Ma) of the W African craton (see Fig. 6 and introductory section).

Elsewhere in these Cadomian orogens, the sequence of late Proterozoic and early Palaeozoic 'supracrustal' rocks has a distinctive character but their relationship to basement rocks is less clear than in Morocco.

Locally in the Avalonian domain, basement rocks have been recognized (Fig. 7, column 7) (Rast & Skehan 1983, p. 266 *et seq.*, Skehan & Rast 1983, columns D, E and H). For example, in New Brunswick (Fig. 7, column 7) this basement, the Brookfield gneiss (830 ± 26 Ma) (Olszewski & Gaudette 1982), is associated with carbonate–orthoquartzite sediments of the Green Head Group (Fig. 7, column 7) (Wardle 1978, Rast & Skehan 1983, p. 266). In N Nova Scotia upper Proterozoic volcanics, the Forchu Group, rest on quartzites, carbonates and gneisses of the George River Group of Green Head aspect (Rast *et al.* 1976, Rast & Skehan 1983, pp. 266–7). Additional examples of basement–cover relationships in the Avalonian terranes are given by Rast & Skehan (1983, pp. 267–9).

Newfoundland

The general stratigraphic relationships of Avalonian terranes can be illustrated by that in the Avalon Peninsula. Here the upper Proterozoic rocks begin with volcanic and volcaniclastic strata of the Harbour Main Group (King 1980, Skehan & Rast 1983, fig. 2). The Harbour Main Group passes laterally into and in part is covered by graded turbidites of the Conception Group. Near the Holyrood pluton (Fig. 7, column 10) (Rast & Skehan 1983, fig. 1) the latter unconformably overlies the former, and their basal conglomerates have pebbles of Holyrood granite (*c.* 595 Ma). The Conception Group contains soft-bodied fossils (King 1980, Rast & Skehan 1983, pp. 258–9).

Stratigraphically higher the upper Proterozoic consists of a thick succession of reddish conglomerates, sandstones and intercalated felsic volcanics collectively represented by the Signal Hill Group (King 1980, Rast & Skehan 1983, p. 260). In view of the presence of both tholeiitic and mildly-alkaline basalts in the upper Proterozoic of the Avalon Peninsula Strong *et al.* (1978) suggested that early volcanicity was rift related and associated with local small oceanic basins.

Such small ocean basins within the rifted Avalonian platform may be represented by the Burin succession (Strong *et al.* 1978, Strong 1979) which starts with breccias and pillow basalts. The age of the mafic volcanics of the Burin Group, dated by an intrusive gabbro, is at least 762 ± 2 Ma (Krogh *et al.* 1983). The Marystown Group (Skehan & Rast 1983, fig. 2) has yielded a Zircon age of 617.5 ± 8 Ma (Dallmeyer *et al.* 1981).

Thus in Newfoundland and throughout the Avalonian domain generally, the lower part of the succession (sediments and volcanics) is dominantly marine, the middle is mixed marine and terrestrial, and the upper is dominantly terrestrial (Rast & Skehan 1983, p. 261).

The upper Proterozoic red beds are overlain by marine Cambro-Ordovician strata that are locally para-conformable but regionally unconformable (Skehan & Rast 1983). Their outliers are in contact with different parts of the Proterozoic sequence (Rast & Skehan 1983, p. 259, fig. 1).

In the Carolina slate belt, SE New England, Newfoundland and the southern British Isles, middle Cambrian sediments have trilobites of *Paradoxides* fauna (Skehan *et al.* 1978, Rayner 1982, Samson *et al.* 1982). In the slate belt, sediments are interbedded with volcanic rocks (Rodgers 1970, Samson *et al.* 1982). Volcanicity extends into the Cambrian in Cape Breton Island and New Brunswick but is unknown in Newfoundland and SE New England. Thus similarities of general successions, regular variations along strike and similar lithological types found in the upper Proterozoic and Cambrian rocks indicate that they are all part of the same major lithotectonic unit (Rast & Skehan 1983, p. 270).

Cadomian–Pan-African

The Cadomian orogenic belt (Fig. 5) is schematically portrayed as lying SE of the northern prong of the Avalonian plate. However, the Cadomian belt is discontinuous and strongly metamorphosed and has been overprinted by Acadian (Rast 1986, personal communication) and Variscan deformations. This Cadomian–Pan-African belt is represented sporadically in thrust sheets (Rast 1986, personal communication) and in all probability is a continuation of the Pan-African system (Rast & Skehan 1983, p. 273). Representative Upper Proterozoic and Lower Palaeozoic sequences are presented in Fig. 7, columns 18–21 (Skehan & Rast 1983, p. 137, columns H and I). In the Cadomian orogenic belt of France small massifs and fragments of older (Pentevrian and Icartian) basement have been recognized (Cogne 1971, Bishop *et al.* 1975, Zwart & Dornsiepen 1978, Rankin *et al.* 1988). Nevertheless the generally oceanic character of the Cadomian orogen in Europe is suggested by Vidal (1977). He pointed out that $^{87}Sr/^{86}Sr$ initial ratios of nearly all older Cadomian plutons in France, Germany and northern Spain are low (0.705) and thus the continental crust of central and western Europe is in general no older than about 700 Ma. This crust surrounds dispersed blocks of older rocks that form massifs within it.

Fullagar & Butler (1979) have advanced a similar argument for the Avalonian of the southern Appalachians where nearly all upper Proterozoic and lower Palaeozoic granitic plutons yield small $^{87}Sr/^{86}Sr$ ratios, suggesting that they have not been recycled or contaminated. Thorpe (1979) claimed that the Avalonian terrane of southern Britain was entirely oceanic prior to 600 Ma. Thus small initial ratios suggest that granites did not originate by crustal anatexis, and therefore sediments deformed by Cadomian–Avalonian orogenesis commonly must be ensimatic (Rast & Skehan 1983, pp. 274–5).

Pre-Arenig metamorphism and timing of deformation

General statement

Suggestions from the Appalachians of pre-Arenig tectonism favourable to the production of metamorphism have only recently led to the question of how extensive and how intense was pre-Arenig metamorphism in the Appalachians and what was the timing of the switch from rifting to compressional tectonism. Such precursor indicators of crustal instability in a progressively more compressive environment include deformation phases which produced olistostromes, melanges, folding, early overthrusting, beginnings of ophiolite obduction and resulting burial of sediments. Metamorphism associated with the obduction of ophiolites is recognized in connection with the Burlingtonian deformation episode (Fig. 7, columns 8 and 9) of early Ordovician age in the Fleur de Lys zone and also of Tremadoc–Arenig age in the Botwood–Gander zones (Dallmeyer 1977, Dewey *et al.* 1983, p. 209).

Metamorphism associated with the Grampian orogeny is well developed in the orthotectonic or Dalradian–Moine belt of the British Isles and Ireland (Fig. 7, columns 13 and 11 respectively). In Scandinavia separation of earlier and later phases of metamorphism has been widely based on terrane-linking upper Ordovician (Ashgill) unconformities developed on obducted ophiolites transported towards the Baltoscandian craton in the Finnmarkian orogeny (Figs 4 and 7, columns 15–17). Peak metamorphic conditions occurred at *c.* 535 Ma and extensive cooling and uplift at *c.* 485 Ma. In SW Norway greenschist–amphibolite-facies metamorphism predating an Ashgillian unconformable sequence is bracketed within the interval 465–535 Ma (Harte 1988).

The most extensive Precambrian–Cambrian deformation and associated, but generally not very intense, metamorphism is within the closely related ACPA orogenic belts. Relationships, however, have been variously obscured by subsequent Taconian, Acadian and Alleghanian metamorphism in N America and by Acadian (Rast 1986, personal communication) and Variscan metamorphism in many parts of Europe and NW Africa.

Appalachian Mountains–Penobscotian orogeny

The distribution of pre-Arenig Palaeozoic metamorphism is not well understood because of polymetamorphism, complex structure and the need for further studies. Nevertheless, evidence for pre-Arenig metamorphism (apart from Grenville events) is found in the northern and central Appalachians (Fig. 7, columns 3–6, 8 and 9). More specifically such metamorphism is mapped in Maritime Canada and eastern New England, southeastern Pennsylvania and northern Virginia (Harte 1988, fig. 1 and table 1). In the southern Appalachians Avalonian-type rocks show rapid lateral facies variations and several similar low-grade belts are separated by higher-grade rocks (Hatcher 1978a, b). The grade of metamorphism of the slaty rocks is generally low and they are intruded by Precambrian and later granites. Thus the general setting and lithologies are similar to Newfoundland, New Brunswick and the British Isles (Rast & Skehan 1983), but a detailed succession is not available.

Zen (1983) and Robinson (1983) interpreted greenschist–amphibolite-facies regional metamorphism in eastern Massachusetts, Rhode Island and eastern Connecticut as pre-Arenig. In part these metamorphic effects may be Avalonian, but on structural grounds there is growing evidence that Alleghanian deformation may be dominant (Dallmeyer 1981, Mosher & Rast 1984, Rast 1984, Skehan *et al.* 1985). Evidence for pre-Arenig greenschist-facies to possibly upper-amphibolite-facies metamorphism in southeastern New Hampshire associated with the 681–619 Ma Massabesic Gneiss Complex is debated. Nevertheless metamorphism possibly extending into Maine and Massachusetts must be older than a 473 Ma pluton (Fig. 7, column 5) which produced contact metamorphic effects in the Merrimack Group.

Olszewski, Gaudette and colleagues have interpreted the 930–550 Ma ages on amphibolite-facies gneisses and metasedimentary rocks from Nova Scotia and New Brunswick as metamorphic ages (636 and 750 Ma respectively) (*cf.* Harte 1988, fig. 1, location 2, and table 1). Stewart (1974) suggested that Precambrian medium-grade metamorphism younger than a 650 Ma

pegmatite is preserved in a fault-bounded block in coastal Maine (Harte 1988, fig. 1, location 4).

In southern Rhode Island late Proterozoic volcanics and sediments (Rast & Skehan 1981a, b) were deformed and lightly metamorphosed prior to intrusion of a granite with an isotopic age of 595 ± 12 Ma (Smith 1978, Smith & Giletti 1978, Rast & Skehan 1983).

In the central Appalachians of southeastern Pennsylvania the earlier of two metamorphisms may be pre-Arenig to Ashgillian, but not Precambrian. In northern Virginia the metamorphism is considered to be pre-Arenig (494–560 Ma) (Harte 1988, fig. 1 and table 1). On the North Carolina–Virginia border there is evidence for a major episode of folding, the Virgilina (Glover & Sinha 1973) (Fig. 7, column 3), accompanied by plutonism and followed by at least one metamorphic event and possibly two. Within the region there is also evidence for Avalonian deformation and metamorphism, probably antedated by formation of high-grade gneisses (Fig. 7, column 3). Until recently not much attention was given to the possibility of pre-Arenig metamorphism and thus little research has been directed to this question. The discussion by Harte (1988) focusses attention on this important problem. The descriptions which follow are concerned with metamorphism and other orogenic manifestations that may be part of major named orogenic episodes which, if not entirely pre-Arenig, are at least pre-Caradoc or earlier.

Penobscotian orogenic phase of Maine and Quebec

In 1861 Hitchcock first recorded the angular unconformity between the Grand Pitch Formation and the overlying beds in northern Maine (Neuman 1967). Neuman, in turn, described the structural and stratigraphic relations of the area. The late Precambrian?–lower Cambrian? Grand Pitch Formation was first deformed before the deposition of the overlying lower middle Ordovician Shin Brook Formation. Neuman named this folding event the Penobscot disturbance and pointed out that it probably affected a widespread area through Maine and southeastern Quebec. Contrasts in deformation between rocks that may be correlative with the Grand Pitch and overlying Ordovician rocks have been described elsewhere in the northern Appalachians including the southern Gaspé Peninsula (Cooke 1955, Riordan 1957, Larrabee *et al.* 1965, E-8). Hall & Roberts (1988) cite evidence for Penobscotian deformation in Massachusetts (Fig. 7, column 4) accompanied by metamorphism that may be more intense and earlier but shorter lived than in the type Penobscotian of Maine (Fig. 7, column 4). These points suggest tectonism of regional extent between the early Cambrian and the early middle Ordovician.

The ophiolite complexes of the internal zone of Quebec are interpreted by Laurent (1973, 1977) and St Julien & Hubert (1975) as obducted flakes of oceanic lithosphere (Fig. 7, column 6). Small massifs and sheets of serpentinite that occur in the Oak Hill, Rosaire and Caldwell Formations (Fig. 3) are regarded by them as remobilized masses of ultramafic rocks located in major thrust faults. The shale–melange assemblage of the thick St Daniel Formation rests conformably on the ophiolite suite and in turn is unconformably overlain by the fossiliferous lower–middle Ordovician Beauceville and alkaline volcanics of the Ascot–Weedon Formations of the Magog Group. The ophiolite complex, in turn, rests with tectonic contact on the Caldwell (Fig. 3) which in turn rests on the Rosaire Group, both of these giving evidence of three phases of folding and one penetrative schistosity. The Oak Hill is considered to be a correlative of the Rosaire. Fossils in the middle of the Oak Hill provide an early Cambrian age. Thus the age of obduction of the Thetford ophiolites is later than early Cambrian and older than the thick St Daniel Formation which is truncated at the top by an unconformity upon which rests the lower–middle Ordovician Magog flysch. Although the basal contact of the St Daniel melange with ophiolite is conformable, the presence of a metamorphic fragment of Cambrian Caldwell in chert associated with the ophiolite suggests that the associated tectonism was early in the Penobscotian cycle.

Thus a major episode of folding and ophiolite obduction took place as a part of the Penobscotian orogeny preceding the deposition of formations of the lower–middle Ordovician Magog Group. The observation that the period of formation of the thick sequence of the St Daniel shale and melange was tectonically unstable allows the interpretation that the deformation was prolonged and substantially antedated the early middle Ordovician.

The evidence from the region as a whole suggests that the Penobscotian orogenic phase is a compressional tectonic event of regional extent and of major importance which produced cleavage, schistosity, metamorphic effects and obduction of ophiolites (Fig. 7, columns 1–7).

Burlington phases of Newfoundland

The Fleur de Lys rocks form a wedge-shaped mass of metamorphosed dominantly-sedimentary sequences just E of the Humber zone in western Newfoundland (Fig. 13). The Fleur de Lys Supergroup has been compared with the Moine and Dalradian rocks of Britain (Kennedy 1975). In the Burlington Peninsula the Fleur de Lys occurs as two divisions. The western units rest unconformably on probably Grenville basement gneiss (de Wit 1974, Bursnall & de Wit 1975) with a basal conglomerate overlain by a succession of dominantly-psammitic rocks with minor pelites and limestones in the lower part. Mafic volcanic rocks and quartz wackes, which may include an ophiolite melange (Williams 1977), form the upper part of this sequence in tectonic contact with an ophiolite complex which separates it from the eastern units. Quartz pebble greywackes and limestone breccias probably form the upper part of this sequence. In the eastern division the succession is from quartz wackes upward into mafic to calc-alkaline mafic and silicic volcanics (Kennedy 1975). The Fleur de Lys is unfossiliferous but contains carbonate breccias similar to the Cow Head Breccia of western Newfoundland, and volcanic rocks within the western division have been tentatively correlated with the basal Cambrian basalts of the platform (Williams & Stevens 1969, Kennedy 1975). U–Pb ages on zircon from the top of this succession in the eastern division indicate an early Ordovician age of 475 Ma (Mattinson 1977). Thus the Fleur de Lys probably contains rocks of late Precambrian to early Ordovician.

Time-stratigraphical equivalents of the Fleur de Lys have been identified in transported sequences of the Taconic allochthons of western Newfoundland. These contain Upper Precambrian to Cambrian clastics at the base, with local mafic volcanics overlain by a Cambrian to lower Ordovician carbonate breccia and flysch sequence which are all NW derived (Stevens 1970). The uppermost part of this succession contains lower Ordovician SE-derived flysch, rich in quartz, feldspar and ophiolitic detritus generally considered to be derived from the Fleur de Lys terrane (Stevens 1970, Williams 1975). Carbonate breccias (Cow Head breccia), interpreted as a bank-edge deposit, locally constitute the middle to lower Ordovician succession within these transported rocks.

Lithological equivalents of the Fleur de Lys have just been referred to in Quebec, and they may include Precambrian to Cambrian quartzites, sandstones and carbonates of the Oak Hill, Rosaire and Caldwell Groups, and parts of other correlative formations from the Gaspé (Kennedy 1979). Calc-alkaline mafic and silicic volcanic rocks occur in both the Fleur de Lys and the Ascot–Weedon Formations of Quebec. The tectonically bounded ophiolite complexes of the Fleur de Lys zone were traced by Williams & St Julien (1982) into Quebec as the discontinuous Baie Verte–Brompton line.

The allochthonous sub-horizontal ophiolites of the Humber zone have produced a dynamo-thermal metamorphism of volcanic rocks over which the ophiolites were thrust (Williams & Smyth 1973). Dallmeyer (1977) has dated this event by $^{40}Ar/^{39}Ar$ at 460 ± 5 Ma for the Humber Arm and 480 ± 5 Ma for the Hare Bay allochthon, indicating diachronous obduction (Fig. 7, column 8). Final assembly of the slices into their present position was accomplished by late Llandeilo, the age of the oldest unit of the neo-autochthonous Long Point Group (Bergstrom *et al.* 1974).

E of the Humber Arm allochthon (5–10 km) metamorphic rocks of the Fleur de Lys Super-group were deformed, metamorphosed and then overthrust during the Ordovician. The age of deformation and metamorphism of the Fleur de Lys, which locally reaches the kyanite zone, is older than the deposition of Silurian rocks (Neale & Kennedy 1967). Detritus of Fleur de Lys is present in easterly-derived Arenig flysch of the Humber Arm allochthon and in early Ordovician conglomerates of the Hare Bay allochthon. The available evidence suggests that the Fleur de Lys deformation and metamorphism is pre-Taconian, and it is referred to by Kennedy (1979) as the Burlingtonian orogeny.

Gander River ultramafic belt

The Gander River ultramafic belt is located in the Gander zone of E central Newfoundland (Fig. 13). These oceanic rocks are considered to have been part of the Botwood zone sequence (Fig. 13). They were overthrust toward the E over the Gander zone rocks in Tremadoc to Arenig time and are associated with polyphase folding and metamorphism to amphibolite facies. This episode is unnamed.

British Isles Dalradian–Grampian orogeny

The Dalradian Supergroup of Ireland, Scotland and probably the Shetland Isles records late Cambrian and early Ordovician deformation and greenschist–amphibolite-facies metamorphism (Fig. 7, columns 11–14) referred to the Grampian orogeny (Rast & Crimes 1969). A summary of the timing of these events is given by Harte (1988, Table 2). D_1–D_3 nappe and other folding events and peak metamorphism are constrained gener-ally between 520 and 480 Ma, on the basis of ages from igneous intrusives and metamorphic rocks. The Ben Vuirich pluton (*c.* 514 Ma) provides

older limits on deformation and metamorphism (Fig. 7, columns 13 and 14). Time constraints appear to be strongest for Connemara, the Ox Mountains of Ireland, and the Barrovian and Buchan metamorphic areas of Scotland (Fig. 7, columns 11–14). Barrovian metamorphism (*s.1.*) generally characterizes most of the Dalradian across the British Isles with the main departures being in the low-pressure assemblages in Conne-mara and northeastern Scotland (Buchan). Im-portant pre-Arenig tectonism may be implied in the evolution of Connemara metamorphism from pressures of at least 7 kbar (Yardley *et al.* 1980) to about 2.5 kbar (Barber & Yardley 1985), possibly culminating in later (460 Ma) post-metamorphic thrusting, uplift and retrograde metamorphism (Harte 1988, table 2). On the basis of considerations of temperature–pressure conditions, Harte (1988) has distinguished several tectono-metamorphic domains or provinces in the Scottish Dalradian.

Whether the Morarian pegmatites (*c.* 800–750 Ma) and the unconformity of the Stoer–Torridon Groups can be assumed to mark the Morarian orogeny, a major tectonothermal event (e.g. van Breemen *et al.* 1974, Lambert *et al.* 1979, Piasecki *et al.* 1981), is disputed because Powell *et al.* (1983) attribute the Precambrian metamorphism to the Grenvillian event (Harte 1988). The Grampian orogenic event ended the Grampian cycle and established the Grampian metamorphic protolith of Dewey's zones B and C (Dewey 1974) extending from the Moine thrust to the Southern Uplands fault (Dewey 1969, Rast & Crimes 1969). Dewey (1974), after accurately stating that 'the age of the Grampian event, that is, the age of the deformation and metamorphism of the Dalradian and (young) Moinian assem-blages, is enigmatic and riddled with apparent paradoxes', proceeds to marshall a variety of arguments for a position statement. On balance, Dewey (1974, p. 225) favours a model for the establishment of a 'Grampian' metamorphic protolith during an early Arenigian–pre-Carado-cian interval, possibly involving diachronous structural and metamorphic phases. Whole-rock K–Ar ages between 500 and 510 Ma in Dalradian rocks along the Highland Border probably reflect the beginning of post-D_1–D_2 uplift in zone B (the NW and Grampian Highlands (Eocaledonia of Ziegler (1970)) and the initiation of the Clew Bay–Highland Boundary fault zone. The rise of isotherms culminating in the M_3 metamorphic peak about 486 Ma may have occurred progres-sively throughout Arenig and early Llanvirn times accompanied by uplift of Zone B elements, which in turn gave rise to molasse and conglom-eratic flysch sedimentation. Dewey (1974) con-

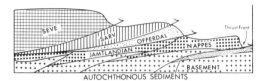

FIG. 15. Schematic cross-section through the nappes of Norway and Sweden indicating their relative stacking position. (Sturt 1984, written comm.)

cludes with 'the only truly unequivocal statement one can make about the age of the Grampian event is that it was completed prior to Caradocian times', as evidenced by the sub-Caradocian unconformity in Tyrone and at Ballantrae.

Scandinavian Caledonides–Finnmarkian orogeny

The Scandinavian Caledonides basically comprise a series of nappes (Fig. 15) with individual metamorphic histories. The tectono-stratigraphic map (Roberts & Gee 1985) separates them into five major units: Parautochthon–Autochthon, lower Allochthon, middle Allochthon, upper Allochthon and uppermost Allochthon (Table 3). Pre-Arenig (pre-Ashgill) evolution of the orogen is of major significance in the uppermost and upper Allochthons, the most distal elements in the geosynclinical belt. In northern Norway, Finnmarkian elements (Fig. 7, columns 15–17) can also be recognized in the lower units where they are marked by progressive metamorphism through the ascending nappe sequence, i.e. northwestward through the original basin of deposition. Bryhni (1988, fig. 3) interpreted the areal distribution of Finnmarkian metamorphism and indicated presumed dates of metamorphism for each of the major tectono-stratigraphic units.

Holtedahl (1920) demonstrated that the Appalachian–European–Arctic geosynclinal belt had evolved through several successive events. For S Norway he separated a major orogenic episode, which he called the Trondheim Disturbance, characterized by upheaval, deep intrusion and deep erosion prior to a later Ordovician event. Vogt (1929, 1945), carrying this work further, claimed that the Trondheim disturbance seemed to represent a significant regional event throughout the Scandinavian Caledonides with a metamorphic break below conglomerate beds. The oldest strata above the unconformity have been dated by graptolites as late middle Arenig (Ryan *et al.* 1980). In the foreland a corresponding 'Trysil phase' was recognized from lower Arenig sandstone (Bryhni 1988).

Outside the Trondheim region and the foreland belt of low-grade sediments, no fossils have been recognized to prove an episode of metamorphic development in the early Ordovician or earlier. However, there are conglomerates overlain by strata carrying Ashgill–Llandovery fossils and containing clasts with pre-depositional metamorphic fabrics and mineral assemblages. Moreover, these conglomerates overlie a terrane-linking unconformity which cuts across major stratigraphic units including obducted ophiolites, such as the Geitung volcanics (Fig. 2, columns D–G and Fig. 7, column 16) (Furnes *et al.* 1983), having an isotopic age of 535 ± 46 Ma. Thus at least some of the Group I ophiolites, of which the Geitung are a part, are Cambrian or older. Some Group I ophiolites are unconformably overlain by Ordovician sediments, the oldest of which are upper middle Arenig (Ryan *et al.* 1980).

The *Parautochthon–Autochthon* (autochthonous sediments of Fig. 15 and Table 3) has experienced Finnmarkian (*c.* 500 Ma) greenschist–sub-greenschist metamorphism, as evidenced by resetting of minerals in the uppermost part of the Precambrian crystalline basement in terms of their $^{40}Ar/^{39}Ar$ (Dallmeyer & Anderson 1984). Locally, evidence for a 650–700 Ma thermal resetting of hornblende is recorded. The sedimentary cover has locally a distinct cleavage dated by Rb–Sr whole-rock isochrons at 504 ± 7 Ma (Reading 1965).

In southern Scandinavia a break is locally present at the base of the Ordovician beds in an otherwise complete sedimentary succession from middle Cambrian to Pridoli. Normally, however, upper Cambrian black shales continue uninterrupted into Tremadocian graptolite shales as, for example, near Oslo. Nevertheless, during late Arenig–early Llanvirn a regional shallowing occurred with contemporaneous volcanism from late Llanvirn to early Caradoc. Bjørlykke (1974) demonstrated that chlorite was first introduced to the sediments in the Arenig and continued to increase in importance through middle Ordovician. Increases in magnesium, iron, nickel and chromium in the shales and detrital chromite occurs in middle Ordovician sediments. Such changes have been related to orogenic activity further W involving emplacement of nappes, such as the Jotun and Trondheim Nappe Complexes (uppermost Allochthon) and the development of island-arc systems (Bjørlykke 1974).

In the *middle Allochthon* there is evidence of pre-Arenig metamorphism in the Laksefjord and Kalak Nappe Complexes. In the former, which is part of the Parautochthon (Fig. 16), the formation of cleavage is dated as 493 ± 45 Ma (Sturt *et al.* 1978). However, some of the mica

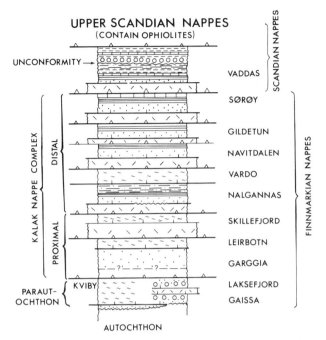

FIG. 16. Stacking order in the Finnmarkian Nappes of the Kalak Nappe Complex relative to the Parautochthon and the Scandian Nappes. (From Ramsey *et al.* 1985, p. 168.)

schists or phyllites in a similar tectonic position further S in Norway may have been metamorphosed at this time. The Western Gneiss region, now considered allochthonous (Gee 1975), records $^{40}Ar/^{39}Ar$ plateau dates at 524 ± 6 Ma for hornblende and 488 ± 2 Ma for biotite (Bryhni *et al.* 1971). Moreover, a recently discovered pre-Ashgillian unconformity in western Norway extends into previously deformed–metamorphosed quartzites of the Dalsfjord Nappe. This early tectonic phase may have produced the tectonic stacking of orthogneisses and psammitic rocks from other parts of the Western Gneiss Complex (Bryhni 1988).

For the *middle Allochthon* (including the Sarv and Kalak Nappes) pronounced differences have been recorded between the southern and northern part of the belt. In the SE there was mainly movement of great crystalline Precambrian blocks with Caledonian metamorphism confined to the thrust zones. An eclogite formed in such a zone gave an isotopic age around 517 Ma. In Sweden the Sarv Nappe (Table 3 and Fig. 15) is composed of psammatic rocks which were metamorphosed in the greenschist facies during Vendian time but were essentially unaffected by later metamorphism outside the thrust zones (Claesson & Roddick 1983). Mylonites between the Sarv Nappe and the underlying Tannas Augen gneiss yielded an age of 485 ± 50 Ma

(Claesson 1980), thus indicating that the thrusting, at least in the thrust zones, was related to Finnmarkian orogenesis (Bryhni 1988).

In Finnmark, however, there was penetrative metamorphism during two orogenic events, extensive migmatization and igneous activity. The Finnmarkian orogeny occurred in this area at an earlier date and reached a more advanced stage of development than in the southern parts of the Scandinavian Caledonides (Sturt *et al.* 1978).

The most characteristic components of the *upper Allochthon*, which are included in the Koli and Seve Nappes (Table 3, Fig. 2, columns D–G, and Fig. 15), are ophiolites and associated eugeosynclinal sequences, and these may have experienced low-grade oceanic metamorphism prior to the intrusion of sheeted dykes and obduction. The Lykling ophiolite, unconformably overlain by an ensimatic island-arc assemblage (Roberts *et al.* 1985) which has been Rb–Sr-dated to 536 ± 46 Ma (Furnes *et al.* 1983), (Fig. 2, column F) was obducted before 464 Ma and the Karmøy ophiolite (Fig. 2, column G) may have been emplaced before 445 Ma (Furnes *et al.* 1983). In western parts of S Norway the obduction was associated with greenschist-facies metamorphism, increasing to lower amphibolite facies at Bergen and other places along the coast. In the Trondheim area there is an indication of a low-grade metamorphic event pre-dating upper middle Arenig which is separated from a younger event in the Llandeilo–Caradoc (Roberts 1980, Ryan *et al*. 1980).

In Sweden there is evidence that the Seve and uppermost parts of the Koli were metamorphosed in the interval 510–450 (Fig. 7, columns 15–17) but at different times in each of these nappes (Dallmeyer *et al*. 1983). High-grade metamorphism is recorded in parts of the Seve (eclogites and glaucophane), and $^{40}Ar/^{39}Ar$ dating of hornblendes indicates an association with the Finnmarkian (Bryhni 1988).

Finnmarkian of the type area

Ramsey & Sturt (1976) proposed the term Finnmarkian phase for the orogenic development of the Kalak Nappe Complex (Fig. 16) and its substrate in northern Scandinavia. The Finnmarkian involved polyphase deformation, metamorphism and plutonism during late Cambrian to early Ordovician (Fig. 4).

Two major cycles of deformation (Fig. 4), D_1 and D_2, occurred before and after the metamorphic peak which reached amphibolite facies with formation of local migmatite complexes. Deformation during D_2 led to initial emplacement of the Kalak Nappe Complex (Fig. 16) and underlying units onto the Baltic shield.

Radiometric dating indicates that the orogenic phase occurred through the interval 535–400 Ma. K–Ar nepheline dates from the D_2 alkaline rocks fall in the range 480–491 Ma, and are possibly cooling ages representing uplift and erosion of the Finnmarkian mountain belt.

Supplementary Rb–Sr isochron dates from tectonic units underlying the Kalak Nappe Complex (Fig. 16) include 493 ± 45 Ma from the Laksefjord Nappe and 504 ± 7 Ma from another locality in the Parautochthon. These dates probably represent the age of cleavage formation in the more marginal parts of the orogen during the Finnmarkian (Bryhni 1988).

Events related to the Finnmarkian orogenic phase of Scandinavia can be summarized as follows (Sturt 1984, written communication).

1 The major stage in accretion of ophiolitic terranes to the Baltic craton was an integral part of the Finnmarkian orogeny.

2 The continental miogeocline–rise prism was the essential configuration of the pre-Finnmarkian continental margin, and its destructive phase relates to the Finnmarkian orogeny. The latter involved thrusting towards the craton, polyphasal folding and metamorphism, syn-orogenic plutonism, and the obduction of ophiolitic terranes (Group 1 ophiolites) including ophiolites *per se* and material of ensimatic island arcs (Fig. 4).

3 This orogenic development was followed by major uplift and erosional stripping during early Ordovician and was covered by an unconformable sequence of Ordovician and Silurian strata (Fig. 7, columns 15–17).

4 The major belt-length Finnmarkian unconformity has been shown to be of a terrane-linking type.

Gondwanaland and some of its fragments

The eastern margin of the AC orogen proper, as far E as the British Isles, is composed of upper Proterozoic and lower Palaeozoic sequences that have had a singular evolutionary history which is in marked contrast with the western margin. These blocks and belts which originated outboard of cratonic N America and its associated volcanic arcs now form a microcontinent (Schenk 1971, 1978) or a collage (Keppie 1985) or domains (Rast *et al*. 1988) whose component terranes are referred to as Avalonian, Cadomian or Pan-African. The identification of these terranes and their associated terminology and geology has been treated by Rast & Skehan (1983), Autran (cited by Rankin *et al*. 1988) and Leblanc & Lancelot (1980).

Upper Proterozoic and lower Palaeozoic rocks of the Appalachians: Avalonian terranes

The Avalon terrane of the Appalachians (Fig. 7, columns 2, 5, 7 and 10, and Fig. 8) consists mainly of upper Proterozoic and Cambrian sedimentary and volcanic rocks that are unmetamorphosed and undeformed by comparison with the Gander terrane immediately W of the Avalon (Fig. 13). The Cambrian volcanic rocks are not known in the Avalonian terranes of southern New England or Newfoundland. In some localities late Proterozoic sedimentary and volcanic rocks pass conformably upward into Cambrian sediments. Elsewhere unconformities and late Proterozoic intrusions are common throughout the length of the Avalonian domain in N America and Britain (Williams & Hatcher 1982, Rast & Skehan 1983).

The Carolina slate belt and the Charlotte belt

The Carolina slate belt, which is of low metamorphic grade and extends from Virginia to Georgia, contains mafic to felsic rocks ranging in age from late Proterozoic to early Palaeozoic. This belt has been intruded by gabbroic to granitic plutons ranging in age from 705 to 510 Ma (Fig. 7, column 2) (Butler & Fullagar 1978). The Charlotte belt of the Carolinas and its equivalents in

Georgia are probably a high-grade (upper-amphibolite facies) portion of the Avalon domain, and although they contain most of the plutons of the southern Appalachians (Hatcher 1978a, b) they are too young to be relevant to the time frame of this paper. Newly discovered Cambrian trilobite fossils of Atlantic affinities (St Jean 1973, Samson *et al.* 1982) have served as a basis for separating Cambrian from late Proterozoic rocks (Secor *et al.* 1983).

Long (1979) suggested that the slate belt developed in a continental rift, but Whitney *et al.* (1978) think that it is a primitive volcanic arc. There are rapid lateral facies variations, such that several similar belts separated by higher-grade rocks are present (Hatcher 1978a, b). The grade of metamorphism of the slaty rocks is typically low. The general setting and lithologies are similar to those of southern New England, Newfoundland, New Brunswick and the British Isles, except for the lack of Cambrian volcanic rocks in southern New England and Newfoundland (Rast & Skehan 1983). It should be noted that, although dated intrusive igneous rocks and volcanic rocks are well represented in the interval from 705 to 445 Ma, there is no evidence for the date of Avalonian orogenesis. The earliest recognized metamorphism (M_1) and folding (D_1) is coeval with emplacement of a mid-Palaeozoic late- to post-kinematic plutonic complex. The $^{40}Ar/^{39}Ar$ hornblende ages in the Charlotte belt (Sutter *et al.* 1983) and whole-rock K–Ar ages from low-grade slates in the North Carolina slate belt (Kish *et al.* 1979) suggest an Ordovician age for D_1 (Secor *et al.* 1983, p. 650).

Southeastern New England

The Avalonian terrane of southeastern New England is in large part underlain by granitic plutons of the Dedham and Esmond plutonic complexes of Massachusetts and Rhode Island respectively. These batholithic masses, which have ages of about 630 Ma, outcrop widely S and W of Boston. N of Boston there are abundant bimodal volcanics and gabbroic plutons older than the 630 Ma plutons. The Westboro Formation (Bell & Alvord 1976) together with the above rocks, the Middlesex volcanic complex and the Lynn volcanics (Smith & Hon 1984) and the sequence of turbidites of Newport, RI are cut by the 630 Ma plutons. In addition, the units of the Blackstone Group of Rhode Island are probably correlated with the Westboro and Middlesex volcanic complex (Skehan & Rast 1983). These rock sequences have recently been recognized as containing olistostromes which were probably deposited in a back-arc basin formed on the continental shelf. The volcanic arc is possibly closely associated with a subduction zone to the S giving rise to rifting and the production of the dominant calc-alkaline plutonic sequences as well as the olistostromes in zones of crustal instability (Skehan *et al.* 1985).

There is strong evidence for D_1, and only D_1, folding and possibly Precambrian metamorphism in schists of the Blackstone Group, prior to the intrusion by Esmond granite of age about 630 Ma (Coyle *et al.* 1984; Dreier, 1984) in northern Rhode Island, and in the Price Neck Formation intruded by a granite of age 595 ± 12 Ma (Smith & Giletti 1978). Olistostromes involving dominantly carbonate and quartz-arenite olistoliths of Green Head aspect with minor serpentinite and detrital spinel have been identified widely over this Avalonian terrane (Skehan *et al.* 1985).

Fossiliferous lower Cambrian limestone in green and maroon slates and middle Cambrian green argillite and dark grey phyllite characterize the southeastern New England terrane (Skehan *et al.* 1978). The lower Cambrian carries a Tommotian pre-trilobitic fauna (Landing 1986, personal communication) and the middle Cambrian carries a *Paradoxides* fauna. In the Carolina slate belt, southeastern New England, Newfoundland and the southern British Isles, the middle Cambrian sediments have trilobites of *Paradoxides* fauna. The fauna of the slate belt are dominated by *Paradoxides* (or *Acadoparadoxides*) (Secor *et al.* 1983, p. 649), and those of southernmost New England are dominated by the diagnostic medial middle Cambrian *Badulesia Tenera* (Harrt) (Skehan *et al.* 1978).

Maritime Provinces

Although details of the Avalonian succession are still obscure in part, the Maritimes (Fig. 7, column 7) together with the central Appalachians (Fig. 7, column 3) may have a stratigraphic and tectonic record that may extend to *c.* 850 Ma and 740 Ma respectively which is comparable with that of the Channel Islands–northern France and Morocco (Fig. 7, columns 21 and 22). Whole-rock Rb–Sr dating of the Brookfield gneiss among the Green Head rocks of New Brunswick has yielded an age of 830 ± 26 Ma (Olszewski & Gaudette 1982). This date may represent an older Avalonian basement which is partly gneissose (Avalonian I) (Fig. 7, column 7) and is associated with carbonate-orthoquartzite sediments—the Green Head Group lying unconformably below the Coldbrook Group volcanics and volcaniclastics. The latter have undergone the later Proterozoic folding, metamorphism and igneous intrusion referred to as Avalonian II (Fig. 7, column 7). Fossiliferous Cambrian rocks were not deformed in pre-Arenig time.

Newfoundland: Avalon Peninsula (type locality)

The thick slightly-metamorphosed late Proterozoic sequence is complicated by faulting and facies variations. These faults are used to divide the Avalon into a series of stratigraphically-distinct packages each characterized by a somewhat different assemblage of lithologies (Strong 1979, King 1980, Rast & Skehan 1983, fig. 2, Skehan & Rast 1983).

The upper Proterozoic sequence of the Avalon Peninsula proper (Figs 8 and 13) begins with volcanic and volcaniclastic beds of the Harbour Main Group which, in part, passes laterally into and is partially covered by graded turbidites of the Conception Group (Fig. 13, Avalon Peninsula column). Near the Holyrood pluton, the latter unconformably overlie the former and their basal conglomerates contain pebbles of Holyrood granite. The Conception Group contains soft-bodied fossils (King 1980).

Stratigraphically-higher red conglomerates, sandstones and interbedded volcanic rocks are interpreted as post-orogenic molasse, and late- to post-orogenic plutons intrude the upper Proterozoic succession on land and on the neighbouring continental shelf (Rast & Skehan 1983, pp. 260–1). In the Proterozoic rocks both tholeiitic and mildly-alkaline basalts are known. Thus early volcanicity may have been rift related and associated with local small oceanic basins (Fig. 17) (Strong *et al.* 1978).

The upper Proterozoic red beds are overlain by marine Cambro-Ordovician strata that are locally para-conformable but regionally unconformable. In the Burin Peninsula (Fig. 13) Strong *et al.* (1978) recognized (a) the lowermost marine upper Proterozoic, (b) the middle terrestrial upper Proterozoic and (c) the mainly marine upper Vendian and lower Palaeozoic beds (Fig. 13) (Rast & Skehan 1983, p. 261). The eastern succession of the Avalon Peninsula (Avalon *sensu stricto*) can be broadly correlated with the western (Burin) sequence. The age of mafic volcanics in Burin is provided by an intrusive gabbro (762 ± 2 Ma) (Krogh *et al.* 1983). The Rock Harbour Group is younger as it contains a clast dated at 620 ± 2 Ma; the Marystown Group has yielded a zircon age of 617 ± 8 Ma which Dallmeyer (1981) correlates with the Love Cove Group (590 ± 30 Ma). The Avalon terrane of Newfoundland is separated from the central mobile belt—the Gander zone—by the Dover–Hermitage Bay fault (Fig. 13). The Avalon zone is only lightly deformed by folding and metamorphism and is intruded by late- to post-tectonic calc-alkaline granitic plutons.

British Isles and Ireland

The upper Proterozoic rocks of southern Britain have been reviewed by Bennison & Wright (1969), Rast & Crimes (1969), Dewey (1974), Harris *et al.* (1975), Rast & Skehan (1983) and Rankin *et al.* (1988).

The 'basement' to the Avalonian terranes of southern Britain in much of central England and Wales, as is the case with other Avalonian terranes in N America, consists of upper Proterozoic low-grade metamorphic rock together with intrusive and extrusive igneous rock and associated sedimentary rock. However, lower to middle Proterozoic basement may be present in southeastern Ireland and forms the basement of the Channel Islands and northern France (Rankin *et al.* 1988).

Southeastern Ireland

These Upper Proterozoic rocks comprise the Rosslare Complex of gneisses and the Cullenstown Group of less-deformed rocks. The Rosslare Complex may have cooled from amphibolite-facies conditions at *c.* 650 Ma. The Rosslare Complex is adjacent to the less-metamorphosed Cullenstown Group which is correlated with the Mona Complex of Anglesey. The Carnsore granodiorite (not to be confused with the Carnsore granite of Wales) intruded the Rosslare at 520 ± 6 Ma (Rankin *et al.* 1988).

Anglesey–Lleyn, N Wales

This locality forms the largest outcrop area of Proterozoic rock in southern Britain and comprises a 'bedded succession' of flysch-type sedimentary rocks more than 7000 m thick which may also include some lower Palaeozoic rocks. The succession also includes mafic and ultramafic rocks which may be related to oceanic crust (Thorpe 1978). The youngest part of the succession is the Gwna Group, a melange interpreted as an olistostrome containing quartzite, carbonate and mafic rocks as is the case in the southern New England succession (Rast & Skehan 1981b).

These rocks of the Mona Complex were folded, metamorphosed (595 ± 12 Ma (Anglesey), 542 ± 17 Ma (Lleyn)) and intruded by plutonic rocks (603 ± 34 Ma (Carnsore granite of Wales—not Carnsore of Rosslare!)) in the Monian orogenic phase (Fig. 7, column 18). Post-orogenic plutons (Sarn Complex) were emplaced at 549 ± 19 Ma.

In N Wales the Arvonian Volcanic Group occurs within the lowermost? Cambrian. Rocks correlated with the Arvonian may indicate a late Proterozoic metamorphic age. The Twt Hill granite, emplaced within the Arvonian, has been dated at 498 ± 7 Ma (Fig. 7, column 18) (Rankin *et al.* 1988).

S Wales–Stanner–Hanter–Malvern

These areas include a variety of volcanic and plutonic rocks. The Johnston Complex of S Wales has been dated at *c.* 700–640 Ma (Fig. 7, column 19) and may represent the earliest igneous activity in southern Britain. The Johnston and Malvern complexes are cut by high-level calc-alkaline intrusions of late Proterozoic–early Cambrian age (Fig. 7, column 19). The Malvern Complex is in tectonic contact with a tholeiitic suite (Warren House Group), suggesting oceanic affinities (Rankin *et al.* 1988).

Welsh Borderlands–central England

The Rushton schist of Shropshire has given an Rb–Sr whole-rock isochron age of 667 ± 20 Ma and is basement to the bimodal Uriconian volcanic suite (558 ± 16 Ma) and the overlying Longmyndian sedimentary sequence (younger than *c.* 600 Ma). The Uriconian rocks have chemical characteristics transitional between volcanic-arc and within-plate lavas consistent with an extensional environment similar to that envisioned for the Avalonian terrane of southeastern New England (Fig. 19). The Longmyndian sediments were deposited within a fault-bounded basin upon the surface of the volcanic rocks. The Uriconian and Longmyndian were folded probably prior to the local Cambrian (Fig. 7, column 20) which is unconformable on the Ercall granite believed to be 560–570 Ma.

Within central England (Rankin *et al.* 1988, fig. 4) the Charnian rocks of Charnwood Forest make up a series of volcaniclastic sedimentary rocks and lavas associated with diorite intrusions. The lavas of late Proterozoic age form a basaltic–andesite–dacite association, and the Charnian rocks were intruded by diorites at 540 ± 57 Ma (Rankin *et al.* 1988).

Channel Islands and northern France

Penteverian basement is recognized in Brittany (Cogne 1959). It has yielded dates of 1200–900 Ma and is overlain unconformably by Brioverian rocks. Icartian orthogneiss has yielded dates of *c.* 2000 Ma (Bishop *et al.* 1975). A variably-metamorphosed sequence of volcanic and sedimentary rocks in Brittany is referred to the lower and middle Brioverian (Fig. 7, column 21). Upper Brioverian volcanics have yielded a Cambrian age (533 Ma).

Cadomian plutonic rocks were emplaced over a long time period. An older group was emplaced *c.* 690–630 Ma before the Cadomian II deformation (Fig. 7, column 21). Gabbro and diorite were intruded at *c.* 600–580 Ma after Cadomian II deformation in the Channel Islands, Brittany and Normandy. In the Channel Islands these mafic rocks were followed by and associated with younger granites including the Mancellian granites of Normandy. The former were emplaced *c.* 570–500 Ma ago and the latter somewhat earlier. The Vire granite (Fig. 7, column 21) emplaced at 617 Ma is overlain unconformably by Cambrian sedimentary rocks (Autran, cited by Rankin *et al.* 1988).

Tectonic setting

It is not a simple matter to relate late Proterozoic events in the Armorican region and the Channel Islands to those of Britain. Magmatism in Wales and the English Midlands can be explained by a SE-dipping subduction zone near Anglesey. Similarly, French geologists have proposed for the Armorican area a SE-dipping subduction zone in the English Channel on the basis of high magnetic anomalies.

In Brittany volcanic rocks have the geochemical characteristics of back-arc tholeiites (Cabanis & Wyns 1984). One Cadomian orogenic cycle has been identified (Rabou *et al.* 1983) and has been dated by associated plutonism at between 585 and 595 Ma (Vidal *et al.* 1972). Autran (Rankin *et al.* 1988) concludes that the Brioverian supracrustal rocks experienced only one Precambrian (Cadomian) orogenic event and urges that the concept of two Cadomian orogenic events in northern France be abandoned.

In the Mancellian area of Normandy, the type area for the Cadomian (Cadomas is the Latin for Caen), there was an important plutonic event between 540 and 520 Ma ago. Odin *et al.* (1983) suggest that this be defined as the Proterozoic–Cambrian boundary.

Cambrian sedimentary rocks in the Armorican massif are only well developed in the Mancellian area where basal conglomerate is overlain successively by a carbonate unit, psammite and pelite. Elsewhere Cambrian deposits are absent and the Tremadocian conglomerate rests on the Brioverian with angular discordance.

In the northwestern Armorican massif, felsic volcanicity followed shortly after the Cadomian orogeny on a NE–SW trend. Ignimbrites overlie with angular discordance Brioverian tuffs dated c. 540 Ma, the latest magmatic event in the subduction cycle (Autran, cited by Rankin et al. 1988). Thus the Cambrian of this region is characterized by abundant volcanicity, represented dominantly by ignimbritic rhyolite with tuff and breccia, and lesser amounts of andesite, dacite and calc-alkaline rhyolite lavas.

About 640 Ma calc-alkaline volcanicity was was well developed on the border of the Icartian craton and is interpreted as island-arc volcanism. The beginning of collision is well dated by calc-alkaline plutonism at 615 Ma and followed the termination of the calc-alkaline volcanicity. The major tectono-metamorphic event is dated by syn-tectonic granodiorite (St Quay-LaLatte, c. 595–585 Ma) (Autran, cited by Rankin et al. 1988). The last tectono-metamorphic Cadomian event involved thrusting of the Icartian basement over the upper Brioverian chert sequence which resulted in local crustal anatexis in the St Malo area at about 540 Ma. Consistent with this model is the presence of a mafic–ultramafic complex in N central Brittany dated at 602 Ma (U–Pb zircon) and interpreted as an ophiolite complex related to a back-arc orogenic setting. Plutonism between 540 and 520 Ma marks the end of the Cadomian orogeny in the Armorican massif. Cambrian volcanicity reflects crustal melting along a zone of intra-plate distention around the Cadomian block (Cabanis 1983, Rankin et al. 1988).

Anti-Atlas Mountains, Morocco

The gneissic rocks of the Eburnean craton near Bou Azzer in the central part of the Anti-Atlas Mountains are overlain unconformably by quartz arenites and stromatolitic limestones which were folded during the major Pan-African deformation (Cadomian I or B) (Leblanc 1972b). This deformation produced recumbent folds with an axial planar slaty cleavage and thrusts which involved a slice of presumed Eburnean gneisses (Fig. 6). Metamorphic clay minerals (schistosity S_1) appear progressively northwards in the Bleida zone and have been dated at 685 ± 15 Ma (Rb–Sr on metamorphic illites (Clauer 1976)). The entire Bou Azzer complex was affected by greenschist-facies metamorphism (Fig. 7, column 22).

The post-tectonic granodiorite of Bleida is dated at 615 ± 12 Ma (U–Pb) (Ducrot & Lancelot 1978). The overlying Tiddiline Formation resting unconformably on the units noted above (Fig. 6 and Fig. 7, column 22) consists of coarse-grained detrital deposits preserved in grabens with meta-volcanics and associated intrusions. The late Pan-African brittle deformation B_2 (Leblanc 1972b) produced upright WNW fracture cleavage par-

allel to the border of the W African craton and is post-dated by the Vendian and Palaeozoic cover. The base of this cover sequence is the Ouarzazate Formation (580 ± 15–565 ± 20 Ma, U–Pb) (Juery et al. 1974, Juery 1976) and the sedimentary Adoudounian Formation containing the Boho lavas (Fig. 6C) (534 ± 10 Ma, U–Pb) (Ducrot & Lancelot 1977, Leblanc 1981, pp. 436–7).

The first complete ophiolitic complex described in the Proterozoic was that of Bou Azzer (Leblanc 1972a, 1975, 1976) which is 4–5 km thick (Leblanc 1981, pp. 437–43) (Fig. 6 and Fig. 7, column 22). The main part of the belt is hidden to the N under the Palaeozoic and Mesozoic cover of the High Atlas. The Bou Azzer ophiolite occurs in an allochthonous setting and has been obducted southward onto the continental margin (Leblanc 1981, p. 445). Other upper Proterozoic ophiolites (Fig. 7, column 18) have subsequently been described in Anglesey, Wales (Baker 1973, Wood 1974, Thorpe 1978).

A phase in the opening of the ocean associated with the W African craton may be indicated by the age 788 ± 9 Ma (Fig. 7, column 22, and Table 4) which is that of mafic volcanism on the continental margin (Rb–Sr whole-rock isochron related to a metamorphic aureole of mafic dykes (Clauer 1976)). On the basis of several assumptions, Leblanc (1981, p. 446) obtained a 1000 km wide oceanic domain N of the continental margin.

Conclusions

Development of the Iapetus Ocean and its borders

Stewart (1976) suggested that at about 850 Ma the tectonics of N America 'changes from a pattern of scattered locally deep epi-cratonic troughs to a pattern of encircling marginal geosynclines'. This change may mean that the beginning of rifting extended almost continuously around the Laurentian–Greenland continent. This implied to him that prior to 850 Ma N America was an interior part of a much larger continent. Tectonic subsidence analyses in mio-geoclines by Bond et al. (1984) in parts of several continents, on the other hand, limits the timing of continental breakup to between 625 and 555 Ma. These results refine the implications of a much broader range of radiometric ages of rift-related igneous rocks and biostratigraphic ages of the transition from active extension to passive subsidence in miogeoclines. Both palaeomagnetic (Uneo et al. 1975) and geological (Gee 1975) data suggest a late Precambrian juxtaposition of the Laurentian and Baltic shields. There is disagree-

TABLE 4. *Sequence of stratigraphic and tectonic events in the Pan-African domain (Anti-Atlas Mountains, Bou Azzer and El Graara)*

		Sequence of events	Date (Ma)		
			U–Pb	Rb–Sr	Phase
Vendian–Cambrian		Adoudounian dolomite (associated with alkaline volcanics and syenite of Jbel Boho)	534 ± 10		
Precambrian	Pan-African orogeny	Infracambrian—base of sedimentary l'Oued Adoudou Formation—bimodal calc-alkaline Ouarzazarte volcanics	563 ± 20	578 ± 15	PIII
		(Cadomian II) B_2—compression, cleavage Tiddiline Formation with volcanics			
		Intrusive quartz–diorite and post-tectonic Bleida Granite; contact metamorphism	615 ± 23	623 ± 18	PII–PIII
		(Cadomian I)—ophiolite obduction B_1—major compression—(closing ocean) metamorphism	685 ± 15		PII
Late		Post-Eburnean: Calcareous and quartzitic sediments (stromatolites), alkaline volcanics on the craton; calcareous to quartzitic sedimentary rocks and alkaline volcanics on the margin; opening of the ocean (ophiolites); metamorphism of the sediments by gabbro and diabase intrusions	788 ± 8		
		West African Shield	2000		PI

Data from Leblanc & Lancelot (1980).

ment, however, about both palaeomagnetic (Piper *et al.* 1973, McGlynn *et al.* 1975) and geological (Schenk 1971, Strong 1977) data concerning the relationship of Laurentia and Africa.

Strong (1979) presents data for the eastern N American Avalon zone indicating a long-lived tensional environment with local rifting and oceanic-crust formation (Fig. 17) at about the time suggested by Stewart (1976) and possibly indicating rifting of the Laurentian–Greenland–Baltic–W African supercontinent at this time. Figure 17, in which this highly tentative position is assumed, shows the continents assembled after the Grenville (Dalslandian, Penteverian) orogeny with the Laurentian and Baltic shields positioned according to the suggestion of Uneo *et al.* (1975) for the best match of pole positions for the 1000–600 Ma interval. The W African craton and intervening terranes are juxtaposed against the others assuming the least relative movements because of the numerous geological similarities discussed by Schenk (1971), Hughes (1972) and Rast & Skehan (1983). A palaeomagnetic basis is lacking, but Cambrian faunal similarities provide some indication that the Baltic shield and N Africa were connected during deposition of the platformal sequence (the Viking province of Jell 1974) and therefore possibly during deposition of the conformably underlying Vendian sequences. Although the late Precambrian Avalonian–Cadomian–Pan-African orogeny may reflect a collision of these terranes during this time (Rast *et al.* 1976), the local nature and irregular timing of these orogenic phases may not indicate major continental collisions until later in Palaeozoic time.

In any case the dominance of bimodal volcanics during the late Precambrian suggests that these terranes were under a tensional platform regime

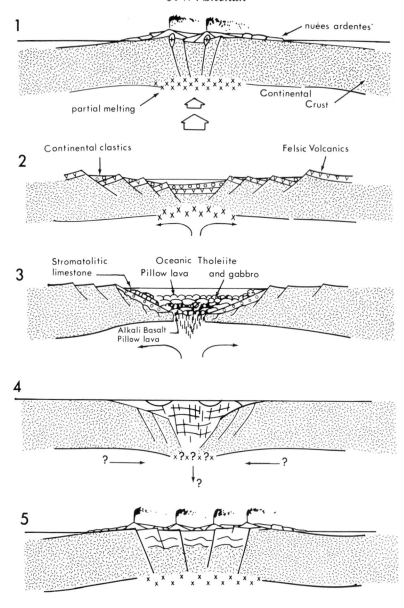

FIG. 17. Stages associated with rifting in the Proterozoic tectonic evolution of the Avalonian domain as inferred from the southern Burin Peninsula. (From Strong 1979, p. 90.)

(Strong 1979) after the Grenville orogeny, as was N America (Stewart 1976) and Scandinavia (Gee 1975, Gee & Sturt 1985). Wynne-Edwards (1976) has suggested that the apparently long time interval for such tension before rupture and proto-Atlantic (Iapetus Ocean) formation may reflect a ductile stretching of the crust as was invoked for Proterozoic orogenesis in general. This may explain the isolated and sporadic

distribution of ophiolites (Fig. 18) with continental rupture occurring in an irregular pattern to form only small isolated basins.

The proto-Atlantic began to develop as a large ocean basin with the separation of the Greenlandian (Laurentian) and Baltic shields at about 700 Ma (Gee 1975), but possibly as late as 600 Ma in eastern Canada (Strong & Williams 1972, Stukas & Reynolds 1976), and continued to a

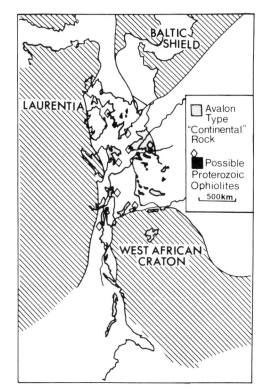

FIG. 18. Assumed relative positions of the Laurentian, Baltic and W African cratons during the late Proterozoic with Avalon-type rocks forming in an intra-cratonic extensional environment. (From Strong 1979, p. 92.)

maximum width at about 500 Ma (Strong 1977, 1979). A faunal difference was maintained between the two stable margins of the Iapetus Ocean until about the middle Ordovician (Neuman 1972) when the closure of Iapetus was well advanced (Stevens *et al.* 1974).

Bimodal volcanism, calc-alkaline plutonism, continental sedimentation and rifting of the continental platform, possibly related to the presence of a shallow dipping subduction zone and ophiolite obduction, may have characterized the Pan-African zone in late Proterozoic time (Fig. 19). Similar rock successions, together with ophiolitic suites, occur throughout late Proterozoic domains of the N Atlantic region and suggest a similar tectonic evolution involving a long period of extension and possibly ductile thinning of continental crust with local and irregular Vendian rupture giving way to Cambrian continental shelf or shelf conditions around volcanic islands and/or archipelagoes.

The stratigraphic, volcanic and plutonic data for the Avalon–Cadomian–Pan-African belts

suggest that the evolution of the rifted margins of Laurentia–Greenland and the Baltic craton is different from that of the W African craton and its associated Pan-African and Avalonian terranes. The eastern margin of the Laurentian–Greenland and the western margin of the Baltic cratons during late Proterozoic time are characterized by rifting of cratonal margins and deposition of rift-facies sediments (Fig. 2). Late Proterozoic sedimentary rocks of the Pan-African and Avalonian terranes consist of quartz-arenite and calcareous sediments of the continental shelf of the Eburnean craton (2000 Ma) upon which were obducted ophiolites of the Bou Azzer sequence (Fig. 6). There is a fundamental coherence between these shelf clastics and carbonates and similar sediments of the Avalonian terranes of New England and the Maritime Provinces and Newfoundland. Moreover, there are later alkaline volcanics of probably continental-shelf rift type.

The Eburnean craton of Morocco and its great thickness of upper Proterozoic shelf clastics and carbonates give evidence of late Proterozoic continental-shelf sedimentation and compressional orogenic episodes (Fig. 6). Cadomian and Avalonian terranes show basically the same kinds of features but are not as readily interpreted nor are the orogenic effects so well developed in the Avalonian domains. The major difference between the Avalonian and Cadomian orogenic belts is that the former structural unit is traceable and readily recognized along the belt by sedimentary and volcanic–plutonic sequences, by its Acado-Baltic or Atlantic fauna and by its generally low grade of metamorphism (Rast & Skehan 1983, pp. 257–8). The Cadomian, however, may not be a continuous orogenic belt as earlier thought by Rast & Skehan (1983, fig. 7), but may consist of isolated blocks and slices of Pan-African–Avalonian sequences distributed throughout the Iberian Peninsula and western and central Europe as tectonic fragments (Rast 1986, personal communication). Skehan *et al.* (1985) (Fig. 19) have interpreted the Avalonian zone of southeastern New England as having evolved as a continental shelf, possibly related to the Eburnean craton, to the W of which developed an eastward-dipping subduction zone. The subduction gave rise to calc-alkaline plutonism and volcanism in a volcanic arc built on the shelf and participated in the rifting of a back-arc basin with its characteristic mafic volcanics, plutonic rocks and olistostromes.

Thus in pre-Arenig times the evolution of the AC orogen appears to have taken place in a time and manner quite different from that of the Pan-African–Cadomian–Avalonian orogen.

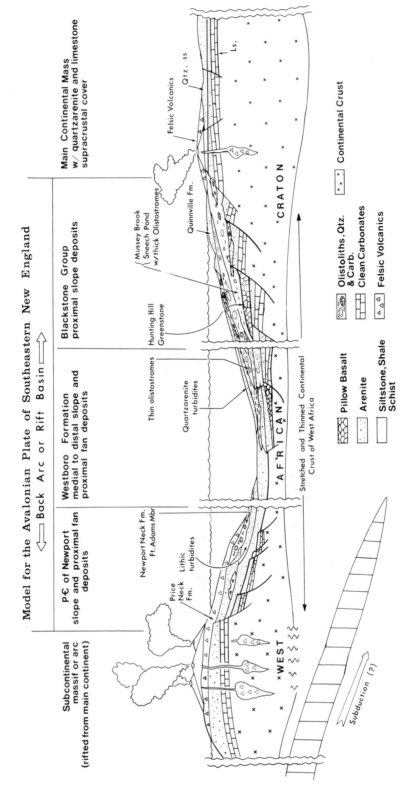

FIG. 19. Schematic profile through the Avalonian terrane of southeastern New England showing possible environments for the production of olistostromes in the Newport and Blackstone areas in Rhode Island and the Lynnfield area (N of Boston) in Massachusetts. The inferred environment is a continental shelf on a cratonal basement which has collapsed by rifting associated with subduction in front of the volcanic arc and the production of a back-arc basin on the shelf. (From Bailey, Skehan, Dreier and Webster 1986 and unpublished data.)

References

BAKER, J. W. 1973. A pre-Dalradian lineament in Connemara. *Scottish Journal of Geology,* **8**, 363–7.

BAMFORD, D., NUNN, K., PRODEHL, C. & JACOB, B. 1978. LISPB-IV. Crustal structure of Northern Britain. *Geophysical Journal of the Royal Astronomical Society,* **54**, 43–60.

BARBER, J. P. & YARDLEY, B. W. D. 1985. Conditions of high grade metamorphism in the Dalradian of Connemara, Ireland. *Journal of the Geological Society, London,* **142** (1), 87–96.

BARR, D., HOLDSWORTH, R. E. & ROBERTS, A. M. 1986. Caledonian ductile thrusting in a Precambrian metamorphic complex: the Moine of northwestern Scotland. *Geological Society of America Bulletin,* **97**, 754–64.

BARTHOLOMEW, M. J. & LEWIS, S. E. 1984. Evolution of Grenville massifs in the Blue Ridge geologic province, southern and central Appalachians. *In:* BARTHOLOMEW, M. J. (ed.) *The Grenville Event in the Appalachians and Related Topics. Geological Society of America Special Paper No. 194,* pp. 229–54.

——, GATHRIGHT, T. M., II, & HENIKA, W. S. 1981. A tectonic model for the Blue Ridge in central Virginia. *American Journal of Science,* **281**, 1164–83.

—— SCHULTZ, A. P., HENIKA, W. S. & GATHRIGHT, T. M., II 1982. Geology of the Blue Ridge and Valley and Ridge at the junction of the central and southern Appalachians. *In:* LYTTLE, P. T. (ed.) *Central Appalachian Geology, NE–SE GSA 1982 Field Trip Guidebook,* 121–70, American Geological Institute, Washington, DC.

BECKINSALE, R. D. & THORPE, R. S. 1979. Rubidium-strontium whole-rock isochron evidence for the ages of the metamorphism and magmatism of the Mona Complex of Anglesey. *Journal of the Geological Society, London,* **136**, 433–9.

BELL, K. G. & ALVORD, D. C. 1976. Pre-Silurian stratigraphy of northeastern Massachusetts. *In:* PAGE, L. R. (ed.) *Contributions to the Stratigraphy of New England, Geological Society of America Memoir No. 148,* 179–216.

BENNISON, G. M. & WRIGHT, A. E. 1969. *The Geological History of the British Isles,* St. Martins Press, New York, 406 pp.

BERGSTROM, S. M., RIVA, J. & KAY, M. 1974. Significance of conodonts, graptolites and shelly faunas from the Ordovician of western and north-central Newfoundland. *Canadian Journal of Earth Sciences,* **11**, 1625–60.

BERTHELSEN, A. 1981. Towards a palinspastic analysis of the Baltic Shield. *In:* COGNE, J. & SLANSKY, M. (eds) *Géologie de l'Europe. Memoires du Bureau de Recherches Géologiques et Minières,* **108**, 5–21.

BISHOP, A. C., ROACH, R. A. & ADAMS, C. J. D. 1975. Precambrian rocks within the Hercynides. *In:* HARRIS, A. L., HOLLAND, C. H. & LEAKE, B. E. (eds) *A Correlation of Precambrian Rocks in the British Isles. Special Report of the Geological Society of London No. 6,* pp. 102–7.

BJØRLYKKE, K. 1974. Geochemical and mineralogical influence of Ordovician island arcs on epicontinental clastic sedimentation: a study of lower Palaeozoic sedimentation in the Oslo Region, Norway. *Sedimentology,* **21**, 251–72.

——, ELVSBORG, A. & HØY, T. 1976. Late Precambrian sedimentation in the central Sparagmite Basin of south Norway. *Norsk Geologisk Tidsskrift,* **56**, 233–290.

—— 1978. The eastern marginal zone of the Caledonide orogen in Norway. *In:* TOZER, E. T. & SCHENK, P. E. (eds) *Caledonian–Appalachian Orogen of the North Atlantic Region. Geological Survey of Canada Paper No. 78-13,* pp. 49–54.

BOND, G. C., NICKESON, P. A. & KOMINZ, M. A. 1984. Breakup of a supercontinent between 625 Ma and 555 Ma: new evidence and implications for continental histories. *Earth and Planetary Science Letters,* **70**, 325–45.

BOONE, G. M. 1983. The Hurricane Mountain Formation melange and unconformably overlying Lower to Middle Ordovician Volcanics, Brassua Lake and Moosehead Lake quadrangles. *In:* CALDWELL, D. W. & HANSON, L. S. (eds) *Guidebook for the Greenville–Millinocket Regions, North Central Maine, Field Trips, New England Intercollegiate Geological Conference, 75th Annual Meeting,* pp. 31–44.

BRACE, W. F. 1953. The Geology of the Rutland area, Vermont. *Vermont Geological Survey Bulletin No. 6,* 120 pp.

VAN BREEMEN, O., HALLIDAY, A. N., JOHNSON, M. R. W. & BOWES, D. R. 1978. Crustal additions in late Precambrian times. *In:* BOWES, D. R. & LEAKE, B. E. (eds) *Crustal Evolution in Northwestern Britain and Adjacent Regions. Special Publication of the Geological Society of London No. 10,* pp. 81–106.

——, PIDGEON, R. T. & JOHNSON, M. R. W. 1974. Precambrian and Paleozoic pegmatites in the Moines of northern Scotland. *Journal of the Geological Society, London,* **130** (6), 493–507.

BROOK, M., POWELL, D. & BREWER, M. S. 1977. Grenville events in the Moine rocks of the Northern Highlands, Scotland. *Journal of the Geological Society, London,* **133**, 489–96.

BRYHNI, I. 1988. Early Palaeozoic metamorphism in the Scandinavian Caledonides. *This volume.*

——, FITCH, F. J. & MILLER, J. A. 1971. $^{40}Ar/^{39}Ar$ dates from recycled Precambrian rocks in the Gneiss Region of the Norwegian Caledonides. *Norsk Geologisk Tidsskrift,* **51**, 391–406.

BURSNALL, J. T. & DE WIT, M. J. 1975. Timing and development of the orthotectonic zone in the Appalachian orogen of northwest Newfoundland. *Canadian Journal of Earth Sciences,* **12**, 1712–22.

BUTLER, J. R. & FULLAGAR, P. D. 1978. Petrochemical and geochronological studies of plutonic rocks in the southern Appalachians. III. Leucocratic adamellites of the Charlotte belt near Salisbury, North Carolina. *Geological Society of America Bulletin,* **89**, 460–6.

CABANIS, B. 1983. Main features of volcanism and

plutonism in late Proterozoic and Dinantian times in France. *In:* SCHENK, P. E. (ed.) *Regional Trends in the Geology of the Appalachian–Caledonian–Hercynian–Mauritanide Orogen*, pp. 187–92, Reidel, Dordrecht.

—— & WYNS, R. 1984. Le volcanisme précambrien des Mauges et ses caractères géochimiques: RCP 705—Géodynamique de Massif Amoricain. *Colloque Journées du Mans, October 1–2, 1984, Hercynia.*

CABY, R., BERTRAND, J. M. L. & BLACK, R. 1981. Pan-African ocean closure and continental collision in the Hoggar–Iforas segment, central Sahara. *In:* KRONER, A. (ed.) *Precambrian Plate Tectonics*, pp. 407–34, Elsevier, Amsterdam.

CHARLOT, R. 1978. Caractérisation des événements éburnéens et pan-africains dans l'Anti-Atlas marocain. Apport de la méthode géochronologique Rb–Sr. *D.Sc. Thesis*, University of Rennes, 220 pp.

CHOUBERT, G. 1947. L'accident majeur de l'Anti-Atlas. *Comptes Rendus Hebdomadaires des Séances de l'Academie des Sciences, Série D,* **224** (16), 1172–3.

CLAESSON, S. 1980. A Rb–Sr isotope study of granitoids and related mylonites in the Tannas Augen Gneiss Nappe, southern Swedish Caledonides. *Geologiska Föreningens i Stockholm Förhandlingar,* **102**, 403–20.

—— & RODDICK, J. C. 1983. ^{40}Ar/^{39}Ar data on the age and metamorphism of the Ottfjallet dolerites, Sarv Nappe, Swedish Caledonides. *Lithos,* **16**, 61–73.

CLAUER, N. 1976. Géochimie isotopique du strontium des milieux sédimentaires. Application à la géochronologie de la couverture du craton ouest-africain. *Thesis, Memoir No. 45*, University of Strasbourg, 256 pp.

COGNE, J. 1959. Données nouvelles sur l'Antecambrien dans l'Ouest de la France: Pentevrien et Brioverien en baie de Saint-Brieuc (Côtes du Nord). *Bulletin de la Société Géologique de France,* **7** (1), 112–18.

—— 1971. Le Massif Armoricain et sa place dans la structure des socles ouest-Europeans: l'arc Hercynien Ibero-Armoricain. *Histoire Structurale du Golfe de Gascogne, Institut Francais Pet. Collect. Colloq. Semin.,* **22** (1), I. 1–1–I. 1–23.

COLTON, G. W. 1970. The Appalachian Basin—its depositional sequences and their geologic relationships. *In:* FISHER, G. W., PETTIJOHN, F. P., REED, J. C., JR. & WEAVER, K. N. (eds) *Studies of Appalachian Geology: Central and Southern*, Wiley-Interscience, New York, pp. 5–47.

COYLE, M., SKEHAN, S. J., J. W. & RAST, N. 1984. The deformation of the "Older Gneisses" of the Avalon Platform in Rhode Island. *Geological Society of America Abstracts with Programs,* **16**, 11.

COOKE, H. C. 1955. An early Palaeozoic orogeny in the eastern townships of Quebec. *Proceedings of the Geological Association of Canada,* **7**, 118–31.

DALLMEYER, R. D. 1975. Incremental ^{40}Ar/^{39}Ar ages of biotite and hornblende from retrograded basement gneisses of the southern Blue Ridge: their bearing on the age of Palezoic metamorphism. *American Journal of Science,* **275**, 444–60.

—— 1977. ^{40}Ar/^{39}Ar age spectra of minerals from the Fleur de Lys terrane in northwest Newfoundland: their bearing on chronology of metamorphism within the Appalachian orthotectonic zone. *Journal of Geology,* **85**, 89–103.

—— 1981. Geochronology of the Newfoundland Appalachians: recent advances. *Geological Society of America Abstracts with Programs,* **13**, 127.

—— & ANDERSON, A. 1984. Tectonothermal evolution of the Precambrian basement terraine of western Troms and northern Nordland: evidence from preliminary ^{40}Ar/^{39}Ar incremental release mineral ages. *Stockholm University Geological Institute Meddelelser,* **255**, 50.

——, GEE, D. G. & BECKHOLMEN, M. 1983. ^{40}Ar/^{39}Ar evidence of superposed metamorphism in the Central Scandinavian Caledonides, Jamtland, Sweden. *Geological Society of America Abstracts with Programs,* **15**, 553.

——, ODOM, A. L., O'DRISCOLL, C. F. & HUSSEY, E. M. 1981. Geochronology of the Swift Current granite and host volcanic rocks of the Love Cove Group, southwestern Avalon zone, Newfoundland: evidence of a late Proterozoic volcanic-subvolcanic association. *Canadian Journal of Earth Sciences,* **18** (9), 699–707.

DEWEY, J. F. 1969. Evolution of the Appalachian/Caledonian orogen. *Nature, London,* **222**, 124–9.

—— 1974. The geology of the southern termination of the Caledonides. *In:* NAIRN, A. E. M. & STEHLI, F. G. (eds) *The Ocean Basin and Margins,* Vol. 2, *The North Atlantic*, pp. 205–31, Plenum Press, New York.

——, KENNEDY, M. J. & KIDD, W. S. F. 1983. A geotraverse through the Appalachians of northern Newfoundland. *In:* RAST, N. & DELANY, F. M. (eds) *Profiles of Orogenic Belts, Geodynamics Series*, Vol. 10, pp. 205–41. American Geophysical Union and Geological Society of America, Washington, DC.

DOWNIE, C., LISTER, T. R., HARRIS, A. L. & FETTES, D. J. 1971. A palynological Investigation of the Dalradian rocks of Scotland. *Institute of Geological Sciences Report No. 71/9*, pp. 1–30.

DRAKE, A. A., JR & LYTTLE, P. T. 1981. The Accotink Schist, Lake Barcroft Metasandstone, and Popes Head Formation—keys to an understanding of the tectonic evolution of the northern Virginia piedmont. *United States Geological Survey Professional Paper No. 1205*, 16 pp.

—— & MORGAN, B. A. 1981. The Piney Branch Complex—a metamorphosed fragment of the central Appalachian ophiolite in northern Virginia. *American Journal of Science,* **281**, 484–508.

DRIER, R. B. 1984. The Blackstone Series: evidence for Alleghanian deformation in an Avalonian Terrane. *Geological Society of America Abstracts with Programs,* **16**, 13.

DUCROT, J. & LANCELOT, J. R. 1977. Problème de la Limite Precambrien–Cambrien: étude radiochronologique par la méthode U–Pb sur zircons du volcan du Jbel Boho (Anti-Atlas-marocain). *Canadian Journal of Earth Sciences,* **14**, 2771–7.

—— & —— 1978. Age pan-africain de la granodiorite de Bleida (Anti-Atlas Maroc) et conséquences. *6me*

Réunion Annuaire des Sciences de la Terre, Orsay, p. 150.

FULLAGAR, P. D. & BUTLER, J. R. 1979. 325 to 265 m.y. old granitic plutons in the Piedmont of the southeastern Appalachians. *American Journal of Science, 279* (2), 161–85.

FURNES, H., AUSTRHEIM, H., AMALIKSEN, K. G. & NORDAS, J. 1983. Evidence for an incipient early Caledonian (Cambrian) orogenic phase in southwestern Norway. *Geological Magazine, 120,* 607–12.

FYFFE, L. R., RANKIN, D., SIZE, W. B. & WONES, D. R. 1983. Volcanism and plutonism in the Appalachian Orogen. *In:* SCHENK, P. E. (ed.) *Regional Trends in the Geology of the Appalachian–Caledonian–Hercynian–Mauritanide Orogen*, pp. 173–85. Reidel, Dordrecht.

GEE, D. G. 1975. A tectonic model for the central part of the Scandinavian Caledonides. *American Journal of Science, 275A,* 468–515.

—— & ROBERTS, D. 1983. Timing of deformation in the Scandinavian Caledonides. *In:* SCHENK, P. E. (ed) *Regional trends in the Geology of the Appalachian–Caledonian–Hercynian–Mauritanide Orogen*, pp. 279–92, Reidel, Dordrecht.

—— & STURT, B. A. (eds) 1985. *The Caledonide Orogen—Scandinavia and Related Areas*, Wiley, Chichester.

GILETTI, B., MOORBATH, S. & LAMBERT, R. St J. 1961. A geochronological study of the metamorphic complexes of the Scottish Highlands. *Quarterly Journal of the Geological Society of London,* **117,** 233–64.

GLOVER, L., III, & SINHA, A. K. 1973. The Virgilina deformation, a late Precambrian to early Cambrian (?) orogenic event in the central Piedmont of Virginia and North Carolina. *American Journal of Science, 273A,* 234–51.

——, SPEER, J. A., RUSSELL, G. S. & FARRAR, S. S. 1983. Ages of regional metamorphism and ductile deformation in the central and southern Appalachians. *Lithos,* **16,** 223–45.

GUSTAVSON, M. 1978. Caledonides of north central Norway. *In:* TOZER, E. T. & SCHENK, P. E. (eds) *Caledonian–Appalachian Orogen of the North Atlantic Region. Geological Survey of Canada Paper No. 78–13*, pp. 25–30.

HADLEY, J. B. 1970. The Ocoee Series and its possible correlatives. *In:* FISHER, G. W., PETTIJOHN, F. P., REED, J. C., JR, & WEAVER, K. N. (eds) *Studies of Appalachian Geology: Central and Southern*, pp. 247–59, Wiley-Interscience, New York.

—— & GOLDSMITH, R. 1963. Geology of the eastern Great Smoky Mountains, North Carolina and Tennessee. *United States Geological Survey Professional Paper No. 349-B*, 118 pp.

HALL, L. M. & ROBERTS, D. 1988. Timing of Ordovician deformation in the Caledonian–Appalachian orogen. *This volume.*

HALLER, J. 1971. *Geology of the East Greenland Caledonides*, Wiley-Interscience, New York, 413 pp.

HARLAND, W. V. & GAYER, R. A. 1972. The Arctic Caledonides and earlier oceans. *Geological Magazine,* **109,** 289–314.

HARRIS, A. L. & PITCHER, W. S. 1975. The Dalradian Supergroup. *In:* HARRIS, A. L., SHACKLETON, R. M., WATSON, J., DOWNIE, C., HARLAND, W. B. & MOORBATH, S. (eds) *A Correlation of Precambrian Rocks in the British Isles. Special Report of the Geological Society of London No. 6*, pp. 52–75

——, BALDWIN, C. T., BRADBURY, H. J., JOHNSON, H. D. & SMITH, R. A. 1978. Ensialic basin sedimentation: the Dalradian Supergroup. *In:* BOWES, D. R. & LEAKE, B. E. (eds) *Crustal Evolution in Northwestern Britain and Adjacent Regions. Special Publication of the Geological Society of London No. 10*, pp. 115–38.

——, HOLLAND, C. H. & LEAKE, B. E. (eds) 1975. *A Correlation of Precambrian Rocks in the British Isles. Special Report of the Geological Society of London No. 6.*, 768 pp.

HARRIS, L. & MILICI, R. C. 1977. Characteristics of thin-skinned style of deformation in the southern Appalachians, and potential hydrocarbon traps. *United States Geological Survey Professional Paper No. 1018.*

HARTE, B. 1988. Lower Palaeozoic metamorphism in the Moine–Dalradian belt of the British Isles. *This volume.*

HATCHER, R. D., JR, 1978a. Synthesis of the southern and central Appalachians, U.S.A. *In:* TOZER, E. T. & SCHENK, P. E. (eds) *Caledonian–Appalachian Orogen of the North Atlantic Region. Geological Survey of Canada Paper No. 78-13*, pp. 149–57.

—— 1978b. Tectonics of the Western Piedmont and Blue Ridge, southern Appalachians, review and speculation. *American Journal of Science, 278,* 276–304.

—— 1984. Southern and central Appalachian basement massifs. *Geological Society of America Special Paper No. 194*, pp. 149–53.

HENRIKSEN, N. 1978. East Greenland Caledonian Fold Belt. *In:* TOZER, E. T. & SCHENK, P. E. (eds) *Caledonian–Appalachian Orogen of the North Atlantic Region. Geological Survey of Canada Paper No. 78-13*, pp. 105–9.

—— 1985. The Caledonides of central East Greenland 70°–76° N. *In:* GEE, D. G. & STURT, B. A. (eds) *The Caledonide Orogen–Scandinavia and Related Areas*, pp. 1095–113, Wiley, Chichester.

—— & HIGGINS, A. K. 1976. The East Greenland Caledonian fold belt. *In:* ESCHER, A. & WATT, W. S. (eds) *Geology of Greenland*, pp. 183–246, Geological Survey of Greenland, Denmark.

HERZ, N. 1984. Rock suites in Grenvillian terrane of the Roseland district, Virginia. Part 2. Lithologic relations. *In:* BARTHOLOMEW, M. J. (ed.) *The Grenville Event in the Appalachians and Related Topics. Geological Society of America Special Paper No. 194*, pp. 175–86.

—— & FORCE, E. R. 1984. Rock suites in Grenvillian terrane of the Roseland district, Virginia. Part 1. Lithologic relations. *In:* BARTHOLOMEW, M. J. (ed.) *The Grenville Event in the Appalachians and Related Topics. Geological Society of America Special Paper No. 194*, pp. 187–200.

HIGGINS, A. K. & PHILLIPS, W. E. A. 1979. East Greenland Caledonides—an extension of the British Caledonides. *In:* HARRIS, A. L., HOLLAND, C. H. & LEAKE, B. E. (eds) *The Caledonides of the British Isles Reviewed. Special Publication of the Geological Society of London No. 8*, pp. 19–32.

HOLTEDAHL, O. 1920. Palaeogeography and distrophism in the Atlantic–Arctic region during Paleozoic time. *American Journal of Science*, **49**, 1–25.

HUGHES, C. J. 1972. Geology of the Avalon Peninsula, Newfoundland and its possible correspondence with Morocco. *Notes et Mémoires du Service Géologique du Maroc*, **236**, 265–75.

IRVING, E. & RUNCORN, S. K. 1957. Analysis of the palaeomagnetism of the Torridonian Sandstone Series of northwest Scotland. *Philosophical Transactions of the Royal Society of London Series A*, **250**, 83–99.

JELL, P. A. 1974. Faunal provinces and possible planetary reconstruction of the middle Cambrian. *Journal of Geology*, **82**, 319–50.

JUERY, A. 1976. Datation U/Pb du socle précambrien du Haut-Atlas (Maroc). *Thesis*, University of Paris VII, 85 pp.

——, LANCELOT, J. R., HAMET, J., PROUST, F. & ALLEGRE, C. J. 1974. L'âge des rhyolites du P III du Haut-Atlas et le problème de la limite Précambrien–Cambrien. *2ᵐᵉ Réunion Annuaire des Sciences de la Terre, Pont-à-Mousson (Nancy)*, p. 230.

KENNEDY, M. J. 1975. Repetitive orogeny in the northeastern Appalachians—new plate models based upon Newfoundland examples. *Tectonophysics*, **28**, 39–87.

—— 1979. The continuation of the Canadian Appalachians into the Caledonides of Britain and Ireland. *In:* HARRIS, A. L., HOLLAND, C. H. & LEAKE, B. E. (eds) *The Caledonides of the British Isles Reviewed, Special Publication of the Geological Society of London No. 8*, pp. 33–64.

KEPPIE, J. D. 1985. The Appalachian collage. *In:* GEE, D. G. & STURT, B. A. (eds) *The Caledonide Orogen–Scandinavia and Related Areas*, pp. 1217–26, Wiley, Chichester.

——, ST JULIEN, P., HUBERT, C., BELAND, J., SKIDMORE, B., FYFFE, L. R., RUITENBERG, A. A., McCUTCHEON, S. R., WILLIAMS, H. & BURSNALL, J. 1983. Times of deformation in the Canadian Appalachians. *In:* SCHENK, P. E. (ed.) *Regional Trends in the Geology of the Appalachian–Caledonian–Hercynian–Mauritanide Orogen*, pp. 307–13, Reidel, Dordrecht.

KILBURN, C., PITCHER, W. S. & SHACKLETON, R. M. 1965. The stratigraphy and origin of the Port Askaig Boulder Bed series (Dalradian). *Geological Journal*, **4**, 343–60.

KING, A. F. 1980. The Birth of the caledonides: late Precambrian rocks of the Avalon Peninsula, Newfoundland, and their correlatives in the Appalachian orogen. *In:* WONES, D. R. (ed.) *The Caledonides in the USA: Proceedings of the International Geological Correlation Program—Caledonide Orogen Project 27, Blacksburg, VA Department of Geological Sciences, Virginia Polytechnic Institute and State University, Memoir No. 2*, pp. 3–8.

KING, P. B. 1964. Geology of the central Great Smoky Mountains, Tennessee. *United States Geological Survey Professional Paper No. 349-C*, 148 pp.

——, HADLEY, J. B., NEWMAN, R. B. & HAMILTON, W. 1958. Stratigraphy of Ocoee Series, Great Smoky Mountains, Tennessee and North Carolina. *Geological Society of America Bulletin*, **69**, 947–66.

KISH, S. A., BUTLER, R. J. & FULLAGAR, P. D. 1979. The timing of metamorphism and deformation in the Canadian Appalachians. *Geological Society of America Abstracts with Programs*, **11**, 184–5.

KROGH, T. E., STRONG, D. F. & PAPEZIK, V. S. 1983. Precise U–Pb ages of zircons from volcanic and plutonic units in the Avalon Peninsula. *Geological Society of America Abstracts with Programs*, **15** (3), 135.

LAMBERT, R. ST J. 1969. Isotopic studies relating to the Pre-Cambrian history of the Moinian of Scotland. *Geological Society of London, Proceedings*, **1652**, 243–4.

——, WINCHESTER, J. A. & HOLLAND, J. G. 1979. Time, space and intensity relationships of the Precambrian and lower Palaeozoic metamorphisms of the Scottish Highlands. *In:* HARRIS, A. L., HOLLAND, C. H. & LEAKE, B. E. (eds) *The Caledonides of the British Isles Reviewed. Special Publication of the Geological Society No. 8*, pp. 363–7.

LARRABEE, D. M., SPENCER, C. W. & SWIFT, D. J. P. 1965. Bedrock geology of the Grand Lake areas, Arrostook, Hancock, Penobscot, and Washington Counties, Maine. *United States Geological Survey Bulletin No. 1201-E*, 38 pp.

LARSEN, O. 1971. K/Ar age determinations from the Precambrian of Denmark. *Danmarks Geologiske Undersögelse (Afhandlinger), Raekke 2*, **97**, 37 pp.

LAURENT, R. 1973. The Thetford-Mines ophiolite: Paleozoic 'flake' of oceanic lithosphere in the Northern Appalachian of Quebec. *Geological Society of America Abstracts with Programs*, **5** (2), 188.

—— 1977. Ophiolites from northern Appalachians of Quebec. *In:* COLEMAN, R. G. & IRWIN, W. P. (eds) *North American Ophiolites. Oregon Department of Geology and Mineral Industries Bulletin No. 95*, pp. 25–40.

LEBLANC, M. 1972a. Un complexe ophiolitique dans le Précambrien II de l'Anti-Atlas central (Maroc): description, interprétation et position stratigraphique. *Notes et Mémoires du Service Géologique du Maroc*, **236**, 119–44.

—— 1972b. Tectonique du Précambrien II de Bou-Azzer–El Graara (Anti-Atlas central). *Notes et Mémoires du Service Géologique du Maroc*, **236**, 59–81.

—— 1975. Ophiolites Précambriennes et gîtes arsenies de cobalt: Bou Azzer (Maroc). *D.Sc. Thesis*, University of Paris VI, 329 pp.

—— 1976. A Proterozoic oceanic crust at Bou Azzer. *Nature, London*, **261**, 34–5.

—— 1981. The Late Proterozoic ophiolites of Bou Azzer (Morocco): evidence for Pan-African plate tectonics. *In:* KRONER, A. (ed.) *Precambrian Plate Tectonics*, pp. 435–51, Elsevier, Amsterdam.

—— & LANCELOT, J. R. 1980. Interprétation géodynamique du domaine pan-africaine (précambrien terminal) de l'Anti-Atlas (Maroc) à partir de données géologiques et géochronologiques. *Canadian Journal of Earth Sciences*, **17**, 142–55.

LONG, L. E. & LAMBERT, R. ST J. 1963. Rb–Sr isotopic ages from the Moine Series. *In:* JOHNSON, M. R. W. & STEWART, F. H. (eds) *The British Caledonides*, pp. 177–88, Oliver & Boyd, Edinburgh.

LONG, T. 1979. The Carolina slate belt—evidence of a continental rift zone. *Geology*, **7**, 180–4.

MCGLYNN, J. C., IRVING, E., BELL, K. & PULLAIH, G. 1975. Paleomagnetic poles and a Proterozoic supercontinent, *Nature, London*, **255**, 318–19.

MATTINSON, J. M. 1977. U–Pb ages of some crystalline rocks from the Burlington Peninsula, Newfoundland and implications for the age of Fleur de Lys metamorphism. *Canadian Journal of Earth Sciences*, **14**, 2316–24.

MICHARD, A. 1976. Eléments de géologie Marocaine. *Notes et Mémoires du Service Géologique du Maroc*, **252**, 408 pp.

MISRA, K. C. & MCSWEEN, H. Y., JR. 1984. Mafic and ultramafic rocks of the Appalachian orogen: an introduction. *American Journal of Science*, **284**, 294–318.

MOORBATH, S. 1969. Evidence for the age of deposition of the Torridonian sediments of northwest Scotland. *Scottish Journal of Geology* **5**, 154–70.

MOSHER, S. & RAST, N. 1984. The deformation and metamorphism of Carboniferous rocks in maritime Canada and New England. *In:* HUTTON, D. H. W. & SANDERSON, D. J. (eds) *Variscan Tectonics of the North Atlantic Region. Special Publication of the Geological Society of London No. 14*, pp. 233–43.

MURRAY, D. P. & SKEHAN, J. W., S. J. 1979. A traverse across the eastern margin of the Appalachian–Caledonide orogen, southeastern New England. *In:* SKEHAN, J. W. S. J. & OSBERG, P. H. (eds) *The Caledonides in the USA: Geological Excursions in the Northeast Appalachians*, pp. 1–35, Weston Observatory, Boston College, Western, MA.

NEALE, E. R. W. & KENNEDY, M. J. 1967. Relationship of the Fleur de Lys Group to younger groups of the Burlington Peninsula, Newfoundland. *In:* NEALE, E. R. W. & WILLIAMS, H. (eds) *Geology of the Atlantic Region. Geological Association of Canada Special Paper No. 4*, pp. 139–69.

NEUMAN, R. B. 1967. Bedrock geology of the Shin Pond and Stacyville quadrangles, Penobscot County, Maine. *United States Geological Survey Professional Paper No. 524-1*, 37 pp.

—— 1972. Brachiopods of Early Ordovician volcanic islands. *Proceedings of the 24th International Geology Congress, Section 7*, pp. 297–302.

ODIN, G. S., AUVRAY, B., BIELSKI, M., DORE, F., LANCELOT, S. R. & PASTEELS, P. 1983. Numerical dating of Precambrian–Cambrian boundary. *Nature, London*, **302**, 21–3.

OLSZEWSKI, W. J., JR & GAUDETTE, H. E. 1982. Age of the Brookville Gneiss and associated rocks, southeastern New Brunswick. *Canadian Journal of Earth Sciences*, **19** (11), 2158–66.

OSBERG, P. H. 1983. Timing of organic events in the U.S. Appalachians. *In:* SCHENK, P. E. (ed.), *Regional Trends in the Geology of the Appalachian–Caledonian–Hercynian–Mauritanide Orogen*, pp. 315–37, Reidel, Dordrecht.

—— 1985. Stratigraphic columns for Eastern Maine. *In:* LINDBERG, F. A. (ed.) *Correlation of Stratigraphic Units of North America (COSUNA) Project: Northern Appalachian Region*. American Association of Petroleum Geologists, Tulsa.

PATCHETT, P. J. & BYLAND, G. 1977. Age of Grenville magnetisation: Rb–Sr and palaeomagnetic evidence from Swedish Dolerites, *Earth and Planetary Science Letters*, **35**, 92–104.

PAVLIDES, L. 1981. The central Virginia volcanic-plutonic belt: an island arc of Cambrian (?) age. *United States Geological Survey Professional Paper No. 1231-A*, 34 pp.

——, ARTH, J. G., DANIELS, D. L. & STERN, T. W. 1982. Island-arc, back-arc and melange terranes of northern Virginia: tectonic, temporal and regional relationships. *Geological Society of America Abstracts with Programs*, **14** (7), 584.

PHILLIPS, W. E. A., STILLMAN, C. J., FRIDERICHSEN, J. D. & JEMELIN, L. 1973. Preliminary results of mapping in the western gneiss and schist zone around Vestfjord and inner Gasefjord, south-west Scoresby Sound. *Rapport Grønlands Geologiske Undersøkelse*, **58**, 17–32.

PIASECKI, M. A. J. 1980. New light on the Moine rocks of the Central Highlands of Scotland. *Journal of the Geological Society, London*, **137**, 41–59.

—— & VAN BREEMEN, O. 1983. Field and isotopic evidence for a *c.* 750 Ma tectonothermal event in Moine rocks in the Central Highland region of the Scottish Caledonides. *Transactions of the Royal Society of Edinburgh: Earth Sciences 4th Series*, **73**, 119–34.

——, & WRIGHT, A. E. 1981. Late Precambrian geology of Scotland, England and Wales. *In:* KERR, J. W. & FERGUSON, A. J. (eds) *Geology of the North Atlantic Borderlands. Canadian Society of Petroleum Geology Memoir No. 7*, pp. 57–94.

PIPER, J. D. A., BRIDEN, J. C. & LOMAX, K. 1973. Precambrian Africa and South America as a single continent. *Nature, London*, **245**, 244–8.

POWELL, D., BROOK, M. & BAIRD, A. W. 1983. Structural dating of a Precambrian pegmatite in Moine rocks of northern Scotland and its bearing on the status of the 'Morarian Orogeny'. *Journal of the Geological Society, London*, **140**, 813–23.

RABOU, D., CHAUVEL, J. J. & CHANTRAINE, J. 1983. Nouvelles propositions pour la lithostratigraphie du Briovérien (Proterozoïque supérieur) et pour l'évolution géodynamique cadomiènne en basie de St. Brieuc (Massif Amoricain). *Bulletin de la Société Géologique de France*, **24** (4), 615–21.

RAMSEY, D. M. & STURT, B. A. 1976. The synmetamorphic emplacement of the Magerøy Nappe. *Norsk Geologisk Tidsskrift*, **56**, 291–308.

——, ——, ZWANN, K. B. & ROBERTS, D. 1985. Caledonides of northern Norway. *In:* GEE, D. G. & STURT, B. A. (eds) *The Caledonide Orogen-Scandinavia and Related Areas*, pp. 163–84, Wiley, Chichester.

RANKIN, D. W. 1968. Magmatic activity and orogeny

in the Blue Ridge province of the southern Appalachian Mountain system in northwestern North Carolina and southwestern Virginia. *Geological Society of America Special Paper No. 115*, p. 181 (abstract).

—— 1975. The continental margin of eastern North America in the southern Appalachians: the opening and closing of the proto Atlantic Ocean. *American Journal of Science*, **275A**, 298–336.

——, FURNES, H., BISHOP, A. C., CABANIS, B., MILTON, D. J., O'BRIEN, S. J. & THORPE, R. S. 1988. Plutonism and volcanism related to the pre-Arenig evolution of the Caledonide–Appalachian orogen. *This volume.*

RAST, N. 1984. The Alleghenian orogeny in eastern North America: *In:* HUTTON, D. H. & SANDERSON, D. J. (eds) *Variscan Tectonics of the North Atlantic Region. Special Publication of the Geological Society of London No. 14*, pp. 197–217.

—— & CRIMES, T. P. 1969. Caledonian orogenic episodes in the British Isles and northwestern France and their tectonic and chronological interpretation. *Tectonophysics*, **7**, 277–307.

—— & KOHLES, K. M. 1986. The origin of the Ocoee Supergroup. *American Journal of Science*, **286**, 593–616.

—— & SKEHAN, J. W., S. J. 1981a. The geology of the Precambrian rocks of Newport and Middletown, Rhode Island. *In:* HERMES, O. D. & BOOTHROYD, J. C. (eds) *Guidebook to Field Stations in Rhode Island and Adjacent Areas. Geological Conference, 73rd Annual Meeting*, pp. 67–92, University of Rhode Island, Kingston, RI.

—— & —— 1981b. Possible correlation of Precambrian rocks of Newport, Rhode Island with those of Anglesey, Wales, *Geology*, **9** (12), 596–601.

—— & —— 1983. The evolution of the Avalonian plate. *Tectonophysics*, **100**, 257–86.

——, O'BRIEN, B. H. & WARDLE, R. J. 1976. Relationships between Precambrian and lower Paleozoic rocks of the 'Avalon Platform' in New Brunswick, the Northeast Appalachians and the British Isles. *Tectonophysics*, **30**, 315–38.

—— *et al.* 1988. Early deformation in the Caledonian–Appalachian orogen. *This volume.*

RAYNER, D. 1982. *Stratigraphy of the British Isles*, 2nd edn, Cambridge University Press, Cambridge, 400 pp.

READING, H. 1965. Eocambrian and lower Paleozoic geology of the Digermul Peninsula, Tanafjord, Finnmark. *Norges Geologiske Undersøkelse*, **234**, 167–91.

RIORDAN, P. H. 1957. Evidence of a pre-Taconic orogeny in southeastern Quebec. *Geological Society of America Bulletin*, **68**, 389–94.

ROBERTS, D. 1975. Marine geology of the Rockall Plateau and Trough. *Philosophical Transactions of the Royal Society of London A*, **278**, 447–509.

—— 1980. Petrochemistry and palaeographic setting of the Ordovician Volcanic rocks of Smøla, Central Norway. *Norges Geologiske Undersøkelse*, **359**, 43–60.

—— & GALE, G. H. 1978. The Caledonian–Appalachian Iapetus Ocean. *In:* TARLING, D. H. (ed.) *Evolution of the Earth's Crust*, pp. 255–342, Academic Press, New York.

—— & GEE, D. G. 1985. An introduction to the structure of the Scandinavian Caledonides. *In:* GEE, D. & STURT, B. A. (eds) *The Caledonide Orogen–Scandinavia and Related Areas*, pp. 55–68, Wiley, Chichester.

——, STURT, B. A. & FURNES, H. 1985. Volcanite assemblages and environments in the Scandinavian Caledonides and the sequential development history of the mountain belt. *In:* GEE, D. & STURT, B. A. (eds) *The Caledonide Orogen—Scandinavia and Related Areas*, pp. 919–30. Wiley, Chichester.

ROBINSON, P. 1983. Realms of regional metamorphism in southern New England, with emphasis on the eastern Acadian metamorphic high. *In:* SCHENK, P. E. (ed.) *Regional Trends in the Geology of the Appalachian–Caledonian–Hercynian–Mauritanide Orogen*, pp. 249–58, Reidel, Dordrecht.

—— & HALL, L. M. 1980. Tectonic synthesis of Southern New England. *In:* WONES, D. R. (ed.) *The Caledonides in the USA: Proceedings of the International Geological Correlation Program—Caledonide Orogen Project 27, Blacksburg, VA. Department of Geological Sciences, Virginia Polytechnic Institute and State University, Memoir No. 2*, pp. 99–106.

RODGERS, J. 1970. *The Tectonics of the Appalachians*, Wiley-Interscience, New York, 271 pp.

—— 1972. Latest Precambrian (post-Grenville) rocks of the Appalachian region. *American Journal of Science*, **272**, 507–20.

RYAN, P. D., WILLIAMS, D. M. & SKEVINGTON, D. 1980. A revised interpretation of the Ordovician stratigraphy of Sør-trøndelag, and its implications for the evolution of the Scandinavian Caledonides. *In:* WONES, D. R. (ed.) *The Caledonides in the USA: Proceedings of the International Geological Correlation Program—Caledonide Orogen Project 27, Blacksburg, VA. Department of Geological Sciences, Virginia Polytechnic Institute and State University, Memoir No. 2*, pp. 99–106.

ST JEAN, J. 1973. A New Cambrian trilobite from the Piedmont of North Carolina. *American Journal of Science*, **237A**, 196–216.

ST JULIEN, P. & HUBERT, C. 1975. Evolution of the Taconian orogen in the Quebec Appalachians. *American Journal of Science*, **275A**, 337–62.

SAMSON, S. L., SECOR, D. T., SNOKE, A. W. & PALMER, A. R. 1982. Geological implications of recently discovered Middle Cambrian trilobites in the Carolina slate belt. *Geological Society of America Abstracts with Programs*, **14**, 607.

SCHENK, P. E. 1971. Southeastern Atlantic Canada, northwestern Africa, and continental drift. *Canadian Journal of Earth Sciences*, **8** (10), 1218–51.

—— 1978. Synthesis of the Canadian Appalachians. *In:* TOZER, E. T. & SCHENK, P. E. (eds) *Caledonian–Appalachian Orogen of the North Atlantic Region. Geological Survey of Canada Paper No. 78-13*, pp. 111–36.

SCHWAB, F. L., NYSTUEN, J. P. & GUNDERSON, L. 1988. Pre-Arenig evolution of the Appalachian–Caledonide orogen: sedimentation and stratigraphy. *This volume.*

SECOR, D. T., JR, SAMSON, S. L., SNOKE, A. W. & PALMER, A. R. 1983. Confirmation of the Carolina slate belt as an exotic terrane. *Science,* **221,** 649–50.

SHACKLETON, R. M. 1979, The British Caledonides: comments and summary. *In:* HARRIS, A. L., HOLLAND, C. H. & LEAKE, B. E. (eds) *The Caledonides of the British Isles Reviewed. Special Publication of the Geological Society of London No. 8,* pp. 299–304.

SINHA, A. K. & BARTHOLOMEW, M. J. 1984. Evolution of the Grenville terrane in the central Virginia Appalachians. *In:* BARTHOLOMEW, M. J. (ed.) *The Grenville Event in the Appalachians and Related Topics. Geological Society of America Special Paper No. 194,* pp. 175–86.

SKEHAN, J. W., S. J. 1961. The Green Mountain anticlinorium in the vicinity of Wilmington and Woodford, Vermont. *Vermont Geological Survey, Bulletin No. 17,* Vermont Development Department, Montpelier, VT, 159 pp.

—— & RAST, N. 1983. Relationship between Precambrian and Lower Palezoic rocks of Southeastern New England and other North Atlantic Avalonian terrains. *In:* SCHENK, P. E. (ed.) *Regional Trends in the Geology of the Appalachian–Caledonian–Hercynian–Mauritanide Orogen,* pp. 131–62, Reidel, Dordrecht.

——, BAILEY, R. H., DREIER, R. B. & WEBSTER, M. J. 1985. Late Proterozoic olistostromes of the Avalon zone, southeastern Massachusetts and Rhode Island. *Geological Society of America Abstracts with Programs,* **17** (7), 719.

—— MURRAY, D. P., PALMER, A. R., SMITH, A. T. & BELT, E. S. 1978. Significance of fossiliferous Middle Cambrian rocks of Rhode Island, to the history of Avalonian microcontinent. *Geology,* **6** (11), 694–8.

SKEVINGTON, D. 1968. British and North American Lower Ordovician correlation: discussion. *Geological Society of America Bulletin,* **79** (9), 1259–64.

SMITH, B. M. 1978. The geology and Rb–Sr whole-rock age of granite rock of Aquidneck and Conanicut Islands, Rhode Island. *M.Sc. Thesis,* Brown University, Providence, RI, 94 pp.

—— & GILETTI, B. J. 1978. Rb–Sr whole-rock study of the deformed prophyritic granitic rocks of Aquidneck and Conanicut Islands, Rhode Island. *Geological Society of America Abstracts with Programs,* **10** (2), 86.

SMITH, C. J. & HON, R. 1984. Geology, petrology, and origin of the Precambrian igneous rocks located in the area north of Boston. *In:* HANSON (ed.) *Geology of the Coastal Lowlands, Boston to Kennebunk Maine, New England Intercollegiate Geological Conference, 76th Annual Meeting,* pp. 292–309.

STANLEY, R. S. & RATCLIFFE, N. M. 1985. Tectonic synthesis of the Taconian orogeny in western New England. *Geological Society of America Bulletin,* **96,** 1227–50.

STEVENS, R. K. 1970. Cambro-Ordovician flysch sedimentation and tectonics in west Newfoundland

and their possible bearing on a Proto-Atlantic Ocean. *In:* LAJOIE, J. (ed.) *Flysch sedimentology in North America. Geological Association of Canada Special Paper No. 7,* pp. 165–77.

——, STRONG, D. F. & KEAN, B. F. 1974. Do some eastern Appalachian ultramafic rocks represent mantle diapirs produced above a subduction zone? *Geology,* **2,** 175–8.

STEWART, A. D. 1969. Torridonian rocks of Scotland reviewed. *In:* KAY, M. (ed.) *North Atlantic— Geology and Continental Drift. American Association of Petroleum Geologists Memoir No. 13,* 595–608.

—— 1975. 'Torridonian' rocks of western Scotland. *In:* HARRIS, A. L., SHACKLETON, R. M., WATSON, J., DOWNIE, C., HARLAND, W. B. & MOORBATH, S. (eds) *A Correlation of Precambrian Rocks in the British Isles. Special Publication of the Geological Society of London No. 6,* pp. 43–51.

STEWART, D. B. 1974. Precambrian rocks of Seven Hundred Acre Island and development of cleavage in the Isleboro Formation. *In:* OSBERG, P. H. (ed.) *Geology of East-central and North-central Maine, New England Intercollegiate Geological Conference, 66th Annual Meeting,* pp. 223–40.

STEWART, J. H. 1976. Late Precambrian evolution of North America, plate tectonics implications. *Geology,* **4,** 11–15.

STRONG, D. F. 1977. Volcanic regimes in the Newfoundland Appalachians. *In:* BARAGAR, W. R. A., COLEMAN, L. C. & HALL, J. M. (eds) *Volcanic Regimes in Canada, Geological Association of Canada Special Paper No. 16,* pp. 61–90.

—— 1979. Proterozoic tectonics of northwestern Gondwanaland, New evidence from eastern Newfoundland. *Tectonophysics,* **55,** 81–101.

—— & WILLIAMS, H. 1972. Early Paleozoic flood basalts of northwestern Newfoundland: their petrology and tectonic significance. *Proceedings of the Geological Association of Canada,* **24** (2), 43–52.

——, O'BRIEN, S. J., TAYLOR, S. W., STRONG, P. G. & WILTON, D. H. 1978. Aborted Proterozoic rifting in eastern Newfoundland. *Canadian Journal of Earth Sciences,* **15,** 117–31.

STUKAS, V. J. & REYNOLDS, P. R. 1976. $^{40}Ar/^{39}Ar$ dating of terrestrial materials: a review of recent studies with particular emphasis on plagioclase release patterns. *Geological Association of Canada— Mineralogical Association of Canada Annual Meeting, Abstracts with Programs,* p. 1.

STURT, B. A. & ROBERTS, D. 1978. Caledonides of northernmost Norway (Finnmark). *In:* TOZER, E. T. & SCHENK, P. E. (eds) *Caledonian–Appalachian Orogen of the North Atlantic Region. Geological Survey of Canada Paper No. 78–13,* pp. 17–24.

—— & THON, A. 1978. Caledonides of southern Norway. *In:* TOZER, E. T. & SCHENK, P. E. (eds) *Caledonian–Appalachian Orogen of the North Atlantic Region. Geological Survey of Canada Paper No. 78–13,* pp. 39–47.

——, PRINGLE, I. R. & RAMSAY, D. M. 1978. The Finnmarkian phase of the Caledonian orogeny. *Journal of the Geological Society, London,* **135** (6), 597–610.

SUTTER, J. F., MILTON, D. J. & KUNK, M. J. 1983.

^{40}Ar/^{39}Ar spectrum dating of gabbro plutons and surrounding rocks in the Charlotte belt of North Carolina. *Geological Society of America Abstracts with Programs,* **15**, 110.

SWETT, K. & SWIT, D. E. 1972. Paleogeography and depositional environments of the Cambro-Ordovician shallow-marine facies of the North Atlantic. *Geological Society of America Bulletin,* **83**, 3223–48.

THOMAS, P. R. 1979. New evidence for a Central Highland root zone. *In:* HARRIS, A. L., HOLLAND, C. H. & LEAKE, B. E. (eds) *The Caledonides of the British Isles Reviewed. Special Publication of the Geological Society of London No. 8,* pp. 205–11.

THOMPSON, J. B., JR 1972. Lower Paleozoic rocks flanking the Green Mountain anticlinorium. *In:* DOOLAN, B. S. & STANLEY, R. S. (eds) *Lower Paleozoic Rocks Flanking the Green Mountain Anticlinorium, New England Intercollegiate Geological Conference, 64th Annual Meeting,* pp. 215–29, University of Vermont, Burlington, VT.

THORPE, R. S. 1974. Geochemical evidence for the original nature of the Rosslare Complex, S.E. Eire. *Proceedings of the Royal Dublin Society,* **5A**, 199–206.

—— 1978. Tectonic emplacement of ophiolitic rocks in the Precambrian Mona Complex of Anglesey. *Nature, London,* **275**, 57–8.

—— 1979. Late Precambrian igneous activity in southern Britain. *In:* HARRIS, A. L., HOLLAND, C. H. & LEAKE, B. E. (eds) *The Caledonides of the British Isles Reviewed, Special Publication of the Geological Society of London No. 8,* pp. 579–85.

UNEO, H., IRVING, E. & McNUTT, R. H. 1975. Paleomagnetism of the Whitestone anorthosite and diorite, the Grenville polar track, and relative motions of the Laurentian and Baltic shields. *Canadian Journal of Earth Sciences,* **12**, 209–26.

VIDAL, P. 1977. Limitations isotopiques à l'âge et l'évolution de la croûte continentale en Europe moyenne et occidentale. *In: La Chaîne Varisique d'Europe Moyenne et Occidentale. Colloques Internationaux du Centre National de le Recherche Scientifique,* **243**, 129–41.

——, AVERY, B., CHAUVET, J. F. & COGNE, J. 1972. L'âge radiometrique de la diorite de Saint Quay Portrieux (Côtes du Nord): ses conséquences sur le Brioverien de la baie de St. Brieuc. *Comptes Rendus Hebdomadiares des Séances de l'Academie des Sciences,* **275**, 1323–6.

VOGT, TH. 1929. Den norske fjellkjedes revolusjonshistorie. *Norsk Geologisk Tidsskrift,* **10**, 97–115.

—— 1945. The geology of part of the Holanda-Horg district, a type area in the Trondheim region. *Norsk Geologisk Tidsskrift,* **25**, 449–528.

WARDLE, R. J. 1978. The stratigraphy and tectonics of the Greenhead Group: its relationship to Hadrynian and Paleozoic rocks, Southern New Brunswick. *Ph.D. Thesis,* University of New Brunswick, Fredericton, New Brunswick.

WATSON, J. & DUNNING, F. W. 1979. Basement–cover relations in the British Caledonides. *In:* HARRIS, A. L., HOLLAND, C. H. & LEAKE, B. E. (eds) *The Caledonides of the British Isles Reviewed. Special*

Publication of the Geological Society of London No. 8, pp. 67–91.

WHITNEY, J. A., PARIS, T. A., CARPENTER, R. H. & HARTLEY, M. E., III 1978. Volcanic evolution of the southern slate belt of Georgia and South Carolina: a primitive oceanic island arc. *Journal of Geology,* **86**, 173–92.

WILLIAMS, A. 1972. An Ordovician Whiterock Fauna in western Ireland. *Proceedings of the Royal Irish Academy, Section B,* 209–19.

WILLIAMS, H. 1975. Structural succession, nomenclature, and interpretation of transported rocks in western Newfoundland. *Canadian Journal of Earth Sciences,* **12**, 1874–94.

—— 1977. Ophiolitic melange and its significance in the Fleur de Lys Supergroup, northern Appalachians. *Canadian Journal of Earth Sciences,* **14**, 987–1003.

—— 1978. *Tectonic Lithofacies Map of the Appalachian Orogen, Map No. 1,* Memorial University of Newfoundland.

—— & HATCHER, R. D., JR. 1982. Suspect terranes and accretionary history of the Appalachian orogen. *Geology,* **10**, 530–6.

—— & —— 1983. Appalachian suspect terranes. *In:* HATCHER, R. D., JR, WILLIAMS, H. & ZIETZ, I. (eds) *Contributions to the Tectonics and Geophysics of Mountain Chains, Geological Society of America Memoir No. 158,* pp. 33–53.

—— & ST JULIEN, P. 1982. The Baie Verte–Brompton line in early Paleozoic continent–ocean interface in the Canadian Appalachians. *In:* ST JULIEN, P. & BELAND, J. (eds) *Major Structural Zones and Faults of the Northern Appalachians. Geological Association of Canada Special Paper, No. 24,* pp. 117–207.

—— & SMYTH, W. R. 1973. Metamorphic aureoles beneath ophiolite suites and Alpine peridotites: tectonic implications with west Newfoundland examples. *American Journal of Science,* **273**, 594–621.

—— & STEVENS, R. K. 1969. Geology of Belle Isle—northern extremity of the deformed Appalachian miogeosynclinal belt. *Canadian Journal of Earth Sciences,* **6**, 1145–57.

DE WIT, M. J. 1974. On the origin and deformation of the Fleur de Lys metaconglomerate, Appalachian fold belt, northwest Newfoundland. *Canadian Journal of Earth Sciences,* **11**, 1168–80.

WOOD, D. S. 1974. Ophiolites, melanges, blueschists, and ignimbrites: early Caledonian subduction in Wales? *In:* DOTT, R. H. & SHAVER, R. H. (eds) *Modern and Ancient Geosynclinal Sedimentation, Society of Economic Palaeontologists and Mineralogists Special Publication No. 19,* pp. 334–44.

WYNNE-EDWARDS, H. R. 1976. Proterozoic ensialic orogenesis: the millipede model of plate tectonics. *American Journal of Science,* **276**, 921–53.

YARDLEY, B. W. D., LEAKE, B. E. & FARROW, C. M. 1980. The metamorphism of Fe-rich pelites from Connemara, Ireland. *Journal of Petrology,* **21**, 365–99.

ZARTMAN, R. E. & NAYLOR, R. S. 1984. Structural implications of some radiometric ages of igneous rocks in southeastern New England. *Geological Society of America Bulletin,* **95**, 522–39.

ZEN, E-AN 1983. Exotic terranes in the New England Applachians: limits, candidates, and ages. A speculative essay. *In:* HATCHER, R. D., JR, WILLIAMS, H. & ZIETZ, I. (eds) *Contributions to the Tectonics and Geophysics of Mountain Chains. Geological Society of America Memoir No. 158*, 55–81.

ZIEGLER, A. M. 1970. Geosynclinal development of the British Isles during the Silurian period. *Journal of Geology,* **78**, 445–79.

ZIEGLER, P. A. 1984. Caledonian and Hercynian crustal consolidation of western and central Europe—a working hypothesis. *Geologie en Mijnbouw,* **63**, 93–108.

ZWART, H. J. & DORNSIEPEN, U. F. 1978. The tectonic framework of central and western Europe. *Geologie en Mijnbouw,* **57**, 627–54.

J. W. SKEHAN, SJ, Weston Observatory, Department of Geology and Geophysics, Boston College, Weston, MA 02193, USA.

Arenig–Wenlock activity in the Caledonian–Appalachian Orogen

CONVENOR
W. S. McKERROW
University of Oxford

Metamorphic activity in the ortho-tectonic zone of the British Isles relating to this period is included in the article by Ben Harte in the previous section.

Articles by Jack Soper and Jo Chaloupski dealing with regional tectonics in Britain and the Bohemian massif and which partly relate to this period appear in the next section.

Arenig to Llandovery faunal distributions in the Caledonides

R. A. Fortey & L. R. M. Cocks

SUMMARY: Faunal distributions in the Arenig to Llandovery period can be seen to be due to an interplay of the following factors: (i) the biofacies and community distributions on the shelves and slopes of continental margins; (ii) the distribution of former continental masses relative to palaeolatitude; (iii) the contemporary transgressive–regressive cycles which cause diachronous shifts of biofacies belts (with a major crisis at the Ordovician–Silurian boundary); (iv) differential dispersal methods and rates of the different invertebrate groups. The distribution of the common brachiopods, trilobites, graptolites and conodonts exemplify these various influences, and these distributions are considered from both the margins and the central areas of the Caledonides. Palaeogeography cannot be reliably reconstructed without due consideration of all these factors which give results which are relatively independent of structural studies.

In a previous discussion of the faunal evidence for continent and ocean distribution in the lower Palaeozoic of Britain (Cocks & Fortey 1982) we concentrated particularly on the evidence that could be adduced to recognize the former extent and latitudinal placing of the continents involved in the complex. We emphasized the importance of comparing appropriate shelf faunas in assessing geographical separations, and the recognition of marginal (slope, oceanic) biofacies in determining the sites of continent edges. Even so, we were able to give only a somewhat static perspective on the faunal distributions through the Ordovician and Silurian—a series of 'snapshots' at particular time intervals designed to reveal the palaeogeography rather than portray the faunal dynamics. The purpose of this paper is to discuss the controls on faunal distribution in the Caledonides from the Arenig to the Llandovery, introducing additional factors such as eustatic events which we specifically excluded from our earlier account. Sea level was probably higher in the Caradoc than at any other time in the Phanerozoic, but much lower level stands are known from other times in our period and the faunal distributions are best understood as the result of the interplay between the biofacies disposition on the former continental shelves and slopes and the siting of continental masses relative to palaeolatitude, both of which are constantly changed and overprinted by the effects of eustatic variations. The faunal changes that take place over this 70 Ma period can be explained by a combination of these historical factors, all of which are testable from independent observations from sedimentology or palaeomagnetics, and without the need for recourse to extraterrestrial catastrophes. In a paper of this length we cannot do justice to the variety of organisms nor to the varied and dispersed literature in which they are discussed,

but some of the more comprehensive relatively recent references are listed in Table 1, although that list does not give proper credit to the work of numerous palaeontologists of the 19th and early 20th centuries, many of whose collections and monographs are still in use. Our concern is to show how an understanding of the faunal distributions can be properly applied to structural or plate-tectonic studies as well as to elucidating the Caledonide faunal history.

Caledonide faunal distributions and facies belts

We have summarized elsewhere (Cocks & Fortey 1982) the faunal evidence which led us to postulate the existence of three distinct continents in the N Atlantic area in lower Ordovician time: America (without the eastern Appalachians to eastern Newfoundland but including NE Ireland, Scotland and a small part of western Norway and Spitsbergen), the Baltic area eastwards to the Urals; and Gondwana. We distinguished marginal facies round each cratonic area of these continents (Fig. 1). Our survey confirmed the faunal evidence for the well-known Iapetus Ocean, but also indicated the separation of Baltica from Gondwana in lower Ordovician times by what we termed Tornquist's Sea. Since deducing the presence of Tornquist's Sea on purely faunal grounds, we have been pleased to learn of other strong evidence for such a suture on structural and tectonic grounds (Anderton 1982, fig. 2, Watson 1984, p. 211) and also on the grounds of the distribution of the radiometric ages of deformation and plutonism under the more recent deposits of the North Sea and northern Europe. These ages are summarized by

From HARRIS, A. L. & FETTES, D. J. (eds), 1988, *The Caledonian–Appalachian Orogen,* Geological Society Special Publication No. 38, pp. 233–246.

TABLE 1. *Representative bibliography for Arenig to Llandovery faunal distributions**

	American craton	American margin	Baltic craton	Baltic margin	Gondwanan margin	Gondwanan craton
Llandovery	Johnson et al. 1981 McCracken & Barnes 1981	McKerrow & Cocks 1978 Cocks & Toghill 1973	Kaljo 1977 Worsley et al. 1983	Bjerreskov 1975 Tomczykowa & Tomczyk 1979	Hutt 1974–5 Ziegler et al. 1968	Ziegler et al. 1968 Harper 1973
Ashgill–Caradoc	Nowlan & Barnes 1981 Bergström 1983	Harper 1984 Williams 1962	Owen & Bruton 1980 Brenchley & Cocks 1982	Bergström & Nilsson 1974 Jaanusson & Bergström 1980	Ingham 1970–7	Havlíček 1977 Hammann 1983
Llandeilo–Llanvirn	Shaw & Fortey 1977 Whittington 1963	Ross & Ingham 1970 Walker et al. 1980	Rõõmusoks 1970 Viira 1974	Tomczykowa & Tomczyk 1970	Williams et al. 1981	Henry 1960 Destombes 1972
Arenig	Whittington & Hughes 1972 Fortey 1975	Cooper & Fortey 1982 Fortey 1974–80	Ulst et al. 1982 Tjernvik 1956	Poulsen 1965	Fortey & Owens 1978 „ „ 1987	Babin et al. 1982

Many of the references listed also deal with faunas outside the areas shown.

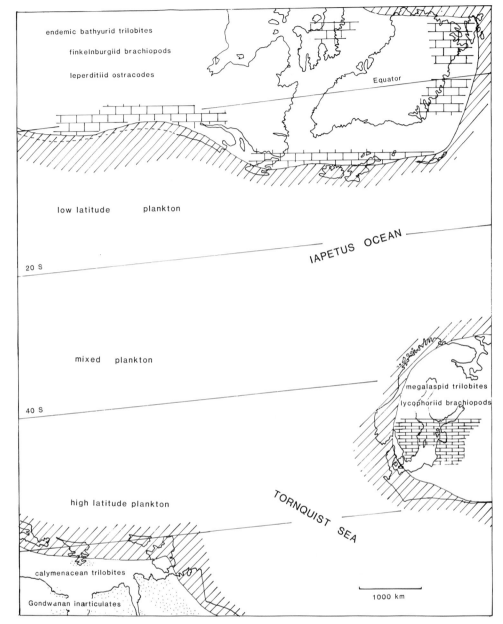

FIG. 1. Arenig distribution of faunas in relation to continents, facies and climatic belts: marginal facies belts are indicated by oblique lines (for clarity, 'suspect terranes' are not restored to their original position); large blocks, tropical shelf limestones and dolomites; small blocks, temperate carbonates; stipple, Grès Armoricain and associated lithologies. Some endemic taxa are indicated for shelf regions. (Adapted from Cocks & Fortey 1982, figs 2–4.)

Ziegler (1982, table 1 and Enclosure 1) and show a broad swathe of boreholes from NE of the Shetlands through the eastern North Sea into southern Denmark and N Germany whose ages range from 454 to 346 Ma, with most in the 435–415 Ma band, i.e. of Silurian age. This represents the aftermath of the closure of Tornquist's Sea, which became narrow enough for the faunal differences on its margins to merge by late Caradoc (Actonian) time and which must have

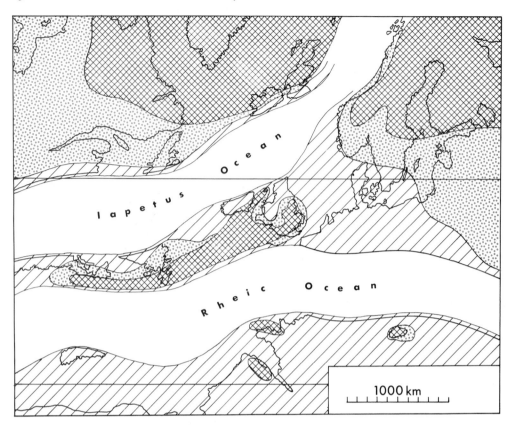

FIG. 2. Upper Llandovery distribution of faunas in relation to continents, facies and climatic belts: cross-hatched ornament, probable land; stipple, shallow-shelf seas with benthic fauna of brachiopods; diagonal shading, shelf sea too deep for benthic fauna; blank areas, deep oceans.

closed between SE Britain and the SW Baltic area in the early Ashgill to early Llandovery, with subsequent post-collision plutonism extending into the late Silurian. Ziegler (1982, p. 20) alludes to the possibility of the southern British (London–Brabant), Armorican, Moldanubian and Aquitaine–Iberian masses being separate microcontinents which rifted off the northern margin of Gondwana in Cambrian and early Ordovician times and which successively migrated northwards to accrete with Baltica. However, this interesting theory does not accord well with the widespread and probably continuous Armorican quartzite facies and the widespread *Neseuretus–Selenopeltis* shallow-shelf faunas over all these areas in Arenig time (Cocks & Fortey 1982, figs 2 and 3), and we prefer to think in terms of a single Gondwanan–Baltic collision event in late Ordovician time although the presence, for example, of probable late Proterozoic ophiolites in southern Brittany does not preclude the possibility that some of these smaller masses may

have accreted separately onto Gondwana in pre-Ordovician times. However, we accept mid-oceanic islands as important mid-oceanic faunal dispersal points (Neuman 1988).

After the Gondwanan–Baltic closure this combined continental mass continued to move towards America and the width of the intervening Iapetus Ocean steadily decreased. To what extent this closure was accompanied by large-scale strike-slip movements is uncertain, since such displacements would have been largely longitudinal and therefore less likely to have had a marked effect on the faunas. However, by the end of the Llandovery the two masses were close enough to have the same faunas on their facing margins (Fig. 2), apart from the ostracods and thelodont fish which dispersed relatively slowly. That America stayed relatively static and Gondwana moved towards it, rather than the other way round, is indicated by the steady increase in warmer-water faunas and sedimentary facies in the southern continent during the period, although that pattern has to be disentangled from the equally noticeable effects of the global variations in climate. Towards the end of the Llandovery, N America, Britain and the Baltic area on the one hand and southern Europe (Armorica, Iberia and Bohemia, representing northern Gondwana) on the other became separated by the Rheic Ocean, but the chief faunal and floral evidence for this separation comes from Wenlock and later times.

Factors affecting faunal distributions independent of palaeogeography

Dispersal

Independent factors influencing biogeography are superimposed upon the distributional constraints dictated by past and present continental positioning. Most important of these are the variable capacities of the different kinds of organisms for dispersal and the transgressive–regressive eustatic cycles which more or less regularly punctuated the Ordovician system. The influence of dispersal is the more difficult factor to assess since it varied not only between different classes of organisms but also *within* a group according to the life habits or habitat requirements of particular species. Thus it has been shown for the trilobites (Cook & Taylor 1975,

Fortey 1975, Ludvigsen 1982) that genera which inhabited deeper-water off-shelf sites have a much wider geographical distribution than shal-lower-water on-shore relatives, and individual species (e.g. *Hedinaspis regalis* in the late Cambrian or *Parabolinella* species in the early Ordovician) can be found off widely separated continents, even at different palaeolatitudes. However, inshore trilobites and brachiopods tend greatly towards endemicity. Even around the early Ordovician equatorial great circle, platform benthic trilobite faunas differed substantially between N America and Australia for example. In contrast, mid-continent conodont faunas and pelagic trilobites between these highly (longitu-dinally) separated areas were substantially the same. From such considerations it is possible to construct a subjective diagram (Fig. 3) showing the relative capacity of the main kinds of animals, divided by habitat and life habits, to disperse between continental plates. Forms with planktic or pelagic habits as adults, especially those in oceanic sites, lead the table; those with direct development without a dispersive larval phase are at the bottom. We might therefore expect provinciality in the restricted sense, referring to relatively shallow-water epeiric faunas, to be indicated from bottom to top of the table. Differences in dispersal patterns between cono-donts and trilobites account for the different ways in which the faunal 'provinces' of both groups are defined (Fortey & Barnes 1977). However,

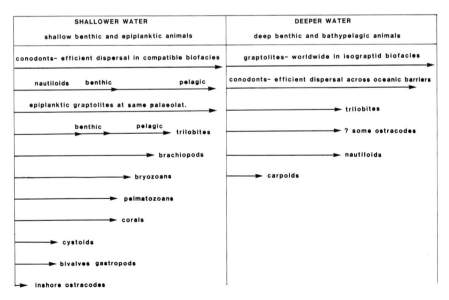

FIG. 3. Schematic representation of the assumed differential dispersal abilities of various kinds of marine animals common in Ordovician faunas. These have been divided into broad habitat types and by life habits. Shallow-water forms disperse at comparable latitudes only.

monographic treatment of some groups, such as ostracods and gastropods, is only now reaching the stage in the Ordovician where judgments about dispersal can begin to be made. It must be stressed that the whole distribution of any fossil group must be analysed separately; one or two genera with an apparently wider distribution than the main mass of the group should be treated with reserve, since exceptional migrations can sometimes occur.

Transgressive–regressive cycles

In the Ordovician and Silurian there were major eustatic oscillations, which in turn affected the major styles of sedimentation (Leggett *et al.* 1981) and had an important influence on the faunal distributions. These major cycles are distinguished from local phenomena by a number of criteria: most important, they should be provably contemporaneous on what were separate continental platforms (McKerrow 1979) so that, for example, when a regressive event affects the N China platform and the N American platform at exactly the same time it is appropriate to look for a global event. The cycles (Fig. 4) affect regional sedimentation in a consistent way so that, for example, a disconformity in a shelf region may correspond to a prograding clastic wedge in an adjacent basin. Only the extreme off-shelf sites will escape the effects of the eustatic events, usually in graptolitic facies; these should form the stratigraphic standard against which the occurrence of the eustatic events is timed. We have plotted elsewhere (Fortey & Cocks 1986) the variation seen between two areas of the Caledonides (N and S Wales) as compared with the worldwide sea-level curve, and hence identified which of the various local transgressions and regressions can be attributed to local orogeny rather than eustatic changes.

The regressive-transgressive event at the Cambrian–Ordovician boundary, at or near the base of the Tremadoc, has been much discussed recently because of the current interest in defining the base of the Ordovician. Most workers in this field would now accept the reality of this event, which was originally suggested by Miller (1976). Fortey (1984) reviewed transgressive–regressive episodes for the whole Ordovician, and the curve he described is compatible in most respects with that independently developed by Barnes (1984) for the earlier Ordovician around the Canadian shield.

Major eustatic events appear to be related to the boundaries between the Ordovician series. Indeed, they may explain why natural major

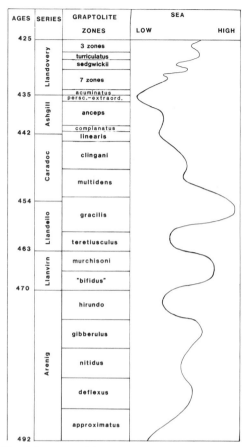

FIG. 4. Summary of the transgressive–regressive cycles which affected shelf seas in the Arenig–Llandovery.

divisions were originally recognized by the geologists of the last century. Short-lived, but extensive, regressions occurred at or near the base of the Arenig and at the top of that series, and again at the top of the Llanvirn, probably extending to the lower Llandeilo. The major regression at the top of the Ashgill associated with the contemporary glaciation is well known (e.g. Brenchley & Cocks 1982). Ensuing transgressions take up much of the Arenig, Llanvirn, Caradoc and Llandovery series.

Locally, of course, tectonic or volcanic circumstances often override the effects of the transgressive–regressive cycles. This applies particularly to mobile belts and to sites where subduction is active. In general, though, shore-lines about volcanic islands and microcontinents will be enlarged in times of regression as more land emerges, and the fossil record of such sites will be at its best just when those of platform regions are deficient since the shallow-platform marine seas will have retreated. This prediction is supported by the common occurrence of Caledonian 'island' brachiopod faunas in Maine, Newfoundland, the Trondheim district and other areas of western Norway (Neuman 1972, 1987, Bruton & Harper 1981) which are described as being of Arenig–Llanvirn or Llandeilo age. Even the recent evidence for a possible microcontinent in the Midland Valley of Scotland (Curry *et al.* 1982) is based on faunas dated as near the Cambrian–Ordovician boundary and the Tremadoc–Arenig boundary respectively.

The effect upon the faunas of these cycles can be briefly summarized as follows (Fig. 5).

1 Biofacies belts move in harmony with the transgressions and regressions. Regressions may restrict shelf biota sufficiently to produce extinction of some stenotopic taxa (Ludvigsen & Westrop 1983). Shelf-edge sites or islands may act as refuges and possibly the source of new taxa. However, the appearance of an apparently 'new' fauna in a given vertical section may be no more than the shift into the area of a particular biofacies accompanying transgression.

2 Transgressive phases spread epeiric habitats far across shallow shelves; if platform endemics evolve, it is at this stage. In the area under consideration we might mention the evolution of bathyurid trilobite endemics on the N American craton, asaphid and clitambonitacean endemics

over platform Baltoscandia and dalmanitacean trilobite and heterorthid brachiopod endemics in Gondwana during the Arenig and Llanvirn transgressive phases.

3 Transgressive phases also bring more oceanic biofacies shelfwards. For the late Llandeilo–early Caradoc transgression (*Nemagraptus gracilis* transgression) this is sufficient to extend such exterior biofacies widely over shelf regions, which is why the Caradoc transgression is considered much more profound than those which preceded it. Since the so-called breakdown of faunal provinces occurred at the same time, it is likely that part of this breakdown is simply the spread of more uniform deeper biofacies.

4 The siting of organic 'mounds'—algal bioherms in the early Ordovician and later reefs—is likely to be influenced by the cycles; bioherms were relatively rare and peripheral at regressive climaxes, as in the latest Ashgill, but occupied shelf sites at transgressive times (e.g. the 'Chazy' reefs of the eastern U.S.A.). Although diverse, 'reef' faunas are taxonomically conservative— some trilobite genera persist from the early Ordovician to the late Silurian, for example— which implies that throughout the period with which we are concerned there was never a time in which the reef environment was wholly eliminated.

5 Inter-continental faunal interchange proceeded in off-shelf biofacies, especially beneath

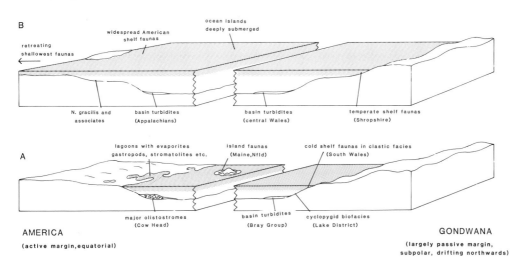

FIG. 5. The effects of transgressive–regressive cycles superimposed upon palaeogeography, shown here in a cartoon of opposing sides of Iapetus. The simplified shelf profile shown omits marginal basins and some suspect terranes. (A) Regression at the end of the Arenig restricts diverse biota to marginal areas, partly exposing shelves or causing hypersalinity or dolomite deposition, while islands tend to be emergent. (B) Transgression during the Llandeilo–Caradoc is most marked during the whole Arenig to Llandovery period; oceanic biofacies impinge widely on shelves with 'breakdown' of provincial faunas accompanying wide spread of *Nemagraptus gracilis* fauna; 'islands' are largely submerged.

the thermocline, even at times when shelf faunas may have been taxonomically distinct. Transgressive phases allow for shelfwards displacement of these forms, which may account for the 'sudden' appearance of, for example, Gondwanan trinucleid trilobites in America (Ross & Shaw 1972). Searching appropriate off-shelf biofacies during regressive phases may trace the earlier history of such apparently rapid changes.

Outline faunal history of the Caledonides

Combining the inferences about distribution of continental masses through the Arenig–Llandovery interval with the supposed eustatic changes and the differing responses of organisms leads to a broad picture of faunal dynamics in the Caledonian region. This broad view ignores local unconformities, which may be extensive in mobile belts such as that removing part of the Caradoc in the Bala area, North Wales. We maintain that it is the state of immersion or geographic position on the continental scale which determines the faunal patterns, even if regional tectonic events outside platform areas can lead to rapid environmental changes in the short term.

Arenig

The base of the Arenig is preceded by a regressive interval corresponding to some or all of the Lancefieldian-2 interval of the Australian graptolitic stratigraphic standard (Fortey 1984, p. 41). The transgressive basal Arenig graptolite zone of *Tetragraptus approximatus* is confined to relatively exterior sites; its equivalents are supposedly absent in Wales, but the discovery of a Lancefieldian graptolite in the Lake District (Rushton 1985) has increased the likelihood of the presence of *T. approximatus* age strata there in the appropriate exterior site. The early Arenig transgression is diachronous in parts of Sweden (Tjernvik 1956), as it probably is over the northern margin of Gondwana from Wales to Shropshire (Whittington *et al.* 1984, p. 20). Endemic speciation, especially of asaphid trilobites, accompanied the flooding of the Baltic platform during the Arenig, with deposits of temperate-limestone lithofacies, often glauconitic. Conversely, on the other side of Tornquist's Sea, limestone lithofacies are absent from the Gondwanan continent over much of which the Arenig transgression is represented by shallow-water clastic lithofacies of the Grès Armoricain type (Dean 1976). The

beginnings of endemic platformal dalmanitacean speciation are confined to Morocco at this time (Destombes 1972). Deeper-water facies are, however, present in Wales, where an upward-deepening succession records a sequence from inshore *Neseuretus* biofacies to oceanic cyclopygid biofacies. Comparable facies are also found in and off the southern edge of Baltica, on Bornholm for example, and it is only in such sites that the few common shelly taxa between Baltica and Gondwana occur. On the N American plate the Arenig transgression is represented by the appearance of a widespread endemic bathyurid/asaphid trilobite fauna, with such genera as *Punka, Petigurus, Bathyurina, Benthamaspis* and *Isoteloides* having individual species extending through Spitsbergen, Greenland, Vermont, Missouri and NW Scotland, always in identical shallow-water tropical limestone lithofacies. Arenig age marginal facies are distinctly rare in the periphery of the N American Caledonides, having been mostly overridden by marginal thrusts or metamorphosed, but remnants are found in the Deepkill section, New York State, Quebec, western Newfoundland (Cow Head), western Norway (as allochthonous slices) and northern Spitsbergen. International correlation is effected by a few cosmopolitan graptolites, in exterior facies only, and the deeper-water 'N Atlantic province' conodonts which do not extend into Gondwana. The Arenig shows well the interaction between geography and eustasy to produce the distinctive biological and lithological 'suites' which were originally recognized on the basis of trilobites by Whittington (1963) as the Bathyurid, Asaphid and Selenopeltis faunal provinces for N America, Baltica and Gondwana respectively.

The late Arenig regression affected platform regions during an interval embraced by the late Castlemainian and Yapeenian of the Australian graptolitic standard. It produces a widespread dolomitic interval over the N American craton in which shelly fossils are absent (Fortey 1980); this unfossiliferous interval is longer in the platform areas flanking the Caledonides than in the Basin Ranges in the W and hence may be overprinted by a tectonic event. Over Baltica a similar hiatus in extreme inshore areas is equated with the reappearance of a series of limestones between the lower and upper Didymograptus shales in the Oslo region. At the edge of Gondwana a comparable change in facies occurs at the top of the Arenig in Wales where a shelf-type trilobite fauna appears rather suddenly between deeper-water faunas with graptolites and cyclopygid biofacies trilobites. 'Island'-fringing faunas are particularly common at this time in Maine, Newfoundland, the Norwegian Caledonides, Ireland and possibly Anglesey.

Llanvirn–Llandeilo

The Llanvirn transgression repeats the pattern of the Arenig transgression. The Llanvirn was originally recognized by the apparently sudden appearance of 'tuning fork' *Didymograptus*, and the arrival of these forms over platform Baltica and Gondwana *does* afford a convenient way of dividing the Ordovician although it reflects the transgressive event rather than evolutionary novelty. These graptolites, and the dark-shale lithofacies that contains them, penetrate into interior platform areas (e.g. Saudi Arabia) where shallow-water facies had been the rule previously and, taken with the comparable on-shelf encroachment of marginal facies in N America, this tends to suggest that the Llanvirn transgression was of greater magnitude than the Arenig. In the Gondwanan Caledonides the Llanvirn transgression brings deep-water biofacies shelfwards into Shropshire, as into Bohemia, and the relative immersion of the Armorican–Iberian–Moroccan region stimulated the endemic radiation of dalmanitacean and calymenacean trilobites described by Destombes (1972), Henry (1960) and Hammann (1983). In Baltica, endemic asaphid trilobite speciation continued in Sweden, and particularly in Estonia, with the graptolitic facies widespread across more exterior sites. As far as the N American continent is concerned the Llanvirn transgression is equivalent to the Whiterock 'stage': it is highly diachronous in its local expression but is well displayed as a succession of upward-deepening lithofacies and biofacies in such sequences as the Table Head Formation, western Newfoundland (Whittington & Kindle 1963). The distribution around the N American craton of Whiterock type biofacies was recorded by Ross & Ingham (1970). It should be noted that the recently published correlation chart of the United States Ordovician (Ross *et al.* 1982) extends the Whiterock down to include the regressive part of the late Arenig. Shallow-water limestone trilobite faunas of Whiterock age are the continuation of the endemic bathyurid faunas of the Arenig. Thus, as a whole, the Llanvirn is a confirmation of the pattern noted in the Arenig, but in deeper-water facies there is already evidence of widespread genera suggesting at least some communication between both sides of Iapetus. For example, in the Hope Shales, Shropshire, the curious benthic trilobite *Seleneceme* occurs—as it does in off-shelf facies in both western Newfoundland and Quebec. Such evidence in the Llanvirn is not yet fully documented but does presage the wider interchange that was to come in the later Ordovician.

The Llandeilo is a relatively short interval compared with the other Ordovician series. In its type development it is surely a regressive interval *plus* part (but quite how much is unclear) of a transgressive interval (Wilcox & Lockley 1981), but because of the facies shifts involved the series has never been precisely defined. It probably included another worldwide regression event, but the correlation problems make this more difficult to prove. Island faunas in the mobile belt of Newfoundland belong here, e.g. the Cobbs Arm limestone, and in platform sequences Llandeilo formations often appear with regressive bases. What is clear is that the late Llandeilo to early Caradoc is a huge transgressive event—the most considerable in the Ordovician. The effects of this transgression are to displace deeper-water facies shelfwards, and the displacement is such as to introduce faunas which have previously occupied off-shelf habitats into shelf regions. This includes, of course, the *Nemagraptus gracilis* graptolite faunas, long recognized as one of those rare horizons where international correlation is apparently without problems, although the *Nemagraptus gracilis* zone was not short. Earlier occurrences of *Nemagraptus*-type graptolite faunas, termed the isograptid biofacies by Fortey (1984), are all in more exterior sites; their shelfward movement is somewhat diachronous, accompanying the encroachment of the appropriate oceanic conditions over N America. It comes as little surprise that the same event is accompanied by a partial breakdown in 'provinces'; for example, this is one of the few lower Palaeozoic occasions when ostracode genera cross the Iapetus (Schallreuter & Siveter 1985), as do the platform conodonts—'North Atlantic Province platform taxa invaded parts of the Mid-Continent Province' (Bergström 1983). Deeper-water trilobites such as *Cryptolithus* and *Flexicalymene* also appear with apparent suddenness at this time over areas which were previously platform, e.g. New York.

Caradoc–Ashgill

Although the Caradoc–Ashgill interval is nearly 20 Ma long, its detailed sea-level fluctuations are less apparent than the periods before or after it, perhaps because they are dwarfed by the very large *gracilis* zone transgression at its base which is known worldwide from rocks of this age. Encroachments occurred onto every landmass, including the type Caradoc area in Shropshire itself, while the Llandeilo–Caradoc boundary is difficult to correlate accurately since it falls within the *gracilis* zone. This transgression played an important part in the transfer and movement of some benthic genera as outlined above (and down to sub-specific level in a few cases, e.g. *Nicolella actoniae actoniae* (Harper 1984)). Nevertheless the basic faunal provinces in the Caledonide area of Baltica, America and N Gondwana did not break down until later. In the case of the Baltic and N Gondwana provinces a substantial transfer of genera across the remnant Tornquist's Sea was under way near the end of Caradoc (Actonian) time, and this transfer continued steadily so that by the mid-Ashgill (Rawtheyan) these two provinces cannot usefully be separated. We assume that the sea-level high at the end of the *gracilis* zone was not maintained since the Gondwanan–American interchange of genera did not persist for long, and most late Caradoc and early to middle Ashgill genera show subsequent endemic speciation in the two areas (e.g. Williams 1973). This situation continued until almost the end of the Ashgill when most of the shallow-water Richmondian brachiopods and trilobites of America are different from their Rawtheyan contemporaries in the Anglo-Baltic area even though many of the sedimentary facies, which included large bioherms with all their attendant diversity of faunas, are similar on both sides of the Iapetus Ocean. Caradoc tectonic activity in N Wales was sufficiently intensive to obliterate the effects of the transgression locally (Fortey & Cocks 1986), but deeper-water conditions, represented by the condensed Nod Glas deposits (Cave 1965), were quickly re-established. These local variations in topography are also reflected in the distribution of the subsequent lower Ashgill trilobite communities (Price & Magor 1984).

At the end of the Ashgill came the greatest regression of our period, which coincided with and was at least partly caused by the contemporary glaciation whose sedimentary traces are so well seen in Africa and elsewhere. This is naturally represented by an unconformity in most sections between the Ashgill and the subsequent Silurian transgressive sediments, but where there is no sedimentary break, e.g. in the Oslo–Asker region, Norway, it is possible to chart a regressive sequence of benthic assemblages representing deeper-shelf to shore-face communities (Brenchley & Cocks 1982) with a subsequent transgression and deeper assemblages in the earliest Llandovery. The latest Ashgill *Hirnantia* fauna is very widespread and is to be found on the border of America, e.g. in Percé (Lespérance & Sheehan 1976) and Anticosti Island, Canada (Cocks & Copper 1981), as well as over most of the Anglo-Baltic area and into Bohemia and N Africa (Rong 1984). It is noteworthy that the ancestors of most of the constituent trilobites and brachiopods of the *Hirnantia* fauna have their ancestors in peri-Gondwanan cooler-water faunas in the earlier Ordovician, and their widespread invasion of hitherto warmer areas in late Ashgill times probably represents a worldwide lowering of temperature including areas far removed from the extensive polar ice caps.

Llandovery

The whole Caledonide area was essentially a single faunal province by this time, which makes direct comparisons much easier over the region, and therefore there is no endemism, apart from the ostracodes, even in the regressive phases. Partly because the graptolite zonation has been so finely divided for so many years, more is known about regressions and transgressions in the Llandovery than in any other period in the Palaeozoic. The general trend is of steady transgression through the 10 Ma period which started from the eustatic low point of the end-Ordovician glaciation. However, by tracing the shifting patterns of the depth-related benthic communities, initially in the Welsh Borderland (Ziegler *et al.* 1968), a more complicated pattern of worldwide sea-level fluctuations has emerged. By analysing these patterns from various continents (McKerrow 1979, Johnson *et al.* 1981) it has been possible to separate the effects of local perturbations from global eustatic events, and three distinct phases of transgressions can be recognized with maximum flooding of shelves and continental margins in the *cyphus*, the start of the *sedgwickii* and the *turriculatus* zones, corresponding to A_4, C_1 and C_5 times in the former zonation from the type Llandovery area. There is no evidence of separate island faunas in Llandovery time, although some of the fossils have been found in very unstable tectonic situations, particularly those on the NW margin of the Iapetus Ocean which appears to have been the active margin from at least Llanvirn times onwards into the mid-Silurian. Such faunas come from places like Girvan, Scotland (Cocks & Toghill 1973) and the central mobile belt of Newfoundland (McKerrow & Cocks 1978), where the typical Llandovery shelf faunas such as the *Stricklandia* community are accompanied by huge clastic piles of sediment including olistostromes and paraconglomerates. In contrast, the SE margin of the Iapetus was characterized by quieter sedimentation, although thick turbidites with occasional graptolite-bearing thinner beds filled some marginal basins such as that of N Wales.

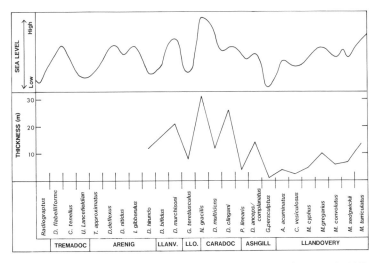

FIG. 6. Sedimentation rates in pelagic environments (from Churkin *et al.* 1977, Carter *et al.* 1980) as measured by the thickness of standard graptolite zones. We also show our eustatic curve, as in Fig. 4, to demonstrate their close correlation. Zones here have been drafted to equal thickness, following Churkin *et al.*

Arenig–Llandovery deep-ocean sedimentation rates—constant or fluctuating?

Presumed constant rates of accumulation of oceanic graptolite shales during the Arenig–Llandovery have been used as a method for subdividing the absolute time-scale (Churkin *et al.* 1977, Odin 1982) and for estimating rates of evolution (Carter *et al.* 1980). The charts published showed the relative thicknesses of pelagic sediments accumulated during the standard graptolite zones: the thicker zones were also assumed to be the longer.

An alternative view is possible. There is an obvious coincidence between the 'thickness' curve and the eustatic curve which is deduced from independent evidence. Figure 6 shows the two together: the thickness curve is taken directly from Churkin *et al.* (1977), with graptolite zones portrayed as having equal duration. The thicker graptolite zones apparently coincide with transgressive intervals and the thinner ones with regressive intervals on the platform. Even allowing for the relatively poor thickness data for the Ordovician (Churkin *et al.* 1977, p. 455) the coincidence is remarkable. Where the thickness data are best—for the Llandovery—the correspondence is especially striking. The minimum of the *persculptus* zone coincides with the maximum glacial eustatic regression. Increasing thicknesses from the *acuminatus* to the *gregarius* zones

correspond to widespread transgressions discussed above, and each subsequent dip and rise in thickness equates exactly with the sea-level curve. A minimum thickness in the *sedgwickii* zone is particularly interesting. This *does* correspond to a regression, but the fact that shelly-fossil evolution during the same interval is sufficient to encompass the origin of two full species of the slowly-evolving brachiopod *Eocoelia* suggests that this zone is certainly the match in duration of any other Llandovery zone.

The thickness data apply only to sediments accumulating in oceanic sites. We presume that in peri-continental environments regressive phases may be relatively thick (prograding clastic wedges, increased frequency of olistostromes). However, when Churkin *et al.* (1977) remark that the thicker zones 'such as *Nemagraptus gracilis* ... are the zones most commonly found' this is scarcely surprising because that zone is transgressive almost everywhere. Conversely, regressive zones, of which Churkin *et al.* (1977) cite the *G. teretiusculus* zone, will be of sporadic and peripheral distribution.

It is still something of a problem to explain the relative thickness of transgressive zones. It is possible that transgressive phases allowed for extensive redeposition into the deep ocean basins of finer sediments, which are the products of sub-aerial weathering during the regressive phases.

ACKNOWLEDGMENT: We are very grateful to Dr A. W. A. Rushton for comments on the first draft of this paper.

References

ANDERTON, R. 1982. Dalradian deposition and the late Precambrian–Cambrian history of the N Atlantic region: a review of the early evolution of the Iapetus Ocean. *Journal of the Geological Society, London*, **139**, 421–31.

BABIN, C., COURTESSOLE, R., MELOU, M., PILLET, M., VIZCAINO, D. & YOCHELSON, E. L. 1982. Brachiopodes (articulés) et mollusques (bivalves, rostroconches, monoplacophores, gastropodes) de l'Ordovicien inférieur (Tremadocien–Arenigien) de la Montagne Noire (France meridionale). *Mémoire de la Societé d'Études Scientifiques de l'Aude*, pp. 1–63, plates 1–15.

BARNES, C. R. 1984. Early Ordovician eustatic events in Canada. *In*: BRUTON, D. L. (ed.) *Aspects of the Ordovician System*, pp. 51–64, Universitetsforlaget, Oslo.

BERGSTRÖM, S. M. 1983. Biogeography, evolutionary relationships, and biostratigraphic significance of Ordovician platform conodonts. *Fossils and Strata*, **15**, 35–58.

—— & NILSSON, R. 1974. Age and correlation of the Middle Ordovician bentonites on Bornholm. *Meddelelserfra Dansk Geologisk Forening*, **23**, 27–48.

BJERRESKOV, M. 1975. Llandoverian and Wenlockian graptolites from Bornholm. *Fossils and Strata*, **8**, 1–93, plates 1–13.

BRENCHLEY, P. J. & COCKS, L. R. M. 1982. Ecological associations in a regressive sequence: the latest Ordovician of the Oslo–Asker district, Norway. *Palaeontology*, **25**, 783–815, plates 85, 86.

BRUTON, D. L. & HARPER, D. A. T. 1981. Brachiopods and trilobites of the early Ordovician serpentine Otta Conglomerate, south central Norway. *Norsk Geologisk Tidsskrift*, **61**, 153–81, plates 1–5.

CARTER, C., TREXLER, J. H. & CHURKIN, M. 1980. Dating of graptolite zones by sedimentation rates: implications for rates of evolution. *Lethaia*, **13**, 279–87.

CAVE, R. 1965. The Nod Glas sediments of Caradoc age in North Wales. *Geological Journal*, **4**, 279–98, plate 12.

CHURKIN, M., CARTER, C. & JOHNSON, B. R. 1977. Subdivision of Ordovician and Silurian time scale using accumulation rates of graptolitic shale. *Geology*, **5** (8), 452–5.

COCKS, L. R. M. & COPPER, P. 1981. The Ordovician–Silurian boundary at the eastern end of Anticosti Island. *Canadian Journal of Earth Sciences*, **18**, 1029–34.

—— & FORTEY, R. A. 1982. Faunal evidence for oceanic separations in the Palaeozoic of Britain. *Journal of the Geological Society, London*, **139**, 465–78.

—— & TOGHILL, P. 1973. The biostratigraphy of the Silurian rocks of the Girvan District, Scotland. *Journal of the Geological Society, London*, **129**, 209–43, plates 1–3.

COOK, H. E. & TAYLOR, M. E. 1975. Early Paleozoic continental margin sedimentation, trilobite biofacies, and the thermocline. *Geology*, **3**, 559–62.

COOPER, R. A. & FORTEY, R. A. 1982. The Ordovician graptolites of Spitsbergen. *Bulletin of the British Museum (Natural History), Geology*, **36**, 157–302, plates 1–6.

CURRY, G. B., INGHAM, J. K., BLUCK, B. J. & WILLIAMS, A. 1982. The significance of a reliable Ordovician age for some Highland Border rocks in central Scotland. *Journal of the Geological Society, London*, **139**, 453–6.

DEAN, W. T. 1976. Some aspects of Ordovician correlation and trilobite distribution in the Canadian Appalachians. *In*: BASSETT, M. G. (ed.) *The Ordovician System*, pp. 227–50, University of Wales Press and National Museum of Wales, Cardiff.

DESTOMBES, J. 1972. Les trilobites au sous-ordre des Phacopina de l'Ordovicien de l'Anti-Atlas (Maroc). *Notes et Mémoires du Service Mines Carte Géologique de Maroc*, **240**, 1–78, plates 1–16.

FORTEY, R. A. 1974–80. The Ordovician trilobites of Spitsbergen. *Skrifter Norsk Polarinstitutt*, **160**, 1–129, plates 1–24; **162**, 1–207, plates 1–41; **171**, 1–163, plates 1–25.

—— 1975. Early Ordovician trilobite communities. *Fossils and Strata*, **4**, 331–52.

—— 1980. The Ordovician of Spitsbergen, and its relevance to the base of the Middle Ordovician in North America. *In*: WONES, D. R. (ed.) *The Caledonides in the USA: Proceedings of the International Geological Correlation Program—Caledonide Orogen Project 27, Blacksburg, VA. Department of Geological Sciences, Virginia Polytechnic Institute and State University, Memoir No. 2*, pp. 33–40.

—— 1984. Global earlier Ordovician transgressions and regressions and their biological implications. *In*: BRUTON, D. L. (ed.) *Aspects of the Ordovician System*, pp. 37–50, Universitetsforlaget, Oslo.

—— & BARNES, C. R. 1977. Early Ordovician conodont and trilobite communities of Spitsbergen: influence on biogeography. *Alcheringa*, **1**, 207–309.

—— & COCKS, L. R. M. 1986. Marginal faunal belts and their structural implications, with examples from the Lower Palaeozoic. *Journal of the Geological Society, London*, **143**, 151–60.

—— & OWENS, R. M. 1978. Early Ordovician (Arenig) stratigraphy and faunas of the Carmarthen District, south-west Wales. *Bulletin of the British Museum (Natural History), Geology*, **30**, 225–94, 11 plates.

—— & —— 1987. The Arenig Series in south Wales. *Bulletin of the British Museum (Natural History), Geology*, **41**, 68–303.

HAMMANN, W. 1983. Calymenacea (Trilobita) aus dem Ordovizium von Spanien; ihre Biostratigraphie, Ökologie und Systematik. *Abhandlungen der Senckenbergischen Naturforschenden Gesellschaft*, **542**, 1–177.

HARPER, C. W. 1973. Brachiopods of the Arisaig Group (Silurian–Lower Devonian) of Nova Scotia. *Bulletin of the Geological Survey of Canada*, **215**, 1–163, plates 1–28.

HARPER, D. A. T. 1984. Brachiopods from the Upper Ardmillan Succession (Ordovician) of the Girvan

District, Scotland. *Palaeontographical Society Monograph*, pp. 1–78, plates 1–11.

HAVLÍČEK, V. 1977. Brachiopods of the order Orthida in Czechoslovakia. *Rozpravy Ústředniho Ústavu Geologického*, **44**, 1–327, plates 1–56.

HENRY, J.-L. 1960. Trilobites ordoviciens du Massif Armoricain. *Mémoires de la Société Géologique et Minéralogique de Bretagne*, **22**, 1–250, plates 1–48.

HUTT, J. E. 1974–5. The Llandovery Graptolites of the English Lake District. *Palaeontographical Society Monograph*, pp. 1–137, plates 1–26.

INGHAM, J. K. 1970–7. The Upper Ordovician Trilobites from the Cantley and Dent Districts of Westmorland and Yorkshire. *Palaeontographical Society Monograph*, pp. 1–121, plates 1–27.

JAANUSSON, V. & BERGSTRÖM, S. M. 1980. Middle Ordovician faunal spatial differentiation in Baltoscandia and the Appalachians. *Alcheringa*, **4**, 89–110.

JOHNSON, M. E., COCKS, L. R. M. & COPPER, P. 1981. Late Ordovician–early Silurian fluctuations in sea level from eastern Anticosti Island, Quebec. *Lethaia*, **14**, 73–82.

KALJO, D. (ed.) 1977. *Facies and fauna of the Baltic Silurian*, Academy of Sciences of the Estonian SSR, Tallinn, 286 pp.

LEGGETT, J. K., McKERROW, W. S., COCKS, L. R. M. & RICKARDS, R. B. 1981. Periodicity in the early Palaeozoic marine realm. *Journal of the Geological Society of London*, **138**, 167–76.

LESPÉRANCE, P. J. & SHEEHAN, P. M. 1976. Brachiopods from the Hirnantian Stage (Ordovician–Silurian) at Percé, Quebec. *Palaeontology*, **19**, 719–731, plates 109–110.

LUDVIGSEN, R. 1982. Upper Cambrian and Lower Ordovician trilobite biostratigraphy of the Rabbitkettle Formation, western District of Mackenzie. *Life Science Contributions of the Royal Ont. Museum*, **134**, 1–187.

—— & WESTROP, S. R. 1983. Trilobite biofacies in the Cambrian–Ordovician boundary interval of northern North America. *Alcheringa*, **7**, 301–20.

McCRACKEN, A. D. & BARNES, C. R. 1981. Conodont biostratigraphy and paleoecology of the Ellis Bay Formation, Anticosti Island, Quebec, with special reference to late Ordovician–early Silurian chronostratigraphy and the systematic boundary. *Bulletin of the Geological Survey of Canada* **329**, 51–134, plates 1–7.

McKERROW, W. S. 1979. Ordovician and Silurian changes in sea level. *Journal of the Geological Society of London*, **136**, 137–45.

—— & COCKS, L. R. M. 1978. A Lower Paleozoic Trench fill sequence, New World Island, Newfoundland. *Bulletin of the Geological Society of America*, **89**, 1121–32.

MILLER, J. F. 1976. Conodont biostratigraphy and international correlations across the Cambrian–Ordovician boundary. *Abstracts of the 25th International Geological Congress*, **1**, 274.

NEUMAN, R. B. 1972. Brachiopods of Early Ordovician volcanic islands. *International Geological Congress*, section 7, 297–302.

—— 1988. Palaeontological evidence bearing on the Arenig–Caradoc development of the Iapetus Ocean basin. *This volume*.

NOWLAN, G. S. & BARNES, C. R. 1981. Late Ordovician conodonts from the Vauréal Formation, Anticosti Island, Quebec. *Bulletin of the Geological Survey of Canada*, **329**, 1–50, plates 1–8.

ODIN, G. S. (ed.) 1982. *Numerical Dating in Stratigraphy*. Wiley, Chichester, 1040 pp.

OWEN, A. W. & BRUTON, D. L. 1980. Late Caradoc-early Ashgill trilobites of the central Oslo Region, Norway. *Palaeontological Contributions of the University of Oslo No. 245*, pp. 1–64, plates 1–10.

POULSEN, V. 1965. An early Ordovician trilobite fauna from Bornholm. *Meddelelserfra Dansk Geologisk Forening*, **16**, 49–113, plates 1–9.

PRICE, D. & MAGOR, P. M. 1984. The ecological significance of variation in the generic composition of Rawtheyan (late Ordovician) trilobite faunas from North Wales, U.K. *Geological Journal*, **19**, 187–200.

RONG, J.-Y. 1984. Distribution of the *Hirnantia* fauna and its meaning. *Palaeontological Contributions of the University of Oslo No. 295*, pp. 101–12.

RÕÕMUSOKS, A. 1970. *Stratigraphy of the Viruan Series (Middle Ordovician) in Northern Estonia*, Vagus, Tallinn, 346 pp.

ROSS, R. J. & INGHAM, J. K. 1970. Distribution of the Toquima–Table Head (middle Ordovician Whiterock) faunal realm in the northern hemisphere. *Geological Society of America Bulletin*, **81**, 393–408.

—— & SHAW, F. C. 1972. Distribution of the Middle Ordovician Copenhagen Formation and its trilobites in Nevada. *United States Geological Survey Professional Paper No. 749*, pp. 1–33, 8 plates.

—— et al. 1982. The Ordovician System in the United States. *International Union of Geological Sciences Publication No. 12*, pp. 1–73.

RUSHTON, A. W. A. 1985. A Lancefieldian graptolite from the Lake District. *Geological Magazine*, **122**, 329–33.

SCHALLREUTER, R. E. L. & SIVETER, D. J. 1985. Ostracodes across the Iapetus Ocean. *Palaeontology*, **28**, 577–98, plates 68–70.

SHAW, F. C. & FORTEY, R. A. 1977. Middle Ordovician facies and trilobite faunas in North America. *Geological Magazine*, **114**, 409–43.

TJERNVIK, T. E. 1956. On the early Ordovician of Sweden: stratigraphy and fauna. *Bulletin of the Geological Institution, University of Uppsala*, **36**, 107–284, 11 plates.

TOMCZYKOWA, E. & TOMCZYK, H. 1970. The Ordovician. *Geology of Poland*, Vol. 1, *Stratigraphy*, Part 1, *Pre-Cambrian and Palaeozoic*, pp. 177–236, Wydawnictwa Geologiczne, Warsaw.

—— & —— 1979. Stratigraphy of the Polish Silurian and Lower Devonian and development of the Proto-Tethys. *Acta Palaeontologica Polonica*, **24**, 165–83.

ULST, R. Z., GAILITE, L. K. & YAKOVLEVA, V. I. 1982. *The Ordovician of Latvia*, pp. 1–294, plates 1–8, Zinatne Riga.

VIIRA, V. 1974. *Ordovician Conodonts of the East Baltic*, pp. 1–142, Valgus, Tallinn.

WALKER, K. R., BROADHEAD, T. W. & KELLER, F. B. 1980. Middle Ordovician carbonate shelf to deepwater basin deposition in the southern Appalachians. *University of Tennessee Department of Geological Science Studies in Geology*, **4**, 1–120.

WATSON, J. 1984. The ending of the Caledonian orogeny in Scotland. *Journal of the Geological Society, London*, **141**, 193–214.

WHITTINGTON, H. B. 1963. Middle Ordovician trilobites from Lower Head, western Newfoundland. *Bulletin of the Museum of Comparative Zoology, Harvard University*, **129**, 1–118, 36 plates.

—— & HUGHES, C. P. 1972. Ordovician geography and faunal provinces deduced from trilobite distribution. *Philosophical Transactions of the Royal Society of London, Series B*, **263**, 235–78.

—— & KINDLE, C. H. 1963. Middle Ordovician Table Head Formation, western Newfoundland. *Geological Society of America Bulletin*, **74**, 745–58.

——, DEAN, W. T., FORTEY, R. A., RICKARDS, R. B., RUSHTON, A. W. A. & WRIGHT, A. D. 1984. Definition of the Tremadoc series and the series of the Ordovician System in Britain. *Geological Magazine*, **121**, 17–33.

WILCOX, C. J. & LOCKLEY, M. G. 1981. A re-assessment of facies and faunas in the type Llandeilo (Ordo-vician) Wales. *Palaeogeography, Palaeoclimatology, Palaeoecology*, **34**, 285–314.

WILLIAMS, A. 1962. The Barr and Lower Ardmillan Series (Caradoc) of the Girvan District, southwest Ayrshire, with descriptions of the Brachiopoda. *Memoirs of the Geological Society of London*, **3**, 1–267, plates 1–25.

—— 1973. Distribution of brachiopod assemblages in relation to Ordovician palaeogeography. *Palaeontological Association Special Papers in Palaeontology No. 12*, pp. 241–69.

——, LOCKLEY, M. G. & HURST, J. M. 1981. Benthic palaeocommunities represented in the Ffairfach group and coeval Ordovician successions of Wales. *Palaeontology*, **24**, 661–94.

WORSLEY, D., AARHUS, N., BASSETT, M. G., HOWE, M. P. A., MØRK, A. & OLAUSSEN, S. 1983. The Silurian succession of the Oslo Region. *Norges Geologiske Undersøkelse*, **384**, 1–57.

ZIEGLER, A. M., COCKS, L. R. M. & MCKERROW, W. S. 1968. The Llandovery transgression of the Welsh Borderland. *Palaeontology*, **11**, 736–82.

ZIEGLER, P. A. 1982. *Geological Atlas of Western and Central Europe*, Shell Internationale, The Hague, 130 pp., 40 enclosures.

R. A. FORTEY & L. R. M. COCKS, Department of Palaeontology, British Museum (Natural History), Cromwell Road, London SW7 5BD, UK.

Arenig–Llandovery stratigraphy and faunas across the Scandinavian Caledonides

David L. Bruton & David A. T. Harper

SUMMARY: The nature and development of Arenig–Llandovery sedimentary environments is reviewed with reference to 18 allochthonous–parautochthonous sections in the Scandinavian Caledonides. The faunas suggest that age constraints are imprecise, and direct correlations with sequences on the adjacent platform are difficult. However, it is possible to recognize a northerly transition from near-shore to offshore facies on Hardangervidda and a platform to slope transition in Jämtland and E Jotunheimen during the early Ordovician. There is no direct evidence of a distinct Finnmarkian orogenic event (late Cambrian–early Ordovician) in the lower Allochthon, while the central Scandinavian upper Allochthon, containing N American shelly fossils, has a pre-Caradoc history far removed from that of the Baltic platform. In the Bergen area no fossils older than Ashgill age are known and the youngest marine rocks are early Llandovery. Locally-important features of the platform sequences, including breaks in sedimentation, the deposition of bentonites, basement faulting and the early termination of marine sedimentation (late Llandovery in the N and W), cannot be directly related to discrete tectonic events in the orogen.

Lithologically diverse rocks of proven Arenig–Llandovery age are well developed within the autochthonous–parautochthonous platform successions of the Baltic craton and occur sporadically throughout the lower and upper Allochthons of the Scandinavian Caledonides. Both the platform and allochthonous sequences occur in a wide variety of geological settings reflecting the concurrent evolution of the Caledonian orogen in Scandinavia. Although there is adequate and often precise faunal control within the platform and a number of adjacent successions, fossil information is sparse throughout much of the Allochthon where thick sedimentary sequences lack adequate age constraints. Nevertheless, many published studies include ostensibly-precise correlations of such sequences with the standard systems principally on the basis of regional correlations of lithological facies and events. Such an assumption of synchronous facies and tectonic development is unsound because 'diachronism of orogenic deformation is indeed the hallmark of the Caledonian mountain belt' (Roberts 1983, p. 90).

There have been a number of attempts to relate events occurring within the evolving mountain belt to those manifest on the adjacent platforms, e.g. Vogt (1928, 1945), Størmer (1967), Gee (1975a) and more recently Bruton et al. (1985). Although the earlier studies, particularly that of Størmer (1967), are conceptually important, imprecise correlations have invalidated many of their conclusions.

In this paper we illustrate and discuss 18 of the better-known successions from the mountain belt containing rocks of Arenig–Llandovery age.

Lithological and faunal data for these sections are presented graphically. These data provide constraints on the nature and timing of orogenic activity, the origin and history of individual thrust sheets and the depositional environment of their constituent sedimentary facies.

The Autochthon

Arenig–Llandovery rocks and successions of the Autochthon have been documented in a number of recent summary articles (Poulsen 1966, Bruton & Williams 1982, Jaanusson & Mutvei 1982, Worsley et al. 1983, Bruton et al. 1985). In marked contrast with coeval sequences within the upper Allochthon there are no major angular unconformities or thick conglomerates and, with the exception of bentonite horizons, volcanic and volcaniclastic rocks are absent. Sequences vary in thickness from less than 250 m in the E of the Baltoscandian area to at least 1500 m to the W in the Oslo region where siliciclastic sediments are locally developed and where basement faulting has played a major part in the rate and mode of sedimentation. The Swedish and E Baltic Ordovician successions are generally thin and characterized by distinctive limestones and marls which were deposited relatively slowly in well-defined confacies belts with fairly constant lithofacies and biofacies types (Jaanusson 1976, Jaanusson & Bergström 1980). In the Oslo region lateral and vertical facies changes are more marked, reflecting a pronounced basement topography and syndepositional fault movement (Bockelie 1978).

From HARRIS, A. L. & FETTES, D. J. (eds), 1988, *The Caledonian–Appalachian Orogen,*
Geological Society Special Publication No. 38, pp. 247–268.

Nevertheless, a more limited set of confacies belts has been recognized across the various districts of the region (Størmer 1967, Bockelie 1978). The successions within the Oslo region are dominated by limestones and mudstones with sandstones best developed at and towards the top of the Ordovician.

Throughout the interval, deposition of the platform sequences was governed by sediment input from two sources. A carbonate source in the E developed at the margins of an area of low relief where terrigenous input was slight, whilst in the W the greater influx of siliciclastic sediments has been ascribed to sources within the rising Caledonides (Jaanusson 1973). The successions thus reflect periods of sediment competition and asymmetry of deposition (Jaanusson 1973, 1984).

The effects of both global and more local events, the latter most probably related to processes within the developing Caledonides, are evident in the platform sequences. The dominant features of the Arenig–Llandovery stratigraphy of the platform are discussed and summarized in Fig. 11 together with recognizable broadly-contemporaneous events in the fold belt.

A number of global and transgressive and regressive events are documented within the sequences on the Baltoscandian platform. Black shales containing graptolites occur at the base of the Arenig and at the Caradoc–Ashgill boundary over much of the southern part of the platform. Above and between these shales widespread differentiation of facies and faunas inhibit very precise correlation of units and events across the Autochthon. A late Arenig–early Llanvirn regression corresponds to the Whiterock regressive event on the N American platform (Jaanusson 1979, Fortey 1984). Similarly, at the top of the Ashgill widespread glacio-eustatic changes are evident across the platform (Brenchley & Newall 1984) and locally a *Hirnantia* fauna is present (Brenchley & Cocks 1982). Regional environmental changes within the carbonate milieu have been suggested by the presence of the 'bioherm-bahamite–warm-water facies' in the upper Caradoc and Ashgill (Jaanusson 1973); Webby (1984) has associated this tropical or warm-water facies with the northward movement of Baltica towards the equator and consequently the closing of the Iapetus Ocean. Faunal provincialism, so marked in the earlier part of the Ordovician, is less clearly defined during this interval.

More local phenomena, some of which may be related to tectonic events within the Caledonian orogen, include the presence of intra-formational conglomerates, e.g. the Lockne conglomerate in Jämtland (Jaanusson & Karis 1982), numerous breaks in sedimentation represented by discontinuity surfaces (Jaanusson 1973, Holmer 1983) and the early termination of marine sedimentation (late Llandovery) in the N and W (Bassett 1981).

A progressive but gradual increase, beginning during the early Llanvirn in the Oslo region, in metallic elements such as manganese, iron, nickel and chromium and in detrital minerals, notably chromite, and higher chlorite to illite ratios in the sediments (Bjørlykke 1974a) may be related to the erosion of earlier or coeval island-arc sequences which may be *in situ*, already obducted or present within an early advancing nappe system during the middle and late Ordovician (Bjørlykke 1974b); significant increases in trace-element concentrations are not apparent until the upper Caradoc and Ashgill. Geographically-extensive bentonite horizons developed during the Llandeilo-Caradoc and the late Llandovery. The Ordovician bentonites can be traced from the Oslo region to Bornholm and as far E as Estonia (Hagemann & Spjeldnæs 1955, Hagemann 1966, Bergström & Nilsson 1974). Significantly, the events cited are not abrupt but occur with varying intensities throughout the middle and upper Ordovician; there is no evidence for changes in direct response to a Finnmarkian event.

In Norway it has been customary to use the succession of the Oslo region as a standard reference for correlation of sequences and events within the fold belt and between those sections on the platform (Vogt 1928, 1945, Størmer 1967). However, the Oslo region is in itself abnormal since there are rapid facies changes over relatively short distances and many sedimentary units are strongly diachronous. Nevertheless, it occupies an intermediate position between the stable platform of Baltoscandia and the developing orogen in the W, and thus features of successions here rather than those of the more stable Swedish platform may be linked to processes occurring within the fold belt presumably westward of the edge of the adjacent Baltic craton (Fig. 1). In this context the parautochthonous rocks of Hardangervidda are significant (Fig. 3) as they are the most complete and best documented of the westerly foreland sections presumably nearest to the locus of the orogen. The succession has been described in detail by Andresen (1978) who erected a formal lithostratigraphy. More recent interpretations have been given by Naterstad *et al.* (1981), Andresen & Færseth (1982) and Bruton *et al.* (1984). The succession is at least 700 m thick, is dominated by coarse siliciclastic rocks and differs markedly from coeval sequences in the Oslo region. In particular, the influx of coarse

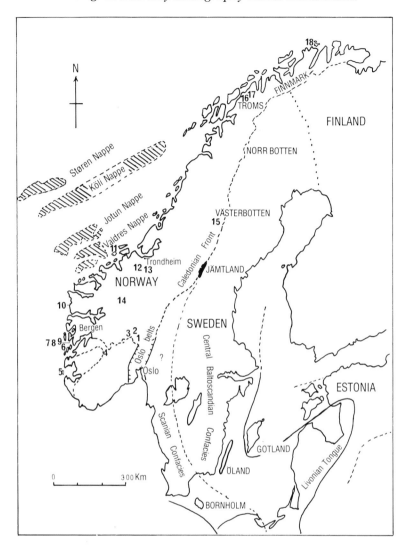

FIG. 1. Map of Scandinavia and adjacent Baltic areas showing the eastern extension of the Caledonian front. Numbers 1–18 refer to the location of the allochthonous sections illustrated and discussed in the text. The approximate boundaries of the relevant confacies (lithofacies) belts of the platform area (Jaanusson 1976) are superimposed. The predominantly carbonate area (central Baltoscandian confacies) covers much of mainland Sweden and extends into Latvia and S Estonia (Livonian tongue). Graptolite shales are predominant in the Scanian confacies belt which merges with the eastern part of the Oslo belt and extends along the Caledonian front and into the parautochthonous segment of E Jotunheimen and Jämtland. The presumed pre-thrust positions prior to the Scandian event of the four major nappe units are also superimposed (those for Valdres and Jotun are after Hossack 1978). The relative positions of the Köli and Støren Nappes are based on faunal evidence and originated much farther W (Bruton & Bockelie 1979, 1980, Bruton & Harper 1981). Distances from the present western coast are in excess of 500 km.

clastic material during and possibly before the Arenig contrasts with the graptolitic facies known from elsewhere in the Autochthon (lower Didymograptus shale and equivalents), across the southern part of the platform and in the lower part of the Allochthon in Gausdal (Williams 1984). The source of the clastic wedge may have been an eroded basement complex although the involvement of other sources cannot be excluded. Andresen (1978) suggested that a northward transition from near-shore to offshore facies can be observed within the area.

The Allochthon

Rocks of Arenig–Llandovery age are variably represented within certain nappes. It is only recently, however, that the concept of Autochthon, Parautochthon and lower, middle, upper and uppermost Allochthon, developed largely for the rocks of the Swedish Caledonides, has been applied to the mountain belt as a whole (Roberts & Gee 1981). Unanimous agreement as to how this terminology should be applied to many of the local nappe sequences is lacking and thus we have elected to discuss the successions within the established regional tectono-stratigraphy for each area. Where possible reference has been made to the more general nappe classification. The successions are from the following areas: (1) E Jotunheimen; (2) Hardangervidda; (3) Bergen; (4) Trondheim region; (5) Jämtland, Västerbotten and Norrbotten; (6) Nordland and Troms; (7) Finnmark.

E Jotunheimen area (Fig. 2, Sections 1–3)

Rocks lying structurally above the Precambrian, Cambrian and Ordovician strata of the foreland, but beneath the Jotun Nappe, can be assigned to one of three structural units: the Aurdal duplex, the Synnfjell duplex and the Valdres thrust sheets (in ascending order) (Hossack et al. 1985). Each contains Cambrian and Ordovician successions both thicker and markedly different from those of the adjacent Autochthon. The allochthonous sequences themselves significantly display mutual contrasts (Fig. 2, Sections 1–3). Reconstruction of the sedimentary environments across the thrust units suggests that a thick clastic wedge, which thickened northwards, was deposited in response to the approaching Jotun nappe (Nickelsen et al. 1985).

Hardangervidda (not figured)

Within the lower Allochthon, rocks of the Cambro-Silurian eastern facies (Strand 1972, 31–32) are well developed, comprising quartzites probably overlain by a thin marble unit which is succeeded by a thick sequence of calcareous mica-schist (Solli et al. 1978). There are marked facies changes within these units and although trace fossils have been found in the basal quartzite (Riis 1977) they are locally overlain by autochthonous black shales with a fauna of middle Cambrian age (Henningsmoen 1952) and are thus presumed to be Precambrian.

The upper Allochthon in this area contains a succession of schists, greywackes and pelites of unknown age which are commonly correlated with fossiliferous successions in the Bergen arcs (Solli et al. 1978). Andersen et al. (1984) have discussed the presence of a dismembered and deformed ophiolite fragment in the lower part of the Allochthon in central Hardangervidda. This is overlain unconformably by a series of metasediments and volcanics thought to be Ordovician in age, although this cannot be confirmed because of the absence of fossils.

Bergen area (Fig. 4, Sections 5 and 6; Fig. 5, Sections 7–9; Fig. 6, Section 10)

Fossiliferous upper Ordovician and lower Silurian rocks have been documented from sections within the lowermost nappe of the Bergen arcs. Although a variety of these sequences have been discussed in detail on the islands of Stord and Karmøy, at Sunnfjord and in the major Bergen arc, the shelly faunas are in need of detailed reappraisal. The rocks of the major and minor schist arcs have been assigned to a eugeosynclinal facies; the sedimentary sequence, which usually

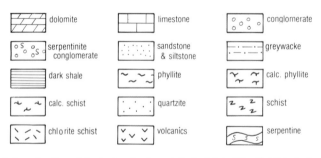

The graphical presentation of sedimentological and palaeontological data (Figs 2–10) is that agreed by the Faunal Province–Sedimentology Working Group of the International Geological Correlation Program Project 27 (Bruton 1979). Faunal symbols are as follows: Al, alga; B, brachiopod; Bi, bivalve; Br, bryozoa; Co, conodont; Cp, cephalopod; Cr, crinoid ossicle; E, echinoderm; G, gastropod; Gr, graptolite; M, miscellaneous; Rc, rugose coral; Sr, stromatolite; T, trilobite; Tc, tabulate coral; TF, trace fossil.

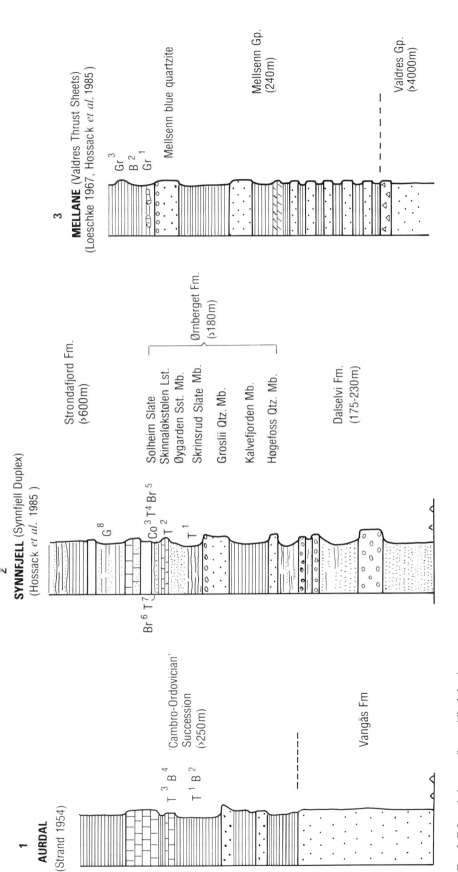

FIG. 2. E Jotunheim area (lower Allochthon).

Section 1   Aurdal: 1–2, trilobite and brachiopod faunas indicating correlation with lower, middle and upper Cambrian (Strand 1954); 3–4, brachiopods and trilobites indicate correlation with Ceratopyge limestone of Oslo region (Strand 1954).

Section 2   Synfjell: 1, *Paradoxides* of middle Cambrian age (Bruton, unpublished data); 2, agnostids of middle Cambrian age (Henningsmoen, cited by Nickelsen *et al.* 1985); 3–5, conodonts, trilobites and brachiopods indicate correlation with Tremadoc and Ceratopyge limestone (Repetski & Henningsmoen, cited by Nickelsen *et al.* 1985, Bruton & Harper, unpublished data); 6, Clitambonitide brachiopods in beds above 'Ceratopyge limestone' (Harper, unpublished data), suggest post-Tremadoc age; 7, *Pliomera* species (Bruton, unpublished data) of probable Arenig–Llanvirn age; 8, graptolites of middle Arenig–early Llanvirn age from equivalent rocks in Gausdal (Lapworth, cited by Bjørlykke 1893, Lapworth 1905, Williams 1984).

Section 3   Mellane: 1, *Dictyonema flabelliforme* (Peach, cited by Nickelsen *et al.* 1985); 2, orthide brachiopods (Loeschke 1967, Peach 1979, personal communication); 3, graptolites of Arenig–Llanvirn age (Bjørlykke 1905).

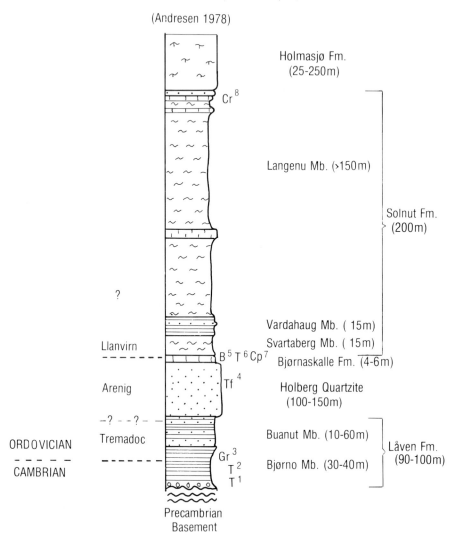

4
HARDANGERVIDDA (south east part)

(Andresen 1978)

FIG. 3. Section 4 Hardangervidda (autochthon–parautochthon): 1, lower Cambrian fauna recorded from basal conglomerate at Ustaoset (Størmer 1925); 2, middle Cambrian fauna described from Bjørno Mb. (Bruton, cited by Bruton *et al.* 1985); 3, *Dictyonema flabelliforme* at several localities (Dahll 1861, Størmer 1941, Andresen 1974); 4, 'tube-like' structures (Andresen 1978); 5–7, brachiopod, trilobite and cephalopod faunas consistent with a late Arenig–early Llanvirn age for the formation suggest correlation with the 'Orthoceras limestone' of the Oslo region (Andresen 1974, Harper, cited by Bruton *et al.* 1984); 8, crinoid stems, middle Ordovician or younger (Bockelie, cited by Andresen 1978, authors' collections).

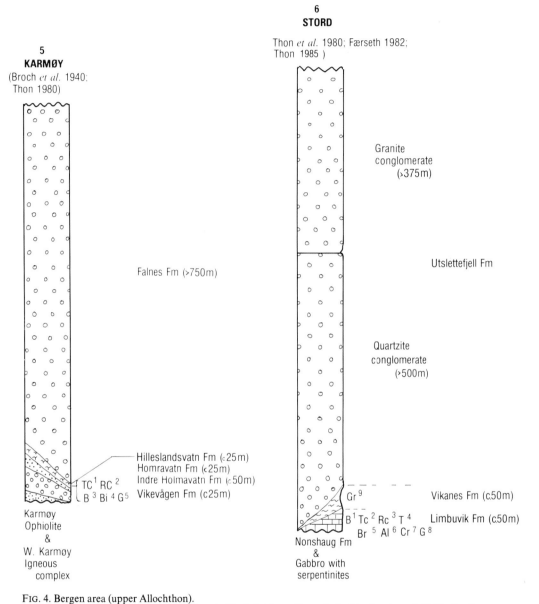

FIG. 4. Bergen area (upper Allochthon).
Section 5 Karmøy: 1–5, shelly fauna of probable Ashgill age (Strand, cited by Broch *et al.* 1940); Skudenes fauna in need of reappraisal (Strand, cited by Broch *et al.* 1940).
Section 6 Stord: 1–8, 'shallow-water' marine shelly fauna (1–4, 7, 8, Kvale 1938; 1–8, Breivik 1975); 9, lower Llandovery graptolite faunas (*Monograptus cyphus* zone (Ryan & Skevington 1976)).

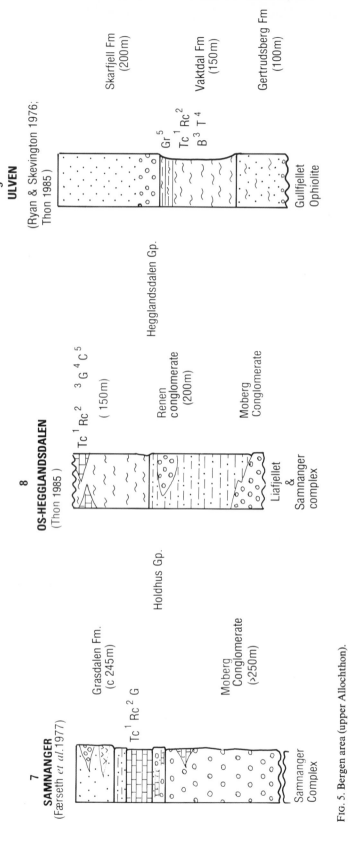

FIG. 5. Bergen area (upper Allochthon).
Section 7 Samnanger: 1–3, shelly fauna dominated by corals indicates correlation with Ashgill (Kolderup & Kolderup 1940).
Section 8 Os-Hegglandsdalen: 1–5, shelly faunas not rich but indicate correlation with Ashgill of the Oslo region (Kolderup & Kolderup 1940).
Section 9 Ulven: 1–4, rich shelly fauna, including brachiopod *Stricklandia lens* J de C. Sowerby which suggests correlation with the upper part of the lower Llandovery of the Oslo region (Kiær, cited by Kolderup & Kolderup 1940); 5, graptolites of early Llandovery age (*Monograptus gregarious* zone (Ryan & Skevington 1976)).

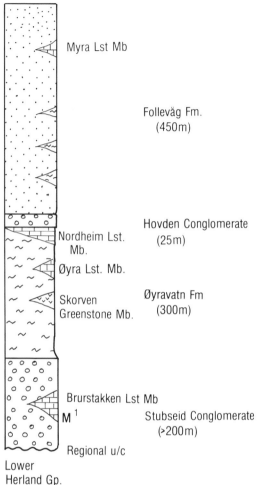

Fig. 6. Section 10   Sunnfjord (upper Allochthon): 1, poorly preserved fauna of middle Ordovician (Reusch 1888), early Silurian (Skjerlie 1969) or Ashgill age (Spjeldnæs, cited by Thon 1985).

unconformably overlies units containing ob-ducted ophiolite fragments—the Samnanger Complex—is designated the Holdhus Group (Sturt & Thon 1976, 1978, Færseth *et al.* 1977, Thon 1985). The age of the unconformity is not known unequivocally (Naterstad 1976, Sturt & Thon 1976); however, the oldest fossils post-dating it are of Ashgill age.

Trondheim region (Fig. 7, Sections 11–13)

The Trondheim region has fulfilled a significant role in the development of tectonic models relating to the orogen as a whole. The N American (Bathyurid) faunal province affinities of the diverse and locally-abundant assemblages from Sør Trondelag have been appreciated for over half a century (Kiær 1932). These data have formed the basis for the bipartite division of the Scandinavian Caledonides into N American and Baltic parts (Wilson 1966, Dewey 1969) separated by a flat-lying suture (Nicholson 1971, 1979). Conflicting evidence from structural, geochemi-cal and faunal studies in this key area has promoted much continuing controversy regard-ing the timing of events and the place of origin of major thrust sheets.

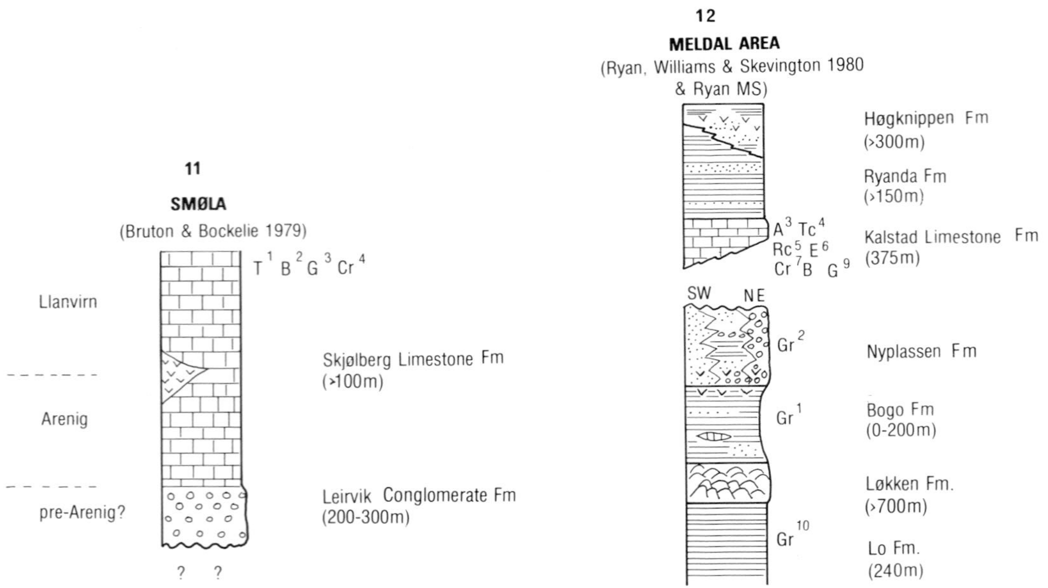

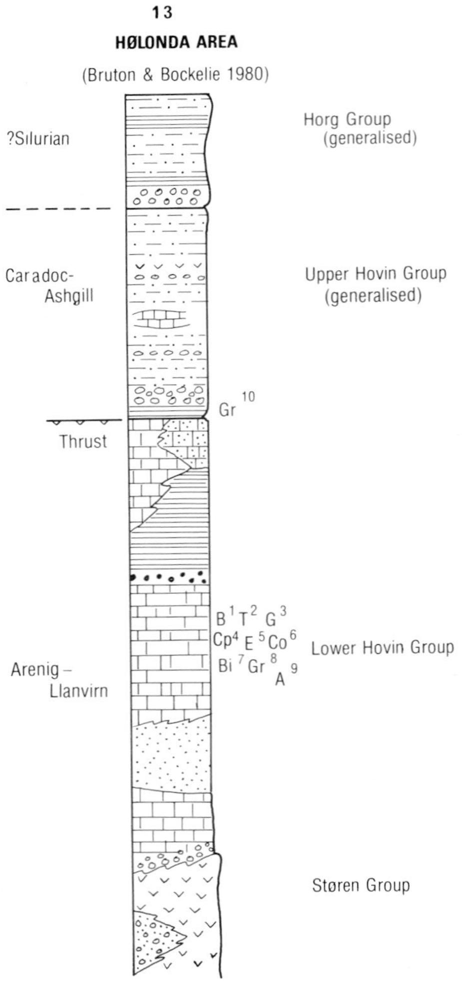

FIG. 7. Trondheim region (upper Allochthon).

Section 11 Smøla: 1, *Goniotelina* cf. *broeggeri* (Bruton, cited by Neuman & Bruton 1974), bathyurid province trilobite of Arenig–Llanvirn age; 2, *Stenocamara* (*Camarella* (*sic*) of Holtedahl (1924) and Strand (1932), and *Camarella* cf. *nuda* of Bruton & Bockelie (1979)). N American affinity and suggests correlation with high Llanvirn (Harper 1981) (fauna also includes *Aporthophyla* (Bruton & Bockelie 1979) and *Syndielasma* (Harper, unpublished data): 3, gastropod fauna (Holtedahl 1915, 1924, Strand 1932, Bruton & Bockelie 1979) of N American affinity.

Section 12 Meldal: 1, diverse graptolite fauna (Blake 1962, Skevington 1963, Berry 1968, Schmidt 1984, personal communication), which is correlated with the *Didymograptus hirundo* zone (Bruton & Bockelie 1982); 2, sparse graptolites of early–middle Llanvirn age (Ryan *et al.* 1980); 3–9, in Kiær (1932); 10, diverse graptolite fauna of mid–late Arenig age (Ryan *et al.* 1980).

Section 13 Hølonda: 1–9, in Kiær (1932), and in addition brachiopods (Neuman, cited by Neuman & Bruton 1974, Neuman, cited by Bruton & Bockelie 1982), trilobites (Strand 1948, Bruton, cited by Neuman & Bruton 1974), echinoderms (Bockelie 1974), gastropods (Yochelson 1977) and conodonts (Bergström 1971, 1979); 10, graptolites of the *Dicranograptus clingani* zone (late Caradoc) Williams in Bruton & Bockelie (1982).

Although rock units within the Köli nappes N of the Grong-Olden Culmination (Fig. 1) may be correlated with fossiliferous units in Västerbotton, it is in the Trondheim Nappe Complex that rich Ordovician faunas occur. In the second-lowest major unit, the Støren Nappe, abundant and diverse fossils occur around Løkken and Hølanda. The late Arenig–early Llanvirn (White-rock) faunas include graptolites (Blake 1962, Skevington 1963, Berry 1968, Ryan *et al.* 1980, Schmidt 1984), trilobites (Strand 1948, Bruton, cited by Neuman & Bruton 1974), brachiopods (Reed, cited by Kiær 1932, Neuman, cited by Neuman & Bruton 1974 and by Bruton & Bockelie 1982, Neuman 1982, personal communication), cephalopods (Foerste, cited by Kiær 1932), echinoderms (Bockelie 1974), gastropods (Yochelson 1977) and conodonts (Bergström 1971, 1979, 1980). The benthonic elements of the fauna have marked N American faunal province affinities (Bruton & Bockelie 1980, Bruton & Harper 1985). The stratigraphy of Hølanda and Meldal is summarized in Fig. 7. In the Hølanda area the lower Hovin Group consists of lime-stones, conglomerates, sandstones and shales, and deposition of clastic sediments with rapid local changes of lateral facies around 'greenstone islands' of the underlying Støren Group is envisaged (Bruton & Bockelie 1980, 1982).

Deeper-water facies of the lower Hovin Group are represented in the Meldal area (Ryan *et al.* 1980). The sedimentary basin was partly filled with detritus from a continental source in the E or NE and was floored by oceanic crust to the W.

Significantly, no continental basement is known from the Støren Nappe. It is also noteworthy that correlation of the Støren Group with the Fundsjø Group in the eastern Trondheim region has recently been questioned (Grenne & Lagerblad 1981). Although these two groups are generally assumed to have occupied the same tectono-stratigraphical levels, the Støren Group greenstones have a chemistry similar to that of ocean-floor tholeiites but those from the Fundsjø Group are more typical of an immature island-arc environment.

Jämtland, Västerbotten and Norrbotten areas (Fig. 8, Sections 14 and 15)

These mountainous areas comprise the eastern part of the Scandes where rocks of the lower, middle and upper Allochthons crop out. Translation of the nappes is thought to have been considerable with estimates of at least 500 km (Gee & Zachrisson 1979) or even of the order of 1000 km (Gee 1978) of eastward movement having been proposed for the highest tectonic units.

The lower Allochthon of central and northern Jämtland contains fossiliferous sequences (Thorslund 1940, 1960, Bassett *et al.* 1982) which contrast markedly with those coeval units represented in the adjacent Autochthon (Gee & Zachrisson 1979, Jaanusson & Karis 1982, Karis 1982). The latter two studies provide detailed stratigraphical data for the allochthonous Jämtland successions which are not reiterated here.

Whilst the middle Allochthon carries an intensely tectonized Precambrian basement and unfossiliferous coarse siliciclastic cover rocks, the upper Allochthon is characterized by a variety of lithologies consistent with formation in island-arc, back-arc and possibly oceanic environments (Gee & Zachrisson 1979). In this unit—the Köli of the Seve-Köli Nappe Complex—sporadically-fossiliferous sequences of Ordovician and Silurian rocks are developed (Fig. 8). Although the full vertical extent of the Köli Group is not precisely known, lithological correlations with the autochthonous Jämtland Supergroup and further indirect evidence (Gee & Zachrisson 1979, fig. 6 and p. 33) suggest that the Köli may range in age from early Cambrian to at least early Silurian (late Llandovery).

The lowest fossiliferous unit is a serpentinite conglomerate of undoubted sedimentary origin (Stigh 1979, 1980) which is developed near the base of the Köli throughout much of the outcrop of the Seve–Köli Nappe Complex. However, only the Otta conglomerate of Norway has yielded a fauna enabling a precise correlation (lower Llanvirn) of the unit locally (Bruton & Harper 1981). Holmqvist (1980, 1982) has suggested a comparable age for a limestone near the top of a similar conglomerate in Västerbotten, but better preserved and more diagnostic material is required to confirm his correlation (Bruton & Harper 1982). The faunal province affinities have been discussed elsewhere (Bruton & Harper 1981, 1985), but on balance indicate mid-oceanic settings for the archipelago around which the Otta fauna lived.

Overlying greenschist and keratophyre (Fig. 8), quartzites, fossiliferous limestones (the Slätdal Formation) and shales (Broken Formation) occur within a succession of greywackes and conglomerates. The shelly fauna from the former unit indicate a late Ordovician (probably Hirnantian) age, whilst the graptolite fauna from the overlying shales suggests an early Llandovery age (Kulling 1933). Although the faunas and sedimentology of this part of the succession are in need of reappraisal, an oceanic setting is indicated (Gee 1975a); significantly, the late Ordovician–early Silurian glacio-eustatic regression–transgression is evident in that part of the sequence.

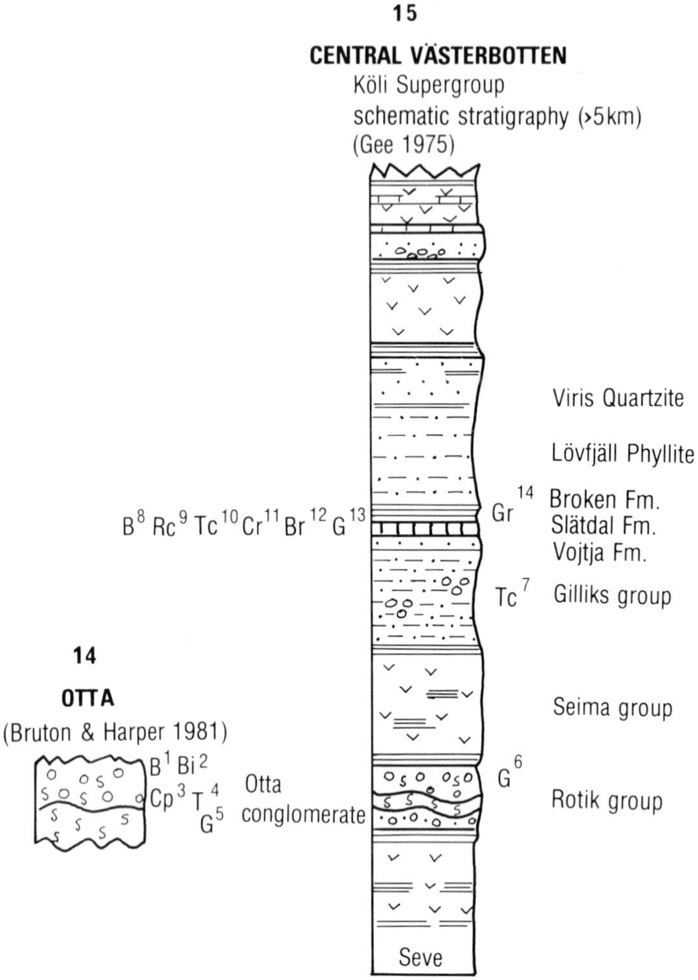

15

CENTRAL VÄSTERBOTTEN

Köli Supergroup

schematic stratigraphy (>5km)

(Gee 1975)

$B^8 Rc^9 Tc^{10} Cr^{11} Br^{12} G^{13}$

Gr ^{14}

Viris Quartzite

Lövfjäll Phyllite

Broken Fm.
Slätdal Fm.
Vojtja Fm.

Tc ^{7} Gilliks group

14

OTTA

(Bruton & Harper 1981)

$B^1 Bi^2$
$Cp^3 T^4$
G^5

Otta
conglomerate

Seima group

G^6 Rotik group

Seve

FIG. 8. Sections 14 and 15   Otta and Västerbotten (upper Allochthon): 1, brachiopods, early Llanvirn age–Celtic province (Hedström 1930, Harper, cited by Bruton & Harper 1981); 2, bivalves (Hedström 1930); 3, cephalopods (Hedström 1930); 4, trilobites, early Llanvirn–Baltic province (Hedström 1930, Jaanusson 1973, 1979, Bruton, cited by Bruton & Harper 1981); 5, gastropods, middle Ordovician, N American province (Yochelson 1963); 6, Macluritacean gastropods (Holmqvist 1980; see also Bruton & Harper 1982, Holmqvist 1982); 7, coral, Caradoc age (Kulling, cited by Strand & Kulling 1972); 8–13, shelly fauna in regressive sequence, brachiopods (including *Holorhynchus giganteus* Kiær), rugose and tabulate corals, crinoids, bryozoans and gastropods of probable Hirnantian age (Kulling 1933); 14, diverse graptolite fauna, early Llandovery age (Kulling 1933).

In summary, the Arenig–Llandovery stratigraphy of the Swedish Köli is dominated by a thick accumulation of volcanic and volcaniclastic rocks associated with deep-water turbidite facies, although there is evidence of the development of insular environments during at least two periods of global regression.

Nordland and Troms areas (Fig. 9, Sections 16 and 17)

Within the upper Allochthon of these areas, middle Ordovician fossils have been reported from Sulitjelma (Vogt 1927, Kautsky 1953, Nicholson 1966, Gustavson 1978) and include crinoids, cystoids and bryozoans.

The 'Middle Nappe' of the Troms area has been correlated with the Seve–Köli Nappe Complex, whereas the 'Upper Nappes' have been assigned to the Rødingfjell and Gasak nappes of Nordland (Gustavson 1978). Fossiliferous sequences of early Silurian age have been documented from the upper part of the Middle Nappe (Olaussen 1976, Binns & Gayer 1980, Bjørlykke & Olaussen 1981) and are schematically illustrated herein.

Finnmark area (Fig. 10, Section 18)

Within the northernmost part of Norway, two clearly defined groups of nappes are present resting adjacent to the autochthonous Precambrian–Tremadoc succession on Digermulen

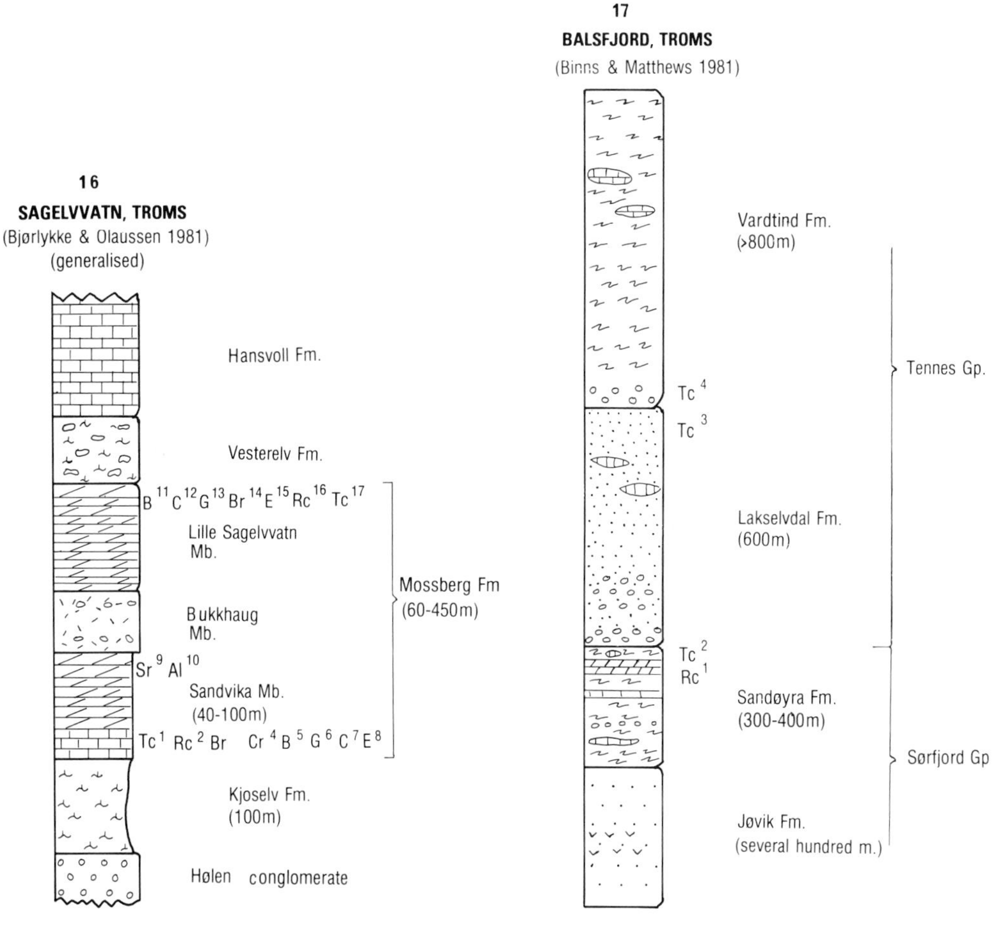

FIG. 9.   Troms (upper Allochthon).
Section 16   Sagelvvatn: 1–8, shelly fauna, association of halysitid corals suggests late Llandovery age (Klaaman, cited by Bjørlykke & Olaussen 1981); 9–10, stromatolites and algal remains (Bjørlykke & Olaussen 1981); 11–13, diverse shelly fauna (Olaussen 1976, Bjørlykke & Olaussen 1981) including streptelasmatid corals similar to lower Silurian genera of the Oslo region (Neuman, cited by Bjørlykke & Olaussen 1981).
Section 17   Balsfjord: 1, 'horn corals' (Binns & Matthews 1981); 2–4, *Favosites* (Binns & Matthews 1981).

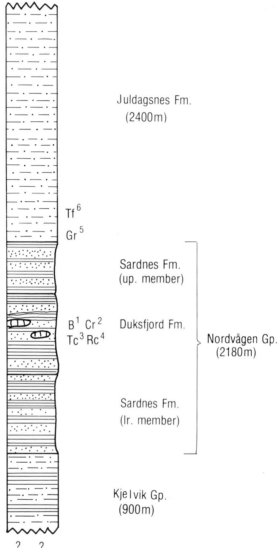

FIG. 10. Finnmark (upper Allochthon).
Section 18   Magerøy: 1–4, lower Silurian shelly fauna of brachiopods, crinoids, tabulate and rugose corals (Henningsmoen 1960); 5, *Monograptus*? (of *sandersoni* group, early Llandovery age (Skevington, cited by Sturt *et al.* 1975)); 6, includes *Protopalaeodictyon* and *Scotia plana* (Andersen 1981).

(Reading 1965). The older Finnmarkian Nappe Complex comprises thin lower parautochthonous units and, above, allochthonous units; the majority of both contain basement–cover sequences of pre-Caledonian rocks and Precambrian to Cambrian strata (Ramsay *et al.* 1985). Emplacement onto the Baltic craton during the late Cambrian– early Ordovician 'Finnmarkian phase' is indicated.

The higher Scandian nappes were emplaced during the late Silurian and early Devonian (Sturt & Roberts 1978). The uppermost tectonic unit—

the Magerøy Nappe—contains about 5.5 km of lower Llandovery metasedimentary rocks comprising the Magerøy Supergroup (Andersen 1979, 1981). Much of the supergroup comprises turbidites, although the middle Nordvågen Group is thought to be of shallow-water origin (Andersen 1981). The interpretations of patterns and depositional environments of much of the succession are inconclusive, but the turbidite deposition may be related to the early development of the Scandian phase of the Caledonian orogeny (Andersen 1981).

Discussion

Each of the segments of the Scandinavian Caledonides investigated possesses a distinctive and exclusive stratigraphy (Fig. 12). The dissimilarity of these sequences invites discussion of their place of origin within the Iapetus Ocean and the time of their interaction with other elements of the mobile belt. The western margin of the Baltic shield clearly had a complex morphology, but it is not clear where and when island-arc sequences of the upper Allochthon were accreted. Sturt (1984, p. 209) has recently emphasized the significance of the 'belt-length' unconformity between ophiolites obducted during the Finnmarkian phase and an often imprecisely dated Ordovician–Silurian succession. There is no clear evidence for this unconformity within the Autochthon or the lower Allochthon (Fig. 2) (*cf.* Sturt 1984, p. 207). In the Skien–Langesund district of the Oslo region the upper part of the 'Orthoceras limestone' (lower Llanvirn) has been thrust over Cambrian shales during a later event associated with movement of the sole thrust within the lowest part of the Palaeozoic rocks of the region (Bockelie & Nystuen 1981, Harper & Owen 1983). Certainly the successions of the Autochthon and lower Allochthon were some distance from the locus of the orogen (Sturt 1984). Nevertheless, the initial interactions of those terranes bearing exotic faunas in the upper Allochthon need not have been with the Baltic shield. The islands themselves may have been in constant interaction with elements of island-arc complexes (Leitch 1984) or even microcontinents (Ramsay & Sturt 1978, Roberts 1980) which contributed considerable and varied detritus to basins marginal to the moving volcanic terranes (Robertson & Woodcock 1983).

Webby (1984) has recently suggested that Baltoscandia moved from high to middle–low latitudes during the early Ordovician and by the end of the period was situated near the equator.

This movement towards an essentially stable N American platform was thus considerable and is pertinent to the analysis of the evolution of both marginal and oceanic environments and particularly the siting of tectonic events. The fact that certain of the nappe complexes contain shelly faunas which clearly originated outside the Baltic province within sedimentary sequences which display quite different depositional histories is also significant. For example the Köli Nappe Complex contains sequences dominated by volcanic and volcaniclastic rocks throughout much of the Ordovician and lower Silurian, in marked contrast with the Silurian succession of the Magerøy nappe which lacks volcanics and consists of turbidites and occasional limestones.

The successive W–E translation of nappe units involved considerable distances, the highest unit being the most far travelled. Hossack (1978) has calculated a minimum displacement of 290 km for the Jotun Nappe. In addition, the estimate of 400 km for the Osen–Røa Nappe Complex (Nystuen 1981) and a significant movement of the Oslo region itself (Bockelie & Nystuen 1981, 1985) must also be taken into account. Study of Figs 2–10 indicates that none of the successions within the Allochthon is comparable with those deposited on the Baltic platform. Nevertheless, a basinward transition is recognized in E Jotunheimen where successively higher tectonic units (Aurdal duplex–Synfjell duplex–Valdres thrust sheets) contain concomitantly more sandstones and greywackes which provide evidence of slope–basin depositional environments. It is significant to note that here in the lower Allochthon, as in the Autochthon, there is no direct evidence of a discrete late Cambrian–early Ordovician deformational event corresponding to the Finnmarkian phase of the Caledonian orogeny (Sturt *et al.* 1978). Throughout the Ordovician and into the early Silurian, sedimentary environments and faunas within the Köli Nappe Complex of the upper Allochthon and its equivalents (Otta Nappe) indicate the existence of island arcs and insular environments. The faunas together with the volcanic and volcaniclastic facies suggest an ocean setting for at least some of these archipelagos (Stigh 1979, 1980, Bruton & Harper 1981, 1985). Associated faunas (Arenig–Llanvirn and late Ashgill) correspond to periods of global regression and the presumed emergence of islands (Fortey 1984). The succeeding Llandovery transgression is represented by graptolitic shales in Västerbotten (Kulling 1933). Other insular environments, e.g. on Smøla and in the Trondheim region (Bruton & Bockelie 1979, 1980), differ from those of the Köli Nappe Complex in having early Ordovician (Arenig–Llanvirn)

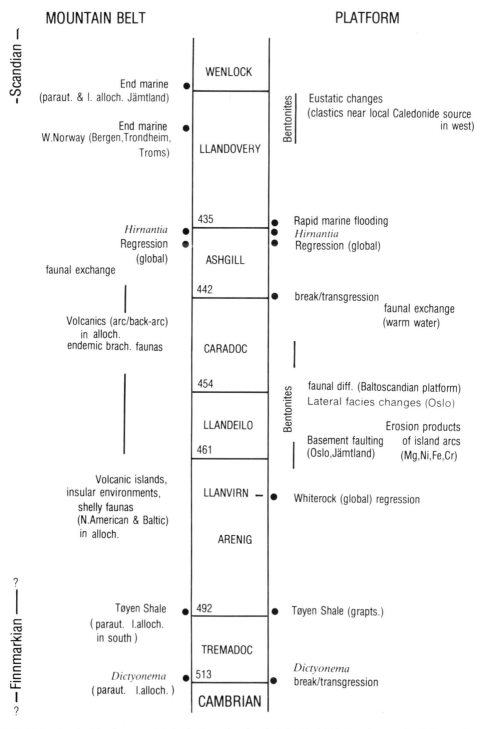

FIG. 11. Major Arenig–Llandovery events in the Scandinavian Caledonide fold belt and across the Baltoscandian platform based on sedimentological and faunal data. Radiometric dates from McKerrow *et al.* (1985).

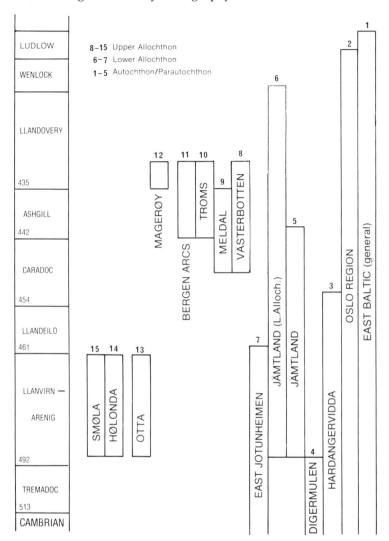

FIG. 12. Major geographical areas in the Scandinavian Caledonides and the stratigraphical ranges of included rock units. Sedimentological and faunal differences over comparable time intervals in areas 1–7 can be explained in terms of facies changes from the E towards the miogeocline in the W. Areas 8–15 are now separated from adjacent areas by major structural discontinuities and are exotic terranes. Areas 8–11 share a similar Ashgill fauna with the platform, whilst areas 10–12 contain Silurian faunas. Areas 13–15 are the most exotic and contain insular shelly faunas of American affinities. Radiometric dates as in Fig. 11.

faunas with N American (Bathyurid) faunal province affinities which developed on oceanic crust. Younger faunas from the latter area are associated with flysch, polymict conglomerates and rhyolitic tuffs derived from developing basins associated with an active plate margin.

In the Bergen area no fossils older than those of probable Ashgill age are known and the youngest undoubted marine rocks are of early Llandovery age. The illustrated sections (Figs 2 and 4–10) indicate the considerable variation in

thickness and sediment type across the Bergen arcs and adjacent outcrop; diverse basement sources and considerable relief are indicated to account for the coarse breccias and conglomerates and the presence of local basins (Thon 1985).

In summary, this brief survey demonstrates that in a traverse from E to W across the Baltoscandian area the Arenig–Llandovery interval is characterized by a complex mosaic of sedimentary environments. In a now considerably foreshortened segment of the orogen and its

eastern margin the following sedimentary regimes are encountered within a belt some 750 km
wide.

Autochthon, Parautochthon and lower Allochthon

1 The tectonically-stable epicontinental platform of Sweden over which depositional rates
were low (2–3 mm per 1000 years) and carbonate
sediments are dominant.

2 The variably developed intra-cratonic basins
of the Oslo region and Jämtland in which
sedimentation rates were markedly higher and
rapid facies changes were governed partly by
basement faulting.

Westwards and northwards there are two distinct
modes of transition which clearly reflect the
complex morphology of the western margin of
the Baltic platform.

3a Transition from the basin and platform
environments of the Oslo region to a variety of
near-shore and offshore slope environments characterized by often rapid sedimentation of silici-
clastics on Hardangervidda.
3b The platform–slope transitions of the E
Jotunheimen and Jämtland areas.

Upper Allochthon

1 The northern and southern extremities of the
orogen represented by the Finnmark and Bergen
areas where variable successions are developed
on thrust sheets and obducted ophiolite fragments
themselves emplaced during the late Cambrian-
early Ordovician (Finnmarkian) phase of the
orogeny.

2 The central Scandinavian upper Allochthon
containing a variety of island-arc and insular
environments developed on oceanic crust adjacent to and far from the western margin of the
Baltic platform. Obduction of the tectono-strati-
graphically higher ophiolite units onto fore-arc
parts of the margin may have occurred during
the middle Ordovician.

ACKNOWLEDGMENTS: We thank Dr A. W. Owen, Dr
D. Roberts and Dr M. G. Bassett for their detailed
constructive comments on the manuscript and Jenny
Orr for her swift and accurate typing. D. L. B.
acknowledges financial assistance from Norges Almenvitenskapelige Forskningsråd; D. A. T. H. acknowledges finance from the Natural Environment Research
Council, Norges Almenvitenskapelige Forskningsråd
and the Paleontologisk Museum, Oslo.

References

ANDERSEN, T. B. 1979. The geology of south-western
   Magerøy, Finnmark, with special reference to the
   tectonometamorphic development. *Thesis*, Uni-
   versity of Bergen, 388 pp (unpublished).
—— 1981. The structure of the Magerøy Nappe,
   Finnmark, North Norway. *Norges Geologiske
   Undersøkelse*, **363**, 1–23.
——, FURNES, H., BREKKE, H., STURT, B. A. &
   NATERSTAD, J. 1984. The Tørvikbygd ophiolite—
   a newly discovered ophiolite fragment with an
   unconformable cover sequence in the central
   Hardanger area, West Norway. *Norsk Geologisk
   Tidsskrift*, **64**, 69–73.
ANDRESEN, A. 1974. New fossil finds from the Cambro-
   Silurian metasediments on Hardangervidda.
   Norges Geologiske Undersøkelse, **304**, 55–60.
—— 1978. Lithostratigraphy of the autochthonous-
   parautochthonous lower Palaeozoic metasedi-
   ments on Hardangervidda, South Norway. *Norges
   Geologiske Undersøkelse*, **338**, 59–69.
—— & FAERSETH, R. 1982. An evolutionary model for
   the southwest Norwegian Caledonides. *American
   Journal of Science*, **282**, 756–82.
BASSETT, M. G. 1981. Silurian stratigraphy and facies
   development in Scandinavia. *Terra Cognita*, **1**, 34.
——, CHERNS, L. & KARIS, L. 1982. The Röde
   Formation. Early Old Red Sandstone facies in the
   Silurian of Jämtland, Sweden. *Sveriges Geologiska
   Undersökning, Serie C*, **793**, 1–24.

BERGSTRÖM, S. M. 1971. Conodont biostratigraphy of
   the middle and upper Ordovician of Europe and
   eastern North America. *In*: SWEET, W. C. &
   BERGSTRÖM, S. M. (eds) *Symposium on Conodont
   Biostratigraphy. Geological Society of America
   Memoir No. 127*, pp. 83–162.
—— 1979. Whiterockian (Ordovician) conodonts from
   the Hølanda Limestone of the Trondheim Region,
   Norwegian Caledonides. *Norsk Geologisk Tidsskrift*, **59**, 295–307.
—— 1980. Conodonts as paleotemperature tools in
   Ordovician rocks of the Caledonides and adjacent
   areas in Scandinavia and the British Isles. *Geologiska Föreningens i Stockholm Förhandlingar*, **102**,
   377–92.
—— & NILSSON, R. 1974. Age and correlation of the
   middle Ordovician bentonites on Bornholm. *Bulletin of the Geological Society of Denmark*, **23**, 27–
   48.
BERRY, W. B. N. 1968. Age of Bogo Shale and western
   Ireland graptolite faunas and their bearing on
   dating early Ordovician deformation and metamorphism in Norway and Britain. *Norsk Geologisk
   Tidsskrift*, **48**, 217–30.
BINNS, R. E. & GAYER, R. A. 1980. Silurian or upper
   Ordovician fossils at Guolasjav'ri, Troms, Norway. *Nature, London*, **284**, 53–5.
—— & MATTHEWS, D. W. 1981. Stratigraphy and
   structure of the Balsfjord Supergroup, Troms,

North Norway. *Norges Geologiske Undersøkelse*, **365**, 39–54.

BJØRLYKKE, A. & OLAUSSEN, S. 1981. Silurian sediments, volcanics and mineral deposits in the Sagelvvatn area, Troms, North Norway. *Norges Geologiske Undersøkelse*, **365**, 1–30.

BJØRLYKKE, K. 1974a. Depositional history and geochemical composition of lower Palaeozoic epicontinental sediments from the Oslo Region. *Norges Geologiske Undersøkelse*, **305**, 1–81.

—— 1974b. Geochemical and mineralogical influence of Ordovician island arcs on epicontinental clastic sedimentation. A study of Lower Palaeozoic sedimentation in the Oslo Region, Norway. *Sedimentology*, **21**, 251–72.

BJØRLYKKE, K. O. 1893. Gausdal. *Norges Geologiske Undersøkelse*, **13**, 1–36.

BLAKE, D. H. 1962. A new Lower Ordovician graptolite fauna from the Trondheim Region. *Norsk Geologisk Tidsskrift*, **42**, 223–38.

BOCKELIE, J. F. 1974. Ordovician echinoderms from the Trondheim Region, Norway. *Norsk Geologisk Tidsskrift*, **54**, 221–6.

—— 1978. The Oslo region during the early Palaeozoic. *In*: RAMBERG, I. B. & NEUMANN, E.-R. (eds) *Tectonics and Geophysics of Continental Rifts*, pp. 195–202, Reidel, Dordrecht.

—— & NYSTUEN, J. P. 1981. The southeastern part of the Scandinavian Caledonides. *Terra Cognita*, **1**, 35.

—— & —— 1985. The southeastern part of the Scandinavian Caledonides. *In*: GEE, D. G. & STURT, B. A. (eds) *The Caledonide Orogen—Scandinavia and Related Areas*, pp. 69–88. Wiley, Chichester.

BREIVIK, H. 1975. Dalskardtjern—a fossil locality on Stord, west Norway. *Norsk Geologisk Tidsskrift*, **55**, 297–8.

BRENCHLEY, P. J. & COCKS, L. R. M. 1982. Ecological associations in a regressive sequence: the latest Ordovician of the Oslo–Asker district, Norway. *Palaeontology*, **25**, 783–815.

—— & NEWALL, G. 1980. A facies analysis of Upper Ordovician regressive sequences in the Oslo Region, Norway—a record of glacio-eustatic changes. *Palaeogeography, Palaeoclimatology, Palaeoecology*, **31**, 1–38.

—— & —— 1984. Late Ordovician environmental changes and their effect on faunas. *In*: BRUTON, D. L. (ed.) *Aspects of the Ordovician System, Paleontological Contributions from the University of Oslo No. 295*, pp. 65–79, Universitetsforlaget, Oslo.

BROCH, O. A., ISACHSEN, F., ISBERG, O & STRAND, T. 1940. Bidrag til Skudenes-sedimentenes geologi. *Norges Geologiske Undersøkelse*, **155**, 1–41.

BRUTON, D. L. 1979. Report of the International Faunal Province—Sedimentology Working Group, International Geological Correlation Program Project 27, Blacksburg, VA, June 8, 1979. *Reports from Meetings of Specialist Study Groups, Blacksburg, 1979*, pp. 1–7 (internal project circular).

—— & BOCKELIE, J. F. 1979. The Ordovician sedimentary sequence on Smøla, west central Norway. *Norges Geologiske Undersøkelse*, **348**, 21–32.

—— & —— 1980. Geology and palaeontology of the Hölanda area, western Norway—a fragment of North America? *In*: WONES, D. R. (ed.) *The Caledonides in the USA: Proceedings of the International Geological Program—Caledonide Orogen Project 27, Blacksburg, VA. Department of Geological Sciences, Virginia Polytechnic Institute and State University, Memoir No. 2*, pp. 41–7.

—— & —— 1982. The Løkken–Hølanda–Støren areas. *In*: BRUTON, D. L. & WILLIAMS, S. H. (eds) *Field Excursion Guide. 4th International Symposium on the Ordovician System. Palaeontological Contributions from the University of Oslo No. 279*, Universitetsforlaget, Oslo.

—— & HARPER, D. A. T. 1981. Brachiopods and trilobites of the early Ordovician serpentine Otta Conglomerate, south central Norway. *Norsk Geologisk Tidsskrift*, **61**, 153–81.

—— & —— 1982. Ordovician gastropods from Vardofjället, Swedish Lapland, and the dating of Caledonian serpentinite conglomerates: a discussion. *Geologiska Föreningens i Stockholm Förhandlingar*, **104**, 189–90.

—— & —— 1985. Early Ordovician (Arenig–Llanvirn) faunas from oceanic islands in the Appalachian–Caledonide orogen. *In*: GEE, D. G. & STURT, B. A. (eds) *The Caledonide Orogen—Scandinavia and Related Areas*, pp. 359–68, Wiley, Chichester.

—— & WILLIAMS, S. H. (eds) 1982. *Field Excursion Guide. 4th International Symposium on the Ordovician System. Palaeontological Contributions from the University of Oslo No. 279*, Universitetsforlaget, Oslo.

——, HARPER, D. A. T., GUNBY, I. & NATERSTAD, J. 1984. Cambrian and Ordovician fossils from the Hardangervidda Group, Haukelifjell, southern Norway. *Norsk Geologisk Tidsskrift*, **64**, 313–24.

——, LINDSTRÖM, M. & OWEN, A. W. 1985. The Ordovician of Scandinavia. *In*: GEE, D. G. & STURT, B. A. (eds) *The Caledonide Orogen—Scandinavia and Related Areas*, pp. 273–282, Wiley, Chichester.

DAHLL, T. 1861. Om Telemarkens geologie. *Nyt. Mag. Naturvidensk.*, **11**, 137–72.

DEWEY, J. F. 1969. Evolution of the Appalachian–Caledonian orogen. *Nature, London*, **222**, 124–9.

FÆRSETH, R. B. 1982. Geology of southern Stord and adjacent islands, southwest Norwegian Caledonides. *Norges Geologiske Undersøkelse*, **371**, 57–112.

——, THON, A., LARSEN, S. G., SIVERTSEN, A. & ELVESTAD, L. 1977. Geology of the Lower Palaeozoic rocks in the Samnanger–Osterøy area, major Bergen arc, western Norway. *Norges Geologiske Undersøkelse*, **334**, 19–58.

FORTEY, R. A. 1984. Global earlier Ordovician transgressions and regressions and their biological implications. *In*: BRUTON, D. L. (ed.) *Aspects of the Ordovician System, Palaeontological Contributions from the University of Oslo No. 295*, pp. 37–50, Universitetsforlaget, Oslo.

GEE, D. G. 1975a. A tectonic model for the central part

of the Scandinavian Caledonides. *American Journal of Science*, **275A**, 485–515.

—— 1975b. A geotraverse through the Scandinavian Caledonides—Östersund to Trondheim. *Sveriges Geologiska Undersökning, Serie C*, **717**, 1–66.

—— & ZACHRISSON, E. 1979. The Caledonides in Sweden. *Sveriges Geologiska Undersökning, Serie C*, **769**, 1–48.

GRENNE, T. & LAGERBLAD, B. 1981. The Fundsjø Group, Central Norway—a Lower Palaeozoic island arc sequence: geochemistry and regional implications. *Terra Cognita*, **1**, 47–8.

GUSTAVSON, M. 1978. Caledonides of North-Central Norway. *In*: TOZER, E. T. & SCHENK, P. E. (eds) *Caledonian–Appalachian Orogen of the North Atlantic Region. Geological Survey of Canada Paper No. 78–13*, pp. 25–30.

HAGEMANN, F. 1966. Silurian bentonites in the Oslo Region. *Norges Geologiske Undersøkelse*, **242**, 44–61.

—— & SPJELDNAES, N. 1955. The Middle Ordovician of the Oslo Region, Norway, 6. Notes on bentonites (K-bentonites) from the Oslo–Asker District. *Norsk Geologisk Tidsskrift*, **35**, 29–52.

HARPER, D. A. T. 1981. The brachiopod *Stenocamara* from the Ordovician of Smøla, Norway. *Norsk Geologisk Tidsskrift*, **61**, 149–52.

—— & OWEN, A. W. 1983. The structure of the Ordovician rocks of the Ringerike District: evidence of a thrust system within the Oslo Region. *Norsk Geologisk Tidsskrift*, **63**, 111–15.

HEDSTRÖM, H. 1930. Om Ordoviciska fossil fran Ottadalen i det centrala Norge. *Avhandlinger Utgitt av det Norske Videnskaps—Akademi i Oslo, Matematisk–Naturvidenskapelig Klasse*, **10**, 1–10.

HENNINGSMOEN, G. 1952. Early Middle Cambrian fauna from Rogaland, S.W. Norway. *Norsk Geologisk Tidsskrift*, **30**, 13–32.

—— 1960. Cambro-Silurian deposits of the Oslo Region. *In*: HOLTEDAHL, O. (ed.) *Geology of Norway. Norges Geologiske Undersøkelse*, **208**, 130–50.

HOLMER, L. E. 1983. Lower Viruan discontinuity surfaces in Central Sweden. *Geologiska Föreningens i Stockholm Förhandlingar*, **105**, 29–42.

HOLMQVIST, A. 1980. Ordovician gastropods from Vardofjället, Swedish Lapland, and the dating of Caledonian serpentinite conglomerates. *Geologiska Föreningens i Stockholm Förhandlingar*, **102**, 439–97.

—— 1982. Ordovician gastropods from Vardofjället, Swedish Lapland, and the dating of Caledonian serpentinite conglomerates: a reply. *Geologiska Föreningens i Stockholm Förhandlingar*, **104**, 191–2.

HOLTEDAHL, O. 1915. V. Fossiler fra Smølen. *Norges Geologiske Undersøkelse*, **69**, 1–14 (Aarbog for 1914).

—— 1924. On the rock formations of Novaya Zemleya. *Report of the Scientific Results of the Norwegian Expeditions to Novaya Zemleya 1921*, Vol. 2 (22), pp. 1–181.

HOSSACK, J. R. 1978. The correction of stratigraphic sections for tectonic finite strain in the Bygdin

area, Norway. *Journal of the Geological Society, London*, **135**, 229–41.

——, GARTON, M. R. & NICKELSEN, R. P. 1985. The geological section from the foreland up to the Jotun thrust sheet in the Valdres area, South Norway. *In*: GEE, D. G. & STURT, B. A. (eds) *The Caledonide Orogen—Scandinavia and Related Areas*, pp. 443–56, Wiley, Chichester.

JAANUSSON, V. 1973. Aspects of carbonate sedimentation in the Ordovician of Baltoscandia. *Lethaia*, **6**, 11–34.

—— 1976. Faunal dynamics in the middle Ordovician (Viruan) of Baltoscandia. *In*: BASSETT, M. G. (ed.) *The Ordovician System: Proceedings of a Palaeontological Association Symposium, Birmingham, September 1974*, pp. 301–26, University of Wales Press, National Museum of Wales, Cardiff.

—— 1979. Ordovician. *In*: ROBISON, R. A. & TEICHERT, C. (eds) *Treatise on Invertebrate Palaeontology*, Part A, *Introduction*, pp. A136–66, Geological Society of America, Boulder, CO, and University of Kansas, Lawrence, KA.

—— 1984. Ordovician benthic macrofaunal associations. *In*: BRUTON, D. L. (ed.) *Aspects of the Ordovician System. Palaeontological Contributions from the University of Oslo No. 295*, pp. 127–39, Universitetsforlaget, Oslo.

—— & BERGSTRÖM, S. M. 1980. Middle Ordovician faunal spatial differentiation in Baltoscandia and the Appalachians. *Alcheringa*, **4**, 89–110.

—— & KARIS, L. 1982. Introduction to the Ordovician in Jämtland. *In*: BRUTON, D. L. & WILLIAMS, S. H. (eds) *Field Excursion Guide. 4th International Symposium on the Ordovician system. Palaeontological Contributions from the University of Oslo No. 279*, pp. 43–6, Universitetsforlaget, Oslo.

—— & MUTVEI, H. 1982. Ordovician of Öland. *Guide to Excursion 3. 4th International Symposium on the Ordovician System*, pp. 1–23, Section of Palaeozoology, Swedish Museum of Natural History, Stockholm.

KARIS, L. 1982. The sequence in the Lower Allochthon of Jämtland. *In*: BRUTON, D. L. & WILLIAMS, S. H. (eds) *Field Excursion Guide. 4th International Symposium on the Ordovician System. Palaeontological Contributions from the University of Oslo No. 279*, pp. 55–63, Universitetsforlaget, Oslo.

KAUTSKY, G. 1953. Der geologische bau des Sulitelma-Salojauregebietes in den Nord-Skandinavischen, Kaledoniden. *Sveriges Geologiska Undersökning, Serie C*, 528 pp.

KIÆR, J. 1932. The Hovin Group in the Trondheim area. *Norske Videnskaps—Akademi Skrifter I, Matematisk–Naturvitenskapelig Klasse*, **4**, 1–175.

KOLDERUP, C. F. & KOLDERUP, N.-H. 1940. Geology of the Bergen Arc system. *Bergens Museums Skrifter*, **20**, 1–137.

KULLING, O. 1933. Bergbyggnaden inom Björkvattnet-Virisen-området i Västerbottenfjällens centrala del. *Geologiska Föreningens i Stockholm Förhandlingar*, **55**, 167–422.

KVALE, A. 1938. Et kaledonsk effusiv-og intrusivfelt på Stord. *Bergens Museums Årbok 1937*, pp. 1–138.

LAPWORTH, C. 1905. Notes on the graptolites from

Bratland Gausdal, Norway. *Norges Geologiske Undersøkelse*, **39** (Appendix), 1–14.

LEITCH, E. C. 1984. Island arc elements and arc-related ophiolites. *Tectonophysics*, **106**, 177–203.

LOESCHKE, J. 1967. Zur Petrographie des Valdres Sparagmites zwischen Bitihorn und Langsuen/ Valdres (Süd-Norwegen). *Norges Geologiske Undersøkelse*, **243**, 67–98.

McKERROW, W. S., LAMBERT, R. ST J. & COCKS, L. R. M. 1985. The Ordovician, Silurian and Devonian Periods. *In:* SNELLING, N. J. (ed.) *The Chronology of the Geological Record. Geological Society of London Memoir No. 10*, pp. 73–80.

NATERSTAD, J. 1976. Comments on the Lower Palaeozoic unconformity in West Norway. *American Journal of Science*, **276**, 394–7.

——, ANDRESEN, A. & GABRIELSEN, R. H. 1981. Caledonides of the Hardangervidda–Ryfylke area. *Terra Cognita*, **1**, 60.

NEUMAN, R. B. & BRUTON, D. L. 1974. Early Middle Ordovician fossils from the Hølanda area, Trondheim Region, Norway. *Norsk Geologisk Tidsskrift*, **54**, 69–115

NICHOLSON, R. 1966. On the relations between volcanic and other rocks in the fossiliferous east Lommivann area, Norwegian Sulitjilma. *Norges Geologiske Undersøkelse*, **242**, 143–56.

—— 1971. Faunal provinces and ancient continents in the Scandinavian Caledonides. *Geological Society of America Bulletin*, **82**, 2349–56.

—— 1979. Caledonian correlations: Britain and Scandinavia. *In:* HARRIS, A. L., HOLLAND, C. H. & LEAKE, B. E. (eds) *The Caledonides of the British Isles Reviewed. Special Publication of the Geological Society of London No. 8*, pp. 3–18.

NICKELSEN, R. P., HOSSACK, J. R., GARTON, M. & REPETSKY, J. Late Precambrian to Ordovician stratigraphy and correlation in the Valdres and Synnfjell thrust sheets of the Valdres area, southern Norwegian Caledonides, with some comments on sedimentation. *In:* GEE, D. G. & STURT, B. A. (eds) *The Caledonide Orogen—Scandinavia and Related Areas*, pp. 369–78, Wiley, Chichester.

NYSTUEN, J. P. 1981. The late Precambrian 'Sparagmites' of southern Norway. A major Caledonian allochthon—the Osen–Røa nappe complex. *American Journal of Science*, **281**, 69–94.

OLAUSSEN, S. 1976. Paleozoic fossils from Troms, Norway. *Norsk Geologisk Tidsskrift*, **56**, 457–9.

POULSEN, V. 1966. Cambro-Silurian stratigraphy of Bornholm. *Medd. Dansk. Geol. Fören.*, **16**, 117–37.

RAMSAY, D. M. & STURT, B. A. 1978. A sub-Caledonian unconformity within the Finnmarkian Nappe sequence and its regional significance. *Norges Geologiske Undersøkelse*, **339**, 107–16.

——, STURT, B. A., ZWANN, K. B. & ROBERTS, D. 1985. Caledonides of northern Norway. *In:* GEE, D. G. & STURT, B. A. (eds) *The Caledonide Orogen—Scandinavia and Related Areas*, pp. 163–184, Wiley, Chichester.

READING, H. G. 1965. Eocambrian and Lower Palaeozoic geology of the Digermul peninsula, Tana Fjord, Finnmark. *Norges Geologiske Undersøkelse*, **234**, 167–91.

REUSCH, H. 1888. Bømmeløen og Karmøen med omgivelser, *Norges Geologiske Undersøkelse*, 422 pp.

RIIS, F. 1977. En petrografisk–strukturgeologisk undersøkelse av Nedstrandområdet, Ryfylke. *Thesis*, University of Oslo, 138 pp. (unpublished).

ROBERTS, D. 1980. Petrochemistry and palaeogeographic setting of the Ordovician volcanic rocks of Smøla, central Norway. *Norges Geologiske Undersøkelse*, **359**, 43–60.

—— 1983. Devonian tectonic deformation in the Norwegian Caledonides and its regional perspectives. *Norges Geologiske Undersøkelse*, **380**, 85–96.

—— & GEE, D. G. 1981. Caledonian tectonics in Scandinavia. *Terra Cognita*, **1**, 69–70.

ROBERTSON, A. H. F. & WOODCOCK, N. H. 1983. Zabyat Formation, Semail Nappe, Oman: sedimentation on to an emplacing ophiolite. *Sedimentology*, **30**, 105–16.

RYAN, P. D. & SKEVINGTON, D. 1976. A re-interpretation of the late Ordovician–early Silurian stratigraphy of the Dyvikvågen and Ulven–Vaktal areas, Hordaland, western Norway. *Norges Geologiske Undersøkelse*, **324**, 1–19.

——, WILLIAMS, D. M. & SKEVINGTON, D. 1980. A revised interpretation of the Ordovician stratigraphy of Sør-Trøndelag and its implications for the evolution of the Scandinavian Caledonides. *In:* WONES, D. R. (ed.) *The Caledonides in the USA: Proceedings of the International Geological Correlation Program—Caledonide Orogen Project 27, Blacksburg, VA. Department of Geological Sciences, Virginia Polytechnic Institute and State University, Memoir No. 2*, pp. 99–103.

SCHMIDT, O. 1984. The graptolitic facies of the Bogo Shale (Arenig–Llanvirn), Sør-Trøndelag, west central Norway. *Geologica et Palaeontologica*, **18**, 17–19.

SKEVINGTON, D. 1963. A note on the age of the Bogo Shale. *Norsk Geologisk Tidsskrift*, **43**, 257–60.

SKJERLIE, F. J. 1969. The pre-Devonian rocks in the Askvoll–Gaular area and adjacent districts, western Norway. *Norges Geologiske Undersøkelse*, **258**, 325–59.

—— 1974. The lower Palaeozoic sequence of the Stavfjord district, Sunnfjord. *Norges Geologiske Undersøkelse*, **302**, 1–32.

SOLLI, A., NATERSTAD, J. & ANDRESEN, A. 1978. Structural succession in a part of the outer Hardangerfjord area, West Norway. *Norges Geologiske Undersøkelse*, **343**, 39–51.

STIGH, J. B. 1979. Ultramafites and detrital serpentinites in the central and southern parts of the Caledonian allochthon in Scandinavia. *Geol. Inst. Chalmers Tekn. Högsk. och Göteborgs Univ. Publ. A27*, pp. 1–222.

—— 1980. Detrital serpentinites of the Caledonian allochthon in Scandinavia. *In:* WONES, D. R. (ed.) *The Caledonides in the USA: Proceedings of the International Geological Correlation Program—Caledonide Orogen Project 27, Blacksburg, VA. Department of Geological Sciences, Virginia Polytechnic Institute and State University, Memoir No. 2*, pp. 149–56.

STØRMER, L. 1925. On a Lower Cambrian fauna at Ustaoset. *Fennia*, **45**, 12–22.

—— 1941. Dictyonema shales outside the Oslo Region. *Norsk Geologisk Tidsskrift*, **20**, 161–9.

—— 1967. Some aspects of the Caledonian geosyncline and foreland west of the Baltic Shield. *Quarterly Journal of the Geological Society of London*, **123**, 183–214.

STRAND, T. 1932. A Lower Ordovician fauna from the Smøla Island, Norway. *Norsk Geologisk Tidsskrift*, **11**, 356–66.

—— 1948. New trilobites from the Hølanda limestone (Trondheim Region, southern Norway). *Norsk Geologisk Tidsskrift*, **25**, 449–528.

—— 1954. Aurdal: Beskrivelse til det geologiske gradteigskart. *Norges Geologiske Undersøkelse*, **185**, 1–71 (in Norwegian with English summary).

—— 1972. The Norwegian Caledonides. VI. Area with Cambro-Silurian deposits along the west coast of South Norway. *In*: STRAND, T. & KULLING, O. (eds) *The Scandinavian Caledonides*, pp. 67–71, Wiley-Interscience, New York.

—— & KULLING, O. (eds) 1972. *The Scandinavian Caledonides*, Wiley-Interscience, New York.

STURT, B. A. 1984. The accretion of ophiolitic terrains in the Scandinavian Caledonides. *Geologie en Mijnbouw*, **63**, 201–12.

—— & ROBERTS, D. 1978. Caledonides of northernmost Norway. *In*: TOZER, E. T. & SCHENK, P. E. (eds) *Caledonian–Appalachian Orogen of the North Atlantic Region. Geological Survey of Canada Paper No. 78–13*, pp. 17–24.

—— & THON, A. 1976. Discussion. The age of orogenic deformation in the Scandinavian Caledonides. *American Journal of Science*, **236**, 385–90.

—— & —— 1978. Caledonides of southern Norway. *In*: TOZER, E. T. & SCHENK, P. E. (eds) *Caledonian–Appalachian Orogen of the North Atlantic Region. Geological Survey of Canada Paper No. 78–13*, pp. 39–47.

——, PRINGLE, I. R. & RAMSAY, D. M. 1978. The Finnmarkian phase of the Caledonian orogeny. *Journal of the Geological Society, London*, **135**, 597–610.

——, —— & ROBERTS, D. 1975. Caledonian nappe sequence in Finnmark, northern Norway, and timing of orogenic deformation and metamorphism. *Geological Society of America Bulletin*, **86**, 710–18.

THON, A. 1985. Late Ordovician and early Silurian cover sequences to the west Norwegian ophiolite fragments: stratigraphy and structural evolution. *In*: GEE, D. G. & STURT, B. A. (eds) *The Caledonide Orogen—Scandinavia and Related Areas*, pp. 407–15, Wiley, Chichester.

——, MAGNUS, C. & BREIVIK, H. 1980. The stratigraphy of the Dyvikvågen Group, Stord: a revision. *Norges Geologiske Undersøkelse*, **359**, 31–42.

THORSLUND, P. 1940. On the Chasmops series of Jemtland and Södermanland (Tvären). *Sveriges Geologiska Undersökning, Serie C*, **436**, 1–191.

—— 1960. *In*: THORSLUND, P. & JAANUSSON, V. (eds) *The Cambrian, Ordovician and Silurian in Västergötland, Närke, Dalarne and Jämtland, central Sweden. Guide to Excursions Nos A23 and C18. International Geological Congress, 21st Session Norden, 1960, Guide Book E*, pp. 1–51.

VOGT, T. 1927. Sulitelmafeltets Geologi og Petrografi. *Norges Geologiske Undersøkelse*, **121**, 560 pp.

—— 1928. Den norske fjellkjedes evolusjonshistorie. *Norsk Geologisk Tidsskrift*, **10**, 97–115.

—— 1945. The geology of part of the Hølanda–Horg district, a type area in the Trondheim Region. *Norsk Geologisk Tidsskrift*, **25**, 449–528.

WEBBY, B. D. 1984. Ordovician reefs and climate: a review. *In*: BRUTON, D. L. (ed.) *Aspects of the Ordovician System. Palaeontological Contributions from the University of Oslo No. 295*, pp. 89–100, Universitetsforlaget, Oslo.

WILLIAMS, S. H. 1984. Lower Ordovician graptolites from Gausdal, central southern Norway: a reassessment of the fauna. *Norges Geologiske Undersøkelse*, **395**, 1–24.

WILSON, J. T. 1966. Did the Atlantic close and then re-open? *Nature, London*, **211**, 676–81.

WORSLEY, D., AARHUS, N., BASSETT, M. G., HOWE, M. P. A., MORK, A. & OLAUSSEN, S. 1983. The Silurian succession of the Oslo Region. *Norges Geologiske Undersøkelse*, **384**, 1–57.

YOCHELSON, E. 1963. Gastropods from the Otta Conglomerate. *Norsk Geologisk Tidsskrift*, **43**, 75–81.

—— 1977. Middle Ordovician gastropods from the Hølanda area, Trondheim Region, Norway. *Norsk Geologisk Tidsskrift*, **57**, 379–84.

D. L. BRUTON, Paleontologisk Museum, Sars gate 1, N-0562 Oslo 5, Norway.
D. A. T. HARPER, Department of Geology, The University, Dundee DD1 4HN, Scotland.
Present address: Department of Geology, University College, Galway, Ireland.

Palaeontological evidence bearing on the Arenig–Caradoc development of the Iapetus Ocean basin

Robert B. Neuman

SUMMARY: Ophiolitic rocks of the Dunnage–Dundee terranes and deep-water sedimentary rocks in the Gander–Greenore terranes indicate the position of the Iapetus Ocean in the Appalachian–Caledonide orogen during the Late Precambrian and Early Ordovician. The few occurrences of fossiliferous Cambrian to Tremadocian peri-insular limestones in the Dunnage terrane suggest a relatively narrow ocean basin within low palaeolatitudes. Late Arenig–early Llanvirn islands in Dunnage and Gander terranes and their equivalents were more abundant; most have little limestone and distinctive Celtic faunal assemblages of middle to high palaeolatitudes, but two (Glensaul–Tourmakeady, central western Ireland, and Hølonda, central western Norway) have abundant limestone and Scoto-Appalachian fossils of low palaeolatitudes. During the obduction of Iapetus Ocean crust, Celtic faunas were replaced by late Llanvirn–Llandeilo warm-water assemblages, indicating movement of these terranes into low palaeolatitudes.

The axial part of the Appalachian–Caledonide orogen is the site of the Cambrian–Ordovician Iapetus Ocean basin. Comparisons of the faunas of this age range within the vestiges of this ocean basin, and the continental rise prisms that bordered it, with those of adjacent miogeoclines and continental platforms contribute to knowledge of the palaeogeography of the orogen.

The most informative of these faunas are those from remnants of islands of various kinds identified at several places through the orogen. Convincing evidence for such islands is forthcoming where rocks of deep-water origin can be traced into those of shallow-water origin and in turn to shore-line deposits and their emergent sources, as in the Hølanda area of W central Norway (Bruton & Bockelie 1980, 1982). Less complete but equally convincing evidence of an insular setting was seen in an offshore-to-onshore progression of fossiliferous volcaniclastic rocks on New World Island, Newfoundland (Horne 1976, Neuman 1976). More subtle indications of peri-insular origin include the presence of ignimbrite immediately beneath fossiliferous tuff in the Shin Brook Formation, Maine, and the small areal extent, disjunct distribution, petrography, local geological relations and mid-orogen location of other formations.

Fossil shallow-water benthic faunas are especially valuable for determining palaeogeography. Like their Recent counterparts, climate strongly influences their composition, as does the limited mobility and dispersal mechanisms of their organisms. Modern island biotas are characterized by their endemic taxa; the degree of endemism varies greatly, and is governed by the geography and history of the individual island or archipelago and by the biological characteristics of the organisms constituting the biota. In general the biotas of near-shore islands within normal dispersal ranges of organisms of nearby habitats are extensions of those habitats, while islands beyond those ranges have special populations. Comparisons of peri-insular fossil faunas with coeval faunas of miogeoclines and continental platforms thus permit an estimate of their former relative positions.

Cambrian to Early Ordovician rocks deposited on the miogeoclines on opposite sides of Iapetus differ greatly. Those on the N American (Laurentian) side are largely carbonates that were deposited in low-latitude warm climates, while those on the opposite (Baltic and Armorican) side are dominantly pelitic and were deposited in cooler waters. The scattered occurrences of rocks of probable peri-insular origin through the axial part of the orogen give some indication of the configuration of Iapetus at successive stages.

This paper is a summary of one recently published on the same subject (Neuman 1984) to which the reader is referred for more complete documentation than is presented here.

Islands in Iapetus

Pre-late Arenig

Although the Cambrian to earliest Ordovician age range of basin deposits in the axial region of the orogen is known from a few widely scattered occurrences of fossils of pelagic organisms and from trace fossils, few contemporaneous islands have been identified.

The late Middle and early Late Cambrian platform limestone within the Dunnage zone in

From HARRIS, A. L. & FETTES, D. J. (eds), 1988, *The Caledonian–Appalachian Orogen,*
Geological Society Special Publication No. 38, pp. 269–274.

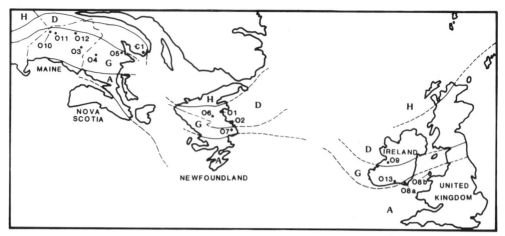

FIG. 1. Terranes of the Appalachian–Caledonide orogen in N America and the British Isles: H, Humber and Hebrides terranes; D, Dunnage and Dundee terranes; G, Gander and Greenore terranes; A, Avalon and Anglesey terranes. Points referred to in the text: Є1, Cambrian suspect island; O1–O13, Ordovician suspect islands. (Terrane nomenclature of Williams (1978); map after Haworth & Jacobi (1983).)

Quebec near Percé (Fig. 1, Є1) which has deep-water correlatives (Fritz et al. 1970) is a suspect island. Two explanations of this anomalous occurrence have been offered (Poole, in Poole & Rodgers 1972): (1) it is an exotic block derived from the edge of the miogeocline; (2) it is part of the N American autochthonous carbonate shelf exposed in a tectonic window. Although the 13 trilobite genera from these rocks are N American, most from the carbonate bank margin but some from the continental interior, the species of the 10 genera that were specifically determinable are endemic (Fritz et al. 1970). Such pervasive endemism suggests genetic isolation that might be afforded by an offshore island or shoal that lay within the same climate zone as the N American bank margin.

Evidence of earliest Ordovician islands is known only from one Tremadoc occurrence and one occurrence that is probably early Arenig, both in the Dunnage zone of Notre Dame Bay, Newfoundland, and both consisting of limestone associated with volcanic rocks. The Tremadocian occurrence, in eastern Notre Dame Bay (Fig. 1, O2), although lacking in provincially diagnostic fossils, is of special interest because it is part of the basal unit of the thick and continuous rock sequence—the Summerford Group—on New World Island (Horne 1970). Higher in the same sequence are distinctive fossiliferous peri-insular late Arenig rocks and late Llanvirn to early Llandeilo limestone that are of special interest.

Early Arenig limestone at South Catcher Pond in western Notre Dame Bay (Fig. 1, O1) yielded

four trilobite genera and one brachiopod genus which, although not provincially distinctive, have congeners in the bank-edge carbonate rocks of western Newfoundland and Quebec (Dean 1970, Boucot 1973). The presence of limestone at both places and the fossils in the latter suggest that this segment of the Dunnage zone shared the same warm climate that prevailed in the mio-geocline at the beginning of the Ordovician. Perhaps the ocean basin during the earliest Ordovician lay largely within the influence of the warm climate that prevailed across the N American craton.

Late Arenig–early Llanvirn

Mid-orogen islands of this age, just prior to Taconic tectonic events, are more numerous than earlier ones. Benthic shelly faunal provinces are well differentiated, permitting the recognition of two very similar schemes of biogeographic prov-inces, each based on a major component of the fauna, brachiopods and trilobites (Whittington & Hughes 1972, Williams 1973). In addition to the assemblages of the N American and Baltic–Armorican platforms in these schemes, a distinc-tive Celtic brachiopod province includes the brachiopod assemblages in seven of the nine peri-insular settings now known (Neuman & Bates 1978).

In these seven occurrences the fossiliferous rocks are of volcanic or epiclastic composition with little or no associated limestone. Five of these are in the northern Appalachians in both the Dunnage and Gander terranes (Fig. 1, O2–O7), one is in the British Isles (Anglesey and southeastern Ireland (Fig. 1, O8a, b)) just off the southeastern edge of the Greenore terrane and one is in the southeastern Scandinavian Caledonides in the Köli Nappe.

The composition of the Celtic assemblage is what might be expected in isolated ocean islands. Brachiopods are more abundant than other fossils: a significant proportion of brachiopod genera are endemic, others are elsewhere temporally or spatially separated and there are several distinctive Baltic forms that suggest linkages with that region. Trilobites, although not as abundant as brachiopods, are similarly distinctive (Dean 1974). Such islands may have been important havens for taxa from a wide variety of environments and for opportunistic forms during a major regression associated with a global lowering of the sea level (Fortey 1984).

The near absence of limestone from sequences containing Celtic assemblages together with the presence of Baltic forms suggests that these islands lay at mid-latitudes near the southern margin of Iapetus. Support for this comes from the discovery of Llanvirn brachiopods of both Celtic and Anglo-Welsh provincial affinities in a debris flow derived from a volcanic island near Builth, on the southern margin of the Welsh Basin (Lockley 1984), (Fig. 2, B).

The two other peri-insular late Arenig–early Llanvirn occurrences, in western Ireland and central western Norway, lie to the NW of the Celtic occurrences nearest them. In Ireland fossiliferous limestones (Glensaul Group and Tourmakeady Beds) (Fig. 2, T) are intimately associated with volcanic rocks (Phillips *et al.* 1969, Williams & Curry 1985) in the Dundee zone (Fig. 1, O9). Those in Norway, both at Hølonda and Smøla (Fig. 2, H) are in siltstones

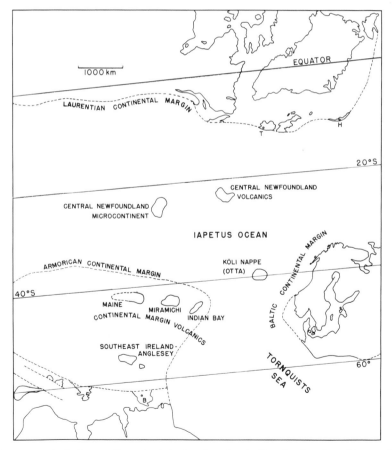

FIG. 2. Insular terranes in the Iapetus Ocean basin in Arenig and early Llanvirn time (from Neuman 1984; adapted from Cocks & Fortey 1982).

associated with thick beds of limestone and hypabyssal intrusives of the highest Caledonide nappe, the Støren Nappe. Brachiopods are the most abundant fossils at these places, but the generic assemblages here have little in common with those of the Celtic Province (Neuman & Bruton 1974, Williams & Curry 1985); although both have several endemic genera, they have in common many that are congeneric with those of the coeval N American carbonate bank (Scoto-Appalachian province of Williams (1973) and the Toquima–Table Head realm of Ross & Ingham (1970)). The similarities between these occurrences and those in N America suggested their original geographic proximity (Cocks & Fortey 1982). An alternative explanation of the Hølonda area is that those rocks were deposited offshore of a microcontinent in waters contiguous with those of the N American continental margin (Neuman & Sturt, in Neuman 1984).

These and other data suggest that the late Arenig–early Llanvirn islands formed two clusters (Fig. 2). Those that have Scoto-Appalachian fossil assemblages were shown by Whittington & Hughes (1972) and Cocks & Fortey (1982) to lie along the N American continental margin. Those that have Celtic assemblages lay at higher palaeolatitudes. The several whose insular rocks overlie continental rise deposits are shown here within the Armorican continental margin, while others of probable oceanic origin are plotted within the ocean basin. The area shown as 'Central Newfoundland Microcontinent' is of special interest because it represents a sequence exposed in a tectonic window that contains non-volcanic greywacke and fossiliferous limestone debris flows (Colman-Sadd & Swinden 1984). Thus the various Celtic islands show some indications of their palaeolatitudes, with the 'microcontinent' and the 'Central Newfoundland Volcanics' (New World Island) lying nearer to the equator than the others while the Irish Sea Horst, the source of the southeastern Ireland and Anglesey deposits, was an island at a much higher palaeolatitude, near the Welsh miogeocline. Scandinavian occurrences were possibly deposited on the opposite shores of a landmass within the ocean basin (Neuman & Sturt, in Neuman 1984), but the implications of this suggestion are not represented in Fig. 2.

Late Llanvirn–Caradoc

A large segment of the ocean crust of Iapetus was destroyed during Llanvirn time when the ophiolites of western Newfoundland and Quebec were emplaced. At the same time the Arenig–early Llanvirn Celtic faunal province was replaced in late Llanvirnian and younger peri-insular settings by shelly benthic faunas of Scoto-Appalachian affinities. This contrast is most apparent in the Summerford Group and related rocks of New World Island, Newfoundland (Horne 1970) (Central Newfoundland Volcanics of Fig. 2), in the Dunnage terrane. Here rocks that contain the late Arenig Celtic assemblage of fossils are tuffs and volcaniclastics that are minor components of a thick sequence of flows. Late Llanvirn to early Llandeilo Scoto-Appalachian assemblages of trilobites and brachiopods occur in the Cobbs Arm limestone immediately above the flows (Dean 1971, McKerrow & Cocks 1977) and in volcaniclastic rocks in a similar stratigraphic position nearby (McKerrow & Cocks 1981). Limestone of about the same age is interbedded with volcanics in the Tetagouche Group in New Brunswick (Miramichi Island Group of Fig. 2) in the Gander terrane, well above that part of the group that has Celtic-assemblage fossils. The Llandeilo limestones here have N Atlantic province conodonts (Nowlan 1981) but no shelly fossils, whereas those of Caradoc age have trilobites of southern Appalachian affinities (Dean 1976) as well as N Atlantic Province conodonts (Nowlan 1981).

Caradoc greywacke rich in clasts of volcanic origin occur at a few places in the Gander zone in Maine (Fig. 1, O10–O12), where their association with black slate, chert and volcanic rocks indicates their peri-insular origin (Neuman 1984). The few brachiopods in these rocks belong to genera that are common in American and Baltic provinces, a mixture classed as a transitory circum-Atlantic province by Williams (1973), further indicating the accessibility of the remnant Iapetus to immigration from both sources.

The abundance of Appalachian genera of brachiopods and trilobites in Llandeilo- to early Caradoc-age limestone in southeastern Ireland (Fig. 1, O13) (Tramore Group) (Carlisle 1979) and in limestone of early Caradoc age on Anglesey (Fig. 1, O8b) (Bates 1972) shows that faunal and lithic contrasts in the Irish and Welsh Caledonides paralleled those in the Appalachians. No fossiliferous rocks of comparable age are known in relevant parts of the Scandinavian Caledonides.

Thus widespread black shale and related rocks of Llandeilo and Caradoc age in the axial part of the Appalachian–Caledonide belt record the persistence of deep waters following Llanvirn subduction–obduction, but the fossils in rocks of peri-insular origin within the belt indicate that the Iapetus Ocean basin had lost much of its width as a consequence.

References

BATES, D. E. B. 1972. The stratigraphy of the Ordovician rocks of Anglesey. *Geological Journal*, **8**, 29–58.

BOUCOT, A. J. 1973. The Lower Ordovician brachiopod *Syntrophia* sp. cf. *S. arethusa* (Billings, 1862) from South Catcher Pond, northeastern Newfoundland. *Canadian Journal of Earth Sciences*, **10**, 427–30.

BRUTON, D. L. & BOCKELIE, J. F. 1980. Geology and paleontology of the Hølonda area, western Norway—a fragment of North America? *In:* WONES, D. R. (ed.) *The Caledonides in the USA: Proceedings of the International Geological Program—Caledonide Orogen Project 27, Blacksburg, VA. Department of Geological Sciences, Virginia Polytechnic Institute and State University, Memoir No. 2*, pp. 41–7.

—— 1982. The Løkken–Hølonda–Støren areas. *In:* BRUTON, D. L. & WILLIAMS, H. S (eds) *4th International Symposium on the Ordovician System, Field Excursion Guide. University of Oslo Palaeontological Contribution No. 279*, pp. 75–91.

CARLISLE, H. 1979. Ordovician stratigraphy of the Tramore area, County Waterford, with a revised Ordovician correlation for southeast Ireland. *In:* HARRIS, A. L., HOLLAND, C. H. & LEAKE, B. E. (eds) *The Caledonides of the British Isles Reviewed. Special Publication of the Geological Society of London No. 8*, pp. 545–54.

COCKS, L. R. M. & FORTEY, R. A. 1982. Faunal evidence for oceanic separations in the Palaeozoic of Britain. *Journal of the Geological Society, London*, **139**, 465–78.

COLMAN-SADD, S. P. & SWINDEN, H. S. 1984. A tectonic window in central Newfoundland? Geological evidence that the Appalachian Dunnage Zone may be allochthonous. *Canadian Journal of Earth Sciences*, **21**, 1349–67.

DEAN, W. T. 1970. Lower Ordovician trilobites from the vicinity of South Catcher Pond, northeastern Newfoundland. *Geological Survey of Canada Paper No. 70-44*, 15 pp.

—— 1971. Ordovician trilobites from the central volcanic mobile belt at New World Island, northeastern Newfoundland. *Geological Survey of Canada Bulletin No. 210*, 37 pp.

—— 1974. Lower Ordovician trilobites from the Summerford Group at Virgin Arm, New World Island, northeastern Newfoundland. *Geological Survey of Canada Bulletin No. 240*, 43 pp.

—— 1976. Some aspects of Ordovician correlation and trilobite distribution in the Canadian Appalachians. *In:* BASSETT, M. G. (ed.) *The Ordovician System: Proceedings of a Palaeontological Association Symposium, Birmingham, September 1974*, pp. 227–50, University of Wales Press and National Museum of Wales, Cardiff.

FORTEY, R. A. 1984. Global earlier Ordovician transgressions and regressions and their biological importance. *In:* BRUTON, D. L. (ed.) *Aspects of the Ordovician System: University of Oslo Palaeontological Contribution No. 295*, pp. 37–50.

FRITZ, W. H., KINDLE, C. H. & LESPÉRANCE, P. J. 1970. Trilobites and stratigraphy of the Middle Cambrian Corner-of-the Beach Formation, eastern Gaspé Peninsula, Quebec. *Geological Survey of Canada Bulletin No. 187*, pp. 43–58.

HAWORTH, R. T. & JACOBI, R. D. 1983. Geophysical correlation between the geological zonation of Newfoundland and the British Isles. *In:* HATCHER, R. D., JR., WILLIAMS, H. & ZIETZ, I. (eds) *Contributions to the Tectonics and Geophysics of Mountain Chains. Geological Society of America Memoir No. 158*, pp. 25–32.

HORNE, G. S. 1970. Complex volcanic–sedimentary patterns in the Magog belt of northeastern Newfoundland. *Geological Society of America Bulletin*, **81**, 1767–88.

—— 1976. Geology of Lower Ordovician fossiliferous strata between Virgin Arm and Squid Cove, New World Island, Newfoundland. *Geological Survey of Canada Bulletin No. 261*, pp. 1–9.

LOCKLEY, M. G. 1984. Faunas in a volcaniclastic debris flow from the Welsh Basin: a synthesis of palaeoecological and volcanological observations. *In:* BRUTON, D. L. (ed.) *Aspects of the Ordovician System. University of Oslo Palaeontological Contribution No. 295*, pp. 195–201.

McKERROW, W. S. & COCKS, L. R. M. 1977. The location of the Iapetus suture in Newfoundland. *Canadian Journal of Earth Sciences*, **14**, 488–95.

—— 1981. Stratigraphy of the eastern Bay of Exploits, Newfoundland. *Canadian Journal of Earth Sciences*, **18**, 751–64.

NEUMAN, R. B. 1976. Early Ordovician (late Arenig) brachiopods from Virgin Arm, New World Island, Newfoundland. *Geological Survey of Canada Bulletin*, **261**, 11–61.

—— 1984. Geology and paleobiology of islands in the Ordovician Iapetus Ocean: review and implications. *Geological Society of America Bulletin*, **95**, 1188–1201; Discussion by W. Gibbons and Reply by R. B. Neuman, 1985, *Geological Society of America Bulletin*, **96**, 1225–6; Discussion by D. A. T. Harper & D. L. Bruton and Reply by R. B. Neuman & B. A. Sturt, *Geological Society of America Bulletin*, **96**, 1597–9.

—— & BATES, D. E. B. 1978. Reassessment of Arenig and Llanvirn age (Early Ordovician) brachiopods from Anglesey, northwest Wales. *Palaeontology*, **21**, 571–613.

—— & BRUTON, D. L. 1974. Early Middle Ordovician fossils from the Hølonda area, Trondheim region, Norway. *Norsk Geologisk Tidsskrift*, **54**, 69–115.

NOWLAN, G. L. 1981. Some Ordovician conodont faunules from the Miramichi anticlinorium, New Brunswick. *Geological Survey of Canada Bulletin*, **345**, 35 pp.

PHILLIPS, W. A. E., KENNEDY, M. J. & DUNLOP, G. M. 1969. Geologic comparison of western Ireland and northeastern Newfoundland. *In:* KAY, M. (ed.) *The North Atlantic—Geology and Continental Drift. American Association of Petroleum Geologists Memoir No. 12*, pp. 194–211.

POOLE, W. H. & RODGERS, J. 1972. Appalachian geotectonic elements of the Atlantic provinces and southern Quebec. *24th International Geological Congress, Guidebook Excursion A63–C63*, 200 pp.

ROSS, R. J. JR & INGHAM, J. K. 1970. Distribution of Toquima–Table Head (Middle Ordovician Whiterock) faunal realm in the northern hemisphere. *Geological Society of America Bulletin*, **81**, 393–408.

WHITTINGTON, H. B. & HUGHES, C. P. 1972. Ordovician geography and faunal provinces deduced from trilobite distribution. *Philosophical Transactions of the Royal Society of London, Series B*, **263**, 235–78.

WILLIAMS, A. 1973. Distribution of brachiopod assemblages in relation to Ordovician palaeogeography. *In:* HUGHES, N. F. (ed.) *Organisms and Continents Through Time. Palaeontological Association Special Papers in Palaeontology No. 12*, pp. 241–69.

—— & CURRY, G. B. 1985. Lower Ordovician (Arenig) brachiopods from the Tourmakeady Limestone, County Mayo, Eire. *British Museum (Natural History), Geology Bulletin*, **38**, 183–269.

WILLIAMS, H. 1978. Geological development of the northern Appalachians: its bearing on the evolution of the British Isles. *In:* BOWES, D. R. & LEAKE, B. E. (eds) *Crustal Evolution in Northwestern Britain and Adjacent Regions. Special Publication of the Geological Society of London No. 10*, pp. 1–22.

R. B. NEUMAN, Department of Paleobiology, E-501 National Museum of Natural History, Smithsonian Institution, Washington, DC 20560, USA.

Ordovician to Silurian volcanism in the Appalachian–Caledonian orogen

C. J. Stillman

SUMMARY: Ordovician to Silurian volcanism in the orogen was primarily associated with the change from a spreading to a closing ocean basin and with the converging margins which involved the development of volcanic arcs, marginal basins and active continental margins as arc–trench systems approached and in some cases were subducted beneath the continental crust. Volcanism was controlled by plate-margin dynamics which differed according to the margin concerned but show remarkable similarities along the length of the orogen.

Arenig to Wenlock volcanism in N America, the British Isles, Europe and Scandinavia are surveyed in this paper in the framework of current plate-tectonic models, and the value of volcanic rocks in tectono-stratigraphic compilation is demonstrated.

Extensive destruction of oceanic crust and margins took place during major Ordovician orogenic events but, although parallel developments on both margins of Iapetus are noted, these events were not synchronous. Similarly, whilst subsequent volcanism was produced by both subduction-related and within-plate activity in most regions, the differences in the timing of this activity lend support to the concept of terrane accretion for the assembly of crustal blocks which make up the Caledonide orogen in its entirety.

At the start of Ordovician times volcanism in the Appalachian–Caledonian orogen was primarily associated with the change from a spreading to a closing Iapetus Ocean basin, a change which had commenced at the end of the Cambrian. Later activity was related to the development of active continental margins as the arc–trench systems approached and in some cases were subducted beneath the continental crust.

To facilitate comparison of the Ordovician volcanic activity along the orogen, Fig. 1 depicts the tectonic elements of the orogen restored to their post-Caledonian, but pre-Mesozoic, positions, as shown by Williams (1983) with tectonic lithofacies terranes added from Williams & Hatcher (1982) and Kennedy (1979). Figure 2 expands the N American sector to show the detail more clearly and Table 1 adds stratigraphic columns to clarify the timing of volcanism in the various terranes. Figure 3 shows the British Isles, using the model of Kelling et al. (1985) with volcanic localities added from Bevins et al. (1985). The Scandinavian sector involves a complex of nappes in which the volcanic rocks are found. Brekke et al. (1984) have presented a concise account of the lower Palaeozoic volcanism, and their map is extensively used in Fig. 4 together with a schematic representation of events in the development of the Scandinavian Caledonides by Sturt (1984).

In considering the volcanic rocks of the various sectors of the orogen, it should be borne in mind that the time interval designated for this account represents only a segment of the total evolution

of the orogen and that certain of the volcanic cycles started before the period whilst others continued beyond it. Some reference to these must therefore be made.

N America

It would be logical to follow the Appalachian belt from S to N, i.e. from Alabama to Newfoundland, but the profound overprint of the Hercynian (Alleghanian) orogeny obscures the original Appalachian features as far N as Long Island Sound. The clearest view of original Appalachian geology is thus perhaps best seen in Newfoundland. It is also doubtful whether any post-Arenig volcanic rocks occur S of New York State, except perhaps for a number of bentonitic tuff horizons in the southern Appalachians (D. Rankin 1984, personal communication), although pre-Arenig island-arc volcanics with associated arc plutonic rocks of possible Ordovician age are known from central Virginia (Pavlides 1981).

Newfoundland

Because of the degree of outcrop and the detail in which Newfoundland geology has been studied, the tectonic lithofacies were here first defined in units grouped to produce terranes which Williams (1978) continued throughout the rest of the Appalachians. Figure 2 depicts the terranes as shown in a recent paper by Williams & Hatcher (1982).

From HARRIS, A. L. & FETTES, D. J. (eds), 1988, *The Caledonian–Appalachian Orogen*, Geological Society Special Publication No. 38, pp. 275–290.

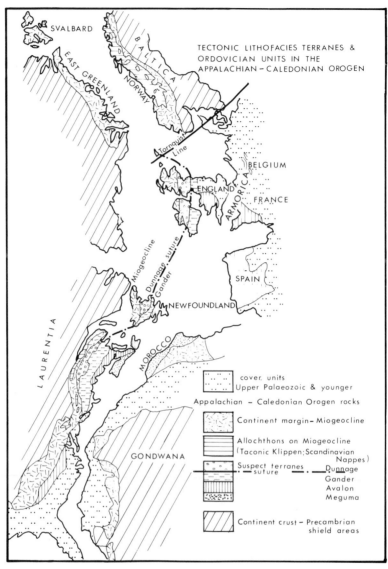

FIG. 1. Tectonic lithofacies terranes in the Appalachian–Caledonian orogen (continents restored to pre-Mesozoic drift configuration). (After Williams 1983.)

A significant feature of the Newfoundland region is that the Caledonian–Appalachian suture, i.e. the junction between what were the northwestern and southeastern margins of Iapetus brought together by the closure of Iapetus with collision in the Acadian orogenic event, is to be found here. This juxtaposes the margin of the N American continent, already modified by the Taconic orogenic event, with the Avalonian continental fragment. This Taconic event was marked by the thrusting of early Appalachian continental margin deposits over the platform edge, and climaxed in the Caradoc (McKerrow 1983). The Reach fault, W of Notre Dame Bay (see Fig. 2), has been interpreted as representing the suture in Newfoundland (Kennedy 1975, McKerrow & Cocks 1976).

The terranes (or zones) W of the Reach Fault are thus regarded here as belonging to the northwestern Iapetus margin through the period up to the Taconic orogenic event. The account which follows has largely been derived from reviews by Williams & Hatcher (1982) and McKerrow (1983) with additions from the recent

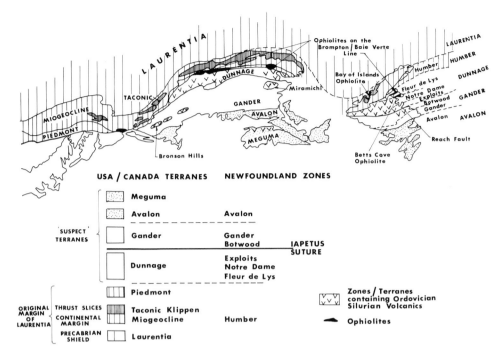

FIG. 2. Terranes of the Appalachian orogen: V, zones containing Ordovician–Silurian volcanics. (After Williams & Hatcher (1982) with details of Newfoundland zones added from Dewey *et al.* (1983).)

TABLE 1. *Summary of timing of volcanism on each side of Iapetus as seen in Newfoundland, Britain and Ireland, and Norway*

paper by Arnott *et al.* (1985). Reconstruction of the volcanic palaeo-environment indicates an offshore island arc built up over an eastward-dipping subduction system extending beneath oceanic lithosphere. This arc apparently collided with the N American passive continental margin during the mid-Ordovician; remnants of the oceanic lithosphere, thrust onto the continental margin, can be seen along the orogenic belt both in Newfoundland and further S. Perhaps the most complete is the Bay of Islands ophiolite (Fig. 3) dated at 504 ± 10 Ma (Mattinson 1976), which forms a Taconic thrust sheet apparently resulting from the attempted subduction of the passive continental margin (Dewey *et al.* 1983).

The continental margin and its overriding thrust sheets of ocean margin rocks are depicted in Fig. 2 as the miogeocline with Taconic klippen which, in Newfoundland, is known as the Humber Arm terrane (Humber zone). The rocks originally occurring seaward of this along the western margin of Iapetus have been designated as the Dunnage terrane, a complex assemblage which has been divided into a number of zones by Dewey *et al.* (1983) (Fig. 2 & Table 1): from W to E these are the Fleur de Lys zone, the Notre Dame zone and the Exploits zone.

The Fleur de Lys zone contains bimodal volcanics: mafic pillow lavas and volcaniclastics, acid volcaniclastics and minor porphyry intrusions. They range in age from Cambrian to early Ordovician (a U–Pb zircon age for silicic eruptives is 475 ± 10 Ma (Mattinson 1977)). The zone also contains the northern end of a most important line of ophiolites—the Baie Verte–Brompton line—which extends down the orogen towards New England. This line represents the now highly modified and originally complex passage from the continental lithosphere of N America to the oceanic lithosphere originally established by late Precambrian rifting (Dewey *et al.* 1983).

The Notre Dame zone is characterized by early Ordovician island-arc volcanics that rest on an ophiolitic basement (Dewey *et al.* 1983). It appears that at an early stage of the subduction of the N American continental margin the offshore island arcs began to split and new oceanic crust was generated to floor the developing marginal basins; it is thought that the Betts Cove ophiolite (Upadhyay *et al.* 1971) may represent such crust (Dewey *et al.* 1983). Volcanic material derived from the arcs was a major component of the infill to these basins. The top of this overlying arc sequence contains tholeiitic pillow lavas with some volcaniclastics (Papezic & Fleming 1967) and minor silicic volcanics. In places some of these volcanics (e.g. the Snooks Arm Group) are clearly seen as a cover sequence

to the new ocean crust, infilling the Arenig intra-arc basin with lavas and volcaniclastics. Palaeontological evidence (Nowlan & Thurlow 1984) now shows that some of the basalt–rhyolite volcanics seen in the Roberts Arm and Buchans Groups, which were previously thought to be Siluro-Devonian, are Arenig–Llanvirn in age.

The Exploits zone is made up largely of volcaniclastic sediment, shales and cherts, with less-abundant mafic pillow and sheet lavas and some silicic volcanics. Again, mafic volcanics predominate at the base and also near the top, where they are probably Llandeilo as they are overlain by extensive late Llandeilo to early Ashgill black shales. The famous Dunnage melange contains blocks of the volcanics and is probably a gravity slide in a fore-arc trough or near-arc basin (Hibberd & Williams 1979). The Exploits zone is terminated to the NE by the transcurrent Reach fault, which is accepted here as marking the Iapetus suture. Across this structure the rocks have different stratigraphy and faunas with little evidence of Ordovician volcanic arcs or inter-arc basins.

The Botwood zone is made up predominantly of a fine-grained sequence of mudstones and shallow marine sandstones. On the eastern margin of the zone is a wedge of ophiolitic rocks; however, these appear to be tectonically emplaced as a thrust slice from the lower part of the succession in the adjacent Gander zone and are probably pre-Ordovician.

The Gander zone is characterized by pre-middle Ordovician, possibly Precambrian, clastic sequences which are believed to have been deposited on gneisses and migmatites on the far side of the ocean from the arc–trench system that provided the Dunnage terrane lithologies (Williams & Hatcher 1982). They have apparently been deformed, metamorphosed and eroded in pre-Caradocian times before deposition of adjacent rocks of the Botwood zone (Dewey *et al.* 1983).

The Avalon zone represents the Avalonian continental fragment in Newfoundland and presents strong contrasts in metamorphism and deformation with the Gander zone (Dewey *et al.* 1983). It is supposedly the crust which bounded Iapetus to the SE and is a late Precambrian construction which has some similarity to the basement beneath the Welsh basin and the English Midland platform. As with the Gander zone, the absence of Ordovician rocks makes impossible any comparisons of Ordovician volcanicity with the zones to the W of the suture.

This description has so far been confined to the pre-Taconic successions. The Taconic orogenic event deformed and uplifted the sequences deposited on, or attached to, the margin of the N American continent. Across the Humber, Fleur de Lys and Notre Dame zones the upper Ordovician is missing and lower and middle Ordovician rocks are unconformably overlain by Siluro-Devonian clastic and volcanic sequences. Further from the margin, in the Exploits zone, the upper Ordovician is represented by a ubiquitous black shale and chert lithology which is widespread throughout the northern Appalachians during this time interval. The period represented by this unconformity has recently been revised, as isotopic studies of volcanics and intrusives in the Notre Dame zone have shown that some of the Siluro-Devonian volcanics are older than was thought. In the NW of the zone the Springdale Group red sandstones and conglomerates contain sub-aerial rhyolites, mainly ignimbrites, and minor basalts with related peralkaline plutons. Recent U–Pb zircon dating by Chandler & Dunning (1983) gives a Landovery age of 431 ± 5 Ma. Other similar volcanics may be of similar age. These calc-alkaline to alkaline bimodal suites can be interpreted from their geochemistry as strike-slip, or pull-apart basin, within-plate volcanics erupted on continental crust (Dewey *et al*. 1983). Perhaps significantly, a similar bimodal assemblage of mafic volcanics and silicic ignimbrites is found in an early Llandovery sequence in the Botwood zone. The implication may be that the Botwood zone was accreted to the N American continent by the Silurian.

Nova Scotia, New Brunswick and New England

The N American continental margin miogeocline can be traced the whole length of the Appalachians with, on its eastern edge, rocks equated with the Piedmont terrane which is properly defined in the southern Appalachians. To the E of this the Dunnage terrane can be followed from Newfoundland to New England (Fig. 2). These two units are thought to represent the rocks forming the northwestern margin of Iapetus throughout its lower Palaeozoic development. Positioned between them on the eastern edge of the Piedmont terrane are ophiolitic complexes which, in Quebec, make up the southward continuation of the Baie Verte line that Dewey *et al*. (1983) consider may represent the primary junction between continental and oceanic crust. Here, in the Brompton sector, it consists of ophiolite slices in a Dalradian-like succession of metasediments, apparently obducted onto the continental margin from the E. In the Thetford Mines area of Quebec the ophiolites have been ascribed to mid-ocean ridge magmas (Laurent *et*

al. 1979) and are overlain by a cover of lavas and volcaniclastics of volcanic-arc origin. The ophiolite is believed to have been the ocean crust of a marginal basin situated between the arc and the continent, which formed by spreading during the late Cambrian and acquired its cover of arc volcanics in the early Ordovician. The volcanics comprise basaltic and andesitic pillow lavas and pyroclastics, and acid volcaniclastics. The intermediate to acid sequence has calc-alkaline chemistry and the entire succession resembles a young arc developed on ocean crust like Tonga or the New Hebrides. Obduction of the oceanic slices appears to have occurred in the lower Ordovician, after which they were covered by a flysch deposit before the Taconic tectonism. Similar primitive arc volcanics are found flanking the eastern margin of the miogeocline in Vermont and Connecticut in the Hawley–Ascott–Weedon belt (Rankin 1983).

Thrust onto the miogeocline and analogous to Newfoundland's Bay of Islands ophiolite are the classic Taconic allochthons of Vermont and New York State. The allochthons are composite and consist of lower structural slices of sedimentary rocks and upper slices of igneous rocks (Williams & Hatcher 1982). The igneous rocks comprise ophiolitic fragments interpreted as oceanic lithosphere overlain by volcanics and plutonics thought to represent seamounts. In various places along the orogen the sedimentary rocks of the lower slices are coeval with westerly parts of the miogeocline, apparently deposited at the ancient continental slope and rise. Again, accretion may be related to westward transport of the allochthons resulting from attempted eastward subduction of the passive N American margin beneath an overriding oceanic plate (Williams & Hatcher 1982).

Eastward of the miogeocline and the Baie Verte–Brompton line, the correlation of terranes with those of Newfoundland becomes more problematical although still feasible for the Dunnage terrane (Williams & Hatcher 1982). This terrane is characterized by early Palaeozoic mafic rocks, marine sediments and melanges which apparently overlie ophiolitic substructure. The age and chemistry of the volcanic rocks indicate that they were produced in island arcs which were active during the development of the miogeocline (Kean & Strong 1975). In the Bathurst region of New Brunswick (Pajari *et al*. 1977) extensive and widely spilitized basalts are found both in the Arenig, where they are associated with melanges and sheeted dykes, and in Llanvirn–Llandeilo sequences where pillow lavas are overlain by Caradoc greywackes and black shales. Pajari *et al*. (1977) suggest that the lower sequence represents oceanic crust from a back-arc basin and the upper sequence represents an island arc.

At Bathurst and elsewhere in the western parts of the terrane the rocks have clearly been involved in the Taconic deformation. Further E this is less evident. A cover of Caradoc shales corresponding to those in the Exploits zone in Newfoundland mark a corresponding reduction in volcanic activity and confirm a similar relationship to the Taconic orogenic event, and further indicate that the Canadian Dunnage terrane must have 'docked' with N America before the upper Ordovician.

Within the Gander terrane, which is supposedly across the Iapetus suture, major difficulties in correlation appear. E of the Dunnage terrane there is the major volcanic and plutonic belt of the Bronson Hills anticlinorium in Connecticut, Massachusetts and New Hampshire and the Miramichi anticlinorium in New Brunswick. These are out of place in a model in which the Gander terrane is characterized by pre-middle Ordovician clastic sequences which are supposed to have been deposited on gneisses on the far side of the Iapetus spreading axis. They would fit better into the Avalon terrane of Williams & Hatcher (1982), but this would still present problems. The Bronson Hills anticlinorium (Robinson 1979) contains the Ammonoosuc volcanics which overlie gneisses in a series of domes which are now thought to contain some Avalon-like crust (P. Robinson 1984, personal communication). The eruptives include pillow basalts, andesites and low-potassium dacites, very like the Tonga arc volcanics, and peraluminous rhyolites. The whole suite is now believed to be derived from a mantle source with no significant contribution from crustal remelts, despite being erupted through sialic continental crust (P. Robinson 1984, personal communication). Rankin (1983) states that, despite their intense metamorphism, these Bronson Hills volcanics have been uncontroversially defined as the products of a mid-Ordovician island arc situated above an E-dipping subduction zone. Along strike in northern Maine there are other Ordovician volcanic rocks which may be of the same origin; some at least are basalts and andesites of recognizable island-arc type (Rankin 1983). Most workers have suggested that the Ammonoosuc volcanic arc was closely involved in the Taconic event. If so, the gneissic basement should be part of the N American crust.

The volcanics of the Miramichi anticlinorium are extensive rhyolites erupted onto sialic crustal rocks and succeeded by a thick clastic succession (Ruitenberg et al. 1978). Like the Ammonoosuc

volcanics they have been ascribed to emplacement above an E-dipping subduction zone (Rast et al. 1976), but the nature of the basement is not so well known. The Ordovician sequence here also shows similarities to that of the Leinster zone of southeastern Ireland, in particular to that of the Avoca copper-mining district.

There is much evidence to suggest that the Dunnage terrane was juxtaposed with the N American miogeocline during the middle Ordovician; there is less to support the collision of the Gander terrane at this time, and the arrival of the Avalon terrane cannot be clearly demonstrated until Siluro-Devonian times (Williams & Hatcher 1982). In the Avalon terrane, which is traced down the orogen to form a major component of the southern Appalachians, there are hardly any Ordovician rocks. In the NE, in Nova Scotia and New Brunswick, the earliest Appalachian volcanics belong to a late Ordovician to Devonian succession which starts with non-marine red beds and volcanics and passes up in the Silurian to shallow-water marine sediments with volcanics. These appear to be rift related and to overlie both the Avalon and the Meguma terranes of Nova Scotia. This provides the earliest evidence of juxtaposition of the Meguma terrane which has a very different early history involving the deposition of Cambrian and lower Ordovician sediments but no volcanics. The Siluro-Devonian volcanics related to the Meguma terrane are the White Rock Group, occurring along the southern side of the Bay of Fundy, which is a bimodal basalt–rhyolite assemblage, in which the basalts are transitional from alkaline to tholeiitic, erupted onto continental crust in an anorogenic or extensional 'within-plate' tectonic setting (Keppie & Dostal 1980). Ordovician basaltic sills from the same area, described by Barr et al. (1983), also have this chemistry as do the basalts of the bimodal assemblage of the Antigonish Highlands which, however, are erupted through Avalon crust. Across the Bay of Fundy the Mascarene–Nerapis belt in New Brunswick, which extends southward to the Maine coastal volcanic belt, is very similar. Here basalts and rhyolites which range from Silurian to Devonian in age are also erupted through Avalonian crust and have extensional within-plate geochemistry (Gates & Moench 1981).

Thus there appears to be a phase of within-plate magmatism in both Avalon and Meguma terranes which started in the late Ordovician and therefore should be mentioned in this account. The magmatism is of importance in dating the accretion of these terranes to the N American continent, for the volcanics do not appear to be subduction related and support the concept of terrane accretion for the assembly of crustal blocks which make up the Caledonide orogen in its entirety.

The British Isles and northwestern Europe

Although the Appalachians and Caledonides are now separated by the Atlantic Ocean, plate reconstructions for the end of the Appalachian–Caledonian orogeny by researchers such as Phillips *et al.* (1976), Williams (1983, fig. 1) and Kennedy (1979) suggest that the major tectonic lithofacies elements of the Appalachians extend to the British Isles and can be recognized in the zones into which the Caledonide rocks have recently been divided by, for example, Kelling *et al.* (1985, fig. 3). The Iapetus suture running through the centre of Ireland and between Scotland and England divides the region almost in half, and in contrast with N America Ordovician volcanism along the margin of the southeastern or Avalon continent is extensive and quite long lived.

In the zones representing the northern continent and its margins the tectonic history of the Appalachian miogeocline with its obduction of ophiolites, uplift and deformation, culminating in the Taconic orogenic event, has its counterpart in the pre-Grampian and Grampian evolution of the Dalradian ensialic basin. This orogenic event terminated in the collision of a volcanic arc flanking the northwestern margin of Iapetus with the N American plate, closing the small marginal and back-arc basins which were interposed between the rising Dalradian cordillera and the active northwestern margin of Iapetus (Kelling *et al.* 1985). Although analogous to the Taconic history of N America, this process culminated somewhat earlier in northern Britain and has preserved far fewer fragments of obducted or tectonically emplaced ocean crust. The difference may be due in part to the short-lived nature of the marginal basins which produced the components of ophiolites so far recognized and perhaps also to the polarity of subduction. There is no evidence of an eastward dip to the pre-Grampian subduction system. The bulk of available evidence refers to the post-Grampian evolution of the orogen and indicates northwesterly subduction beneath the Scottish Midland Valley and Highlands. The accretionary history of the Southern Uplands during the Caradoc to Wenlock period and the chemical zonation of Siluro-Devonian volcanics from the S of Scotland to the Highlands (Thirlwall 1981) both support this model. However, Kelling *et al.* (1985, fig. 4) feel

sufficiently confident in the scanty evidence that is available to suggest northerly-directed subduction from the middle Cambrian onwards. If the pre-Grampian direction of subduction was indeed northwestward, the tendency would have been for the continent to ride up over the ocean slab, making obduction more difficult.

The Highland Boundary fault separates the Dalradian basin from the Midland Valley and Southern Uplands–Longford Down zones which equate with the Dunnage terrane. Volcanism N of this fault is largely pre-Arenig or post-Wenlock. Along the fault zone the Highland Border complex contains serpentinites, gabbros, spilites, amphibolites, cherts, clastic sediments and limestones, some of which are of Arenig age (Curry *et al.* 1982). The complex may perhaps be the equivalent of ophiolitic fragments on the Baie Verte–Brompton line. It has been ascribed to northward transport (by subduction and reverse faulting) of oceanic crust from a marginal basin or back-arc sequence formed S of the fault (van Breemen & Bluck 1981). An alternative suggestion by Henderson & Robertson (1982) is that it formed in a small ocean basin within the Dalradian and was obducted towards the SE. Other representatives of similar ocean crust may be the basic metavolcanics of Arran and Bute (Ikin 1983), the Tyrone igneous complex in Northern Ireland (Hutton *et al.* 1985) and perhaps the Deer Park complex of Clew Bay in the W of Ireland (Dewey 1982, Ryan *et al.* 1983).

In the Midland Valley zone lower Palaeozoic rocks are largely concealed beneath upper Palaeozoic cover; however, there is evidence from granitoid and acid volcanic clasts in Ordovician sediments at Girvan that an early pre-Arenig island arc may have existed in a region N of the Southern Uplands fault (Bluck 1983). Such an arc must have been uplifted in middle Ordovician times to permit erosion and inclusion of these boulders in upper Ordovician sediments (Longman *et al.* 1979); uplift at this time would coincide with the event which closed the source basin for the Highland Border complex and produced the Margie Series molasse which is deposited on the ophiolitic rocks of the latter complex.

In the W of Ireland the lower Palaeozoic rocks of the small Curlew Mountains inlier and the larger S Mayo basin represent the Midland Valley zone. On the southern flank of the S Mayo basin Tremadocian island-arc tholeiitic volcanism of the Lough Nafooey Group passes upwards into calc-alkaline pillow basalts and andesites (Ryan *et al.* 1980). Subsequent Arenig to Llanvirn volcanism is largely acid. The lowest Arenig sediments contain abundant calc-alkaline granitic clasts, suggesting an arc-core unroofing situa-

BRITISH ISLES

FIG. 3. Caledonian zones of Britain and Ireland. (Boundaries partly after Kelling *et al.* (1985); volcanic outcrops after Bevins *et al.* (1985).)

tion analogous to that postulated for the Scottish Midland Valley by Bluck (1983), and the depositional sequence is terminated by a major post-Llanvirn–Llandeilo pre-upper Llandovery unconformity which may well be related to the uplift at this time in the Midland Valley in Scotland.

In the SW of the Scottish Midland Valley, S of the Ordovician sediments at Girvan, is the Ballantrae complex. This has been interpreted as an ophiolitic slice of hot ocean crust obducted, together with other assemblages of possible island-arc origin, in Arenig times (475±4 Ma) (Bluck *et al.* 1980). These workers believe that the source was an Arenigian short-lived marginal basin; the complex contains gabbros with a U–Pb age of 484±4 Ma, formed S of the Midland Valley zone, and has an island arc on its southerly edge. Others have argued that the ophiolite is true ocean crust (Lambert & McKerrow 1976) or part of an island arc (Lewis & Bloxham 1977), but a more recent publication (Thirlwall & Bluck 1983) uses isotopic and chemical evidence to show that the ophiolite contains at least four different and tectonically juxtaposed units.

Separated from the Midland Valley zone by the Southern Uplands fault, the Southern Uplands–Longford Down zone comprises Ordovician and Silurian sediments and volcanics emplaced in what has been interpreted as an accretionary prism (Leggett *et al.* 1976). The northern part consists of Arenig sequences containing ocean-floor volcanics of two chemical facies, which Lambert *et al.* (1981) have designated as ocean-floor tholeiites and oceanic-fracture volcanics. Later Llandeilo–Caradoc volcanics are of mildly-alkaline oceanic-island composition and they are of relatively minor extent. These volcanics have all been erupted in an ocean basin and indicate that the prism has accreted from the oceanward side of a trench; no volcanics generated on or above the subduction zone have as yet been observed, which suggests that the entire sequence was emplaced within a relatively short distance, probably less than 100 km, of the trench.

The zones so far described contain rocks which were apparently emplaced on the northwestern margin of Iapetus, and they are bounded to the S by the Iapetus suture which occupies a position analogous to the suture in N America: the rocks to the S of it have been emplaced on the opposite side of Iapetus. The suture itself lies concealed beneath upper Palaeozoic rocks, but S of it lower Palaeozoic rocks crop out in the Lake District, eastern and southeastern Ireland and Wales (Fig. 3). Williams (1983) assigns them to the Gander and Avalon terranes, but such exact equivalence is arguable; as Kelling *et al.* (1985) say, 'the south-eastern margin of the British Caledonides is characterized by an Avalon-type history', and from the suture southwards there are volcanics which apparently belong to volcanic arcs and basins marginal to a continental mass. The initial direction of the subduction system above which the arcs were first erupted is as yet unknown; it is only with the establishment of a clearly zoned sequence in Caradoc to Ashgill times that a southeasterly direction of subduction can be ascribed with any degree of certainty.

The volcanic arc nearest to the suture extends in a NE–SW direction from the N of the Lake District to eastern Ireland (see Fig. 3), and the earliest activity is seen in the Llanvirn rocks of the Eycott district of the Lake District. Here tholeiites, initially of rather primitive island-arc type, evolved towards calc-alkaline compositions, whilst new centres of primitive arc volcanism appeared further along the arc, the inception of arc magmatism apparently migrating in a southwesterly direction to produce the Caradoc volcanic sequences of Balbriggan and Lambay in N Leinster. Precise determination of this migration is precluded by subsequent strike-slip shuffling of crustal blocks resulting in the juxtaposition of small-scale exotic terranes such as that containing the Llanvirn mildly-alkaline ocean-island volcanics of Bellewstown, Collon and Grangegeeth.

Along this arc, from the Lake District to the southeastern Irish coast, a Llanvirn to lower Llandeilo hiatus was succeeded by a voluminous and extensive phase of activity which continued for almost 20 Ma into Ashgill times. Stratiform composite volcanoes were constructed which rose from below the sea to build sub-aerial plateaux with inter-montane lakes or shallow seas. The andesite–dacite–rhyolite Borrowdale volcanics of the Lake District, whose eruption is dated by an Sm–Nd age on garnets as 457 ± 4 Ma (Thirlwall & Fitton 1983), produced volcanoes resembling those of the Cascades Range of present-day northwestern America (Moseley 1983). In southeastern Ireland, upper Llandeilo volcanoes were submarine and erupted basalts and basaltic andesites of tholeiitic and transitional calc-alkaline chemistry. By Caradoc times the volcanism was still partly submarine, although dominantly acid, with extrusive rhyolite domes and was in some cases associated with Kuroko-type

mineralization (Sheppard 1980). Trace-element and isotopic studies (Davies 1984) confirm earlier geochemical studies (Stillman & Williams 1979) that indicated a zonation above a SE-dipping subduction system from an outer volcanic arc in N Leinster to continental margin activity well within the plate in Waterford on the SE Irish coast.

Between this extensive volcanic arc and the Welsh basin there is interpolated now the Irish Sea horst, a wedge of Proterozoic basement separated from the Welsh basin by the faults of the Menai Straits system which may well be transcurrent. On Anglesey this basement has a cover of lower Palaeozoic rocks which include Caradoc rhyolites.

The Welsh basin appears to have initiated during the early Cambrian, when extensional tectonics led to foundering of blocks of the Proterozoic crust. The relationship of this extensional situation to the inception of subduction is not clear, but by later Tremadoc times widespread tectonism was associated with island-arc volcanism as can be seen in the arc tholeiites of Rhobell Fawr and the Trefgarne volcanics of Dyfed. Such subduction-related magmatism was short lived: the succeeding widespread basal Arenig transgression was followed by volcanism which throughout the Ordovician seems to have been related to back-arc extension, typically a bimodal basalt–rhyolite association. The basic rocks resemble those of modern ensialic marginal basins in which basalts are transitional from ocean-floor to arc-like compositions. Minor volumes of andesite to rhyodacite resulted from low-pressure fractional crystallization of the tholeiitic basalts. The more voluminous rhyolites may, at least in part, have been generated by crustal fusion, although in some instances evolution by crustal fractionation from intermediate magma has been proposed (Kokelaar *et al.* 1984, Bevins *et al.* 1985). The significance of crustal fracturing in controlling the eruptions is very apparent, especially in Snowdonia (Howells 1977, p. 404). and it is now thought likely that fissures in central Snowdonia were related to the subsidence of a large caldera (M. F. Howells 1985, personal communication).

On the eastern edge of the Welsh basin, Llanvirn to Caradoc volcanism with calc-alkaline affinities has been recognized in the Builth Wells and Shelve–Breiden Hills inliers. If the accepted plate-tectonic model for the Ordovician postulates a single SE-dipping subduction system below the Lake District–Irish arc with the Welsh basin situated above the crystalline margin of the continent, the chemistry of these volcanics presents a problem.

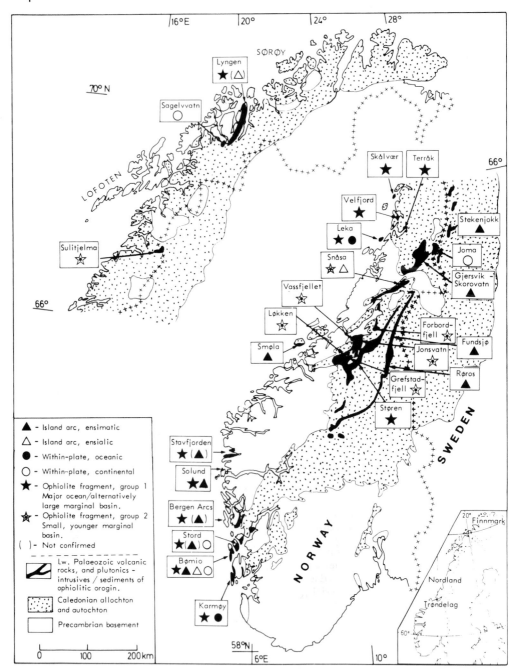

FIG. 4. Distribution of Caledonian ophiolites and volcanic arc sequences in Norway and Sweden. (From Brekke *et al.* (1984, fig. 1) with a summary of Iapetus development history and the time of generation of Norwegian ophiolites from Sturt (1984, fig. 2).)

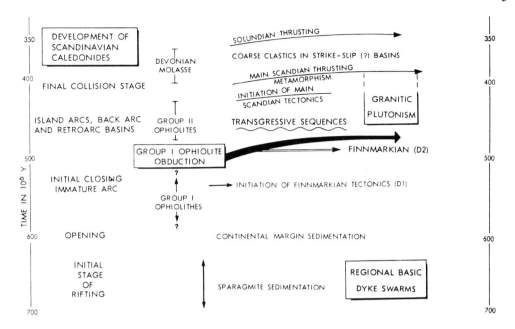

Another problem is given by the alkaline hawaiites, mugearites and rhyolites of Skomer Island off the Dyfed coast, which are of ocean-island chemistry and interbedded with sediments originally thought to be Llandovery (Sanzen Baker 1972) but now believed to be Caradoc (R. E. Bevins 1985, personal communication).

The Caledonian volcanics have generally been described as marginal to the 'Avalon' continental crust—here the 'English microcontinent'—erupted on the miogeocline and active margin of this continent. Owing to the post-Caledonian cover on the continental plate, little is known of intra-continental volcanism on the plate itself in England nor of the relationship of this segment of continental crust to the 'Armorican' crustal plate of northwestern Europe. Small inliers of Llandovery age are found at Tortworth, Gloucestershire, and the Mendips, Somerset (Van de Kamp 1969), and there is a suite of calc-alkaline intrusions in the English Midlands (Le Bas 1982).

Cabanis (1983) summarized Caledonian–Hercynian volcanism in France, where plutonism was more significant than volcanism during the Ordovician. Earlier intrusions were associated with the build-up of Cadomian crust, and the calc-alkaline activity with tholeiitic and alkaline admixture which continued into the Ordovician is interpreted as being due to progressive rifting of continental crust. Much of this activity is seen in Armorica, and later activity both here and further to the S is complicated by the tectonics and magma genesis probably associated with the

development of the Rheic Ocean, about which there seems to be little general agreement.

The southward and eastward extent of the Armorican plate is likewise far from clear. New data from Belgium may add a significant contribution (André & Michot 1981, Andre & Deutsch 1984, J. Hertogen & L.André 1985, personal communication in a summary report for IGCP 27). Acid lavas and tonalite intrusions of upper Cambrian to lower Ordovician age in the Ardennes massif were followed by gabbros and diabases in the upper Ordovician to Silurian both in the Ardennes and to the N in the Brabant massif. The Brabant rocks are calc-alkaline, whilst those from the Ardennes are of back-arc basalt or arc tholeiite composition. It is suggested by these workers that the regions were situated on an active continental margin during Ordovician to Silurian times and that the magmatism is related to SE-directed subduction beneath the northeastern margin of the Armorican plate prior to its docking with the Baltic plate. They also suggest that development of the mid-European Caledonides may thus be related to closure of a Palaeozoic Medio-European (Rheic) ocean during the northward drift and docking of the Armorican plate.

Scandinavia

In the Caledonides of Norway and Sweden the rocks occur within nappe units which are stratigraphic packages bounded by tectonic junctions and stacked one above the other; hence exact correlation of the volcanics and their original geometry of distribution can only be a matter of guesswork. Although evidence of most of the environments seen elsewhere in the orogen can be found, the terrane analysis of N America and Britain is clearly more dubious here. However, there are sufficient differences to suggest that, at least throughout the lower Palaeozoic, Scandinavia was not linked to any of the British terranes. The Scandinavian Caledonides, however, do bear many resemblances to the Appalachians despite their development on the opposite side of Iapetus. The Taconic orogenic event, which affected rocks deposited on the NW side of Iapetus, has a somewhat older parallel in Scandinavia in the pre-mid-Arenig Finnmarkian event (Sturt *et al.* 1978). This represents a major cycle that affected the continental rise prism and produced widespread polyphase deformation and metamorphism together with translative thrusting onto the Baltic craton. The major stage of Iapetus destruction apparently occurred during the Finnmarkian orogeny, and ophiolites representing vestiges of Iapetus ocean floor were accreted onto the Baltic craton at that time (Sturt 1984).

This view is contested by Stephens & Gee (1985) who maintain that the ophiolitic terranes accreted to the N American continent and were first moved over the Baltic craton during the later Silurian Scandian orogeny. Much of the evidence for this rests in recognition of a N American affinity to the Arenig to mid-Llanvirn faunas in sediments and volcaniclastics overlying ophiolitic rocks in the Trondheim region. Roberts *et al.* (1984) believe that these rocks were emplaced in a back-arc marginal basin and, to explain the faunas, propose a model in which the arc and basin volcanism and sedimentation is related to a destructive plate margin along the northwestern side of an elongate microcontinental plate within Iapetus.

Wherever these rocks were first erupted, they are now allochthonously situated above the Baltic craton in nappes which also contain succeeding Ordovician, Silurian and lower Devonian sequences. The nappes have been grouped into four major complexes, the lower, middle, upper and uppermost Allochthons (Roberts & Gee 1985); most volcanic sequences are found in the upper Allochthon but some are also found in each of the others (Furnes, cited by Bevins *et al.* 1985). Ordovician volcanics, which are found mainly in the two highest, have been interpreted as a complex sequence of arc, marginal-basin and continental-margin magmatism which, as far as southwestern Norway is concerned, suggests

convergent plate-margin activity with successive segments of Iapetus crust and that its suprasubduction margin has been brought eastward and stacked on the Baltic craton.

It seems that there are grounds for postulating an assemblage of terranes, again not unlike the Appalachian collage, and support for this concept may come from interpretation of the ophiolitic fragments which have been classified into two groups (Furnes *et al.* 1985). The older group (group I) is found along the whole length of the Norwegian Caledonides and is believed to represent Iapetus crust generated during the ocean-spreading period of the Cambrian and obducted during the Finnmarkian orogenic event. The younger group (group II) is of Arenig to Llanvirn age and is found only in the Trondheim region, in the marginal basin described by Roberts *et al.* (1984), which may represent a separate terrane.

The most complete sequence of convergent margin volcanics is seen in SW Norway on the islands of Karmøy, Bømlo and Stord, and much of this has been described by Brekke *et al.* (1984) who have shown correspondences with other upper Allochthon sequences along the length of the Norwegian Caledonides. The ophiolite, with an overlying ensiamatic-arc sequence dated at 535 ± 46 Ma, was emplaced on the Baltic craton probably in Arenig times. After a period of deep erosion, ensialic strike-slip volcanism of Basin and Range type occurred: basic and intermediate lavas below, acid pyroclastics and lavas above. Rhyolite flows have been dated at 464 ± 16 Ma. Chemically the basic rocks closely resemble continental basalts from the central Sierra Nevada and western Mexico (Brekke *et al.* 1984).

This phase of activity was followed by a hiatus in the magmatism and a widespread weak phase of vertical tectonism, possibly owing to the successful subduction of a spreading ridge. This produced a mid-upper Ordovician unconformity which is present along the length of the Norwegian Caledonides. The break in magmatic activity persisted for some 10–40 Ma, and was followed by Ashgill–Llandovery calc-alkaline sub-aerial volcanism which passes up into basin-fill volcanosedimentary lithologies in which the basalt chemistry is compatible with the early stages of ensialic back-arc basin development. Subsequent sedimentation is consistent with the continued development of a marine basin behind a western volcanic chain. The evolution of this basin is somewhat different from that of the Trondelag basin in the Trondheim region (Roberts *et al.* 1984) or at Sulitjelma (Sturt *et al.* 1983), where group II ophiolites intrude older crust and interdigitate with basin-fill lithologies, testifying to actual rifting of continental crust and active back-arc spreading. There is no evidence in Bømlo for actual rifting and spreading, only for crustal attenuation and basin formation.

A final point of interest is that the strike-slip basin magmatism of the upper Ordovician is recognized particularly in SW Norway, and it may be no coincidence that the Baltic crust seems to have been separated from the NW European crust until the end of the Ordovician by the Tornquist line, which is interpreted by some as a 'sub-Baltic' transform (Keppie 1977). The strike-slip basin may have developed within the stress system associated with the Tornquist line.

Conclusions

The assumptions underlying this paper, which was compiled in an attempt to correlate the volcanic activity taking place in a time-slice along the whole orogen, have changed significantly since its inception. The concept of terrane analysis questions the validity of long-range correlation, and indeed the findings reported here support the view that, whilst the tectono-magmatic setting of Ordovician volcanism was very largely related to continental margins, throughout much of the period the regions concerned must be treated as separate entities. Volcanic rocks related to obducted ocean crust, developing and closing marginal basins, volcanic arcs and active continental margins can be recognized in each of them, but often the parallel developments took place at different times. The linking factor seems to be the Iapetus Ocean whose formation and demise provided the causative relationship between the magmatic activity in the various regions that bordered it.

There is evidence to suggest that major destruction of oceanic crust and its margins took place during the Taconic, Grampian and Finnmarkian orogenic events, with the emplacement of remnants of the igneous rocks produced during the earlier constructional period onto the respective continental margins. However, these events, although apparently equivalent, are not synchronous.

Subsequent volcanism in many of the zones apparently accreted to the continents is mainly of within-plate character, such as in the Siluro-Devonian sequences of the Dunnage, Gander, Avalon and Meguma terranes of Newfoundland and Nova Scotia–New Brunswick. Perhaps

equivalent to this, on the other side of Iapetus, are the examples of the post-lower Arenig marginal-basin magmatism of the Welsh basin and the post-Caradoc ensialic back-arc magmatism of southwestern Norway. In both cases the igneous activity took place in an ensialic basin in which there is no evidence for major rifting and formation of new oceanic crust, and in both cases this development succeeded an earlier period of subduction-related magmatism; however, the initiation of the basins is separated by more than 40 Ma.

Nevertheless, quite different activity was taking place simultaneously in regions which are now almost adjacent. Examples are found in the Lake District–Leinster zone in the British Isles, where subduction-related volcanic arcs were erupting at the same time as the Snowdonia ensialic basin centres, or the Trondelag basin in central Norway, where ocean crust was forming in an active back-arc setting at the same time as the Bømlo and Stord Basin and Range type volcanism.

In attempting to assess the value of this study it is clear that the recognition of tectono-magmatic settings permitted by modern geochemical and isotopic studies of volcanic rocks, although providing only rather inconclusive evidence at present, will be of value to the ultimate unravelling of the history of the orogen when taken in conjunction with other stratigraphic and structural evidence in the terrane analysis now being undertaken.

ACKNOWLEDGMENTS. This work is a contribution to the International Geophysical Correlation Program (IGCP) Caledonides Orogen Project. The author owes a debt of gratitude to his colleagues who have allowed him the use of much new and as yet largely unpublished material in this compilation (referred to as 'personal communication' in the text) and who have made many helpful suggestions. In particular, acknowledgment is due to R. E. Bevins, B. P. Kokelaar, H. Brekke, H. Furnes, D. Roberts and B. A. Sturt for permitting quotation from papers which are currently in the press, and to J. Hertogen and L. André for quotation from their contribution to the IGCP Project 27 Final Report. Special thanks are also due to D. Rankin, the late D. Wones, L. Fyfe and M. J. Kennedy, who have read, amended and corrected the N America section of this paper, and to M. F. Howells and W. S. McKerrow whose careful reviews have done much to improve the first draft.

References

ANDRÉ, L. & DEUTSCH, S. 1984. Les porphyres de Quenast et de Lessines géochronologie, géochimie isotopique et contribution au problème de l'âge du socle précambrien du Massif du Brabant (Belgique). *Bulletin de la Société Belge de Géologie, de Paléontologie et d'Hydrologie*, **93**, 375–84.

——, —— & MICHOT, J. 1981. Données géochronologiques concernant le développement tectono-métamorphique du segment Caledonian Braban-çon. *Annales de la Société Géologique de Belgique*, **104**, 241–53.

ARNOTT, R. J., MCKERROW, W. S. & COCKS, L. R. M. 1985. The tectonics and depositional history of the Ordovician and Silurian rocks of Notre Dame Bay, Newfoundland. *Canadian Journal of Earth Sciences*, **22**, 607–18.

BARR, S. M., DOYLE, E. & TRAPASSO, L. 1983. Geochemistry and tectonic implications of mafic sills in lower Palaeozoic formations of southwestern Nova Scotia. *Marine Sediments and Atlantic Geology*, **19**, 73–87.

BEVINS, R. E., KOKELAAR, B. P. & DUNKLEY, P. N. 1984. Petrology and geochemistry of early to mid-Ordovician igneous rocks in Wales: a volcanic arc to marginal basin transition. *Proceedings of the Geologists' Association*, **95** (4), 337–47.

——, STILLMAN, C. J. & FURNES, H. 1985. A review of Caledonian volcanicity in the British Isles and Scandinavia. *In:* GAYER, R. (ed.) *The Tectonic Evolution of the Caledonian–Appalachian Orogen*, Vieweg, Braunschweig.

BLUCK, B. J. 1983. The role of the Midland Valley of Scotland in the Caledonian orogeny. *Transactions of the Royal Society of Edinburgh, Earth Science*, **74**, 119–36.

——, HALLIDAY, A. M., AFTALION, M. & MACINTYRE, R. M. 1980. Age and origin of the Ballantrae ophiolite and its significance to the Caledonian orogeny and the Ordovician time scale. *Geology*, **8**, 492–5.

VAN BREEMEN, O. & BLUCK, B. J. 1981. Episodic granite plutonism in the Scottish Caledonides. *Nature, London*, **291**, 113–7.

BREKKE, H., FURNES, H., NORDAS, J. & HERTOGEN, J. 1984. Lower Palaeozoic convergent plate margin volcanism on Bømlo, SW Norwegian Caledonides. *Journal of the Geological Society, London*, **141**, 1015–32.

CABANIS, B. 1983. Main features of volcanism and plutonism in late Proterozoic and Dinantian times in France. *In:* SCHENK, P. E. (ed.) *Regional Trends in the Geology of the Appalachian–Caledonian–Hercynian–Mauretanide Orogen*, Reidel, Dordrecht.

CHANDLER, F. W. & DUNNING, G. R. 1983. Fourfold significance of an early Silurian U–Pb zircon age from rhyolite in red beds, southwest Newfoundland. *Current Research, Part B, Geological Survey of Canada Paper No. 83-1B*, pp. 419–21.

CURRY, G. B., INGHAM, J. K., BLUCK, B. J. & WILLIAMS, A. 1982. The significance of a reliable Ordovician age for some Highland Border rocks in Central Scotland. *Journal of the Geological Society, London*, **139**, 451–4.

DAVIES, G. 1984. The isotopic evolution of the British lithosphere. *Ph. D. Thesis*, Open University, Milton Keynes (unpublished).

DEWEY, J. F. 1982. Plate tectonics and the evolution of the British Isles. *Journal of the Geological Society, London*, **139**, 371–412.

——, KENNEDY, M. J. & KIDD, S. W. F. 1983. A geotraverse through the Appalachians of Northern Newfoundland. *Profiles of Orogenic Belts, Geodynamic Series*, Vol. 10, pp. 201–41, American Geophysical Union, Washington, DC.

FURNES, H., RYAN, P. D., GRENNE, T., ROBERTS, D., STURT, B. A. & PRESTVIK, T. 1985. Geological and geochemical classification of the ophiolite fragments in the Scandinavian Caledonides. *In:* GEE, D. G. & STURT, B. A. (eds) *The Caledonide Orogen—Scandinavia and Related Areas*, Wiley, Chichester.

GATES, O. & MOENCH, R. H. 1981. Bimodal Silurian and lower Devonian volcanic rock assemblages in the Machias–Eastport area, Maine. *United States Geological Survey Professional Paper No. 1184*.

HENDERSON, W. G. & ROBERTSON, A. H. F. 1982. The Highland Border rocks and their relation to marginal basin development in the Scottish Caledonides. *Journal of the Geological Society, London*, **139**, 433–50.

HIBBERD, J. P. & WILLIAMS, H. 1979. Regional setting of the Dunnage melange in the Newfoundland Appalachians. *American Journal of Science*, **279**, 993–1021.

HOWELLS, M. F. 1977. The varying pattern of volcanicity and sedimentation in the Bedded Pyroclastic/Middle Crafnant volcanic formations in the Ordovician of central and eastern Snowdonia. *Journal of the Geological Society, London*, **133**, 401–11.

HUTTON, D. H. W., AFTALION, M. & HALLIDAY, A. N. 1985. An Ordovician ophiolite in County Tyrone, Ireland. *Nature, London*, **315**, 210–12.

IKIN, N. P. 1983. Petrochemistry and tectonic significance of Highland Border Suite mafic rocks. *Journal of the Geological Society, London*, **140**, 267–78.

KEAN, B. F. & STRONG, D. F. 1975. Geochemical evolution of an Ordovician island arc of the Central Newfoundland Appalachians. *American Journal of Science*, **275**, 97–118.

KELLING, G., PHILLIPS, W. E. A., HARRIS, A. L. & HOWELLS, M. F. 1985. The Caledonides of the British Isles: a review and appraisal. *In:* GEE, D. G. & STURT, B. A. (eds) *The Caledonide Orogen—Scandinavia and Related Areas*, Wiley, Chichester.

KENNEDY, M. J. 1975. Repetitive orogeny in the northeastern Appalachians—new plate models based upon Newfoundland examples. *Tectonophysics*, **28**, 39–87.

—— 1979. The continuation of the Canadian Appalachians into the Caledonides of Britain and Ireland. *In:* HARRIS, A. L., HOLLAND, C. H. & LEAKE, B. E. (eds) *The Caledonides of the British Isles Reviewed*.

Special Publication of the Geological Society of London No. 8, pp. 33–64.

KEPPIE, J. D. 1977. Plate tectonic interpretation of Palaeozoic World Maps (with emphasis on Circum-Atlantic orogens and southern Nova Scotia). *Nova Scotia Department of Mines Paper No. 77-3.*

—— & DOSTAL, J. 1980. Palaeozoic volcanic rocks of Nova Scotia. *In:* WONES, D. R. (ed.) *The Caledonides in the USA: Proceedings of the International Geological Correlation Program—Caledonide Orogen Project 27, Blacksburg, VA. Virginia Polytechnic Institute and State University, Memoir No. 2,* pp. 249–56.

KOKELAAR, B. P., HOWELLS, M. F., BEVINS, R. E., ROACH, R. A. & DUNKLEY, P. N. 1984. The Ordovician marginal basin of Wales. *In:* KOKELAAR, B. P. & HOWELLS, M. F. (eds) *Volcanism and Associated Sedimentary and Tectonic Processes in Modern and Ancient Marginal Basins. Special Publication of the Geological Society of London No. 16,* pp. 245–70.

LAMBERT, R. ST J. & MCKERROW, W. S. 1976. The Grampian orogeny. *Scottish Journal of Geology,* **12,** 271–92.

——, HOLLAND, J. G. & LEGGETT, J. K. 1981. Petrology and tectonic setting of some upper Ordovician volcanics from the Southern Uplands of Scotland. *Journal of the Geological Society, London,* **128,** 421–36.

LAURENT, R., HEBERT, R. & HEBERT, Y. 1979. Tectonic setting and petrological features of the Quebec Appalachian Ophiolites. *In:* MALPAS, J. & TALKINGTON, R. W. (eds) *Ophiolites of the Canadian Appalachians and Soviet Urals. Memorial University of Newfoundland Department of Geology Report No. 8,* pp. 53–77.

LE BAS, M. J. 1982. The Caledonian granites and diorites of England and Wales. *In:* SUTHERLAND, D. S. (ed.) *Igneous Rocks of the British Isles,* pp. 191–201, Wiley, New York.

LEGGETT, J. E., MCKERROW, W. S. & EALES, M. H. 1976. The Southern Uplands of Scotland, a lower Palaeozoic accretionary prism. *Journal of the Geological Society, London,* **136,** 755–70.

LEWIS, A. D. & BLOXHAM, T. W. 1977. Petrochemical environment of the Girvan–Ballantrae lavas, from rare-earth element distributions. *Scottish Journal of Geology,* **13,** 211–22.

LONGMAN, C. D., BLUCK, B. J. & VAN BREEMEN, O. 1979. Ordovician conglomerates and the evolution of the Midland Valley. *Nature, London,* **280,** 578–81.

MATTINSON, J. M. 1976. Ages of zircons from the Bay of Islands ophiolite complex, Western Newfoundland. *Geology,* **4,** 393–4.

—— 1977. U–Pb ages of some crystalline rocks from the Burlington Peninsula, Newfoundland. *Canadian Journal of Earth Sciences,* **14,** 2316–24.

MCKERROW, W. S. 1983. The northern margin of the Iapetus ocean during the early Palaeozoic. *American Association of Petroleum Geologists Memoir No. 34,* pp. 521–33.

—— & COCKS, L. R. M. 1976. Progressive faunal migration across Iapetus Ocean. *Nature, London,* **263,** 304–6.

MOSELEY, F. 1983. *The Volcanic Rocks of the Lake District.* McMillan, London.

NOWLAN, G. S. & THURLOW, J. G. 1984. Middle Ordovician conodonts from the Buchans Group, central Newfoundland, and their significance for regional stratigraphy of the Central Volcanic Belt. *Canadian Journal of Earth Sciences,* **21,** 284–96.

PAJARI, G. E., RAST, N. & STRINGER, P. 1977. Palaeozoic volcanicity along the Bathurst–Dalhousie Geotraverse, New Brunswick, and its relation to structure. *In:* BARAGAR, W. R. A., COLEMAN, L. C. & HALL, J. M. (eds) *Volcanic Regimes in Canada. Geological Association of Canada Special Paper No. 16,* pp. 111–24.

PAPEZIC, V. S. & FLEMING, J. M. 1967. Basic volcanic rocks of the Whaleback area, Newfoundland. *In:* NEALE, R. W. & WILLIAMS, H. (eds) *Geology of the Atlantic Region. Geological Association of Canada Special Paper No. 4,* pp. 181–92.

PAVLIDES, L. 1981. The Central Virginia volcanic–plutonic belt: an island arc of Cambrian(?) age. *United States Geological Survey Professional Paper No. 1231-A.*

PHILLIPS, W. E. A., STILLMAN, C. J. & MURPHY, T. 1976. A Caledonian plate tectonic model. *Journal of the Geological Society, London,* **132,** 579–609.

RANKIN, D. 1983. Volcanism in the Appalachians of the United States. *In:* SCHENK, P. E. (ed.) *Regional Trends in the Geology of the Appalachian–Caledonian–Hercynian–Mauretanide Orogen,* pp. 173–7, Reidel, Dordrecht.

RAST, N., KENNEDY, M. J. & BLACKWOOD, R. F. 1976. Comparison of some tectono-stratigraphic zones in the Appalachians of Newfoundland and New Brunswick. *Canadian Journal of Earth Sciences,* **13,** 868–75.

ROBERTS, D. & GEE, D. G. 1985. Caledonian tectonics in Scandinavia. *In:* GEE, D. G. & STURT, B. A. (eds) *The Caledonide Orogen—Scandinavia and Related Areas,* Wiley, Chichester.

——, GRENNE, T. & RYAN, P. D. 1984. Ordovician marginal basin development in the central Norwegian Caledonides. *Journal of the Geological Society, London,* in press.

ROBINSON, P. 1979. Bronson Hills anticlinorium and Merrimac synclinorium in central Massachusetts. *In:* SKEHAN, J. W., S. J. & OSBERG, P. (eds) *The Caledonides in the USA: Geological Excursions in the Northeast Appalachians,* pp. 126–50, Weston Observatory, Boston College, Weston, Ma.

RUITENBERG, A. A., FYFFE, L. R., MCCUTCHEON, S. R., ST PETER, G. J., IRRINKI, R. R. & VENUGOPAL, D. V. 1978. Evolution of pre-Carboniferous tectonostratigraphic zones in the New Brunswick Appalachians. *Geoscience, Canada,* **4,** 171–81.

RYAN, P. D., FLOYD, P. A. & ARCHER, J. B. 1980. The stratigraphy and petrochemistry of the Lough Nafooey Group (Tremadocian), W Ireland. *Journal of the Geological Society, London,* **137,** 443–58.

——, SAWAL, V. K. & ROWLANDS, A. S. 1983. Ophiolite melange separates ortho and paratectonic Caledonides in W Ireland. *Nature, London,* **302,** 50–2.

SANZEN BAKER, I. 1972. Structural relations and sedimentary environment of the Silurian and early Old Red Sandstone of Pembrokeshire. *Proceedings of the Geologists' Association*, **83**, 139–69.

SHEPPARD, W. A. 1980. The ores and host rock geology of the Avoca Mines, Co. Wicklow, Ireland. *Norges Geologiske Undersøkelse*, **360**, 269–84.

STEPHENS, M. B. & GEE, D. G. 1985. A plate tectonic model for Caledonian orogenesis in the central Scandinavian Caledonides. *In:* GEE, D. G. & STURT, B. A. (eds) *The Caledonide Orogen—Scandinavia and Related Areas*, Wiley, Chichester.

STILLMAN, C. J. & WILLIAMS, C. T. 1979. Geochemistry and tectonic setting of some Upper Ordovician volcanics in east and southeast Ireland. *Earth and Planetary Science Letters*, **41**, 288–310.

STURT, B. A. 1984. The accretion of ophiolite terranes in the Scandinavian Caledonides. *Geologie en Mijnbouw*, **63**, 201–12.

——, PRINGLE, I. R. & RAMSAY, D. M. 1978. The Finnmarkian phase of the Caledonian orogeny. *Journal of the Geological Society, London*, **135**, 597–610.

——, ROBERTS, D. & FURNES, H. 1983. A conspectus of Scandinavian Caledonian ophiolites. *In:* GASS, I. G., LIPPARD, S. J. & SHELTON, A. W. (eds) *Ophiolites and Oceanic Lithosphere. Special Publication of the Geological Society of London No. 13*, pp. 381–92.

THIRLWALL, M. F. 1981. Implications for Caledonian plate models of chemical data from volcanic rocks of the British Old Red Sandstone. *Journal of the Geological Society, London*, **138**, 123–38.

—— & BLUCK, B. J. 1983. Sr–Nd isotope and chemical evidence that the Ballantrae 'ophiolite', SW Scotland, is polygenetic. *In:* GASS, I. G., LIPPARD, S. J. & SHELTON, A. W. (eds) *Ophiolites and Oceanic Lithosphere. Special Publication of the Geological Society of London No. 13*, pp. 215–30.

—— & FITTON, J. G. 1983. Sm–Nd garnet age for the Ordovician Borrowdale Volcanic Group, English Lake District. *Journal of the Geological Society, London*, **140**, 511–18.

UPADHYAY, H. D., DEWEY, J. F. & NEALE, E. R. W. 1971. The Betts Cove ophiolite complex, Newfoundland: Appalachian oceanic crust and mantle. *Proceedings of the Geological Association of Canada*, **24**, 27–33.

VAN DE KAMP, P. C. 1969. Silurian volcanic rocks of the Mendip Hills, Somerset and Tortworth, Gloucestershire, England. *Geological Magazine*, **106**, 542–55.

WILLIAMS, H. 1978. Tectonic lithofacies map of the Appalachian orogen. *Memorial University of Newfoundland Map No. 1a.*

—— 1983. *Tectonic Elements of the Restored North Atlantic*, MUNCL, St John's.

—— & HATCHER, R. D. 1982. Suspect terranes and accretionary history of the Appalachian Orogen. *Geology*, **10**, 530–6.

C. J. STILLMAN, Department of Geology, Trinity College, Dublin, Eire.

Timing of Ordovician deformation in the Caledonian–Appalachian orogen

Leo M. Hall & David Roberts

SUMMARY: Evidence for Ordovician deformation is variably present throughout the Caledonides. The Grampian (late Cambrian–early Ordovician) and Taconian (middle to late Ordovician) major orogenies occurred during this time period and involved plutonism and metamorphism as well as deformation. The Taconian is particularly important in N America, whereas the Grampian (Penebscot), although locally identified, seems less important. Conversely, the Grampian appears to be more important in Scotland and in Scandinavia, where it is termed the Finnmarkian and constituted a major orogenic phase. Subduction and oceanic closure seems to have been an important Ordovician process, as indicated by abundant ophiolites. In Scandinavia the principal phase of thrust emplacement of the ophiolites occurred in the early to middle Ordovician. Major deformation in central E Greenland is of late Ordovician age.

Timing of Ordovician deformation in the Caledonides derives mainly from stratigraphic–palaeontological studies tied to structural relationships and from radiometric data that identify times of metamorphism and plutonic igneous activity in relation to deformation. On the maps that accompany this paper and show the distribution of Ordovician times of deformation, large regions of Silurian and younger rocks are shown as being deformed in the Ordovician. These are places where pre-Silurian rocks are inferred to be present at depth and to have been deformed during the Ordovician.

Two Ordovician orogenic episodes are recognized in the Caledonides. The earlier, which is referred to as Grampian in Britain and Ireland, Penobscotian in the USA and Canada, and Finnmarkian in Scandinavia, overlaps the Cambrian–Ordovician boundary and is arbitrarily defined as pre-480 Ma. The later is the Taconian, which is arbitrarily defined here as having occurred during the Ordovician but after 480 Ma.

Papers appearing in *Regional Trends in the Geology of the Appalachian–Caledonian–Hercynian–Mauritanide Orogen* (Schenk 1983), and especially those by Gee & Roberts, Powell, Max, Keppie *et al.* and Osberg have been heavily drawn upon as source material for this review.

Appalachians in N America

General statement

Five major regions, the S Appalachians, central Appalachians, New England, mainland Canada and Newfoundland (Fig. 1) will be discussed in that order. Each of these regions is sub-divided into segments parallel to the length of the mountain chain.

Ordovician deformation is widespread in the Appalachians (Figs 2 and 3) and involved two episodes, the late Cambrian–early Ordovician Penobscotian arbitrarily defined as pre-480 Ma and the middle to late Ordovician Taconian. Owing to either insufficient data or overlap of the two episodes it is not clear in many places whether one or both episodes occurred. Consequently the times of Ordovician deformation are shown in three patterns on the map (Fig. 2), one for Penobscotian, one for Taconian (middle and late Ordovician) and one for Penobscotian and/or Taconian.

Discussions of the timing of Ordovician deformation in N America and comparisons with Europe are greatly confused by the inconsistent terminology of sub-division of the Ordovician. In the scheme adopted for the Decade of N American Geology in 1983 the early Ordovician includes Tremadoc and Arenig, middle Ordovician includes Llanvirn and Llandeilo, and late Ordovician includes Caradoc and Ashgill. In the correlation of New York State (Fisher 1977), which has heavily influenced thinking on the Appalachians, Llanvirn and Llandeilo are designated as 'early medial Ordovician', Caradoc is designated as 'late medial Ordovician' and Ashgill is designated as 'late Ordovician'. In New England and New York rocks known or thought to be Caradocian are usually described as middle Ordovician, and the Caradocian emplacement of the frontal allochthon of the Taconic mountains is considered to be the best-dated phase of the 'middle Ordovician' Taconian orogeny. Only the more distal Taconian flysch which is spread well W onto the N American platform falls into the 'late Ordovician' Ashgill. In this paper the middle–late boundary is, as much as possible, taken approximately at the Llandeilo–Caradoc boundary to conform to more general usage.

From HARRIS, A. L. & FETTES, D. J. (eds), 1988, *The Caledonian–Appalachian Orogen,*
Geological Society Special Publication No. 38, pp. 291–309.

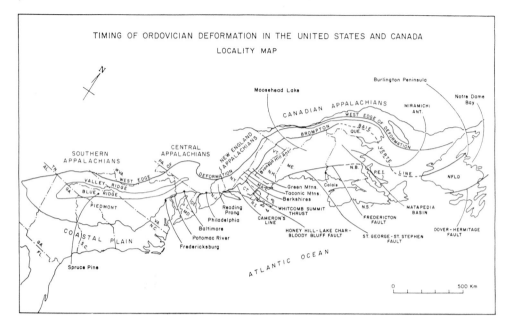

FIG. 1. Location map of the geographical localities and geological features in the Appalachians.

S Appalachians

Palaeozoic deformation in the S Appalachians extended from the Cambrian to the Permian (Tull 1980). Taconian metamorphism has been recognized and may be widespread (Hatcher *et*

al. 1980), but there may be some confusion between Penobscotian and Taconian effects as well as with Acadian.

Pre-deformation plutons about 560 Ma old and post-deformation plutons about 400 Ma old constrain the times of deformation and metamorph-

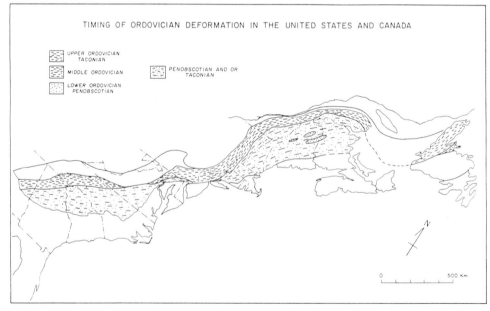

FIG. 2. Areal distribution of Ordovician deformation in the Appalachians of the USA and Canada.

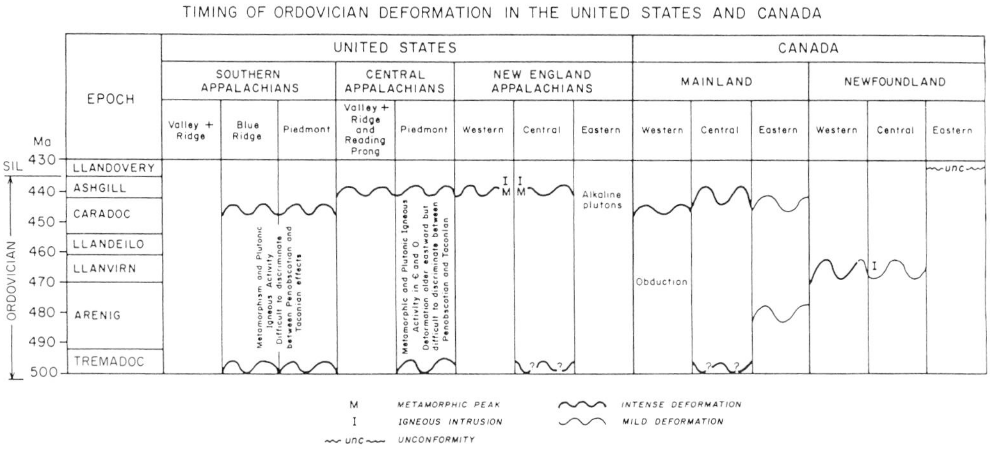

TIMING OF ORDOVICIAN DEFORMATION IN THE UNITED STATES AND CANADA

FIG. 3. Chart showing the timing of Ordovician deformation in the Appalachians of the USA and Canada.

ism in the central and eastern Piedmont of N Carolina (Kish *et al.* 1979). Cambrian slates in this region yield evidence for Penobscotian metamorphism yielding ages of 483 Ma (K–Ar). Zircon dating of pegmatites in the Spruce Pine region of the Blue Ridge in N Carolina indicates that their age is 380–430 Ma (Butler 1973). The pegmatites intruded already isoclinally folded (Penobscotian or Taconian) rocks that subsequently underwent peak metamorphism at about 450 Ma (Butler 1973). Dallmeyer (1975), interpreting $^{40}Ar/^{39}Ar$ incremental gas release ages of biotites and hornblendes from Grenvillian basement gneisses in the Blue Ridge of SW North Carolina (Fig. 1), calculated an uplift rate which indicates metamorphism at about 480 Ma (Penobscotian?).

Taconian effects extended across the S Appalachians from the western Blue Ridge to the eastern Piedmont (Hatcher *et al.* 1980), but earlier deformation (Hatcher *et al.* 1980) occurred from the Western Blue Ridge eastward to the Kings Mountain Belt.

Central Appalachians

This region is divided into two segments: (1) the Valley and Ridge and the Reading Prong; (2) the Piedmont (Figs 1 and 3). In the Valley and Ridge the Caradocian Martinsburg Shale is folded and thrust, with structures related to this deformation truncated by an unconformity at the base of the overlying Silurian Shawangunk Conglomerate. The intensity of deformation increases southeastward to the Reading Prong which includes large nappes involving Precambrian basement gneisses as well as lower Palaeozoic rocks as

young as the middle to late Ordovician Martinsburg (Drake 1980).

Timing of deformation is problematical in the very complex Piedmont of the central Appalachians which consists of thrust sheets and multiply-folded and metamorphosed rocks (Drake 1980); there is insufficient information to discriminate clearly between Penobscotian and Taconian deformation, apart from possible Cadomian (late Precambrian) effects. Deformation for this region is shown as Penobscotian and/or Taconian in Fig. 2.

Taconian deformation of the highly metamorphosed strata in the Baltimore and Philadelphia regions is indicated by analogy with the structural style of rocks, including middle to late Ordovician strata, in the Reading Prong region to the N (Amenta 1974, Drake 1980). Also, if the stratigraphy of the Baltimore and Philadelphia regions is correlated with the Cambrian–Ordovician strata to the N and W, the early deformation must be interpreted to involve middle to late Ordovician rocks. Grauert & Wagner (1975), on the basis of a 440 Ma date from Wilmington Complex zircons, conclude that there was a major Taconian metamorphism in this region. Interpretation of the deformational history in this area is further complicated by the effects of subsequent Acadian and/or Alleghenian deformation (Drake 1980).

Radiometric data from rocks in this part of the Piedmont seem to favour early Palaeozoic but pre-Taconian (pre-480 Ma) deformation (Osberg 1983). Small granite bodies and associated pegmatites transect previously metamorphosed and multiply-deformed rocks in the Potomac River allochthon (Drake 1980) of the Glenarm Terrane near Washington, DC. Rb–Sr mineral dates of 469 Ma from pegmatite muscovite rocks (Muth *et al.* 1979) place a minimum age on early deformation and favour Penobscotian for this. Drake (1980) points out similarities between the Potomac River allochthon and the Smith River allochthon of Virginia and N Carolina; thus Penobscot deformation may also be important in those rocks. Drake & Lyttle (1981) have defined three thrust sheets of multiply-deformed and metamorphosed late Precambrian–Cambrian strata unconformably overlain by younger, but still late Precambrian–Cambrian, strata of the Popes Head Formation. The Occoquan granite cuts the unconformity and its age thus places a minimum date on the early deformation. Unfortunately, the Occoquan zircon date of 560 Ma (Seiders *et al.* 1975) is in question (Drake & Lyttle 1981), although the Occoquan is at least 500 Ma old (Drake 1984, personal communication). Further S, near Fredericksburg, Virginia (Fig. 1), the Quantico Formation (late Ordovician or younger) rests unconformably on deformed and metamorphosed late Precambrian–Cambrian strata (Chopawamsic and its correlatives) intruded by the Occoquan granite (Pavlides 1980). This relationship is consistent with Cadomian or Penobscotian deformation. Pavlides *et al.* (1982) point out that, during westward transport along thrust faults, magmatic arc rocks about 550 Ma old yielded mélange which was itself deformed before emplacement of the 440 Ma Ellisville pluton of N Virginia. These relationships are consistent with Penobscotian or Taconian deformation.

Thrusting in the central Appalachian Piedmont appears to have occurred later and to have been directed successively westwards in that the earlier thrusts lie E of and above the later thrusts except where modified by later folding. It is possible that the older thrust sheets, especially those containing oceanic crust and related rocks, were assembled and transported westward during the Penobscotian. In some cases the rocks in these thrust sheets may have been deformed and even metamorphosed prior to or during thrusting (Drake & Morgan 1981, Pavlides *et al.* 1982). The lower, younger and more westward thrusts involving middle to late Ordovician strata may have developed during the Taconian. Taconic folding and metamorphism of all the assembled allochthons is indicated by radiometric data (Grauert & Wagner 1975).

New England–New York Appalachians

The western region of the New England–New York Appalachians lies W of the Cameron's Line–Whitcomb Summit thrust (Fig. 1), while the central region is separated from the eastern region by the Honey Hill–Lake Char–Bloody Bluff fault array in Connecticut and Massachusetts and the St George–St Stephen fault in Maine (Fig. 1).

There is clear-cut evidence for both Penobscotian and Taconian deformation in the New England–New York Appalachians, the type area for both events. Taconian deformation is defined by geological evidence in the western New England Appalachians (Figs 1 and 2). Wildflysch that occurs beneath the lowest and westernmost large Taconic thrust sheet (Giddings Brook slice) was developed in front of this fault as it was transported westwards (Zen 1961). The matrix of the wildflysch contains graptolites of zones 12 and 13, which indicates that this Taconic thrust fault was active in the Caradocian. Deformed Caradocian strata as well as the Giddings Brook thrust itself are truncated by the classic Taconic unconformity beneath late Silurian and/or early Devonian strata in eastern New York State (Fisher *et al.* 1970, Ratcliffe *et al.* 1975). Grenvillian basement in the Berkshires and Green Mountains of New York, Connecticut, Massachusetts and parts of Vermont has been transported westward along thrusts that locally truncate middle Ordovician strata.

Such thrusts of basement and of previously metamorphosed strata are believed by Zen *et al.* (1983) and Stanley & Ratcliffe (1985) to be younger than and to cut through the earlier thrusts that emplaced the Giddings Brook slice.

Preliminary zircon dating indicates an Ordovician age for a granite that cuts one of these basement thrusts in Massachusetts (Ratcliffe & Zartman 1976), and thus Taconian deformation is bracketed there.

Hall (1980) has shown that in southeastern New York and adjacent Connecticut post-Giddings Brook deformation, rather than thrusts, involved major W-directed recumbent fold nappes of basement, subsequently refolded by more upright folds in both the Taconian and the Acadian. Along and near the W margin of the Giddings Brook slice Bosworth & Kidd (1985) have identified a series of hard rock thrusts and tectonic mélanges that truncate a slaty cleavage superimposed on the Giddings Brook thrust and that are unconformably overlain by Silurian–Devonian strata in the Hudson Valley region.

Consequently there is ample evidence to constrain the time of occurrence of Taconian deformation in the W New England Appalachians.

Towards the E in New England the Cameron's Line–Whitcomb Summit thrust is a major tectonic boundary E of the Berkshires and the Green

Mountains (Fig. 1) (Robinson & Hall 1980, Stanley & Ratcliffe 1983). Rocks E of and above this boundary, the western part of the central region of the New England Appalachians, are inferred to represent an oceanic terrane that was transported onto N American continental crust during Taconian deformation. Mafic and ultramafic rocks occur near this tectonic boundary and are associated with thrust sheets to the E (Stanley *et al.* 1984, Stanley & Ratcliffe 1985). They constitute the evidence for interaction with oceanic crust and overlying strata in an accretionary wedge. Some of the thrusting and associated deformation in this zone E of the Cameron's Line–Whitcomb Summit thrust is probably Penobscotian, similar to that in the central Appalachians discussed earlier.

In this zone in N Vermont there is local evidence of an early blueschist-facies metamorphism (Laird & Albee 1981) with K–Ar ages suggesting cooling around 470 Ma, as well as coarse hornblende in a probable ophiolite contact aureole yielding an age of around 500 Ma (Laird *et al.* 1984). Evidence for Taconian deformation E of the Cameron's Line–Whitcomb Summit thrust is neither spectacular nor clear-cut, but a post-deformational erosional interval is evident from the unconformity beneath the Silurian Shaw Mountain Formation–Russell Mountain Formation in Vermont, Massachusetts and W Connecticut as well as beneath the Silurian Clough quartzite in New Hampshire, Massachusetts and E Connecticut. Hatch (1982) has described this unconformity in W Connecticut, Massachusetts and Vermont as the Taconian Line and interprets it to be a décollement in places. Although no angular unconformity is known by local truncation along the boundary, Hatch (1982) has pointed out that folds in nearby pre-Silurian strata seem to be absent in the Silurian rocks and that different pre-Silurian rock types occur beneath the unconformity on a regional scale. An angular unconformity at the base of the Clough Quartzite is well documented (Thompson *et al.* 1968).

Penobscotian deformation is evident from geological relations in several areas in N Maine, but only some of these are mentioned here. The Penobscot disturbance was named after Penobscot County, Maine, where rocks of the Cambrian, or possibly late Precambrian, Grand Pitch Formation, bearing *Oldhamia*, were deformed before the deposition of the fossiliferous early Ordovician or earliest middle Ordovician (late Arenig) Shin Brook Formation (Neuman 1967). This unconformity indicates that the Grand Pitch was deformed in the Cambrian and/or early Ordovician. The Shin Brook Formation is itself deformed, but its deformational features are

similar to those in the overlying Ordovician, Silurian and lower Devonian strata and, although evidence for Taconian deformation is thus difficult to identify (Neuman 1967), a disconformity between upper Llandovery and Ashgill strata may represent the Taconian. To the SW in the vicinity of Moosehead Lake, Maine (Fig. 1), there are late Cambrian to early Ordovician rocks (Dead River Formation) that were folded with the development of a slaty cleavage before deposition of the overlying lower, middle and upper Ordovician rocks (Lobster Mountain volcanics and Kennebec Formation) (Boone 1983). Although there may have been continuous deposition through the time of Taconian deformation in places in Maine, there is also evidence for Taconian deformation where Silurian rocks rest unconformably on Ashgill rocks. Osberg (1983) suggested that Penobscotian effects may be present southward along the Bronson Hill anticlinorium. Robinson (cited by Robinson & Hall 1980) identified a conglomerate at the base of the middle Ordovician Ammonoosuc volcanics in the Bronson Hill anticlinorium in Massachusetts which supports the interpretation that the Ammonoosuc and associated Partridge Formation probably unconformably overlie gneisses in the core of this anticlinorium (Thompson *et al.* 1968). One of the gneiss units, Monson gneiss, has been dated at 440 Ma (zircon) and another gneiss unit, Dry Hill gneiss, has been dated at 556 Ma (zircon) (Zartman & Naylor 1984).

If Robinson's lithic correlation of the Monson with known late Precambrian gneisses on the SE Connecticut coast is correct and if the Monson zircons have been heavily reworked by Ordovician and/or Acadian metamorphism, it is possible that these gneisses were deformed and metamorphosed in the Ordovician prior to deposition of the Ammonoosuc volcanics (Hall & Robinson 1982) and are consistent with Penobscotian deformation in this region.

This is supported by relics of a pre-Ammonoosuc granulite-facies metamorphism in pelitic schists associated with the Dry Hill gneiss, although such relics have not been found in the Monson gneiss (Robinson *et al.* 1975, Roll 1986). Taconian deformation also occurred in this region and is represented by the unconformity below the Silurian Clough quartzite that rests on probable Caradocian and older strata. Thus both Penobscotian and Taconian deformation are shown for the central region in Fig. 2.

There is evidence for pre-Silurian metamorphism on the eastern side of the central New England region (Fig. 1) where the deformed migmatitic Andover granite occurs in rocks of the Nashoba Formation adjacent to the apparently undeformed Sharpners Pond diorite. The Sharpners Pond is dated at 430 Ma (zircon) (Zartman & Naylor 1984) and, since it is less deformed than the Andover granite, it is interpreted as the younger of the two. Radiometric dating of the Andover granite must be interpreted with caution, but it is likely that it is late Ordovician or older (Zartman & Naylor 1984). Thus metamorphism and deformation may have occurred in this region in the late Ordovician during and after the formation of the Andover but prior to the intrusion of the Sharpners Pond.

Evidence for Ordovician deformation in the eastern region of New England is sparse. Lower Silurian strata near Calais, Maine, rest on Tremadoc beds, but there is little or no structural disparity between the rocks on each side of this contact (Osberg 1983). Some alkalic anorogenic pluton igneous activity involved the emplacement of the Cape Ann and Quincy granites in E Massachusetts during the Late Ordovician but there is no evidence for Taconian deformation (Skehan & Murray 1980).

Mainland Canada Appalachians

Western, central and eastern regions of the Appalachians in mainland Canada are continuations of those in New England. The Baie Verte–Brompton Line separates the western and central regions and the Fredericton fault forms the E boundary of the central region (Fig. 1). The Fredericton fault is extrapolated northeastward beneath Carboniferous strata. Taconian thrust faults and folds developed in the Llandeilo and Caradoc of the western region, and later folding with associated metamorphism occurred about 450 Ma ago (St Julien & Hubert 1975). Fossiliferous wildflysch deposits indicate that thrust nappe emplacement commenced in Llandeilo and was completed in Caradoc times. Thrusts involved in this deformation are successively younger toward the NW. Late Caradoc metamorphism that accompanied folding and associated cleavage development has been identified by the interpretation of radiometric dates (St Julien & Hubert 1975), taking into account effects of Acadian resetting (Gariepy & Hubert 1981).

In the central region SE of the Brompton Line pre-Taconian deformation is well documented in S Quebec (St Julien & Hubert 1975), where an ophiolite section was obducted onto the N American margin in the lower Ordovician and subsequently overlain by the St Daniel mélange. These rocks were further deformed in the middle and late Ordovician along with the adjacent western region. Taconian deformation in the central region is also evident in the Miramichi

anticlinorium where deformed mid-Caradoc strata are unconformably overlain by Ludlow rocks (Keppie *et al.* 1983). Penobscotian deformation clearly affected N Maine, and Penobscotian effects are likely to be present in New Brunswick by extrapolation of the relations in Maine. Neuman (1967) cites evidence for an unconformity related to Penobscotian deformation in Quebec. Consequently, the entire central region is shown on the map (Fig. 2) as being affected by Penobscotian and/or Taconian deformation. Evidence for Taconian deformation is lacking in parts of the central region such as the central part of the Matapedia Basin (Fig. 1), since here there was continuous deposition during the period of Taconian deformation (Fyffe 1982). This situation is analogous to that in Maine where rocks deformed in the Taconian occur near areas that were undergoing continuous coeval deposition (Neuman 1967).

Evidence for Ordovician deformation is restricted in SE New Brunswick and Nova Scotia. Lower Silurian strata are locally unconformable on Cambrian–Ordovician rocks in the eastern region. Although this unconformity indicates some Ordovician deformation, it is not widespread (Keppie *et al.* 1983).

Newfoundland

In Newfoundland the Baie Verte–Brompton Line separates the western and central regions and the Dover–Hermitage fault separates the central and eastern regions.

As is the case with mainland Canada and New England–New York, there is clear evidence for Taconian deformation in the western region. Cambrian and Ordovician strata are thrust and folded and the youngest rocks involved in this Taconian episode are Llanvirn. They are unconformably overlain by the Caradocian Long Point Formation which constrains the time of deformation (Bergstrom *et al.* 1974) to Llandeilo. Thrusting associated with obduction occurred along the Baie Verte Line in the early Ordovician (Williams & St Julien 1982). This early movement and obduction is similar to that suggested for areas to the S in Quebec and New England where rocks along and above the Cameron's Line–Whitcomb Summit thrust may have undergone pre-Taconian imbrication or accretion.

Unlike the case in mainland Canada, there is not much evidence for Ordovician deformation in the central region of Newfoundland except near the Baie Verte line. The deformed Burlington granodiorite has been dated at 461 Ma (Keppie *et al.* 1983). It is unconformably overlain by Silurian–Devonian rocks, suggesting Taconian deformation. Since some of the deformation near the Baie Verte Line may be Penobscotian, the area is shown on the map (Fig. 2) as having been affected by one or both of the Ordovician deformational episodes. Elsewhere in the central region Ordovician and Silurian rocks are conformable and there is little evidence for Taconian deformation other than that associated with active sedimentation and the formation of mélanges. Ordovician deformation does not seem to have been important in the eastern region, although Williams *et al.* (1974) report late Ordovician open flexural folding.

Caledonides in Britain and Ireland

It is convenient to divide the Caledonides of Britain and Ireland into an early or orthotectonic zone where metamorphism has been pervasive and a later paratectonic zone where metamorphic effects are less important (Fig. 4). The orthotectonic zone lies N of the Highland Border fault in Scotland (Johnson *et al.* 1979) which is now regarded by many workers as a major terrane boundary marked by considerable strike-slip displacement—probably sinistral—and N of the

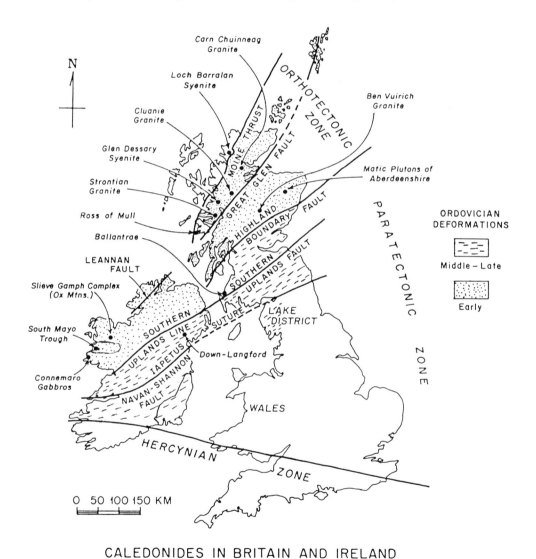

CALEDONIDES IN BRITAIN AND IRELAND

FIG. 4. Principal tectonic and zonal boundaries in Britain and Ireland, and the distribution of the times of main Ordovician deformation.

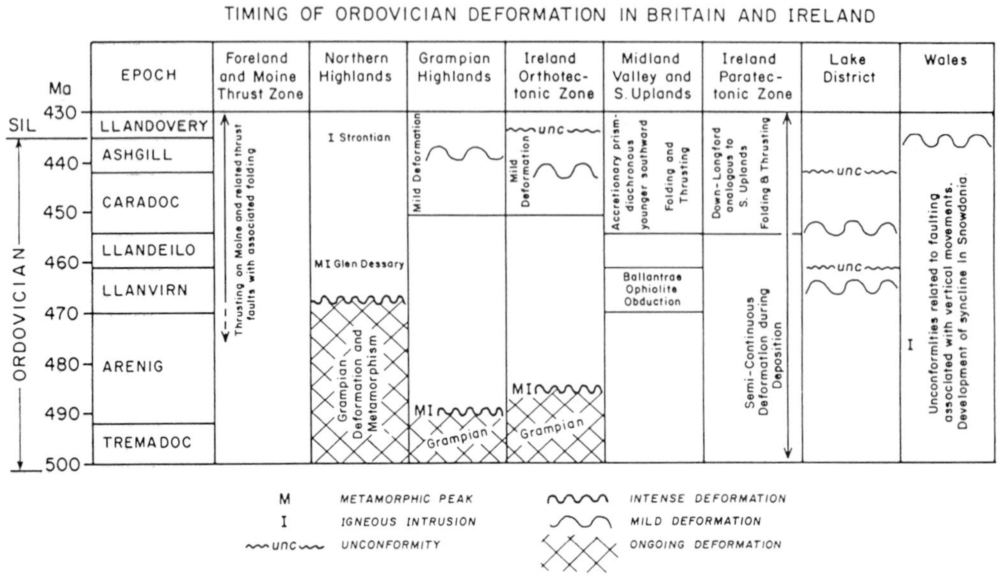

TIMING OF ORDOVICIAN DEFORMATION IN BRITAIN AND IRELAND

FIG. 5. Chart showing the timing of Ordovician deformation in Britain and Ireland.

Southern Uplands line in Ireland (Max 1983). Further subdivision of the region (Powell & Phillips 1985) is useful for looking at the timing of deformation (Figs 4 and 5).

Rocks in the Moine thrust zone were folded, faulted and sheared to produce mylonitic textures presumably beginning in the Llanvirn, since Arenig rocks are involved in the deformation (Powell 1983). Movement clearly could have begun before this, since initially the allochthonous rocks were much further SE when thrusting commenced and were not being thrust against the Durness carbonates but against rocks that permitted the production of mylonitic textures in siliceous rocks. At least 100 km of transport was involved in bringing rocks previously metamorphosed about 1000 Ma above the Moine thrust onto the foreland (Watson 1984). Movement associated with rocks of the Moine thrust zone involved numerous faults and was complex, involving both contractional and extensional faults and occurring over a long period (Coward 1982, Fettes & Harris 1986). The Loch Borrolan syenite (430± Ma, zircon) is post-deformational (Fig. 6) or late syn-deformational and marks the end of deformation associated with movement on the Moine thrust in that sector (Powell 1983, Watson 1984), and the Ross of Mull granite (414 Ma) was emplaced shortly after movement on the Moine thrust ceased (Pankhurst *et al.* 1982, Watson 1984). The Moine thrust is interpreted as the westernmost and youngest of a series of Caledonian thrusts of which the Sgurr Beag slide (ductile thrust) is one (Rathbone *et al.*

1983, Barr *et al.* 1986). The Sgurr Beag slide is believed (Kelley & Powell 1983) to pre-date the Moine thrust by about 25 Ma and is folded on a regional scale during the same deformation that foliated the Glen Dessary syenite (456±5 Ma).

Radiometric dating of the Carn Chuinneag granite (555±10 Ma, Rb–Sr), the Glen Dessary syenite (456±5 Ma, zircon), the Strontian granite (435±10 Ma, zircon), the Cluanie granite (425±4 Ma, zircon) and the Ross of Mull granite (414±3 Ma, Rb–Sr) is important in bracketing the timing of deformation in the Northern Highlands. The Carn Chuinneag granite was emplaced after deformation began (Harris 1983) in that it post-dates early deformation (Precambrian?) and displays a foliation associated with subsequent (probably early Ordovician) deformation (Powell 1983). The Glen Dessary syenite (456 Ma) post-dates early deformation and metamorphism (Precambrian?), but is syn-metamorphic with respect to later thrust-related events (Roberts *et al.* 1984, Barr *et al.* 1986) and has been considered to have been intruded at the climax of Ordovician metamorphism (Watson 1984, Harte 1987). The Strontian granite (435 Ma) was emplaced into hot country rocks still undergoing deformation, while the post-tectonic and post-metamorphic Cluanie granite (425 Ma) approximately constrains the end of deformation and metamorphism.

Nappes and ductile faults, many of which are apparently extensional, developed in the Grampian Highlands during deformation associated with the Grampian orogeny. Two phases of

SELECTED DATED PLUTONS IN SCOTLAND

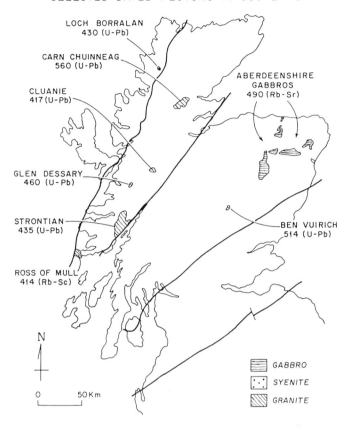

LOCH BORRALAN
430 (U-Pb)

CARN CHUINNEAG
560 (U-Pb)

CLUANIE
417 (U-Pb)

ABERDEENSHIRE
GABBROS
490 (Rb-Sr)

GLEN DESSARY
460 (U-Pb)

STRONTIAN
435 (U-Pb)

BEN VUIRICH
514 (U-Pb)

ROSS OF MULL
414 (Rb-Sc)

N

0   50 Km

GABBRO
SYENITE
GRANITE

FIG. 6. Map showing the locations of selected dated plutons in Scotland and their isotopic ages.

deformation, D_1 and D_2, were of prime importance in nappe development (Bradbury *et al.* 1979, Thomas 1979). The Ben Vuirich granite (514 ± 6 Ma, zircon) was emplaced between D_2 and D_3 prior to the metamorphic climax (Bradbury *et al.* 1976) and thus post-dates nappe development. Although metamorphism occurred during D_1 and D_2 (i.e. pre-514 Ma) the climax of metamorphism was about 490 Ma ago (Fettes 1983, Watson 1984), about 20–30 Ma later. The metamorphic climax has been dated by the time of emplacement of essentially syn-metamorphic mafic igneous plutons in Aberdeenshire. A third phase of deformation (D_3) overlaps and post-dates the metamorphic climax (Bradbury 1979) and further deformed the nappes. Post-tectonic 'Newer Granites' emplaced 425–400 Ma ago constrain the youngest time of deformation at about 430 Ma. Thus deformation proceeded in the Grampian Highlands from about 520 Ma to 435 Ma, perhaps to 425 Ma, and included the development of nappes and their subsequent

deformation which produced features such as the 'down-bend' at the Highland Border (Harris 1983, Dempster 1985). Strike-slip faulting such as that along the Great Glen apparently commenced about 425 Ma ago, as the WNW regional transport of the rocks ceased (Watson 1984).

The orthotectonic zone in Ireland lies N of the Southern Uplands line and is divided into a NW block and SE block by the Leannan fault (Fig. 7) (Johnson *et al.* 1979). Much of the orthotectonic zone in Ireland is comparable to the SW Highlands (Grampian Highlands) of Scotland in terms of stratigraphy and deformational history. The rocks underwent intense deformation and metamorphism in the late Cambrian–early Ordovician Grampian orogeny (Max 1983). The Connemara gabbros yield a 510 Ma zircon age and combined with the 490 Ma date based on whole-rock Rb–Sr studies of metasediments indicates that the time of main deformation was about 500 Ma ago (Johnson *et al.* 1979). The Slieve Gamph Complex in the Ox Mountains

(Fig. 7) is syn-tectonic and has been dated at 477 Ma (Johnson *et al.* 1979). It post-dates earlier deformational features that may be Caledonian or Precambrian (Max 1983). Folds in middle Ordovician strata in the S Mayo Trough (Fig. 7) are truncated by an unconformity beneath Silurian strata, which provides strong evidence for Taconian deformation (Max 1983). The S Mayo Trough is an Ordovician–Silurian basin of paratectonic aspect within the orthotectonic zone (Max 1983).

The Southern Uplands has been interpreted as an accretionary prism developed during the closing of Iapetus (Leggett *et al.* 1983). Faults associated with the development of the accretionary prism are progressively younger from N to S, and considerable dip-slip and strike-slip displacements are postulated along segment boundaries within the prism. Ballantrae ophiolitic rocks were apparently obducted in the Arenig, and earliest accretion of rocks in the Southern Uplands did not commence until 20–25 Ma later in the late Caradoc according to available evidence (Leggett *et al.* 1983). Development of the accretionary prism continued through the Wenlock to early Ludlow (Leggett *et al.* 1983).

Ordovician rocks in the paratectonic zone of Ireland were likely to have been undergoing more

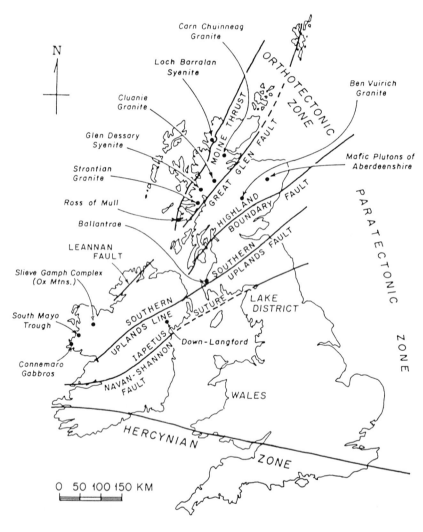

CALEDONIDES IN BRITAIN AND IRELAND

FIG. 7. Location map for geographic localities in Britain and Ireland.

or less continuous deformation during deposition (Max 1983). The rocks of the Down–Longford region and paratectonic inliers to the SW have a depositional and deformational history comparable with that of the Southern Uplands of Scotland in that they constitute an accretionary prism developed in the late Ordovician and Silurian (Anderson & Cameron 1979). Caledonian deformation is simpler to the S of the Navan–Shannon fault (Iapetus suture) (Fig. 7) than it is to the N (Phillips *et al.* 1979), and only mild deformation and tilting are recognized as Ordovician (Max 1983).

Two phases of Ordovician deformation are recorded by unconformities in the Lake District of N England. The earlier one is equivocal, being marked by either soft sediment or tectonically formed folds in Arenig–Llanvirn sedimentary and volcanic rocks (Johnson *et al.* 1979). These folds are truncated by an unconformity beneath the Llandeilian Borrowdale volcanics and thus developed in the late Llanvirn–early Llandeilo (Powell 1983). A second phase of major regional folding in the Borrowdale volcanics and older rocks occurred in early Caradoc to early Ashgill time (Johnson *et al.* 1979). These folds are truncated by an unconformity beneath the upper Ordovician Coniston Group.

Vertical tectonics accomplished by faulting and arching is indicated by some discontinuities in the Ordovician strata of Wales, but Ordovician deformational features are not extensively developed (Coward & Siddans 1979). The rim syncline around the Ordovician volcanic region in Snowdonia was apparently developed in relation to ring fracturing related to uprising magma in the Ordovician. Open folds developed in the late Ordovician in the Welsh Borderland areas (Coward & Siddans 1979).

Caledonides in Scandinavia, Svalbard and East Greenland

Scandinavia

Geological and radiometric evidence has clearly demonstrated that Ordovician deformation was important in Scandinavia (Fig. 8) (Sturt *et al.* 1967, 1978, Roberts & Wolff 1981, Gee & Roberts 1983, Dallmeyer *et al.* 1985), although this early, pre-Scandian, Palaeozoic deformation is sometimes difficult to distinguish from Precambrian tectonism and is masked by intense Scandian overprinting in the mid-Silurian–early Devonian.

The late Cambrian–early Ordovician deformation was most extensive in rocks comprising the lower and middle Allochthons in N Norway (Fig. 9). In Finnmark deformation and metamorphism proceeded successively from W to E, slightly pre-dating piggy-back nappe transport and accretion. Further south, the generation and obduction of oceanic crust also occurred at this time, and parts of the miogeoclinal sedimentary sequences were deformed and translated southeastward onto the Baltoscandian platform.

The late Cambrian to early Ordovician deformation, metamorphism and plutonism are ascribed to the *Finnmarkian* phase of the Caledonian orogeny (Ramsay & Sturt 1976). Evidence for the Finnmarkian is most widespread in N Norway where numerous radiometric ages have been determined for a variety of rock types in several nappes, particularly the plutonic rocks of the Seiland Petrographic Province in the Kalak Nappe Complex (Sturt *et al.* 1978). Two major episodes of deformation, separated by peak metamorphism, have been identified in the Finnmarkian. Rb–Sr isochron ages for Seiland

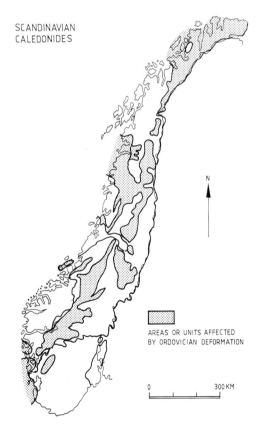

SCANDINAVIAN CALEDONIDES

N

AREAS OR UNITS AFFECTED BY ORDOVICIAN DEFORMATION

0   300 KM

FIG. 8. Distribution of areas or geological units (generally nappe complexes) affected by Ordovician deformation in the Scandinavian Caledonides.

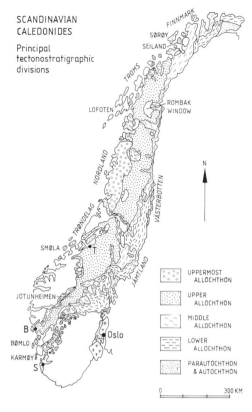

SCANDINAVIAN
CALEDONIDES

Principal
tectonostratigraphic
divisions

LOFOTEN

ROMBAK
WINDOW

FINNMARK
SØRØY
SEILAND
TROMS

NORDLAND

TRØNDELAG

VÄSTERBOTTEN

N

SMØLA

T

JAMTLAND

JOTUNHEIMEN

B

Oslo

BØMLO

KARMØY

S

		UPPERMOST ALLOCHTHON
		UPPER ALLOCHTHON
		MIDDLE ALLOCHTHON
		LOWER ALLOCHTHON
		PARAUTOCHTHON & AUTOCHTHON

0   300 KM

FIG. 9. Simplified map showing the principal tectonostratigraphic divisions of the Caledonides in Scandinavia and the geographic locations mentioned in the main text: B, Bergen; S, Stavanger; T, Trondheim. The non-ornamented areas are those of the crystalline autochthon in the E and tectonic windows within and to the W of the main Caledonian nappes. Crosses near Oslo represent Permian igneous rocks.

Province syn-tectonic plutonic rocks range from 540 to 490 Ma, with early gabbros on Sørøy showing the oldest dates of 540–527 Ma. In addition, nepheline from nepheline-syenite dykes on Seiland and Sørøy have produced K–Ar ages of 500–488 Ma (Sturt *et al.* 1967) (recalculated). Further E, slates (493 Ma, Rb–Sr isochron) in the Laksefjord Nappe below the Kalak and lower Cambrian slates (504 Ma, Rb–Sr) in the Parautochthon suggest that slaty cleavage or schistosity development occurred approximately 490–500 Ma ago during the later, main phase of the Finnmarkian orogeny. The youngest fossils found in the highest parts of the deformed sedimentary pile are Tremadoc. Preliminary ^{40}Ar/^{39}Ar dating suggests that slaty cleavages formed about 485 Ma ago in the Laksefjord and subjacent Gaissa Nappes (R. D. Dallmeyer 1985, personal

communication). Thus the isotopic data together with the geological information indicate that the major foliation-producing metamorphic event of the Finnmarkian orogenesis occurred in the period from about 505 to 485 Ma. The earlier phase is recorded only in the highest part of the Kalak Nappe Complex, W Finnmark, in plutonic rocks of the Seiland Province. Deformation and metamorphism of rocks of the Caledonian allochthon during the Finnmarkian apparently started in the NW and migrated in an easterly to southeasterly direction along with detachment and emplacement of the various nappes onto the Baltoscandian platform during the second and most widespread episode of deformation (Roberts 1985).

Elsewhere in Scandinavia, radiometric data indicative of pre-Silurian Caledonian deformation are available from different parts of the allochthon (Roberts & Gee 1985). Metamorphism represented by hornblende growth in cleavage developed in association with early thrusting has been dated at about 450 Ma (K–Ar) in the Rombak area of Norway (Hodges *et al.* 1982), although Hodges (1985) now prefers to regard these dates as being 'unreasonably old and reflect excess radiogenic argon'. Nevertheless, relationships in the Lofoten–Rombak area suggested to Hodges *et al.* (1982) that there had been a collision between the Baltic and Laurentian cratons beginning in the middle to late Ordovician. Migmatites (442 Ma, Rb–Sr) and syn-tectonic granite (438 Ma, Rb–Sr) (Gee & Roberts 1983) in the higher Köli Nappes in Västerbotten, Sweden, indicate mid-Ordovician deformation and metamorphism. In the same region, in the uppermost Allochthon, granitic dykes (447 Ma, Rb-Sr) postdate penetrative deformation and metamorphism of the Rödingsfjället Nappe; these relationships were interpreted by Claesson (1979) to indicate strong middle Ordovician deformation. Further W, in the Beiarn Nappe in Nordland, Norway, Rb–Sr ages on granite and monzonitic gneiss suggest both late Cambrian–early Ordovician and middle Ordovician deformation (Cribb 1981, Tørudbakken & Brattli 1985). Hornblende from rocks in eastern parts of the Köli and Seve Nappes in Jämtland, Sweden, have yielded ^{40}Ar/^{39}Ar plateau ages of 510–480 Ma and 480–450 Ma respectively, and are interpreted to indicate an early Caledonian (Finnmarkian) metamorphism and diachronous cooling in early to middle Ordovician time (Dallmeyer *et al.* 1985). Also in Jämtland, but in the middle Allochthon, mylonitic rocks that separate the Särv Nappe from the underlying Tännäs Nappe developed at the time of thrusting at around 485 Ma (Rb–Sr) (Claesson 1980) and indicate early Ordovician deformation.

In Trøndelag, central Norway, trondhjemites within the Gula Nappe truncate an early schistosity but are themselves involved in the early Caledonian deformation and metamorphism. In one area this deformation affects phyllites containing a Tremadoc fauna and also involves the Støren ophiolite slice and Fundsjø ensimatic arc rocks (Gee & Roberts 1983). The oldest fossiliferous metasediments which lie unconformably upon the deformed Gula and Støren rocks are of mid-Arenig age (Ryan & Williams 1980). Thus the biostratigraphic constraints on the age of this early Ordovician deformation in Trøndelag are quite narrow (Fig. 10), and the isotopic dates of 480–450 Ma (Rb–Sr and zircon) (Klingspor & Gee 1981) from the cross-cutting trondhjemites lend support to this view. On the island of Smøla in this same part of Norway, Arenig–Llanvirn sediments and calc-alkaline volcanic rocks have been metamorphosed at low grade and display tight to open folds cross-cut by a quartz-diorite intruded about 436 Ma (Rb–Sr) (Roberts & Sturt 1980, Roberts 1985); this deformation would then be about mid-Ordovician. Ryan & Williams (1980) also reported a minor folding event in SW Trøndelag, in the period Llanvirn to mid-Caradoc, time-equivalent to the Taconian.

In W and SW Norway, rock units in both the gneissic basement and the upper Allochthon in the Bergen–Stavanger region provide evidence for probable early Ordovician orogenesis (Bryhni *et al.* 1971, Bryhni & Sturt 1985). A pre-Ashgill unconformity is present in the Major Bergen Arc (Fig. 10), below which occurs a multiply-deformed complex including ophiolite fragments (Sturt & Thon 1976). On Karmøy, the pre-Ashgill granitoids which cut the deformed ophiolite have yielded an Rb–Sr errorchron age of about 450 Ma.

On the neighbouring island of Bømlo, however, an ensimatic island-arc assemblage occurs on top of the ophiolite (Nordås *et al.* 1984), and a quartz-keratophyre from this unit has given an Rb–Sr age of 535 Ma (Furnes *et al.* 1983). Both the ophiolite and the island-arc volcanics were polyphasally deformed and then overlain unconformably by sub-aerial basaltic to rhyolitic volcanites of the Siggjo Complex (Nordås *et al.* 1984). An andesite and a rhyolite from this complex have yielded Rb–Sr isochron ages of 468 Ma and 464 Ma respectively. Thus an orogenic event of early to middle Ordovician age appears to have affected the Caledonian nappe rocks of SW Norway.

Elsewhere in S Norway, on the southeastern side of Jotunheimen, the Strondafjord Formation near Fagernes includes rocks interpreted as a clastic wedge deposited in front of the higher Valdres and Jotun thrust sheets during their emplacement (Hossack *et al.* 1981). Rock fragments carrying a pre-depositional cleavage in clastics of the Strondafjord indicate deformation in the source rock prior to sedimentary accumulation. Graptolites in the slates associated with the Strondafjord Formation indicate that it is middle to upper Ordovician and thus denote thrusting and deformation at that time (Hossack *et al.* 1981).

In summary, the evidence from Scandinavia points to an important polyphase orogenesis, the Finnmarkian, in latest Cambrian to early Ordovician time. In some parts of the fold belt this deformation was restricted to the Ordovician, affecting metasediments containing Tremadoc fossils. In Finnmark, N Norway, for example, the principal folding and metamorphism occurred in the early Ordovician, but an early

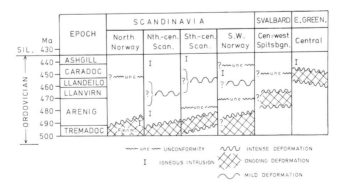

FIG. 10. Chart showing the timing of Ordovician deformation in the Caledonides of Scandinavia, W Svalbard and central E Greenland. The sloping deformation belts (time periods) for Scandinavian areas signify W (left) to E (right) diachronism of deformation. An E–W diachronism is indicated for E Greenland but this has not been proved.

episode in the NW dates to late Cambrian time. Isotopic evidence, with some support from faunas, is also suggesting that elsewhere deformation and metamorphism occurred locally in the middle Ordovician, broadly equivalent to the Taconian, especially in nappes in Nordland, around Smøla and in parts of W and SW Norway.

Svalbard

Indications of Ordovician deformation on Svalbard are found in the western part of the island of Spitsbergen. In one area, a blueschist–eclogite complex has yielded two K–Ar muscovite ages of 475–470 Ma (Horsfield 1972), while rocks of a nearby flyschoid sequence, the Bulltinden Formation, have yielded early to middle Silurian fossils (Scrutton *et al.* 1976). This tectonometamorphic phase is broadly equivalent to the post-Llanvirn–pre-Wenlock deformation in central N Spitsbergen (Harland 1978). Recent work by Ohta *et al.* (1983) in Central W Spitsbergen has revealed an unconformity at the base of the Bulltinden Formation. Clasts in the basal conglomeratic limestone include rocks from the subjacent high-pressure metamorphic complex. Moreover, gastropods and other fossils in the limestone matrix and in newly discovered localities within the Bulltinden limestones (Ohta, in prep.) include *Maclurites* of probable middle–late Ordovician age (Y. Ohta & J. S. Peel 1984, personal communication) and conodonts of Caradoc–Ashgill age (Y. Ohta, H. A. Armstrong & H. A. Nakrem 1985, personal communication). Thus the phase of high-pressure deformation and metamorphism in this part of Svalbard is middle Ordovician or older (Fig. 10).

E Greenland

Recently discovered fossils allied to radiometric data have constrained the main Caledonian orogeny in central E Greenland to the Ordovician (Henriksen 1985), which is somewhat older than previously thought (Fig. 10). Moreover, no evidence survives for a middle Cambrian to lower Ordovician hiatus in the stratigraphic succession.

The youngest sediments involved in the main deformation are of upper Chazyan age (late middle Ordovician). Although the oldest molasse sediments post-dating orogenesis are middle Devonian, there are many late- to post-tectonic Ordovician and Silurian granitoids. According to Henriksen (1985) a post-tectonic granite which truncates folded Ordovician sediments and which is dated at 445 Ma (Rb–Sr) (Rex & Gledhill 1981) provides perhaps the most reasonable minimum

age available. These lines of evidence place a late Ordovician age on the main orogenic event in this part of Caledonide Greenland. In the northern part of E Greenland the main Caledonian deformation was younger. Wenlock turbidites are the youngest sediments involved in the nappes there.

Summarizing remarks

Ordovician deformational effects are widespread in the Caledonide orogen. Two main episodes are identified: the earlier is referred to as the Grampian, Penobscotian or Finnmarkian in Britain and Ireland, N America and Scandinavia respectively; the later is referred to as Taconian and its effects are widespread, especially in N America. In some places, such as the paratectonic zone of Ireland, deformation may have been more or less continuous during the Ordovician (Figs 4 and 5), whereas elsewhere the two episodes are distinct. It is difficult to discriminate between the Grampian and the Taconian in some regions, either because data are insufficient or because the two episodes overlapped and effects of both are present. Areas where Grampian and Taconian effects cannot be distinguished or where they overlap, are indicated by a separate ornament in Fig. 2.

Recognition of the significance of Grampian (Penobscot) deformation in the Appalachian part of the orogen is becoming more widespread. Large parts of the Appalachians exhibit evidence which either requires Penobscot deformation or is consistent with its occurrence (Fig. 2).

Deformation in the early Ordovician was important in the development of imbricate thrust faults that involved the obduction of oceanic crust. Stacking of thrust sheets occurred and was accompanied, or slightly preceded, by metamorphism in some areas. The stacked thrust sheets were transported onto continental crust later in the period of deformation. Ordovician deformational effects are progressively younger towards the craton: northwesterly in N America, Britain, Ireland and E Greenland, and easterly to southeasterly in Scandinavia. Thus the Taconian is important along the western or northwestern side of the Appalachians. The timing of Ordovician deformation is also diachronous from SE to NW across the Highlands of Scotland where compressional deformation began about 520 Ma ago in the Southern Highlands and ended about 430 Ma ago at the Moine thrust zone.

In Scandinavia, deformation and metamorphism ascribed to the Finnmarkian are most widespread in the N, in Norway, but are now being recognized more extensively in central and southern areas. In Sweden, whereas until a few years ago the main Caledonian deformation was ascribed almost solely to the Silurian (the Scandian event), there is now appreciable evidence supporting early Ordovician orogenesis. There is also isotopic evidence of a mid-Ordovician deformation in parts of central and western Norway. It is also clear that oceanic closure and the obduction of ophiolitic rocks was of major importance during early to middle Ordovician times in the Caledonide orogen. The deformation associated with this is diachronous and generally progressively younger towards the neighbouring cratons, although post-Giddings Brook thrusting

in New England may be an exception. In N America, Grampian (Penobscot) deformational effects may be much more widespread than is known at the present time.

ACKNOWLEDGEMENTS: We wish to thank Avery Drake, Philip Osberg and Peter Robinson for numerous discussions and helpful comments on the original manuscript, and Brian Sturt for his critical reading of the sections on Britain, Ireland and Scandinavia.

EDITORIAL NOTE: Professor Leo Hall died before an earlier version of this manuscript could be revised. The editors wish to acknowledge the major contribution of Dr David Roberts in revising and supplementing the original manuscript.

References

AMENTA, R. V. 1974. Multiple deformation and metamorphism from structural analysis of the eastern Pennsylvania Piedmont. *Geological Society of America Bulletin*, **85**, 1647–60.

ANDERSON, T. B. & CAMERON, T. D. J. 1979. A structural profile of Caledonian deformation in Down. *In*: HARRIS, A. L., HOLLAND, C. H. & LEAKE, B. E. (eds) *The Caledonides of the British Isles Reviewed. Special Publication of the Geological Society of London No. 8*, pp. 263–7.

BARR, D., HOLDSWORTH, R. E. & ROBERTS, A. M. 1986. Caledonian ductile thrusting in a Precambrian metamorphic complex: the Moine of northwestern Scotland. *Geological Society of America Bulletin*, **97**, 754–64.

BERGSTROM, S. M., RIVA, J. & KAY, M. 1974. Significance of conodonts, graptolites, and shelly faunas from the Ordovician of western and north-central Newfoundland. *Canadian Journal of Earth Sciences*, **11**, 1625–60.

BOONE, G. M. 1983. The Hurricane Mountain Formation melange and unconformably overlying lower to middle Ordovician volcanics, Brassua Lake and Moosehead Lake quadrangles. *In*: CALDWELL, D. W. & HANSON, L. S. (eds) *New England Intercollegiate Geologic Conference Guidebook for Field Trips, 75th Annual Meeting*, pp. 31–44.

BOSWORTH, W. & KIDD, W. S. F. 1985. Thrusts, melanges, folded thrusts and duplexes in the Taconic foreland. *Guidebook, Annual Meeting, New York State Geological Association, Skidmore College*, pp. 117–47.

BRADBURY, H. J. 1979. Migmatisation, deformation and porphyroblast growth in the Dalradian of Tayside, Scotland. *In*: HARRIS, A. L., HOLLAND, C. H. & LEAKE, B. E. (eds) *The Caledonides of the British Isles Reviewed. Special Publication of the Geological Society of London No. 8*, pp. 351–6.

——, SMITH, R. A. & HARRIS, A. L. 1976. Older granites as time-markers in Dalradian evolution. *Journal of the Geological Society, London*, **132**, 4.

——, HARRIS, A. L. & SMITH, R. A. 1979. Geometry and emplacement of nappes in the Central Scottish

Highlands. *In*: HARRIS, A. L., HOLLAND, C. H. & LEAKE, B. E. (eds) *The Caledonides of the British Isles Reviewed. Special Publication of the Geological Society of London No. 8*, pp. 213–20.

BRYHNI, I. & STURT, B. A. 1985. Caledonides of Southwestern Norway. *In*: GEE, D. G. & STURT, B. A. (eds) *The Caledonide Orogen—Scandinavia and Related Areas*, pp. 89–107, Wiley, Chichester.

——, FITCH, F. J. & MILLER, J. A. 1971. ^{40}Ar–^{39}Ar dates from recycled Precambrian rocks in the gneiss region of the Norwegian Caledonides. *Norsk Geologisk Tidsskrift*, **51**, 391–406.

BUTLER, J. R. 1973. Paleozoic deformation and metamorphism in part of the Blue Ridge thrust sheet, North Carolina. *American Journal of Science*, **273A**, 72–88.

CLAESSON, S. 1979. Pre-Silurian orogenic deformation in the north-central Scandinavian Caledonides. *Geologiska Föreningens i Stockholm Förhandlingar*, **101**, 353–6.

—— 1980. A Rb-Sr isotope study of granitoids and related mylonites in the Tannas Augen Gneiss Nappe, Southern Swedish Caledonides. *Geologiska Föreningens i Stockholm Förhandlingar*, **102**, 403–20.

COWARD, M. P. 1982. Surge zones in the Moine thrust zone of NW Scotland. *Journal of Structural Geology*, **4**, 247–56.

—— & SIDDANS, A. W. B. 1979. The tectonic evolution of the Welsh Caledonides. *In*: HARRIS, A. L., HOLLAND, C. H. & LEAKE, B. E. (eds) *The Caledonides of the British Isles Reviewed. Special Publication of the Geological Society of London No. 8*, pp. 187–98.

CRIBB, S. J. 1981. Rb-Sr geochronological evidence suggesting a reinterpretation of part of the north Norwegian Caledonides. *Norsk Geologisk Tidsskrift*, **61**, 97–110.

DALLMEYER, R. D. 1975. Incremental ^{40}Ar/^{39}Ar ages of biotite and hornblende from retrograded basement gneisses of the southern Blue Ridge: their bearing on the age of Paleozoic metamorphism. *American Journal of Science*, **275**, 444–60.

——, GEE, D. G. & BECKHOLMEN, M. 1985. $^{40}Ar/^{39}Ar$ mineral age record of early Caledonian tectonothermal activity in the Baltoscandian miogeocline. *American Journal of Science*, **285**, 532–68.

DEMPSTER, T. J. 1985. Uplift patterns and orogenic evolution on the Scottish Dalradian. *Journal of the Geological Society, London*, **142**, 111–28.

DRAKE, A. A., JR 1980. The Taconides, Acadides, and Alleghenides in the Central Appalachians. *In*: WONES, D. R. (ed.) *The Caledonides in the USA: Proceedings of the International Geological Correlation Program—Caledonide Orogen Project 27, Blacksburg, VA. Department of Geological Sciences, Virginia Polytechnic Institute and State University, Memoir No. 2*, pp. 179–87.

—— & LYTTLE, P. T. 1981. The Accotink Schist, Lake Barcroft Metasandstone, and Popes Head Formation—keys to an understanding of the tectonic evolution of the northern Virginia piedmont. *United States Geological Survey Professional Paper No. 1205*, 16 pp.

—— & MORGAN, B. A. 1981. The Piney Branch Complex—a metamorphosed fragment of the central Appalachian ophiolite in nothern Virginia. *American Journal of Science*, **281**, 484–508.

FETTES, D. J. 1983. Metamorphism in the British Caledonides. *In*: SCHENK, P. E. (ed.) *Regional Trends in the Geology of the Appalachian–Caledonian–Hercynian–Mauritanide Orogen*, pp. 205–19, Reidel, Dordrecht.

—— & HARRIS, A. L. (eds) 1986. *Synthesis of the Caledonian Rocks of Britain. NATO Advanced Study Institute, Series C, Mathematical and Physical Sciences*, **175**, 350 pp.

FISHER, D. W. 1977. Correlation of the Hadrynian, Cambrian and Ordovician Rocks in New York State. *New York State Museum Map and Chart Series No. 25*, 75 pp.

——, ISACHSEN, Y. W. & RICKARD, L. V. 1970. Geologic map of New York. *New York State Museum and Science Service Map and Chart Series No 15*.

FURNES, H., AUSTRHEIM, H., AMALIKSEN, K. G. & NORDÅS, J. 1983. Evidence for an incipient early Caledonian (Cambrian) orogenic phase in southwestern Norway. *Geological Magazine*, **120**, 607–12.

FYFFE, L. R. 1982. Taconian and Acadian structural trends in central and northern New Brunswick. *In*: ST JULIEN, P. & BELAND, J. (eds) *Major Structural Zones and Faults of the Northern Appalachians. Geological Association of Canada Special Paper No. 24*, pp. 117–30.

GARIEPY, C. & HUBERT, C. 1981. An appraisal of the geochemistry of the Quebec Appalachians. *Geological Society of America, Abstracts with Programs*, **13**, 134.

GEE, D. G. & ROBERTS, D. 1983. Timing of deformation in the Scandinavian Caledonides. *In*: SCHENK, P. E. (ed.) *Regional Trends in the Geology of the Appalachian–Caledonian–Hercynian–Mauritanide Orogen*, pp. 279–92, Reidel, Dordrecht.

GRAUERT, B. & WAGNER, M. E. 1975. Age of the granulite facies metamorphism of the Wilmington Complex, Delaware–Pennsylvania piedmont. *American Journal of Science*, **275**, 683–91.

HALL, L. M. 1980. Basement–cover relations in western Connecticut and southeastern New York. *In*: WONES, D. R. (ed.) *The Caledonides in the USA: Proceedings of the International Geological Correlation Program—Caledonide Orogen Project 27, Blacksburg, VA. Department of Geological Sciences, Virginia Polytechnic Institute and State University, Memoir No. 2*, pp. 73–82.

—— & ROBINSON, P. 1982. Stratigraphic–tectonic subdivisions of southern New England. *In*: ST JULIEN, P. & BELAND, J. (eds) *Major Structural Zones and Faults of the Northern Appalachians. Geological Association of Canada Special Paper No. 24*, pp. 15–41.

HARLAND, W. B. 1978. The Caledonides of Svalbard. *Geological Survey of Canada No. 78–13*, pp. 3–11.

HARRIS, A. L. 1983. The growth and structure of Scotland. *In*: CRAIG, G. Y. (ed.) *Geology of Scotland*, 2nd edn, pp. 1–22, Wiley, New York.

HARTE, B. 1987. Lower Palaeozoic metamorphism in the Moine–Dalradian belt of the British Isles. *This volume*.

HATCH, N. L., JR 1982. Taconian line in western New England and its implications to Paleozoic tectonic history. *In*: ST JULIEN, P. & BELAND, J. (eds) *Major Structural Zones and Faults of the Northern Appalachians. Geological Association of Canada Special Paper No. 24*, pp. 67–85.

HATCHER, R. D., JR, BUTLER, J. R., FULLAGAR, P. D., SECOR, D. T. & SNOKE, A. W. 1980. Geologic synthesis of the Tennessee–Carolinas–Northeast Georgia southern Appalachians. *In*: WONES, D. R. (ed.) *The Caledonides in the USA: Proceedings of the International Geological Correlation Program—Caledonide Orogen Project 27, Blacksburg, VA. Department of Geological Sciences, Virginia Polytechnic Institute and State University, Memoir No. 2*, pp. 83–9.

HENRIKSEN, N. 1985. The Caledonides of central East Greenland 70–76°N. *In*: GEE, D. G. & STURT, B. A. (eds) *The Caledonide Orogen—Scandinavia and Related Areas*, pp. 1095–113, Wiley, Chichester.

HODGES, K. V. 1985. Tectonic stratigraphy and structural evolution of the EfjordSitasjaure area, northern Scandinavia Caledonides. *Norges Geologiske Undersøkelse, Bulletin No. 399*, pp. 41–60.

——, BARTLEY, J. M. & BURCHFIEL, B. C. 1982. Structural evolution of an A-type subduction zone, Lofoten–Rombak Area, northern Scandinavian Caledonides. *Tectonics*, **1**, 441–62.

HORSFIELD, W. T. 1972. Glaucophane schists of Caledonian age from Spitzbergen. *Geological Magazine*, **109**, 29–36.

HOSSACK, J. R., KOESTLER, A. G., LUTRO, O., MILNES, P. T. & NICKELSON, R. P. 1981. A traverse from the foreland through the thrust sheet complex of Jotunheimen. *Uppsala Caledonide Symposium, Excursion B3, International Geological Correlation Program—Caledonide Orogen Project 27.*

JOHNSON, M. R. W., SANDERSON, D. J. & SOPER, N. J. 1979. Deformation of the Caledonides of England,

Ireland and Scotland. *In*: HARRIS, A. L., HOLLAND, C. H. & LEAKE, B. E. (eds) *The Caledonides of the British Isles Reviewed. Special Publication of the Geological Society of London No. 8*, pp. 165–86.

KELLEY, S. P. & POWELL, D. 1983. Relationships between marginal thrusting and movement on major internal shear zones in the northern Highland Caledonides, Scotland. *Journal of Structural Geology*, **7**, 161–74.

KEPPIE, J. D., ST JULIEN, P., HUBERT, C., BELAND, J., SKIDMORE, B., FYFFE, L. R., RUITENBERG, A. A., McCUTCHEON, S. R., WILLIAMS, H. & BURSNALL, J. 1983. Times of deformation in the Canadian Appalachians. *In*: SCHENK, P. E. (ed.) *Regional Trends in the Geology of the Appalachian–Caledonian–Hercynian–Mauritanide Orogen*, pp. 307–13, Reidel, Dordrecht.

KISH, S. A., BUTLER, R. J. & FULLAGAR, P. D. 1979. The timing of metamorphism and deformation in the central and eastern piedmont of North Carolina. *Geological Society of America, Abstracts with Programs*, **11**(4), 184.

KLINGSPOR, I. & GEE, D. G. 1981. Isotopic age-determination studies of the Trøndelag trondhjemites. *Terra Cognita*, **1**, 55 (abstract).

LAIRD, J. & ALBEE, A. L. 1981. Pressure, temperature and time indicators in mafic schist: their application to reconstructing the polymetamorphic history of Vermont. *American Journal of Science*, **281**, 127–75.

——, LAMPHERE, M. A. & ALBEE, A. L. 1984. Distribution of Ordovician and Devonian metamorphism in mafic and pelitic schists from northern Vermont. *American Journal of Science*, **284**, 376–413.

LEGGET, J. K., McKERROW, W. S. & SOPER, N. J. 1983. A model for the crustal evolution of southern Scotland. *Tectonics*, **2**, 187–210.

MAX, M. D. 1983. Deformation in the Irish Caledonides. *In*: SCHENK, P. E. (ed.) *Regional Trends in the Geology of the Appalachian–Caledonian–Hercynian–Mauritanide Orogen*, pp. 301–6, Reidel, Dordrecht.

MUTH, K. G., ARTH, J. G. & REED, J. C., JR 1979. A minimum age for high-grade metamorphism and granite intrusion in the piedmont of the Potomac River gorge near Washington, DC, *Geology*, **7**, 349–50.

NEUMAN, R. B. 1967. Bedrock geology of the Shin Pond and Stacyville quadrangles Penobscot County, Maine. *United States Geological Survey Professional Paper No. 524-I*, 1–37.

NORDÅS, J., AMALIKSEN, K. G., BREKKE, H., SUTHREN, R., FURNES, H., STURT, B. A. & ROBINS, B. 1984. Lithostratigraphy and petrochemistry of Caledonian rocks on Bømlo, southwest Norway. *In*: GEE, D. G. & STURT, P. A. (eds) *The Caledonide Orogen—Scandinavia and Related Areas*, pp. 679–82, New York, Chichester.

——, HIRAJIMA, T. & HIROI, Y. 1985. Caledonian high-*P* metmamorphism in central West Spitsbergen. *In*: EVANS, B. W. & BROWN, E. H. (eds) Blueschists and Eclogites. *Geological Society of America Memoir No. 164*.

——, HIROI, Y. & HIRAJIMA, T. 1983. Additional evidence of pre-Silurian high-pressure metamorphic rocks in Spitzbergen. *Polar Research*, **1**, 215–8.

OSBERG, P. H. 1983. Timing of orogenic events in the U.S. Appalachians. *In*: SCHENK, P. E. (ed.) *Regional Trends in the Geology of the Appalachian–Caledonian–Hercynian–Mauritanide Orogen*, pp. 315–37, Reidel, Dordrecht.

PANKHURST, R. J., SUTHERLAND, D. S., BROWN, G. C. & PITCHER, W. J. 1982. Caledonian granites and diorites of Scotland and Ireland. *In*: SUTHERLAND, D. S. (ed.) *Igneous Rocks of the British Isles*, pp. 149–90, Wiley, New York.

PAVLIDES, L. 1980. Revised nomenclature and stratigraphic relationships of the Fredericksburg Complex and Quantico Formation of the Virginia piedmont. *United States Geological Survey Professional Paper No. 1146*, 29 pp.

——, ARTH, J. G., DANIELS, D. L. & STERN, T. W. 1982. Island-arc, back-arc, and melange terranes of northern Virginia: tectonic, temporal and regional relationships. *Geological Society of America, Abstracts with Programs*, **14**(7), 584.

PHILLIPS, W. E. A., FLEGG, A. M. & ANDERSON, T. B. 1979. Strain adjacent to the Iapetus suture in Ireland. *In*: HARRIS, A. L., HOLLAND, C. H. & LEAKE, B. E. (eds) *The Caledonides of the British Isles Reviewed. Special Publication of the Geological Society No. 8*, pp. 257–62.

POWELL, D. 1983. Time of deformation in the British Caledonides. *In*: SCHENK, P. E. (ed.) *Regional Trends in the Geology of the Appalachian–Caledonian–Hercynian–Mauritanide Orogen*, pp. 293–9, Reidel, Dordrecht.

—— & PHILLIPS, W. E. A. 1985. Time of deformation in the Caledonide Orogen of Britain and Ireland. *In*: HARRIS, A. L. (ed.) *Geological Society of London, Memoir No. 9*, 17–39.

RAMSAY, D. M. & STURT, B. A. 1976. The synmetamorphic emplacement of the Mageroy Nappe. *Norsk Geologisk Tidsskrift*, **56**, 291–308.

RATCLIFFE, N. M., BIRD, J. M. & BAHRAMI, B. 1975. Structural and stratigraphic chronology of the Taconide and Acadian polydeformational belt of the central Taconics of New York State and Massachusetts. *In*: RATCLIFFE, N. M. (ed.) *New England Intercollegiate Geological Conference Guidebook for Field Trips, 67th Annual Meeting*, pp. 55–86.

—— & ZARTMAN, R. E. 1976. Stratigraphy, isotopic ages, and deformational history of basement and cover rocks of the Berkshire massif, southwestern Massachusetts. *In*: PAGE, L. R. (ed.) *Contributions to the Stratigraphy of New England, Geological Society of America Memoir No. 148*, pp. 373–412.

RATHBONE, P. A., COWARD, M. P. & HARRIS, A. L. 1983. Cover and basement: a contrast in style and fabric. *Mem. geol. Soc. A.* **158**, 213–23.

REX, D. C. & GLEDHILL, A. R. 1981. Isotopic studies in the East Greenland Caledonides (72° 74°N): Precambrian and Caledonian ages. *Rapport Grønlands Geologiske Undersøkelse No. 104*.

ROBERTS, A. M., SMITH, D. I. & HARRIS, A. L. 1984. The structural setting and tectonic significance of the Glen Dessary syenite, Inverness-shire. *Journal of the Geological Society, London*, **141**, 1033–42.

ROBERTS, D. 1985. The Caledonian fold belt in Finnmark. *Norges Geologiske Undersøkelse Bulletin No. 403*, pp. 161–77.

—— & STURT, B. A. 1980. Caledonian deformation in Norway. *Journal of the Geological Society, London*, **137**, 241–50.

—— & GEE, D. G. 1985. An introduction to the structure of the Scandinavian Caledonides. *In*: GEE, D. G. & STURT, B. A. (eds) *The Caledonide Orogen—Scandinavia and Related Areas*, pp. 55–68, Wiley, Chichester.

—— & WOLFF, F. C. 1981. Tectonostratigraphic development of the Trondheim region Caledonides, Central Norway. *Journal of Structural Geology*, **3**, 487–94.

ROBINSON, P. & HALL, L. M. 1980. Tectonic synthesis of Southern New England. *In*: WONES, D. R. (ed.) *The Caledonides in the USA: Proceedings of the International Geological Correlation Program—Caledonide Orogen Project 27, Blacksburg, VA. Department of Geological Sciences, Virginia Polytechnic Institute and State University, Memoir No. 2*, pp. 73–82.

——, TRACY, R. J. & ASHWAL, L. D. 1975. Relict sillimanite–orthoclase assemblage in kyanite–muscovite schist, Pelham dome, west-central Massachusetts. *Transactions of the American Geophysical Union*, **56**, 466 (abstract).

ROLL, M. A. 1986. Effects of Acadian prograde kyanite-zone metamorphism on relict garnet from pre-Acadian granulite facies metamorphism, Mt. Mineval Formation, Pelham dome, Massachusetts. *Geological Society of America, Abstracts with Programs*, **18**, 63.

RYAN, P. D. & WILLIAMS, D. M. 1980. A revised interpretation of the Ordovician stratigraphy of Sor-Trøndelag and its implications for the evolution of the Scandinavian Caledonides. *In*: WONES, D. R. (ed.) *The Caledonides in the USA: Proceedings of the International Geological Correlation Program—Caledonide Orogen Project 27, Blacksburg, VA. Department of Geological Sciences, Virginia Polytechnic Institute and State University, Memoir No. 2*, pp. 99–106.

SCHENK, P. E. (ed.) 1983. *Regional Trends in the Geology of the Appalachian–Caledonian–Hercynian–Mauritanide Orogen*, Reidel, Dordrecht.

SCRUTTON, C. T., HORSFIELD, W. T. & HARLAND, W. B. 1976. Silurian fossils from western Spitsbergen. *Geological Magazine*, **103**, 519–23.

SEIDERS, V. M., MIXON, R. B., STERN, T. W., NEWELL, M. F. & THOMAS, C. B., JR 1975. Age of plutonism and tectonism and a new minimum age limit on the Glenarm Series in the northeast Virginia Piedmont near Occuquan. *American Journal of Science*, **275**, 481–511.

SKEHAN, J. W., S. J. & MURRAY, D. P. 1980. Geologic profile across southeastern New England. *Tectonophysics*, **69**, 285–319.

ST JULIEN, P. & HUBERT, C. 1975. Evolution of the Taconian orogen in the Quebec Appalachians. *American Journal of Science*, **275A**, 337–62.

STANLEY, R. S. & RATCLIFFE, N. M. 1983. Simplified lithotectonic synthesis of pre-Silurian rocks in western New England. *Vermont Geological Survey Special Bulletin No. 5.*

—— & —— 1985. Tectonic synthesis of the Taconian orogeny in western New England. *Geological Society of America Bulletin*, **96**, 1227–50.

——, ROY, D. L., HATCH, N. L., JR & KNAPP, D. A. 1984. Evidence for tectonic emplacement of ultramafic and associated rocks in the pre-Silurian eugeoclinal belt of western New England—vestiges of an ancient accretionary wedge. *American Journal of Science*, **284**, 559–95.

STURT, B. A. & THON, A. 1976. The age of orogenic deformation in the Swedish Caledonides: a discussion. *American Journal of Science*, **276**, 385–90.

——, MILLER, J. A. & FITCH, F. J. 1967. The age of alkaline rocks from West Finnmark, northern Norway, and their bearing on the dating of the Caledonian orogeny. *Norsk Geologisk Tidsskrift*, **47a**, 255–73.

——, PRINGLE, I. R. & RAMSAY, D. M. 1978. The Finnmarkian phase of the Caledonian orogeny. *Journal of the Geological Society, London*, **135**, 597–610.

THOMAS, P. R. 1979. New evidence for a Central Highland root zone. *In*: HARRIS, A. L., HOLLAND, C. H. & LEAKE, B. E. (eds) *The Caledonides of the British Isles Reviewed. Special Publication of the Geological Society of London No. 8*, pp. 205–11.

THOMPSON, J. B., JR, ROBINSON, P., CLIFFORD, T. N. & TRASK, N. J., JR 1968. Nappes and gneiss domes in west-central New England. *In*: ZEN, E-AN, WHITE, W. S., HADLEY, J. B. & THOMPSON, J. B. (eds) *Studies in Appalachian Geology: Northern and Maritime*, pp. 203–18, Wiley, Interscience.

TØRUDBAKKEN, B. O. & BRATTLI, B. 1985. Ages of metamorphic and deformational events in the Beiarn Nappe Complex, Nordland, Norway. *Norges Geologiske Undersøkelse Bulletin No. 399*, pp. 27–39.

TULL, J. F. 1980. Overview of the sequence and timing of deformational events in the southern Appalachians: evidence from the crystalline rocks North Carolina. *In*: WONES, D. R. (ed.) *The Caledonides in the USA: Proceedings of the International Geological Correlation Program—Caledonide Orogen Project 27, Blacksburg, VA. Department of Geological Sciences, Virginia Polytechnic Institute and State University, Memoir No. 2*, pp. 167–77.

WATSON, J. 1984. The ending of the Caledonian orogeny in Scotland. *Journal of the Geological Society, London*, **141**, 139–214.

WILLIAMS, E. & ST JULIEN, P. 1982. The Baie Verte–Brompton Line: early Paleozoic continent–ocean interface in the Canadian Appalachians. *In*: ST JULIEN, P. & BELAND, J. (eds) *Major Structural Zones and Faults of the Northern Appalachians. Geological Association of Canada Special Paper No. 24*, pp. 177–207.

WILLIAMS, H., KENNEDY, M. J. & NEALE, E. R. W. 1974. The northeastward termination of the Appalachian orogen. *In*: NAIRN, A. E. M. & STEHLI,

F. G. (eds) *The Ocean Basins and Margins*, Vol. 2, *The North Atlantic*, pp. 79–123, Plenum, New York.

ZARTMAN, R. E. & NAYLOR, R. S. 1984. Structural implications of some radiometric ages of igneous rocks in southeastern New England. *Geological Society of America Bulletin*, **195**, 522–39.

ZEN, E-AN 1961. Stratigraphy and structure at the north end of the Taconic Range in west-central Vermont. *Geological Society of America Bulletin*, **72**, 293–338.

——, GOLDSMITH, R., RATCLIFFE, N. M., ROBINSON, P. & STANLEY, R. S. 1983. *Bedrock Map of Massachusetts* (scale 1:250,000), United States Geological Survey, Washington, DC.

L. M. HALL*, Department of Geology and Geography, University of Massachusetts, Amherst, MA 01003, USA.

D. ROBERTS, Norges Geologiske Undersøkelse, Post Box 3006, 7002 Trondheim, Norway.

*Deceased. Requests for reprints should be directed to Dr Roberts.

Arenig to Wenlock age metamorphism in the Appalachians

Jo Laird

SUMMARY: Arenig to Wenlock age metamorphism is best defined in the western part of the Appalachian orogen but may well be preserved in some terranes to the E that are underlain by basement which is not N. American regional metamorphism is primarily medium pressure, but low- to medium-pressure facies series metamorphism also occurs in the central Appalachians, and high-pressure metamorphism is locally preserved in northern Vermont and adjacent Quebec. Metamorphic grade varies from prehnite–pumpellyite to granulite facies; the isograds are generally parallel to the regional NE structural trend. Delimitation of the isograds has been hampered by widespread polymetamorphism, uncertainties in interpretation of field and isotopic data, and the need for more detailed mapping and petrological studies.

Metamorphic maps for the United States and Canadian Appalachians compiled by G. W. Fisher and W. E. Trzcienski, Jr, are the basis for Figs 2, 5 and 8 and the following discussion. The assignment of isograds to Arenig to Wenlock age metamorphism is hampered by disagreement concerning the ages of metamorphism and their relative metamorphic grade and facies series. This is due in part to the structural complexity of the rocks, the paucity of good outcrop, especially in the southern Appalachians, and the effects of polydeformation and polymetamorphism. The basis for assigning the metamorphism in various areas to Arenig to Wenlock age is presented below. Eskola's facies classification is used to distinguish the intensity of metamorphism in Figs 2, 5 and 8. Many of the maps from which these figures were compiled use the grade of pelitic rocks to distinguish metamorphic intensity. In general, the following correlations apply:

Facies	Grade of pelitic rocks
Greenschist	Chlorite and biotite
Epidote–amphibolite	Garnet
Lower amphibolite (K)	Staurolite–kyanite
Lower amphibolite (A)	Staurolite–andalusite
Medium amphibolite	Sillimanite + muscovite
Upper amphibolite	Sillimanite + K-feldspar

Following the terminology of Miyashiro (1973, pp. 71–8), kyanite- or andalusite-bearing pelitic schist indicates medium- or low-pressure facies series metamorphism respectively. High-pressure facies series metamorphism is indicated by mafic schist with glaucophane and omphacite + quartz + garnet. Mafic schist with sodic–calcic amphibole + chlorite + epidote + plagioclase + quartz is assigned to a medium- to high-pressure facies series as Laird & Albee (1981b) and Laird et al. (1984) show that these rocks were metamor-phosed at a pressure between that indicated for blueschist and that indicated for mafic schist associated with kyanite-bearing pelitic schist in Vermont.

The Appalachians have traditionally been divided into three parts: northern, central and southern. This division will be used below. The term Taconian will be used for Arenig to Wenlock age metamorphism in rocks underlain by Grenville age basement. Terranes within the Appalachians that are not considered to be underlain by N American basement, but are suspected to have been metamorphosed during this time period, will also be discussed. These terranes may have been metamorphosed elsewhere, but their metamorphic history provides constraints on Appalachian tectonic history during the Arenig to Wenlock.

Figures 1, 4 and 7 show the localities mentioned in the text. Abbreviations for localities are used in the text and on the figures; these are defined in Table 1.

Northern Appalachians

Timing of metamorphism

Taconian metamorphism is recorded in gneisses from the Grenville basement of the Green Mountain (GMM), Berkshire (BM) and Hudson Highlands (HHM) massifs and in the metasedimentary and meta-igneous rocks that overlie them. Recent summaries of available isotopic age data have been presented by Sutter et al. (1985) and Laird et al. (1984). Pertinent data are summarized in Fig. 1 and Table 2.

The best estimate for the timing of Taconian metamorphism within the BM (Sutter et al. 1985) and HHM (Dallmeyer & Sutter 1976) E of the Hudson River (HR) is 466 Ma based on ^{40}Ar/

From HARRIS, A. L. & FETTES, D. J. (eds), 1988, *The Caledonian–Appalachian Orogen,* Geological Society Special Publication No. 38, pp. 311–345.

TABLE 1. *Abbreviations*

States

AL	Alabama	NH	New Hampshire
CT	Connecticut	NY	New York
DE	Delaware	PA	Pennsylvania
GA	Georgia	PQ	Province of Quebec, Canada
MA	Massachusetts	RI	Rhode Island
MD	Maryland	SC	South Carolina
ME	Maine	TN	Tennessee
NC	North Carolina	VA	Virginia
NJ	New Jersey	VT	Vermont

Northern Appalachians

AD	Adamstown pluton	HHM	Hudson Highlands massif
ADM	Adirondacks massif	HM	Housatonic massif
AG	Andover granite	HR	Hudson River
AT	Attean pluton	MG	Mount Grant
BM	Berkshire massif	MP	Manhattan Prong
CC	Cortlandt plutonic complex	NM	Northfield Mountains
CL	Chain Lakes massif	NP	Newburyport complex
CM	Canaan Mountain	NZ	Nashoba zone
DC	Dutchess County	PG	Preston gabbro
EM	Elmore Mountain	SP	Sharpners Pond diorite
EP	Exeter pluton	TM	Taconic Mountains
GMM	Green Mountain massif	WD	Waterbury dome
HC	Highlandcroft pluton	WM	Worcester Mountains

Central Appalachians

AA	Avondale anticline	OB	Occoquan batholith
BGD	Baltimore gneiss domes	PR	Potomac River
BR	Blue Ridge Mountains	RF	Rosemont fault zone
CP	Columbia pluton	SR	Susquehanna River
FRG	Falls Run granite	WC	Wilmington complex
HBU	Honey Brook Upland	WCP	West Chester Prong
JRS	James River synclinorium		

Southern Appalachians

AMS	Ashe metamorphic suite	KAG	Kowaliga augen gneiss
AWB	Ashland–Wedowee belt	KB	Kiokee belt
BR	Blue Ridge Mountains	KMB	Kings Mountain belt
BZ	Brevard zone	LW	Leatherwood granite
CB	Charlotte belt	MA	Mount Airy pluton
CGC	Corbin gneiss complex	MS	Murphy syncline
CK	Cherokee, NC	NB	Newberry granite
CSB	Carolina slate belt	PM	Pine Mountain window
DT	Ducktown, TN	RB	Raleigh belt
EDG	Edgemoor granite	SMA	Sauratown Mountains anticlinorium
EQD	Elkhatchee quartz diorite	SPD	Spruce Pine district
FG	Farmington gabbro	SRA	Smith River allochthon
GF	Great Falls granite	TB	Talladega belt
GMW	Grandfather Mountain window	VAR	Valley and Ridge
GSM	Great Smoky Mountains	W	Waxhall granite porphyry
HF	Hayesville fault	WG	Weddington gabbro
IP	Inner Piedmont	ZG	Zana granite

Age data

123	^{40}Ar/^{39}Ar hornblende	123R	Rb–Sr whole-rock
123B	^{40}Ar/^{39}Ar biotite	123Br	Rb–Sr whole-rock + biotite
123M	^{40}Ar/^{39}Ar muscovite	123MR	Rb–Sr whole-rock + muscovite
123	K–Ar whole-rock	123N	Nd–Sm whole-rock
123B	K–Ar biotite	123S	U–Pb sphene
123M	K–Ar muscovite	123Z	U–Pb zircon
123H	K–Ar hornblende		

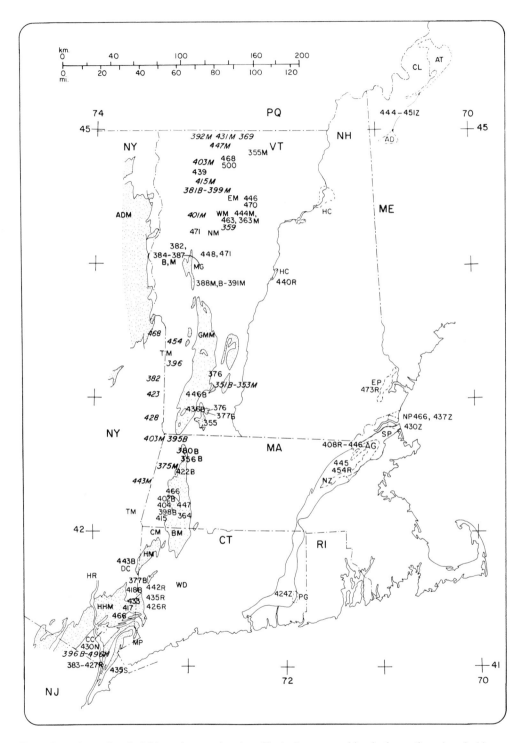

FIG. 1. Isotopic age data (in Ma) pertinent to Arenig to Wenlock metamorphism in the northern Appalachians, USA. Abbreviations are defined in Table 1. The stippled pattern indicates Grenville age basement.

TABLE 2. *Isotopic age data: northern Appalachians*

Location*	Rock type	Dating method	Age†(Ma)	Reference
Northern Vermont: Eugeoclinal rocks (pre-Silurian section)				
45°00'N, 72°33'W	Felsic schist	K–Ar muscovite	392±8	Harper 1968
44°59'N, 72°30'W	Felsic schist	K–Ar muscovite	431±8	Harper 1968
44°57'N, 72°15'W	Slate	K–Ar whole-rock	369±8	Harper 1968
44°52'N, 72°32'W	Felsic schist	K–Ar muscovite	447±8	Harper 1968
44°52.0'N, 72°19.3'W	Quartz and slate pebble, phyllitic conglomerate	^{40}Ar/^{39}Ar total fusion, muscovite	355±5.2	Laird et al. 1984
44°48.3'N, 72°33.0'W	Mafic schist	^{40}Ar/^{39}Ar total fusion, glaucophane	468±6.4	Laird et al. 1984
44°46.4'N, 72°33.0'W	Mafic schist	^{40}Ar/^{39}Ar total fusion, barroisite	490±8.0	Laird et al. 1984
44°46.4'N, 72°33.0'W	Mafic schist	^{40}Ar/^{39}Ar plateau, barroisite	505±19.5	Laird et al. 1984
44°46.4'N, 72°33.0'W	Mafic schist	^{40}Ar/^{39}Ar isochron, barroisite	500±7.7	Laird et al. 1984
44°46'N, 72°36'W	Felsic schist	K–Ar muscovite	388±8	Harper 1968
44°44'N, 72°45'W	Felsic schist	K–Ar muscovite	403±8	Harper 1968
44°41.7'N, 72°54.6'W	Mafic schist	^{40}Ar/^{39}Ar total fusion, actinolite	439±10.0	Laird et al. 1984
44°39'N, 72°46'W	Felsic schist	K–Ar muscovite	415±8	Harper 1968
44°33'N, 72°47'W	Felsic schist	K–Ar biotite	381±8	Harper 1968
44°33'N, 72°47'W	Felsic schist	K–Ar muscovite	399±8	Harper 1968
44°31.2'N, 72°32.2'W (EM)	Mafic schist	^{40}Ar/^{39}Ar total fusion, hornblende cores and actinolite rims	415±3.8	Laird et al. 1984
44°31.2'N, 72°32.2'W (EM)	Mafic schist	^{40}Ar/^{39}Ar plateau, hornblende cores and actinolite rims	470±12.6	Laird et al. 1984
44°31.2'N, 72°32.2'W (EM)	Mafic schist	^{40}Ar/^{39}Ar isochron, hornblende cores and actinolite rims	460±6.1	Laird et al. 1984
44°30.6'N, 72°33.2'W (EC)	Mafic schist	^{40}Ar/^{39}Ar total fusion, hornblende cores and actinolite rims	446±6.7, 449±9.0	Laird et al. 1984
44°29'N, 72°44'W	Felsic schist	K–Ar muscovite	413±8	Harper 1968
44°21.1'N, 72°40.5'W (WM)	Quartz vein	^{40}Ar/^{39}Ar plateau, muscovite	444±9	Lanphere & Albee 1974
44°21.1'N, 72°40.5'W (WM)	Pelitic schist	^{40}Ar/^{39}Ar plateau, muscovite pseudomorphous after kyanite	363±4	Lanphere & Albee 1974
44°24.2'N, 72°40.5'W (WM)	Mafic schist	^{40}Ar/^{39}Ar total fusion, hornblende	463±43	Lanphere & Albee 1974
44°17'N, 72°58'W	Felsic schist	K–Ar muscovite	401±8	Harper 1968
44°17'N, 72°39'W	Phyllite	K–Ar whole-rock	359±8	Harper 1968
44°13.1'N, 72°57.4'W	Mafic schist	^{40}Ar/^{39}Ar total fusion, hornblende	471±5.8	Laird et al. 1984
44°08'N, 72°40'W	Phyllite	K–Ar whole-rock	349±8	Harper 1968
44°5.4'N, 72°57'W	Mafic schist	^{40}Ar/^{39}Ar total fusion, biotite	387±4	Lanphere 1983, personal communication
44°5.4'N, 72°57'W	Mafic schist	^{40}Ar/^{39}Ar total fusion, hornblende	382±3	M. A. Lanphere 1983, personal communication
44°2.9'N, 72°56.9'W (MG)	Felsic schist	^{40}Ar/^{39}Ar total fusion, biotite	384±4.2	Laird et al. 1984

Location	Rock type	Method	Age	Reference
44°2.9'N, 72°56.8'W (MG)	Pelitic schist	^{40}Ar/^{39}Ar total fusion, muscovite	386±4.5	Laird et al. 1984
44°2.7'N, 72°56.9'W (MG)	Pelitic schist	K–Ar biotite	383±5.0	Laird et al. 1984
44°2.7'N, 72°56.3'W (MG)	Felsic schist	K–Ar white mica	376±5.5	Laird et al. 1984
44°3.0'N, 72°56.9'W (MG)	Pelitic schist	K–Ar white mica	385±5.3	Laird et al. 1984
44°1.4'N, 72°50.1'W	Mafic schist	^{40}Ar/^{39}Ar total fusion, barroisite cores and actinolite rims	448±5.1, 471±10.6	Laird et al. 1984
44°1.4'N, 72°50.1'W	Quartz vein	^{40}Ar/^{39}Ar total fusion, actinolite	471±7.2	Laird et al. 1984
44°56'N, 72°56'W	Felsic schist	K–Ar muscovite	391±8, 388±8	Harper 1968
44°56'N, 72°56'W	Felsic schist	K–Ar biotite	389±8	Harper 1968
Taconic Range, SW Vermont and New York				
43°34'N, 73°20'W	Slate	K–Ar whole-rock	468±8	Harper 1968
43°30'N, 73°15'W	Slate	K–Ar whole-rock	454±8	Harper 1968
43°16'N, 73°12'W	Slate	K–Ar whole-rock	396±8	Harper 1968
43°13'N, 73°17'W	Slate	K–Ar whole-rock	382±8	Harper 1968
43°3'N, 73°21'W	Slate	K–Ar whole-rock	423±8	Harper 1968
42°51'N, 73°21'W	Slate	K–Ar whole-rock	428±8	Harper 1968
42°43.4'N, 73°16.6'W	Phyllite	K–Ar muscovite	403±14	Sutter et al. 1985
42°15'N, 73°29'W	Phyllite	K–Ar muscovite	443±16	Sutter et al. 1985
Southern Vermont: Green Mountain massif and domes of Grenville age basement to the E				
42°58'N, 72°57.5'W	Gneiss	^{40}Ar/^{39}Ar plateau, biotite	446.5±4.2	Sutter et al. 1985
42°53.7'N, 72°58.7'W	Gneiss	^{40}Ar/^{39}Ar plateau, biotite	436.5±4.1	Sutter et al. 1985
42°52.5'N, 72°54.7'W	Gneiss	^{40}Ar/^{39}Ar plateau, biotite	363.0±2.7	Sutter et al. 1985
SE Vermont: pre-Silurian rocks E of the Green Mountain massif				
43°7.9'N, 72°43.2'W	Amphibolite	^{40}Ar/^{39}Ar total fusion, hornblende	376±5.0	Laird et al. 1984
43°4'N, 72°43'W	Pelitic schist	K–Ar muscovite	353±8	Harper 1968
43°4'N, 72°43'W	Pelitic schist	K–Ar biotite	351±8	Harper 1968
42°53.5'N, 72°51.5'W	Biotite gneiss	^{40}Ar/^{39}Ar plateau, biotite	377.3±4.2	Sutter et al. 1985
42°53.5'N, 72°51.5'W	Amphibolite	^{40}Ar/^{39}Ar plateau, hornblende	376.1±5.0	Sutter et al. 1985
42°51'N, 72°47.2'W	Amphibolite	^{40}Ar/^{39}Ar plateau, hornblende	355.2±4.8	Sutter et al. 1985
NW Massachusetts: thrust fault zones				
42°31.3'N, 73°19.2'W	Phyllonite	K–Ar muscovite	375±13	Sutter et al. 1985
42°42.8'N, 73°13.1'W	Blastomylonite	K–Ar biotite	395±14	Sutter et al. 1985
Western Massachusetts: Berkshire massif				
42°36'N, 73°5'W	Felsic gneiss	^{40}Ar/^{39}Ar plateau, biotite	379.6±4.2	Sutter et al. 1985
42°28.7'N, 73°7.7'W	Felsic gneiss	^{40}Ar/^{39}Ar plateau, biotite	356.5±3.8	Sutter et al. 1985
42°27.5'N, 73°10'W	Felsic gneiss	^{40}Ar/^{39}Ar plateau, biotite	421.6±4.6	Sutter et al. 1985
42°18'N, 73°13.5'W	Gneiss	^{40}Ar/^{39}Ar plateau, hornblende	466.5±5.1	Sutter et al. 1985
42°16.2'N, 73°8.5'W	Gneiss	^{40}Ar/^{39}Ar plateau, hornblende	446.6±6.2	Sutter et al. 1985

TABLE 2. *Continued*

Location*	Rock type	Dating method	Age†(Ma)	Reference
Western Massachusetts: Berkshire massif—*Continued*				
42°11.2'N, 73°18.8'W	Gneiss	^{40}Ar/^{39}Ar plateau, hornblende	415.4±4.6	Sutter et al. 1985
42°11.2'N, 73°18.8'W	Gneiss	^{40}Ar/^{39}Ar plateau, biotite	397.7±3.0	Sutter et al. 1985
42°14.5'N, 73°12.7'W	Blastomylonite	^{40}Ar/^{39}Ar plateau, biotite	402.1±4.4	Sutter et al. 1985
42°14.5'N, 73°12.7'W	Blastomylonite	^{40}Ar/^{39}Ar plateau, hornblende	404.0±4.5	Sutter et al. 1985
42°11.5'N, 73°9.5'W	Gneiss	^{40}Ar/^{39}Ar plateau, hornblende	406.2±4.5	Sutter et al. 1985
42°11.2'N, 73°3.7'W	Gneiss	^{40}Ar/^{39}Ar plateau, hornblende	364.2±4.1	Sutter et al. 1985
Dutchess County, New York				
41.7°N, 73.6°W	Pelitic schist (garnet–staurolite zone)	^{40}Ar/^{39}Ar plateau, biotite	443±3	Bence & McLelland 1976
41.6°N, 73.6°W	Pelitic schist (kyanite zone)	^{40}Ar/^{39}Ar plateau, biotite	418±15	Bence & McLelland 1976
41.6°N, 73.5°W	Pelitic schist (sillimanite + muscovite)	^{40}Ar/^{39}Ar plateau, biotite	377±5	Bence & McLelland 1976
Hudson Highlands massif E of the Hudson River				
41.4°N, 73.6°W	Gneiss	^{40}Ar/^{39}Ar plateau, hornblende	433±10	Dallmeyer & Sutter 1976
41.4°N, 73.6°W	Gneiss	^{40}Ar/^{39}Ar plateau, hornblende	417±10	Dallmeyer & Sutter 1976
41.4°N, 73.6°W	Gneiss	^{40}Ar/^{39}Ar plateau, hornblende	466±10	Dallmeyer & Sutter 1976
Cortlandt complex				
41.2°N, 74°W (Stony Point)	Biotite diorite	Rb–Sr biotite	383±15	Ratcliffe et al. 1982
41.2°N, 74°W (Stony Point)	Cortlandtite	K–Ar hornblende	483±10	Ratcliffe et al. 1982
41.2°N, 74°W (Stony Point)	Biotite diorite	K–Ar biotite	422±6	Ratcliffe et al. 1982
41.2°N, 74°W (Stony Point)	Biotite diorite	K–Ar biotite	396±8	Ratcliffe et al. 1982
41.2°N, 73.9°W (E of HR)	Norite	Rb–Sr biotite	423±20	Ratcliffe et al. 1982
41.3°N, 73.9°W (E of HR)	Hornblende norite	K–Ar hornblende	496±7	Ratcliffe et al. 1982
41.3°N, 73.9°W (E of HR)	Hornblende diorite	K–Ar hornblende	419±8	Ratcliffe et al. 1982
41.2°N, 73.9°W (E of HR)	Pegmatitic norite	K–Ar hornblende	426±8	Ratcliffe et al. 1982
41.2°N, 73.9°W (E of HR)	Pegmatitic norite	K–Ar biotite	412±8	Ratcliffe et al. 1982
41.3°N, 73.9°W (E of HR)	Norite and pyroxenite	Nd–Sm whole-rock isochron	430±34	Domenick & Basu 1982
41.3°N, 73.9°W (E of HR)	Hornblende diorite	^{40}Ar/^{39}Ar plateau, hornblende	430±10	Dallmeyer 1975c
41.3°N, 73.9°W (E of HR)	Norite	Rb–Sr whole-rock isochron	427±30(λ?)	Ratcliffe et al. 1983, p. 23
Manhattan Prong				
41°38'N, 73.4°W	Granite gneiss	Rb–Sr whole-rock isochron	442±10	Mose & Nagel 1982a
41°37'N, 73.4°W	Granite gneiss	Rb–Sr whole-rock isochron	435±12	Mose & Nagel 1982a
41°29'N, 73.4°W	Granite gneiss	Rb–Sr whole-rock isochron	426±49	Mose & Nagel 1982a
41°2.7'N, 73°50.9'W	Granite gneiss	^{207}Pb/^{206}Pb, sphene	435	Aleinikoff 1985

Plutons and country rocks, eastern Massachusetts, eastern Connecticut and SE New Hampshire

Exeter pluton (EP)	Diorite	Rb–Sr whole-rock	473 ± 37	Gaudette et al. 1984
Newburyport complex (NP)	Granodiorite and quartz monzonite, porphyritic phase	U–Th–Pb, zircon	437 ± 2	Zartman & Naylor 1984
NP	Granodiorite and quartz monzonite	U–Th–Pb, zircon	466 ± 4	Zartman & Naylor 1984
Sharpners Pond diorite (SP)	Diorite and granodiorite	U–Th–Pb, zircon	430 ± 5	Zartman & Naylor 1984
Andover granite (AG)	Peraluminous granite gneiss, granite and aplite	Rb–Sr whole-rock isochron	408 ± 22	Zartman & Naylor 1984
AG	Peraluminous granite gneiss and granite	Rb–Sr whole-rock	446 ± 32	Zartman & Naylor 1984
Preston gabbro (PG)	Trondhjemite	U–Th–Pb, zircon	424 ± 5	Zartman & Naylor 1984
Nashoba zone (NZ)	Metasediments	Rb–Sr whole-rock isochron	454 ± 22	Olszewski 1980
NZ	Metavolcanics	Rb–Sr whole-rock isochron	445 ± 30	Olszewski 1980

Ordovician plutons in western New Hampshire and adjacent Vermont and Maine

Attean, Adamstown and Highlandcroft plutons (AT, AD, HC)	Granite	U–Th–Pb, zircon	444–451(λ?)	Lyons et al. 1983
43°56.1'N, 72°7.2'W and 44°19'N, 71°50'W	Granite	Rb–Sr whole-rock isochron	440 ± 40	Naylor 1969

* See Fig. 1 for locations. Abbreviations used here correspond to those in Fig. 1 and Table 1.
† Decay constants λ used in age calculations are those recommended by Steiger & Jäger (1977).

[39]Ar hornblende plateau ages. Younger plateau ages on biotite and hornblende from the GMM, BM and HHM are interpreted as cooling ages. As summarized by Ratcliffe et al. (1982, 1983), the Cortlandt plutonic complex (CC), which intruded near the regional metamorphic maximum and contact metamorphosed Cambrian and Ordovician rocks from the northern HHM and Manhattan Prong (MP), has been dated at 383–496 Ma by several isotopic methods.

[40]Ar/[39]Ar plateau ages on biotite and muscovite from Dutchess County (DC), New York, range from 443 to 377 Ma (Bence & Rajamani 1972, Bence & McLelland 1976). These are apparently cooling ages as higher-grade rocks give lower ages. E of the Grenville basement in Connecticut Mose & Nagel (1982a) reported Rb–Sr whole-rock isochron ages of 442–426 Ma on granitic gneisses that may have been emplaced at the peak of metamorphism (Jackson & Hall 1982).

Recently published data support earlier arguments that Taconian age metamorphism is widespread in the Taconic Mountains (TM) and the pre-Silurian cover rocks of the GMM. Metamorphism in the TM cannot be older than Caradocian based on the presence of graptolites of zones 12 and 13 (Berry 1968). K–Ar whole-rock and muscovite ages from both the autochthon and allochthon range from 468 to 382 Ma. Sutter et al. (1985) suggested that ages from 380 to 400 Ma are cooling ages and anomalously young.

In N central Vermont [40]Ar/[39]Ar total fusion, plateau and isochron ages on amphibole, muscovite and biotite from eugeoclinal rocks range from 505 to 439 Ma (Lanphere & Albee 1974, Laird et al. 1984). Taconian metamorphism is also widespread in pre-Silurian rocks from adjacent Quebec (Guidotti et al. 1983, p. 236). All but one of the samples studied by Laird et al. (1984) give ages between about 470 and 440 Ma, consistent with the interpretation of Sutter et al. (1985) that the peak of Taconian metamorphism within the northern Appalachians occurred at about 466 ± 5 Ma.

The age of lower amphibolite (kyanite) and adjacent epidote–amphibolite-facies metamorphism between the Green Mountain anticlinorium and Grenville age basement, W central Vermont (Fig. 1, MG and vicinity) is shown as Ordovician in Fig. 2, but it is not clear that Devonian high-grade metamorphism did not occur here. [40]Ar/[39]Ar total fusion ages on muscovite, biotite and hornblende are the same (387–382 Ma). However, [40]Ar/[39]Ar amphibole ages farther N and E indicate Ordovician metamorphism at 471 Ma.

Interpretation of the isotopic data is complicated by polymetamorphism. Zen (1981) reported two periods of metamorphism within the TM, SW Massachusetts and adjacent Connecticut and New York: (1) low grade and (2) lower than biotite grade to staurolite + kyanite grade. He suggested that the first was Taconian and the second Acadian. However, recent isotopic data (as discussed above) indicate that the latter is Taconian. Both periods of metamorphism must therefore be Taconian as the rocks are Ordovician. Norton (1975) presented textural data for three periods of metamorphic mineral growth in the BM and cover rocks; Cheney (1980) identified two periods of metamorphism. Sutter et al. (1985) give a historical review of the age assignments for metamorphism and show that the highest grade is Taconian rather than Acadian as was suggested previously.

The oldest sample from northern Vermont studied by Laird et al. (1984) (about 500 Ma) is significantly older than the other samples, and incremental release spectra show no clear evidence of later resetting (Laird et al. 1984, p. 393). The sample is from mafic schist spatially associated with a large asbestos body and is interpreted to have been metamorphosed prior to being emplaced tectonically. Actinolite rims on barroisite- and winchite-rich cores are a common occurrence in mafic schist from northern Vermont (Laird & Albee 1981b). Locally (Fig. 1, EM) kyanite is pseudomorphed by chloritoid + white mica, garnet is pseudomorphed by chlorite + magnetite and hornblende is overgrown by actinolite (Albee 1957, Laird & Albee 1981b). A stepwise heating experiment on amphibole that gave a 415 Ma total fusion age also gave a 470 Ma plateau age and a 460 Ma isochron age; the first 36% of the [39]Ar released gave a 376 Ma apparent age (Laird et al. 1984, tables 2 and 3, fig. 4). Farther S along the same anticlinorial structure (Fig. 1, WM) coarse-grained muscovite 'protected' in a quartz vein gave a 444 Ma age, while muscovite pseudomorphing kyanite in the same sample gave a 363 Ma age ([40]Ar/[39]Ar isochron ages) (Lanphere & Albee 1974). Therefore Laird et al. (1984) suggested that the zoned amphibole and pseudomorphed pelitic minerals are a manifestation of Taconian metamorphism overprinted by Acadian metamorphism.

Sutter et al. (1985), however, suggested that Acadian metamorphism is not recorded in the pre-Silurian rocks of northern Vermont. They agreed with Harper (1968) who proposed that K–Ar whole-rock and muscovite ages of 447–345 Ma in N central Vermont are cooling ages. Stanley et al. (1984, p. 587) concurred with the latter interpretation and concluded from detailed map-

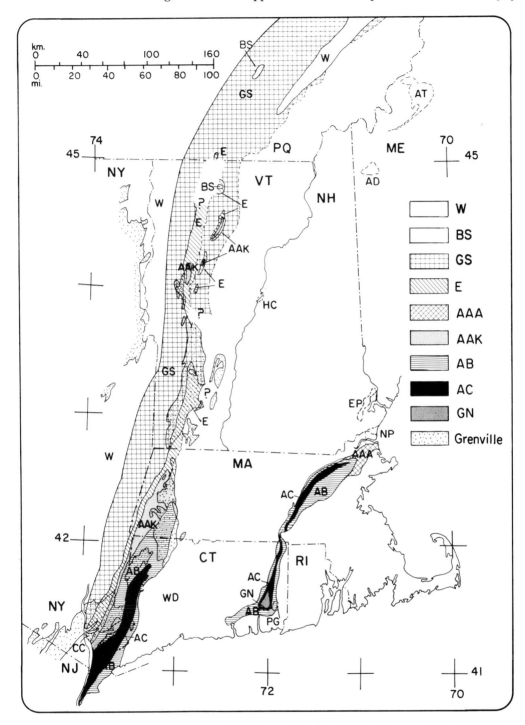

FIG. 2. Arenig to Wenlock regional metamorphism in the northern Appalachians from compilations by G. W. Fisher (USA) and W. E. Trzcienski (Canada) for International Geological Correlation Program (IGCP) Project 27. Contact metamorphism is associated with the igneous rocks labelled AT, AD, CC, EP, HC and NP (see Table 1 for abbreviations). Other abbreviations: W, weakly metamorphosed; BS, blueschist facies; GS, greenschist facies; E, epidote–amphibolite facies; AAA, amphibolite facies, andalusite; AAK, amphibolite facies, kyanite; AB, medium amphibolite facies; AC, upper amphibolite facies; GN, granulite facies; stippled, Grenville age basement.

ping and structural analysis that the folding and faulting associated with the formation of the amphibole cores and rims form a continuum without an obvious break during the Taconian.

As $^{40}Ar/^{39}Ar$ ages reported for amphibole and biotite in pre-Silurian and Silurian–Devonian metamorphic rocks from SE Vermont are Devonian, Sutter *et al.* (1985) suggested that Taconian metamorphism is not recorded E of the GMM. However, Rosenfeld (1968), Karabinos (1984a, b) and Laird & Albee (1981b) identified textural unconformities in garnet and amphibole and suggested that Devonian (Acadian) metamorphism may have overprinted Taconian metamorphism, consistent with the Taconian ages reported for rocks of the GMM.

Arenig to Wenlock metamorphism is recorded farther E (Fig. 1 and Table 2), but there is no clear relationship with the Taconian metamorphism of rocks underlain by N American (Grenville) basement. Olszewski (1980) interpreted Rb–Sr whole-rock dates of 454 and 445 Ma on meta-sedimentary and metavolcanic rocks in the Nashoba zone (NZ), Massachusetts, as meta-morphic ages. More recently Zartman & Naylor (1984) presented ages, obtained by several iso-topic methods, for plutonic rocks within the NZ that indicate late Ordovician to early Silurian metamorphism. The unmetamorphosed Sharp-ners Pond diorite is 430 Ma old, while the nearby Andover granite gives ages of 446 and 408 Ma and appears to be coeval with high-grade meta-morphism. In SE Connecticut high-grade meta-morphism occurred before 424 Ma, the age of the post-metamorphic Preston gabbro.

Late Ordovician age contact metamorphism is suspected at the Vermont–New Hampshire and Maine–Quebec borders owing to intrusion of felsic plutonic rocks (Fig. 1, HC, AD and AT) dated at 440–451 Ma by several isotopic methods (Naylor 1969, Lyons *et al.* 1983). Ordovician contact metamorphism is recognized in SE New Hampshire and adjacent NE Massachusetts owing to the intrusion of the Exeter pluton (EP) and Newburyport complex. The former has been dated at 473 Ma (Rb–Sr whole-rock) (Gaudette *et al.* 1984), and the latter gives zircon ages of 466 and 437 Ma (Zartman & Naylor 1984).

Distribution and estimates of temperature and pressure

Recent summary papers regarding Arenig to Wenlock age metamorphism in the northern Appalachians include those by Robinson (1983), Guidotti *et al.* (1983), Sutter *et al.* (1985) and Laird *et al.* (1984). The distribution of metamor-phic grade and facies series is shown in Fig. 2.

The temperatures and pressures that have been estimated are summarized in Table 3. Petrologi-cal evidence for metamorphic facies series and grade are discussed below.

Rocks underlain by N American basement primarily record medium-pressure facies series metamorphism characterized by kyanite in high-grade pelitic rocks. As reported by Zen (1981), Barth (1936) and Bence & McLelland (1976), the sequence of mineral assemblages (highest grade in each area) observed in pelitic rocks from (1) the TM, SW Massachusetts and adjacent Con-necticut and New York, and (2) DC, New York (Fig. 3) is similar to that reported by Harte & Hudson (1979, path B) SW of Stonehaven, Scotland. Taconian metamorphism occurred at somewhat higher pressure along the BM and to the N in Vermont as the sequence of the pelitic assemblages reported by Cheney (1980) and Albee (1965, 1968) indicate that chloritoid be-comes unstable before the garnet–chlorite pair becomes unstable (chloritoid + biotite + kyanite are stable in the TM and DC).

In N central Vermont glaucophane- and om-phacite-bearing mafic schist occurs locally (Fig. 2, BS) indicating high-pressure facies series metamorphism (Laird & Albee 1981a). The presence of barroisite and Na^{M4}-rich calcic amphibole in mafic schist containing the assem-blage amphibole + chlorite + epidote + plagio-clase + quartz indicates that medium- to high-pressure facies series metamorphism is preserved over a more extended area (Laird *et al.* 1984, Fig. 7). As stated by Guidotti *et al.* (1983) high-pressure anomalies occur in southern Quebec as indicated by the presence of crossitic amphibole (Trzcienski 1976, 1977) and very aluminous pumpellyite (Trzcienski & Birkett 1982).

High-pressure metamorphism (of unknown age) may also be preserved in central western Connecticut (Fig. 1, CM) where sillimanite-grade metamorphism has overprinted a possible eclo-gitic assemblage in allochthonous mafic dykes resulting in a clinopyroxene + plagioclase sym-plectite of omphacite(?) and the 'moth-eaten' appearance of garnet (Harwood 1976). Dietsch (1985) reported high-pressure–high-temperature metamorphism near the Waterbury dome (Table 3) and suggested that it was Taconian. Barth (1936, pp. 793–4) reported glaucophane in DC, but suggested that it was 'the product of some special thermodynamic conditions acting locally in a small restricted area'. To my knowledge this occurrence has not been relocated.

The metamorphic grade along the W margin of the Taconic orogen is chlorite or lower. Prehnite- and pumpellyite-bearing mineral as-semblages have been reported from eastern New

TABLE 3. *Temperature and pressure data for Arenig to Wenlock age metamorphism in the Northern Appalachians*

Location*	Rock type	Facies/grade	Method†	Temperature and pressure	Reference
Vermont					
W of PꞒ, central VT	Metalimestone	Weakly metamorphosed	cc–dol, O and C isotopes (cc–dol)	210–295°C	Sheppard & Schwarcz 1970
W of PꞒ, central and southern VT	Metalimestone, dolomite and marble	Greenschist/biotite	cc–dol, O and C isotopes (cc–dol)	255–400°C	Sheppard & Schwarcz 1970
N of PꞒ, central VT	Pelitic schist	Greenschist/biotite	O isotopes (qtz–mus)	435°C	Garlick & Epstein 1967
44°5.4′N, 72°57′W	Mafic schist	Epidote–amphibolite/garnet	cc–dol	489°C	Laird & Albee 1981b
Mount Grant (MG)	Pelitic schist	Lower amphibolite/kyanite	O isotopes (qtz–mgt, qtz–mus)	420–465°C	Garlick & Epstein 1967
44°48.3′N, 72°33′W	Mafic schist	Blueschist/garnet	Gar–cpx and isopleths on ab=jd+qtz	500±50°C 11.5±1.5 kbar	Laird & Albee 1981a Laird, unpublished data
Taconic Range in SW Massachusetts and adjacent Connecticut and New York					
TM	Pelitic phyllite to schist	Weakly metamorphosed to lower amphibolite/ <chlorite to staurolite–kyanite	Pertinent experimental data	400–600°C c. 4 kbar	Zen 1981, pp. 1, 38–41
TM	Pelitic schist	Epidote–amphibolite to lower amphibolite/garnet to staurolite	Gar–bio (effect of high Mn and Ca content in gar?)	457–500°C	Zen 1984, personal communication
SE New York					
Dutchess County (DC)	Pelitic schist	Epidote–amphibolite/garnet	O isotopes (qtz–mus)	470°C	Garlick & Epstein 1967
DC	Pelitic schist	Lower amphibolite/staurolite–kyanite	O isotopes (qtz–mus)	490–555°C	Garlick & Epstein 1967
DC	Pelitic schist	Medium amphibolite/sillimanite–muscovite	O isotopes (qtz–mus, qtz–mgt)	470–595°C	Garlick & Epstein 1967
MP in contact with CC	Emery	Contact metamorphism	Pertinent mineral equilibria, granite minimum	800–900°C, >7 kbar	Tracy *et al.* 1984
Waterbury dome (WD)					
WD	Pelitic and felsic gneisses	Upper amphibolite/kyanite + K-feldspar	Pertinent mineral equilibria	700–765°C, 8.5–9 kbar	Dietsch 1985

*See Fig. 1 for general locations and Table 1 for abbreviations.
†Abbreviations: ab, albite; bio, biotite; cc, calcite; cpx, clinopyroxene; dol, dolomite; gar, garnet; jd, jadeite; mgt, magnetite; mus, muscovite; qtz, quartz. Stable isotope temperatures were determined from the fractionation curves compiled by Friedman & O'Neil (1977) using the 1000 ln α data from the original reference.

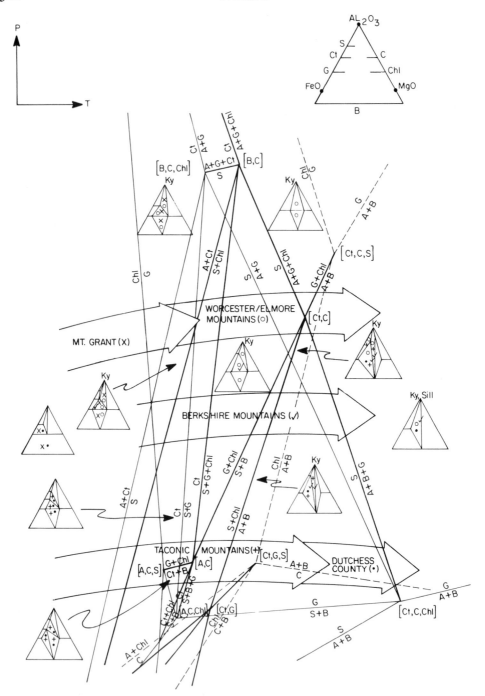

FIG. 3. Petrogenetic grid for pelitic schist (after Harte & Hudson 1979, Fig. 2) showing the mineral assemblages reported in pelitic rocks from Vermont, western Massachusetts and SE New York. The pressure–temperature slopes are schematic. All AFM diagrams are projected from quartz and muscovite; two phase fields are shown as single lines for clarity. Sources of data: Albee (1965, 1968, 1972) for Vermont (Mount Grant, Elmore–Worcester Mountains); Cheney (1980) for the Berkshire Mountains; Zen (1960, 1981) for the Taconic Range; Bence & McLelland (1976) for Dutchess County. Abbreviations: A, Al$_2$SiO$_5$; B, biotite; C, cordierite; Chl, chlorite; Ct, chloritoid; G, garnet; Ky, kyanite; S, staurolite; Sill, sillimanite; bold lines, reactions within the system K$_2$O–FeO–MgO–Al$_2$O$_3$–SiO$_2$–H$_2$O (KFMASH); light lines, KFASH reactions; broken lines, KMASH reactions.

York and southern Quebec (Zen 1974, Trzcienski & Birkett 1982). The grade increases eastward with the highest metamorphic grade centred about the Grenville age basement massifs and cores of anticlinoria (Fig. 2). It reaches sillimanite + muscovite and sillimanite + K-feldspar within the cores of BM, HM, HHM and MP. Farther N it reaches the kyanite zone in the northern BM, N central Vermont and Quebec (external/internal domains (Guidotti *et al.* 1983, Fig. 1)). If Taconian metamorphism is preserved in pre-Silurian rocks E of the GMM, SE Vermont, it reached at least garnet grade (Rosenfeld 1968, Karabinos 1984a,b).

Farther E within the NZ (basement which is not N American), eastern Massachusetts and Connecticut, amphibolite- and granulite-facies low-pressure facies series metamorphism occurs. The metamorphic grade decreases successively from sillimanite + garnet + cordierite to sillimanite + K-feldspar to sillimanite + muscovite and to andalusite zones (Fig. 2) (Robinson 1983, Zen 1983).

The contact metamorphic aureole associated with the mafic to ultramafic CC contains sillimanite $\pm$ K-feldspar and, at lower grade, kyanite (Ratcliffe *et al.* 1982, 1983). Tracy *et al.* (1984) reported temperatures as great as 800–900°C and a pressure greater than 7 kbar for emery present as roof pendants and xenoliths. Rumble & Finnerty (1974) interpreted euhedral cores of garnet in metavolcanic rocks near HC plutonic rocks, W central New Hampshire, as contact metamorphic. (Poikiloblastic overgrowths formed during a later regional metamorphism are generally inferred to be Devonian.) In SE New Hampshire contact metamorphism due to the intrusion of the EP is generally biotite grade, but andalusite and perhaps cordierite occur within a few metres of the contact.

Central Appalachians

Timing of metamorphism

In SE Pennsylvania and northern Delaware Arenig to Wenlock and possibly pre-Arenig age metamorphism has occurred in gneisses from the Wilmington complex (WC) and in basement gneiss and metasedimentary rocks near the WC. Isotopic data are summarized in Table 4 and Fig. 4. Granulite-facies metamorphism in the WC may be late Ordovician on the basis of a 441 Ma lower-intercept age on zoned zircons (Grauert & Wagner 1975). However, Crawford & Crawford (1980, Table 2, M2) suggested that this metamorphism may be older than 440 Ma but not Precambrian. This interpretation is supported by the observation that plutons within the WC, including the Arden pluton dated at 502 Ma, deform the metamorphic foliation of the WC (Srogi *et al.* 1983). The first period of metamorphism recorded in the metasedimentary rocks near the WC may also be this age (Crawford & Mark 1982).

Later lower-grade metamorphism recognized in the Grenville basement, its overlying metasedimentary rocks and the WC may be Taconian (Crawford & Crawford 1980, Table 2, M3). This interpretation is consistent with a lower-intercept zircon age of 450 Ma from the Grenville basement (Grauert *et al.* 1973, 1974), a $^{40}Ar/^{39}Ar$ age spectrum date on hornblende of 465 Ma (Sutter *et al.* 1980) and a biotite cooling age of 403 Ma (Crawford & Hoersch 1984, p. 113).

In the Piedmont of Maryland and northern Virginia, complex structural relationships and equivocal interpretation of isotopic age data make it difficult to define the number of metamorphic events, their ages and their relative metamorphic isograds. It is particularly disconcerting that many of the U–Pb zircon ages obtained are of questionable value in interpreting the age of metamorphism because of inherited radiogenic lead as discussed by Higgins *et al.* (1977). The basis for assigning particular isograds shown in Fig. 5 to the Arenig to Wenlock is discussed below. Further details of pertinent isotopic age data are given in Table 4.

Major metamorphism near the domes of Baltimore gneiss (Fig. 4, BGD) appears to be Arenig to Wenlock in age. The peak of metamorphism occurred after the Baltimore mafic complex was thrust or possibly intruded (Hobson 1964, p. 142, Southwick 1969, p. 409, Fisher *et al.* 1979, Muller & Chapin 1984, p. 141) at 490 Ma (Shaw & Wasserburg 1984). A minimum age for this metamorphism is given by the 400–469 Ma ages for relatively undeformed pegmatites and granite. However, deformation probably spanned the Taconian to Acadian (Muller & Chapin 1984, p. 137). E of the gneiss domes in metavolcanics and gneiss, 470 Ma Rb–Sr whole-rock ages are interpreted to date the age of metamorphism (Lesser & Sinha 1982).

Metamorphism in the Piedmont of northern Virginia E of the Triassic basin (Fig. 5) is older than the cross-cutting Occoquan batholith (OB). The age of the OB is controversial (Higgins *et al.* 1977), but it appears to be pre-Arenig (Table 4). If metamorphism occurred farther S before the intrusion of the 415–385 Ma Falls Run granite, which is polydeformed and metamorphosed (Pavlides *et al.* 1979), no petrological data that

TABLE 4. Isotopic age data: central Appalachians

Location*	Rock type	Dating method	Age†(Ma)	Reference
SE Pennsylvania				
Wilmington complex (WC)	Gneiss	U–Pb zircon, lower intercept (nearly concordant)	441	Grauert & Wagner 1975
WC, Arden pluton	Anorthosite, charnockite	Rb–Sr whole-rock	502 ± 20	Foland & Muessig 1978
West Chester Prong (WCP)	Grenville basement gneiss	U–Pb zircon, lower intercept	c. 450	Grauert et al. 1973, 1974
Rosemont fault zone (RF)	Amphibolite	$^{40}Ar/^{39}Ar$ age spectrum hornblende	$465(\lambda?)$	Sutter et al. 1980
S of RF	Pelitic schist	$^{40}Ar/^{39}Ar$ age spectrum, biotite	$410(\lambda?)$	Sutter et al. 1980
Between WC and HBU	Mafic amphibolite gneiss	$^{40}Ar/^{39}Ar$ age spectrum, biotite	$403(\lambda?)$	Crawford & Hoersch 1984, p. 113
Avondale anticline (AA)	Gneiss	$^{40}Ar/^{39}Ar$ age spectrum, hornblende	$375(\lambda?)$	Sutter et al. 1980
AA	Gneiss	$^{40}Ar/^{39}Ar$ age spectrum, biotite	$360(\lambda?)$	Sutter et al. 1980
Maryland–northern Virginia Piedmont				
39°19′N, 76°48′W to 39°42′N, 76°12′W	Norite, gabbro, websterite, orthopyroxenite	Nd–Sm whole-rock isochron	490 ± 20	Shaw & Wasserburg 1984
SW of SR ≈ 39.6°N, 76.3°W	Tholeiite-dacite suite with trondhjemitic affinities	Rb–Sr whole-rock	$470 \pm 20(\lambda?)$	Lesser & Sinha 1982
Baltimore gneiss domes (BGD)	Pegmatite	Rb–Sr, muscovite and microcline	$400–450(\lambda?)$	Hobson 1964, p. 196
38°58.8′N, 77°14.4′W	Granite and pegmatite	Rb–Sr model age, muscovite	469 ± 20	Muth et al. 1979
Occoquan batholith (OB)	Granite to tonalite and quartz granitoid	U–Pb zircon, upper intercept	558	Seiders et al. 1975
OB	Granite and quartz granitoid	Rb–Sr whole-rock isochron	494 ± 14	Mose & Nagel 1982b
Falls Run granite (FRG)	Granite gneiss	U–Pb and Rb–Sr	$385–415(\lambda?)$	Pavlides et al. 1979
Columbia pluton (CP)	Granite to tonalite	Rb–Sr whole-rock isochron	$454 \pm 9, 417 \pm 37$	Mose & Nagel 1982b
Blue Ridge, James River and Columbia synclinoria, Virginia				
38.6°N, 78.4°W	Metabasalt	Rb–Sr whole-rock	470 ± 77	Mose & Nagel 1984
38.6°N, 78.4°W	Metarhyolite	Rb–Sr whole-rock	420 ± 4	Nagel & Mose 1984
37.7°N, 79°W	Nelsonite dike	Rb–Sr whole-rock (two points)	c. 475	Pettingill et al. 1984
37°29.3′N, 79°10.1′W	Biotite gneiss	K–Ar biotite	$464, 468 \pm 37$	Robison 1978
37°27.7′N, 79°11.1′W	Plagioclase–biotite migmatite	K–Ar biotite	394 ± 28	Robison 1978
37°27.7′N, 79°11.1′W	Porphyritic diopside–biotite gneiss	K–Ar biotite	$378–383 \pm 19$	Robison 1978
37°26′N, 79°12.2′W	Hornblende–biotite gneiss	K–Ar hornblende, biotite	$408 \pm 20, 407 \pm 20$	Robison 1978
37°26′N, 79°12.2′W	Hornblende–feldspar gneiss	K–Ar hornblende	428 ± 21	Robison 1978
37°25.2′N, 79°8.3′W	Mica schist	K–Ar biotite	$484, 479 \pm 31$	Robison 1978
37°24.7′N, 79°7.9′W	Biotite gneiss	K–Ar biotite	403 ± 20	Robison 1978
37°24.7′N, 79°7.9′W	Mica schist	K–Ar biotite	420 ± 21	Robison 1978
37°22.5′N, 79°20′W	Biotite gneiss	K–Ar biotite	$432 \pm 22, 413 \pm 21$	Robison 1978
37°1.9′N, 79°25.2′W	Biotite gneiss	K–Ar biotite	$450 \pm 23, 440 \pm 22, 447 \pm 22$	Robison 1978
37°1.2′N, 79°28.5′W	Biotite gneiss	K–Ar muscovite	399 ± 40	Robison 1978
			$310–317 \pm 16$	Robison 1978

Location	Rock type	Method	Age	Reference
38°21'N, 79°10.3'W	Phyllite	K–Ar sericite	313, 328 ± 16	Robison 1978
37°20.8'N, 79°26'W	Biotite gneiss	K–Ar biotite	364, 373 ± 18	Robison 1978
37°18.5'N, 79°27.1'W	Biotite gneiss	K–Ar biotite	356, 358 ± 18	Robison 1978
37°16.7'N, 79°26.9'W	Hornblende gneiss	K–Ar hornblende	407 ± 20	Robison 1978
37°16.4'N, 79°29.5'W	Biotite gneiss	K–Ar biotite	396, 394 ± 30	Robison 1978
37°15.6'N, 79°24.6'W	Hornblende–feldspar gneiss	K–Ar hornblende	470 ± 50, 494 ± 25	Robison 1978
37.8°N, 78.8°W to 36.9°N, 80.3°W	Garnetiferous biotite and two-mica gneisses	Rb–Sr whole-rock isochron	571 ± 21	Fullagar & Dietrich 1976
37°N, 79.9°W	Garnetiferous two-mica gneisses	Rb–Sr whole-rock isochron	509 ± 32	Fullagar & Dietrich 1976
37°N, 79.9°W	Garnetiferous two-mica gneisses	Rb–Sr whole-rock + biotite	325	Fullagar & Dietrich 1976
37°N, 80.5°W	Phyllite and slate	Rb–Sr whole-rock isochron	520 ± 19	Fullagar & Dietrich 1976
37°N, 80.5°W	Phyllite and slate	Rb–Sr whole-rock + muscovite	339	Fullagar & Dietrich 1976

* See Fig. 4 for locations. Abbreviations here correspond to those in Fig. 4 and Table 1.
† Decay constants λ used in age calculations are those recommended by Steiger & Jäger (1977).

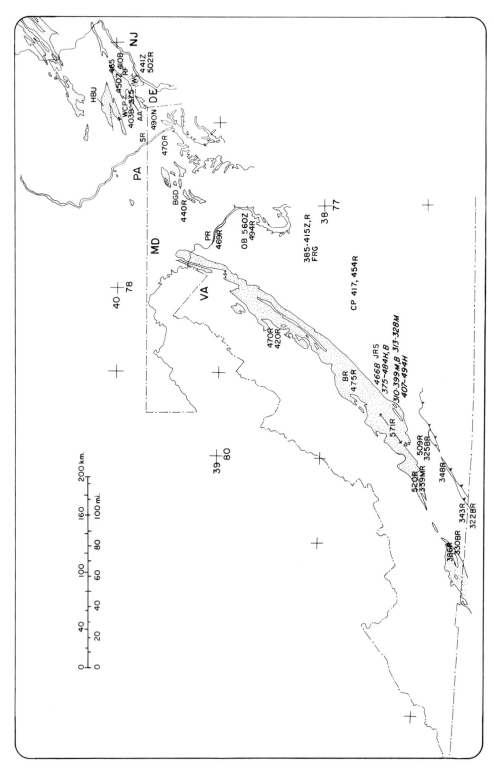

Fig. 4. Isotopic age data (in Ma) pertinent to Arenig to Wenlock metamorphism in the Central Appalachians. Abbreviations are defined in Table 1. The stippled pattern indicates Grenville age basement.

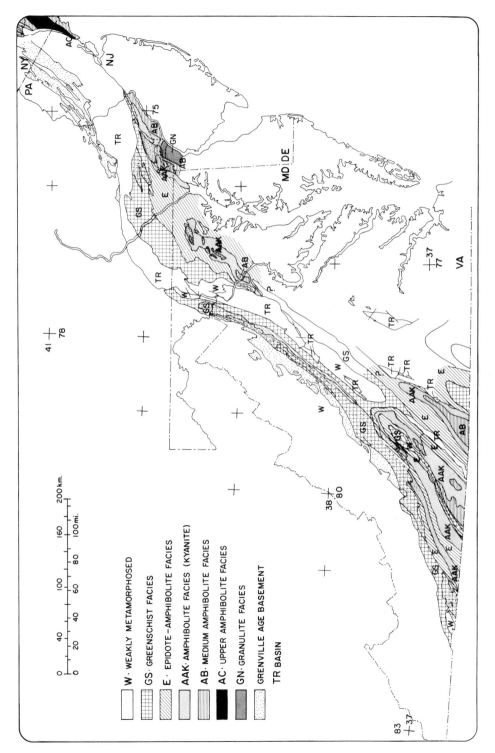

FIG. 5. Arenig to Wenlock regional metamorphism in the Central Appalachians (compiled by G. W. Fisher for IGCP Project 27).

indicate the grade of metamorphism are available.

Clarke (1984, p. 159) stated that rocks in the Blue Ridge anticlinorium (BR), northern Virginia, were metamorphosed to greenschist facies during the Taconic orogeny. Rb–Sr whole-rock ages of 470 Ma and 475 Ma for metabasalt and a Nelsonite dyke respectively (Mose & Nagel 1984, Pettingill *et al.* 1984) are consistent with Taconian metamorphism in the BR. Nagel & Mose (1984) obtained an Rb–Sr whole-rock age of 420 Ma on metarhyolite which they interpreted to be the age of metamorphism. Farther S in the Virginia BR Fullagar & Dietrich (1976) appealed to pre-Arenig dewatering or metamorphism and to Carboniferous redistribution of rubidium and strontium isotopes to explain whole-rock and whole-rock plus mineral ages.

In the James River synclinorium, southern Virginia, Robison (1976, 1978) suggested that K–Ar ages of 494–407 Ma on hornblende and 484–356 Ma on biotite were the result of Taconian metamorphism. Farther E Mose & Nagel (1982b, p. 28) suggested that migmatite adjacent to the Columbia pluton (Fig. 4, CP), which yielded Rb–Sr whole-rock ages of 417 and 454 Ma, formed during the intrusion of the pluton. High-grade metamorphic rocks (felsic and mafic) merge into the migmatite. Is this metamorphism Arenig to Wenlock in age? Later low-grade metamorphism of the CP is indicated by whole-rock plus mica ages of 278–347 Ma (Mose & Nagel 1982b).

Distribution and estimates of temperature and pressure

Crawford & Crawford (1980), Crawford & Mark (1982) and Crawford & Hoersch (1984) have presented generalized geological and metamorphic maps of SE Pennsylvania and distinguished the distribution of metamorphic facies as a function of the age of metamorphism. Figure 5 shows the highest grade of metamorphism attained during the M2 (pre-Arenig? (see above)) and M3 (Taconian) events. M2 varied from low-pressure granulite facies in the WC and adjacent basement gneisses and metasedimentary rocks to amphibolite facies farther N. Overprinting Grenville age metamorphism (M1) and M2 is greenschist- to amphibolite-facies metamorphism (M3).

M2 in pelitic and semi-pelitic schists is characterized by low-pressure facies series metamorphism (Fig. 6) as indicated by the presence of cordierite + sillimanite + biotite near the WC and relict andalusite to the NE (Crawford & Mark 1982). M3 is characterized by higher-pressure metamorphism based on the presence of

kyanite pseudomorphs after andalusite and sillimanite and on sillimanite + biotite pseudomorphs after cordierite (see Fig. 6 and Table 5 for the relative pressure and temperature). M3 overprints of M2 are strongest where water was available and where deformation was the most intense (Crawford & Mark 1982, p. 337).

In the metasedimentary rocks near the WC, pressure and temperature estimates for the peak of M2 and M3 based on pertinent mineral equilibria (Fig. 6 and Table 5) are consistent with the pressure–temperature path calculated by Spear & Selverstone (1983) for garnet growth. Amphibolite- to granulite-facies metamorphism in the WC occurred at greater temperature and pressure than those of M2 in the overlying rocks (Table 5).

M3 metamorphism NE of the WC varies from staurolite to kyanite + K-feldspar and perhaps sillimanite grade. Farther W Grenville age granulite- to amphibolite-facies gneisses (M1) were overprinted by M3 greenschist- to granulite-facies metamorphism. In the highest-grade rocks Wagner & Crawford (1975) reported that Taconian metamorphism resulted in the formation of garnet coronas on the mafic minerals formed earlier (M1), kyanite pseudomorphs of sillimanite and kyanite rims on green spinel. Post-Grenville age diabase dykes were also metamorphosed at this time. The metamorphic intensity in the gneisses and dykes varied from high-pressure granulite facies (temperature about 700°C and pressure about 8.5–9.5 kbar (Wagner 1982)) under 'dry' conditions to amphibolite facies under 'wet' conditions.

In Maryland, the metamorphic grade increases from greenschist to amphibolite facies toward the cores of several gneiss domes (Figs 4 and 5, BGD). Pelitic mineral assemblages are similar to those from SE Pennsylvania (Fig. 6). Kyanite occurs; andalusite is not reported N of the Potomac River (PR). If the biotite–cordierite–chlorite invariant point is at 18 kbar (Harte & Hudson 1979, p. 334), pelitic rocks near the Susquehanna River (SR) indicate high-pressure metamorphism (Fig. 6).

Southwick (1969, pp. 13–14, Fig. 7) reported that sillimanite (fibrolite) occurs sporadically in the staurolite and kyanite zones, replacing porphyroblasts of garnet, staurolite and kyanite. He suggested that the sillimanite formed after the peak of metamorphism owing to a decrease in pressure during uplift or to reheating. Hobson (1964, p. 76) also reported that sillimanite (prismatic and fibrolitic) occurred associated with garnet and kyanite and suggested that the sillimanite might be 'late'.

Summaries of the petrography and petrology

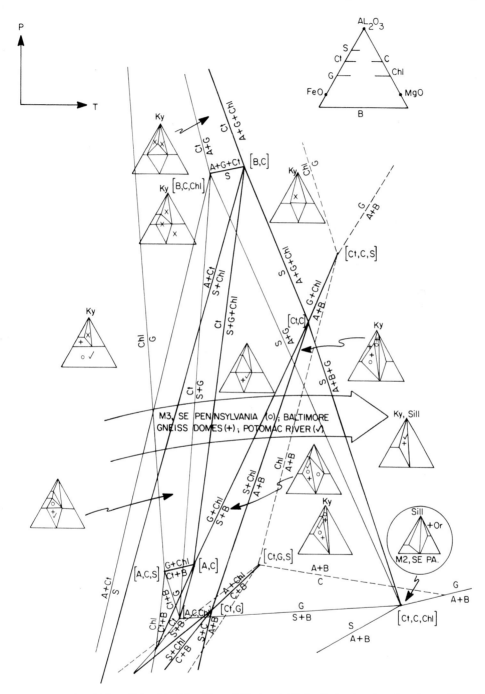

FIG. 6. Petrogenetic grid for pelitic schist (after Harte & Hudson 1979, fig. 2) showing the mineral assemblages in SE Pennsylvania and Maryland. The pressure–temperature slopes are schematic. All AFM diagrams are projected from quartz and muscovite except for M2 assemblages from SE Pennsylvania which are projected from quartz and orthoclase. Two phase fields are shown as single lines for clarity. Sources of data: Crawford & Mark (1982), Crawford & Crawford (1980) and Crawford & Hoersch (1984) for SE Pennsylvania; Southwick (1969) for SW of the Susquehanna River (x) and near the Baltimore gneiss domes; Fisher (1970) for the area along the Potomac River. Abbreviations and distinction between the bold, light and broken lines as for Fig. 3.

TABLE 5. *Temperature and pressure data for Arenig to Wenlock and possible pre-Arenig age metamorphism in the central Appalachians (SE Pennsylvania and northern Delaware)*

Location*	Rock type	Facies/grade	Method†	Temperature and pressure	Reference
Wilmington complex (WC)	Felsic, mafic and pelitic gneisses	Amphibolite to granulite	gar–bio, opx–cpx	750–825 °C	Srogi *et al.* 1983
WC	Felsic, mafic and pelitic gneisses	Amphibolite to granulite	opx–gar–plg–qtz, cpx–gar–plg–qtz	4.5–6 kbar	Srogi *et al.* 1983
N and E of WC	Pelitic schist, migmatite	Lower amphibolite to granulite/andalusite to sillimanite + orthoclase (M2, pre-Arenig?)	Pertinent phase equilibria, garnet zoning profile	>550 °C, <5 kbar 605 °C, 1.9–3.8 kbar	Crawford & Mark 1982 Spear & Selverstone 1983
N and E of WC	Pelitic schist, migmatite (retrograded)	Lower amphibolite/staurolite–kyanite (M3, Arenig to Wenlock)	Pertinent phase equilibria, gar–bio–plg	550–650 °C 6.5–7 kbar	Crawford & Mark 1982
West Chester Prong (WCP)	Gneiss	Granulite, amphibolite if more H_2O/kyanite	Pertinent phase equilibria	650–700 °C 7–8 kbar	Wagner & Crawford 1975
WCP	Gneiss	Granulite	gar–cpx–plg–qtz	8.5–9.5 kbar 700 °C	Wagner 1982

* See Fig. 4 for general locations and Table 1 for abbreviations.
† Abbreviations: bio, biotite; cpx, clinopyroxene; gar, garnet; opx, orthopyroxene; plg, plagioclase; qtz, quartz.

of rocks that crop out along the PR can be found in the papers by Hobson (1964, p. 88 ff.) and Fisher (1970). The metamorphic grade varies from chlorite to sillimanite + muscovite. Pelitic mineral assemblages are the same as those near the BGD (Fig. 6) but the pressure is probably lower. Andalusite, sillimanite and pseudomorphs of kyanite(?) indicate pressures near the Al_2SiO_5 triple point. Hobson (1964, p. 97) suggested that the pseudomorphs of kyanite(?) are sillimanite, and Reed & Jolly (1963) reported that cordierite pseudomorphs may occur, indicating a lower pressure (Fig. 6). Migmatite and pegmatite occur in the highest-grade areas, indicating temperatures near the water-saturated muscovite granite minimum. As muscovite + quartz is present, the maximum temperature of metamorphism would be about 650°C, which is the temperature of the intersection of the second sillimanite isograd and the granite minimum for $X_{H_2O} = 0.5$–1.0 (Kerrick 1972).

Southern Appalachians

Timing of metamorphism

Papers summarizing the timing of metamorphism in the southern Appalachians have recently been published by Hatcher *et al.* (1980), Tull (1980) and Glover *et al.* (1983). Stratigraphic data indicating Arenig to Wenlock or earlier metamorphism in the BR include (1) a thick clastic wedge of middle Ordovician rocks in the Valley and Ridge (VAR) that probably came from a southeasterly source that was being uplifted and eroded rapidly (Colton 1970) and (2) a conglomerate in these middle Ordovician rocks with pebbles and cobbles of metamorphosed rock that may have come from rocks now cropping out in the BR (Kellberg & Grant 1956).

Butler (1972) compiled previously published isotopic ages and suggested that 430 Ma is a minimum age for Palaeozoic metamorphism in the BR. Subsequent isotopic data, summarized in Table 6 and Fig. 7, support his conclusion that Arenig to Wenlock metamorphism is recorded. K–Ar whole-rock ages of 480 Ma for slates from Tennessee are reported by Kish (1982). A cross-cutting pegmatite S of Cherokee, North Carolina (Fig. 7, CK), has an Rb–Sr whole-rock age of 440 Ma (Kish *et al.* 1976). $^{40}Ar/^{39}Ar$ hornblende and biotite total-gas ages on retrograded Grenville basement near CK are 429–423 Ma and 357–350 Ma respectively (Dallmeyer 1975a). Dallmeyer (1975b) also reported $^{40}Ar/^{39}Ar$ plateau ages of 468–362 Ma (hornblende) and 345–317 Ma (biotite) from retrograded Grenville

basement W of the Grandfather Mountain window (GMW). He suggested that the peak of metamorphism occurred at about 480 Ma. NE of the GMW the Mount Airy pluton, which post-dates metamorphism (Rankin *et al.* 1973, De-Rosset & Hewitt 1979), is one of a group of calc-alkaline granodiorite plutons of age 420 Ma, and possibly 460 Ma, located along the BR (Kish *et al.* 1976). Abbott (1983) stated that high-grade metamorphism in NW N Carolina (Fig. 7, AMS) is older than 475 Ma, and Abbott & Raymond (1984) assigned the highest grade of metamorphism observed here to the Taconian.

Metamorphism in the BR may have continued past Wenlock times. Mose & Stransky (1973) concluded that the peak of metamorphism in the N Carolina–Tennessee BR was between 350 and 380 Ma. Near Ducktown, Tennessee (DT), Fullager *et al.* (1979) obtained an incremental release age of 400 Ma on hornblende and concluded that hornblende ages as high as 1066 Ma resulted from excess ^{40}Ar. Pegmatites interpreted as contemporaneous with the maximum grade of metamorphism in the N Carolina BR (Spruce Pine district (Fig. 7, SPD)) (Butler 1973, Rankin *et al.* 1973) give Rb–Sr whole-rock ages of about 400 Ma (Kish *et al.* 1976). U–Pb, Rb–Sr and K–Ar mineral ages of these pegmatites tabulated by Butler (1972) range from 420 to 335 Ma. N of the GMW in N Carolina and SW Virginia Fullagar & Dietrich (1976) reported Rb–Sr whole-rock ages of 394–343 Ma on metasedimentary rocks. Abbott & Raymond (1984) assigned retrograde metamorphism of the AMS to the Acadian and Alleghanian.

The southern extent of Arenig to Wenlock metamorphism in the western part of the southern Appalachians is in question. Glover *et al.* (1983, Fig. 2) suggested that Arenig to Wenlock metamorphism occurred NW of the Hayesville–Fries fault in Virginia, N Carolina and Tennessee. Tull (1980, Fig. 2) showed Ordovician metamorphism at the N Carolina–Georgia border. As summarized by McConnell & Costello (1984, pp. 271–5), isotopic ages near Grenville age basement, NW Georgia (Fig. 7, CGC), have been interpreted as cooling ages from Grenville age metamorphism or ages reflecting ductile deformation. Arenig to Wenlock metamorphism is precluded in the Talladega slate belt (TB) to the S where Devonian fossils occur, although areas where early Ordovician faunas occur (Harris *et al.* 1984) could, in principle, have been metamorphosed during this period.

The Ashland–Wedowee belt (AWB), which is the probable SW extension of the BR, may record Arenig to Wenlock metamorphism. Tull (1978) proposed that only one period of metamorphism

TABLE 6. *Isotopic age data: southern Appalachians*

Location*	Rock type	Dating method	Age† (Ma)	Reference
Blue Ridge: Grenville basement and cover rocks				
36.8°N, 80°W	Pelitic schist	Rb–Sr whole-rock isochron	348 ± 9	Fullagar & Dietrich 1976
36.7°N, 80.9°W	Pelitic gneiss	Rb–Sr whole-rock isochron	386 ± 27	Fullagar & Dietrich 1976
36.7°N, 80.9°W	Pelitic gneiss	Rb–Sr whole-rock + biotite	330	Fullagar & Dietrich 1976
36.6°N, 80.7°W	Pelitic gneiss and schist	Rb–Sr whole-rock isochron	343 ± 28	Fullagar & Dietrich 1976
36.6°N, 80.7°W	Pelitic gneiss and schist	Rb–Sr whole-rock + biotite	322	Fullagar & Dietrich 1976
36.5°N, 81.2°W	Pelitic gneiss	Rb–Sr whole-rock isochron	394 ± 98	Fullagar & Dietrich 1976
36.4°N, 81.2°W	Pelitic gneiss	Rb–Sr whole-rock isochron	363 ± 17	Fullagar & Dietrich 1976
36.4°N, 81.2°W	Pelitic gneiss	Rb–Sr whole-rock + biotite	310	Fullagar & Dietrich 1976
W of GMW	Grenville basement gneiss	$^{40}Ar/^{39}Ar$ plateau, biotite	345–317 ± 10	Dallmeyer 1975b
W of GMW	Grenville basement gneiss	$^{40}Ar/^{39}Ar$ plateau, hornblende	468–362 ± 10	Dallmeyer 1975b
SPD	Pegmatite	Rb–Sr whole-rock isochron	c. 400(λ?)	Kish et al. 1976
35.5°N, 83.3°W (CK)	Grenville basement gneiss	$^{40}Ar/^{39}Ar$ total fusion, biotite	350 ± 15	Dallmeyer 1975a
35.4°N, 83.3°W (CK)	Grenville basement gneiss	$^{40}Ar/^{39}Ar$ total fusion, hornblende	429 ± 15	Dallmeyer 1975a
35.4°N, 83.4°W	Grenville basement gneiss	$^{40}Ar/^{39}Ar$ total fusion, biotite	350 ± 15	Dallmeyer 1975a
35.4°N, 83.4°W	Grenville basement gneiss	$^{40}Ar/^{39}Ar$ total fusion, biotite	357 ± 15	Dallmeyer 1975a
35.4°N, 83.4°W	Grenville basement gneiss	$^{40}Ar/^{39}Ar$ total fusion, hornblende	423 ± 15	Dallmeyer 1975a
35.4°N, 83.4°W	Pegmatite	Rb–Sr whole-rock isochron	440 ± 13(λ)	Kish et al. 1976
GSM, Tennessee	Slate	K–Ar whole-rock isochron	480(λ?)	Kish 1982
GSM, Tennessee	Slate	K–Ar whole-rock isochron	430–370(λ?)	Kish 1982
Ducktown, TN(DT)	Ore zone	K–Ar age spectrum, hornblende	400 ± 20(λ?)	Fullagar et al. 1979
Ashland–Wedowee belt				
EQD	Quartz diorite	U–Pb zircon	516	Thomas et al. 1980, p. 95
EQD	Quartz diorite	Rb–Sr whole-rock isochron	490 ± 26	Thomas et al. 1980, p. 95
ZG and KAG	Granite and augen gneiss	U–Pb zircon	460	Thomas et al. 1980, p. 95
Brevard zone				
35°8′N, 82°45′W	Henderson gneiss	U–Pb zircon (residue of acid wash)	c. 440	Sinha & Glover 1978
Smith River allochthon				
Leatherwood granite (LW)	Granite	Rb–Sr whole-rock isochron	454 ± 20	Odom & Russell 1975
Inner Piedmont (IP)				
SW of SMA	Granite gneiss	Rb–Sr whole-rock isochron	431, 429 ± 22	Odom & Russell 1975
W of KMB	Amphibolite	$^{40}Ar/^{39}Ar$ plateau, hornblende	>360 (high-temperature steps) 345–335(λ?) (low-temperature steps)	Sutter et al. 1984

Location	Rock type	Method	Age	Reference
Elberton granite (ELB)	Granite	Rb–Sr whole-rock isochron	350 ± 11	Ellwood et al. 1980
ELB	Granite	U–Pb zircon (upper intercept)	$320 \pm 20(\lambda?)$	Dallmeyer et al. 1981, p. 590
Traverse across IP, 33.5°N–34°N	Gneiss and amphibolite	$^{40}Ar/^{39}Ar$ total fusion, biotite	$324–241 \pm 5$	Dallmeyer 1978
Traverse across IP, 33.5°N–34°N	Gneiss and amphibolite	$^{40}Ar/^{39}Ar$ total fusion, hornblende	$362–306 \pm 5$	Dallmeyer 1978
Kings Mountain belt				
KMB, High Shoals batholith	Biotite granite	U–Pb zircon, concordant	$317(\lambda?)$	Horton & Stern 1983
KMB, country rock	Amphibolite?	$^{40}Ar/^{39}Ar$ high temperature plateau, hornblende	$322(\lambda?)$	Sutter et al. 1984
Charlotte belt				
Farmington gabbro (FG)	Gabbro	$^{40}Ar/^{39}Ar$ plateau, hornblende	$406 \pm 4(\lambda?)$	Sutter et al. 1983
Weddington gabbro (WG)	Gabbro	$^{40}Ar/^{39}Ar$ plateau, hornblende	$408 \pm 1(\lambda?)$	Sutter et al. 1983
Country rock associated with FG and WG	Amphibolite	$^{40}Ar/^{39}Ar$ plateau, hornblende	$425–430(\lambda?)$	Sutter et al. 1983
Just E of KMB	Amphibolite	$^{40}Ar/^{39}Ar$ plateau, hornblende	>430 (high-temperature steps) c. 320 (low-temperature steps) $(\lambda?)$	Sutter et al. 1984
E of KMB	Amphibolite	$^{40}Ar/^{39}Ar$ plateau, hornblende	$430(\lambda?)$	Sutter et al. 1984
Waxhall granite porphyry (W)	Metagranite	Rb–Sr whole-rock isochron	495 ± 13	Fullagar 1981
34°49.5'N, 80°58.1'W (EDG)	Granite (metamorphosed?)	Rb–Sr whole-rock isochron	535 ± 30	Fullagar 1971, 1981; Fullagar & Kish 1981
Great Falls granite (GF)	Metagranite	Rb–Sr whole-rock isochron	543 ± 63	Fullagar 1971, 1981
Newberry granite (NB)	Granite	Rb–Sr whole-rock isochron	415 ± 9	Fullagar 1981; Fullagar & Kish 1981
Carolina slate belt				
35.9°N, 79°W	Dacite metatuff	Rb–Sr whole-rock isochron	$459 \pm 5(\lambda?)$	Black & Fullagar 1976; Kish 1982
35.4°N, 80.2°W	Argillite	K–Ar whole-rock isochron	$481 \pm 13, 483 \pm 15(\lambda?)$	Kish et al. 1979

*See Fig. 7 for locations. Abbreviations here correspond to those in Fig. 7 and Table 1.
†Decay constants λ used in age calculations are those recommended by Steiger & Jäger (1977).

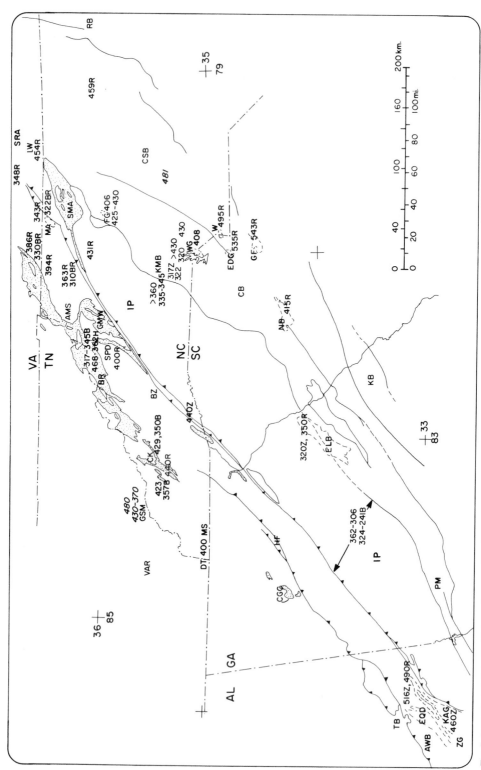

FIG 7. Isotopic age data (in Ma) pertinent to Arenig to Wenlock metamorphism in the Southern Appalachians. Abbreviations are defined in Table 1. The stippled pattern indicates Grenville age basement.

affected the northern Alabama Piedmont and that this metamorphic event must be younger than the early to middle Devonian fossils within the TB. However, Glover *et al.* (1983, p. 237, Fig. 2) suggested that high-grade metamorphism may have occurred during both the Taconian and Acadian. Bieler & Deininger (1984) have recently identified deformation and metamorphism in the Alabama AWB associated with emplacement of 460 Ma granite and augen gneiss (as reported by Thomas *et al.* 1980, p. 95). Russell *et al.* (1984) have also suggested that Arenig to Wenlock age metamorphism may be associated with the emplacement of these granitic rocks.

In recent summary papers by Hatcher *et al.* (1980), Glover *et al.* (1983) and Williams & Hatcher (1983) it has been concluded that Arenig to Wenlock metamorphism occurred in the Brevard zone (BZ) and Inner Piedmont (IP). The following isotopic data constrain a period of metamorphism to pre-Arenig or Arenig to Wenlock in southern Virginia and N Carolina. Metamorphosed and deformed rocks in the Smith River allochthon (SRA) have been intruded by the Leatherwood granite dated at 464 Ma by Odom & Russell (1975). In the IP near the BZ, N Carolina, granitic gneiss of age 438–440 Ma postdates metamorphism (Odom & Russell 1975). From a detailed study of zircons Sinha & Glover (1978) proposed that 440 Ma is the best age of metamorphism of the Henderson gneiss along the BZ and adjacent IP, southern N Carolina. However, Dallmeyer & Hatcher (1985) have recently obtained ^{40}Ar/^{39}Ar plateau ages of 368–325 Ma on hornblende from metavolcanic and metasedimentary rocks from the eastern BR, BZ and IP.

Definitive evidence for Arenig to Wenlock metamorphism is lacking in the IP W of the Kings Mountain belt (KMB) and into S Carolina, Georgia and Alabama. Glover *et al.* (1983, pp. 237–8, fig. 2) suggested that metamorphism may have been high grade during both Taconian and Acadian times. W of the KMB Sutter *et al.* (1984) reported that a discordant hornblende ^{40}Ar/^{39}Ar spectrum gave an age of greater than 360 Ma for the high-temperature steps and of 335–345 Ma for the low-temperature steps. Dallmeyer *et al.* (1981) asserted that the peak of metamorphism within the Georgia IP was at about 400 Ma. Earlier, Dallmeyer (1978) suggested that regional metamorphism occurred at about 365 Ma based on ^{40}Ar/^{39}Ar biotite and hornblende ages of 324–241 Ma and 362–306 Ma respectively. Metamorphism must have occurred before the intrusion of the Elberton granite (350 Ma, Rb–Sr whole-rock; 320 Ma, zircon) as it is not metamorphosed but does include polydeformed and

metamorphosed schists and gneisses (Ellwood *et al.* 1980, Dallmeyer *et al.* 1981).

The areas discussed above (except perhaps the IP) are underlain by Grenville age basement. Geophysical, geochemical, palaeontological and isotopic data indicate different basement to the E (Wenner 1981, Rankin *et al.* 1983, Secor *et al.* 1983, Williams & Hatcher 1983). The main metamorphism in the Charlotte belt (CB) and Carolina slate belt (CSB) has been attributed to Arenig to Wenlock time by some students of the southern Appalachians and to the Devonian by others (Secor & Snoke 1978, Hatcher *et al.* 1980, Snoke *et al.* 1980, Bearce *et al.* 1982, Glover *et al.* 1983). The two belts may have been metamorphosed at the same time (Butler 1972, Secor *et al.* 1982). The Kiokee belt (KB) to the E may also have been metamorphosed at this time but was overprinted by later higher-grade metamorphism (Secor *et al.* 1982.)

Silurian age metamorphism appears to have occurred E of the KMB, N Carolina–S Carolina, where Sutter *et al.* (1983, 1984) reported ^{40}Ar/^{39}Ar plateau ages of 425–430 Ma on hornblende from amphibolite. Rb–Sr whole-rock isochron ages summarized by Fullagar (1981) and Fullagar & Kish (1981) show that metamorphism within the S Carolina CB is bracketed between (1) the Rb–Sr whole-rock ages of pre-metamorphic granitic rocks (543–495 Ma) and (2) the 415 Ma age of a polymetamorphic granite (Fig. 7, NB) that includes rotated xenoliths of metamorphic rock (Secor *et al.* 1982, p. 6951). Glover *et al.* (1983, Fig. 2) proposed that the primary metamorphism was Taconian and that it was overprinted by Acadian metamorphism.

Regional metamorphism within the CSB is poorly bracketed between (1) the protolith age, which is 670–494 Ma based on Rb–Sr whole-rock ages of metavolcanic rocks (Fullagar & Butler 1976, Fullagar 1981) and on the presence of late Proterozoic to middle Cambrian fossils in slate (St Jean 1973, Secor *et al.* 1983, Gibson *et al.* 1984), and (2) the Rb–Sr whole-rock ages of crosscutting plutons (323–285 Ma) (Fullagar & Butler 1979, Fullagar 1981). Arenig to Wenlock metamorphism within the N Carolina CSB is indicated by a K–Ar whole-rock age of 481 Ma argillite and slate (Kish *et al.* 1979, Kish 1982) and by an Rb–Sr whole-rock isochron age of 459± Ma for dacite metatuff (Black & Fullagar 1976). Briggs *et al.* (1978) stated that regional metamorphism in the northern N Carolina CSB occurred at about 350 Ma. Wright & Seiders (1980) obtained a lower intercept age of 340 Ma on zircon from felsic volcanic rocks of the N Carolina slate belt, suggesting Devonian metamorphism. However, they noted that, because their data points cluster

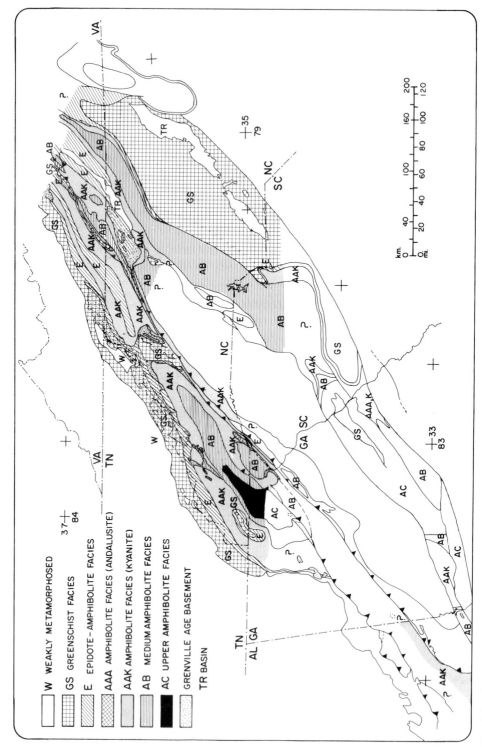

FIG. 8 Arenig to Wenlock regional metamorphism in the southern Appalachians (compiled by G. W. Fisher for IGCP Project 27). The age(s) of isograds S of the question marks is a subject of debate (see text).

at the upper concordia intercept, control on the lower intercept is poor. Glover *et al.* (1983) suggested that the metamorphism was primarily Taconian. The conflict is not yet resolved.

Distribution and estimates of temperature and pressure

Metamorphic facies for probable Taconian metamorphism are shown on Fig. 8. (Because ages of metamorphism are uncertain the highest grades of metamorphism for other areas, as compiled by G. W. Fisher for IGCP Project 27, are also indicated.) Determining metamorphic isograds and the effects of polymetamorphism is particularly difficult in the southern Appalachians because of poor exposure of bedrock. Some of the 'isograds' are extrapolated from minerals found in panned alluvial samples (Carpenter 1970), but detailed petrological studies are sparse.

In general, metamorphism appears to be medium-pressure facies series; kyanite is common in high-grade pelitic rocks. Palaeozoic metamorphism increases from weakly metamorphosed rocks in the VAR to upper amphibolite facies in the BR (see also the summary papers and metamorphic maps by Carpenter (1970), Hadley & Nelson (1971), Rankin *et al.* (1972, 1973), Espenshade *et al.* (1975) and Rankin (1975)). This metamorphism has overprinted granulite-facies metamorphism of the Grenville age basement. Within sillimanite-grade rocks SW of the GMW, pegmatite and granitic rocks may have formed by partial melting at the peak of the metamorphism (Rankin *et al.* 1973, p. 34). Farther S in the AWB of Alabama, Bieler & Deininger (1984) report kyanite-grade and perhaps sillimanite + muscovite-grade metamorphism associated with Ordovician granitic rocks (Fig. 7, EQD, KAG, ZG).

Taconian metamorphism in the vicinity of the BZ appears to be kyanite grade in both the BR and IP of N Carolina (Hadley & Nelson 1971). Much of the IP shows sillimanite + muscovite-grade metamorphism; migmatite is common (Hatcher *et al.* 1980, Goldsmith, in preparation). High-grade metamorphism also occurs farther SW in the IP, but definitive evidence that this is Arenig to Wenlock is lacking.

High-grade metamorphism is observed in two other terranes that may have been metamorphosed at the same time as the IP. The metamorphic grade within the SRA varies from staurolite + kyanite to sillimanite + muscovite. The Sauratown Mountains anticlinorium (SMA) exhibits kyanite-grade metamorphism except in the gneissic core where lower-grade rocks (epidote–amphibolite facies?) occur.

Terranes farther SE that are not underlain by N American basement and that may show Arenig to Wenlock age metamorphism are the CB and CSB. In the Carolinas the CB primarily shows sillimanite + muscovite-grade metamorphism and the CSB primarily shows greenschist-facies metamorphism. Metamorphic isograds are closely spaced at the CB–CSB contact; in S central N Carolina the two belts are juxtaposed along a fault.

Pressure and temperature estimates for pelitic, mafic and calc-silicate rocks from the BR are summarized in Table 7. The pressure of metamorphism appears to have been less in the Murphy syncline (MS) than elsewhere. Staurolite–kyanite-grade metamorphism in the MS occurred at about 4.5 kbar, whereas pressures of 6 kbar and 6.6 kbar are estimated for the same grade (and similar temperatures) at DT, Tennessee, and the N end of the MS respectively. Abbott & Raymond (1984) estimated that staurolite–kyanite-grade metamorphism in the AMS N of the GMW occurred at a pressure of more than 7 kbar. They mapped three reactions of the invariant point [Ct, C] (Fig. 3) in pelitic rocks and showed that progressive metamorphism, as represented by mineral assemblages at the present erosion surface, was similar to the EM–WM path in Fig. 3 (temperature greater than that of the chloritoid out-reactions).

Nesbitt & Essene (1983) estimated that the composition of the volatile phase associated with rocks from DT and MS was similar (Table 7) owing to similar protolith compositions and to internal buffering during metamorphism. At the N end of the MS, southwestern N Carolina, Mohr & Newton (1983) showed that sulphur fugacity was very important in controlling the mineral assemblages and mineral compositions that occur in epidote–amphibolite- to amphibolite-facies schist. In the amphibolite-facies rocks, for example, kyanite occurs in sulphur-rich rocks but staurolite does not. However, staurolite occurs in sulphur-poor rocks but kyanite does not. Consequently, 'isograds' drawn on the first occurrence of staurolite or of kyanite may not represent reactions in pressure–temperature space at all but, rather, a difference in bulk composition.

Conclusions

Recent isotopic dating shows that Arenig to Wenlock metamorphism is more widespread in the Appalachians than was thought previously. Data now available indicate that on the western side of the orogen metamorphism in the Grenville basement and overlying metasedimentary and

TABLE 7. *Temperature, pressure and fluid composition data for Arenig to Wenlock age metamorphism in the southern Appalachians*

Location*	Rock type	Facies/grade	Method	Temperature, pressure, fluid composition	Reference
NW of GMW, c. 36°15'N, 81°30'W	Pelitic schist	Lower amphibolite/staurolite–kyanite	Pertinent phase equilibria	700 °C, >7 kbar	Abbott & Raymond 1984
c. 35°25'N, 83°35'W	Pelitic schist	Lower amphibolite/staurolite–kyanite	Pertinent phase equilibria, gar–plg–Al silicate–qtz, pyrrhotite composition	580±35 °C, 6.6±0.9 kbar, $P_{CO_2} = 1-7$kbar, $P_{H_2O} > 0.85 P_{total}$	Mohr & Newton 1983
Ducktown (DT)	Ore surrounding calcareous metasediments	Lower amphibolite/staurolite–kyanite	cc–dol	540±40 °C	Nesbitt & Essene 1982
DT	Ore surrounding pelitic, felsic and calcareous metasediments	Lower amphibolite/staurolite–kyanite	O isotopes (qtz–mgt, cc–mgt, qtz–bio)	407–554 °C	Addy & Ypma 1977
DT	Pelitic, felsic and calcareous metasediments	Lower amphibolite/staurolite–kyanite	Pertinent phase equilibria	6±1 kbar, $X_{H_2O}=0.90-0.80±0.05$, $\log f_{S_2} > -7.0±0.5$, $\log f_{O_2} > -21.4±0.7$	Nesbitt & Essene 1982, 1983
Murphy syncline (MS) NC & GA, ~35°N, 84°W	Marble	Greenschist/biotite	cc–dol	425±40 °C	Nesbitt & Essene 1982
MS	Marble	Epidote–amphibolite/garnet	cc–dol	475±30 °C	Nesbitt & Essene 1982
MS	Calcareous and felsic metasediments	Greenschist and epidote–amphibolite/biotite and garnet	Pertinent phase equilibria	$X_{H_2O}=0.95-0.70$, $\log f_{S_2} > -8±0.7$, $\log f_{O_2} > -23.6±0.6$	Nesbitt & Essene 1983
MS	Calcareous, felsic and pelitic metasediments	Lower amphibolite/staurolite–kyanite	cc–dol, pertinent phase equilibria	540±30 °C, 4.5±1 kbar	Nesbitt & Essene 1982
MS	Pelitic schist	Medium amphibolite/sillimanite–muscovite	Pertinent phase equilibria	650–675 °C, 6.5–7.5 kbar	Dallmeyer et al. 1978

* See Fig. 7 for general locations and Table 1 for abbreviations.
† Abbreviations: bio, biotite; cc, calcite; dol, dolomite; gar, garnet; mgt, magnetite; plg, plagioclase; qtz, quartz.

metavolcanic rocks occurred at about 470–460 Ma in the northern Appalachians. In the central Appalachians 440 Ma metamorphism is recognized in SE Pennsylvania, and metamorphism at about 470 Ma occurred in Maryland S to the PR and in central Virginia. 440–480 Ma metamorphism is recorded in western N Carolina and adjacent Virginia and Tennessee. How much farther S Taconian metamorphism occurs in the southern Appalachians is a matter of much debate.

Several areas farther E that are underlain by basement which is not N American appear to have been metamorphosed at about the same time but perhaps far from their present positions. In the northern Appalachians metamorphism in eastern Massachusetts and Connecticut has been dated at about 450 Ma. There is significant disagreement as to the age(s) of metamorphism in the southern Appalachian Piedmont. Arenig to Wenlock metamorphism does appear to have occurred in N Carolina and probably in northern S Carolina (430 Ma in the CB; 460–480 Ma in the CSB), but the age of metamorphism farther S is uncertain.

In the northern Appalachians the pressure attendant during Taconian metamorphism appears to decrease towards the S. High-pressure facies series metamorphism is recognized in mafic rocks from northern Vermont and adjacent Quebec, while medium-pressure facies series is mapped farther S. Pelitic assemblages show that the pressure of metamorphism is greater in the eugeoclinal rocks of Vermont and Massachusetts than in the allochthonous and autochthonous (miogeoclinal section) rocks farther W and S (Fig. 3). Medium-pressure facies series metamorphism, apparently well above Al_2SiO_5 triple point, occurs in the central Appalachians N of the PR and in the southern Appalachians N and W of the MS. In SE Pennsylvania high temperature–low pressure metamorphism preceded medium-pressure metamorphism and may be pre-Arenig in age. In the MS medium-pressure metamorphism (4.5 kbar at 540°C (Table 7)) occurs slightly above the Al_2SiO_5 triple point.

Andalusite in pelitic rocks from the eastern northern Appalachians indicates low-pressure metamorphism. Ordovician age plutons are common here, unlike the case farther W in rocks underlain by Grenville basement, consistent with high-temperature and low-pressure metamorphism. In the southern Appalachians rocks underlain by basement which is not N American were either metamorphosed at low grade (CSB, greenschist facies) or high grade (CB, amphibolite facies). Kyanite occurs, indicating pressure above that of the Al_2SiO_5 triple point.

Combined field, structural, petrological and isotopic studies have been very helpful in sorting out the complex metamorphic history in several areas. Further interdisciplinary studies will help to answer remaining questions such as the following.

What is the metamorphic history in areas not studied in detail petrologically? Does extrapolation of 'isograds' across areas where there are no data give a false impression of the continuity of the metamorphic grade?

Can separate isograds be mapped for distinct metamorphic events such as has been done by Crawford & Crawford (1980), Crawford & Mark (1982), Robinson (1983), Laird *et al.* (1984) and Sutter *et al.* (1985)?

Are there distinct Taconian events? Can conflicting interpretations regarding Devonian and later metamorphic overprinting be resolved? $^{40}Ar/^{39}Ar$ dating of zoned amphiboles may be very helpful in this regard.

Is some apparent textural evidence for polymetamorphism really due to changes in mineral composition and assemblage during progressive metamorphism?

Are the apparent differences in facies series due to differential erosion of isogradic surfaces or are exotic terranes with distinct metamorphic histories juxtaposed?

ACKNOWLEDGMENTS: Countless geologists have helped me wrestle with trying to understand better the complex metamorphic history of the Appalachians. Thank you; I apologize if I have inadvertently misrepresented any of your data. Reviews by W.A. Bothner, M.A. Boxwell, B. Harte and an anonymous reviewer are very much appreciated. Support from National Science Foundation grant EAR-8319383 (for drafting and photographic services) is gratefully acknowledged.

References

ABBOTT, R. N., JR 1983. Metamorphism in the Ashe Formation and associated ultramafic rocks, northwest North Carolina. *Geological Society of America Abstract with Programs*, **15**, 51.

—— & RAYMOND, L. A. 1984. The Ashe Metamorphic Suite, northwest North Carolina: metamorphism and observations on geologic history. *American Journal of Science*, **284**, 350–75.

ADDY, S. K. & YPMA, P. J. M. 1977. Origin of massive sulfide deposits at Ducktown, Tennessee: an oxygen, carbon, and hydrogen isotope study. *Economic Geology*, **72**, 1245–68.

ALBEE, A. L. 1957. Bedrock geology of the Hyde Park quadrangle, Vermont. *United States Geological Survey Geologic Quadrangle Maps of the United States, Map No. GQ102.*

—— 1965. Phase equilibria in three assemblages of kyanite-zone pelitic schists, Lincoln Mountain quadrangle, central Vermont. *Journal of Petrology,* **6**, 246–301.

—— 1968. Metamorphic zones in northern Vermont. *In:* ZEN, E-AN, WHITE, W. S., HADLEY, J. B. & THOMPSON, J. B., JR (eds) *Studies of Appalachian Geology: Northern and Maritime,* pp. 329–41, Wiley-Interscience, New York.

—— 1972. Metamorphism of pelitic schists: reaction relations of chloritoid and staurolite. *Geological Society of America Bulletin,* **83**, 3249–68.

ALEINIKOFF, J. N. 1985. Isotopic and morphologic evidence for the age of the Fordham gneiss. *American Journal of Science,* **285**, 459–79.

BARTH, T. F. W. 1936. Structural and petrologic studies in Dutchess County. New York, Part II. Petrology and metamorphism of the Paleozoic rocks. *Geological Society of America Bulletin,* **47**, 775–850.

BEARCE, D. N., BLACK, W. W., KISH, S. A. & TULL, J. F. (eds) 1982. Tectonic Studies in the Talladega and Carolina Slate Belts, Southern Appalachian Orogen. *Geological Society of America Special Paper No. 191,* p. v.

BENCE, A. E. & MCLELLAND, J. M. 1976. Progressive metamorphism in Dutchess County, New York. *New York State Geological Association Field Guidebook, 48th Annual Meeting, Poughkeepsie, NY,* pp. B-7-1–B-7-27.

—— & RAJAMANI, V. 1972. ^{40}Ar/^{39}Ar incremental heating 'ages' of muscovites and biotites from a progressive metamorphic terrane. *Geological Society of America Abstracts with Programs,* **4**, 449.

BERRY, W. B. N. 1968. Ordovician paleogeography of New England and adjacent areas based on graptolites. *In:* ZEN, E-AN, WHITE, W. S., HADLEY, J. B. & THOMPSON, J. B., JR (eds) *Studies of Appalachian Geology: Northern and Maritime,* pp. 23–4, Wiley-Interscience, New York.

BIELER, D. B. & DEININGER, R. W. 1984. Evidence for a fourth lithotectonic block in the Alabama Piedmont. *Geological Society of America Abstracts with Programs,* **16**, 125.

BLACK, W. W. & FULLAGAR, P. D. 1976. Avalonian ages of metavolcanics and plutons of the Carolina slate belt near Chapel Hill, North Carolina. *Geological Society of America Abstracts with Programs,* **8**, 136.

BRIGGS, D. F., GILBERT, M. C. & GLOVER, L., III 1978. Petrology and regional significance of the Roxboro Metagranite, North Carolina. *Geological Society of America Bulletin,* **89**, 511–21.

BUTLER, J. R. 1972. Age of Paleozoic regional metamorphism in the Carolinas, Georgia, and Tennessee Southern Appalachians. *American Journal of Science,* **272**, 319–33.

—— 1973. Paleozoic deformation and metamorphism in part of the Blue Ridge thrust sheet, North Carolina. *In:* GLOVER, L., III & RIBBE, P. H. (eds) *American Journal of Science,* **273A**, 72–88.

CARPENTER, R. H. 1970. Metamorphic history of the Blue Ridge Province of Tennessee and North Carolina. *Geological Society of America Bulletin,* **81**, 749–62.

CHENEY, J. T. 1980. Chloritoid through sillimanite zone metamorphism of high-alumina pelites from the Hoosac Formation, western Massachusetts. *Geological Society of America Abstracts with Programs,* **12**, 401.

CLARKE, J. W. 1984. The core of the Blue Ridge anticlinorium in northern Virginia. *In:* BARTHOLOMEW, M. J. (ed.) *The Grenville Event in the Appalachians and Related Topics. Geological Society of America Special Paper No. 194,* pp. 155–60.

COLTON, G. W. 1970. The Appalachian Basin—its depositional sequences and their geological relationships. *In:* FISHER, G. W., PETTIJOHN, F. J., REED, J. C., JR & WEAVER, K. N. (eds) *Studies of Appalachian Geology: Central and Southern,* pp. 5–47, Wiley-Interscience, New York.

CRAWFORD, M. L. & CRAWFORD, W. A. 1980. Metamorphic and tectonic history of the Pennsylvania Piedmont. *Journal of the Geological Society, London,* **137**, 311–20.

—— & MARK, L. E. 1982. Evidence from metamorphic rocks for overthrusting, Pennsylvania Piedmont, U.S.A. *Canadian Mineralogist,* **20**, 333–47.

CRAWFORD, W. A. & HOERSCH, A. L. 1984. The geology of the Honey Brook Upland, southeastern Pennsylvania. *In:* BARTHOLOMEW, M. J. (ed.) *The Grenville Event in the Appalachians and Related Topics. Geological Society of America Special Paper No. 194,* pp. 111–25.

DALLMEYER, R. D. 1975a. Incremental ^{40}Ar/^{39}Ar ages of biotite and hornblende from retrograded basement gneisses of the southern Blue Ridge: their bearing on the age of Paleozoic metamorphism. *American Journal of Science,* **275**, 444–60.

—— 1975b. ^{40}Ar/^{39}Ar ages of biotite and hornblende from a progressively remetamorphosed basement terrane: their bearing on interpretation of release spectra. *Geochimica et Cosmochimica Acta,* **39**, 1655–69.

—— 1975c. ^{40}Ar/^{39}Ar release spectra of biotite and hornblende from the Cortlandt and Rosetown plutons, New York, and their regional implications. *Journal of Geology,* **83**, 629–43.

—— 1978. ^{40}Ar/^{39}Ar incremental-release ages of hornblende and biotite across the Georgia Inner Piedmont: their bearing on late Paleozoic–early Mesozoic tectonothermal history. *American Journal of Science,* **278**, 124–49.

—— & HATCHER, R. D., JR 1985. The Alto allochthon: Part 2, Geochronological constraints on tectonothermal evolution. *Geological Society of America Abstracts with Programs,* **17**, 86.

—— & SUTTER, J. F. 1976. ^{40}Ar/^{39}Ar incremental-release ages of biotite and hornblende from variably retrograded basement gneisses of the northeasternmost Reading Prong, New York: their bearing on early Paleozoic metamorphic history. *American Journal of Science,* **276**, 731–47.

——, COURTNEY, P. S. & WOOTEN, R. M. 1978. Stratigraphy, structure, and metamorphism east of the Murphy syncline: Georgia–North Carolina. *Georgia Geological Society Field Excursion*, Georgia Geological Society, Atlanta, GA, 74 pp.

——, Hess, J. R. & Whitney, J. A. 1981. Post-magmatic cooling of the Elberton granite: bearing on the late Paleozoic tectonothermal history of the Georgia Inner Piedmont. *Journal of Geology*, **89**, 585–600.

DeRosset, W. H. M. & Hewitt, D. A. 1979. Emplacement and late cooling history of the Mt. Airy, North Carolina, granite. *Geological Society of America Abstracts with Programs*, **11**, 176.

Dietsch, C. W. 1985. Geology of the Waterbury dome. *In*: Tracy, R. J. (ed.) *Guidebook for Field Trips in Connecticut and Adjacent Areas of New York and Rhode Island. New England Intercollegiate Geological Conference, 77th Annual Meeting, New Haven, CT*, pp. A1–1–A1–23, Boston University, Boston, MA.

Domenick, M. A. & Basu, A. R. 1982. Age and origin of the Cortlandt Complex, New York: implications from Sm–Nd data. *Contributions to Mineralogy and Petrology*, **79**, 290–4.

Ellwood, B. B., Whitney, J. A., Wenner, D. B., Mose, D. & Amerigian, C. 1980. Age, paleomagnetism, and tectonic significance of the Elberton granite, northeast Georgia Piedmont. *Journal of Geophysical Research*, **85** (B11), 6521–33.

Espenshade, G. H., Rankin, D. W., Shaw, K. W. & Neuman, R. B. 1975. Geologic map of the east half of the Winston-Salem quadrangle, North Carolina–Virginia. *United States Geological Survey Miscellaneous Geological Investigation Series Map No. I-709-B* (Scale, 1:250 000).

Fisher, G. W. 1970. The metamorphosed sedimentary rocks along the Potomac River near Washington, D.C. *In*: Fisher, G. W., Pettijohn, F. J., Reed, J. C., Jr & Weaver, K. N. (eds) *Studies of Appalachian Geology: Central and Southern*, pp. 299–315, Wiley-Interscience, New York.

——, Higgins, M. W. & Zietz, I. 1979. Geological interpretations of aeromagnetic maps of the crystalline rocks in the Appalachians, northern Virginia to New Jersey. *Maryland Geological Survey Report of Investigations No. 32*, 43 pp.

Foland, K. A. & Muessig, K. W. 1978. A Paleozoic age for some charnockitic–anorthositic rocks. *Geology*, **6**, 143–6.

Friedman, I. & O'Neil, J. R. 1977. Compilation of stable isotope fractionation factors of geochemical interest. *In*: Fleischer, M. (ed.) *Data of Geochemistry*, 6th edn, *United States Geological Survey Professional Paper No. 440-kk*, pp. kk1–kk12.

Fullagar, P. D. 1971. Age and origin of plutonic intrusions in the Piedmont of the southeastern Appalachians. *Geological Society of America Bulletin*, **82**, 2845–62.

—— 1981. Summary of Rb–Sr whole-rock ages for South Carolina. *South Carolina Geology*, **25**, 29–32.

—— & Butler, J. R. 1976. Timing of Paleozoic igneous activity in the southern Piedmont and Blue Ridge. *Geological Society of America Abstracts with Programs*, **8**, 178.

—— & —— 1979. 325 to 265 M.Y.-old granitic plutons in the Piedmont of the southeastern Appalachians. *American Journal of Science*, **279**, 161–85.

—— & Dietrich, R. V. 1976. Rb–Sr isotopic study of the Lynchburg and probably correlative formations of the Blue Ridge and western Piedmont of Virginia and North Carolina. *American Journal of Science*, **276**, 347–65.

—— & Kish, S. A. 1981. Mineral age traverses across the Piedmont of South Carolina and North Carolina. *In*: Horton, J. W., Jr, Butler, J. R. & Milton, D. M. (eds) *Geological Investigations of the Kings Mountain Belt and Adjacent Areas in the Carolinas. Carolina Geological Society Field Trip Guidebook 1981*, pp. 155–65.

——, ——, Odom, A. L., Bottino, M. L. & Dallmeyer, R. D. 1979. Apparent excess ^{40}Ar in hornblendes from the Ore Knob, N.C., and Ducktown, TN, massive sulfide deposits. *Geological Society of America Abstracts with Programs*, **11**, 179.

Garlick, G. D. & Epstein, S. 1967. Oxygen isotope ratios in coexisting minerals of regionally metamorphosed rocks. *Geochimica et Cosmochimica Acta*, **31**, 181–214.

Gaudette, H. E., Bothner, W. A., Laird, J., Olszewski, W. J., Jr & Cheatham, M. M. 1984. Late Precambrian/early Paleozoic deformation and metamorphism in southeastern New Hampshire—confirmation of an exotic terrane. *Geological Society of America Abstracts with Programs*, **16**, 516.

Gibson, G. G., Teeter, S. A. & Fedonkin, M. A. 1984. Ediacarian fossils from the Carolina slate belt, Stanly County, North Carolina. *Geology*, **12**, 387–90.

Glover, L., III, Speer, J. A., Russell, G. S. & Farrar, S. S. 1983. Ages of regional metamorphism and ductile deformation in the central and southern Appalachians. *Lithos*, **16**, 223–45.

Goldsmith, R. (ed.) Preliminary isograd map of the Charlotte quadrangle, North Carolina and South Carolina. *United States Geological Survey Map* in preparation.

Grauert, B. & Wagner, M. E. 1975. Age of the granulite-facies metamorphism of the Wilmington Complex, Delaware–Pennsylvania Piedmont. *American Journal of Science*, **275**, 683–91.

——, Crawford, M. L. & Wagner, M. E. 1973. U–Pb isotopic analyses of zircons from granulite and amphibolite facies rocks of the West Chester prong and the Avondale anticline, Southeastern Pennsylvania. *Carnegie Institution of Washington, Year Book*, **72**, 290–3.

——, Wagner, M. E. & Crawford, M. L. 1974. Age and origin of amphibolite-facies rocks of the Avondale anticline (southeastern Pennsylvania) as derived from U–Pb isotopic studies on zircon. *Carnegie Institution of Washington, Year Book*, **73**, 1000–3.

Guidotti, C. V., Trzcienski, W. E. & Holdaway, M. J. 1983. A northern Appalachian metamorphic transect—Eastern Townships, Quebec Maine Coast to the central Maine coast. *In*: Schenk, P. E. (ed.) *Regional Trends in the Geology of*

the Appalachian–Caledonian–Hercynian–Mauritanide Orogen, pp. 235–48, Reidel, Dordrecht.

HADLEY, J. B. & NELSON, A. E. 1971. Geologic map of
the Knoxville quadrangle, North Carolina, Tennessee, and South Carolina. United States Geological Survey Miscellaneous Geological Investigations
Map No. I-654 (Scale, 1 : 250 000).

HARPER, C. T. 1968. Isotopic ages from the Appalachians and their tectonic significance. Canadian
Journal of Earth Sciences, 5, 49–59.

HARRIS, A. G., REPETSKI, J. E., TULL, J. F. & BEARCE,
D. N. 1984. Early Paleozoic conodonts from the
Talladega slate belt of the Alabama Appalachi-
ans—tectonic implications. Geological Society of
America Abstracts with Programs, 16, 143.

HARTE, B. & HUDSON, N. F. C. 1979. Pelite facies series
and the temperatures and pressures of Dalradian
metamorphism in E Scotland. In: HARRIS, A. L.,
HOLLAND, C. H. & LEAKE, B. E. (eds) The
Caledonides of the British Isles Reviewed. Special
Publication of the Geological Society of London No.
8, pp. 323–37.

HARWOOD, D. S. 1976. Clinopyroxene—plagioclase
symplectite after omphacite and polymetamorphism of allochthonous rocks in northwestern Connecticut. Geological Society of America Abstracts
with Programs, 8, 189 (author's name given incor-
rectly as Hardwood).

HATCHER, R. D., JR, BUTLER, J. R., FULLAGAR, P. D.,
SECOR, D. T. & SNOKE, A. W. 1980. Geologic
synthesis of the Tennessee–Carolinas–northeast
Georgia southern Appalachians. In: WONES,
D. R. (ed.) The Caledonides in the USA: Proceedings
of the International Geological Correlation Pro-
gram—Caledonide Orogen, Project 27, Blacksburg,
VA. Department of Geological Sciences, Virginia
Polytechnic Institute and State University, Memoir
No. 2, pp. 83–90.

HIGGINS, M. W., SINHA, A. K., ZARTMAN, R. E. &
KIRK, W. S. 1977. U–Pb zircon dates from the
central Appalachian Piedmont: a possible case of
inherited radiogenic lead. Geological Society of
America Bulletin, 88, 125–32.

HOBSON, C. A. 1964. The crystalline rocks of Howard
and Montgomery Counties. In: CLOOS, E. (ed.) The
Geology of Howard and Montgomery Counties,
pp. 27–215, Maryland Geological Survey.

HORTON, J. W., JR & STERN T. W. 1983. Late Paleozoic
(Alleghanian) deformation, metamorphism, and
syntectonic granite in the central Piedmont of the
Southern Appalachians. Geological Society of
America Abstracts with Programs, 15, 599.

JACKSON, R. A. & HALL, L. M. 1982. An investigation
of the stratigraphy and tectonics of the Kent area,
western Connecticut. In: JOESTEN, R. & QUARRIER,
S. S. (eds) Guidebook for Field Trips in Connecticut
and South-central Massachusetts. New England
Intercollegiate Geological Conference, 74th Annual
Meeting, Storrs, CT, pp. 213–246, Boston University, Boston, MA.

KARABINOS, P. 1984a. Deformation and metamorphism
on the east side of the Green Mountain massif in
southern Vermont. Geological Society of America
Bulletin, 95, 584–93.

—— 1984b. Polymetamorphic garnet zoning from
southeastern Vermont. American Journal of Science,
284, 1008–25.

KELLBERG, J. M. & GRANT, L. F. 1956. Coarse
conglomerates of the middle Ordovician in the
southern Appalachian Valley. Geological Society of
America Bulletin, 67, 697–716.

KERRICK, D. M. 1972. Experimental determination of
muscovite + quartz stability with $P_{H_2O} < P_{total}$.
American Journal of Science, 272, 946–58.

KISH, S. A. 1982. The application of potassium–argon
dating of slates to the study of the metamorphic
history of the southern Appalachian Piedmont and
Blue Ridge. Geological Society of America Abstracts
with Programs, 14, 31.

——, FULLAGER, P. D. & DABBAGH, A. E. 1976.
Palaeozoic plutonic activity in the Blue Ridge of
North Carolina. Geological Society of America
Abstracts with Programs, 8, 211–12.

——, BUTLER, J. R. & FULLAGER, P. D. 1979. The
timing of metamorphism and deformation in the
central and eastern Piedmont of North Carolina.
Geological Society of America Abstracts with Programs, 11, 184–5.

LAIRD, J. & ALBEE, A. L. 1981a. High-pressure
metamorphism in mafic schist from northern
Vermont. American Journal of Science, 281, 97–
126.

—— & —— 1981b. Pressure, temperature, and time
indicators in mafic schist. Their application to
reconstructing the polymetamorphic history of
Vermont. American Journal of Science, 281, 127–
75.

——, LANPHERE, M. A. & ALBEE, A. L. 1984.
Distribution of Ordovician and Devonian metamorphism in mafic and pelitic schists from
Northern Vermont. American Journal of Science,
284, 376–413.

LANPHERE, M. A. & ALBEE, A. L. 1974. ^{40}Ar/^{39}Ar age
measurements in the Worcester Mountains. Evidence of Ordovician and Devonian metamorphic
events in northern Vermont. American Journal of
Science, 274, 545–55.

LESSER, R. P. & SINHA, A. K. 1982. The Cambro-
Ordovician volcanic/plutonic province of the Cen-
tral Appalachians. Geological Society of America
Abstracts with Programs, 14, 545.

LYONS, J. B., ZARTMAN, R. E. & ALEINIKOFF, J. N.
1983. U–Pb ages of zircons from the Ordovician
Highlandcroft plutonic suite and Silurian intrusives. Geological Society of America Abstracts with
Programs, 15, 187.

MCCONNELL, K. I. & COSTELLO, J. O. 1984. Basement-
cover rock relationships along the western edge of
the Blue Ridge thrust sheet in Georgia. In:
BARTHOLOMEW, M. J. (ed.) The Grenville Event in
the Appalachians and Related Topics. Geological
Society of America Special Paper No. 194, pp. 263–
80.

MIYASHIRO, A. 1973. Metamorphism and Metamorphic
Belts, Wiley, New York, 492 pp.

MOHR, D. W. & NEWTON, R. C. 1983. Kyanite-
staurolite metamorphism in sulfidic schists of the
Anakeesta Formation, Great Smoky Mountains,

North Carolina. *American Journal of Science*, **283**, 97–134.

MOSE, D. G. & NAGEL, S. 1982a. Chronology of metamorphism in western Connecticut: Rb–Sr ages. *In*: JOESTEN, R. & QUARRIER, S. S. (eds) *Guidebook for Field Trips in Connecticut and South-central Massachusetts. New England Intercollegiate Geological Conference, 74th Annual Meeting, Storrs, CT*, pp. 247–62, Boston University, Boston, MA.

—— & —— 1982b. Plutonic events in the Piedmont of Virginia. *Southeastern Geology*, **23**, 25–39.

—— & —— 1984. Rb–Sr age for the Robertson River pluton in Virginia and its implication on the age of the Catoctin Formation. *In*: BARTHOLOMEW, M. J. (ed.) *The Grenville Event in the Appalachians and Related Topics. Geological Society of America Special Paper No. 194*, pp. 167–74.

—— & STRANSKY, T. 1973. Radiometric age determinations in the southern Appalachian Blue Ridge. *Geological Society of America Abstracts with Programs*, **5**, 422.

MULLER, P. D. & CHAPIN, D. A. 1984. Tectonic evolution of the Baltimore Gneiss anticlines, Maryland. *In*: BARTHOLOMEW, M. J. (ed.) *The Grenville Event in the Appalachians and Related Topics. Geological Society of America Special Paper No. 194*, pp. 127–48.

MUTH, K. G., ARTH, J. G. & REED, J. C., JR 1979. A minimum age for high-grade metamorphism and granite intrusion in the Piedmont of the Potomac River gorge near Washington, D.C. *Geology*, **7**, 349–50.

NAGEL, M. S. & MOSE, D. G. 1984. A revised geochemical and geochronological picture of the Catoctin Formation. *Geological Society of America Abstracts with Programs*, **16**, 182.

NAYLOR, R. S. 1969. Age and origin of the Oliverian domes, central-western New Hampshire. *Geological Society of America Bulletin*, **80**, 405–28.

NESBITT, B. E. & ESSENE, E. J. 1982. Metamorphic thermometry and barometry of a portion of the southern Blue Ridge province. *American Journal of Science*, **282**, 701–29.

—— & —— 1983. Metamorphic volatile equilibria in a portion of the southern Blue Ridge province. *American Journal of Science*, **283**, 135–65.

NORTON, S. A. 1975. Chronology of Paleozoic tectonic and thermal metamorphic events in Ordovician, Cambrian, and Precambrian rocks at the north end of the Berkshire massif, Massachusetts. *United States Geological Survey Professional Paper No. 888*, pp. 21–31.

ODOM, A. L. & RUSSELL, G. S. 1975. The time of regional metamorphism of the Inner Piedmont, N.C., and Smith River allochthon: inference from whole-rock ages. *Geological Society of America Abstracts with Programs*, **7**, 522–3.

OLSZEWSKI, W. J., JR 1980. The geochronology of some stratified metamorphic rocks in northeastern Massachusetts. *Canadian Journal of Earth Sciences*, **17**, 1407–16.

PAVLIDES, L., STERN, T. W., ARTH, J. G., MUTH, K. G., NEWELL, M. F. & CRANFORD, S. L. 1979. Middle and late Paleozoic plutonic suites in the Piedmont near Fredericksburg, Virginia. *Geological Society of America Abstracts with Programs*, **11**, 208.

PETTINGILL, H. S., SINHA, A. K. & TATSUMOTO, M. 1984. Age and origin of anorthosites, charnockites, and granulites in the central Virginia Blue Ridge: Nd and Sr isotopic evidence. *Contributions to Mineralogy and Petrology*, **85**, 279–91.

RANKIN, D. W. 1975. The continental margin of eastern North America in the Southern Appalachians: the opening and closing of the proto-Atlantic Ocean. *American Journal of Science*, **275A**, 298–336.

——, ESPENSHADE, G. H. & NEUMAN, R. B. 1972. Geologic map of the west half of the Winston–Salem quadrangle, North Carolina, Virginia, and Tennessee. *United States Geological Survey Miscellaneous Geologic Investigations Map No. I-709-A* (Scale, 1:250 000).

——, —— & SHAW, K. W. 1973. Stratigraphy and structure of the metamorphic belt in northwestern North Carolina and southwestern Virginia: a study from the Blue Ridge across the Brevard fault zone to the Sauratown Mountains anticlinorium. *American Journal of Science*, **273A**, 1–40.

——, STERN, T. W., McLELLAND, J., ZARTMAN, R. E. & ODOM, A. L. 1983. Correlation chart for Precambrian rocks of the eastern United States. *United States Geological Survey Professional Paper No. 1241-E*, 18 pp.

RATCLIFFE, N. M., ARMSTRONG, R. L., MOSE, D. G., SENESCHAL, R., WILLIAMS, N. & BAIAMONTE, M. J. 1982. Emplacement history and tectonic significance of the Cortlandt complex, related plutons, and dike swarms in the Taconide zone of southeastern New York based on K–Ar and Rb–Sr investigations. *American Journal of Science*, **282**, 358–90.

——, BENDER, J. F. & TRACY, R. J. 1983. Tectonic setting, chemical petrology, and petrogenesis of the Cortlandt Complex and related igneous rocks of southeastern New York State. *Field Guide, Northeastern Section Geological Society of America Meeting, Kiamesha Lake, NY, March 1, 1983*.

REED, J. C., JR & JOLLY, J. 1963. Crystalline rocks of the Potomac River Gorge near Washington, D.C. *United States Geological Survey Professional Paper No. 414-H*, 16 pp.

ROBINSON, P. 1983. Realms of regional metamorphism in southern New England, with emphasis on the eastern Acadian metamorphic high. *In*: SCHENK, P. E. (ed.) *Regional Trends in the Geology of the Appalachian–Caledonian–Hercynian–Mauritanide Orogen*, pp. 249–58, Reidel, Dordrecht.

ROBISON, M. S. 1976. Paleozoic metamorphism of the Piedmont–Blue Ridge boundary region in west-central Virginia: evidence from K–Ar dating. *Geological Society of America Abstracts with Programs*, **8**, 257–8.

—— 1978. Potassium/argon geochronology of the Piedmont/Blue Ridge boundary region near Lynchburg, Virginia. *PhD Thesis*, University of Pittsburgh (unpublished).

ROSENFELD, J. L. 1968. Garnet rotations due to the major Paleozoic deformations in southeast Vermont. *In*: ZEN, E-AN, WHITE, W. S., HADLEY, J. B. & THOMPSON, J. B., JR (eds) *Studies of Appalachian Geology: Northern and Maritime*, pp. 185–202, Wiley-Interscience, New York.

RUMBLE, D., III & FINNERTY, T. A. 1974. Devonian grossularite–spessartine overgrowths on Ordovician almandine from eastern Vermont. *American Mineralogist*, **59**, 558–62.

RUSSELL, G. S., RUSSELL, C. W. & GOLDEN, B. K. 1984. The Taconic history of the northern Alabama Piedmont. *Geological Society of America Abstracts with Programs*, **16**, 191.

SECOR, D. T., JR & SNOKE, A. W. 1978. Stratigraphy, structure, and plutonism in the central South Carolina Piedmont. *In*: SNOKE, A. W. (ed.) *Geological Investigations of the Eastern Piedmont, Southern Appalachians. Carolina Geological Society Field Trip Guidebook 1978*, pp. 65–123.

——, PECK, L. S., PITCHER, D. M., PROWELL, D. C., SIMPSON, D. H., SMITH, W. A. & SNOKE, A. W. 1982. Geology of the area of induced seismic activity at Monticello Reservoir, South Carolina. *Journal of Geophysical Research*, **87**, 6945–57.

——, SAMSON, S. L., SNOKE, A. W. & PALMER, A. R. 1983. Confirmation of the Carolina slate belt as an exotic terrane. *Science*, **221**, 649–51.

SEIDERS, V. M., MIXON, R. B., STERN, T. W., NEWELL, M. F. & THOMAS, C. B., JR 1975. Age of plutonism and tectonism and a new minimum age limit on the Glenarm Series in the northeast Virginia Piedmont near Occoquan. *American Journal of Science*, **275**, 481–511.

SHAW, H. F. & WASSERBURG, G. J. 1984. Isotopic constraints on the origin of Appalachian mafic complexes. *American Journal of Science*, **284**, 319–49.

SHEPPARD, S. M. F. & SCHWARCZ, H. P. 1970. Fractionation of carbon and oxygen isotopes and magnesium between coexisting metamorphic calcite and dolomite. *Contributions to Mineralogy and Petrology*, **26**, 161–98.

SINHA, A. K. & GLOVER, L., III 1978. U/Pb systematics of zircons during dynamic metamorphism. A study from the Brevard fault zone. *Contributions to Mineralogy and Petrology*, **66**, 305–10.

SNOKE, A. W., KISH, S. A. & SECOR, D. T., JR 1980. Deformed Hercynian granitic rocks from the Piedmont of South Carolina. *American Journal of Science*, **280**, 1018–34.

SOUTHWICK, D. L. 1969. Crystalline rocks in Harford County. *The Geology of Harford County, Maryland*, pp. 1–76, Maryland Geological Survey.

SPEAR, F. S. & SELVERSTONE, J. 1983. Quantitative P–T paths from zoned minerals: theory and tectonic applications. *Contributions to Mineralogy and Petrology*, **83**, 348–57.

SROGI, L., WAGNER, M. E., LUTZ, T. M. & HAMRE, J. 1983. Metamorphic and tectonic history of a Paleozoic granulite facies terrane, Delaware–Pennsylvania Piedmont. *Geological Society of America Abstracts with Programs*, **15**, 694.

ST JEAN, J. 1973. A new Cambrian trilobite from the Piedmont of North Carolina. *American Journal of Science*, **273A**, 196–216.

STANLEY, R. S., ROY, D. L., HATCH, N. L., JR & KNAPP, D. A. 1984. Evidence for tectonic emplacement of ultramafic and associated rocks in the pre-Silurian eugeoclinal belt of western New England—vestiges of an ancient accretionary wedge. *American Journal of Science*, **284**, 559–95.

STEIGER, R. H. & JÄGER, E. 1977. Subcommission on geochronology: Convention on the use of decay constants in geo- and cosmochronology. *Earth and Planetary Science Letters*, **36**, 359–62.

SUTTER, J. F., CRAWFORD, M. L. & CRAWFORD, W. A. 1980. $^{40}Ar/^{39}Ar$ age spectra of coexisting hornblende and biotite from the Piedmont of SE Pennsylvania: their bearing on the metamorphic and tectonic history. *Geological Society of America Abstracts with Programs*, **12**, 85.

——, HORTON, J. W., JR & KUNK, M. J. 1984. Timing of Alleghenian metamorphism in the Kings Mountain Belt of North Carolina and South Carolina. *Geological Society of America Abstracts with Programs*, **16**, 201.

——, MILTON, D. J. & KUNK, M. J. 1983. $^{40}Ar/^{39}Ar$ age spectrum dating of gabbro plutons and surrounding rocks in the Charlotte Belt of North Carolina. *Geological Society of America Abstracts with Programs*, **15**, 110.

——, RATCLIFFE, N. M. & MUKASA, S. B. 1985. $^{40}Ar/^{39}Ar$ and K–Ar data bearing on the metamorphic and tectonic history of western New England. *Geological Society of America Bulletin*, **96**, 123–36.

THOMAS, W. A., TULL, J. F., BEARCE, D. N., RUSSELL, G. & ODOM, A. L. 1980. Geologic synthesis of the southernmost Appalachians, Alabama and Georgia. *In*: WONES, D. R. (ed.) *The Caledonides in the USA: Proceedings of the International Geological Correlation Program—Caledonide Orogen Project 27, Blacksburg, VA. Depeartment of Geological Sciences, Virginia Polytechnic Institute and State University, Memoir No. 2*, pp. 91–8.

TRACY, R. J., McLELLAN, E. L. & WALDRON, K. A. 1984. Disequilibrium features in contact metamorphosed emery, Cortlandt Complex, New York. *Geological Society of America Abstracts with Programs*, **16**, 68.

TRZCIENSKI, W. E., JR 1976. Crossitic amphibole and its possible tectonic significance in the Richmond area, southeastern Quebec. *Canadian Journal of Earth Sciences*, **13**, 711–4.

—— 1977. Petrology and tectonics of the Cambro-Ordovician sequence in the Quebec Appalachians. *Geological Survey of Canada Paper No. 77-1B*, pp. 77–9.

—— & BIRKETT, T. C. 1982. Compositional variations of pumpellyite along the western margin of the Quebec Appalachians. *Canadian Mineralogist*, **20**, 203–9.

TULL, J. F. 1978. Structural development of the Alabama Piedmont northwest of the Brevard zone. *American Journal of Science*, **278**, 442–60.

—— 1980. Overview of the sequence and timing of deformational events in the Southern Appalachians: evidence from the crystalline rocks, North Carolina to Alabama, *In*: WONES, D. R. (ed.) *The Caledonides in the USA: Proceedings of the Inter-*

national Geological Correlation Program—Caledonide Orogen Project 27, Blacksburg, VA. Department of Geological Sciences, Virginia Polytechnic Institute and State University, Memoir No. 2, pp. 167–77.

WAGNER, M. E. 1982. Taconic metamorphism at two crustal levels and a tectonic model for the Pennsylvania–Delaware Piedmont. *Geological Society of America Abstracts with Programs*, **14**, 640.

—— & CRAWFORD, M. L. 1975. Polymetamorphism of the Precambrian Baltimore Gneiss in southeastern Pennsylvania. *American Journal of Science*, **275**, 653–82.

WENNER, D. B. 1981. Oxygen isotopic compositions of the late orogenic granites in the southern Piedmont of the Appalachian Mountains, U.S.A., and their relationship to subcrustal structures and lithologies. *Earth and Planetary Science Letters*, **54**, 186–99.

WILLIAMS, H. & HATCHER, R. D., JR 1983. Appalachian suspect terranes. *In*: HATCHER, R. D., JR, WILLIAMS, H. & ZIETZ, I. (eds) *Contributions to the Tectonics and Geophysics of Mountain Chains.* Geological Society of America Memoir No. 158, pp. 33–54.

WRIGHT, J. E. & SEIDERS, V. M. 1980. Age of zircon from volcanic rocks of the central North Carolina Piedmont and tectonic implications for the Carolina volcanic slate belt. *Geological Society of America Bulletin*, **91**, 287–94.

ZARTMAN, R. E. & NAYLOR, R. S. 1984. Structural implications of some radiometric ages of igneous rocks in southeastern New England. *Geological Society of America Bulletin*, **95**, 522–39.

ZEN, E-AN 1960. Metamorphism of lower Paleozoic rocks in the vicinity of the Taconic range in west-central Vermont. *American Mineralogist*, **45**, 129–75.

—— 1974. Prehnite- and pumpellyite-bearing mineral assemblages, west side of the Appalachian metamorphic belt, Pennsylvania to Newfoundland. *Journal of Petrology*, **15**, 197–242.

—— 1981. Metamorphic mineral assemblages of slightly calcic pelitic rocks in and around the Taconic Allochthon, southwestern Massachusetts and adjacent Connecticut and New York. *United States Geological Survey Professional Paper No. 1113*, 128 pp.

—— (ed.) 1983. Bedrock geologic map of Massachusetts. *United States Geological Survey Map* (Scale, 1:250 000).

J. LAIRD, Department of Earth Sciences, University of New Hampshire, Durham, NH 03824, USA.

Arenig to Wenlock regional metamorphism in the Paratectonic Caledonides of the British Isles: a review

G. J. H. Oliver

SUMMARY: Between Arenig and Wenlock times the various terranes of the Paratectonic Caledonides in the British Isles were metamorphosed by a variety of processes such as sedimentary burial in volcanic arcs, inter-arc basins and fore-arc and back-arc basins (e.g. Wales, SE and W Ireland, the Lake District and the Midland Valley of Scotland), tectonic burial in an accretionary prism (e.g. Ballantrae, the Southern Uplands and the Longford–Down Massif), hydrothermal alteration associated with the generation of oceanic crust (e.g. Ballantrae and the Highland Border Complex, the Southern Uplands and the Tyrone spilites), dynamothermal metamorphism accompanying obduction of oceanic mantle and crust (e.g. Ballantrae and the Highland Border complexes) and tectonic burial by nappes (e.g. the NW Foreland beneath the Moine Thrust). The region has suffered low-grade regional metamorphism ranging from zeolite facies through prehnite–pumpellyite and pumpellyite and pumpellyite–actinolite facies into greenschist facies, with the localized development of amphibolite and granulite facies.

Prior to the commencement of International Geological Correlation Programme (IGCP) Project 27, The Caledonide Orogen, in 1975 little was known about the regional metamorphism of the Paratectonic Caledonides of the British Isles. The Paratectonic Caledonides are defined as those tectonized lower Palaeozoic rocks lying S of the Highland Boundary Fault (Read 1961, Dewey 1969). Most workers regarded the region as unmetamorphosed compared with the Orthotectonic Caledonides (defined as those tectonized lower Palaeozoic rocks lying to the N of the Highland Boundary Fault (Read 1961, Dewey 1969)). This view was held despite the numerous reports of pumpellyite and prehnite from the British Isles (Balsillie 1932, 1937, Bloxam 1958, Nicholls 1959, Kelling 1962, Jenkins & Ball 1964, Raam et al. 1969) and the erection of the zeolite and prehnite–pumpellyite facies by Coombs (1954, 1960) and Coombs et al. (1959). However, Vallance (1965) and Coombs (1974) did ascribe the occurrence of pumpellyite in the Paratectonic Caledonides to low-grade metamorphism.

With the incentive of IGCP Project 27 systematic studies of regional metamorphism have been undertaken in Ireland (Ryan & Archer 1977, Oliver 1978, Ryan et al. 1980), Wales (Bevins 1978, Roberts 1981, Bevins & Rowbotham 1983, Merriman & Roberts 1985, Roberts & Merriman 1985), Scotland (Oliver & Leggett 1980, Hepworth et al. 1982, Oliver et al. 1984, Johnson et al. 1985, Kemp et al. 1985), and the English Lake District (Fettes et al. 1985). These papers are synthesized in this paper and new graptolite reflectance data from Wales and Ireland are included in an attempt to describe regional metamorphism in the Paratectonic Caledonides during the period from the Arenig to the Wenlock.

Tectonostratigraphic terranes

The evolution of the British Caledonides in terms of plate tectonic theory is now generally accepted (Phillips et al. 1976, Harris et al. 1979, Bluck 1983, Leggett et al. 1983, McKerrow 1983, Mitchell 1984). Figure 1 has been adapted from Leggett et al. (1983). However, a comparison of the literature shows that there is continuing debate concerning the details of the closure of the Iapetus Ocean. In particular, there is still speculation on the significance of the Highland Boundary Fault, the Southern Uplands Fault and the Iapetus suture (see Fig. 1) in terms of the amounts and directions of movement (Dewey & Shackleton 1984, Soper & Hutton 1984). Since the Iapetus probably closed with oblique convergence, the suspicion exists that strike-slip motions were important on one or more of these major faults and that the various terranes shown on Fig. 1 are allochthonous with respect to each other. The inference is that the metamorphism of the various tectonostratigraphic terranes shown on Fig. 1 did not necessarily occur in the same relative geographical positions as those in which they are located at present. However, petrographic evidence suggests that by Wenlock times sedimentation in the Southern Uplands, the Lake District and the Welsh Basin occurred in shared basins, indicating the closeness of the opposing margins of the Iapetus (Mitchell 1984).

From HARRIS, A. L. & FETTES, D. J. (eds), 1988, *The Caledonian-Appalachian Orogen*, Geological Society Special Publication No. 38, pp. 347–363.

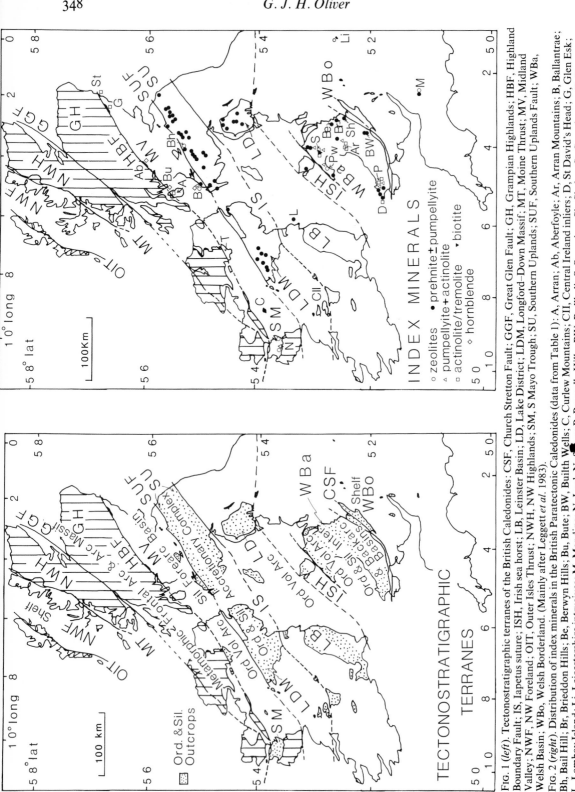

FIG. 1 (*left*). Tectonostratigraphic terranes of the British Caledonides: CSF, Church Stretton Fault; GGF, Great Glen Fault; GH, Grampian Highlands; HBF, Highland Boundary Fault; IS, Iapetus suture; ISH, Irish sea horst; LB, Leinster Basin; LD, Lake District; LDM, Longford–Down Massif; MT, Moine Thrust; MV, Midland Valley; NWF, NW Foreland; OIT, Outer Isles Thrust; NWH, NW Highlands; SM, S Mayo Trough; SU, Southern Uplands; SUF, Southern Uplands Fault; WBa, Welsh Basin; WBo, Welsh Borderland. (Mainly after Leggett *et al.* 1983).

FIG. 2 (*right*). Distribution of index minerals in the British Paratectonic Caledonides (data from Table 1): A, Arran; Ab, Aberfoyle; Ar, Arran Mountains; B, Ballantrae; Bh, Bail Hill; Br, Brieddon Hills; Bu, Bute; BW, Builth Wells; C, Curlew Mountains; CII, Central Ireland inliers; D, St David's Head; G, Glen Esk; L, Lambay Island; Li, Leicestershire intrusives; M, Mendips; N, Loch Na Valley; P, Prescelly Hills; PW, Pwllheli; S, Snowdon; Sh, Shelve; St, Stonehaven; T, Tyrone. Abbreviations for tectonostratigraphy as in Fig. 1.

Grade of regional metamorphism

The most convenient method of displaying variation in metamorphic grade across a particular region is by way of a metamorphic facies map. This is relatively simple for terranes of medium- and high-grade metamorphism (e.g. the Orthotectonic Caledonides (Fettes 1979)) where there is an abundance of index minerals in a wide range of rock compositions. However, terranes of sub-greenschist facies pose problems because diagnostic minerals tend to form only in rocks of basic compositions. The Paratectonic Caledonides of the British Isles is a region of low-grade regional metamorphism and, although there is a reasonable distribution, large areas are devoid of basic rocks. Therefore metamorphic indicators other than index minerals must be utilized. In the following sections the metamorphic grade in the region is defined using clay mineralogy, conodont coloration and graptolite reflectance in addition to index minerals. The data are summarized in Tables 1 and 2 and Figs 2–6.

Index minerals

Rather than repeat the descriptions of index mineral occurrences in the Paratectonic Caledonides given in reviews by Oliver *et al.* (1984) and Bevins *et al.* (1985) the data are summarized in Table 1 and Fig. 2. New data published in 1985 are also included. From the distribution of index minerals shown in Fig. 2 it can be concluded that regional metamorphism has affected large areas of the Paratectonic Caledonides. The lack of index minerals in the Silurian inliers of the Midland Valley, the southern belt of the Southern Uplands, the southern area of the Lake District, the inliers of Central Ireland and large areas of Central Wales is accounted for by the lack of suitable basic lithologies. The apparent lack of index minerals in the County Monaghan section of the Longford–Down Massif and the Leinster Basin is probably due to the fact that no one has critically examined the basic lithologies which are known to occur in these areas. Most indexed areas have suffered prehnite–pumpellyite-facies metamorphism. However, there is a trend of increasing grade from the zeolite facies of the English Midlands shelf region to prehnite–pumpellyite facies in the eastern area of the Welsh Basin and to pumpellyite–actinolite and greenschist facies in the thickest sequences of Central and NW Wales.

Clay minerals

The results of studies of clay minerals in sediments in the Paratectonic Caledonides are summarized in Table 2 and Fig. 3. Illite crystallinity can be used to define grades of metamorphism in pelites. Kubler (1968) defined the diagenetic, anchizone and epizone in terms of illite (001) peak widths at half-height. Weber (1972) proposed an Hbrel index which is a ratio of the illite (001) peak width at half-height to the quartz (100) peak width at half-height. Weber's index is preferred since it allows inter-laboratory correlation. Illite crystallinity results complement the findings of thin-section petrography (index minerals) and in addition delineate the grade of metamorphism where rocks of basic composition are absent. Anchizone and epizone areas directly correlate with prehnite–pumpellyite- and greenschist-facies areas respectively in the Southern Uplands, Longford–Down Massif and Wales, agreeing with the correlations given by Kisch (1983). In addition, the illite crystallinity results delineate diagenetic zones in the Silurian inliers of the Midland Valley, the southern belt of Southern Uplands (Kirkcudbright area), the Coldingham Bay slope deposits and the shelf of the NW Foreland (also with anchizone illites) in Scotland, in the Welsh Borderland area and in NW Wales. None of these diagenetic areas has zeolite occurrences but the association of kaolinite, saponite (mixed layered clays) and celadonite confirms the sub-anchizone grade and its probable equivalence to zeolite facies (Kisch 1983).

Conodont temperature

The thermally induced colour alteration of conodonts was first described by Epstein *et al.* (1977). Figure 4 shows the distribution of conodont colour alteration indexes (CAIs) in the Paratectonic Caledonides. The CAI values of 5, 6 and 7 are here correlated with slightly lower temperatures than those estimated by Epstein *et al.* (1977) since prehnite–pumpellyite occurrences in the Southern Uplands are co-located with CAI 6–7 and the experimental stability of pumpellyite is at a maximum of 375 °C at 5 kbar (Schiffman & Liou 1980). The correlation between conodont CAI, clay mineralogy and index mineralogy is good. Low CAI values of 1–2.5 are found in kaolinite-bearing sediments of the Welsh Borderland and the cover to the Ballantrae Complex. Kaolinite has a maximum stability of about 200 °C (Dunoyer de Segonzac 1970). CAI values of 4–5 correspond to the prehnite–pumpellyite areas in the Lake District and Wales. The metamorphic grade in areas without data for index or clay minerals is delimited by conodonts in the S Leinster Basin, County Monaghan, and part of the NW Foreland. The latter occurrence, with CAI 5, is thought to have been metamor-

TABLE 1. Summary of data for index minerals from the Paratectonic Caledonides of the British Isles

Locality	Protolith (and age)	Metamorphic minerals	Metamorphic facies	Metamorphic environment	Age of metamorphosis	References
Midland Valley *Highland Border Complex*						
Stonehaven	Ophiolite + sediments	Alb + Trem + Chl + Carb	Greensch	Ocean ridge + burial?	Arenig?	Henderson & Fortey 1982
Glen Esk	(Arenig)	Chl + Carb	Greensch	Ocean ridge + burial?	Arenig?	Ikin 1983
Bute	(Arenig)	Gnt + Hbl	Amphib	Dynamo thermal sole to obducted ocean crust	Arenig?	Ikin 1983
Aberfoyle	(Arenig)	Gnt + Hbl	Amphib		Arenig?	Henderson & Fortey 1982
Ballantrae Complex						
Millenderdale	Ocean floor	Hbl + Plag	Hornb	Ocean ridge	Arenig	Jelinek et al. 1980
		Pyrox + Hbl + Plag	Hornfels / Pyrox Hornfels	Ocean ridge morphism	487 ± 8 Ma / Arenig	Bluck et al. 1980
Slockenray	Island-arc volcanics (Arenig)	Chl + Sap	Zeolite	Autometamorphism on eruption	487 ± 8 Ma / Arenig	Bluck 1982
Knocklaugh	Oceanic mantle (Arenig)	Gnt + Pyrox + Hbl + Spin / Hbl + Plag / Epid + Alb + Act + Chl	Gran / Amphib / Greensch	Dynamothermal sole to obducted ocean crust	Arenig / 478 ± 4 Ma	Church & Gayer 1973; Spray & Williams 1980; Treloar et al. 1980; Bluck et al. 1980
Girvan– Ballantrae region	Ocean floor, island arc, oceanic island (Arenig)	Sap ± Analt ± Nat ± Pr / Alb + Chl / Pr + Pu / Alb + Chl / Pu + Act	Zeolite / Pr–Pum / Pu–Act	Burial by tectonic piling during obductive accretion	Arenig	Oliver & Smellie in Oliver et al. 1984; Bevins et al. 1985
Tyrone Igneous Complex						
Tyrone	Island-arc volcanic sediments (Caradoc)	Alb + Chl + Epid	Pr–Pu?	Burial	Caradoc	Hartley 1933; Phillips et al. 1976
S Mayo Trough						
Lough Nafooey	Island-arc volcanics + sediments (Tremadoc)	Alb + Act + Epid / Pu + Act + Epid / Lau	Greensch / Pu–Act / Zeolite	Burial by 10 km of volcanics + sediments	Arenig & Llavirn	Ryan & Archer 1977; Ryan et al. 1980
Partry Group	Dolerite sill + sediments (Lavirn)	Nat + Chab	Zeolite	Burial	Llavirn	McManus 1972
Curlew mountain	Granophyre (Caradoc)	Alb + Chl + Pu + ...	Pr–Pu	Burial?	Caradoc?	Oliver 1978

Region	Rock type	Assemblage	Facies	Process	Timing	Reference
Northern + Central Belts	Basic-clast sandstones, ocean-floor spilites (Arenig–Wenlock)	Alb+Musc+Pr+ Pu+Chl+Cal± Hem	Pr–Pu	Tectonic burial in accretionary complex	Diachronous from Caradoc through to Wenlock	Oliver 1978; Oliver & Leggett 1980; Hepworth et al. 1982
Bail Hill	Oceanic sea-mount (Landeilo-Caradoc)	Pr+Pu+Chl+ Thom+Anal	Zeolite	Autometamorphism + tectonic burial in accretionary complex	Llandeilo-Caradoc	McMurtry in Hepworth et al. 1982
Lake District–Leinster Basin						
Eycott	Island-arc volcanics (Lanvirn)	Alb+Chl+Epd+ Pr+Pu+Sph+ Cal+Musc	Pr–Pu	Sedimentary burial	Llandeilo end Sil	Thomas in Bevins et al. 1985
Borrowdale volcanics	Island-arc volcanics (Llandeilo?-Caradoc)	Alb+Chl+Pr+Pu+ Epid+Cal	Pr–Pu	Sedimentary burial	Caradoc end Sil	Thomas & Oliver in Oliver et al. 1984
Lambay Island volcanics	Island-arc volcanics (Caradoc)	Alb+Chl+Pr+Pu+ Sph+Cal	Pr–Pu	Sedimentary burial	Caradoc end Sil	Oliver 1978
Welsh Basin						
Builth Wells	Basic volcanics	Alb+Chl+Pu+Pr+ Sph	Pr–Pu	Sedimentary burial	Ord + Sil	Coombs 1974
North Pembrokeshire	Basic volcanics, dolerite	Alb+Chl+Pr+Pu+ Epid+Sph±Stil	Pr–Pu	Sedimentary burial	Ord + Sil	Bevins 1978
Pwllheli	Basic volcanics + dolerite (Caradoc)	Sap+Pr+Anal veins	Zeolite	Sedimentary burial	Burial metamorphism from Caradoc onwards with an end Sil thermal event	Roberts 1981; Bevins in Fettes et al. 1985
Northern Snowdonia + Llŷn	Basic volcanics + dolerite (Caradoc)	Alb+Chl+Pr+Pu+ Stil	Pr–Pu	Sedimentary burial	Burial metamorphism from Caradoc onwards with an end Sil thermal event	Roberts 1981
		Alb+Chl+Pu+ Act+Sph+Pr	Pu–Act	Sedimentary burial	Burial metamorphism from Caradoc onwards with an end Sil thermal event	Bevins & Rowbotham 1983
Central Snowdonia	Basic volcanics + dolerite (Caradoc)	Ab+Act+Chl+ Clz+Kfels+ Musc+Qtz+Sph+ Stil	Lowest Greensch	Sedimentary burial	Burial metamorphism from Caradoc onwards with an end Sil thermal event	Roberts 1981; Bevins & Rowbotham 1983
		Alb+Bio+Cal+ Chl+Kfels+ Musc+Qtz+Sph+ Stil	Biotite zone Greensch	Sedimentary burial	Burial metamorphism from Caradoc onwards with an end Sil thermal event	Roberts 1981

TABLE 1 (*continued*). *Summary of data for index minerals from the Paratectonic Caledonides of the British Isles*

Locality	Protolith (and age)	Metamorphic minerals	Metamorphic facies	Metamorphic environment	Age of metamorphosis	References
Anglesey Berwyn Hills, Breidden Hills, Shelve, Builth	Basic volcanics + dolerite (Llandeilo-Caradoc)	Chl + Alb + Pr + Pu + Sph + Epid	Pr–Pu	Sedimentary burial	Burial metamorphism from Caradoc onwards with an end Sil thermal event	Bevins & Rowbotham 1983
Aran Mountains Prescelly Hills	Basic volcanics + dolerite (Llandeilo-Caradoc)	Chl + Alb + Pr + Pu Act + Sph + Epid	Pu–Act	Sedimentary burial	Burial metamorphism from Caradoc onwards with an end Sil thermal event	Bevins & Rowbotham 1983
St David's Head Aran Mountains Prescelly Hills	Basic volcanics + dolerite (Llandeilo-Caradoc)	Chl + Alb + Sph + Epid + Act ± Stil ± Cal	Lowest Greensch	Sedimentary burial	Burial metamorphism from Caradoc onwards with an end Sil thermal event	Bevins & Rowbotham 1983
English Shelf						
Mendips	Basic volcanics (Sil)	Pu + Lau	Zeolite	Sedimentary burial	End Sil or possibly Hercynian	Bevins et al. 1985
Leicestershire	Dolerite (Ord)	Lau + Anal	Zeolite	Sedimentary burial	?	Bevins in Fettes et al. 1985

Act, actinolite; Alb, albite; Anal, analcite; Bio, biotite; Cal, calcite; Chab, chabasite; Clz, clinozoisite; Epid, epidote; Gnt, garnet; Hbl, hornblende; Hem, hematite; Kfels, potassium feldspar; Lau, laumonite; Musc, muscovite; Nat, natrolite; Plag, plagioclase; Pr, prehnite; Pu, pumpellyite; Pyrox, pyroxene; Qtz, quartz; Sap, saponite; Sph, sphere; Stil, stilpnomelane. Ord, Ordovician; Sil, Silurian.

TABLE 2. *Summary of data for clay mineralogy from the Paratectonic Caledonides of the British Isles*

Locality/ formations	Age of sediment	Illite crystallinity	Diagnostic clays	Reference
Midland Valley of Scotland				
Lesmahagow Hagshaw Pentlands Craighead Girvan	Llandov	Anchizone transition to diagenetic zone (av. $b_0 = 9.03$ Å)	Kaolinite & mixed layered clays Corrensite illite–mont	Evans & Oliver in Oliver *et al.* 1984
Ballantrae Complex	Arenig	Anchizone transition to diagenetic zone (av. $b_0 = 9.03$ Å)	Caledonite + saponite	Smellie & Oliver in Oliver *et al.* 1984
Southern Uplands Longford–Down Massif				
Northern & Central Belts in Scotland & Ireland	Ord & Sil	Anchizone (av. $b_0 = 9.03$ Å)		Oliver *et al.* 1984
Central Ireland inliers		Anchizone (av. $b_0 = 9.03$ Å)		
Bail Hill volcanic sediments	Caradoc	Diagenetic	Kaolinite	Hepworth *et al.* 1982
Coldingham Bay— prism slope deposits	Wenlock	Anchizone– diagenetic zone (av. $b_0 = 9.00$ Å)		Casey in Oliver *et al.* 1984
Southern Belt (Kirkcudbright)	Wenlock	Anchizone to diagenetic zone (av. $b_0 = 9.02$ Å)	Mixed layered clays, illite-mont	Kemp in Oliver *et al.* 1984 Kemp *et al.* 1985
Southern Belt (Langholm)	Wenlock	Anchizone (av. $b_0 = 9.04$ Å)		Kemp *et al.* 1985.
Lake District				
Skiddaw Slates	Arenig	Anchizone (av. $b_0 = 8.99$ Å)		Thomas & Oliver in Oliver *et al.* 1984
Borrowdale volcanics	Llandeilo?-Caradoc	Anchizone (av. $b_0 = 9.01$ Å)		Thomas & Oliver in Oliver *et al.* 1984
Southern Lake District	Ashgill–Wenlock	Anchizone (av. $b_0 = 9.04$ Å)		Thomas & Oliver in Oliver *et al.* 1984
Leinster Basin				
New Ross	Camb–Sil	Anchizone		Oliver & Shannon in Bevins *et al.* 1985
Welsh Basin				
Welsh Borderland	Ord–Sil	Diagenetic zone	Kaolinite	Robinson & Bevins in Bevins *et al.* 1985
North & Central Pembrokeshire	Ord	Anchizone		Robinson *et al.* 1980
South Pembrokeshire	Ord	Diagenetic zone		Robinson & Bevins, unpublished (see Fig. 2 of Bevins *et al.* 1985)
St David's Head	Camb	Epizone		Robinson *et al.* 1980
Llŷn	Ord	Diagenetic zone		Merriman & Roberts 1985
Snowdonia & Harlech Dome	Camb + Ord	Epizone + anchizone		Bevins *et al.* 1981 Merriman & Roberts 1985
Arfon	Ord	Diagenetic zone		Merriman & Roberts 1985
Prescelly Hills	Ord	Epizone		Bevins *et al* 1981
Central and NE Wales	Ord + Sil	Anchizone		Bevins *et al.* 1981
Pwllheli	Ord	Diagenetic zone	Saponite	Merriman & Roberts 1985
English Shelf				
Mendips	Sil	Diagenetic zone	Celadonite	Bevins *et al.* 1985
NW Foreland (Scottish Shelf)				
Ullapool	Camb–Ord	Diagenetic– anchizone (av. $b_0 = 9.00$ Å)		Johnson *et al.* 1985

mont, montmorillonite; b_0, lateral spacing; Camb, Cambrian; Ord, Ordovician; Sil, Silurian.

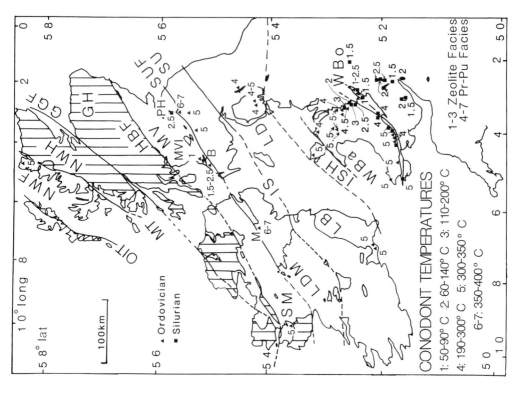

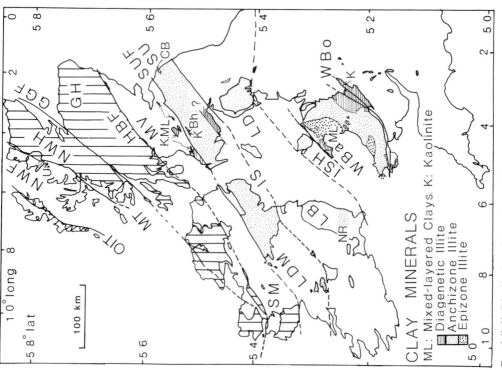

FIG. 3 (*left*). Distribution of clay minerals in the British Paratectonic Caledonides (data from Table 2): Bh, Bail Hill; CB, Coldingham Bay; NR, New Ross; U, Ullapool. Abbreviations for tectonostratigraphy as in Fig. 1.

FIG. 4 (*right*). Distribution of conodont temperatures in the British Paratectonic Caledonides: data from Bergström (1980) and Higgins (personal communication) for NWF, Aldridge (personal communication) for Ballantrae (B), the Pentland Hills (PH), the Lake District (LD) and Wales, and Bassett & Savage (personal communication) for Wales; MVl, Midland Valley Silurian inliers; M, County Monaghan. Abbreviations for tectonostratigraphy as in Fig. 1. Sources: Silurian

phosed when Moine rocks were thrust onto the Foreland shelf along the Moine Thrust in late Llandovery times (Johnson *et al.* 1985). The colour of thermally altered acritarchs (270 °C) (Downie 1982) and the diagenetic and anchizone illites in the Cambrian strata (Johnson *et al.* 1985) confirm the heating of the Foreland.

Graptolite reflectance

Watson (1976) showed that the mean maximum reflectance $\bar{R}_0$(max) of graptolites increase towards dykes and granite plutons in the Southern Uplands. Hepworth (1981) and Hepworth *et al.* (1982) used this method to compare the relatively higher grade of regional metamorphism in the Northern Belt to the lower grade in the Central Belt of the Southern Uplands. Oliver (cited by Kemp *et al.* 1985) applied this method to the whole of the Southern Uplands and compared the results with those from clay mineral studies. Diagenetic illites in Kirkcudbright compare with $\bar{R}_0$(max) < 1.9, whereas anchizone illites compare with $\bar{R}_0$(max) > 2.6 (compare Figs 3 and 5). Graptolites from the Bail Hill sequence have $\bar{R}_0$(max) = 2.2 and coexist with kaolinite-bearing volcaniclastics (i.e. less than 200 °C (see above)). Thomsonite and analcime at Bail Hill indicate temperatures of less than 328 °C and less than 200 °C respectively (Coombs *et al.* 1959, Liou 1971). On the basis of these results, Oliver (cited by Kemp *et al.* 1985) suggested that the boundary between the zeolite and prehnite–pumpellyite facies corresponds to $\bar{R}_0$(max) = 2.5. Kisch (1974) equated vitrinite $\bar{R}_0$(max) = 3.0 with this boundary.

The author has measured the reflectivity of graptolites from the Welsh Borderland, the Welsh Basin, the Lake District, the Longford–Down Massif, and the Glen App and Girvan region of the Midland Valley (Fig. 5). Reflectivity values from the Welsh Borderland are constant on the shelf E of the Church Stretton Fault and increase to the NW in the Shelve and Long Mountain areas (Fig. 6). Further again to the NW the values increase dramatically and systematically towards the greenschist-facies area of Snowdonia and also towards the SW in the Prescelly Hills area (Figs 5 and 7).

Comparison of Figs 2 and 5 suggests that pumpellyite–actinolite-facies graptolites have $\bar{R}_0$(max) > 8.0 and that greenschist-facies graptolites may have $\bar{R}_0$(max) > 10.0. Graptolite reflectance results from County Longford and County Cavan (Fig. 5) are not as systematic as those from the Southern Uplands. It may be that buried granite plutons have affected the reflectivity in Ireland; in Scotland, Watson (1976) found

that the Loch Doon and Fleet granites affected graptolites up to 2 km from granite contacts. If buried granites are absent in Ireland, the County Longford and County Cavan graptolite results confirm the prehnite–pumpellyite grade of metamorphism and also suggest that pumpellyite–actinolite assemblages might be found in suitable rock compositions.

The Silurian rocks of the Lake District show graptolites with $\bar{R}_0$(max) indicative of progressive burial metamorphism from the zeolite facies in Ludlovian sediments to prehnite–pumpellyite facies in Ashgillian sediments (see Table 3). One sample from the Skiddaw Slates shows a prehnite–pumpellyite value. The zeolite values for reflectance disagree with the anchizone illite crystallinity results obtained from the same Ludlovian rocks (compare Figs 3 and 5); however, Thomas (cited by Oliver *et al.* 1984) has noted the relatively coarse grain size of illites in the Silurian rocks of the Lake District and has suggested that it is largely clastic in origin.

The results from Ordovician strata N of the Glen App Fault are significantly lower than those to the S in the Southern Uplands. Graptolites in the Ordovician strata overlying the Ballantrae Complex are lower still and comparable with the shelf of the Welsh Borderland. Graptolite reflectance results from across the Paratectonic Caledonides are shown as a cross-section in Fig. 7. The relative importance of the faults separating the various tectonostratigraphic terranes can clearly be seen.

Timing of metamorphism

Midland Valley

It is apparent from Table 1 that the ophiolitic rocks of the Midland Valley have had a complex metamorphic history. Indeed, various elements of the Ballantrae Complex appear to have suffered ocean-floor metamorphism at a spreading ridge, dynamothermal metamorphism during obduction, burial metamorphism during sedimentary burial by younger volcanics (e.g. less than 7 km of volcanics and volcaniclastics occur in the Pinbain block (Bluck 1982)) and tectonic burial metamorphism after obduction had piled up the various ocean-floor sediments (Oliver *et al.* 1984). All these processes occurred within a 20 Ma period of the Arenig (Bluck *et al.* 1980). Similar relationships will probably be seen in the Tyrone Igneous Complex, part of which is now recognized as an ophiolite fragment (Hutton *et al.* 1985).

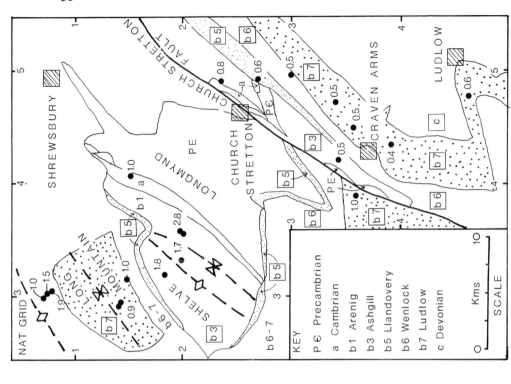

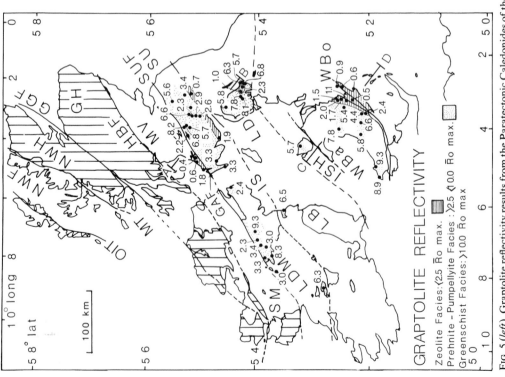

FIG. 5 (*left*). Graptolite reflectivity results from the Paratectonic Caledonides of the British Isles: **BH**, Bail Hill; **GAF**, Glen App Fault. The values of the mean maximum reflectivity $\bar{R}_o$ (max) are the average of at least 10 measurements. The tectonostratigraphic abbreviations are as in Fig. 1. Data for the Central Belt of the Southern Uplands from Watson (1976), for the Northern Belt of the Southern Uplands from Hepworth *et al.* (1982) and for the Southern Belt from Kemp *et al.* (1985). The remaining data are new; details of the sample locations can be obtained from the author. Where data are abundant in the Southern Uplands, an average value has been used.

FIG. 6 (*right*). Graptolite reflectivity results from the Welsh Borderland. Values of the mean maximum reflectivity $\bar{R}_o$ (max) (average of 10 or more measurements)

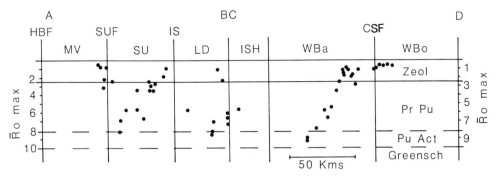

FIG. 7. Cross-sections A–B and C–D (from Fig. 5) showing graptolite reflectivity results from the various tectonostratigraphic terranes of the British Paratectonic Caledonides (abbreviations as in Fig. 1). Data have been extrapolated onto the sections from along strike. Note the northwestwards increase in $\bar{R}_0(\text{max})$ in both the Welsh Basin and the Southern Uplands. Where data are abundant in the Southern Uplands an average value has been used. Abbreviations as in Fig. 1; CSF, Church Stretton Fault.

South Mayo Trough

Ryan *et al.* (1980) described greenschist-facies assemblages in the base of the Lough Nafooey Group Tremadoc-age island-arc volcanics. Prehnite–pumpellyite-facies and then zeolite-facies assemblages are found successively higher in the sequence. 10 km of flysch and molasse overlie the volcanics, with the youngest sediment having a Caradocian age. Therefore Ordovician burial metamorphism is quite feasible. The Ordovician sequence has been folded once prior

to burial by 3 km of upper Llandoverian to Ludlovian flysch which was itself deformed in the lower Devonian. Consequently the Ordovician strata have had the potential of being metamorphosed twice by burial. Lower Devonian regional cleavage is found in both Ordovician and Silurian pelites.

Southern Uplands and Longford–Down Massif

There is circumstantial evidence that tectonic burial metamorphism in the accretionary com-

TABLE 3. *Graptolite reflectivity results from the upper Ordovician and Silurian, Lake District*

Stages	Main inlier	Howgill Fells	Litho-stratigraphy
	(1000 m)		SHF + KMF
	1.0	∼∼∼∼∼∼	Bannisdale Slates
	(1500 m)	— — —	
Ludlow		2.3	
			Coniston Grits
	(1800 m)		
	(100 m)	(200 m)	Coldwell Beds
Wenlock		6.4	Brathay Flags
	7.0	7.3	
	(400 m)	(250 m)	
	8.1	6.3 5.4	Stockdale Shales
Llandovery	8.5	5.9	
	(50 m)	(65 m)	

$\bar{R}_0(\text{max})$, mean maximum reflectivity (average of 10 or more readings); SHF, Scout Hill Flags; KMF, Kirby Moor Flags. Stage thicknesses from Furness *et al.* (1967) and Rickards (1978).

plex was diachronous. Kemp (cited by Oliver *et al.* 1984) and Kemp *et al.* (1985) have demonstrated that the youngest accreted sediments (of Wenlock age), in the Southern Belt at Kirkcudbright, are uncleaved and are of the lowest metamorphic grade. Cleavage is only progressively developed to the NW in older sediments of higher metamorphic grade, as indicated by illite crystallinity and graptolite reflectance. The conclusion is that cleavage and metamorphism were produced during progressive accretion. Graptolite fauna date the sequential accretion, and therefore the sequential metamorphism of sediments, starting in Caradoc times in the Northern Belt and continuing through to Wenlock times in the SE (Kemp & White 1985). In the Northern Belt, in County Cavan, one set of prehnite–pumpellyite veins in sandstones are folded with the regional cleavage formed parallel to their axial planes whilst a second set cross-cuts the cleavage (Oliver 1978). Therefore prehnite–pumpellyite-facies metamorphism preceded and followed cleavage formation in these Ordovician sediments. Furthermore, Oliver & Leggett (1980) described detrital prehnite in sandstones of Silurian age in the Southern Uplands, which themselves were metamorphosed to prehnite–pumpellyite facies. They suggested that the detrital prehnite had been cannibalized from previously metamorphosed sediments of Ordovician age eroded from the emergent trench-slope break (Cockburnland of Walton 1963).

The Lake District and the Leinster Basin

Thomas (cited by Bevins *et al.* 1985) has pointed out that the age of Lake District metamorphism is uncertain. Illite (and chlorite) in all Lake District sediments has grown parallel to bedding as well as to the later cleavage. The earlier bedding-parallel illite presumably grew during burial. Pumpellyite in the Eycott and Borrowdale volcanics is unrelated to cleavage and its growth is presumably also a burial-related event. Therefore the Skiddaw Slates mineralogy may have developed during burial by the Llanvirn Eycott group; subsequently the Eycott and Skiddaw Slates groups were buried unconformably by the Borrowdale volcanics of Caradoc age. Finally the Borrowdale volcanics (but not the Eycott or Skiddaw Slates groups) were buried unconformably by the Ashgill and Silurian sediments of the southern Lake District (Moseley 1978). Therefore burial metamorphism in the Lake District would have accompanied each burial episode. Presumably, illite crystallinity produced by an early burial event would be largely preserved unless either a later burial produced temperatures

greater than before, or strain-induced metamorphism associated with the lower Devonian regional cleavage overprinted the burial illite (see discussion of Wales below). Illite grown along the regional cleavage in the Arenig Skiddaw Slates has been dated radiometrically at 395 Ma (K–Ar) (lower Devonian) by Ineson & Mitchell (cited by Wadge *et al.* 1974). This age agrees with evidence from the Shap and Skiddaw granite aureoles. At Shap, contact biotite has grown across the cleavage in some places but deflects the cleavage in others (Soper & Roberts 1971). Soper & Moseley (1978) use this evidence to suggest that both granites were emplaced during the final stages of cleavage formation. The Shap granite is dated at 379 ± 7 Ma (K–Ar; biotite) (Wadge *et al.* 1974) and the Skiddaw granite is dated at 392 ± 4 Ma (K–Ar; biotite) (Shepherd *et al.* 1976).

The possibility therefore arises that the crystallinity measurements in Lake District sediments are a composite of bedding and cleavage, with illite of various ages ranging from Arenig to the lower Devonian in the case of the Skiddaw Slates.

Wales

Roberts (1981) reasoned that the biotite isograd in Snowdonia is discordant to the Snowdonia syncline. Actinolite and stilpnomelane appear to grow across the tectonic fabric. He suggested that a thermal dome existed and that metamorphic crystallization was in part post-tectonic, i.e. early Devonian. However, he noted the correspondence of grade to intensity of deformation, and therefore syn-deformational, i.e. early Devonian, metamorphism must have occurred. The deformation is assumed to be early Devonian since Ludlow strata are deformed in Wales.

Bevins & Rowbotham (1983) and Bevins *et al.* (1985) note that the highest grades of metamorphism in Wales correspond to the areas of thickest sedimentary sequences (about 13 km thick (Kelling 1978)). It is reasonable to assume that burial metamorphism would progress during the accumulation of this great thickness of Cambrian, Ordovician and Silurian sediments, albeit interrupted by the sub-Arenig unconformity, and would cease at the onset of end-Silurian regional deformation and uplift. Supporting evidence for burial metamorphism is given by Craig *et al.* (1982), who argued that chlorite-mica stacks in pelites from central Wales formed during diagenesis and low-grade burial metamorphism through mimetic growth of a primary bedding fabric composed of clay minerals. Textural criteria indicate that the stacks formed prior to the regional cleavage.

Merriman & Roberts (1985) and Roberts & Merriman (1985) have subsequently shown that the metamorphic evolution of N Wales is more complicated than a simple model of burial followed by deformation. Isocrysts (lines of equal illite crystallinity) are concordant above and below most of the trace of the sub-Arenig unconformity. However, there is discordance at certain localities where the unconformity is strongest. Roberts & Merriman (1985) conclude that pre-Arenig burial metamorphism indurated the Cambrian strata sufficiently for them to resist further metamorphosis.

Merriman & Roberts (1985) note that low-grade corrensite, rectorite and pyrophyllite occur in uncleaved contact-metamorphosed pelites adjacent to probable Caradocian intrusions in N Wales. Higher-grade cleaved pelites occur *away* from the aureoles. This apparent contradiction is explained by proposing that the aureole rocks were indurated during contact metamorphism and resisted the formation of the regional penetrative cleavage. Therefore the low-grade contact minerals are metastable and probably Caradocian.

A direct relationship between illite crystallinity and strain exists in N Wales; high strain in fold hinges equates with high metamorphic grade. Roberts & Merriman (1985) proposed that, immediately before the onset of Caledonian deformation, ambient temperatures, possibly controlled by heat flow and depth of burial, had somewhat overstepped the mineral assemblages. Strain heating (by mineral sliding, fracturing and rotation) associated with cleavage development in zones of high strain was sufficient to activate endothermic illite reactions. However, Roberts & Merriman did not discuss the possible role of pressure solution and hydraulic pumping in high-strain zones (Sibson 1977). Dewatering from hotter deeper levels to cooler higher levels would introduce relatively hot fluid, reducing rock strength and thus allowing higher strain while causing prograde illite reactions and recrystallization. There is a danger of a circular argument here in that there is the question of what caused the original dewatering at depth. Was it strain-induced dehydration reactions or did an increase in temperature caused by increased depth of burial or increased heat flow cause the dehydration? In any case, the work of Roberts (1981), Bevins & Rowbotham (1983), Merriman & Roberts (1985) and Roberts & Merriman (1985) shows that regional metamorphism in Wales during the period between the lower Cambrian and upper Silurian was a consequence of depth of burial and heat flow during that time combined with strain-related recrystallization and thermal

doming during the early Devonian cleavage formation.

Conclusions

1 The Paratectonic Caledonides have been regionally metamorphosed; the grade varies from zeolite to greenschist facies. Locally higher grades of metamorphism occur in ophiolitic rocks (Fig. 8).

2 The grade of metamorphism can be measured using a variety of methods: index mineralogy, clay mineralogy, including illite crystallinity, conodont colour alteration and graptolite reflectance.

3 Graptolite reflectance appears to be the most refined method of assessing metamorphic grade.

4 At least seven types of metamorphic process can be distinguished: (a) hydrothermal auto-metamorphism of lava; (b) hydrothermal metamorphism of ocean crust at a spreading ridge; (c) dynamothermal metamorphism by obduction of ocean crust and mantle; (d) tectonic burial metamorphism by obductive accretion; (e) tectonic burial metamorphism in a subductive accretionary complex; (f) sedimentary burial metamorphism in subsiding basins; (g) tectonic burial due to thrusting of nappes. These processes are summarized in Table 4.

5 The timing of regional metamorphism varies throughout the Paratectonic Caledonides. Metamorphism in the Southern Uplands accretionary complex was diachronous throughout the Ordovician and Silurian. Metamorphism in the Ballantrae Complex occurred in the Arenig. Burial metamorphism was initiated with the commencement of sedimentation in subsiding basins in Ireland, the Lake District and Wales. Therefore burial metamorphism in certain basins would have commenced in Cambrian time and continued to Silurian time. Areas with repeated unconformities would be repeatedly metamorphosed. In Wales, pre-Arenig burial metamorphism at anchizone grade was not everywhere overprinted by post-Arenig burial metamorphism. Pre-Arenig induration resisted the later burial effects. Metamorphism in the Ballantrae Complex occurred in the Arenig.

6 In Wales strain-induced metamorphism, associated with early Devonian regional cleavage development, overprinted the burial effects in high-strain zones in the cores of folds. Lower-strain zones presumably mostly record the burial effects.

7 In Wales low-grade contact metamorphism has indurated the aureole rocks around intrusions such that higher-grade regional metamorphism has not overprinted the earlier burial episode.

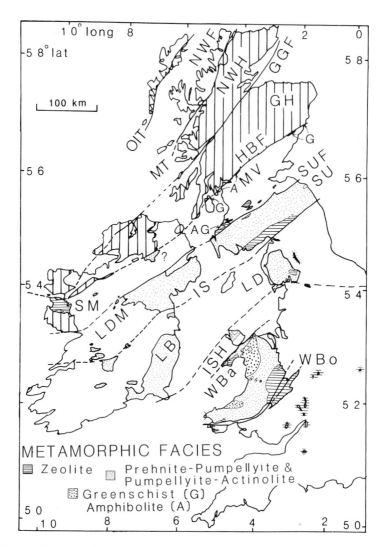

FIG. 8. Distribution of metamorphic facies in the Paratectonic Caledonides of the British Isles.
Tectonostratigraphic abbreviations as in Fig. 1. This map has been compiled by combining the information
obtained from index minerals (Fig. 2), clay minerals (Fig. 3), conodont temperatures (Fig. 4) and graptolite
reflectivity (Fig. 5).

ACKNOWLEDGMENTS: The author would like to thank
the Natural Environment Research Council and Tara
Mines Limited for financial support. The use of electron-
probe facilities at Cambridge, Edinburgh and Glasgow
Universities is acknowledged. R. J. Aldridge, R. E.
Bevins, M. G. Bassett, B. J. Bluck, L. Craig, L. J.
Evans, G. Fitton, A. Herriot, M. Johnson, A. Maltman,
S. Molyneux, D. Robinson, M. Savage, R. Smith and
D. Winter are thanked for the loan of samples and thin
sections and for allowing their unpublished results to
be used. The technical assistance of M. Oliver, A. Reid
and J. Allan is especially appreciated. C. Finlay and J.
Galloway are thanked for typing the manuscript.

TABLE 4. *Metamorphic processes in the Paratectonic Caledonides*

	Type of metamorphism	Examples	Grade of metamorphism
1	Hydrothermal autometamorphism of erupting lavas	Ballantrae Complex and possibly others	Zeo
2	Hydrothermal metamorphism at spreading centres	Highland Border Complex, Ballantrae Complex	Amph, Greens
3	Dynamothermal metamorphism by obduction of ocean mantle	Highland Border Complex, Ballantrae Complex	Gran, Amph., Greens
4	Tectonic burial metamorphism by obductive accretion of oceanic crust and sediments	Ballantrae Complex	Zeo, Pr–Pu, Pu–Act, Greens (?)
5	Tectonic burial metamorphism by subductive accretion of ocean crust and sediments	Southern Uplands, Longford–Down Massif	Zeo, Pr–Pu
6	Sedimentary burial metamorphism in subsiding basins	S Mayo, Welsh Basin and Borderlands Lake District, Leinster Basin	Zeo, Pr–Pu, Pu–Act, Greens
7	Tectonic burial metamorphism by nappes	NW Foreland, Moine Thrust	Pr–Pu

Amph, amphibolite; Gran, granulite; Greens, greenschist; Pr–Pu, prehnite–pumpellyite; Pu–Act, pumpellyite–actinolite; Zeo, zeolite.

References

BALSILLIE, D. 1932. The Ballantrae Igneous Complex, south Ayrshire. *Geological Magazine*, **69**, 107–31.
—— 1937. Further observations on the Ballantrae Igneous Complex, south Ayrshire. *Geological Magazine*, **74**, 20–33.
BERGSTRÖM, S. M. 1980. Conodonts as palaeotemperature tools in Ordovician rocks of the Caledonides and adjacent areas in Scandinavia and the British Isles. *Geologiska Föreningens i Stockholm Förhandlingar*, **102**, 377–92.
BEVINS, R. E. 1978. Pumpellyite-bearing basic igneous rocks from the Lower Ordovician of North Pembrokeshire. *Mineralogical Magazine*, **42**, 81–3.
—— & ROWBOTHAM, G. 1983. Low-grade metamorphism within the Welsh sector of the paratectonic Caledonides. *Geological Journal*, **18**, 141–67.
——, OLIVER, G. J. H. & THOMAS, L. J. 1985. Low-grade metamorphism in the paratectonic in Caledonides of the British Isles. *In:* GAYER, R. A. (ed.) *The Tectonic Evolution of the Caledonian–Appalachian Orogeny. Earth Evolution Sciences Memoir No. 1*, 57–79.
——, ROBINSON, D., ROWBOTHAM, G. & DUNKLEY, P. N. 1981. Low grade metamorphism in the Welsh Caledonides. *Journal of the Geological Society, London*, **138**, 634.
BLOXAM, T. W. 1958. Pumpellyite from Ayrshire. *Mineralogical Magazine*, **31**, 811–13.

BLUCK, B. J. 1982. Hyalotuff deltaic deposits in the Ballantrae ophiolite of SW Scotland: evidence for crustal position of the lava sequence. *Transactions of the Royal Society of Edinburgh, Earth Sciences*, **72**, 217–28.
—— 1983. Role of the Midland Valley of Scotland in the Caledonian Orogeny. *Transactions of the Royal Society of Edinburgh, Earth Sciences*, **74**, 119–36.
—— & HALLIDAY, A. N. 1982. Age and origin of Ballantrae ophiolite and its significance to the Caledonian orogeny and the Ordovician time scale (Reply to comment by Barrett *et al.* 1982). *Geology*, **10**, 331–3.
CHURCH, W. R. & GAYER, R. A. 1973. The Ballantrae ophiolite. *Geological Magazine*, **110**, 157–80.
COOMBS, D. S. 1954. The nature and alteration of some Triassic sediments from Southland, New Zealand. *Transactions of the Royal Society of New Zealand*, **82**, 65–109.
—— 1960. Lower grade mineral facies in new Zealand. *Report of the International Geological Congress, 21st Session, Norden*, **13**, 339–51.
—— 1974. On the mineral facies of spilitic rocks and their genesis. *In:* AMSTUTZ, G. C. (ed.) *Spilites and Spilitic Rocks*, pp. 373–85, Springer, Berlin.
——, ELLIS, A. J., FYFE, W. S. & TAYLOR, A. M. 1959. The zeolite facies, with comments on the interpret-

ation of hydrothermal syntheses. *Geochimica Cosmochimica Acta,* **17**, 53–107.

CRAIG, J., FITCHES, W. R. & MALTMAN, A. J. 1982. Chlorite-mica stacks in low strain rocks from central Wales. *Geological Magazine,* **119**, 234–56.

DEWEY, J. F. 1969. Evolution of the Appalachian/ Caledonian orogen. *Nature, London,* **222**, 124–9.

DEWEY, J. F. & SHACKLETON, R. M. 1984. A model for the evolution of the Grampian tract in the early Caledonides and Appalachians. *Nature, London,* **312**, 115–21.

DOWNIE, C. 1982. Lower Cambrian aritarchs from Scotland, Norway, Greenland and Canada. *Transactions of the Royal Society of Edinburgh, Earth Sciences,* **72**, 257–85.

DUNOYER DE SEGONZAC, G. 1970. The transformation of clay minerals during diagenesis and low-grade metamorphism: a review. *Sedimentology,* **15**, 281–346.

EPSTEIN, A. G., EPSTEIN, J. B. & HARRIS, L. D. 1977. Conodont colour alteration—an index to organic metamorphism. *United States Geological Survey Professional Paper No. 995.*

FETTES, D. J. 1979. A metamorphic map of the British and Irish Caledonides. *In:* HARRIS, A. L., HOLLAND, C. H. & LEAKE, B. E. (eds) *The Caledonides of the British Isles Reviewed. Special Publication of the Geological Society of London No. 8,* pp. 307–22.

——, LONG, C. B., BEVINS, R. E., MAX, M. D., OLIVER, G. J. H., PRIMMER, T. J., THOMAS, L. J. & YARDLEY, B. W. D. 1985. Grade and time of metamorphism in the Caledonian Orogen of Britain and Ireland. *In:* HARRIS, A. L. (ed.) *The Nature and Timing of Orogenic Activity in the Caledonian Rocks of the British Isles. Geological Society of London Memoir No. 9,* pp. 41–53.

FURNESS, R. R., LLEWELLYN, P. G., NORMAN, T. N. & RICKARDS, R. B. 1967. A review of the Wenlock and Ludlow stratigraphy and sedimentation in N.W. England. *Geological Magazine,* **104**, 132–47.

HARRIS, A. L., HOLLAND, C. H. & LEAKE, B. E. (eds) 1979. *The Caledonides of the British Isles Reviewed. Special Publication of the Geological Society of London No. 8.*

HARTLEY, J. J. 1933. The geology of north-eastern Tyrone and the adjacent portions of Co. Londonderry. *Proceedings of the Royal Irish Academy, Section B,* **61**, 218–84.

HENDERSON, W. G. & FORTEY, N. J. 1982. Highland Border rocks at Loch Lomond and Aberfoyle. *Scottish Journal of Geology,* **18**, 227–45.

HEPWORTH, B. C. 1981. Geology of the Ordovician rocks between Leadhills and Abington, Lanarkshire. *University of St. Andrews.* (unpublished) *Ph.D. Thesis.*

——, OLIVER, G. J. H. & McMURTRY, M. J. 1982. Sedimentology, volcanism, structure and metamorphism of the northern margin of a Lower Palaeozoic accretionary complex—Bail Hill-Abington area of the Southern Uplands of Scotland. *In:* LEGGETT, J. K. (ed.) *Trench Fore–Arc Geology. Special Publication of the Geological Society of London No. 10,* pp. 521–33.

HUTTON, D. H. W., AFTALION, M. & HALLIDAY, A. N.

1985. An Ordovician ophiolite in County Tyrone, Ireland. *Nature, London,* **315**, 210–12.

IKIN, N. P. 1983. Petrochemistry and tectonic significance of the Highland Border Suite mafic rocks. *Journal of the Geological Society, London,* **140**, 267–78.

JELÍNEK, E., SOUCEK, J., BLUCK, B. J., BOWES, D. R. & TRELOAR, P. J. 1980. Nature and significance of beerbachites in the Ballantrae ophiolite, SW Scotland. *Transactions of the Royal Society of Edinburgh, Earth Sciences,* **71**, 159–79.

JENKINS, D. A. & BALL, D. F. 1964. Pumpellyite in Snowdonian soils and rocks. *Mineralogical Magazine,* **33**, 1093–6.

JOHNSON, M. R. W., KELLEY, S. P., OLIVER, G. J. H. & WINTER, D. A. 1985. Thermal effects and timing of thrusting in the Moine Thrust zone. *Journal of the Geological Society, London,* **142**, 863–73.

KELLING, G. 1962. The petrology and sedimentation of Upper Ordovician rocks of the Rhinns of Galloway. *Transactions of the Royal Society of Edinburgh,* **65**, 107–37.

—— 1978. The paratectonic Caledonides. *In: IGCP Project 27: Caledonian–Appalachian Orogen of the North Atlantic Region. Geological Survey of Canada Paper No. 78–13,* pp. 89–95.

KEMP, A. E. S. & WHITE, D. E. 1985. Silurian trench sedimentation in the Southern Uplands, Scotland: implications of new age data. *Geological Magazine,* **122**, 275–7.

——, OLIVER, G. J. H. & BALDWIN, J. R. 1985. Low grade metamorphism and accretion tectonics: Southern Uplands Terrain, Scotland. *Mineralogical Magazine,* **49**, 335–44.

KISCH, H. J. 1983. Mineralogy and petrology of burial diagenesis (burial metamorphism) and incipient metamorphism in clastic rocks. *In:* LARSEN, G. & CHILINGAR, G. V. (eds) *Diagenesis in sediments and sedimentary rocks, 2. Developments in Sedimentology B,* **25**, 289–493.

KUBLER, B. 1968. *La Cristallinité de l'illite et les Zones Toutàfait Supérieur du Métamorphism Etages Tectoniques,* pp. 105–22, Baconniere, Neuchâtel, Switzerland.

LEGGETT, J. K., McKERROW, W. S. & SOPER, N. J. 1983. A model for the crustal evolution of Southern Scotland. *Tectonics,* **2**, 187–210.

LIOU, J. G. 1971. Analcime equilibria. *Lithos,* **4**, 389–402.

McKERROW, W. S. 1983. The northwest margin of the Iapetus Ocean during the Early Palaeozoic. *American Association of Petroleum Geologists Memoir No. 341,* pp. 521–33.

McMANUS, J. 1972. The stratigraphy and structure of the Lower Palaeozoic rocks of eastern Murrisk, Co. Mayo. *Proceedings of the Royal Irish Academy,* **72B**, 307–33.

MERRIMAN, R. J. & ROBERTS, B. 1985. A survey of white mica crystallinity and polytypes in pelitic rocks of Snowdonia and Llyn, N. Wales. *Mineralogical Magazine,* **49**, 305–20.

MITCHELL, A. H. G. 1984. The British Caledonides: interpretations from Cenozoic analogues. *Geological Magazine,* **121**, 35–46.

MOSELEY, F. (ed.) 1978. *The Geology of the Lake District. Special Publication of the Yorkshire Geological Society, Leeds.*

NICHOLLS, G. D. 1959. Autometasomatism in the lower Spilites of the Builth Volcanic Series. *Quarterly Journal of the Geological Society of London,* **114,** 137–61.

OLIVER, G. J. H. 1978. Prehnite–pumpellyite facies metamorphism in Co. Cavan, Ireland. *Nature, London,* **274,** 242–3.

—— & LEGGETT, J. K. 1980. Metamorphism in an accretionary prism: prehnite–pumpellyite facies metamorphism of the Southern Uplands of Scotland. *Transactions of the Royal Society of Edinburgh, Earth Sciences,* **71,** 235–46.

——, SMELLIE, J. L., THOMAS, L. J., CASEY, D. M., KEMP, A. E. S., EVANS, L. J., BALDWIN, J. R. & HEPWORTH, B. C. 1984. Early Palaeozoic metamorphic history of the Midland Valley, Southern Uplands—Longford–Down Massif and the Lake District, British Isles. *Transactions of the Royal Society of Edinburgh, Earth Sciences,* **75,** 245–58.

PHILLIPS, W. E. A., STILLMAN, C. J. & MURPHY, T. 1976. A Caledonian plate tectonic model. *Journal of the Geological Society, London,* **132,** 579–609.

RAAM, A., O'REILLY, S. Y. & VERNON, R. H. (1969). Pumpellyite of deuteric origin. *American Mineralogy,* **54,** 320–4.

READ, H. H. 1961. Aspects of Caledonian magmatism in Britain. *Liverpool and Manchester Geological Journal,* **2,** 653–83.

RICKARDS, R. B. 1978. Silurian. *In:* MOSELEY, F. (ed.) *Geology of the Lake District. Special Publication of the Yorkshire Geological Society, Leeds,* pp. 130–45.

ROBERTS, B. 1981. Low grade and very low grade regional metabasic Ordovician rocks of Llŷn and Snowdonia, Gwynedd, North Wales. *Geological Magazine,* **118,** 189–200.

—— & MERRIMAN, R. J. 1985. The distinction between Caledonian burial and regional metamorphism in pelites from North Wales: an analysis of isocryst patterns. *Journal of the Geological Society, London,* **142,** 615–24.

ROBINSON, D., NICHOLLS, A. & THOMAS, L. J. 1980. Clay mineral evidence for low-grade Caledonian and Variscan metamorphism in south-western Dyfed, South Wales. *Mineralogical Magazine,* **43,** 857–63.

RYAN, P. D. & ARCHER, J. B. 1977. The South Mayo Trough: a possible Ordovician Gulf of California-type marginal basin in the west of Ireland. *Canadian Journal of Earth Sciences,* **14,** 2453–61.

——, FLOYD, P. A. & ARCHER, J. B. 1980. The stratigraphy and petrochemistry of the Lough Nafooey Group (Tremadocian), western Ireland. *Journal of the Geological Society, London,* **137,** 443–58.

SCHIFFMAN, P. & LIOU, J. G. 1980. Synthesis and stability relations of Mg–Al pumpellyite $Ca_4Al_5MgSi_6O_4(OH)_7$. *Journal of Petrology,* **21,** 441–74.

SHEPHERD, T. J., BECKINSALE, R. D., RUNDLE, R. D. & DURHAM, J. 1976. Genesis of the Carrock Fell tungsten deposits, Cumbria: fluid inclusion and isotope study. *Transactions of the Institution of Mining and Metals B,* **85,** 63–73.

SIBSON, R. H. 1977. Fault rocks and fault mechanisms. *Journal of the Geological Society, London,* **133,** 191–213.

SOPER, N. J. & HUTTON, D. W. H. 1984. Late Caledonian sinistral displacements in Britain: implications for a three plate collision model. *Tectonics,* **3,** 781–94.

—— & MOSELEY, F. 1978. Structure. *In:* MOSELEY, F. (ed.) *The Geology of the Lake District. Special Publication of the Yorkshire Geological Society, Leeds,* pp. 45–67.

—— & ROBERTS, D. E. 1971. Age of cleavage in the Skiddaw Slates in relation to the Skiddaw aureole. *Geological Magazine,* **108,** 293–302.

SPRAY, J. G. & WILLIAMS, G. D. 1980. The sub-ophiolite metamorphic rocks of the Ballantrae Igneous Complex, S.W. Scotland. *Journal of the Geological Society, London,* **137,** 359–68.

TRELOAR, P. J., BLUCK, B. J., BOWES, D. R. & DUDOK, A. 1980. Hornblende–garnet metapyroxenite beneath serpentinite in the Ballantrae Complex of S.W. Scotland and its bearing on the depth provenance of obducted oceanic lithosphere. *Transactions of the Royal Society of Edinburgh, Earth Sciences,* **71,** 201–12.

VALLANCE, T. G. 1965. On the chemistry of pillow lavas and the origin of spilites. *Mineralogical Magazine,* **34,** 471–81.

WADGE, A. J., HARDING, R. R. & DARBYSHIRE, D. P. F. 1974. The rubidium–strontium age and field relationships of the Threlkeld Microgranite. *Proceedings of the Yorkshire Geological Society,* **40,** 211–22.

WALTON, E. K. 1963. Sedimentation and structure in the Southern Uplands. *In:* JOHNSON, M. R. W. & STEWART, F. H. (eds) *The British Caledonides,* pp. 71–97. Oliver & Boyd, Edinburgh.

WATSON, S. W. 1976. The sedimentary geochemistry of the Moffat shales: a carbonaceous sequence in the Southern Uplands of Scotland. *Ph.D. Thesis,* University of St. Andrews (unpublished).

WEBER, K. 1972. Kristallinität des illites in Tonschiefern und andre Kriterien schwacher Metamorphism im nordastlichen Rheimischen Schiefergebirge. *Neues Jahrbuch für Geologie und Palaeontologie,* **141,** 333–63.

G. J. H. OLIVER, Department of Geology, University of St Andrews, St Andrews, Fife KY16 9ST, Scotland.

Polyphase tectonothermal evolution of the Scandinavian Caledonides

R. D. Dallmeyer

SUMMARY: A polyphase tectonothermal evolution characterizes many of the allochthonous sequences which constitute the Scandinavian Caledonides. Initial Late Cambrian consumption of Iapetus oceanic crust occurred outboard of the Baltoscandian margin with development of an island-arc above a west-dipping subduction complex. Imbrication, polydeformation and variably high-grade metamorphism of Baltoscandian miogeoclinal rocks and underlying Precambrian crystalline basement occurred within an accretionary prism which developed in the subduction complex. This resulted in eastward younging, diachronous metamorphism throughout the Early and Middle Ordovician. Cooling during subsequent uplift was regionally variable, and is reflected by the wide range of radiometric dates reported for the Baltoscandian allochthons (455–535 Ma). This early Caledonian activity has been termed the Finnmarkian orogeny; however, it is best viewed as a complex, diachronous series of tectonothermal events which variably affected the Baltoscandian margin from the Late Cambrian through the Middle Ordovician.

Almost complete closure of the Iapetus Ocean appears to have been accomplished by the Late Ordovician when eugeoclinal terranes which had developed along the Laurentian margin were tectonically juxtaposed with eroded remnants of the Late Cambrian–Middle Ordovician arc. Initial imbrication of the Laurentian eugeoclinal sequences with the arc occurred during the Early Silurian (Late Llandovery). These were subsequently imbricated and infolded with predeformed Baltoscandian allochthons. The resultant composite allochthon was subsequently thrust eastward onto Silurian sedimentary successions deposited over previously metamorphosed Caledonian basement. This sequence of Early Silurian to Early Devonian tectonic events has been collectively termed the Scandian orogeny; however, they are regionally diachronous and should be bracketed with the local controls available. Scandian dates of 425–430 Ma are locally recorded in allochthons along eastern portions of the orogen and they probably date initial nappe translation to higher crustal levels along the Baltoscandian margin. In lower structural units Scandian dates range from 410 Ma in central to 385 Ma in western portions of the orogen. These are interpreted to date rapid cooling during the uplift associated with a crustal rebound which followed eastward translation of overriding allochthons.

The Scandinavian Caledonides are characterized by a sequence of large-scale nappes (Fig. 1) which were transported variable distances eastward across autochthonous rocks of the Baltoscandian platform during early to middle Paleozoic closure of the Iapetus Ocean (Harland & Gayer 1972, Stephens & Gee 1985). The nappes are of varying metamorphic grade and display marked differences in the complexity of internal deformation. As a result, correlation of specific metamorphic, deformational and thrusting events along the length of the orogen has been uncertain and controversial (Gee & Roberts 1983).

Lower tectonic units within central and southern portions of the Scandinavian Caledonides are represented by low-grade metasedimentary successions of late Proterozoic to Middle Silurian age. These originated along the Baltoscandian continental margin both during separation of Baltica and Laurentia and during subsequent closure of the Iapetus oceanic tract. Significant thicknesses of westerly-derived clastic material

of Middle Ordovician and Early to Middle Silurian age in these successions provide evidence of two periods of outboard instability along the Baltoscandian margin (Gee 1975a). Although early attempts to describe the tectonic evolution of this segment of the Caledonian orogen noted this instability (Gee 1975b), most of the internal deformation, metamorphism and nappe translation has been largely considered to be of Middle Silurian to Early Devonian (Scandian) age (Gee & Wilson 1974). High-level tectonic units within the central Scandinavian Caledonides locally contain sequences of oceanic character and have uncertain palinspastic relationships with the late Proterozoic–early Paleozoic margin of the Baltoscandian platform (Stephens & Gee 1985). These higher units contain fossil-bearing successions which range up into the Early Silurian (Llandovery), confirming a major component of Scandian nappe translation within higher level segments of the orogen.

In more northerly portions of the Scandinavian

From HARRIS, A. L. & FETTES, D. J. (eds), 1988, *The Caledonian–Appalachian Orogen,*
Geological Society Special Publication No. 38, pp. 365–379.

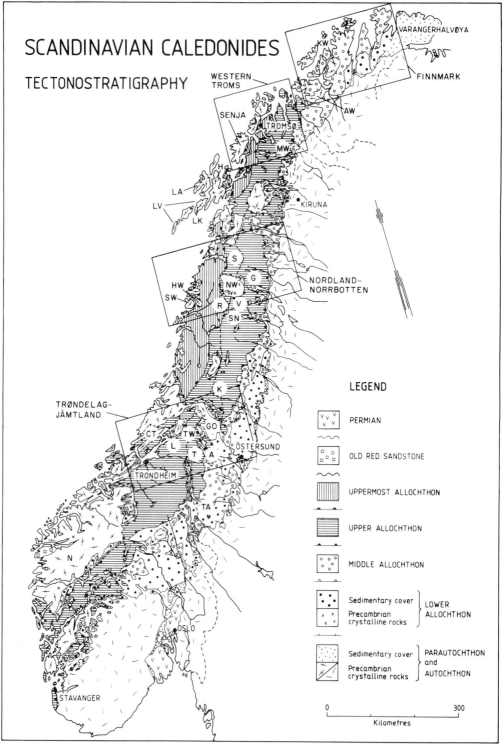

FIG. 1. Tectonostratigraphy of the Scandinavian Caledonides. Finnmark (from Gee & Sturt 1985): KW, Komagfjord window; AW, Alta window. Western Troms: MW, Mauken window (island of Senja is located). Lofoten–Vesterålen archipelago (LV): LA, Langøy; LK, Lekness; H, Hinnøy. Nordland–Norrbotten: NW, Nassafjäll window; SW, Sjona window; HW, Hogtuva window; S, Sulitjelma area; G, Grapesvare; V, Vilasund granite; SN, location of sample suite for the Rb–Sr whole-rock isochron in the Storfjället nappe; R, location of sample suite for the Rb–Sr whole-rock isochron in the Rodingsfjället nappe; K, Kvarnbergsvattnet. Trøndelag–Jämtland: A, Åre; T, Tännforsen; GO, Grong-Olden culmination; TW, Tømmerås window; L, Levanger window; CT, ^{40}Ar/^{39}Ar mineral-age traverse. Others: N, Nordfjord area; TA, Tännäs area.

Caledonides, sedimentary sequences within lower tectonic units only range up into the Tremadoc and therefore provide little chronological control for translation of overlying nappes. However, deformed and variably metamorphosed sequences within several of the higher allochthons are locally intruded by syntectonic plutons which record crystallization dates of 530–490 Ma (Sturt *et al.* 1975). (All radiometric ages listed in this paper are based on the decay constants and isotopic abundance ratios presented by Steiger & Jäger (1977).) Host metasedimentary sequences are thought to correlate with others developed elsewhere within the Baltoscandian miogeocline, and the radiometric controls therefore indicate that a major period of Late Cambrian–Early Ordovician polyphase folding, metamorphism and initial nappe imbrication occurred along this segment of the continental margin of Baltica. This event has been termed the Finnmarkian orogeny.

The suggested diachronism of tectonothermal activity (Finnmarkian to Scandian) along the early to middle Paleozoic continental margin of Baltoscandia has been difficult to reconcile with otherwise almost continuous sedimentological, stratigraphic and tectonic trends. Several systematic ^{40}Ar/^{39}Ar mineral-dating studies have recently been completed within various segments of the central and northern Scandinavian Caledonides, and results provide a more complete understanding of local thermal overprinting relationships than was previously possible. These results and their tectonic significance are briefly summarized here.

Regional geological setting

The Scandinavian Caledonides can be described in terms of several major tectonic units (Gee & Sturt 1985) including (Fig. 1): (1) autochthonous and parautochthonous sequences, (2) lower middle, upper and uppermost allochthons and (3) neoautochthonous molasse deposits of Early to Middle Devonian age. Although the various allochthons generally thin westward, most can be traced across the entire orogen. The nappes were affected by regional northeast–southwest folding following their final emplacement onto the Baltoscandian platform.

The overall tectonostratigraphy of the Scandinavian Caledonides has been discussed at length elsewhere (Gee 1975b, Dyrelius *et al.* 1980, Gee *et al.* 1984) and will not be reviewed here. A variety of variably metamorphosed, largely metasedimentary sequences characterize lower,

middle and lower portions of the upper allochthon. These appear to have originated within the Baltica miogeocline. Eugeoclinal successions of uncertain palinspastic affinities dominate upper portions of the upper allochthon. These probably originated at various locations within the Iapetus oceanic tract. The uppermost allochthon is largely represented by a variety of gneissic rocks together with platformal meta-sedimentary cover sequences which, at least in part, are thought to represent components of the Laurentian miogeocline (Stephens & Gee 1985).

North Norwegian Caledonides

Finnmark

Introduction

The regional geological setting of the Finnmark area has been summarized by Ramsay *et al.* (1985). Autochthonous and parautochthonous sequences are exposed east of the orogenic front and within several tectonic windows (Fig. 1). These consist of Archean gneisses and associated catazonal granites which are overlain by a supracrustal sequence which includes clastic sedimentary and mafic volcanic units. Both sequences were penetratively deformed and metamorphosed during the Svecokarelian orogeny about 1700–1800 Ma ago. Two successions of variably metamorphosed late Proterozoic to early Paleozoic (Tremadoc) clastic sedimentary sequences unconformably overlie the Svecokarelian basement.

A spectrum of allochthonous units is exposed in the Finnmark area. The Gaissa nappe (lower allochthon) is structurally the lowest and contains penetratively cleaved, slightly metamorphosed (lower greenschist facies) lithostratigraphic sequences which are similar to those within the foreland succession. Pringle (1973) reported an Rb–Sr whole-rock isochron age of 514 ± 30 Ma for cleaved shales within the Gaissa nappe and interpreted this to date a penetrative deformation. The tectonically overlying Laksefjord Nappe (middle allochthon) is lithologically similar but at a slightly higher metamorphic grade (middle greenschist facies). Pringle (1973) and Sturt *et al.* (1975) reported an Rb–Sr whole-rock isochron age of 485 ± 45 Ma for slates of the Laksefjord Nappe exposed in the Friarfjorden quarry. They interpreted this to date cleavage formation.

Polydeformed and generally higher-grade units are found in the overlying Kalak Nappe Complex (middle allochthon). These include structural units of variably retrograded middle Proterozoic crystalline basement and late Proterozoic–Cambrian metasedimentary cover. The metasedimentary succession is polydeformed and records at least four distinct regional folding episodes. A variety of igneous rocks of the Seiland Petrographic Province were emplaced during deformation of the Kalak Nappe Complex. Sturt *et al.* (1975) presented Rb–Sr whole-rock isochron crystallization ages for several members of this igneous suite. The Breivikbotn Gabbro was emplaced synchronously with development of D_1 strains. An age of 533 ± 17 Ma was reported for an aplitic granodiorite which appears to have developed by anatexis within the contact aureole of the pluton. Biotite–whole-rock Rb–Sr dates of 425, 410 and 396 Ma were also reported for the granodiorite. A 520 ± 27 Ma crystallization age was listed for the Hasvik Gabbro which was intruded between D_1 and D_2 and during maintenance of high-grade regional metamorphic conditions. A 483 ± 27 Ma crystallization age for the late- to post-D_2 emplacement of the Breivikbotn alkalic complex was considered to date terminal stages of the Cambrian–Lower Ordovician orogenic activity. A 400 ± 12 Ma biotite–whole-rock Rb–Sr date was also reported for the alkalic complex. Nepheline within the alkaline complex yielded conventional K–Ar dates of 491 and 495 Ma (Sturt *et al.* 1967). K–Ar dates of biotite were markedly younger, ranging from 392 to 420 Ma. A K–Ar age of 429 Ma was reported for one muscovite concentrate.

The Magerøy Nappe (uppermost allochthon) structurally overlies units of the Kalak Nappe Complex along a ductile, high-temperature thrust fault. Metasedimentary rocks comprise most of the nappe, and local fossil-bearing sequences indicate a Lower Silurian (Llandovery) and possibly Upper Ordovician depositional age. The rocks are polydeformed and variably metamorphosed up to middle amphibolite grade (Anderson 1981). Anderson *et al.* (1982) reported Rb–Sr whole-rock isochron crystallization ages of 411 ± 7 Ma for the synkinematic Finnvik granite and 410 ± 28 Ma for migmatitic portions of the structurally-underlying Kalak Nappe Complex. These results suggest that Scandian emplacement of the Magerøy Nappe was synchronous with an internally penetrative tectonothermal event.

$^{40}Ar/^{39}Ar$ geochronology

Introduction. Published geochronology suggests that components of Finnmarkian and Scandian tectonothermal activity are regionally recorded in the North Norwegian Caledonides. To resolve local overprinting relationships and provide a more detailed calibration of the individual orogenic events, a comprehensive $^{40}Ar/^{39}Ar$ mineral age dating program has been carried out (Dallmeyer 1987a; Dallmeyer & Reuter 1987a, b; Dallmeyer *et al.* 1987). Representative results are presented here because they provide significant insight into the regional effects of Finnmarkian versus Scandian tectonothermal activity.

Gaissa and Laksefjord Nappes. Penetratively cleaved slate samples were collected at four locations within the Gaissa Nappe. All record internally discordant age spectra with total-gas whole-rock ages ranging from 482 to 551 Ma. The spectra of two samples collected within the hinge zones of isoclinal folds display well-defined plateaux over intermediate experimental temperatures (accounting for 75%–90% of the total gas released) which correspond to ages of 474 and 482 Ma. These are interpreted to approximately date cleavage formation at these locations. High-temperature increments yield markedly older ages which probably reflect outgassing of more refractory detrital feldspar grains.

Four slate samples from the Laksefjord Nappe have been analysed. A sample from the Friarfjorden quarry displays an internally concordant age spectrum defining a plateau age of 485 Ma. The other three samples record slightly discordant spectra in which low- and intermediate-temperature gas fractions yield dates between 475 and 485 Ma, while high-temperature and fusion gas fractions record markedly older apparent dates. These probably reflect experimental outgassing of a small population of more refractory detrital feldspar grains.

Kalak Nappe Complex. Muscovite $^{40}Ar/^{39}Ar$ plateau dates of 429 and 435 Ma have been determined for samples from the Nalganas Nappe. Hornblende in three samples from the Nalganas and Sørøy Nappes displays internally discordant age spectra; however, most discordance can be attributed to low-temperature experimental evolution of loosely bound extraneous (excess) argon components. As a result intermediate- and high-temperature experimental gas fractions yield plateau dates between 473 and 494 Ma.

Autochthon and parautochthon in the Alta and Komagfjord windows. Pharaoh *et al.* (1982) reported conventional K–Ar dates of 1806–2096 Ma for amphiboles separated from metabasalt and metagabbro within Karelian supracrustal sequences exposed in the Komagfjord window (Fig. 1). These ages are similar to those defined for Karelian orogenesis elsewhere in the Baltic Shield and indicate that any subsequent Caledonian thermal overprint must have been insufficient to reset intracrystalline argon systems within hornblende (less than about 500 °C; Harrison 1981). Slate samples were collected within Karelian supracrustal sequences in both the Alta and Komagfjord windows to evaluate the extent to which Caledonian metamorphism(s) affected intracrystalline argon systems of the constituent fine-grained white micas. Eight samples from interior portions of the two windows display internally discordant age spectra in which apparent dates of about 420–430 Ma are recorded in initial, low-temperature gas fractions. Apparent ages systematically increase to define intermediate- and high-temperature plateaus of 1750–1800 Ma. Six samples collected progressively closer to structurally-overlying sequences of the Kalak Nappe Complex record dates of about 420–430 Ma in both low- and intermediate-temperature gas fractions. High-temperature increments record systematically older apparent ages. Eight samples collected immediately adjacent to the fault contact display variably concordant age spectra defining plateau dates of 420–430 Ma.

Interpretation. The ^{40}Ar/^{39}Ar results confirm a polyorogenic evolution for this portion of the North Norwegian Caledonides. Cleavage within units of the lower allochthon appears to have formed at about 475–485 Ma and therefore was probably related to Finnmarkian tectonothermal activity. Although there is considerable debate regarding radiometric calibration of the Paleozoic time-scale (Gale *et al.* 1980, McKerrow *et al.* 1980, Harland *et al.* 1982, Palmer 1983), dates of 475–485 Ma correspond to the Late Tremadoc or Early Arenig according to most workers. These dates are therefore compatible with the Tremadoc age of the stratigraphically highest formations in the Gaissa Nappe. Whole-rock slate systems in the autochthon, parautochthon and lower allochthon show no record of any Scandian thermal overprint, which suggests that this activity must have been confined to higher and more westerly portions of the tectonostratigraphy.

The 473–494 Ma hornblende plateau ages are similar to K–Ar dates previously reported for nepheline from alkalic complexes in the Kalak Nappe Complex. They are interpreted to date post-Finnmarkian metamorphic cooling through approximately 500 °C. When combined with Rb–Sr whole-rock isochron dates for synkinematic plutons in the Kalak Nappe Complex, the data suggest that Finnmarkian orogenesis extended about 50–60 Ma from initial D_1 deformation and low-grade metamorphism until post-D_2 cooling through approximately 500 °C (at 475–495 Ma). This is an unusually protracted tectonic range, and suggests a poly-orogenic Finnmarkian evolution which likely involved several distinct and chronologically separated deformational and metamorphic events. Markedly younger 429–435 Ma plateau dates are recorded by muscovite in the Kalak Nappe Complex. These are probably related to post-Scandian metamorphic cooling through appropriate argon closure temperatures (about 350 °C: Jäger 1979). The ^{40}Ar/^{39}Ar age variations suggest that thermal conditions of Scandian metamorphism in the Kalak Nappes were in the range of 425–475 °C (exceeding those required to reset intracrystalline argon systems in muscovite but not affecting those in hornblende). The 429–435 Ma post-Scandian cooling dates recorded by muscovite within lower structural units of the Kalak Nappe Complex are significantly older than the 407–411 Ma dates reported by Anderson *et al.* (1982) to date high-grade Scandian tectonothermal activity within the Mageröy Nappe and its ductile imbrication with the Kalak Nappe Complex. The apparent east–west diachronism in Scandian tectonothermal activity suggests that lower portions of the Kalak Nappe Complex may already have been emplaced to higher structural levels on the Baltoscandian margin prior to imbrication of western structural levels with the Mageröy Nappe.

Whole-rock slate systems within Karelian supracrustal sequences exposed in the Komagfjord and Alta windows appear to have been variably affected by a Scandian thermal event. The extent of resetting is spatially related to the proximity of structurally overlying units of the Kalak Nappe Complex. Muscovite within adjacent portions of the Kalak Nappe Complex records plateau ages similar to those which appear to date Scandian resetting of the whole-rock slate systems (420–430 Ma), suggesting that the overprint was not caused by a regional metamorphism of the Baltoscandian autochthon but, instead, was a result of the tectonic emplacement of predeformed and metamorphosed allochthons which were maintained at elevated temperatures. The variably overprinted slate systems present no record of any Late Cambrian or Early Ordovician thermal activity, thereby indicating that Finnmarkian orogenesis must have occurred significantly outboard of and was subsequently transported onto this portion of the Baltoscandian margin.

Western Troms

Introduction

The regional geological setting of the western Troms portion of the North Norwegian Caledonides has been reviewed by Andresen *et al.* (1985). Middle Proterozoic crystalline basement rocks are exposed along the Norwegian coast (western gneiss terrane) and within the Mauken window (Fig. 1). Autochthonous to parautochthonous low-grade metasedimentary cover sequences are exposed along the eastern border of the Mauken window. These are structurally overlain by variably-mylonitic, generally low-grade psammites and pelites of the Målselv Nappe (lower allochthon). A series of middle amphibolite grade marbles, mica schists and quartzites of the Senja Nappe (middle allochthon) structurally overlie the Målselv Nappe in eastern portions of the area and are in direct tectonic contact with the western gneiss terrane along the coast. High-grade, polydeformed, largely pelitic sequences of the Dyrøy Nappe (lower portion of the upper allochthon?) are structurally positioned between the Senja Nappe and the Lyngen Nappe Complex (upper portion of the upper allochthon) which is represented by three distinct lithotectonic units. The lowest is characterized by locally garnet-bearing phyllites. These are structurally overlain by the Lyngen Gabbro Complex which has been interpreted to represent a partially dismembered ophiolitic sequence (Furnes *et al.* 1985). The Ullsfjord Group is in overlying thrust or unconformable contact with the Lyngen Gabbro. Coarse basal clastic sequences contain clasts of deformed and metamorphosed Lyngen Gabbro. These sequences can be traced upwards into interbedded slates and metasandstones which locally include Lower Silurian fossil-bearing carbonate sequences (Olaussen 1977).

The highest tectonic unit in western Troms is the composite Tromsø Nappe Complex (uppermost allochthon). Lower structural units are characterized by quartzofeldspathic and amphibolitic gneisses which are pervasively intruded by amphibole-bearing anorthositic dykes. An Rb–Sr whole-rock isochron age of 433 ± 12 Ma has been determined for the felsic gneisses, and K–Ar dates of 420–430 Ma were reported for hornblendes from the anorthositic dykes (Andresen *et al.* 1985). Upper portions of the Tromsø Nappe Complex are represented by high-grade metasedimentary units which include eclogites. The Tromsø Nappe Complex appears to have been emplaced while maintained at high postmetamorphic temperatures because a thermal aureole developed within underlying phyllites of the Lyngen Nappe Complex along the ductile thrust contact. This decreases in intensity structurally downward from the thrust.

$^{40}Ar\!-\!^{39}Ar$ geochronology

Introduction. Detailed mapping and integrated geochronological studies have been completed within the western gneiss terrane and Caledonian nappes exposed in the southwestern portion of the island of Senja (Fig. 1) (Clark *et al.* 1985, Cumbest & Dallmeyer 1985, Williams *et al.* 1985). Here the western gneiss terrane consists of three lithotectonic units including an older (Karelian?) polydeformed gneissic terrane which is host to a series of plutonic rocks of early Svecokarelian age (about 1750 Ma). Both the gneisses and the intrusive suite record widespread ductile strains. Over extensive areas they are represented by blastomylonitic gneisses. Both deformed and undeformed portions of this terrane are cut by a younger series of plutonic rocks of late Svecokarelian age (about 1650 Ma). The structurally-overlying Senja Nappe is largely represented by penetratively mylonitic marble and garnet–mica schist with subordinate amphibolite. Textural characteristics suggest that high-grade metamorphic conditions were attained prior to and maintained during eastward Caledonian thrusting of the metasedimentary sequence. Blastomylonitic fabrics are developed in the basement terrane along the Senja Nappe thrust contact. These are locally overgrown by decussate porphyroblastic muscovite. A younger set of ductile shear zones has been mapped throughout the western gneiss terrane. The largest of these offsets the Senja Nappe contact and clearly developed after emplacement of the Caledonian allochthon. Porphyroblastic hornblende locally overgrows blastomylonitic layering within the younger ductile strain zones.

Results. Hornblende porphyroblasts overgrowing ductile strain zones within the western gneiss terrane and across the penetrative mylonitic layering in the Senja Nappe display variably discordant $^{40}Ar/^{39}Ar$ age spectra. This discordance is largely a result of incorporation of extraneous argon components, and most samples record well-defined plateau dates between 475 and 495 Ma. Low-temperature experimental gas fractions evolved from several samples suggest that minor diffusive argon loss may have occurred during a thermal overprint at about 425–430 Ma. Porphyroblastic muscovite within both the western gneiss terrane and the Senja Nappe records plateau dates of 380–390 Ma.

Interpretation. Oxygen isotopic studies within

several ductile strain zones developed in the western gneiss terrane exposed on Senja (Cumbest *et al.* 1983, Cumbest & Dallmeyer 1985) suggest that initial dynamic recrystallization occurred at about 500 °C. Because these temperatures are sufficient to reset intracrystalline argon systems within hornblende, the 475–495 Ma plateau dates recorded by hornblende porphyroblasts overgrowing strain zone fabrics are interpreted to date cooling following the ductile strain. This requires earlier emplacement of the predeformed and metamorphosed Senja Nappe, indicating a significant Finnmarkian tectonothermal record in the western gneiss terrane. Scandian temperatures in excess of those required to reset muscovite argon systems (about 350 °C) but below those required to totally reset hornblende argon systems were attained in the Lower Devonian throughout the Senja Nappe and western gneiss terrane. Hames & Sinha (1985) reported a 389±4 Ma whole-rock and internal-mineral Rb–Sr isochron for a relatively undeformed metadiorite representative of the younger plutonic sequence in the western gneiss terrane on Senja. This also indicates significant Scandian metamorphism. This regional heating was probably responsible for the textural annealing of the Finnmarkian ductile fabrics observed across southwestern portions of the island.

The Tromsø Nappe Complex appears to have been emplaced as a hot allochthon onto Lower Silurian sequences of the Lyngen Nappe Complex. The 420–435 Ma Rb–Sr whole-rock and K–Ar hornblende dates reported for the Tromsø Nappe Complex by Andresen *et al.* (1985) therefore probably date post-Scandian assembly and emplacement of the composite allochthon to higher structural levels on the Lyngen Nappe Complex. This must have occurred outboard of the previously imbricated Finnmarkian nappes which were subsequently overridden during the Late Silurian translation of pre-assembled Scandian allochthons into their final position on the Baltic margin. Therefore the 380–390 Ma Rb–Sr mineral and whole-rock ages and the $^{40}Ar/^{39}Ar$ muscovite ages from the Finnmarkian nappes on Senja probably date cooling associated with the subsequent uplift. The east–west diachronism is similar to that outlined previously for the Finnmark area.

The mapping and geochronology completed on southwestern Senja indicates that here the western gneiss terrane is allochthonous with respect to the Baltic Shield and probably represents a crystalline structural unit of the middle allochthon. Complex imbrication of predeformed and metamorphosed cover sequences (Senja Nappe) with the basement occurred prior to 475–495 Ma under maintenance of high-grade metamorphic conditions. Continued basement shortening was accommodated along ductile shear zones following emplacement of the Senja Nappe and prior to regional post-Finnmarkian cooling through about 500 °C (at about 475–495 Ma).

A generally similar thermal evolution appears to be appropriate for components of the western gneiss terrane exposed in the Lofoten–Vesterålen archipelago (Fig. 1). Biotite from the vicinity of Lekeness (Tull 1978), Hinnøy (Broch 1964, Tull 1978) and Langøy (Broch 1964) yield conventional K–Ar dates between 349 and 575 Ma. Hornblende from a ductile strain zone near Lekeness yields a $^{40}Ar/^{39}Ar$ plateau date of about 460 Ma (Tull 1978).

Bryhni *et al.* (1971) presented preliminary $^{40}Ar/^{39}Ar$ mineral-age data from the western gneiss terrane near Nordfjord in southwestern Norway (Fig. 1). The hornblende analysed displayed an internally-discordant age spectra in which initial low-temperature experimental ages were anomalously old (more than 2000 Ma). Apparent ages systematically decreased through intermediate-temperature fractions to define a high-temperature plateau of about 535 Ma. This type of discordancy is typical of experimental evolution of extraneous argon components at low temperatures, and suggests that a high-grade pre-Scandian thermal event may also be recorded in southern portions of the Norwegian Caledonides.

Central Scandinavian Caledonides

Nordland–Norrbotten

Introduction

Aspects of geological relations within the Nordland–Norrbotten area of the north-central Scandinavian Caledonides have been discussed by Stephens *et al.* (1985). Representatives of the lower, middle, upper and uppermost allochthons are encountered (Fig. 1). The central portion of the area is dominated by the composite Nasafjäll window developed along an antiformal culmination.

Much of western Norrbotten and eastern Nordland is underlain by generally flat-lying tectonic units corresponding to lower portions of the upper allochthon (Seve Nappes). Predominant lithologies include a variety of polydeformed psammitic schists and amphibolites together with local occurrences of retrogressed eclogites (An-dréasson et al. 1985). The metamorphic grade varies from lower to upper amphibolite facies. Units of the Seve Nappe Complex are in tectonic contact with generally lower-grade, polyde-formed rocks of the overlying Köli Nappe Complex which represent higher structural levels of the upper allochthon. The Köli Nappes are composite and consist of several tectonic units which include a variety of phyllite and micasch-ists with locally significant metaclastic sequences. The metamorphic grade varies from middle greenschist to lower amphibolite facies. The lowermost tectonic units of the Köli Nappes contain Late Ordovician–Early Silurian fossil-bearing sequences (Kulling 1972); however, the upper tectonic units are barren. Gee & Wilson (1974) reported an Rb–Sr whole-rock isochron crystallization age of 438 ± 6 Ma for the syntec-tonic Vilasund granite (Fig. 1) which intrudes the Storfjället Nappe (upper Köli sequences). This is similar to a 442 ± 30 Ma Rb–Sr whole-rock isochron date reported by Reymer (1979) for a metamorphic suite of the Storfjället Nappe collected at another locality (Fig. 1). Both suggest a significant pre-Scandian tectonothermal history for the upper Köli Nappes. This must have been followed by later (Scandian) imbrication with the fossil-bearing lower Köli sequences. Wilson (1981) presented Rb–Sr whole-rock isochron crystallization dates of 424 ± 11, 422 ± 8 and 418 ± 14 Ma for a series of post-D_1 and pre-D_2 granitic intrusions in the Sulitjelma Schist se-quence (Gasak Nappe) of the upper Köli Nappes (Fig. 1). These appear to have been intruded after thrust imbrication of Upper Ordovician se-quences and therefore attest to a pre-Scandian deformation record.

Western portions of Nordland are underlain by a variety of nappes of the uppermost allo-chthon. These are largely represented by polyde-formed middle to upper amphibolite facies gneisses, marbles and various hornblende-mica schists and amphibolite sequences. Claesson (1980) presented a composite Rb–Sr whole-rock isochron date of 447 ± 7 Ma for a suite of post-tectonic granitic dikes which intrude polyde-formed and previously metamorphosed high-grade rocks within the Rodingsfjället Nappe of the uppermost allochthon (Fig. 1). Comparable evidence for an early Caledonian tectonothermal event in the Beiarn Nappe of the uppermost allochthon has been reported by Tørudbakken & Brattli (1985).

$^{40}Ar/^{39}Ar$ geochronology

Seve Nappes of the upper allochthon. Retrogressed

eclogites and host polydeformed psammatic schists within the Seve Nappe Complex are exposed in the vicinity of Grapesvare, Norrbotten County (Fig. 1). Andréasson et al. (1985) suggest that the eclogite assemblages formed at temper-atures of 550–750 °C and pressures of about 15 kbar. These were variably retrogressed during formation of a regional foliation in the host metasedimentary rocks. Hornblendes from two retrograde selvages display internally concordant $^{40}Ar/^{39}Ar$ age spectra which yield identical plateau dates of 491 ± 8 Ma (Dallmeyer & Gee 1986). Phengitic muscovite from adjacent host Seve metasedimentary rocks record plateau dates of 436 ± 7 and 447 ± 7 Ma. These results have been interpreted to suggest that late Proterozoic rift-facies dolerite dikes intruding Baltoscandian miogeoclinal sequences were converted to eclo-gite, retrograded to amphibolite and cooled through 500 °C prior to 490 Ma. This was followed by a distinct Late Ordovician–Early Silurian thermal disturbance which reset muscov-ite intracrystalline argon systems. The muscovite ages are similar to Rb–Sr whole-rock isochron crystallization dates reported for syntectonic granites within the Köli Nappes and portions of the uppermost allochthon in this general region and may indicate a widespread tectonothermal record of this age.

Retrogressed eclogites also occur within the Seve metasedimentary sequences exposed near Kvarnbergsvattnet (Fig. 1: van Roermund 1985). Hornblende within retrogressive assemblages define $^{40}Ar/^{39}Ar$ plateau dates of about 490 Ma (Dallmeyer & Gee 1987), similar to those reported for the Grapesvare area. Hornblende and mus-covite within lower and middle Köli Nappe units yield markedly younger plateau dates (417–435 Ma). Locally within the Seve Nappes, horn-blende isotopic systems were totally rejuvenated by Scandian metamorphism and record plateau ages of 430–435 Ma.

Coastal windows. Hornblendes have been ana-lysed (Dallmeyer 1987b) from blastomylonitic Precambrian crystalline rocks exposed in the Sjona and Hogtuva windows along the Norwe-gian coast (Fig. 1). Samples record variably discordant release spectra, largely as a result of incorporation of extraneous argon components. However some spectra display well-defined pla-teau dates between 401 and 418 Ma. These are interpreted to date post-Scandian metamorphic cooling through about 500 °C, and indicate a post-Finnmarkian thermal evolution very differ-ent from that of the eclogite-bearing Seve Nappes to the east.

Trøndelag–Jämtland

Introduction

The geological setting of the Jämtland–Trøndelag area has been summarized by Gee *et al.* (1985). Exposures of lower portions of the upper allochthon are represented by the Seve Nappe Complex (Fig. 1) which consists of several tectonic units. The lowermost is largely represented by polydeformed psammitic schists and amphibolites. These record upper greenschist-facies to upper amphibolite-facies regional metamorphic assemblages. Complex textures indicate a polymetamorphic evolution. The middle unit is dominated by a polydeformed granulite-facies complex together with minor metabasic rocks (Åreskutan and Snasahögarna Nappes). The contact between this unit and underlying Seve metasedimentary rocks is tectonic and marked by development of a high-temperature mylonitic zone (Arnbom 1980, Sjöström 1983a, b). Recent geochronological work by Claesson (1981) indicates a middle Proterozoic history for at least a portion of the gneissic terrane within the Åreskutan Nappe. Rb–Sr and U–Pb zircon studies by Claesson in this area also suggest that the Seve rocks underwent high-grade Scandian metamorphism between about 415 and 390 Ma. Stepwise zircon dissolution experiments indicate the possibility of earlier Caledonian thermal events.

Upper portions of the upper allochthon are represented by the Köli Nappe Complex. Several distinct structural units have been defined along the Helags–Tännforsen synform (Beckholmen 1978, 1982, Sjöström 1983a, b). The lowest Köli tectonic unit (Duved Nappe) is separated from structurally underlying Seve Nappes by a major mylonite zone. The Duved Nappe consists of a variety of low-grade polydeformed metasedimentary and minor metavolcanic rocks. Although diagnostic fossils are lacking, the overall lithic character and stratigraphic succession is similar to that of fossil-bearing Upper Ordovician–Lower Silurian Köli sequences described farther north in Vasterbotten County (Zachrisson 1969). Overlying structural units in the Tännforsen Köli consist largely of polydeformed generally low-grade phyllite, calcareous mica schist and hornblende garbenschieffer. Several different nappe units have been mapped. Intervening tectonic contacts are marked by development of superposed ductile and brittle fabrics which suggest a polygenetic internal imbrication history. The Tännforsen Köli Nappes thin westward where they are tectonically overlain by the Trondheim Nappe Complex. Low-grade polydeformed calc-phyllites and calc-schists of the Tännforsen type

reappear in western Trøndelag near Levanger (Fig. 1). Rocks of the Trondheim Nappe Complex represent upper structural portions of the upper allochthon. Although the internal structure of the Nappe Complex has long been controversial, most workers agree that a generally northeast-trending predominantly metasedimentary unit (Gula Nappe) is bordered on the west and the east by metasedimentary and metavolcanic units of generally lower grade. The western sequences (Støren nappe) locally contain fossil-bearing rocks of Arenig–Ashgill age. The eastern succession is represented by the Meråker Nappe, with uppermost units containing graptolite-bearing Llandovery phyllites. Many units of the Gula, Støren and Meråker Nappes record polydeformational fabrics and locally complex metamorphic textures. Therefore, details of the tectonothermal evolution of the Trondheim Nappe Complex are uncertain. Clearly some of the metamorphism and deformation must be of Scandian age because fossil-bearing sequences of Lower Silurian age are affected. However, numerous internal tectonic contacts preclude assigning all the tectonothermal record to this orogenic event. Rb–Sr whole-rock and U–Pb zircon analyses of trondhjemite dikes cutting polydeformed and previously metamorphosed rocks of the Gula Nappe possibly suggest Ordovician crystallization ages (Klingspor & Gee 1981), indicating at least a local pre-Scandian tectonothermal record. Biotite from these dikes yield conventional K–Ar dates of about 400 Ma (Wilson *et al.* 1973), suggesting a prolonged and complex thermal evolution for the Gula Nappe. In addition, Wilson *et al.* (1973) reported conventional K–Ar dates for minerals from the Meråker Nappe. Hornblende dates range between 426 and 550 Ma, whereas muscovite and biotite ages range between 411 and 444 Ma. Because of the possible incorporation of extraneous argon components during Scandian metamorphism, unequivocal interpretation of these data is not possible.

$^{40}Ar/^{39}Ar$ geochronology

Results. Dallmeyer *et al.* (1985) presented $^{40}Ar/^{39}Ar$ results from initial phases of a comprehensive dating program in the Trøndelag–Jämtland area. Hornblende from various structural units of the Seve Nappe Complex exposed in the Åre synform (Fig. 1) record plateau dates of 455–458 Ma. Biotite from similar rocks yields plateau dates of 427–429 Ma. Biotite and muscovite from Seve Nappes exposed along the international border yield younger plateau dates of 408 and 415 Ma.

Hornblende from upper portions of the Köli

Nappe Complex exposed along the Tännforsen synform (Middagsfjället Nappe) yield variably-discordant age spectra as a result of widespread incorporation of extraneous argon components. Ages systematically decrease throughout most analyses to yield variably well-defined plateau ages between 475 and 510 Ma. Muscovite from these units record mutually concordant plateau dates between 409 and 425 Ma. Hornblende and biotite from a structurally lower portion of the Middagsfjället Nappe yield mutually similar plateau dates of 414 and 418 Ma. Biotites within a lower tectonic unit of the Tännforsen Köli (Gevsjön Nappe) yield plateau dates between 415 and 427 Ma.

Additional $^{40}Ar/^{39}Ar$ ages have been determined as a result of an ongoing research program in this area (Dallmeyer, unpublished). Hornblende from amphibolitic portions of the parautochthon and middle allochthon exposed in the Grong–Olden culmination and the Tømmerås window (Fig. 1) generally display very complex patterns of internal discordance which do not yield meaningful geological dates (largely a result of polyphase incorporation of extraneous argon components). Muscovite yields more consistent results with plateau dates ranging from 395 to 410 Ma. Results have also been obtained from samples of Tännforsen-type hornblende garbenschiefer collected within Köli Nappes exposed between the Tømmerås and Levanger windows. The hornblende concentrates display internally-discordant $^{40}Ar/^{39}Ar$ age spectra which suggest that a thermal event at about 425–435 Ma affected minor gas loss from intracrystalline argon systems which had initially cooled through approximately 500 °C about 470–480 Ma ago. In addition, a suite of hornblende samples has been examined along a traverse across the western coastal terrane of infolded middle allochthon and parautochthonous crystalline basement. These consistently record plateau ages between 394 Ma (westernmost samples) and 410 Ma (easternmost samples). Muscovites from the samples yield similar $^{40}Ar/^{39}Ar$ plateau ages.

Interpretation. Hornblende results from lower (Seve) and upper (Köli) portions of the upper allochthon suggest a complex polyphase pre-Scandian thermal history. The 455–458 Ma hornblende dates from the Seve Nappes clearly indicate a younger period of cooling through approximately 500 °C than the 475–510 Ma dates in the Köli Nappes. The thermal conditions of Caledonian metamorphism in both areas do not appear to have been greatly in excess of the approximately 500 °C needed for intracrystalline retention of argon in hornblende; therefore it is

unlikely that the difference in ages reflects diachronous cooling following a single tectonothermal event. It is more likely that separate pre-Scandian tectonothermal events are recorded. The effects of Scandian orogenesis were regionally of sufficient magnitude to reset all mica argon systems and locally modify or totally reset hornblende argon systems. There appears to have been a significant diachronism between post-Scandian metamorphic cooling in eastern portions of the area (427–429 Ma biotite dates from the Seve Nappes at Åre) and coastal areas (394–410 Ma hornblende and muscovite dates). This is consistent with the east–west younging trend in post-Scandian thermal decay outlined for more northerly portions of the orogen. In the Trøndelag–Jämtland area, post-Scandian cooling, although apparently diachronous, was everywhere relatively rapid because similar dates are recorded by minerals with widely different argon closure temperatures (e.g. hornblende and muscovite in the Tännforsen Köli and in the coastal section).

The $^{40}Ar/^{39}Ar$ plateau ages recorded by hornblende within lower portions of the upper allochthon exposed in the Tännforsen synform reflect significant orogenic activity during and/or just prior to 475–510 Ma. A 475–510 Ma range corresponds to an Early Ordovician interval on most time-scale calibrations, perhaps extending into the latest Cambrian. In contrast, lower tectonic units of the Tännforsen Köli (Duved Nappe) contain metasedimentary successions which appear to be direct lithostratigraphic correlatives with Ashgill–Llandovery Köli sequences exposed at similar tectonic levels elsewhere in the Scandinavian Caledonides. These Tännforsen sequences must therefore have been tectonically imbricated with the older metamorphic terrane during a late- to post-Llandovery phase of assembly of the Köli Nappe Complex. All Köli Nappes exposed in the Tännforsen synform record a 410–425 Ma overprint, although it is of variable grade. According to most time-scale calibrations this interval corresponds to the Middle to Late Silurian (Wenlock–Pridoli) and suggests that this thermal event was probably associated with late phases of tectonic imbrication of the Köli Nappe Complex. This is consistent with development of mylonitic zones along internal thrust contacts within the Köli Nappe Complex which indicate that at least some components of thrust translation occurred under elevated temperatures. However, tectonic movement appears to have outlasted maintenance of elevated metamorphic conditions because most internal thrust contacts display evidence of later brittle reactivation (Beckholmen

1982). This is consistent with the rapid Late Silurian post-metamorphic cooling suggested by the $^{40}Ar/^{39}Ar$ mineral dates and probably reflects final phases of assembly of the Köli Nappe Complex during its translation to higher structural levels within the succession of Caledonian allochthons.

The tectonothermal evolution of the Seve Nappe Complex in the Trøndelag–Jämtland area also appears to have been polyphase. High-grade early Caledonian metamorphic crystallization must have occurred prior to cooling through hornblende retention temperatures between 455 and 460 Ma. Imbrication of basement (granulite terrane) and cover components of the Seve Nappe Complex must have occurred earlier because Arnbom (1980) provided evidence that high temperatures (above 550 °C) were maintained during development of mylonitic rocks along intervening tectonic contacts. These results combine to suggest that cooling through about 500 °C (appropriate for intracrystalline retention of argon in hornblende) probably occurred when the contrasting metamorphic terranes were translated to higher crustal levels during the initial tectonic assembly of the basement and cover components of the Seve Nappe Complex. Both nappe units appear to have experienced a similar thermal evolution following their initial imbrication.

Regional tectonothermal evolution

Introduction

A polyphase tectonothermal record has been documented in all the areas previously discussed. Both Finnmarkian and Scandian orogenesis must in some way have been related to consumption of Iapetus oceanic lithosphere and attendant destruction of the Baltoscandian miogeocline. Sequences within the autochthon and the lower and middle allochthons contain no significant igneous components, suggesting that any pre-Scandian subduction along the Baltoscandian continental margin was likely directed westward. This is consistent with development of various volcanic/volcaniclastic sequences within upper portions of the upper allochthon (Zachrisson 1969, Stephens 1980, Stephens & Gee 1985). Rb–Sr whole-rock isochron and U–Pb zircon crystallization ages of 480–490 Ma have been reported by Claesson *et al.* (1983) for some of these volcanic units, suggesting that the outboard arc was active during the Early Ordovician. It seems likely therefore that the pre-Scandian orogenesis recorded within the Baltoscandian succession developed in response to westward-dipping subduction. Dallmeyer & Gee (1986) presented the following tectonic model to explain the polyphase tectonothermal evolution of the Baltoscandian margin (Fig. 2).

Late Cambrian–Early Ordovician

The 490 Ma $^{40}Ar/^{39}Ar$ ages recorded by retrograde hornblende within eclogite alteration assemblages in lower portions of the upper allochthon date uplift and associated cooling following a high-pressure metamorphic event. These imply that the progressive development of an accretionary prism along outer portions of the Baltoscandian margin was under way in the Early Ordovician (Fig. 2, B). An associated outboard volcanic arc was constructed (Virisen terrane of Stephens & Gee 1985). Host sedimentary sequences within distal portions of the Baltoscandian miogeocline together with rift-facies dolerite dikes had previously been carried to significant crustal depths along the subduction zone. Eclogite assemblages had formed, undergone variable retrogression and been uplifted through hornblende argon retention temperatures by the Arenig. Initial high-temperature ductile imbrication of crystalline Baltica basement and late Proterozoic cover was at least locally accomplished, as is shown by the pre-475–500 Ma ductile imbrication of crystalline Precambrian basement and cover sequences in the middle allochthon (both in western Troms and in southern Jämtland) and the Seve Nappes of the upper allochthon (Åreskutan Nappe). Hornblende within polydeformed variably metamorphosed upper portions of the upper allochthon (Köli Nappes) records $^{40}Ar/^{39}Ar$ plateau dates between 475 and 510 Ma. The volcaniclastic protoliths probably developed in association with construction of the Late Cambrian arc on the western side of the subduction complex. These were probably deformed and metamorphosed as they were imbricated with Baltoscandian sequences during evolution of the accretionary prism.

Middle Ordovician

Continued development of the accretionary prism appears to have led to eastward-younging diachronous metamorphism (Fig. 2, C). As a result, cooling during subsequent uplift was variable, and is reflected by the wide range of pre-Scandian $^{40}Ar/^{39}Ar$ hornblende plateau dates reported for the Seve Nappes (455–490 Ma). Middle Ordovician uplift of the accretionary prism was probably the erosional source for both westerly-derived

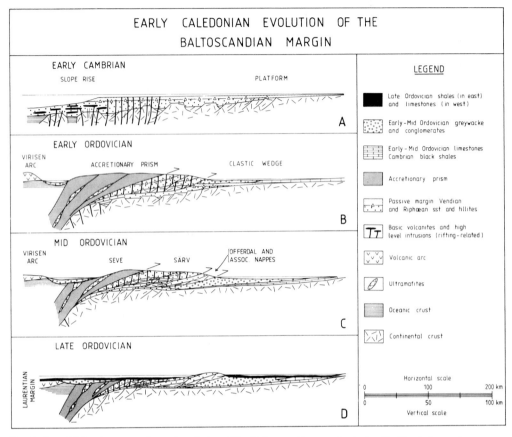

FIG. 2. A model for the tectonothermal evolution of the Baltoscandian margin during the Cambrian and Ordovician (see text for discussion). (From Dallmeyer 1984, Dallmeyer & Gee 1986.)

turbidites which were deposited along the western margin of the Baltoscandian platform and turbidites and fanglomerates which accumulated within the outboard arc terrane.

Scandian history

Almost complete closure of the Iapetus Ocean appears to have been accomplished by the Late Ordovician when eugeoclinal terranes which had developed at various locations in the Iapetus oceanic tract were juxtaposed with volcanic-arc sequences of the Virisen terrane. After relative tectonic quiescence throughout the Late Ordovician and Early Silurian, Scandian orogenesis commenced in the Late Llandovery with thrusting of eugeoclinal sequences onto the extensively eroded island-arc terrane. These were subsequently imbricated and folded with the Baltoscandian accretionary prism. The resultant composite allochthon was then thrust eastward

over the Ordovician clastic wedge and onto Silurian sedimentary successions. Sequential transport of the nappe complex onto the Baltoscandian platform appears to have occurred throughout the Middle and Late Silurian with significant east–west diachronism in post-metamorphic cooling. In more southerly areas this transport appears to have continued into the Early Devonian.

Emplacement of composite Scandian allochthons onto the crystalline middle Proterozoic basement terrane of western Scandinavia resulted in its depression to depths appropriate for formation of eclogite assemblages. These record U–Pb zircon and Sm–Nd mineral-whole-rock crystallization ages of about 425 Ma (Krogh et al. 1974, Griffin & Brueckner 1980). Scandian ^{40}Ar/^{39}Ar mineral ages within easternmost exposures of the Seve Nappes are also about 425–430 Ma. These are interpreted to date the initial translation to higher crustal levels across imbricated

Finnmarkian nappe complexes which had previously been emplaced onto the Baltoscandian margin. Because similar dates are recorded by radiometric systems with very different closure characteristics, relatively rapid cooling is suggested to have accompanied the Scandian thrusting. Scandian ^{40}Ar/^{39}Ar mineral dates range from about 410 Ma in central portions of the orogen to about 385 Ma in western portions. These probably date rapid cooling during uplift

which resulted from crustal rebound following the eastward translation of overriding allochthons.

ACKNOWLEDGMENTS: Various portions of the ^{40}Ar/^{39}Ar Scandinavian dating program have been supported by grants from the U.S. National Science Foundation (EAR-8407027), the North Atlantic Treaty Organization, the Norwegian Marshall Fund, and the University of Tromsø.

References

ANDERSON, T. B. 1981. The structure of the Magerøy Nappe, Finnmark, North Norway. *Norsk Geologiske Undersøkelse*, **363**, 1–23.

——, AUSTRHEIM, H., STURT, B. A., PEDERSEN, S. & KJAERSRUD, K. 1982. Rb–Sr whole-rock ages from Magerøy, north Norwegian Caledonides. *Norsk Geologisk Tidsskrift*, **62**, 79–85.

ANDRÉASSON, P.-G., GEE, D. G. & SUKOTJO, S. 1985. Seve eclogites in the Norrbotten Caledonides, Sweden. *In:* GEE, D. G. & STURT, B. A. (eds) *The Caledonide Orogen—Scandinavia and Related Areas,* pp. 887–901, Wiley, Chichester.

ANDRESEN, A., FARETH, E., BERGH, S., KRISTENSEN, S. E. & KROGH, E. 1985. Review of Caledonian lithotectonic units in Troms, north Norway. *In:* GEE, D. G. & STURT, B. A. (eds) *The Caledonide Orogen—Scandinavia and Related Areas,* pp. 596–678, Wiley, Chichester.

ARNBOM, J. O. 1980. Metamorphism of the Seve rocks on Åreskutan, southern Swedish Caledonides. *Geologiska Föreningen i Stockholm Förhandlingar,* **102**, 359–72.

BECKHOLMEN, M. 1978. Geology of the Nordhallen–Duved–Greningen area in Jämtland, central Swedish Caledonides. *Geologiska Föreningen i Stockholm Förhandlingar,* **100**, 335–47.

—— 1982. Mylonites and pseudotachylites associated with thrusting of the Köli Nappes, Tännforsfaltet, central Swedish Caledonides. *Geologiska Föreningen i Stockholm Förhandlingar,* **104**, 23–32.

BROCH, O. A. 1964. Age determination of Norwegian minerals up to March 1964. *Norsk Geologiske Undersøkelse,* **228**, 84–113.

BRYHNI, I., FITCH, F. J. & MILLER, J. A. 1971. ^{40}Ar/^{39}Ar dates from recycled Precambrian rocks in the gneiss region of the Norwegian Caledonides. *Norsk Geologisk Tidsskrift,* **51**, 391–406.

CLAESSON, S. 1980. Pre-Silurian orogenic deformation in the north-central Scandinavian Caledonides. *Geologiska Föreningen i Stockholm Förhandlingar,* **101**, 353–6.

—— 1981. Caledonian metamorphism of Proterozoic Seve rocks on Mt. Åreskutan, southern Swedish Caledonides. *Geologiska Föreningen i Stockholm Förhandlingar,* **103**, 291–304.

——, KLINGSPOR, I. & STEPHENS, M. B. 1983. U–Pb and Rb–Sr isotopic data on an Ordovician volcanic/subvolcanic complex from the Tjopasi Group, Köli Nappes, Swedish Caledonides. *Geologiska Föreningen i Stockholm Förhandlingar,* **105**, 9–15.

CLARK, A. H., DALLMEYER, R. D. & ANDRESEN, A. 1985. Basement/cover relations along the eastern margin of the Western Gneiss Terrane, Senja, Troms, Norway. *Geological Society of America, Abstracts with Programs,* **17**(1), 11.

CUMBEST, R. J. & DALLMEYER, R. D. 1985. Polyphase Caledonian tectonothermal evolution of the Western Gneiss Terrane, Senja, Troms, Norway. *Geological Society of America, Abstracts with Programs,* **17**(1), 14.

——, —— & SOLOMON, C. 1983. Age and origin of ductile fabrics in the Western Gneiss Terrane of the Norwegian Caledonides (Troms). *Geological Society of America, Abstracts with Programs,* **15**(6), 322.

DALLMEYER, R. D. 1987a (in press) Polyorogenic ^{40}Ar/^{39}Ar mineral age record within the Kalak Nappe Complex, northern Scandinavian Caledonides. *Journal of the Geological Society of London.*

—— 1987b (in press) ^{40}Ar/^{39}Ar mineral ages from retrogressed basement within the Sjona and Hogtuva windows, northwestern Norwegian Caledonides. *Norsk Geologisk Tidsskrift.*

—— & REUTER, A. 1987a (in press) ^{40}Ar/^{39}Ar dating of cleavage formation in diagenetic-lower anchizone autochthonous sequences in eastern Finnmark, northern Scandinavian Caledonides. *Isotope Geology.*

—— & —— 1987b (in press) ^{40}Ar/^{39}Ar dating of cleavage formation in the Gaissa and Laksefjorden Nappes, northernmost Scandinavian Caledonides, Finnmark, Norway. *Geological Society of American Bulletin.*

——, MITCHELL, J. G., PHARAOH, T. C., REUTER, A. & ANDRESEN, A. 1987 (in press) K-Ar and ^{40}Ar/^{39}Ar whole-rock ages of slate/phyllite from autochthonous-parautochthonous sequences in the Komagfjord and Alta-Kvaenangen tectonic windows, northern Scandinavian Caledonides: Evaluating

the extent and timing of Caledonian tectonothermal activity. *Geological Society of America Bulletin.*

—— & GEE, D. G. 1987 (in press) Polyorogenic ^{40}Ar/
^{39}Ar mineral age record in the Seve and Köli
Nappes of the Gäddede Area, northwestern Jämtland, central Scandinavian Caledonides. *Journal
of Geology.*

—— & GEE, D. G. 1986. Polyphase Caledonian
orogenesis within the Baltoscandian Miogeocline:
evidence from ^{40}Ar/^{39}Ar mineral dates from
retrogressed eclogites. *Geological Society of America
Bulletin,* **97**, 26–34.

——, —— & BECKHOLMEN, N. 1985. ^{40}Ar/^{39}Ar mineral
age record of early Caledonian tectonothermal
activity in the Baltoscandian Miogeocline. *American Journal of Science,* **285**, 532–68.

DYRELIUS, D., GEE, D. G., GORBATSCHEV, R., RAM-
BERG, H. & ZACHRISSION, E. 1980. A profile
through the central Scandinavian Caledonides.
Tectonophysics, **69**, 247–84.

FURNES, H., RYAN, P. D., GRENNE, T., ROBERTS, D.,
STRURT, B. A. & PRESTUILIC, T. 1985. Geological
and chemical classification of the opholite fragments in the Scandinavian Caledonides. *In:* GEE,
D. G. & STURT, B. A. (eds) *The Caledonide
Orogen—Scandinavia and Related Areas,* pp. 657–
670, Wiley, Chichester.

GALE, N. H., BECHINSALE, R. D. & WADGE, A. J. 1980.
Discussion of a paper by McKerrow, Lambert and
Chamberlain on the Ordovician, Silurian, and
Devonian time scales. *Earth and Planetary Science
Letters,* **51**, 9–17.

GEE, D. G. 1975a. A geotraverse through the Scandinavian Caledonides–Östersund to Trondheim.
*Sveriges Geologiska Undersökning, Series C, No.
717,* 66 pp.

—— 1975b. A tectonic model for the central part of the
Scandinavian Caledonides. *American Journal of
Science,* **275A**, 468–515.

—— & ROBERTS, D. 1983. Timing of deformation in
the Scandinavian Caledonides. *In:* SCHENK, P. E.
(ed.) *Regional Trends in the Geology of the Appalachian–Caledonian–Hercynian–Mauritanide Orogen,*
pp. 279–92, Reidel, Dordrecht.

—— & STURT, B. A. 1985. *The Caledonide Orogen—
Scandinavia and Related Areas,* Wiley, Chichester.

—— & WILSON, M. R. 1974. The age of orogenic
deformation in the Swedish Caledonides. *American
Journal of Science,* **274**, 1–9.

——, GORBATSCHEV, R. & RAMBERG, H. 1984. The
Scandinavian Caledonides. *In:* RAST, N. & DE-
LANY, F. (eds) *Profiles of Orogenic Belts. American
Geophysical Union Geodynamics Series,* Vol. 10, pp.
45–51.

——, GUEZOU, J. C., ROBERTS, D. & WOLFF, F. C.
1985. The central-southern part of the Scandinavian Caledonides. *In:* GEE, D. G. & STURT, B. A.
(eds) *The Caledonide Orogen—Scandinavia and
Related Areas,* pp. 109–34, Wiley, Chichester.

GRIFFIN, W. L. & BRUECKNER, H. K. 1980. Caledonian
Sm–Nd ages and a crustal origin for Norwegian
eclogites. *Nature, London,* **285**, 319–21.

—— & TAYLOR, P. N. 1978. Geology and age relations
on Vaeroy, Lofoten, north Norway. *Norges Geologiske Undersøkelse,* **338**, 71–82.

HAMES, W. E. & SINHA, A. 1985. Rb–Sr geochronology
of ductile strain zones in the Western Gneiss
Terrane, Senja, Troms, Norway. *Geological Society
of America, Abstracts with Programs,* **17**(2), 23.

HARLAND, W. B. & GAYER, R. A. 1972. The Arctic
Caledonides and earlier oceans. *Geological Magazine,* **109**, 289–314.

——, COX, A. V., LLEWELLYN, P. G., PICTON, C. A.
G., SMITH, A. G. & WALTERS, R. 1982. *A Geological
Time-scale,* Cambridge University Press, Cam-
bridge, 131 pp.

HARRISON, T. M. 1981. Diffusion of ^{40}Ar in hornblende.
Contributions to Mineralogy and Petrology, **78**, 324–
31.

JÄGER, E. 1979. Introduction to geochronology. *In:*
JÄGER, E. & HUNZIKER, J. C. (eds) *Lectures in
Isotope Geology,* pp. 1–12, Springer-Verlag, Berlin.

KLINGSPOR, I. & GEE, D. G. 1981. Isotopic age-
determination studies of the Trøndelag trondhjemites. *Terra Cognita,* **1**, 55.

KROGH, T. E., MYSEN, B. O. & DAVIES, G. L. 1974. A
Palaeozoic age for the primary minerals of a
Norwegian eclogite. *Annual Report of the Geophysical Laboratory, Carnegie Institute, Washington,* **73**,
575–6.

KULLING, O. 1972. The Swedish Caledonides. *In:*
STRAND, T. & KULLING, O. (eds) *The Scandinavian
Caledonides,* pp. 147–285, Wiley-Interscience,
New York.

MCKERROW, W. S., LAMBERT, R. ST. J. & CHAMBER-
LAIN, V. E. 1980. The Ordovician Silurian and
Devonian time scales. *Earth and Planetary Science
Letters,* **51**, 1–8.

OLAUSSEN, S. 1977. Palaeozoic fossils from Troms,
Norway. *Norsk Geologiske Tidsskrift,* **56**, 457–9.

PALMER, A. R. 1983. The decade of North American
geology 1983 geologic time scale. *Geology,* **11**, 503–
4.

PHARAOH, T. C., MACINTYRE, R. M. & RAMSAY, D. M.
1982. K–Ar age determinations on the Raipas
suite in the Komagfjord window, northern Norway. *Norsk Geologisk Tidsskrift,* **62**, 51–7.

PRINGLE, I. R. 1973. Rb–Sr age determinations on
shales associated with the Varanger Ice Age.
Geological Magazine, **109**, 465–72.

RAMSAY, D. M., STURT, B. A., ZWAAN, K. B. &
ROBERTS, D. 1985. Caledonides of northern Nor-
way. *In:* GEE, D. G. & STURT, B. A. (eds) *The
Caledonide Orogen—Scandinavia and Related
Areas,* pp. 163–84, Wiley, Chichester.

REYMER, A. P. S. 1979. Investigations into the metamorphic nappes of the central Scandinavian
Caledonides on the basis of Rb–Sr and K–Ar age
determinations. *Thesis,* University of Leiden, 123
pp.

VAN ROERMUND, H. L. M. 1985. Eclogites of the Seve
Nappe, central Scandinavian Caledonides. *In:*
GEE, D. G. & STURT, B. A. (eds) *The Caledonide
Orogen—Scandinavia and Related Areas,* pp. 873–
86, Wiley, Chichester.

SJÖSTRÖM, H. 1983a. The Seve–Köli nappe complex of the Handøl–Storlien–Essandsjoen area, Scandinavian Caledonides. *Geologiska Föreningens i Stockholm Föhandlingar*, **105**, 1–24.

—— 1983b. Structure and metamorphism of the Seve–Köli nappe complex in the Handøl–Storlien area, Scandinavian Caledonides. *Thesis*, University of Uppsala, 17 pp.

STEIGER, R. H. & JÄGER, E. 1977. Subcommission on geochronology convention on the use of decay constants in geo- and cosmochronology. *Earth and Planetary Science Letters*, **36**, 359–62.

STEPHENS, M. B. 1980. Occurrence, nature, and tectonic significance of volcanic and high-level intrusive rocks within the Swedish Caledonides. *In:* WONES, D. R. (ed.) *The Caledonides in the USA: Proceedings of the International Geological Program—Caledonide Orogen Project 27, Blacksburg, VA.* Department of Geological Sciences, Virginia Polytechnic Institute and State University, Memoir No. 2, pp. 289–98.

—— & GEE, D. G. 1985. A tectonic model for the evolution of the eugeoclinal terranes in the central Scandinavian Caledonides. *In:* GEE, D. G. & STURT, B. A. (eds) *The Caledonide Orogen—Scandinavia and Related Areas*, pp. 953–78, Wiley, Chichester.

——, GUSTAVSON, M., RAMBERG, I. B. & ZACHRISSON, E. 1985. The Caledonides of central-north Scandinavia—a tectonostratigraphic overview. *In:* GEE, D. G. & STURT, B. A. (eds) *The Caledonide Orogen—Scandinavia and Related Areas*, pp. 135–62, Wiley, Chichester.

STURT, B. A., MILLER, J. A. & FITCH, F. J. 1967. The age of alkaline rocks from west Finnmark, northern Norway, and the timing of orgenic deformation and metamorphism. *Norsk Geologische Tidsskrift*, **47**, 255–73.

——, PRINGLE, I. R. & ROBERTS, D. 1975. Caledonian nappe sequence of Finnmark, northern Norway, and the timing of orogenic deformation and metamorphism. *Geological Society of America Bulletin*, **86**, 710–18.

TØRUDBAKKEN, B. O. & BRATTLI, B. 1985. Ages of metamorphic and deformational events in the Beiarn nappe Complex, Nordland, Norway. *Norges Geologiske Undersøkelse*, **399**, 27–39.

TULL, J. F. 1978. The geology and structure of Vestvågøy, Lofoten, north Norway. *Norges Geologiske Undersøkelse*, **333**, 59.

WILLIAMS, T., CLARK, A. H., DALLMEYER, R. D. & ANDRESEN, A. 1985. Litotectonic character of the western gneiss terrane, Senja, Troms, Norway. *Geological Society of America, Abstracts with Programs*, **17**(1), 70.

WILSON, J. R. 1981. Geochronological results from Sultijelma, Norway: Abstract, Uppsala Caledonide Symposium, *Terra Cognita*, **1**, 1.

WILSON, M. R., ROBERTS, D. & WOLFF, F. C. 1973. Age determinations from the Trondheim region of the Caledonides, Norway: A preliminary report. *Norges Geologiske Undersøkelse*, **288**, 53–63.

ZACHRISSON, E. 1969. Caledonian geology of northern Jamtland—southern Vasterbotten. *Sveriges Geologiska Undersökning, Series C, No. 644*, 33 pp.

R. D. DALLMEYER, Department of Geology, University of Georgia, Athens, GA 30602, USA.

A brief review of early Ordovician to Devonian plutonism in the N American Caledonides

David R. Wones & A. K. Sinha*

SUMMARY: The distribution of mafic and felsic plutonic rocks has been used to constrain tectonic and thermal events in portions of the N American Caledonides. In the central and southern Appalachians studies of plutonic rocks identify an early island-arc environment followed by an episode of melting during over-thrusting. Devonian plutonism can be associated with both decompressional melting and rifting. The northern Appalachians also show evidence of early island-arc activity followed by collision of the N American plate with a collection of oceanic arcs and continental fragments. Devonian plutons reflect a more static environment (rift?) where incremental melting of a protolith provides the observed variations in the composition of the magmas.

The distribution and age of plutonic rocks can provide information about thermal events in the geological past. Their mineralogy and composition also provide clues to the nature of the deep crust and mantle beneath a particular piece of the Earth's crust during past events. Although volcanic rocks provide a more direct comparison with contemporary tectonic settings, they are susceptible to erosion, thus leaving the plutonic rocks as the only record of past igneous activity and the thermal and material sources of ancient magmas.

Placing plutonic rocks of the Appalachian Caledonides into their appropriate palaeogeographic and palaeotectonic settings is difficult because of the fault-bounded nature of many of the component blocks of the accreted mountain belt (Williams *et al.* 1972, Hatcher *et al.* 1980, Andrew *et al.* 1983). Plutonic rocks have also been used to make correlations across strike from one block to another (King 1980, Rast 1980, Robinson & Hall 1980) and to establish times of accretion (Zartman & Sinha 1980).

The age of a pluton can be constrained by (1) the age of the country rocks, (2) the age of rocks that intrude or overlie the pluton or (3) radiometric age determination. Fossil evidence is absent over large regions of the N American Caledonides, so that radiometric methods remain the only method for establishing a reliable geological age.

Gross correlations between plutonic events based simply on radiometric methods have been used to define the Avalon terrane, although a wide range in age exists for such rocks within that terrane. Detailed petrographic and chemical studies have shown that a variety of processes

*The second author revised the manuscript after the tragic death of David Wones. Newer models for the tectonic evolution for the central and southern Appalachians are by Sinha. All other conclusions and suggestions are credited to Wones.

may be contemporary and that a satisfactory assignment of plutonic rocks to an age, a terrane and a tectonic environment remains to be made for much of eastern N America.

Ordovician plutonism

There are very few geologically reliable radiometric ages in the central and southern Appalachians (Alabama to Delaware). However, even with the limited data it is possible to separate two distinct plutonic cycles. Early Ordovician tonalitic to granodioritic bodies (Elkahatchee, Leatherwood, Melrose, Columbia, Occoquan, Georgetown, Port Deposit and Arden) have been interpreted as having formed in a continental island-arc environment (Fig. 1). Associated in time with these plutonic rocks are remnants of a weakly-bimodal volcanic suite (James Run Formation and its equivalents) preserved only in the central Appalachians (Sinha *et al.* 1980, Pavlides 1981). The Wilmington Complex in Delaware and Pennsylvania is made up of plutonic rocks intruded into a high-grade metamorphic terrane (Foland & Muessig 1978) that may be equivalent to the James Run Formation. Although this trend of volcanic and plutonic rocks is not contiguous, it is probable that they are associated with the N American continental margin subduction-related magmatism (Pavlides 1981, Sinha & Guy, in press).

Plutons of middle Ordovician age also extend from Maryland to Alabama but lie in two distinct belts. Some of these rocks coincide both spatially and temporally with a regional metamorphism of Ordovician age. In Alabama, Deininger (1975), Russell (1978) and Size & Dean (1982) have demonstrated that these plutons are strongly peraluminous and are often intimately associated

From HARRIS, A. L. & FETTES, D. J. (eds), 1988, *The Caledonian–Appalachian Orogen*, Geological Society Special Publication No. 38, pp. 381–388.

FIG. 1. Geological map of the central and southern Appalachians showing the distribution of selected plutons of Ordovician and Devonian ages. Plutons encircled by a broken line are interpreted to be Devonian in age as no reliable radiometric ages are available.

with the intruded country rocks. They are not similar to the hornblende-bearing granodiorites and tonalites of the circum-Pacific Mesozoic batholiths. They appear to be products of anatexis of volcanically-derived greywackes and lie within the Blue Ridge Province. Further E, Ordovician plutons are found in the Charlotte belt, but it is not clear whether they are spatially associated with magmatism or metamorphism on the N American plate.

Although mafic plutons are common in the central and southern Appalachians, very few have been studied in detail. One such body, the Baltimore mafic complex, occurs in Maryland and has yielded an Nd–Sm age of 480 Ma (Shaw & Wasserburg 1984). Although this complex was once considered to be a true oceanic ophiolite, more recent petrological and isotopic studies show evidence of extensive crustal contamination (Hanan 1980, Shaw & Wasserburg 1984) leading to the interpretation that it formed in a back-arc ensialic environment (Sinha *et al.* 1985).

Between Pennsylvania and southern New York State there is no record of Ordovician plutonism, except for a small intrusive complex at Beamerville in New Jersey.

The Cortlandt complex of southeastern New York State is a mafic intrusive that has had a complex magmatic history (Bender *et al.* 1984). This oval-shaped alkaline gabbroic complex is more characteristic of a cratonic setting than of a convergent plate margin.

A group of small plutons extends from southwestern Connecticut N into Massachusetts just E of the Berkshire Highlands. These rocks range from diorites and granodiorites to granites. They are small bodies and little is known about them. Because of Taconic thrusting, the position of this group of intrusives relative to the Ordovician N American continental shelf is unknown.

Plutons of Ordovician age which occur along the Bronson Hill anticlinorium are the remnants of an intra-oceanic arc that acquires a continental

aspect to the N (Leo 1980). This group of plutons is made up of tonalites, granodiorites and, in the N, monzogranites (Fig. 2). The plutons make up a coherent group from central Connecticut through Massachusetts and New Hampshire to E central Maine. Billings (1956) originally assigned only the Highlandcroft pluton to this series, while the remainder were termed Oliverian of early Devonian age. Naylor (1969) found that the latter group also yielded Ordovician radiometric ages and lay unconformably beneath the Silurian Clough Formation. In northwestern Maine the chain of plutons bifurcates, with the western trend culminating in the Attean pluton (monzogranite) and the eastern trend in the Rockabema granodiorite and the Howe Brook pluton (also granodiorite). An analogy with the Kermadec–New Zealand system, where an oceanic–oceanic arc becomes an oceanic–continental arc, does not seem out of place for this group of plutons.

The plutons of the Bronson Hill anticlinorium were deformed by the Taconic orogeny. In the Pliny complex Czamanske *et al.* (1977) demonstrated that the Pliny syenite intruded the deformed volcanic rocks associated with the Ordovician plutons. Foland & Loiselle (1981) established an age of 441 Ma for the Pliny syenite which defines the minimum age for the Taconic orogeny.

The Nashoba terrane in eastern Massachusetts contains a peraluminous granitic gneiss called the Andover granite (Zen 1983). This pluton is intruded by the Silurian Sharpners Pond tonalite and by younger, possibly Devonian, aplites and pegmatites. Previous efforts at geochronology did not distinguish between the two muscovite-bearing granitoids, so that the ages are not well determined. Zartman & Naylor (1984) suggested that an Ordovician age is likely for the older material. Wones (1984) determined that the Casco Bay terrane in S central Maine contains intrusive rocks that are similar to the sequence

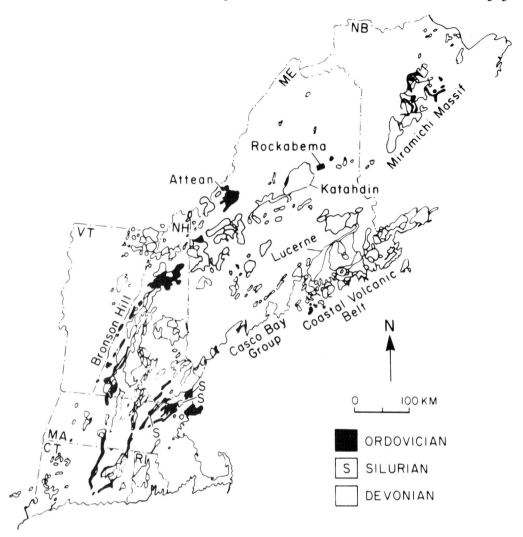

FIG. 2. Map of the northern Appalachians showing the distribution of igneous rocks.

found in the Nashoba zone of Massachusetts. This correlation has not been proved.

The Nashoba zone is bounded on the N by the Merrimack Group which is thought to be correlative with rocks of the central Maine slate belt (Osberg *et al*. 1984) and of Silurian age. However, the Kittery Formation is intruded by the Newburyport complex, part of which has been dated by Zartman & Naylor (1984) as Ordovician. Thus the Merrimack Group may be part of the Nashoba zone and the Casco Bay Group, rather than being correlated with the rocks of the Maine slate belt.

The Miramichi massif (Fyffe *et al*. 1981) contains a complex suite of Ordovician and Devonian plutons and may also be correlative

with the Casco Bay Group and the Nashoba Group. The Miramichi massif contains volcanic and plutonic rocks; the latter have well-defined intrusive contacts and are unlike the migmatitic fabrics that are characteristic of the Nashoba and Casco Bay terranes. Osberg (1978) and Ludman (1981) have previously suggested that these terranes might be correlated.

Newfoundland contains several plutonic suites of Ordovician age that are tonalitic to granodioritic in composition and are consistent with an origin in an intra-oceanic arc. In the Dunnage zone, these units occur in allochthonous blocks (Malpas 1977) and are excellent evidence for the accretion of the island arc onto eastern N America during the Taconic orogeny (Williams *et al*. 1972).

The most appropriate modern analogue of the N American (Laurentian) plate during the Ordovician is probably the Indo-Australian plate in the southwestern Pacific where a continental crustal mass is colliding with a collection of oceanic arcs and continental fragments. Hamilton (1981) has made an effective case that the Australian plate is a modern analogue of the northern Appalachians.

The most difficult problem from a plutonic (or magmatic) point of view is the lack of a continental arc made up of andesitic volcanic rocks, although tonalitic to granodioritic plutons along the continental margin of Ordovician N America have been reported in the central and southern Appalachians. The lack of more widespread continental margin igneous rocks could be because (1) the boundary between the craton and oceanic crust was not the plate boundary, (2) the boundary between the craton and oceanic crust was a system of transform faults or (3) the convergent boundary was marked by a volcanic arc that has been successfully concealed by the convergent tectonics of the Acadian and Alleghanian orogenies.

In the Dedham–Milford terrane of eastern Massachusetts and Rhode Island alkaline to peralkaline granitic plutons of middle Devonian to Ordovician ages have been found (Zartman 1977). Associated with these plutons are alkaline gabbros that are somewhat older (Zartman & Naylor 1984). Hermes *et al.* (1978) demonstrated that similar rocks lie E of Massachusetts within the Gulf of Maine. These plutons are indicative of a stable cratonic environment during the Ordovician, and indicate that the craton had been dehydrated prior to this heating event (Anderson 1983, Wones 1984).

Silurian plutonism

The Silurian period is not represented by many N American Caledonian plutons. The period lasted for 35 Ma, so that a 10% error in rocks 400 Ma old will eclipse that period. Even with this in mind, it is difficult to assign many plutons to a Silurian age. Those that do exist are found mainly in the easternmost portions of the orogen of the northern Appalachians and perhaps in the central Appalachians. In the central Appalachians, two-mica plutons like Woodstock, Ellicott City and Guilford could be earliest Silurian or late Ordovician (Sinha *et al.* 1980, 1985). The Ellicott City pluton may contain magmatic epidote, suggesting formation at great depths (about 8 kbar) (Zen & Hammarstrom 1984), and is probably a result of melting subsequent to over-

thrusting during the middle Ordovician (Sinha *et al.* 1985).

In the Nashoba zone of Massachusetts, the Sharpners Pond tonalite corresponds well to the rocks associated with convergent oceanic–continental boundaries. It intrudes older two-mica granites and metavolcanic rocks (Zen 1983) and is itself intruded by younger two-mica granites. Zartman & Naylor (1984) have obtained a U–Pb zircon age of 430 Ma.

No Silurian age intrusions have been identified within the Casco Bay Group, but the Winterport granite is a tonalite that has been intruded by 410 Ma old pegmatites (Wones 1944, Osberg *et al.* 1984).

The similarity to the Nashoba zone is striking, and suggests that the two terranes may well be equivalent. Rocks of similar age have been found in the Gander zone of Newfoundland (Keppie 1982), and the later Devonian intrusive rocks of Newfoundland (Strong 1980) have characteristics very similar to those of the Maine coastal volcanic belt (Wones 1974, 1980). This argues for a Silurian continental arc on the W side of the Avalonian plate (Schenck 1971). If convergence rates of several centimetres per year are assumed, a maximum of 750–1000 km of oceanic crust could be subducted in this time. This suggests that the Iapetus was not a particularly large ocean, at least during Silurian time.

Devonian plutonism

Devonian plutonism in the southern Appalachians is confined to two discrete belts (Fig. 1). In the Blue Ridge Province some of the trondhjemitic plutons associated with the Spruce Pine pegmatites are Devonian (Kish 1983). This migmatitic and plutonic association is probably the result of decompressional melting after the Ordovician thrust stacking common in the southern Appalachians (Higgins *et al.* 1984, Sinha *et al.* 1985).

A more extensive zone of plutons exists in the Charlotte belt where over 30 plutons occupy a linear zone 200 km long by 50 km wide. The group contains syenites and gabbros (McSween *et al.* 1984), is characterized by K_2O-enriched rocks more characteristic of rifting areas than subduction zones (Hund 1987) and may be associated with strike-slip accretion of Avalonia during Siluro-Devonian periods (Sinha *et al.* 1985). Pavlides *et al.* (1982) have identified a small Devonian pluton in northern Virginia. Much of the area between this pluton and the group in the Charlotte belt is covered by Coastal Plain sediments or has been intruded by Carboniferous plutons, so that correlation is extremely difficult.

The Dedham–Milford zone of eastern Massachusetts is marked by a suite of alkaline intrusives which cut Ordovician plutonic rocks of this region, and are in turn intruded by Pennsylvanian age two-mica granites (Narragansett Pier and Westerly (Hermes & Murray 1988)). The Dedham–Milford zone is disrupted by younger Alleghanian faulting. It is tempting to correlate alkaline plutons with compositionally-similar plutons of the Charlotte Belt, even though the southern group averages around 400 Ma (Fullagar 1983, McSween *et al.* 1984, Hund 1985), whereas the Massachusetts and Rhode Island bodies are 370 Ma old (Zartman 1977, Hermes & Zartman 1982).

An important distinction between the northern and southern Appalachians igneous histories is in the age of the major intrusive events of the two regions. In the N the Devonian period is the time of maximum activity. The belt of plutons in the N reaches from northern Vermont to Nova Scotia in breadth and from Connecticut to Newfoundland in length. In the S the maximum activity is in the Carboniferous and extends from Georgia to Maryland in length, and from the Inner Piedmont to the Coastal Plain where it disappears under Mesozoic and Cenozoic sediments (Fullagar & Butler 1979, Sinha & Zeitz 1982).

In the northern Appalachians the earliest plutons are peraluminous granodiorites intimately involved in the emplacement of the nappe structures of central New England (Nielsen *et al.* 1976, Robinson & Hall 1980). These intrusives extend from central Massachusetts to northern New Hampshire (Fig. 2) and are the very essence of what Chappell & White (1977) term S-type granites. These plutons intrude lower Devonian sediments. In Maine similar magmas are not caught up in nappes, but are associated with gabbros and are present as the shallow Flagstaff Lake and Katahdin plutons. Ages for these plutons have been determined as 412 Ma for the Cardigan pluton (Lyons & Livingston 1977) and 395 Ma for the Katahdin pluton (Loiselle & Naylor 1983). Loiselle *et al.* (1983) report 410–416 Ma for both zircon and Rb–Sr whole-rock ages for a group of plutons in central Maine that intrude Devonian and/or Silurian strata that have undergone Devonian deformation.

Following these earliest plutons and the formation of the nappes are a series of tonalitic rocks, characterized by the Hardwick pluton in Massachusetts, the Spaulding quartz diorite (tonalite) in New Hampshire (Billings 1956, Lyons & Livingston 1977), and the Debsconeag and Horserace diorite in Maine (Hon 1980).

These plutons are transitional between I- and S-type granites and appear to be the product of anatexis of volcanic rocks or volcanic-rich sediments. These bodies have ages of about 400 Ma. Plutons of the same age appear in the Maine coastal volcanic belt, where bimodal plutonism is dominant, with extensive gabbros associated with granites in what Chapman (1962) called the Bays-of-Maine complex. The Bays-of-Maine can be extended into New Brunswick as demonstrated by Fyffe *et al.* (1981). Thus we have the N Appalachians marked by two parallel belts of older plutonic rocks that are mixtures of gabbros and granites (Thompson 1984).

In Newfoundland the distinction between belts becomes obscure. Strong (1979) demonstrated that the Mount Peyton batholith is the result of magma mixing, so that we have clear evidence of the co-existence of mafic and silicic magmas. The largest peralkaline pluton in the Appalachians, the Topsails, is also 400 Ma old (Taylor *et al.* 1980) and was intruded along the fault contact between the Dunnage zone and the Humber zone. This occurrence does not match the observations made in New England and the southern Appalachians, where the peralkaline granites tend to be associated with the Avalon-related rocks on the eastern side of the orogen. If the presence of peralkaline rocks indicates a source region of dehydrated cratonic crust, the Topsails indicates that the craton extends eastward under part of the Dunnage zone while further to the E we find plutons with sedimentary and volcanic source regions (Strong 1980).

There is a large and rather diffuse occurrence of plutons of late Devonian age. The most northwesterly group in Vermont is of this age (Naylor 1971), as are the plutons in the South Mountain batholith of Nova Scotia (Clarke *et al.* 1980). Between these occurrences are a variety of plutons that range from 400 to 350 Ma. There are many plutons that are not satisfactorily dated, and even those that have been studied by geochronology lack modal and mineralogical studies to establish magma sources and processes. However, two patterns emerge in the available data. In regions where there are sequences of plutons, the earliest plutons are gabbroic. If gabbros are not present, the earliest plutons tend to be peraluminous granites. These may be followed by biotite- or hornblende-bearing granites. If additional plutons occur, they will be dioritic, gabbroic or peralkaline in nature. This sequence occurs in the Katahdin region, where the Katahdin granite is intruded by the Debsconeag granodiorite and the Horserace diorite (Hon 1980), and in the Penobscot Bay region, where the Wallamatogus, a peraluminous pluton, is intruded by the Lucerne, a biotite-bearing granite which crystallized from a magma of low water content (Wones 1980). The Lucerne is followed by the younger Tunk Lake pluton of alkaline affinity (Karner 1968).

This same pattern is seen in central Massachusetts, where the Coys Hill peraluminous granite is followed by the Hardwick tonalite, the Prescott diorite complex and the Belchertown mafic pluton in that order (Robinson & Hall 1980).

These types of sequences, in which magmas of a lower melting point intrude earlier than magmas of higher melting points, indicate a static source region where incremental melting would take place (Brown & Fyfe 1970). Such a situation would occur where mantle magmas rise up to the crust and, because of compression, pool at the base of the crust. In subduction zone regimes the source material (either mantle or crust) is re-newed, so that there is a repetition of magma types during the intrusive sequence (Bateman *et al.* 1963, Bateman 1983). Strong (1980) suggested that the agency for tapping the mantle magma would be a megashear. If rift zones form as a result of mantle processes rather than a coupled mantle–crust effect, this underplating, and the gabbroic rocks found within the Acadian orogen, may be related to long-lived mantle sources that were overridden by the eastern edge of N America during the Palaeozoic and were reactivated in the Mesozoic to become the mid-Atlantic ridge system.

ACKNOWLEDGMENTS: We wish to acknowledge the support of National Science Foundation, Earth Science Division, Grants EAR-8206825 to David R. Wones and EAR-8206822 and EAR-8416575 to A. K. Sinha.

References

ANDERSON, J. L. 1983. Proterozoic anorogenic granite plutonism of North America. *Geological Society of America Memoir No. 161*, pp. 133–54.

ANDREW, A. S., LOISELLE, M. C. & WONES, D. R. 1983. Granitic plutonism as an indicator of microplates in the Paleozoic of central and eastern Maine. *Earth and Planetary Science Letters*, **66**, 151–65.

BATEMAN, P. C. 1983. A summary of critical relations in the central part of the Sierra Nevada batholith, California, U.S.A. *Geological Society of America Memoir No. 159*, pp. 241–59.

——, CLARK, L. D., HUBER, N. K., MOORE, J. G. & RINEHART, C. D. 1963. The Sierra Nevada batholith—a synthesis of recent work across the central part. *United States Geological Survey Professional Paper No. 414-D*, 46 pp.

BENDER, J. F., HANSON, G. N. & BENCE, A. E. 1984. Cortlandt complex: differentiation and contamination in plutons of alkali basalt affinity. *American Journal of Science*, **284**, 1–57.

BILLINGS, M. P. 1956. *Geology of New Hampshire*, New Hampshire Planning and Development Commission, 203 pp.

BROWN, G. C. & FYFE, W. 1970. The production of granitic melts during ultrametamorphism. *Contributions to Mineralogy and Petrology*, **28**, 310–18.

CHAPMAN, C. A. 1962. Bays-of-Maine igneous complex. *Geological Society of America Bulletin*, **73**, 883–8.

CHAPPELL, B. W. & WHITE, A. J. R. 1977. Ultrametamorphism and granitoid genesis. *Tectonophysics*, **43**, 7–22.

CLARKE, D. B., BARR, S. M. & DONOHOE, H. V. 1980. Granitoid and other plutonic rocks of Nova Scotia. *In:* WONES, D. R. (ed.) *The Caledonides in the USA: Proceedings of the International Geological Correlation Program—Caledonide Orogen Project 27, Blacksburg, VA. Depeartment of Geological Sciences,*

Virginia Polytechnic Institute and State University, Memoir No. 2, pp. 107–16.

CZAMANSKE, G. K., WONES, D. R. & EICHELBERGER, J. C. 1977. Mineralogy and petrology of the intrusive complex of the Pliny Range, New Hampshire. *American Journal of Science*, **277**, 1073–123.

DEININGER, R. W. 1975. Granitic rocks in northern Alabama piedmont. *In:* NEATHERY, T. L. & TULL, J. F. (eds) *Geologic Profile of the Northern Alabama Piedmont. Alabama Geological Society Guidebook, 13th Annual Field Trip*, pp. 49–62, Alabama Geological Society, Montgomery, AL.

FOLAND, K. A. & LOISELLE, M. C. 1981. Oliverian syenites of the Pliny region, northern New Hampshire. *Geological Society of America Bulletin*, **92**, 1179–88.

—— & MUESSIG, K. W. 1978. A Paleozoic age for some charnockitic-anorthositic rocks. *Geology*, **6**, 143–6.

FULLAGAR, P. D. 1983. Post-metamorphic Siluro-Devonian plutons in the Charlotte belt of South Carolina. *Geological Society of America Abstracts with Programs*, **15**, 64.

—— & BUTLER, J. R. 1979. 325 to 265 m.y. old granitic plutons in the Piedmont of the southeastern Appalachians. *American Journal of Science*, **279**, 161–85.

FYFFE, L. R., PAJARI, G. E., JR & CHERRY, M. E. 1981. The Acadian plutonic rocks of New Brunswick. *Maritime Sediments and Atlantic Geology*, **17**, 23–36.

HAMILTON, W. B. 1981. Crustal evolution by arc magmatism. *Philosophical Transactions of the Royal Society of London, Series A*, **301**, 279–91.

HANAN, B. B. 1980. The petrology and geochemistry of the Baltimore mafic complex, Maryland. *Ph.D*

Dissertation, Virginia Polytechnic Institute and State University, Blacksburg, VA.

HATCHER, R. D., JR, BUTLER, J. R., FULLAGAR, P. D., SECOR, D. T. & SNOKE, A. W. 1980. Geologic synthesis of the Tennessee–Carolinas–northeast Georgia southern Appalachians. *In*: WONES, D. R. (ed.) *The Caledonides in the USA: Proceedings of the International Geological Correlation Program—Caledonide Orogen Project 27, Blacksburg, VA. Department of Geological Sciences, Virginia Polytechnic Institute and State University, Memoir No. 2*, pp. 83–90.

HERMES, O. D. & MURRAY, D. P. 1988. Middle Devonian to Permian plutonism and volcanism in the N American Appalachians. *This volume*.

—— & ZARTMAN, R. E. 1982. Timing of plutonic events in Rhode Island. *Geological Society of America Abstracts with Programs*, **14**, 25.

——, BALLARD, R. D. & BANKS, P. O. 1978. Upper Ordovician peralkalic granites from the Gulf of Maine. *Geological Society of America Bulletin*, **89**, 1761–74.

HIGGINS, M. W., ATKINS, R. L., CRAWFORD, T. J., CRAWFORD, R. F. & COOK, R. B. 1984. A brief excursion through two thrust stacks that comprise most of the crystalline terrane of Georgia and Alabama. *Georgia Geological Society Guidebook, 9th Annual Field Trip*, Georgia Geological Society, Atlanta, GA, 67 pp.

HON, R. 1980. Geology and petrology of igneous bodies within the Katahdin pluton. *In*: ROY, D. C. (ed.) *A Guidebook to the Geology on Northeastern Maine and Neighboring New Brunswick, New England Intercollegiate Geological Conference, 72nd Annual Meeting*, pp. 65–79.

HUND, E. 1987. Siluro-Devonian plutonism in the southern Appalachians, *M.S. Thesis*, Virginia Polytechnic Institute and State University, Blacksburg, VA, 76 pp.

KARNER, F. R. 1968. Compositional variation in the Tunk Lake granite pluton, southeastern Maine. *Geological Society of America Bulletin*, **79**, 193–221.

KEPPIE, J. D. 1982. Structural map in the Appalachian orogen in Canada. *Memoirs of the University of Newfoundland Map No. 4*.

KING, A. F. 1980. The birth of the Caledonides: late Precambrian rocks of the Avalon Peninsula, Newfoundland, and their correlatives in the Appalachian orogen. *In*: WONES, D. R. (ed.) *The Caledonides in the USA: Proceedings of the International Correlation Program—Caledonide Orogen Project 27, Blacksburg, VA. Department of Geological Sciences, Virginia Polytechnic Institute and State University, Memoir No. 2*, pp. 3–8.

KISH, S. A. 1983. A geochronological study of deformation and metamorphism in the Blue Ridge and Piedmont of the Carolinas. *Ph.D. Dissertation*, University of North Carolina, Chapel Hill, NC, 220 pp.

LEO, G. W. 1980. Petrology and geochemistry of Oliverian core gneisses, a progress report. *Geological Society of America Abstracts with Programs*, **12**, 69.

LOISELLE, M. & NAYLOR, R. S. 1983. Age of the Katahdin batholith, Maine. *Geological Society of America Abstracts with Programs*, **15**, 146.

——, ERIKSSON, S., WONES, D. R. & SINHA, A. K. 1983. Timing and emplacement of post-Acadian plutons in central and eastern Maine. *Geological Society of America Abstracts with Programs*, **15**, 187.

LUDMAN, A. 1981. Significance of transcurrent faulting in eastern Maine and location of the sutures between Avalonia and North America. *American Journal of Science*, **281**, 463–83.

LYONS, J. E. & LIVINGSTON, D. E. 1977. Rb–Sr age of the New Hampshire plutonic series. *Geological Society of America Bulletin*, **88**, 1808–12.

MALPAS, J. 1977. Two contrasting associations from transported ophiolites in western Newfoundland. Initial report. *In*: BARKER, F. (ed.) *Dacites, Trondhjemites and Related Rocks*, pp. 465–88, Elsevier, Amsterdam.

McSWEEN, H. Y., JR, SANDO, T. W., CLARK, S. M., HARDEN, J. T. & STRANGE, E. A. 1984. The gabbro–metagabbro association of the southern Appalachian Piedmont. *American Journal of Science*, **284**, 437–61.

NAYLOR, R. S. 1969. Age and origin of the Oliverian domes, central western New Hampshire. *Geological Society of America Bulletin*, **80**, 405–28.

—— 1971. Acadian orogeny: an abrupt and brief event. *Science*, **172**, 558–60.

NIELSON, D. L., CLARK, R. G. & LYONS, J. B. 1976. Gravity models and mode of emplacement of the New Hampshire plutonic series. *Geological Society of America Memoir No. 146*, pp. 301–18.

OSBERG, P. H. 1978. Synthesis of the geology of the northeastern Appalachians, U.S.A. *Geological Survey of Canada Paper No. 78-13*, pp. 137–48.

——, HUSEY, A. M., II & BOONE, G. M. 1984. Bedrock geologic map of Maine. *Geological Survey Open File No. 84-1*.

PAVLIDES, L. 1981. The central Virginia plutonic-volcanic belt: an island arc of Cambrian(?) age. *United States Geological Survey Paper No. 1231-A*, 34 pp.

——, STERN, T. W., ARTH, J. G., MUTH, K. G. & NEWELL, M. F. 1982. Middle and upper Paleozoic granitic rocks in the Piedmont near Fredericksburg, Virginia: geochronology. *United States Geological Survey Paper No. 1231-B*, 9 pp.

RAST, N. 1980. The Avalonian plate in the northern Appalachians and Caledonides. *In*: WONES, D. R. (ed.) *The Caledonides in the USA: Proceedings of the International Geological Correlation Program—Caledonide Orogen Project 27, Blacksburg, VA. Department of Geological Sciences, Virginia Polytechnic Institute and State University, Memoir No. 2*, pp. 63–6.

ROBINSON, P. & HALL, L. M. 1980. Tectonic synthesis of southern New England. *In*: WONES, D. R. (ed.) *The Caledonides in the USA: Proceedings of the International Geological Correlation Program—Caledonide Orogen Project 27, Blacksburg, VA. Department of Geological Sciences, Virginia Polytechnic Institute and State University, Memoir No. 2*, pp. 73–82.

RUSSELL, G. S. 1978. U–Pb, Rb–Sr, and K–Ar isotopic

studies bearing on the tectonic development of the southernmost Appalachian orogen, Alabama. *Ph.D. Dissertation*, Florida State University, Tallahassee, FL.

SCHENCK, P. E. 1971. Southeastern Canada, northwestern Africa, and continental drift. *Canadian Journal of Earth Sciences*, **8**, 1218–51.

SHAW, H. & WASSERBURG, G. J. 1984. Isotopic constraints on the origin of Appalachian mafic complexes. *American Journal of Sciences*, **284**, 319–49.

SINHA, A. K. & GUY, R. Cambro-Ordovician igneous history of the eastern margin of North America. *In*: HATCHER, R. D., JR (ed.) *Decade of North American Geology: The Appalachian and Ouachita Regions*, in press.

—— & ZEITZ, I. 1982. Geophysical and geochemical evidence for a Hercynian magmatic arc, Maryland to Georgia. *Geology*, **10**, 593–6.

——, GUY, R., HUND, E. & TAMBURRO, E. 1985. Thermal and tectonic evolution of the central and southern Appalachians: evidence from distribution, age and origin of granitic rocks. *Geological Society of America Abstracts with Programs*, **17**, 466.

——, SANS, J. R., HANAN, B. B. & HALL, S. T. 1980. Igneous rocks of the Maryland Piedmont: indicators of crustal evolution. *In*: WONES, D. R. (ed.) *The Caledonides in the USA: Proceedings of the International Geological Correlation Program— Caledonide Orogen Project 27, Blacksburg, VA. Department of Geological Sciences, Virginia Polytechnic Institute and State University, Memoir No. 2*, pp. 131–6.

SIZE, W. B. & DEAN, L. S. 1982. Trondhjemite magmatism and tectonic setting in the southern Appalachian Piedmont. *Geological Society of America Abstracts with Programs*, **14**, 82.

STRONG, D. F. 1979. The Mount Peyton batholith, central Newfoundland; a bimodal calc-alkaline suite. *Journal of Petrology*, **20**, 119–38.

—— 1980. Granitoid rocks and associated mineral deposits of eastern Canada and western Europe. *In*: STRANGWAY, D. W. (ed.) *The Continental Crust and its Mineral Deposits. Geological Association of Canada Special Paper No. 20*, pp. 741–70.

TAYLOR, R. P., STRONG, D. F. & KEAN, B. F. 1980. The Topsails igneous complex: Silurian–Devonian peralkaline magmatism in western Newfoundland. *Canadian Journal of Earth Sciences*, **17**, 425–39.

THOMPSON, J. F. H. 1984. Acadian synorogenic mafic intrusions in the Maine Appalachians. *American Journal of Science*, **284**, 462–83.

WILLIAMS, H., KENNEDY, M. J. & NEALE, E. R. M. 1972. The Appalachian structural province. *Geological Society of Canada Special Paper No. 11*, pp. 181–261.

WONES, D. R. 1974. Igneous petrology of some plutons in the northern part of the Penobscot Bay area, Maine. *In*: OSBERG, P. H. (ed.) *Guidebook for Field Trips in East Central and North Central Maine. New England Intercollegiate Geological Conference, 66th Annual Meeting*, pp. 99–125.

—— 1980. Contributions of crystallography, mineralogy, and petrology to the geology of the Lucerne pluton, Hancock County, Maine. *American Mineralogist*, **65**, 411–37.

—— 1984. Plutonic sequences in orogenic zones: the New England collage. *Geological Society of America Abstracts with Programs*, **16**, 699–700.

ZARTMAN, R. E., 1977. Geochronology of some alkalic rock provinces in eastern and central United States. *Annual Reviews of Earth and Planetary Sciences*, **5**, 257–86.

—— & NAYLOR, R. S. 1984. Structural implications of some radiometric ages of igneous rocks in southeastern New England. *Geological Society of America Bulletin*, **95**, 522–39.

—— & SINHA, A. K. 1980. Timing of igneous events in the Appalachians and their tectonic implication. *Geological Society of America Abstracts with Programs*, **12**, 554.

ZEN, E-AN 1983. Exotic terranes in the New England Appalachians—limits, candidates and ages: a speculative essay. *In*: HATCHER, R. D., WILLIAMS, H. & ZIETZ, I. (eds) *Contributions to the Tectonics and Geophysics of Mountain Chains. Geological Society of America Memoir No. 158*, pp. 55–81.

—— & HAMMARSTROM J. M. 1984. Magmatic epidote and its pretrologic significance. *Geology*, **12**, 515–18.

A. K. SINHA, Department of Geological Sciences, Virginia Polytechnic Institute and State University, Blacksburg, VA 24061, USA.

Granitoid plutonism in the Caledonian orogen of Europe

W. E. Stephens

SUMMARY: Granitoid plutonism is a feature of all major segments of the Caledonian orogen in NW Europe and Greenland. Available data on geological setting, age and composition are presented for each segment and are collated for use as the basis for a regional and temporal interpretation of magmatism during the Caledonian. Magmatism close to the northwestern foreland was dominantly alkaline whereas both alkaline and peraluminous compositions are represented on the southern foreland. Within the orogen early magmatism N of the Iapetus suture line was dominantly S-type resulting from crustal anatexis of dominantly metasedimentary rocks, while there is a later shift to predominantly I-type granitoid plutonism. S of the Iapetus suture line plutonism within the orogen in Scandinavia is essentially I-type, whereas in Britain and Ireland it has more S-type characteristics supporting recent propositions of two separate southerly plates. The overall pattern of plutonism contrasts markedly with that of younger subduction-related batholiths.

Granitoid plutonism was a feature of all major segments of the orogen in Europe from early Ordovician to Devonian. A wide variety of compositional types was generated in response to prevailing tectonic and metamorphic conditions as well as varying source regions and further modification by igneous processes. The object of this paper is to collate data on geological setting, geochronology and composition of the granitoids in terms of their spatial and temporal distributions and to use these data to relate Caledonian plutonism to the dynamic development of the orogen in Europe. It is convenient first to consider plutonism within a framework of present segments of the Caledonian orogen (Fig. 1), and for this purpose the E Greenland and N African segments have been included with European segments. The availability of detailed information on plutonism in the various segments is highly variable, being rather sparse in remote areas such as Svalbard and E Greenland. Perhaps the greatest uncertainties concern the emplacement ages of plutons because radiometric techniques date time elapsed since passing through a blocking temperature. This becomes a problem in slow-cooling terranes or in plutons which have been subsequently metamorphosed above the blocking temperature. Available radiometric ages have been viewed critically, but detailed revision of the scheme presented here will be necessary as better geochronological data becomes available.

The geological setting of plutonism is considered on a regional scale in a generalized way by relating plutons to their environment, i.e. whether they were emplaced into old (Archaean or early mid-Proterozoic) crystalline basement or young (late Proterozoic–early Palaeozoic) geosynclinal sequences. A consistent ornamentation for each

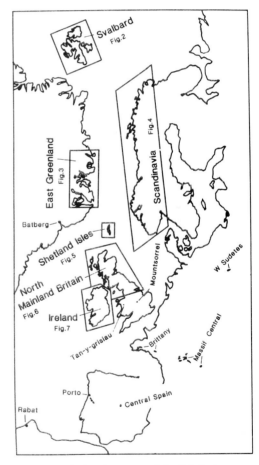

FIG. 1. Boundaries of segments of the Caledonian orogen described in this paper and expanded in Figs 2–7, together with locations of other sites of granitoid magmatism described in the text. Continental reconstruction after Le Pichon *et al.* (1977).

From HARRIS, A. L. & FETTES, D. J. (eds), 1988, *The Caledonian–Appalachian Orogen*, Geological Society Special Publication No. 38, pp. 389–403.

segment (Figs 2–7) is used to illustrate the host rock types and younger cover rocks for each segment. In summarizing the compositional features of granitoids the I- and S-type classification scheme of Chappell & White (1974) has been adopted along with the later addition of A-types (Loiselle & Wones 1979) and a separate category for truly alkaline plutonism. The Chappell–White classification is based on several compositional parameters, and although only some are available for most plutons there is often sufficient mineralogical and isotopic information available to make a reliable assignment; the most generally applied in this study is the strontium isotope initial ratio and modal mineralogy for the practical reason that these are the most widely available of the critical parameters. The value of this classification is that it generally reflects source regions and prevailing tectonic/metamorphic environments, with many orogens showing evolutionary trends from early S-types related to metamorphic climax to later I-types. Subduction-related plutons as exemplified by the Cordilleran batholiths, however, are almost exclusively I-types with only very minor S-types associated towards the continental interior. There have been criticisms of the application of this classification to the Caledonian of Britain (e.g. Plant *et al.* 1983) where minor mineralization in some Scottish plutons appears to differ from that predicted by the granitoid classification. An exposition of the role of A-types by Collins *et al.* (1982) satisfactorily accounts for these apparent contradictions.

Plutonic activity

Svalbard

The Svalbard segment of the Caledonian orogen is 700 km long by 400 km wide and plutonic activity of presumed Silurian–Devonian age has been recorded associated with crystalline basement and the Hecla Hoek sequence of late Proterozoic and early Palaeozoic age (Fig. 2).

On Nordaustlandet grey granites have been described which are invariably associated with schists and gneisses of the metamorphic complexes (Sandford 1950) and the Kap Hansteen Formation (Sandford 1956) both of which have given Caledonian metamorphic ages, but the emplacement ages for the granitoids are not known. A suite of pink and red felsic granodiorites, possibly of Devonian age, is apparently later judging by the lack of tectonism (Sandford 1950). No intrusions have been described as cutting the folded but unmetamorphosed sedimentary cover

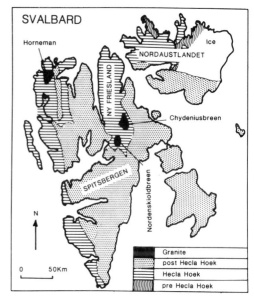

FIG. 2. Distribution of Caledonian plutons in Svalbard.

of the Murchisonfjorden Supergroup of the Hecla Hoek sequence.

On Ny Friesland (Fig. 2) Harland (1959) was able to define two plutons from the scattered outcrops and moraines. The Chydeniusbreen pluton (approximately 30 km × 11 km) forms discordant intrusive contacts with rocks of the Hinlopenstretet Supergroup of the upper Hecla Hoek. The Nordenskioldbreen pluton (about 10 km in diameter) also intrudes the Stubendorffbreen Supergroup of the lower Hecla Hoek. These plutons post-date the main Caledonian tectonism and have yielded ages of 385–406 Ma (Gayer *et al.* 1966). The granitoids are dominantly pink and are petrographically biotite-rich granites and granodiorites with occasional hornblende and clinopyroxene; some more syentic varieties are known from the Nordenskioldbreen pluton (Harland 1959).

Radiometric ages are unavailable for the scattered red granitoids of Nordaustlandet but it is likely that they are closely related to the similar granitoids of Ny Friesland. No geochemical data are available for these granitoids, but petrological indications are that they are all I-type granitoids. On Nordaustlandet only the metamorphic basement appears to have been intruded, whereas on Ny Friesland granitoids have intruded the eugeosynclinal Hecla Hoek sequence. This late plutonic activity (about 420–380 Ma) post-dates the Ny Friesland orogeny with its metamorphic peak at about 440–450 Ma, although some later metamorphism overlapping with plutonic activity has been recorded. The Horneman pluton in the W has yielded young ages of 318–340 Ma, although it is not yet clear whether these reflect time of emplacement or cooling history.

E Greenland

This considerable segment of the orogen extends for more than 1300 km between 70 and 82°N with a long history of Caledonian plutonism (Fig. 3). Much of the segment comprises a central metamorphic complex of gneisses and granites of a variety of ages (mostly pre-Caledonian). This is bordered or overlain by folded geosynclinal rocks of late Proterozoic and lower Palaeozoic ages (Eleonore Bay Group, Tillite Group and Hagen Fjord Group) which show low-grade or no Caledonian metamorphism. In central E Greenland these are overlain by Devonian molasse sediments.

Granitoid plutons have been found only S of 76°N and are abundant, ranging from those being closely associated with the metamorphic complexes and probably pre-Caledonian in age to those having discordant contacts with late Precambrian to lower Palaeozoic sediments (probably true Caledonian intrusions) to yet others stratigraphically constrained to the middle or upper Devonian (Henriksen & Higgins 1976). The chronology of emplacement through radiometric dating is not yet well known, although several Rb–Sr studies, notably those of Hansen & Tembusch (1979), Steiger *et al.* (1979) and Rex & Gledhill (1981), supported by the U–Pb studies

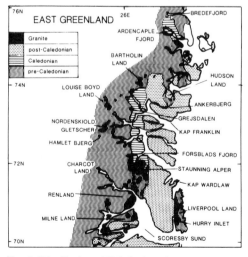

FIG. 3. Distribution of Caledonian plutons in E Greenland.

of Steiger *et al.* (1979) are particularly important in this respect. The pioneering K–Ar work of Haller & Kulp (1962) must now be regarded with caution in view of its tendency to give young ages reflecting cooling rather than emplacement. Another difficulty stems from the fact that younger plutonic activity was most intense in the same areas as older plutonism. Most studies hitherto have been of the reconnaissance type, and the relationships between plutonism and tectonism are not yet well understood. The geochronological data for Caledonian plutons appear to indicate a continuum of activity from Arenig to mid-Devonian with no apparent peak(s), although this is probably in part a reflection of sampling. Plutonic activity presumed to be Caledonian on geological grounds (based on the conclusions of Henriksen & Higgins 1976) or on geochronological evidence is shown on Fig. 3.

The largest area of Caledonian granitoids is in the N Staunning Alper–Schaffhauserdalen–Forsblads Fjord region where plutons were emplaced between metasediments of the Eleonore Bay Group and earlier migmatitic granites of the central crystalline complex. These granitoids are late- to post-orogenic and are generally leucocratic granodiorites or muscovite biotite granites. One such muscovite biotite granite body on Forsblads Fjord gave a good Rb–Sr whole-rock isochron age of 445 ± 5 Ma (Rex *et al.* 1976) with an initial strontium isotope ratio of 0.719. Nearby, a suite of sillimanite and garnet-bearing granite dykes gives a whole-rock isochron age of 430 ± 48 Ma (Rex & Gledhill 1981) with a very high strontium isotope initial ratio of 0.737.

Several Caledonian plutons have been identified in the Scoresby Sund region, particularly in Renland and Milne Land. A large hypersthene monzonite body in the form of a lopolith some 500 m thick can be traced for about 40 km and is associated with diorites. It has given a whole-rock Rb–Sr age of 467 ± 27 Ma and has an initial ratio of 0.710 which is high for such rocks (Steiger *et al.* 1979). This sheet was not involved in tectonism but is believed to pre-date a second Caledonian phase of migmatization in the Staunning Alper region. A biotite hornblende granite stock and a grey-pink granite sheet in E Renland were analysed for U–Pb isotopes in zircons by Steiger *et al.* (1979). The former failed to yield an age but the grey-pink granite gave a lower concordia intercept of 356 ± 1 Ma. Rb–Sr mineral ages on biotites from this same body gave ages of 406 ± 11 and 422 ± 10 Ma, and these workers suggested that the older age is that of emplacement and the 356 Ma age reflects an uplift event. Both samples showed evidence of upper concordia intercepts indicating older crustal precursors in the source with approximate ages of 1100–1500 Ma.

In E Milne Land the largest pluton (13 km in diameter) is a sheet-like body of hornblende biotite granite with marginal diorites which has given an Rb–Sr whole-rock age of 453 ± 23 Ma and a strontium isotope initial ratio of 0.707 (Hansen & Tembusch 1979). The pink granites, which are geologically late, form three main plutons and several smaller bodies and have given an Rb–Sr whole-rock age of 373 ± 9 Ma and a high strontium isotope initial ratio of 0.716 (Hansen & Tembusch 1979).

In the Grejsdalen region a 14 km × 7 km dome-shaped body is composed of quartz monzonite and two-mica granite. Rex & Gledhill (1981) quoted an Rb–Sr whole-rock age of 377 ± 89 Ma based on aplites and monzonites with different strontium isotope initial ratios of 0.742 and 0.716 respectively. Nearby at Gneisdal a muscovite granite sheet gave an Rb–Sr whole-rock age of 480 ± 85 Ma with an initial ratio of 0.730, and a little further S at Djaevlekloften a muscovite leucogranite sheet gave an Rb–Sr whole-rock age of 433 ± 68 Ma and an initial ratio of 0.735 (Rex & Gledhill 1981).

The Nordenskiold Gletscher pluton is an elongate body some 60 km long emplaced into an anticlinal structure and consists mainly of leuco-cratic muscovite biotite granite, but it has not been dated. The Hamlet Bjerg pluton is about 20 km to the S along strike in Goodenough Land and has yielded a whole-rock–mineral isochron age of 415 ± 23 Ma and an initial strontium isotope ratio of 0.721 (Rex & Gledhill 1981). Along strike to the N in Louise Boyd Land a large body revealed by scattered nunataks appears to be an extension of a Nordenskiold Gletscher–Hamlet Bjerg batholith but has given whole-rock Rb–Sr ages of 650–765 Ma for different granitoid facies with relatively low strontium isotope initial ratios of 0.708–0.709 and is thus unlikely to be Caledonian (Rex & Gledhill 1981).

At Kap Wardlaw a small (10 km²) biotite granite body is undated. Farther S on Liverpool Land a large (more than 20 km long) post-tectonic biotite granite on Hurry Inlet has given an Rb–Sr mineral age of 434 Ma (Hansen & Steiger 1971). Fission-track studies of sphene, zircon and apatite from the same granite body generated a cooling curve indicating gradual uplift of a presumed deep-level pluton within the orogen (Gleadow & Brooks 1979).

At Ankerbjerg on Hudson Land a small pluton forms a complex of granodiorites and monzonites; it has not been radiometrically dated but invades Eleonore Bay Group sediments. In the Kap Franklin district the plutonism can be stratigraphically constrained to the middle and upper Devonian and appears to be more alkaline with alkali granites and porphyries represented and associated with volcanic rocks.

In the N within the Ardencaple Fjord–Bredefjord graben several stocks and plutons which appear to have been emplaced by a variety of mechanisms including stoping, sheeting and forceful intrusion were described by Haller (1971). The only available age date is a K–Ar muscovite age of 394 Ma (Haller & Kulp 1962) on a small body at the head of Bredefjord.

Two post-tectonic plutons on Bartholin Land are emplaced into Eleonore Bay sediments (Haller 1971). A batholith some 40 km long occurs in Charcot Land, and zircons from a quartz diorite have yielded a discordia with an upper intercept of about 1900 Ma and a lower intercept of about 370 Ma (Steiger & Henriksen 1972) suggesting Caledonian reworking of old crust. A muscovite granite from the same region has given a Caledonian Rb–Sr mineral age of 417 Ma (Hansen et al. 1973) although most such rocks are much older and in the age range 1600–1800 Ma.

Perhaps the most unusual Caledonian plutonic activity has been recorded from Batberg (Fig. 1) amongst the Tertiary centres of the Kangerdlugssuaq district. The complex consists of pyroxenites, dunites, melteigitic rocks and syenites including undersaturated varieties. The complex is clearly strongly alkaline and is the only such body recorded from the Caledonian of E Greenland; it is petrologically similar to the Loch Borrolan complex of Scotland. Ages of about 440 Ma have been obtained using K–Ar and Rb–Sr mineral dating methods (Brooks et al. 1976). Fission-track studies by Gleadow & Brooks (1979) indicate that uplift and erosion in this area was minimal for much of the upper Palaeozoic.

Caledonian plutonism as a whole in E Greenland does not readily conform to any simple model; there are no systematic age–composition variations. The majority of plutons have the characteristics of S-type granites with strongly peraluminous mineral assemblages and very high strontium isotope initial ratios. A few plutons may belong to the I-type category, and these tend to be located on the eastern margin of the segment including the Hurry Inlet, Ankerbjerg and some of the E Milne Land–Renland plutons. The available petrological and isotopic characteristics of most of these plutons are quite unlike those of subduction-related plutons of the Cordillera. A more appropriate model is the Hercynotype granite of Pitcher (1979) in which S-type granites are associated with migmatites and have a close temporal and spatial connection with regional deformation and metamorphism, with only very minor associated volcanics. The type has been ascribed by Pitcher (1982) to continental collision, and such an interpretation would imply a protracted period of collision for this segment of the orogen. The alkaline complex at Batberg is of the type more commonly associated with thrust zones such as the Moine Thrust in Scotland or with rift zones.

Scandinavia

This 1700-km-long segment of the Caledonian orogen is notable for its small area of exposed granitoid plutons in proportion to the rest of the orogen (Fig. 4) although a broad range of petrological types is represented, principally in Norway. The region consists of a series of Caledonian nappes of westerly derivation lying on a crystalline basement. The granitoid plutons are concentrated in the higher nappes of the upper and uppermost allochthons in the W of the segment.

The largest area of plutonic rocks is that of the Bindal batholith within the Helgeland Nappe

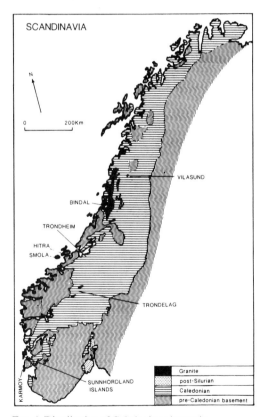

FIG. 4. Distribution of Caledonian plutons in Scandinavia.

Complex. It is a plutonic complex dominated by tonalites, granodiorites and granites, while monzonites are present in small areas. Two mica granodiorites and granites are found as late sheets (Nordgulen 1984). The region has been divided into separate intrusive centres. The main granitoid mass has given an Rb–Sr whole-rock age of 415 ± 26 Ma with an initial ratio of 0.708 (Priem *et al.* 1975). The Bindal complex is surrounded by a broad migmatite zone, as are other similar complexes to the N (Strand & Kulling 1972). A detailed study of the Krakfjellet pluton in the Bindal batholith (Nordgulen 1984) indicates it to be largely I-type in character despite its moderately high strontium isotope initial ratio.

The Sunnhordland Islands define a batholithic area comprising dominantly quartz diorites, tonalites and granodiorites with lesser gabbros and granites. The Fana granite has given an Rb–Sr whole-rock age of 411 ± 50 Ma and an initial strontium ratio of 0.706 (Brueckner 1972), while the nearby Sotra granite gave a whole-rock Rb–Sr age of 431 ± 31 Ma with an initial strontium ratio of 0.707 (Sturt *et al.* 1975). Other granodiorites and granites associated with older gabbros of the Sunnhordland batholith have not yet been dated, but associated rhyolites have given ages of 413 ± 5 Ma (Priem & Torske 1973). These rocks also appear to be generally I-types with slightly elevated strontium isotope initial ratios.

The W Karmoy complex (Ledru 1980), which intrudes the Karmoy ophiolite and comprises various granitoids from quartz diorites to biotite granites, is of similar age to the Sunnhordland batholith. Whole-rock ages of around 445 Ma have been obtained from late dykes associated with this complex (Sturt *et al.* 1979, Ledru 1980). The islands of Hitra and Smola in central Norway are granitoid complexes which have wide petrological ranges from ultrabasic to acid types with diorites, trondhjemites and granodiorites predominating. A whole-rock Rb–Sr age of 436 ± 7 Ma has been obtained (Roberts 1980) from the Smola complex with an initial strontium isotope ratio of 0.705.

Trondhjemite bodies in Trondelag have been shown not to be consanguineous and some were generated syntectonically early in the Ordovician. One such body (Vakkerlia) has yielded a zircon U–Pb age of 477 ± 5 Ma, an Rb–Sr whole-rock age of 474 ± 23 Ma, an Rb–Sr mineral–whole-rock isochron of 412 ± 2 Ma and a K–Ar mineral–whole-rock age of 415 ± 19 Ma. The former two ages probably represent emplacement ages and the latter two cooling ages. The strontium isotope initial ratios for four of these bodies are around 0.705. Another trondhjemite in the Gula Group allochthon has given an Rb–Sr isochron age of

473 Ma (Berthomier *et al.* 1972). Trondhjemites from the type Trondheim region are generally lenticular bodies comprising quartz diorites, granodiorites and granites.

The Finnvik complex in Finnmark intrudes Llandovery rocks and has yielded an Rb–Sr whole-rock age of 411 ± 7 Ma and an initial strontium isotope ratio of 0.755 (Andersen *et al.* 1982).

Caledonian granitoids are rare in Sweden, the principal area being S of Lake Overuman. The Vilasund granite in this area has given a whole-rock Rb–Sr isochron of 447 ± 6 Ma and an initial ratio of 0.706 (Gee & Wilson 1974).

Three periods of granitoid magmatism are suggested by the age data. The first period at about 475 Ma is represented by some of the trondhjemites, a later period around 440 Ma is represented best in the Karmoy complex and finally the main period at about 415 Ma is represented by the Bindal and other masses. However, cooling ages in some complexes are also set at this time. As a whole the segment exhibits I-type granitoid magmatism over a protracted period, although strontium isotope initial ratios tend to be somewhat higher than for normal I-types and it is probable that some crustal melting and/or contamination contributed to the magmatism.

E Europe

Remnants of the Caledonian orogen have been recognized in the Western Sudetes of the Poland–Czechoslovakia–E German boundary region and form the basis of three-plate models for this part of the orogen. The Rumburk granites and Izera gneisses represent a plutonic complex of alkaline composition in the Western Sudetes (Fig. 1) which was reworked in Varsican times but was probably emplaced between 500 and 450 Ma ago with a strontium isotope initial ratio of 0.709 (Borkowska *et al.* 1980). These workers considered the complex to be anorogenic in origin, but the high strontium isotope initial ratio and the quoted chemical analyses are indicative of a peraluminous composition derived from an S-type source.

Shetland Isles

Five complexes in the E of Shetland (Fig. 5), namely the Graven, Brae, Spiggie, Channerwick and Cunningsburgh granites, are Caledonian (*sensu stricto*), whereas in the W the Sandsting and Northmaven complexes have yielded K–Ar ages around 360 Ma (Miller & Flinn 1966). Most of these complexes have intruded Caledonian metasediments which have been correlated with

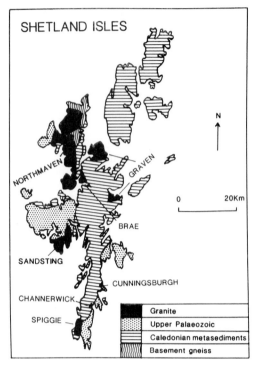

FIG. 5. Distribution of Caledonian plutons in the Shetland Isles.

the Moine and Dalradian rocks of Scotland. The Northmaven complex also intrudes older basement gneisses which have been correlated with the Lewisian of Scotland.

The Graven and Cunningsburgh granites have given K–Ar dates around 400 Ma (Miller & Flinn 1966). The Graven complex is unusual for Caledonian granitoids in consisting of superimposed vein complexes with wide petrological variety including appinites, diorites, granodiorites, monzonites and granite pegmatites. The Brae complex consists of ultrabasic masses in a host of mainly pyroxene diorite, a rock type encountered in contemporaneous complexes on mainland Britain. The Spiggie complex comprises more acid rock types, principally granodiorite and granite but earlier monzonites and ultrabasic rocks are represented. The Channerwick granite may differ from these otherwise essentially I-type granitoids in bearing muscovite, although it is a very small mass and consists of a number of interconnected dyke-like bodies.

The western post-orogenic complexes also show wide petrological variations. The Northmaven complex includes granites, granophyre, diorite and gabbro, and a few outcrops of ultrabasic rocks. The Sandsting complex has early diorites and gabbros intruded by granites and granodiorites.

Although isotopic information is lacking for all these complexes (apart from the K–Ar ages quoted above), the petrographic variations are typical of I-type granitoids in both the eastern and western groups of complexes.

Mainland Britain

This segment is of great importance in that it includes Caledonian plutons emplaced into both margins of the Iapetus Ocean as well as the NW foreland (Fig. 6). The greatest intensity of plutonic activity on mainland Britain was in Scotland and the N of England with at least 55 separate intrusive bodies. Various reviews of plutonism have been published in recent years including those of Brown (1983) and Pankhurst & Sutherland (1982) for Scotland and Le Bas (1982) for England and Wales. Detailed descriptions will not be repeated here. The following is a very general summary of the age and composition variations over the segment based on a

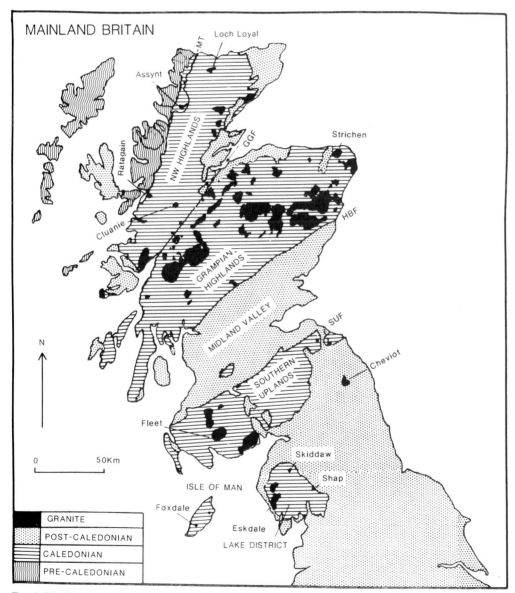

Fig. 6. Distribution of Caledonian plutons in N mainland Britain.

geochemical database of more than a thousand samples representative of the province (Stephens & Halliday 1984) and considerable isotopic information mainly from the work of A. N. Halliday and co-workers. An alternative interpretation of the Chappell–White classification applied to the Caledonian granitoids of Britain has been presented by Plant and co-workers (Plant *et al.* 1983, Fowler 1984, Atherton & Plant 1985, O'Brien *et al.* 1985) in which their assignments are often at variance with those presented here.

In NW Scotland there is a well-defined province of alkaline plutons and hypabyssal rocks in Assynt and Loch Loyal. Other plutons in the NW Highlands have alkaline tendencies of shoshonitic type including Ratagain and Cluanie. Some other plutons in this region are I types with calcalkaline compositions (e.g. Strontian), and available age dates suggest that plutonism in the W of this region took place in the interval 456–417 Ma with the main activity some 20 Ma before the main period of post-tectonic plutonism S of the Great Glen Fault. Plutons in the W intruded rocks still hot after rather late regional metamorphism (Ashworth & Tyler 1983). In the E of this region plutonism is entirely I-type with alkaline varieties restricted to a western zone within 25 km of the Moine Thrust and the Lewisian foreland.

In the Grampian Highlands early plutonism in the interval 480–440 Ma was generally of S-type two-mica granites with high strontium isotope initial ratios and located mainly in the NE and N of the region. Pankhurst (1974) first recognized this group of plutons including Strichen with ages of around 450–470 Ma and strontium isotope initial ratios of 0.714–0.717. This has been extended westwards by Van Breemen & Piasecki (1983) and Zaleski (1982). The main period of plutonic activity, however, was in the interval 420–395 Ma and of predominantly I-type. Amongst these later plutonics there is a wide variety of petrological types and emplacement mechanisms, although Stephens & Halliday (1984) recognized three geochemically-distinct suites, i.e. the Argyll suite in the SW, Cairngorm in the N and NE, and the S of Scotland in the S (including the Southern Uplands). Although this plutonism was principally I-type, some of the granitoids of the Cairngorm suite have characteristics transitional between evolved I-types and A-types (Stephens & Halliday 1984).

Plutonism in the Southern Uplands is characterized by concentrically zoned I-type plutons except for the Cairnsmore of Fleet which has bulk chemical, strontium and oxygen isotope characteristics of an S-type pluton. Plutonism

dates from about 400–410 Ma except for the Cairnsmore of Fleet which dates from 392 Ma (Halliday *et al.* 1980b).

In the Lake District of England a few plutons span a wide temporal and compositional range. The main period of granitoid magmatism was Silurian to early Devonian in which the Eskdale, Ennerdale, Skiddaw and Shap bodies were emplaced. These appear to have high primary ^{18}O values, although strontium isotope initial ratios are not very high (see compilation by O'Brien *et al.* 1985) and U–Pb, common lead and neodymium isotope studies strongly favour a crustal source (see Hampton & Taylor 1983). This suggests a rather young source which has gone through a sedimentary cycle (immature S-type). To the E is the buried Weardale granite and the Wensleydale granite which has yielded a strontium isotope initial ratio of 0.721 (Dunham 1974).

Elsewhere in England the Cheviot is a plutonic–volcanic centre lying along the postulated line of Iapetus suturing. On the Isle of Man there are two small granites of which one (Foxdale) appears to have features in common with Eskdale of the Lake District. Further S in mainland Britain there is Caledonian I-type plutonism at Mountsorrel (Fig. 1) which has given a zircon U–Pb age of 452 ± 8 Ma (Pidgeon & Aftalion 1978). In Wales the Tan-y-Grisiau microgranite (Fig. 1) is probably Ordovician in age but has given a younger K–Ar age of 420 Ma (Fitch *et al.* 1969). This pluton has alkaline affinities with one facies bearing riebeckite.

Ireland

Recent reviews which have described the plutonism of Ireland include those of Leake (1978), Stillman (1981), Pankhurst & Sutherland (1982) and Kennan (1979). The reader is referred to these for details; general features only are presented here.

Plutonic activity is mainly related to the late Silurian and early Devonian stages of the orogeny, but earlier magmatism has been recognized at Slieve Gamph (Fig. 7) in the Ox Mountains which is a granodiorite and granite complex. It has yielded an Rb–Sr whole-rock age of 477 ± 6 Ma with an initial strontium isotope ratio of 0.706 (Pankhurst *et al.* 1976). The Oughterard granite in Connemara has given a poor but apparently younger isochron age with an initial strontium isotope ratio of 0.710. The available compositional characteristics of these earlier intrusives are neither unequivocally I- or S-type.

Younger plutonism of late Silurian and early Devonian age is centred in Donegal, Galway, Newry and Leinster and, as in mainland Britain,

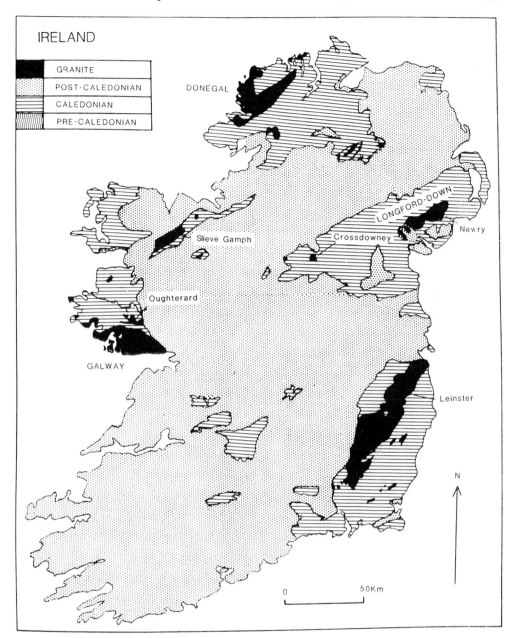

FIG. 7. Distribution of Caledonian plutons in Ireland.

is important in that it is found on both sides of the generally accepted line of suturing of the Iapetus Ocean.

In Donegal eight main plutons (730 km²) display a remarkable range of intrusion mechanisms and compositional diversity which were emplaced within a very short time interval. They comprise the most thoroughly investigated group of plutons in the orogen; the work was performed under the leadership of Professor W. S. Pitcher and has been summarized by Pitcher & Berger (1972). If this region is a microcosm of plutonism in the Caledonian orogen, it is clear that a considerable amount of basic research remains to be done elsewhere before granitoid plutonism in the orogen will be understood in any detail.

The isotopic work of Halliday *et al.* (1980a) and O'Connor *et al.* (1982) indicates that the strontium isotope initial ratios vary little about a value of 0.706 and as a whole the Donegal granites have I-type characteristics with occasional S-type features displayed by the Thorr, Rosses and Trawenagh Bay plutons.

In Galway the largest granitoid is the Galway batholith with its several satellite plutons composed largely of biotite granites and granodiorites (Leake 1978). An exception is the late-stage Murvey granite which is garnet and muscovite bearing. Isotopic data for Galway as a whole (Leggo *et al.* 1966) are consistent with an I-type source, but in the absence of isotopic data it is tentatively suggested that the Murvey facies is S-type on the basis of its markedly peraluminous mineral assemblage.

In the Longford–Down massif the Newry complex ranges from ultramafic rocks to granites in three contiguous plutons; the northeasterly body gives an Rb–Sr isochron age of 403 ± 3 Ma with an initial ratio of 0.705 (Meighan & Neeson 1979). To the SW is a small stock (Crossdowney) of granodiorite and granite.

The Leinster granite on the southern side of the Iapetus suture line is the largest plutonic body in Ireland. It consists of five *en échelon* domed units forming a composite body which comprises early quartz diorite and tonalite, with later adamellitic granite including a facies which has muscovite megacrysts and is occasionally garnet bearing. The Leinster granite has yielded an Rb–Sr isochron age of 404 ± 24 Ma and an initial strontium ratio of 0.708 (O'Connor & Bruck 1978). Early rock types are of I-type although late types have peraluminous mineral assemblages which, along with high strontium isotope initial ratios, suggests a transition towards S-type.

Overall plutonism in Ireland is late (405 ± 15 Ma) except for minor early plutonism in the N (about 470 Ma). It is dominantly of I-type and emplaced into late Proterozoic and early Palaeozoic rocks by a variety of mechanisms. S of the Iapetus suture line late magmatism has significantly higher strontium isotope initial ratios and has clearly been derived from a different source having more in common geochemically with the Lake District along strike on mainland Britain than with its neighbours across the suture to the N.

W Europe

Some Caledonian plutonism has been recognized as post-dating the Cadomian in France although commonly reworked by the Hercynian, particularly in Brittany and the Massif Central (Fig. 1).

In Brittany a suite of lens-shaped potassic granites has yielded ages in the range 470–430 Ma, along with 470 Ma trondhjemitic granodiorites; the latter have been interpreted as crustal melts (Cabanis 1983). Plutonism of calc-alkaline composition was prevalent in the Massif Central during Ordovician times whereas there was a shift to more alkaline character in Silurian times. Zircon U–Pb dating by Pin & Lancelot (1982) has established a 415 ± 6 Ma age for trondhjemitic magmatism in the S Massif Central.

The bulk of plutonic activity in Iberia is Hercynian in age but radiometric evidence exists for earlier Caledonian magmatism. In Portugal these form a belt from Porto along the edge of the Central Iberian and Ossa Morena zones (Fig. 1) and show a range of ages from 512 to 402 Ma using Rb–Sr whole-rock techniques (Pinto 1983). Although data are sparse, they appear to indicate periods of magmatism at about 500, 435 and 400 Ma. Initial strontium isotope ratios are in the range 0.704–0.708 (Pinto 1983) but apparently have S-type chemical characteristics. In central Spain alkaline plutonics including undersaturated varieties of anorogenic type have been dated around 466 ± 12 Ma (Guy-Tamain 1978). As in France there is potentially much more Caledonian granitoid plutonism in Iberia hitherto unrecognized owing to overprinting by Hercynian events.

Mauritanides

This segment of the orogen extends for about 2000 km from S Morocco to Liberia. In Morocco the Rabat–Tiflet granite (Fig. 1) has been dated at 430 ± 2 Ma using the Rb–Sr method. It has compositional features akin to anorogenic alkaline granitoids (Michard & Pique 1980) and was emplaced into a flysch sequence of probable Cambrian age (Pique 1983).

Discussion

The data presented above for Caledonian plutonic activity in this portion of the orogen primarily concern composition and geochronology. This is a result of the types of studies undertaken; for example, few plutons outside the UK and Ireland have been investigated for their emplacement mechanisms. This is partly a result of poor accessibility, poor exposure or subsequent tectonism. Therefore in the remainder of this paper we shall concentrate on the better known compositional aspects in relation to spatial and temporal patterns with a view to generating a regional perspective of this period of plutonic activity and ultimately to constrain better the tectonic processes responsible for their petrogenesis.

Plutonism in the segments described above has been interpreted where possible in terms of I- or S-type characteristics defined by White & Chappell (1977) or as alkaline plutons, making use of all available information. This information has been plotted on a reconstruction of the orogen after Le Pichon *et al.* (1977) (Fig. 8) to examine regional variations in composition and on a stratigraphic column (Fig. 9) to examine temporal variations in composition.

Alkaline magmatism, typically associated with intracontinental magmatism, is found along the edge of the orogen on the NW margin (Greenland and NW Scotland) and is of late Ordovician to early Silurian age. Alkaline magmatism on the SE margin of the orogen in N Africa, Iberia and the French Massif Central forms a belt of anorogenic plutons of Ordovician and Silurian ages. Hercynian reworking of these plutons presents difficulties for their detailed interpretation.

Within-orogen magmatism displays temporal–spatial–composition patterns that have tectonic implications. In Scotland early S-type plutonism contemporaneous with, or immediately post-dating, the peak of metamorphism gives way to I-type magmatism. The exceptional very late S-type magmatism in the Cairnsmore of Fleet is probably related to the end-closure events and Lake District magmatism. Plutonism along strike in the E Greenland and Svalbard segments is less well resolved but is generally consistent with this pattern. S of the Iapetus suture line in England and Ireland most of the plutonism is S type with the probable exceptions of Mountsorrell and Tan-y-Grisiau. This pattern seems to extend to Iberia, Brittany and Poland but is not repeated in Scandinavia where most plutonism is of I type. The long-term inconsistency of compositions in Scandinavia is apparent on Fig. 9 and supports propositions of an additional plate centred on Scandinavia and involved in Caledonian tectonic process as has recently been suggested by several workers (e.g. Ziegler 1981). Although the I-type plutonism can generally be described as calc-alkaline in nature, comparisons with cordilleran granites are few and, considering the extensive S-type plutonism, normally very minor in the major cordilleran batholiths (Miller & Bradfish 1980); the case for subduction generation of this Caledonian plutonism remains to be proved.

The use of trace-element and isotopic characteristics of granitoids is helping to identify terrane boundaries through characterization of deep lithospheric source regions. At present such data are only available in sufficient detail for the Scottish segment of the orogen where significant boundaries have been identified which do not correlate simply with major surface lineaments and must reflect fundamental deep structures such as the postulated mid-Grampian line (Halliday 1984). As this information is accumulated the large temporal and geographical spread of granitoids in the Caledonian orogen should prove a powerful aid to tectonic reconstruction and the recognition of terranes.

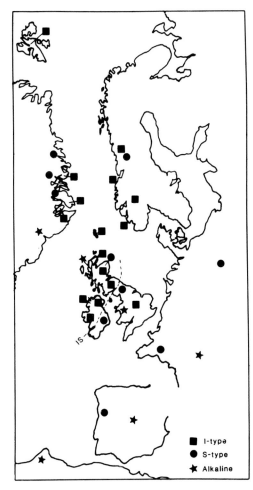

FIG. 8. Regional variations in compositions of granitoid plutons in the 'European' portion of the Caledonian orogen: IS, the postulated line of the Iapetus suture. Continental reconstruction after Le Pichon *et al.* (1977).

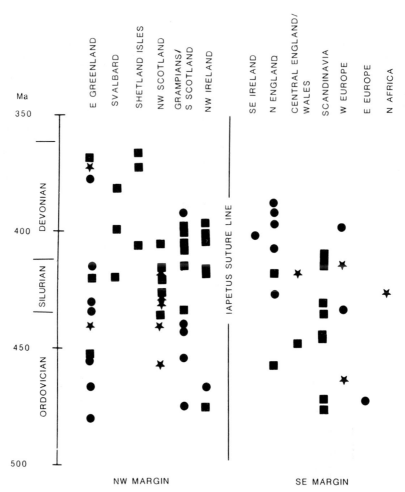

FIG. 9. Temporal variations in composition in various segments of the 'European' portion of the Caledonian orogen. Key to compositional types as in Fig. 8.

ACKNOWLEDGMENTS Financial support for research on UK Caledonian granites comes from the Natural Environment Research Council (NERC Research Grant GR3/4633), the Carnegie Trust for the Univer-sities of Scotland and Chivas Brothers. My gratitude is also extended to Bruce Chappell, Alex Halliday, Peter Holden, Donny Hutton, Oystein Nordgulen, Graeme Oliver, Wally Pitcher and Eva Zaleski.

References

ANDERSEN, T. B., AUSTRHEIM, H., STURT, B. A., PEDERSEN, S. & KJAERSRUD, K. 1982. Rb–Sr whole rock ages from Mageroy, North Norwegian Caledonides. *Norsk Geologisk Tidsskrift,* **62**, 79–85.

ASHWORTH, J. R. & TYLER, I. M. 1983. The distribution of metamorphic temperatures around the Strontian granite. *Geological Magazine,* **120**, 281–90.

ATHERTON, M. P. & PLANT, J. 1985. High heat production granites and the evolution of the Andean and Caledonian continental margins. *In:* *High Heat Production Granites, Hydrothermal Circulation and Ore Genesis,* Institute of Mining and Metallurgy, London.

BERTHOMIER, C., LACOUR, A., LEUTWEIN, F., MALLIOT, J. & SOUCT, J. 1972. Some trondhjemites of Norway: Geochronological and geochemical study. *Science de la Terre,* **17**, 341–57.

BORKOWSKA, M., HAMEURT, J. & VIDAL, P. 1980. Origin and age of Izera gneisses and Rumburk granites in the Western Sudetes. *Acta Geologica Polonica,* **30**, 123–45.

BROOKS, C. K., FAWCETT, J. J. & GITTINS, J. 1976. Caledonian magmatic activity in south-eastern Greenland. *Nature, London*, **260**, 694–6.

BROWN, P. E. 1983. Caledonian and earlier magmatism. *In:* CRAIG, G. Y. (ed.) *Geology of Scotland*, pp. 167–204, Scottish Academic Press.

BRUECKNER, H. 1972. Interpretation of Rb–Sr ages from the Precambrian and Palaeozoic rocks of southern Norway. *American Journal of Science*, **272**, 334–58.

CABANIS, B. 1983. Main features of volcanism and plutonism in late Proterozoic and Dinantian times in France. *In:* SCHENK, P. E. (ed.) *Regional Trends in the Geology of the Appalachian–Caledonian–Hercynian–Mauritanide Orogen*, pp. 187–92, Reidel, Dordrecht.

CHAPPELL, B. W. & WHITE, A. J. R. 1974. Two contrasting granite types. *Pacific Geology*, **8**, 173–4.

COLLINS, W. J., BEAMS, S. D., WHITE, A. J. R. & CHAPPELL, B. W. 1982. Nature and origin of A-type granites with particular reference to south-eastern Australia. *Contributions to Mineralogy and Petrology*, **80**, 189–200.

DUNHAM, K. C. 1974. Granite beneath the Pennines in north Yorkshire. *Proceedings of the Yorkshire Geological Society*, **40**, 191–4.

FITCH, F. J., MILLER, J. A., EVANS, A. L., GRASTY, R. L. & MENEISY, M. Y. 1969. Isotopic age determinations on rocks from Wales and the Welsh borders. *In:* WOOD, A. (ed.) *Precambrian and Lower Palaeozoic Rocks of Wales*, pp. 23–54, University of Wales Press, Cardiff.

FOWLER, M. B. 1984. Discussion. *Transactions of the Institution of Mining and Metallurgy*, **93**, B48–9.

GAYER, R. A., GEE, D. G., HARLAND, W. B., MILLER, J. A., SPALL, H. R., WALLIS, R. H. & WINSNES, T. S. 1966. Radiometric age determinations on rocks from Spitsbergen. *Norsk Polarinstitutt Skrifter*, **137**, 1–39.

GEE, D. G. & WILSON, M. R. 1974. The age of orogenic deformation in the Swedish Caledonides. *American Journal of Science*, **274**, 1–9.

GLEADOW, A. J. W. & BROOKS, C. K. 1979. Fission track dating, thermal histories and tectonics of igneous intrusions in East Greenland. *Contributions to Mineralogy and Petrology*, **71**, 45–60.

GUY-TAMAIN, A. L. 1978. L'évolution caledono-varisque des Hesperides (Meseta iberique). *In:* TOZER, E. T. & SCHENK, P. E. (eds) *Caledonian–Appalachian Orogen of the North Atlantic region. Geological Survey of Canada Paper No. 78-13*, pp. 183–210.

HALLER, J. 1971. *Geology of the East Greenland Caledonides*. Wiley-Interscience, New York, 413 pp.

—— & KULP, J. L. 1962. Absolute age determinations in East Greenland. *Meddelelser om Grønland*, **171**, 1–77.

HALLIDAY, A. N. 1984. Coupled Sm–Nd and U–Pb (zircon) systematics in the late Caledonian granites and the nature of the basement under Northern Britain. *Nature*, **307**, 229–33.

——, AFTALION, M. & LEAKE, B. E. 1980a. A revised age for the Donegal granite. *Nature, London*, **284**, 542–3.

——, STEPHENS, W. E. & HARMON, R. S. 1980b. Rb–Sr and O isotopic relationships in 3 zoned Caledonian granitic plutons, Southern Uplands, Scotland: evidence for varied sources and hybridization in magmas. *Journal of the Geological Society, London*, **137**, 329–48.

HAMPTON, C. M. & TAYLOR, P. N. 1983. The age and nature of the basement of southern Britain: evidence from Sr and Pb isotopes in granites. *Journal of the Geological Society, London*, **140**, 499–509.

HANSEN, B. T. & STEIGER, R. H. 1971. The geochronology of the Scoresby Sund area. I. Rb/Sr mineral ages. *Rapport Grønlands Geologiske Undersøkelse*, **37**, 55–7.

—— & TEMBUSCH, H. 1979. Rb–Sr isochron ages from east Milne Land, Scoresby Sund, East Greenland. *Rapport Grønlands Geologiske Undersøkelse*, **95**, 96–101.

——, OBERLI, F. & STEIGER, R. H. 1973. The geochronology of the Scoresby Sund area. Progress report 4: Rb/Sr whole rock and mineral ages. *Rapport Grønlands Geologiske Undersøkelse*, **58**, 55–8.

HARLAND, W. B. 1959. The Caledonian sequence in Ny Friesland, Spitsbergen. *Quarterly Journal of the Geological Society of London*, **114**, 307–42.

HENRICKSEN, N. & HIGGINS, A. K. 1976. East Greenland Caledonian fold belt. *In:* ESCHER, A. & WATT, W. S. (eds) *Geology of Greenland. The Geological Survey of Greenland*, pp. 182–246.

KENNAN, P. S. 1979. Plutonic rocks of the Irish Caledonides. *In:* HARRIS, A. L., HOLLAND, C. H. & LEAKE, B. E. (eds) *The Caledonides of the British Isles Reviewed. Special Publication of the Geological Society of London No. 8*, pp. 705–11.

LEAKE, B. E. 1978. Granite emplacement: the granites of Ireland and their origin. *In:* BOWES, D. R. & LEAKE, B. E. (eds) *Crustal Evolution in Northwestern Britain and Adjacent Regions. Special Publication of the Geological Society of London No. 10*, pp. 221–48.

LEDRU, P. 1980. Evolution structurale et magmatique du complexe plutonique de Karmoy (Sud-Ouest des Caledonides norvégiennes). *Bulletin de la Société Géologique et Minéralogique de Bretagne*, **7**, 1–106.

LE BAS, M. J. 1982. The Caledonian granites and diorites of England and Wales. *In:* SUTHERLAND, D. S. (ed.) *Igneous Rocks of the British Isles*, pp. 191–201, Wiley, New York.

LEGGO, P. J., COMPSTON, W. & LEAKE, B. E. 1966. The geochronology of the Connemara granites and its bearing on the antiquity of the Dalradian series. *Quarterly Journal of the Geological Society of London*, **122**, 91–118.

LE PICHON, X., SIBUET, J.-C. & FRANCHETEAU, J. 1977. The fit of the continents around the North Atlantic. *Tectonophysics*, **38**, 169–209.

LOISELLE, M. C. & WONES, D. R. 1979. Characteristics and origin of anorogenic granites. *Geological*

Society of America, Abstracts with Programs, **11**, 468.

MEIGHAN, I. G. & NEESON, J. C. 1979. The Newry igneous complex, County Down. *In:* HARRIS, A. L., HOLLAND, C. H. & LEAKE, B. E. (eds) *The Caledonides of the British Isles Reviewed. Special Publication of the Geological Society of London, No. 8,* pp. 719–25.

MICHARD, A. & PIQUE, A. 1980. The Variscan belt in Morocco: structure and development model. *In:* WONES, D. R. (ed.) *The Caledonides in the USA: Proceedings of the International Geological Program—Caledonide Orogen Project 27, Blacksburg, VA. Department of Geological Sciences, Virginia Polytechnic Institute and State University, Memoir No. 2,* pp. 317–22.

MILLER, C. F. & BRADFISH, L. J. 1980. An inner Cordilleran belt of muscovite-bearing plutons. *Geology,* **8**, 412–6.

MILLER, J. A. & FLINN, D. 1966. A survey of the age relations of Shetland rocks. *Geological Journal,* **5**, 95–116.

NORDGULEN, O. 1984. The geology and emplacement of the Krakfjellet pluton, Bindal, central Norway. *Thesis (unpublished),* University of Bergen, Norway.

O'BRIEN, C., PLANT, J. A., SIMPSON, P. R. & TARNEY, J. 1985. The geochemistry, metasomatism and petrogenesis of the granites of the English Lake District. *Journal of the Geological Society, London,* **142**, 1139–57.

O'CONNOR, P. J. & BRUCK, P. M. 1978. Age and origin of the Leinster granite. *Journal of Earth Sciences, Royal Society of Dublin,* **1**, 105–13.

——, LONG, C. B., KENNAN, P. S., HALLIDAY, A. N., MAX, M. D. & RODDICK, J. C. 1982. Rb–Sr isochron study of the Thorr and Main Donegal granites, Ireland. *Geological Journal,* **17**, 279–95.

PANKHURST, R. J. 1974. Rb–Sr whole-rock chronology of Caledonian events in northeast Scotland. *Geological Society of America, Bulletin,* **85**, 345–50.

—— & SUTHERLAND, D. S. 1982. Caledonian granites and diorites of Scotland and Ireland. *In:* SUTHERLAND, D. S. (ed.) *Igneous rocks of the British Isles,* pp. 141–90, Wiley, New York.

——, ANDREWS, J. R., PHILLIPS, W. E. A., SANDERS, I. S. & TAYLOR, W. E. G. 1976. Age and structural setting of the Slieve Gamph igneous complex, Co. Mayo, Eire. *Journal of the Geological Society, London,* **132**, 327–36.

PIDGEON, R. T. & AFTALION, M. 1978. Cogenetic and inherited zircon U–Pb system in granites: Palaeozoic granites of Scotland and England. *In:* BOWES, D. R. & LEAKE, B. E. (eds) *Crustal Evolution in Northwestern Britain and Adjacent Regions. Special Publication of the Geological Society of London No. 10,* pp. 183–220.

PIN, C. & LANCELOT, J. 1982. U–Pb dating of an Early Palaeozoic bimodal magmatism in the French Massif Central and of its further metamorphic evolution. *Contribution to Mineralogy and Petrology,* **79**, 1–12.

PINTO, M. S. 1983. Geochronology of Portuguese granitoids: a contribution. *Studia Geologica Salmanticensia,* **18**, 277–306.

PIQUE, A. 1983. Structural domains of the Hercynian belt in Morocco. *In:* SCHENK, P. E. (ed.) *Regional trends in the Geology of the Appalachian–Caledonian–Hercynian–Mauritanide Orogen,* pp. 339–45, Reidel, Dordrecht.

PITCHER, W. S. 1979. The nature, ascent and emplacement of granitic magmas. *Journal of the Geological Society, London,* **136**, 627–62.

—— 1982. Granite type and tectonic environment. *In:* HSU, K. (ed.) *Mountain Building Processes,* pp. 19–40. Academic Press, London.

—— & BERGER, A. R. 1972. *The Geology of Donegal: A Study of Granite Emplacement and Unroofing,* Wiley-Interscience, New York, 435 pp.

PLANT, J., SIMPSON, P. R., GREEN, P. M., WATSON, J. V. & FOWLER, M. B. 1983. Metalliferous and mineralized Caledonian granites in relation to regional metamorphism and fracture systems in northern Scotland. *Transactions of the Institution of Mining and Metallurgy, Series B,* **92**, 33–42.

PRIEM, H. N. A. & TORSKE, T. 1973. Rb–Sr isochron age of Caledonian acid volcanics from Stord, western Norway. *Norges Geologiske Undersøkelse,* **300**, 83–5.

——, BOELRIJK, N. A. I. M., HEBEDA, E. H., VERDURMEN, E. A. & VERSCHURE, R. H. 1975. Isotopic dating of the Caledonian Binadal and Svenningdal granitic massifs, central Norway. *Norges Geologiske Undersøkelse,* **319**, 29–36.

REX, D. C. & GLEDHILL, A. R. 1981. Isotopic studies in the East Greenland Caledonides (72°–74°N)-Precambrian and Caledonian ages. *Rapport Grønlands Geologiske Undersøkelse,* **104**, 47–72.

——, GLEDHILL, A. R. & HIGGINS, A. K. 1976. Progress report on geochronological investigations in the crystalline complexes of the east Greenland Caledonian fold belt between 72° and 74°N. *Rapport Grønlands Geologiske Undersøkelse,* **80**, 127–33.

ROBERTS, D. 1980. Petrochemistry and palaeogeographic setting of the Ordovician volcanic rocks on Smola, central Norway. *Norges Geologiske Undersøkelse,* **348**, 43–60.

SANDFORD, K. S. 1950. Observations on the geology of the northern part of North-East Land (Spitsbergen). *Quarterly Journal of the Geological Society of London,* **105**, 461–91.

—— 1956. The stratigraphy and structure of the Hecla Hoek formation and its relationship to a subjacent metamorphic complex in North-East Land (Spitsbergen). *Quarterly Journal of the Geological Society of London,* **112**, 339–60.

STEIGER, R. H. & HENRICKSEN, N. 1972. The geochronology of the Scoreby Sund area. Progress Report 3: Zircon ages. *Rapport Grønlands Geologiske Undersøkelse,* **48**, 109–14.

——, HANSEN, B. T., SCHULER, C., BAR, M. T. & HENRICKSEN, N. 1979. Polyorogenic nature of the southern Caledonian fold belt in East Greenland. *Journal of Geology,* **87**, 475–95.

STEPHENS, W. E. & HALLIDAY, A. N. 1984. Geochemical contrasts between late Caledonian granitoid plutons of northern, central and southern Scotland.

Transactions of the Royal Society of Edinburgh, Earth Sciences, **75**, 259–73.

STILLMAN, C. J. 1981. Caledonian igneous activity. *In:* HOLLAND, C. H. (ed.) *A Geology of Ireland,* pp. 83–106, Scottish Academic Press.

STRAND, T. & KULLING, O. 1972. *Scandinavian Caledonides,* Wiley, New York, 302 pp.

STURT, B. A., SKARPENES, O., OHANIAN, A. T. & PRINGLE, I. R. 1975. Reconnaissance Rb/Sr isochron study in the Bergen arc system and regional implications. *Nature, London,* **253**, 595–9.

——, THON, A. & FURNES, H. 1979. The Karmoy ophiolite, southwest Norway. *Geology,* **7**, 316–20.

VAN BREEMEN, O. & PIASECKI, M. A. J. 1983. The Glen Kyllachy granite and its bearing on the nature of the Caledonian orogeny in Scotland. *Journal of the Geological Society, London,* **140**, 47–62.

WHITE, A. J. R. & CHAPPELL, B. W. 1977. Ultrametamorphism and granitoid genesis. *Tectonophysics,* **43**, 7–22.

ZALESKI, E. 1982. The geology of Speyside and Lower Findhorn granitoids. *Thesis (unpublished).* University of St. Andrews.

ZIEGLER, P. A. 1981. Late Caledonian framework of western and central Europe. *Terra Cognita,* **1**, 162.

W. E. STEPHENS, Department of Geology, University of St Andrews, Purdie Building, St Andrews, Fife KY16 9ST, Scotland.

The development of the Iapetus Ocean from the Arenig to the Wenlock

W. S. McKerrow

SUMMARY: In addition to the large continents of N America, Scandinavia and Gondwana, the regions around the early Palaeozoic Iapetus Ocean contained several small terranes. These included an island arc, which collided with various parts of N America to produce, in succession, the Grampian, Humberian and Taconic orogenies. They also included the terrane of Avalonia, a later Precambrian arc which had rifted off a margin of Gondwana by the middle Ordovician. Large sinistral strike-slip faults in Scotland suggest a total displacement of around 1500 km, so that by the Silurian an elongate Scotland lay to the W of Norway. Continental collisions took place in three stages: a Llandovery stage, perhaps related to eastward subduction below Svalbard, when W-verging nappes were emplaced in E Greenland, a later Silurian (Scandian) stage when westward subduction below Scotland can be related to E-verging nappes in Norway, and an early Devonian stage when Avalonia collided with N America (Acadian orogeny).

The first suggestion that a wide ocean was present in the early Palaeozoic between America and Europe (Wilson 1966) was based primarily on faunal differences. This ocean was named Iapetus (Harland & Gayer 1972) after the father of Atlas (from whom the Atlantic Ocean takes its name). Dewey (1969) was the first to propose a model for the development of Iapetus in terms of plate tectonics; since then, later models have had to take account of new data which are slowly revealing the increasing complexity of this development.

As well as distinguishing the times during which the various margins were active and passive, we now recognize the presence of island arcs (Aleinikoff 1977, Robinson & Hall 1980, Hall & Robinson 1982, Hatch 1982, Lyons et al. 1982) and oceanic islands (Neuman 1972, 1984). The presence of a mid-ocean island arc would imply that there were several discrete parts of Iapetus which closed at different times. There were also other oceans: the Tornquist Sea to the E of England (Cocks & Fortey 1982) and the Rheic Ocean to the S (McKerrow & Ziegler 1972, Cocks & Fortey 1982) were, like Iapetus, first proposed on the basis of palaeontological evidence (Fig. 1). More recently, exotic terranes have been postulated (Williams & Hatcher 1982, 1983, Zen 1983): some of these are separated by oceanic sutures, but others appear to be terranes which have shifted by strike-slip along the margin of the parent continent for many hundreds of kilometres in a similar manner to those recorded in the Cordillera of western N America (Coney et al. 1980).

Many collisions, between continent and continent or between arc and continent, are the result of the subduction of a relatively old cool oceanic crust, which may be completely buried so that ophiolite outcrops do not provide a record of all oceanic sutures. Many Cambrian and Ordovician ophiolites show evidence of amphibolite-facies metamorphism and appear to have been hot when obducted; some have been interpreted (Williams & Smyth 1973) as hot oceanic crust which had only been formed shortly before obduction, perhaps in small marginal basins. The Iapetus Ocean did not close finally until the Silurian (in Greenland and Norway) or the Devonian (in the northern Appalachians), but many exposed ophiolites have been dated as Cambrian or Ordovician. Clearly there were different parts of Iapetus which 'closed' at different times, and many of the Ordovician closures were related to marginal basins.

If ophiolites are not proof of a wide ocean and if oceanic sutures are seldom marked by ophiolites, what evidence do we have for the Iapetus Ocean? There are four categories of relevant data.

1 Faunal distributions are sometimes different between continents, although there have always been some animals which have greater mobility and it is clear that the study of fossil biogeography is not as simple as it once appeared (McKerrow & Cocks 1986).

2 Sedimentary facies changes can indicate the margins of continents (Rodgers 1968), and the distributions of such sediments as evaporites, reefs, tillites and certain clastic deposits can give fairly precise indications of latitude (Ziegler et al. 1981).

3 Rock types and structures characteristic of active margins include calc-alkaline igneous rocks, accretionary prisms and large strike-slip

From HARRIS, A. L. & FETTES, D. J. (eds), 1988, The Caledonian–Appalachian Orogen, Geological Society Special Publication No. 38, pp. 405–412.

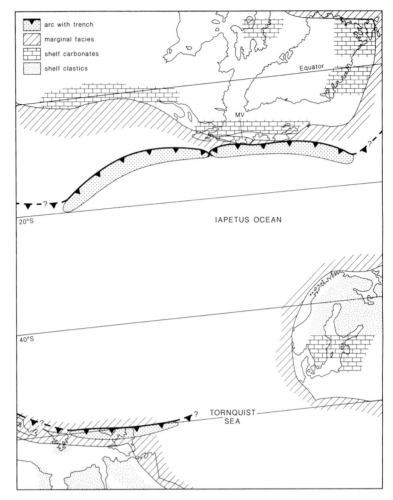

FIG. 1. A diagrammatic map of the Iapetus Ocean in the Arenig just after the collision of an island arc to produce
the Grampian orogeny in Scotland. The westerly continuation of the same arc is poised to collide with
Newfoundland in the Llanvirn and Llandeilo, and with New Brunswick and New England in the Caradoc to
produce the Taconic orogeny. England and Avalon are shown adjacent to France, Spain and Morocco, but it is
not at all certain to which part of Gondwana they were attached nor when they rifted away (they may have rifted
in the Cambrian).

faults. All these can be recognized along the
borders of Iapetus and help to indicate where and
when subduction was taking place along the
continental margins.

4   Palaeomagnetism was instrumental in convincing many geologists during the 1950s and
1960s that the continents are mobile. However,
the best results come from cratons and not from
orogens; rocks which have been deformed produce confusing magnetic signals (Cisowski 1984).
The results from the Appalachians and Caledonides have not helped very much in our understanding of the development of Iapetus (Briden *et al.*
1988).

The continents bordering Iapetus

Early Ordovician faunal and facies distributions
indicate that three continents—N America, Scandinavia and Gondwana—were present in the
Appalachian–Caledonian region at that time.

N America is characterized by benthic trilobites of the Bathyuridae family, nautiloids such
as *Plioceras*, many particular brachiopod genera
(e.g. *Hesperonomiella*) and the so-called 'mid-
continent conodont province' (Cocks & Fortey
1982, Fortey & Cocks 1988). Most of the faunas
which are restricted to the continent are shallow-
water benthos; many deeper-water benthos (oc-

curring mainly around the continental margins) and some of the pelagic animals were capable of spreading to other continents.The more mobile faunas include a few ostracods (Schallreuter & Siveter 1985) which appear to have been surprisingly widely distributed in the Ordovician.

During the Ordovician, the dominant shelf facies in N America were limestones and dolomites, with oolites, stromatolites and reefs; these persisted throughout the period (Webby 1984), suggesting that the continent straddled the equator for the whole of the Ordovician. An equatorial position for N America can also be deduced from the palaeomagnetic data (Scotese 1984).

In the Arenig, Scandinavia contained a distinctive group of asaphid trilobites (the 'megistaspids' of Cocks & Fortey 1982) and some brachiopods, including *Lycophoria* and *Clitambonites*, which are not known in N America or Gondwana. These faunas extend SE to the Holy Cross Mountains in southern Poland where deeper Arenig facies are present, perhaps indicating the southern margin of the Scandinavian continent. The pelagic graptolites and those trilobites which are thought to be pelagic show a mixture of genera, some of which also occur in N America and Gondwana. If their distribution is related to climate the Scandinavian faunas would appear to indicate latitudes intermediate between those of the other two continents (Cocks & Fortey 1982, Fortey & Cocks 1988).

The sedimentary facies of Scandinavia include nodular detrital limestones but they show no evidence of a very warm climate (Jaanusson 1973) and reefs are absent until the late Ordovician (Webby 1984). Thus both the faunal and facies evidence suggest that Scandinavia was situated in middle latitudes during the early Ordovician.

During the Cambrian and early Ordovician Gondwana had many of the same faunas and facies as Avalonia (England, Wales, southern Ireland, eastern Newfoundland, Nova Scotia, coastal New Brunswick and coastal New England). In many areas shallow-marine sands and silts, like the Armorican quartzite, are typical of the Arenig, while the Llanvirn is often represented by deeper-water shales. There is a complete absence of limestones. These beds contain the trilobites *Neseuretus* and *Selenopeltis*, together with characteristic trace fossils (*Cruziana* and *Rusophycus* species), obolid Lingulida (including *Ectenoglossa*) and the bivalve *Babinka prima* (Cocks & Fortey 1982). Much of Avalonia contains deeper-water facies than those in cratonic Gondwana; in these rocks there are mixtures of endemic forms with those that also occur in other continents. Similar marginal facies also occur in the Ardennes and Bohemia, showing that all of Europe SE of the Tornquist Sea lay along the margins of Gondwana until the early Ordovician (Fig. 1).

Terranes

There are numerous regions in the Caledonides and northern Appalachians which have had different tectonic histories from the presently adjacent parts of the three large continents. Some of these may have formed oceanic islands, while others may have undergone strike-slip along the continental margins.

The early Ordovician margin of N America can be recognized by a change in facies along the edge of the platform carbonates (Rodgers 1968); this line lies very close to the Baie Verte–Brompton line, an ophiolitic belt which is the 'surface trace of a structural junction between deformed rocks of an ancient continental margin and bordering ocean' (Williams & St Julien 1978). In the northern Appalachians many terranes have been described (Keppie 1981, 1985, Williams & Hatcher 1982, 1983, Zen 1983). These can be grouped into three categories.

1 Fragments of an early Ordovician island arc, which in places appears to be resting on oceanic crust, while elsewhere is perhaps an old continental crust.
2 Fragments of Avalonia, a continental mass with late Precambrian arc rocks which had Gondwana affinities until the early Ordovician but which separated from Gondwana, perhaps in more than one piece, before colliding with N America in the Devonian Acadian orogeny.
3 The Meguma terrane, which shows no close affinities with the rest of Avalonia until the early Devonian plutons were emplaced. It may have been incorporated with N America separately from the rest of Nova Scotia (Keppie 1985).

In New England and New Brunswick the complex Acadian deformation and metamorphism has made the interpretation of the palaeogeography difficult to unravel, but many workers now agree that the Bronson Hill and Tetagouche massifs consist of early Ordovician arc rocks lying, at least in part, on oceanic crust (Doolan *et al.* 1982, Hall & Robinson 1982, Hatch 1982). This arc appears to have lain above a SE-dipping subduction zone and to have collided with N America in the late Ordovician to produce the Taconic nappes (Figs 1 and 2).

In Newfoundland there is a similar suite of early Ordovician arc rocks, the Lush's Bight Group (Dean 1978, Williams 1979, Arnott *et al.*

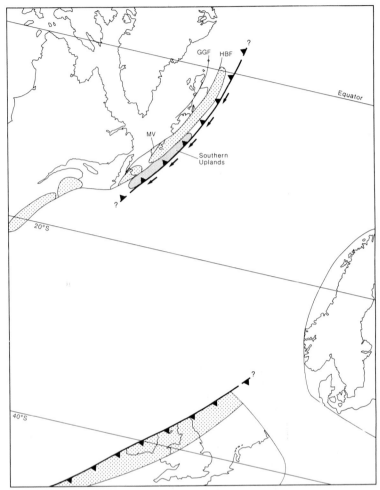

FIG. 2. By Caradoc time the island arc had collided with N America; the Bronson Hill and Tetagouche parts of the arc appear to be in a position close to their original points of collision. The accretionary prism of the Southern Uplands has started to develop off western Newfoundland, and the Midland Valley and Grampian Highlands were offset along the Highland Boundary and Great Glen faults. By the late Caradoc, England and eastern Avalonia had similar faunas to those of Scandinavia and were becoming faunally distinct from Gondwana as the Rheic Ocean widened. The trench shown to the N of England could well have been to the NE.

1985), which rested, at least in part, on ophiolites representing old ocean crust. Thrusting in western Newfoundland, which can be dated as Llanvirn (around Hare Bay) and Llandeilo (Bay of Islands and Humber Arm), has been interpreted (Hibbard 1983) as being due to collision of the Lush's Bight island arc with N America.

In the British Isles the early Ordovician Grampian orogeny can also be interpreted (Dewey 1982, Mitchell 1984) as being due to collision of an island arc, but in this case there are no unequivocal exposure of contemporary island-arc rocks immediately oceanwards of the deformed rocks. The diagrammatic map (Fig. 1)

for the Arenig shows that it is possible that all the arc rocks in the northern Appalachians might be continuous with each other and with an arc to the S of the Grampian Highlands. Modern arcs are commonly several thousand kilometres long, and therefore if this Ordovician arc were of a similar length it might be expected not merely to reach Scotland but to extend well to the N. This extension may be present in the Ballantrae Complex in the SW of the Scottish Midland valley (Bluck *et al.* 1980, Bluck 1984); it may also be present in some of the Ordovician volcanic rocks in the allochthons of Scandinavia (Gale & Roberts 1974). The progressive southeastward migration of the timing of the successive orogenies from the Tremadoc Grampian orogeny in Scotland through the Llanvirn–Llandeilo Humberian orogeny in Newfoundland to the Caradoc Taconic orogeny in New Brunswick and New England is also in agreement with the hypothesis of a single arc colliding obliquely with N America.

Strike-slip movements

In the northern Appalachians the remains of the Bronson Hill, Tetagouche and Lush's Bight arc rocks are still situated near the nappes formed during collision (Fig. 2). This is not so obviously the case in Britain, where a total of around 1500 km of sinistral strike-slip movements may have taken place in Scotland along the Great Glen, Highland Boundary, Southern Upland and other faults. The evidence of sinistral strike-slip is twofold: first, the results of detailed structural studies (Stringer & Treagus 1981, Anderson 1986, Kemp 1986, Knipe *et al.* 1986) performed in the vicinity of the major faults and within the Southern Uplands, and secondly the provenance of clasts in conglomerates adjacent to these faults.

Bluck (1983, 1984) has summarized the sedimentary provenance of conglomerate clasts along both margins of the Midland Valley. Along the northern margin the carbonate- and shale-bearing Ordovician successions (Curry *et al.* 1982) show no indication of the Grampian orogeny which took place in the Tremadoc to the N of the Highland Boundary fault, and even by the late Silurian and early Devonian granite clasts in the Midland Valley are indicating that a different terrane was present to the N (van Breemen & Bluck 1981). Along the southern margin of the Midland Valley exotic clasts are also present in Ordovician and Silurian conglomerates. The large granite clasts in the shallow-water conglomerates of the Barr Group (Ince 1984) are derived neither from the Grampian nor from the Southern Upland terranes. Similarly, the clasts in the Silurian igneous and quartzite conglomerates in the southern inliers of the Midland Valley are derived from the S (Bluck 1983) but do not come from the Southern Uplands. This sedimentological evidence shows clearly that movements persisted on both the Highland Boundary and Southern Upland faults until the late Silurian or early Devonian.

Petrographic studies in mass-flow conglomerates in the Southern Uplands show that in the late Ordovician a provenance terrane with granite plutons with ages of *c.* 1200 Ma and 500–460 Ma lay to the NW (Elders 1986). These granites can be matched petrographically with plutons of similar ages now exposed in N and W Newfoundland, which strongly suggests that the Southern Uplands of Scotland were situated off Newfoundland in the late Ordovician (Fig. 2).

Silurian reconstruction of Iapetus

If the Southern Uplands were adjacent to western Newfoundland in the late Ordovician and if the northern Highlands of Scotland had not moved relative to N America before the opening of the Atlantic, the Southern Uplands would have moved some 1500 km to its present position in Scotland. If this 1500 km movement were confined to the Great Glen, Highland Boundary and Southern Uplands faults there would be around 500 km displacement on each fault. However, it is probable that sinistral shear has taken place along many zones within the Grampian, Midland Valley and Southern Uplands terranes (Soper & Hutton 1984) and that the movements on each of the three major faults may only be of the order of 300 km.

If the terranes which now make up Scotland are extended by 1500 km (Figs 2 and 3), a reasonable Silurian palaeogeography can be envisaged for the N Iapetus region. The E-verging nappes in Norway were emplaced in two phases: an earlier Finnmarkian phase, which may conceivably be attributed to an arc colliding with the eastern margin of Scandinavia in the early Ordovician, and a mainly late Silurian Scandian phase (Gee & Roberts 1983). In contrast, the nappes in E Greenland are W verging, and it now appears that emplacement commenced in the latest Llandovery (Hurst *et al.* 1983). Thus it would appear improbable that Greenland collided with Norway when the N Iapetus closed in the Silurian. However, if Scotland is stretched by 1500 km (Fig. 3) the nappes in Greenland and Norway are no longer opposed to each other. Not only may the different times of collision be explained, but also the different sense of vergence. If a subduction zone extended down eastwards, possibly below Svalbard and/or the Barents Sea continent, the W-verging nappes could have been emplaced by collision in the late Llandovery. Further S, Norway (with its E-verging nappes) would be opposite Scotland. The abundant volcanic and plutonic calc-alkaline rocks (Thirlwall 1981) of Silurian and early Devonian age strongly suggest a westerly-inclined subduction zone, which is consistent with the E-verging nappes of Norway (Fig. 3).

In Fig. 3 the N Sea is shown with its present-day width. It has clearly undergone some crustal

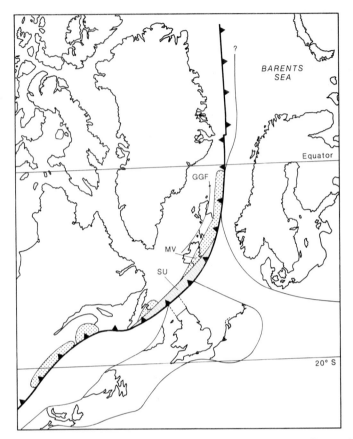

Fig. 3. By Wenlock time collision had taken place between Greenland and the Barents Sea continent with easterly subduction. However, later westerly subduction, below the still elongate Scotland, was responsible for the E-verging nappes in Norway. The gap shown between the present coast of Norway and the trench to the W may have been occupied by Scandinavian continental crust which became subducted below Scotland (Soper & Hutton 1984). The southern part of the Iapetus between Avalonia and N America did not finally close until the early Devonian Acadian orogeny.

stretching to allow for the subsidence since the Carboniferous. Thus the Silurian map should show Norway even closer to the Midland Valley. Could Norway be the source for the exotic clasts in the Midland Valley Silurian conglomerates?

Summarizing remarks

In the Arenig three continents existed: N America to the W of Iapetus, and Scandinavia and Gondwana to the E of Iapetus and separated by the Tornquist Sea. An island arc was present offshore to the E of N America; perhaps part of it had collided with Scotland in the Tremadoc (to give the Grampian orogeny), and possibly it had a northern extension which was obducted in some Scandian nappes in Scandinavia.

In the Cambrian or early Ordovician, England,

Wales and SE Ireland parted from Gondwana, so that by Caradoc times their faunas became identical with those of Scandinavia. The absence of late Ordovician faunas in western Avalonia makes it uncertain whether coastal New England and eastern Newfoundland were attached to England or whether they left Gondwana independently and remained isolated in the Iapetus Ocean until collision with N America in the early Devonian Acadian orogeny.

The Humberian and Taconic orogenies were caused by collision of the Lush's Bight, Tetagouche and Bronson Hill island arcs during the Ordovician; the thrust episodes show a southward migration with time from early Ordovician (Llanvirn) in northern Newfoundland to late Caradoc in Massachusetts and New York.

Sinistral strike-slip movements on the Great Glen, Highland Boundary and Southern Upland faults in Scotland are indicated by detritus from western Newfoundland in conglomerates in the Southern Uplands. Strike-slip movements persisted until the early Devonian, so that Scotland was still elongate when Silurian collision occurred with Norway. The different times of collision and the different vergence of the nappes suggests that these two continents did not collide with each other. It is suggested that Greenland collided with a 'Barents Sea' continent, while Norway collided with the still elongate Scotland. It is probable that final continental collision did not occur between Avalonia and N America until the early Devonian Acadian orogeny.

ACKNOWLEDGMENTS: Thanks are due to Robin Cocks, Chris Elders, Richard Fortey and Jack Soper for fruitful discussions.

References

ALIENIKOFF, J. N. 1977. Petrochemistry and tectonic origin of the Ammonoosuc Volcanics, New Hampshire–Vermont. *Geological Society of America Bulletin*, **99**, 1546–52.

ANDERSON, T. B. 1986. The onset and timing of Caledonian sinistral shear in County Down. *Geological Society Newsletter*, **15** (1), 9–10 (abstract).

ARNOTT, R. J., MCKERROW, W. S. & COCKS, L. R. M. 1985. The tectonics and depositional history of the Ordovician and Silurian rocks of Notre Dame Bay, Newfoundland. *Canadian Journal of Earth Sciences*, **22**, 607–18.

BLUCK, B. J. 1983. Role of the Midland Valley of Scotland in the Caledonian Orogeny. *Transactions of the Royal Society of Edinburgh, Earth Sciences*, **74**, 119–36.

—— 1984. Pre-Carboniferous history of the Midland Valley of Scotland. *Transactions of the Royal Society of Edinburgh, Earth Sciences*, **75**, 275–95.

——, HALLIDAY, A. N., AFTALION, M. & MACINTYRE, R. M. 1980. Age and origin of Ballantrae ophiolite and its significance to the Caledonian orogeny and Ordovician time scale. *Geology*, **8**, 492–5.

VAN BREEMEN, O. & BLUCK, B. J. 1981. Episodic granite plutonism in the Scottish Caledonides. *Nature, London*, **291**, 113–7.

BRIDEN, J. C., KENT, D. V., LAPOINTE, P. L., LIVERMORE, R. A., ROY, J. L., SEGUIN, M. K., SMITH, A. G., VAN DER VOO, R. & WATTS, D. R. 1988. Palaeomagnetic constraints on the evolution of the Caledonian–Appalachian orogen. *This volume.*

CISOWSKI, S. M. 1984. Evidence for early Tertiary remagnetisation of Devonian rocks from the Orcadian Basin, northern Scotland, and associated transcurrent fault motion. *Geology*, **12**, 369–72.

COCKS, L. R. M. & FORTEY, R. A. 1982. Faunal evidence for oceanic separations in the Palaeozoic of Britain. *Journal of the Geological Society, London*, **139**, 465–78.

CONEY, P. J., JONES, D. L. & MONGER, J. W. H. 1980. Cordilleran suspect terranes. *Nature, London*, **288**, 329–33.

CURRY, G. B., INGHAM, J. K., BLUCK, B. J. & WILLIAMS, A. 1982. The significance of a reliable Ordovician age for some Highland Border rocks in Central Scotland. *Journal of the Geological Society, London*, **139**, 451–4.

DEAN, P. L. 1978. The volcanic stratigraphy and metallurgy of Notre Dame Bay, Newfoundland. *Memorial University of Newfoundland Geology Report No. 7*, 204 pp.

DEWEY, J. F. 1969. Evolution of the Appalachian/ Caledonian orogen. *Nature, London*, **222**, 124–9.

—— 1982. Plate tectonics and the evolution of the British Isles. *Journal of the Geological Society, London*, **139**, 371–412.

DOOLAN, B. L., GALE, M. H., GALE, P. N. & HOAR, R. S. 1982. Geology of the Quebec Re-entrant: possible constraints from early rifts and the Vermont–Quebec Serpentine Belt. *Geological Association of Canada Special Paper No. 24*, pp. 87–115.

ELDERS, C. F. 1986. The provenance of granite boulders in the Northern and Central Belts. *Geological Society Newsletter*, **15** (1), 8. (abstract).

FORTEY, R. A. & COCKS, L. R. M. 1988. Arenig to Llandovery faunal distributions in the Caledonides. *This volume.*

GALE, N. H. & ROBERTS, D. 1974. Trace element geochemistry of Norwegian lower Palaeozoic basic volcanics and its tectonic implications. *Earth and Planetary Science Letters*, **22**, 380–90.

GEE, D. G. & ROBERTS, D. 1983. Timing of deformation in the Scandinavian Caledonides. *In*: SCHENK, P. E. (ed.) *Regional Trends in the Geology of the Appalachian–Caledonian–Hercynian–Mauritanide Orogen*, pp. 279–92, Reidel, Dordrecht.

HALL, L. M. & ROBINSON, P. 1982. Stratigraphic-tectonic subdivisions in Southern New England. *Geological Association of Canada Special Paper No. 24*, pp. 15–41.

HARLAND, W. B. & GAYER, R. A. 1972. The Arctic Caledonides and earlier oceans. *Geological Magazine*, **109**, 289–314.

HATCH, N. L. 1982. The Taconian Line in Western New England and its implications to Palaeozoic tectonic history. *Geological Association of Canada Special Paper No. 24*, pp. 67–85.

HIBBARD, J. 1983. Geology of the Baie Verte Peninsula, Newfoundland. *Department of Mines and Energy, Newfoundland and Labrador, Memoir No. 2*, 239 pp.

HURST, J. M., MCKERROW, W. S., SOPER, N. J. & SURLYK, F. 1983. The relationship between Caledonian nappe tectonics and Silurian turbidite deposition in North Greenland. *Journal of the Geological Society, London*, **140**, 123–31.

INCE, D. 1984. Sedimentation and tectonism in the Middle Ordovician of the Girvan district, SW Scotland. *Transactions of the Royal Society of Edinburgh, Earth Sciences*, **75**, 225–37.

JAANUSSON, V. 1973. Aspects of carbonate sedimentation in the Ordovician of Baltoscandia. *Lethaia*, **6**, 11–34.

KEMP, A. E. S. 1986. Tectonic development of the Southern Belt in the Southern Uplands. *Geological Society Newsletter*, **15** (1), 9 (abstract).

KEPPIE, J. D. 1981. The Appalachian collage. *Terra Cognita*, **1**, 54.

—— 1985. The Appalachian collage. *In*: GEE, D. G. & STURT, B. A. (eds) *The Caledonide Orogen— Scandinavia and Related Areas*, pp. 1217–26, Wiley, Chichester.

KNIPE, R. J., NEEDHAM, R., CHAMBERLAIN, M. & PAGE, A. 1986. Deformation histories in the western Southern Uplands. *Geological Society Newsletter*, **15** (1), 9 (abstract).

LYONS, J. B., BOUDETTE, E. L. & ALIENIKOFF, J. N. 1982. The Avalonian and Gander Zones in Central Eastern New England. *Geological Association of Canada Special Paper No. 24*, pp. 43–66.

MCKERROW, W. S. & COCKS, L. R. M. 1986. Oceans, island arcs and olistostromes: the use of fossils in distinguishing sutures, terranes and environments around the Iapetus Ocean. *Journal of the Geological Society, London*, **143**, 185–191.

—— & ZIEGLER, A. M. 1972. Palaeozoic oceans. *Nature, London, Physical Science*, **240**, 92–4.

MITCHELL, A. H. G. 1984. The British Caledonides; interpretation from Cenozoic analogues. *Geological Magazine*, **121**, 35–46.

NEUMAN, R. B. 1972. Brachiopods of early Ordovician volcanic islands. *24th International Geological Congress*, Section 7, pp. 297–302.

—— 1984. Geology and palaeobiology of islands in the Ordovician Iapetus Ocean: review and implications. *Geological Society of America Bulletin*, **95**, 1188–201.

ROBINSON, P. & HALL, L. M. 1980. Tectonic synthesis of southern New England. *In*: WONES, D. R. (ed.) *The Caledonides in the USA: Proceedings of the International Geological Correlation Program— Caledonide Orogen Project 27, Blacksburg, VA. Virginia Polytechnic Institute and State University, Department of Geological Sciences, Memoir No. 2*, pp. 73–82.

RODGERS, J. 1968. The eastern edge of the North American continent during the Cambrian and Early Ordovician. *In*: ZEN, E-AN, WHITE, W. S., HADLEY, J. B. & THOMSON, J. B. (eds) *Studies in Appalachian Geology: Northern and Maritime*, pp. 141–9, Wiley-Interscience, New York.

SCHALLREUTER, R. E. L. & SIVETER, D. J. 1985. Ostracodes across the Iapetus Ocean. *Palaeontology*, **28**, 577–98.

SCOTESE, C. R. 1984. Paleozoic paleomagnetism and the assembly of Pangea. *In*: VAN DER VOO, R., SCOTESE, C. R. & BONHOMMET, N. (eds) *Plate Reconstruction from Paleozoic Paleomagnetism. Geodynamics Series*, Vol. 12, pp. 1–10, American Geophysical Union, Washington, DC.

SOPER, N. J. & HUTTON, D. H. W. 1984. Late Caledonian sinistral displacements in Britain: implications for a three-plate collision model. *Tectonics*, **3**, 781–94.

STRINGER, P. & TREAGUS, J. E. 1981. Asymmetrical folding in the Hawick Rocks of the Galloway area, Southern Uplands. *Scottish Journal of Geology*, **17**, 129–48.

THIRLWALL, M. F. 1981. Plate tectonic implications of chemical data from volcanic rocks of the British Old Red Sandstone. *Journal of the Geological Society, London*, **138**, 123–38.

WEBBY, B. D. 1984. Ordovician reefs and climate. *In*: BRUTON, D. L. (ed.) *Aspects of the Ordovician System*, pp. 89–100, Universitetsforlaget, Oslo.

WILLIAMS, H. 1979. The Appalachian Orogen in Canada. *Canadian Journal of Earth Sciences*, **16**, 792–807.

—— & HATCHER, R. D. 1982. Suspect terranes and accretionary history of the Appalachian Orogen. *Geology*, **10**, 530–6.

—— & —— 1983. Appalachian suspect terranes. *In*: HATCHER, R. D., JR, WILLIAMS, H. & ZIETZ, I. (eds) *Tectonics and Geophysics of Mountain Chains, Geological Society of America Memoir No. 158*, pp. 33–53.

—— & ST JULIEN, P. 1978. The Baie Verte–Brompton line in Newfoundland and regional correlations in the Canadian Appalachians. *Geological Survey of Canada Paper No. 78–1A*, pp. 225–9.

—— & SMYTH, W. R. 1973. Metamorphic aureoles beneath ophiolite suites and Alpine peridotites: tectonic implications with west Newfoundland examples. *American Journal of Science*, **273**, 594–621.

WILSON, J. T. 1966. Did the Atlantic close and then re-open? *Nature, London*, **211**, 676–81.

ZEN, E-AN. 1983. Exotic terranes in the New England Appalachians—limits, candidates and ages: a speculative essay. *Geological Society of America Memoir No. 158*, 55–81.

ZIEGLER, A. M., BARRETT, S. F. & SCOTESE, C. R. 1981. Palaeoclimate, sedimentation and continental accretion. *Philosophical Transactions of the Royal Society of London, Series A*, **301**, 253–64.

W. S. MCKERROW, Department of Earth Sciences, Parks Road, Oxford OX1 3PR, UK.

Wenlock to Mid-Devonian Activity in the Caledonian–Appalachian Orogen

CONVENOR
R. D. HATCHER
University of Tennessee
Knoxville

Plutonism relating to this period is dealt with in articles by Ed Stephens and by the late David Wones and Krishna Sinha in the previous section.

Wenlock to mid-Devonian volcanism of the Caledonian–Appalachian orogen

M. F. Thirlwall

SUMMARY: Volcanic rocks of Siluro-Devonian age form two distinct petrological provinces in the Caledonian–Appalachian orogen roughly corresponding to regions which last suffered major deformation in the Permo-Carboniferous or the Siluro-Devonian. In France, Germany and SW England the minor volcanism was dominantly marine and mostly produced enriched tholeiites. Abundant volcanism about 410 Ma old in Scotland is calc-alkaline and related to subduction on the NW margin of Iapetus, while volcanism in Shetland, E Greenland and Norway is rather younger and more acidic but is calc-alkaline, at least in Shetland. Apart from a metatholeiite in Alabama, Siluro-Devonian volcanism in N America is restricted to New England and the Canadian Appalachians where two major volcanic belts run NE–SW. Chemical data for these rocks are limited but do suggest that at least some rocks in both belts are related to subduction processes. This need not necessarily greatly constrain tectonic models.

The period Wenlock to mid-Devonian was one of intense volcanism in many areas of western Europe and eastern N America. Final closure of Iapetus between N America, Baltica and Avalonia occurred during this period and the change in sedimentary facies from marine to continental was accompanied by dominantly sub-aerial volcanism in the developing Old Red Sandstone continent. In principle, this volcanism could be related to active subduction at either margin of Iapetus, to subduction-related processes such as back-arc spreading or to processes occurring within the new continental plate after final suturing. In contrast, the region S of Avalonia remained dominantly marine throughout the period, and the relatively minor spilitic volcanism is most probably related to within-plate rifting events or possibly to immature island arcs. This contribution will concentrate on the volcanism associated with Iapetus closure and will attempt to discuss to what extent it may be related to subduction processes.

Considering the volcanism separately from related plutonism is very artificial for in many places erosion has removed the volcanic record. Unfortunately the relationships between volcanics and plutonics have only been explored in a few areas, but it is hoped that this paper will be read in conjunction with the companion papers on plutonism.

Age of volcanism

One of the greatest problems in obtaining useful tectonic information from igneous rocks is the question of how palaeontologically dated sediments can be correlated with isotopically dated igneous rocks. Isotopic dating is, of course, often necessary in volcanic suites because of the scarcity or poor preservation of fossils. The problem is not just one of the geological time-scale, which has seen very major fluctuations around the Siluro-Devonian boundary (compare, for example, Gale et al. 1979 and McKerrow et al. 1980), but is also caused by ambiguity in interpreting isotopic ages. It has recently become clear that Rb–Sr whole-rock isochrons in fine-grained acid igneous rocks, which are the principal source of geochronological data for Caledonian Siluro-Devonian volcanics, are highly susceptible to resetting during hydrothermal alteration or low-grade metamorphism (e.g. McKerrow et al. 1980). For example, McKerrow et al. note that the relative Rb–Sr whole-rock ages for Siluro-Devonian lavas in Maine are inconsistent with their stratigraphic ages, although the errors quoted in the original data of Bottino & Fullagar (1966) yield on reprocessing an appreciably higher error in the isochron age (± 19 Ma) than that quoted by McKerrow et al. (1980). Although coarse-grained igneous rocks (plutonics) appear less susceptible to resetting of Rb–Sr systematics during alteration, care must still be taken in using their whole-rock isotopic ages because of the possibilities both of resetting and of heterogeneity in initial $^{87}Sr/^{86}Sr$ ratios.

In addition to the uncertain affects of alteration, older published isotopic ages often use decay constants and methods of error estimation appreciably different from the modern ones used to estimate the geological time-scale. For example, Brookins et al. (1973) reported Rb–Sr whole-rock ages of 390 ± 5 Ma, 393 ± 6 Ma and 387 ± 9 Ma for three volcanic units from Penobscot Bay, Maine, which do not appear to be wholly

From HARRIS, A. L. & FETTES, D. J. (eds), 1988, *The Caledonian–Appalachian Orogen*, Geological Society Special Publication No. 38, pp. 415–428.

inconsistent with the Gedinnian fossil ages of the first two. Recalculation using modern methods and constants (York 1969 (2σ error multiplied by the square root of MSWD), Steiger & Jager 1977) gives ages of 370 ± 38 Ma, 384 ± 22 Ma and 366 ± 22 Ma respectively, which are so imprecise as to have little value for either time-scale or plate-tectonic reconstruction work.

However, sufficient high quality modern age determinations do exist for us to be fairly confident that the base of the Devonian lies around 410 Ma, the base of the upper Devonian around 370 Ma and the base of the Wenlock around 425 Ma (McKerrow *et al.* 1985). These modern dates should form the basis of any hypotheses linking Caledonian igneous activity to plate-tectonic events.

Volcanic rock—tectonic setting relationships

The principal objective of conducting a review of Siluro-Devonian volcanic activity throughout the Caledonides must be to describe what clues the volcanism can provide about its plate tectonic environment. It is therefore important to discuss some of the logic behind the deduction of tectonic environment and to pinpoint some of the pitfalls. Three distinct paths can be taken: the first involves lithological comparisons between ancient and modern volcanics of known tectonic environment, the second involves chemical comparisons and the third compares petrogenetic processes operating in ancient and modern volcanics.

Lithological comparison of rock types, mineralogy and relative rock abundances has been the commonest method of inferring tectonic setting used in the literature. Whereas this method is readily applicable on a very broad scale (e.g. a large rhyolite province is hardly likely to be generated at a spreading ridge), it can be very misleading in detail because of problems related to field or petrographic distinction between basalt and andesite and to the estimation of abundances of rock types in poorly preserved ancient volcanic terranes. For example, Mykura & Phemister (1976) described a bimodal suite of Devonian 'basalts' and rhyolites from Papa Stour, Shetland, but recent chemical work has shown that the 'basalts' contain around 57% SiO_2 (Thirlwall 1979). Similarly, a 'pyroxene–andesite' reported by Mykura & Phemister from Sandness, Shetland, contains 50% SiO_2 (Thirlwall 1979). The problem is well illustrated by Bradley's (1983) discussion of the Coastal Volcanic Arc, Maine, which some workers have viewed as bimodal

(and thus probably related to within-plate rifting) and others as andesite dominated (and thus probably subduction related). Apart from the disruption to the original volcanic terranes produced by Acadian tectonism, the observed relative abundances of rock types may bear little relationship to those erupted because of the possibility that a large part of the composition range is erupted as readily eroded pyroclasts.

While major-element analysis of ancient volcanic rocks can at least allow distinction between basalts and andesites, alteration and metamorphism may completely obliterate original normative characteristics, may cause addition of H_2O and CO_2 and consequently result in appreciably lower SiO_2 contents, may seriously affect alkali contents and thus K–Si relations, and may modify or completely mask the distinctive fractionation trends used to differentiate calc-alkaline from tholeiitic rocks. While these chemical features are undoubtedly useful in suggesting tectonic environments, they should only be used in conjunction with some measure of extent of alteration such as the volatile content or the presence of fresh igneous mineralogy. It is not sufficient to use large numbers of analyses of highly altered rocks, for example, to infer a calc-alkaline trend on an AFM diagram because alteration may produce a systematic change in the Fe/Mg ratio. This is particularly true for metavolcanics; Acadian metamorphism produced amphibolite-facies Siluro-Devonian metavolcanics in southern New England and major-element classification of these would be rather hazardous.

Pearce & Cann (1973), Wood *et al.* (1979) and other workers have popularized the concept that many trace elements are 'immobile' in hydrothermally altered and weakly metamorphosed basic volcanics and that their relative abundances are diagnostic of tectonic setting. The elements involved are principally the high field strength elements (HFSEs) (Zr, Nb, Ti, P, Hf, Ta), the rare earth elements (REEs), and Th, Ni and Cr. They are regarded as immobile because of their resistance to transportation by hydrothermal fluids. Some workers have questioned this immobility, but problems only really seem to arise where there is substantial metasomatic alteration. Further, immobility can be tested by examining the interrelationships of several elements; these should display normal igneous features if the rocks are unaltered. A more serious problem with this approach is that the composition fields thought to be diagnostic of particular tectonic settings are based on relatively limited chemical data for modern volcanics, and that the processes generating the different fields reflect both source composition effects, which are likely to be related to tectonic setting throughout Earth history, and fractional crystallization effects, which are mostly dependent on local conditions such as pressure, temperature and water activity. Thus the differences between basaltic groups on the Ti–Zr diagram of Pearce & Cann (1973) could be generated by different fractional-crystallization histories, while the Cr–Ti diagram (Pearce 1975) is wholly dependent on the different fractionation paths usually operating in ocean-floor and island-arc basalts. Further, the general significance of some commonly used diagrams can be seriously questioned; for example, Wood (1980) showed that Tertiary within-plate volcanics from Skye plotted in all the fields of his Th–Hf–Ta diagram and attributed this to crustal contamination of within-plate basalts. This is of little help in interpreting ancient volcanic rock chemistry in the absence of comprehensive isotopic data; further, isotopic work by Dickin (1981) and Thirlwall & Jones (1983) shows that many of the Skye lavas falling in the normal mid-ocean ridge basalt (N-type MORB) field are uncontaminated.

I believe that the only satisfactory way of investigating tectonic settings of ancient volcanics is to use petrography, full chemistry and preferably isotopes. These can be used together to investigate petrogenetic relationships within and source materials of each ancient volcanic suite and to compare these with the distinctive processes operating in modern tectonic settings. The most convenient way of using chemistry to illustrate broad-scale petrogenetic processes operating in lavas is by means of normalized incompatible element diagrams ('spidergrams') relative to chondrite or estimated bulk Earth (Sun 1980) or to MORB (e.g. Pearce 1983). In the case of Sun's diagrams the elements are ordered in leftward-increasing estimated incompatibility in standard lherzolite phase assemblages, and MORB and ocean island basalts usually show relatively smooth concave-downwards patterns ranging from MORB which is strongly depleted in incompatible elements to highly enriched alkali basalts (e.g. Sun 1980, Thirlwall & Bluck 1984, Thompson *et al.* 1984). These differences could reflect source-composition effects, differences in the extent of partial melting or conceivably differences in the extent and style of fractionation (e.g. O'Hara & Mathews 1981).

In contrast, arc lavas (e.g. Sun 1980, Thirlwall & Graham 1984, Thompson *et al.* 1984) and contaminated continental basalts (e.g. Thirlwall & Jones 1983, Thompson *et al.* 1984) show very 'spiky' spidergrams resulting from the incorporation of some form of continental component, either subducted or during the passage of magmas through the crust. In both cases the addition of crustal material results in elevated hydrophile elements (K, Rb, Ba, Sr, Pb) and sometimes light REEs, Th and U relative to HFSEs. Conventional diagrams of the Pearce & Cann (1973) type will not satisfactorily distinguish arc lavas from contaminated continental lavas because they may incorporate essentially similar crustal components. Only very detailed studies permit clear resolution of the differences (e.g. Thirlwall & Graham 1984; see also Thompson *et al.* 1984) but it is possible to suggest some guidelines to permit distinction:

1 Crustally contaminated lavas are unlikely to have elevated Sr relative to REEs etc. because of the stability of plagioclase as a crustal phase. Arc lavas typically have elevated strontium resulting from its preferential transport in hydrous fluids from the subducting lithosphere (e.g. Hawkesworth & Powell 1980). However, positive Sr 'anomalies' can be gained by continental basalts and lost by arc lavas through plagioclase fractionation; for success, therefore, this criterion should only be used in relatively primitive lavas.

2 Isotopically uncontaminated lavas with smooth spidergrams are likely to be available in most continental volcanic piles; in contrast, few, if any, arc volcanics lack 'spiky' spidergrams and in particular almost all have prominent depletion in Nb relative to hydrophile elements, thorium and light REEs. Indeed, in some cases (e.g. Thirlwall & Graham 1984) where arc lavas have subsequently been contaminated in the crust, their spikiness has been reduced by the subsequent contamination process, whereas, in contrast, continental basalt patterns owing their spikiness to contamination become more spiky with greater contamination. The two lava groups will thus exhibit different behaviour relative to indices of contamination, which should preferably be isotope ratios although fractionation indices may also be used if some assumptions are made about contamination models.

It must be stressed that, with the exception of niobium depletion, all the elements (K, Rb, Ba, Sr, U) used in discriminating arc volcanics are highly susceptible to alteration. Spidergrams can also be of considerable assistance in identifying which elements have been mobile (e.g. Thirlwall & Bluck 1984) because groups of closely related lavas should give near-parallel or systematically related patterns. Erratic deviations from near parallelism are very suggestive of alteration.

It is clear that the logical procedures available for relating lava chemistry to tectonic setting are very ambiguous, and to be most successful require a fairly complete petrogenetic understanding of the volcanic rocks, which itself requires many complete chemical and isotopic analyses of relatively unaltered lavas. With the exception of parts of northern Britain, insufficient chemical data are available from Caledonian Siluro-Devonian volcanics to permit testing of petrogenetic models to the extent where a fairly reliable assignment of tectonic environment can be given. What is known of the Siluro-Devonian volcanics is summarized in the rest of this paper, and it is emphasized that any tectonic environments inferred are subject to the wide range of ambiguities discussed in this section.

Siluro-Devonian volcanics in the Appalachians

Siluro-Devonian igneous activity is present throughout the Appalachian orogenic belt, but with one exception volcanic rocks are not preserved S of New England. The exception is the Hillabee Greenstone, which has an along-strike outcrop of 100 miles (170 km) in Alabama and was described by Tull & Stow (1980). This is a 2600 ft (800 m) complex of mafic phyllites and greenstones containing about 15% metaquartz-dacite which rests conformably on the early to

mid-Devonian shallow marine Talladega sedimentary group. Tull & Stow (1980) quote a K–Ar age on relict igneous hornblende of 382 ± 14 Ma. Although the complex has suffered low-greenschist-facies Acadian metamorphism, they consider that igneous geochemistry is preserved in samples with low volatile content and use the Pearce & Cann (1973) diagrams to suggest an arc tholeiite origin. Unfortunately, these can only be distinguished from ocean floor basalts by using the Ti–Zr–Sr diagram, which can be adversely affected by alteration, and their Nb data are insufficiently precise to allow investigation of possible Nb anomalies. Even with this ambiguity, the greenstone appears to provide important evidence of an oceanic environment in the Southern Appalachians immediately before Acadian orogeny.

Siluro-Devonian volcanism in New England and New Brunswick falls in essentially two NE–SW striking belts (Fig. 1). One belt runs from the Gaspé Peninsula (e.g. Mont Alexandre, Quebec) through central Maine to central Massachusetts and consists of Llandovery to middle Devonian volcanics and related plutons sited on an earlier Ordovician arc massif (Bronson Hill zone, Miramichi massif) which may have late Precambrian basement. This Piscataquis volcanic belt (Rankin

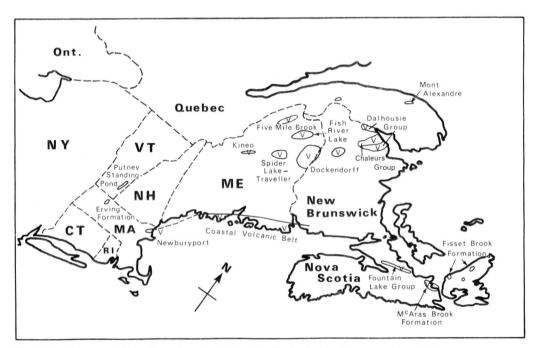

FIG. 1. Location map of Siluro-Devonian volcanics in New England and adjacent provinces of Canada.

1968) is bounded to the W by the Connecticut Valley–Gaspé trough, a region of rapid subsidence during the Silurian and earliest Devonian which includes minor volcanics in western Maine. To the E, the Merrimack–Fredericton trough contains deep-water turbidites and black shales of Silurian and early Devonian age but lacks volcanics unless the metamorphosed mafic–ultramafic complexes tentatively regarded as dismembered ophiolites by Bradley (1983) are partially Siluro-Devonian volcanics. Finally, in the E the coastal volcanic belt runs from NE Massachusetts through coastal Maine to New Brunswick, and has Wenlock to lower Devonian volcanics resting on late Precambrian Avalonian (about 600 Ma) volcanic basement. All these rocks are older than Acadian tectonic movements and metamorphism. The latter changes strongly in intensity from a sub-chlorite zone in the NE to amphibolite facies in the SW, and in places causes severe problems in identifying the original characteristics of volcanics and estimating their ages.

Piscataquis belt

In the western belt the major volcanic sequences occur in northern New Brunswick and N central Maine. In addition, there are minor volcanics on the Gaspé Peninsula, Quebec, and in Vermont, New Hampshire and Massachusetts. The latter include volcanic members of the Erving, Gile Mountain, Littleton and Kidderville Formations (e.g. Green & Guidotti 1968) and the Standing Pond volcanics of Vermont (Hepburn 1981). All these are mafic greenschists and amphibolites, together with some metafelsic volcanics, but detailed studies are difficult because of the high metamorphic grade. Hepburn (1981) describes the Standing Pond volcanics as including basalts enriched and depleted in incompatible elements, the mean compositions of which are shown as spidergrams on Fig. 2 (J. C. Hepburn, unpublished data). Hepburn (1981) suggested an extensional/back-arc setting for these as they form part of the Connecticut Valley–Gaspé trough, while Bradley (1983) suggested that they may be E-derived arc tholeiites. Despite the metamorphism, the chemistry does provide some clarification of this in that the enriched metabasalts show strong Nb enrichment relative to other incompatible elements, a feature unknown in arc environments and often found in alkali basalts. The depleted metabasalts show Nb depletion, but this is probably not analytically significant at the very low Nb concentrations involved. Thus Hepburn's (1981) original view is preferred here.

The Siluro-Devonian volcanics of northern New Brunswick have been briefly described by

CANADA–U.S.A WESTERN VOLCANIC BELT

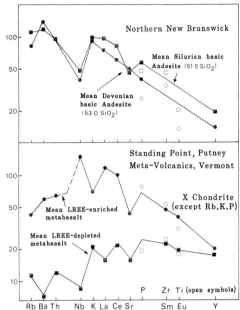

FIG. 2. Spidergrams for mean basalts and andesites from northern New Brunswick (M. F. Thirlwall & L. R. Fyffe, unpublished data) and for mean amphibolite-facies metabasalts from Vermont (J. C. Hepburn, unpublished data). Normalization after Sun (1980).

Fyffe *et al.* (1981). They occur on the N side of the Miramichi massif (Ordovician arc) and form part of an essentially conformable sequence of mafic volcanics with Gedinnian marine fossils (Dalhousie Group) resting on sub-aerial rhyolites, which in turn rest on shallow-water mafic volcanics conformable with sediments bearing a Wenlock fauna (Chaleurs Group). Fyffe *et al.* (1981) describe the Chaleurs volcanics as a bimodal calc-alkaline to mildly alkaline suite, while the Dalhousie volcanics are 'unimodal with abundant intermediate rocks'. Syn- and post-Acadian plutons which range in age from early Devonian to Carboniferous are bimodal and show no compositional polarity. This led Fyffe *et al.* (1981) to infer an origin unrelated to subduction, but the plutons may be appreciably younger than the volcanics. Samples of the latter provided by L. R. Fyffe have been analysed using recently upgraded X-ray fluorescence (XRF) techniques at the Royal Holloway and Bedford New College, London (RHBNC). The samples are dominantly basalt or basic andesite, and, although several have normative nepheline, in almost all cases this appears to be an alteration effect. Spidergrams for the means of analysed Silurian (21) and Devonian (15) mafic lavas are plotted in Fig. 2. Both are basalts or basic andesites and show niobium depletion relative to light REEs and to some extent depletion in P and Ti relative to middle REEs as projected between La, Ce, Nd and Y (Fig. 2). They show no clear enrichment in hydrophile elements (Rb, K, Ba, Sr) relative to light REEs, and, unlike the relatively smooth patterns for 'immobile' elements, these tend to behave very erratically on individual spider-grams, suggesting alteration. Thus the lack of enrichment in K etc. shown in the mean may not be representative of the original lava composition but an effect of alteration. Insufficient data are available to discuss whether the lavas enriched with K and Rb represent primary material with the rest a result of secondary alkali loss, or vice versa. Again, insufficient data are available to discuss whether the niobium depletion is a result of subduction processes or of light REE enrich-ment during crustal contamination, but in view of the uniformity of the Nb depletion, I margin-ally prefer the former hypothesis. It is of interest that the Ti–Zr–Y diagram of Pearce & Cann (1973) is ambiguous for the northern New Brunswick basalts—all samples fall close to the boundary between within-plate and calc-alkaline basalt fields, although the Silurian basalts tend to have higher TiO_2 contents. This is not thought to be very significant.

No chemical data are available or published for the volcanics in northern Maine. These include the Piscataquis volcanic belt proper (Rankin 1968) along strike from northern New Brunswick and the early Devonian Fish River Lake Formation and late Silurian Fivemilebrook Formation within the Connecticut Valley–Gaspé trough. These latter include rocks interpreted as transitional to alkaline basalts with anatectic rhyolites and are thought to have been erupted in an extensional setting behind the Piscataquis arc (Hon & Roy 1981, R. Hon, personal communi-cation 1984). Recent palaeomagnetic work pro-vides evidence of significant separation between the Piscataquis belt and the N American craton in the early Devonian (Spariosu & Kent 1983). In NE Maine the Dockendorff group consists of 4000 ft (1200 m) of acid pyroclasts with andesite and sediments of the Hedgehog Formation overlain by 4200 ft (1300 m) of 'calc-alkaline pyroxene–biotite andesites' of the Edmunds Hill Formation (Sargent et al. 1981). Bottino & Fullager (1966) obtained a whole-rock Rb–Sr isochron of 406 ± 11 Ma (recalculated) for the Hedgehog Formation.

In contrast, the volcanics of the rest of the Piscataquis belt are dominantly rhyodacitic ash

flow tuffs, in places often garnetiferous and peraluminous. Rankin (1980) describes the 10 500 ft (3200 m) Traveller rhyolite, but further thick ash flows occur to the SW at Kineo. These were probably mostly sub-aerial and are associ-ated with early Devonian shallow marine sand-stones. Presumably because of the dominance of rhyolite, Rankin (1980) did not believe that these volcanics were related to subduction, but Hon et al. (1981) have noted that the rhyolites are associated with gabbro–diorite–granite plutons which in parts are chemically very similar to the Edmunds Hill andesite (R. Hon, personal com-munication 1984).

It therefore appears that a significant part of the igneous activity in the Piscataquis belt and its continuations in New Brunswick and central New England could be related to subduction processes, but it must be stated here that the data available at present are far from unambiguous.

Coastal volcanic belt

Even fewer chemical data are available for the Siluro-Devonian volcanics of coastal New Eng-land and New Brunswick. Three distinct areas can be recognized: Eastport (eastern Maine and neighbouring New Brunswick), the Penobscot Bay area (central coastal Maine) and Newbury, NE Massachusetts (Fig. 1). Around Eastport, the Wenlock–lower Devonian is represented by over 25 000 ft (7600 m) of sediments with interbedded volcanics, i.e. the Dennys (Wenlock), Edmunds (Ludlow), Pembroke (Pridoli) and Eastport (Ged-innian–Siegenian) Formations (Gates 1969). The sediments change upwards from shallow marine to terrestrial in the Eastport Formation. Bottino & Fullagar (1966) report an Rb-Sr whole-rock isochron age of 401 ± 10 Ma (recalculated with half estimated errors) for the acid volcanics of the Eastport Formation. Other rock types de-scribed include basalt and andesite, although Gates (1978) described the sequence as bimodal. However, any such comments are premature without chemical data, as discussed in an earlier section. In Penobscot Bay three fault-bounded sequences of Siluro-Devonian volcanics were dated by Brookins et al. (1973) but, as noted earlier, their isochrons should be treated with great care. The thickest sequence consists of the Ludlow–Pridoli Ames Knob Formation sedi-ments overlain by a thick (4400 ft (1340 m)) 'pyroxene–andesite' sequence (Thorofare ande-site) and the Gedinnian Vinalhaven rhyolite (2500 ft (760 m)). While this sequence appears to be dominantly andesitic, the neighbouring Cas-tine volcanics are described as bimodal with pillow basalts and spherulitic rhyolites (Brookins *et al.* 1973). These coastal Maine volcanics have been regarded as both rift related (Gates 1978) and subduction related (Gates 1969, Bradley 1983); this confusion is not surprising with the lack of chemical work.

The Newbury volcanic complex, NE Massachusetts, has been described in detail by Shride (1976). 9500 ft (2900 m) of volcanic rock is present, of which over half is described by Shride as porphyritic andesite lavas and tuffs. Relatively small volumes of rhyolite, ash flow tuff and basalt are also present. Much was probably sub-aerial, but shallow marine incursions in the andesite unit yield Pridoli brachiopods (Shride 1976). A spidergram of a Newbury basic andesite (52.6% SiO_2, collected by R. Hon and analysed by XRF at RHBNC) is shown in Fig. 3 and is representative of the six samples analysed. There is enrichment in K and Ba and strong depletion in Nb and P relative to REEs. The patterns for all six samples are sub-parallel except for K, Rb and Sr, again suggesting an alteration problem. Samples with the lowest K content have very high Na and low Ca, suggesting spilitic alteration and that fresher samples may be enriched in hydrophile elements. The strong negative Nb anomaly is largest in the most primitive samples available, suggesting that it is not a function of contamination. Ti–Zr–Y contents for the most mafic samples (less than 53% SiO_2) fall in the calc-alkaline basalt field of Pearce & Cann (1973). The available evidence therefore suggests fairly strongly that the Newbury volcanics were generated in response to subduction, but to extend this to the rest of the coastal volcanic belt requires further data.

In addition to the Newbury volcanics, the Lynn and Mattapan volcanics near Boston, Massachusetts, have been thought to be Siluro-Devonian in age (see discussion in Shride (1976)), but Kaye & Zartman (1980) report zircon concordia of 602 ± 3 Ma for these, suggesting a much greater age.

Nova Scotia

The province of Nova Scotia (NS) lies to the E of the coastal volcanic belt and volcanics of upper Silurian to lower Devonian age appear to be absent. In contrast, the Llandovery–Wenlock White Rock Series of southern NS has minor basalt and rhyolitic tuff as do parts of the Arisaig Group in northern NS (Keppie 1979). Dostal *et al.* (1983) have described the middle Devonian to Carboniferous volcanics of NS which crop out in three units in northern NS and Cape Breton Island (Fig. 1). These include 200 ft or so of basalt lavas with, in places, 10 000 ft of rhyolite. Spidergrams of some of their basalt chemical data are presented in Fig. 3, and at first glance seem inconsistent with their interpretation of an intraplate rifting setting because of the presence of negative Nb anomalies in all except the Fountain Lake Group basalt (Fig. 3). These are small, however, and in the case of the McAras Brook Formation the La/Nb ratio increases from 0.90 (chondritic) to 1.4 with fractionation, suggesting a crustal contamination effect. Insufficient data are reported to test this possibility for the Fisset Brook basalts, but the Ballantynes Cove alkali basalts show La/Nb ratios substantially greater than chondritic and also a positive Sr anomaly (Fig. 3). These features should be characteristic of arc volcanics, perhaps indicating that the mantle source for the Ballantynes Cove lavas had been affected by some subduction event. While a within-plate origin of these younger Nova Scotian basalts can in general be favoured, the chemical

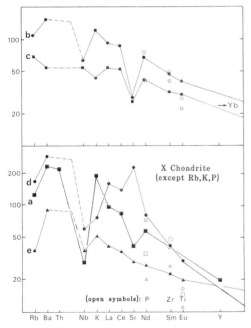

CANADA–USA COASTAL VOLCANIC BELT

FIG. 3. Spidergrams for lavas from the Appalachian coastal volcanic belt and Nova Scotia: (a) = basic andesite NV7B (52.6% SiO_2), Newbury, Massachusetts; (b) = basalt 14, Fisset Brook Formation (upper Devonian); (c) = basalt 19, Fountain Lake Group (middle Devonian); (d) = average basalt, Ballyantynes Cove (middle Devonian); (e) = basalt 2, McAras Brook Formation. ((a) From M. F. Thirlwall & R. Hon, unpublished data; (b)–(e) from Dostal *et al.* 1983.) Normalization after Sun (1980).

data usefully illustrate the ambiguities of these chemical methods.

Newfoundland

Siluro-Devonian volcanics in Newfoundland have been well reviewed by Strong (1977) and Kean *et al.* (1981). All occur within the central volcanic belt of Newfoundland, but three distinct E–W groupings have been recognized. In the W Wenlock–lower Devonian sub-aerial basalts, rhyolites and ignimbrites form the Springdale, MicMac, Cape St John and Upper Cutwell Groups, in the centre the Roberts Arm, Buchans, Cottrells Cove and Chanceport Groups are dominated by pillow basalts with rare acid rocks and in the eastern Botwood belt there are thin felsic and mafic lavas associated with continental sediments. Very substantial thicknesses of volcanics exist (several of these groups are 10000 ft thick) and some of the rock is in greenschist or amphibolite facies. Few fossil or isotopic ages are available and correlation is difficult. Despite the bimodality, the rocks are broadly calc-alkaline (Strong 1977) but have been regarded as post-subduction because of other stratigraphic evidence. Strong (1977) shows striking differences between the chemistries of the Cape St. John and central region volcanics, with the former appearing to be transitional to within-plate tholeiites, but care is required in interpreting the major-element chemistry of rocks metamorphosed to amphibolite facies.

Siluro-Devonian volcanics in Britain

In contrast with the Appalachians, Siluro-Devonian volcanics in the British Caledonides are almost wholly restricted to the region NW of the Iapetus suture (Fig. 4). All are associated with the continental sediments of the Old Red Sandstone, which is usually regarded as Devonian in age, but in places the facies extends into the Wenlock and the Carboniferous. Recent geochronological work (Thirlwall 1983a, b, and unpublished data) has shown that volcanism in the Scottish Highlands and Midland Valley (Fig. 4) occurred close to 410 Ma (i.e. ± about 6 Ma), which is probably near the Silurian–Devonian boundary (Richardson *et al.* 1984). In contrast, volcanism in the Cheviot Hills (Fig. 4) is about 392 Ma, probably late in the lower Devonian, while volcanism in Shetland and Orkney (Fig. 4) is mostly associated with middle and upper Devonian sediments (Mykura 1976, Marshall, personal communication 1984). The stratigraphic

relationships and chemistry of the volcanics have been described by Thirlwall (1979, 1981) and aspects of their Sr–Nd isotope systematics by Thirlwall (1982, 1983a), and a Pb isotope study has recently been published (Thirlwall 1986). The 410 Ma volcanics in the Midland Valley and SW Highlands form a coherent calc-alkaline–shoshonitic suite, showing progressive changes in chemistry and Nd–Pb isotopes northwestwards (Thirlwall 1981, 1982, 1986). In the SW Highlands about 3000 ft (1000 m) of basalts and andesites rest unconformably on Dalradian metasediments deformed in the Cambro-Ordovician; thick rhyolites and ignimbrites (2000 ft (600 m)) are restricted to the Glencoe caldera. In the northern part of the Midland Valley up to 8000 ft (2400 m) of basalts and andesites with rare rhyolites are exposed but no base is seen, whereas in the southern part of the Midland Valley 1000–6000 ft (300–1800 m) of basalts, andesites and rhyolites are exposed. In places these are conformable on Silurian sediments which show a progressive change from deep marine through to continental facies, and N of the Southern Upland Fault there is no evidence for orogenic activity between the mid-Ordovician and the mid-Devonian. This is an important point which is discussed in detail by Thirlwall (1981), for in the Southern Uplands during this period an accretionary prism developed above a N-dipping subduction zone (Leggett *et al.* 1979). This allows the approximately 410 Ma volcanics to be associated with active subduction prior to Iapetus closure, a conclusion which is amply justified by their chemical and isotopic characteristics (Thirlwall 1981, 1982). Thirlwall (1983a) suggested that the rather late onset of volcanism was a consequence of the termination of accretion and the first subduction of greywackes in the Wenlock; the chemistries of Midland Valley lavas show a strong signature of subducted greywacke.

Spidergrams of mean mafic lavas of the northern Midland Valley and SW Highlands (basic andesites with more than 100 ppm Ni (Thirlwall 1981)) are presented in Fig. 5 for comparison; the strong Nb, P and Ti depletion relative to REEs is characteristic of subduction-related volcanics as discussed earlier, as also is the Ba, K and Sr enrichment of lavas of the SW Highlands. The Midland Valley lavas show a relatively smooth pattern apart from Nb, but Thirlwall (1983a) has documented how this changes with the progressive incorporation of subducted turbidites.

In N Ireland about 2000 ft (600 m) of acid andesites are exposed in the Curlew Mountains and Fintona (Fig. 4) with minor acid tuffs further W (Phillips 1974, Graham 1981); these are

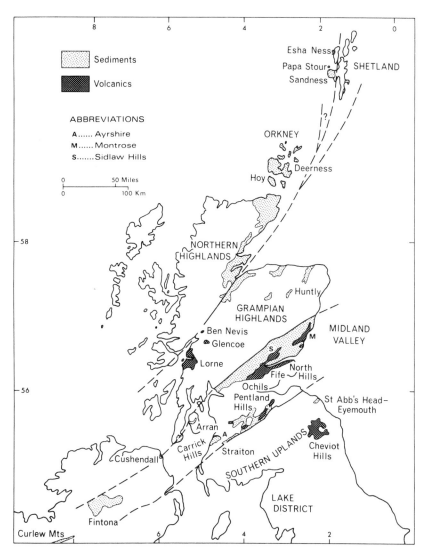

FIG. 4. Distribution of lower and middle Old Red Sandstone sediments and volcanic rocks in northern Britain. (From Thirlwall 1981.)

broadly similar to the Scottish Midland Valley lavas (Fig. 6), whereas the Cushendall and Arran volcanics (Fig. 4) closely resemble the lavas of the SW Highlands (Thirlwall 1981). The chemistry provides a good constraint on the orientation of the trace of the subduction zone if it is assumed that changes in the incompatible-element content are directly related to the depth of the Benioff zone (Thirlwall 1981).

The Cheviot Hills are an approximately 3000 ft (900 m) pile of monotonous two pyroxene acid andesites resting unconformably on Wenlock turbidites. Although they are undoubtedly calc-alkaline they lie across the inferred position of the Iapetus suture and are therefore not easily related to Iapetus subduction. They show marked petrographic, chemical (Thirlwall 1979, 1981) and isotopic differences from the volcanics further N in Scotland and are at least 10 Ma younger (Thirlwall, unpublished data). A spidergram for the mean Cheviot andesite (Thirlwall 1981 and unpublished data) is shown in Fig. 6

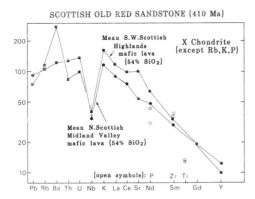

FIG. 5. Spidergrams for mean lavas with more than 100 ppm Ni from the North Midland Valley and SW Highlands of Scotland (Thirlwall 1981, 1986). Normalization after Sun (1980).

and displays the Nb depletion and Rb and K enrichment characteristic of subduction-related volcanics. The significance of the Cheviot lavas is far from clear at present.

Shetland is an important location (Fig. 4) for linking the Scandinavian and British Caledonides. Three distinct volcanic sequences are found in the Shetland Old Red Sandstone (Mykura 1976, Thirlwall 1979), and recent spore work has concluded that all are probably of middle Devonian age (Marshall, personal communication 1984). The rocks are transitional from tholeiitic to calc-alkaline (Thirlwall 1981) and have spidergrams characteristic of subduction-related volcanics (Fig. 6). One of the sequences (Sandness) is bimodal, but the other two have abundant andesite. These features have been discussed by Thirlwall (1981, 1983b) and Astin (1983), and it is believed that the Shetland volcanics and the closely similar Eday lavas of Orkney were developed relatively close to the surface trace of a subduction zone. This need not imply that the ocean closed in the Shetland region as late as middle Devonian, but polyphase deformation in some of the middle Devonian sediments could suggest this. The final Old Red Sandstone volcanism in Scotland produced the Hoy lavas in the upper Devonian of Orkney. These are alkali olivine-basalts and hawaiites (Thirlwall 1979), apparently marking the start of Carboniferous alkaline volcanism (Francis 1988). A spidergram for the most primitive, and very fresh, Hoy lava is shown in Fig. 6 where it is compared with that of a Carboniferous hawaiite (OC151) (Browne & Thirlwall 1981). The latter shows a smooth pattern apart from Sr depletion (plagioclase

fractionation?) while the Hoy basalt shows marked Nb and Ti depletion relative to light REEs although not to K, perhaps suggesting some form of subduction relationship.

To the S of the suture in Britain, there is a 1700 ft (500 m) sequence of probably continental pyroxene-andesite and dacite lavas and tuffs in the Wenlock of the Mendip Hills near Bristol (Van de Kamp 1969, Hancock 1982). Van de Kamp (1969) presents chemical data for these, although their significance has been doubted by Ponsford (1970) who suggested that the 'rhyodacites' were a result of secondary silicification of andesites. This does not seem likely on careful examination of the data, for MgO correlates well with Ni, Sc and Co and is negatively correlated with SiO_2. La/Nb ratios are very high, suggesting a large negative Nb anomaly and, again, some form of relationship to subduction processes. Finally, rhyolite flows and pyroclasts and 'tholeiitic andesite' flows are known from the Siluro-Devonian Dingle Beds in SW Ireland (Stillman 1981).

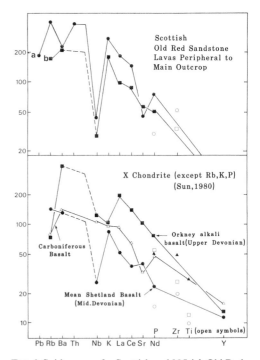

FIG. 6. Spidergrams for Scottish and N Irish Old Red Sandstone lavas remote from main outcrop: (a) = mean Cheviot acid andesite (392 Ma) (Thirlwall 1981 and unpublished data); (b) = andesite NI11 (57% SiO_2; Curlew Mountains, Ireland) (Thirlwall 1979), mean Shetland basalt (Thirlwall 1981), Orkney alkali basalt OR3 (Thirlwall 1979) and Carboniferous basalt OC151 (Browne & Thirlwall 1981).

Siluro-Devonian volcanics in Greenland and Scandinavia

Only limited data are available for Siluro-Devonian volcanics to the N of Britain, which in this area are all associated with Old Red Sandstone continental sediments. The volcanics in Greenland have been reviewed by Haller (1971) who describes predominantly bimodal volcanism of middle and upper Devonian age in the Old Red Sandstone of central E Greenland between 71 and 74°N. The rocks are folded and thrust by late Caledonian tectonic events but post-date the major deformation and metamorphism. Great thicknesses (more than 3000 ft (1000 m)) of volcanics are present in the Cape Franklin, Cape Fletcher, Cape Graah and Cape Kolthoff Series; although the basaltic volcanics are thinner they can be traced over great distances. No modern chemical data are available; Haller (1971) reports that the basalts are 'calc-alkaline' whereas the rhyolites are both 'alkaline' and 'calc-alkaline'.

In western Norway two flows of rhyolite and trachyte are associated with middle Devonian (?) continental sediments at Solund near Sognefjord (Furnes & Lippard 1983), although recent work has indicated a substantially greater thickness than was at first realized with considerable amounts of mafic volcanics (Furnes, personal communication 1984). The lavas described by Furnes & Lippard (1983) have a total thickness of about 130 ft (40 m) and have high concentrations of incompatible elements, particularly Zr, Nb, Y and light REEs, similar to many peralkaline rhyolites. Furnes & Lippard (1983) suggested a continental rift environment, and it is clear that the lavas are unrelated to subduction and chemically unlike the volcanics of equivalent age in Shetland.

Siluro-Devonian volcanism in the Hercynides

Siluro-Devonian volcanism is present in many of the Hercynian massifs of western Europe. The volcanics are often metamorphosed to greenschist facies and above, and the major-element data available in many areas are of little use except to confirm that most have suffered spilitic alteration. For many regions stratigraphic control is limited and the age ranges of volcanism are little known. The following descriptions are based principally on the review by Floyd (1982), who divided the volcanism into a series of E–W-trending zones.

Rheno-Hercynian zone

This zone includes SW England and the Rheinische Schiefergebirge and Harz Mountains of central Germany. In both regions the volcanics are essentially submarine and bimodal; in Germany, lower Devonian acid volcanics are followed by mid-Devonian basalts regarded by Floyd (1982) as intra-plate continental tholeiites, while in SW England basic and acid volcanics occur throughout the Devonian. Substantial chemical data are available for the SW England lavas (e.g. Floyd 1982, 1984) which show a northward transition from basalts similar to E-type MORB seen as lower to middle Devonian clasts in the Roseland–Meneage melange in S Cornwall, through lower Devonian intra-plate tholeiites in the Mylor group to sparse alkali basalts in the middle Devonian of N Cornwall and Devon. Floyd (1984) interprets this as a rifted passive continental margin becoming truly oceanic to the S, where the Lizard complex may represent Devonian oceanic crust. Figure 7 shows a partial spidergram for a mean SW England Devonian basalt (Floyd 1982); there is no sign of Nb, Zr or Ti depletion relative to REEs, and the high K content is most probably an effect of alteration. There is no evidence of subduction-related volcanism in this zone.

Saxo-Thuringian zone

This zone includes the lower and middle Devonian pillow basalts of Brittany and the middle Devonian volcanics of the Schimeck massif (Vosges). Cabanis *et al.* (1982) have described the chemistry of some of the volcanics in Brittany; these appear to be broadly similar to the SW England Devonian volcanics (Fig. 7). Cabanis

HERCYNIAN SUBMARINE BASALTS
(DEVONIAN)

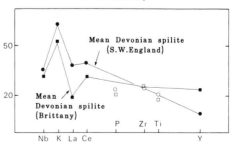

FIG. 7. Spidergrams normalized to chondrite (Sun 1980) for mean Devonian spilites from SW England and Brittany (Floyd 1982).

(1983) has noted that although there is substantial evidence for mid-Palaeozoic subduction beneath Brittany no arc volcanics are known. Further E, the Schimeck massif may include mid-Devonian calc-alkaline lavas (Floyd 1982).

Moldanubian zone

This includes the Hercynian blocks of the French Massif Central, the southern Vosges and the SW German Black Forest. Floyd (1982) notes the existence of Devonian tholeiites in all of these, but little more is known. Further to the S, Palaeozoic volcanic rocks occur in Iberia, the Pyrenees and the French and Austrian Alps but little is known of their ages and chemistry, although Loeschke (1973) has described an alkali basalt differentiation sequence in Austria.

Discussion and conclusions

Striking differences exist between Wenlock–mid-Devonian volcanic rocks in the European Hercynian regions and those of the Caledonian–Appalachian orogen. In the former region volcanism was almost wholly marine and of ocean-floor or intra-plate character; in the latter, volcanism was wholly continental, dominantly sub-aerial and mostly subduction related. In northern Britain and in the Piscataquis and coastal volcanic belts of the Appalachians all analysed volcanics show a subduction signature to their chemistry, but this should not necessarily be taken as evidence that subduction was active when the lavas were erupted. As many of the lavas involved are basalts or the products of basalt differentiation a mantle source is required (cf. Thirlwall 1982), and this mantle source must also have possessed the chemical and isotopic subduction signature. In places an apparent subduction signature may have arisen through crustal contamination, but there is certainly a true subduction signature in northern Britain and most probably in the Appalachians. As the mantle signature is thought to have arisen through metasomatism by hydrous fluids and siliceous melts from the subducting slab (e.g. Saunders et al. 1980), it will continue to be produced as long as the slab is available and is likely to remain in the mantle for a significant period after subduction ceases. Chemically it is therefore impossible to deduce a relationship to active subduction; rather, stratigraphic arguments must be used such as those of Thirlwall (1981) who suggested that the 410 Ma N British Old Red Sandstone volcanics were related to active subduction because they were the only significant calc-alkaline volcanic event related to the NW-directed subduction known to have operated from at least Caradoc to Wenlock times, because there is no regional deformation event implying continental collision until after the volcanism and because igneous activity also occurred significantly later (about 390 Ma) around the continental suture.

ACKNOWLEDGMENTS: I am grateful to L. R. Fyffe and R. Hon for providing rock samples, J. N. Walsh for preliminary ICP analyses of the U.S.A. samples, Rosemary Frischer for patient typing, Craig Hildrew for the diagrams and many colleagues for information on sectors of the orogen with which I am unfamiliar.

References

ASTIN, T. R. 1983. Discussion on implications for Caledonian plate tectonic models of chemical data from volcanic rocks of the British Old Red Sandstone. Journal of the Geological Society, London, 140, 315–8.

BOTTINO, M. L. & FULLAGAR, P. D. 1966. Whole-rock rubidium–strontium age of the Silurian–Devonian boundary in northeastern North America. Geological Society of America Bulletin, 77, 1167–76.

BRADLEY, D. C. 1983. Tectonics of the Acadian Orogeny in New England and adjacent Canada. Journal of Geology, 91, 381–400.

BROOKINS, D. G., BERDAN, J. M. & STEWART, D. B. 1973. Isotopic and palaeontological evidence for correlating three volcanic sequences in the Maine Coastal Belt. Geological Society of America Bulletin, 84, 1619–28.

BROWNE, M. A. E. & THIRLWALL, M. F. 1981. An occurrence of Lower Carboniferous lavas at Monksgrave (Powmill) near Dollar. Scottish Journal of Geology, 17(4), 275–9.

CABANIS, B. 1983. Main features of volcanism and plutonism in Late Proterozoic and Dinantian times in France. In: SCHENK, P. E. (ed.) Regional Trends in the Geology of the Appalachian–Caledonian–Hercynian–Mauritanide Orogen, pp. 187–92, Reidel, Dordrecht.

——, CHANTRAINE, J., HERROUIN, T. & TREUIL, M. 1982. Etude géochimique (majeure et traces) des spilites et dolerites de Bolazec. Mise en évidence d'un domaine en distension crustale au dévonien inférieur en Bretagne Centre-Ouest. Bulletin du Bureau de Recherches Géologiques et Minières (France), Section 1, 1–2, 47–61.

DICKIN, A. P. 1981. Isotope geochemistry of Tertiary igneous rocks from the Isle of Skye, Scotland. Journal of Petrology, 22, 155–89.

DOSTAL, J., KEPPIE, J. D. & DUPUY, C. 1983. Petrology

and geochemistry of Devono-Carboniferous volcanic rocks in Nova Scotia. *Maritime Sediments*, **19**, 59–71.

FLOYD, P. A. 1982. Chemical variation in Hercynian basalts relative to plate tectonics. *Journal of the Geological Society, London*, **139**, 505–20.

—— 1984. Geochemical characteristics and comparison of the basic rocks of the Lizard Complex and the basaltic lavas within the Hercynian troughs of SW England. *Journal of the Geological Society, London*, **141**, 61–70.

FRANCIS, E. H. 1988. Mid-Devonian to early Permian volcanism: Old World. *This volume*.

FURNES, H. & LIPPARD, S. J. 1983. Devonian lavas from Solund, West Norway—field relationships and geochemistry. *Norges Geologiske Undersøkelse*, **382**, 1–15.

FYFFE, L. R., PAJARI, G. E. & CHERRY, M. E. 1981. The Acadian plutonic rocks of New Brunswick. *Maritime Sediments*, **17**, 23–36.

GALE, N. H., BECKINSALE, R. D. & WADGE, A. J. 1979. A Rb–Sr whole rock isochron for the Stockdale Rhyolite of the English Lake District and a revised mid-Palaeozoic time scale. *Journal of the Geological Society, London*, **136**, 235–42.

GATES, O. 1969. Lower Silurian–Lower Devonian volcanic rocks of New England coast and southern New Brunswick. *American Association of Petroleum Geologists*, **12**, 484–503.

—— 1978. The Silurian–Lower Devonian marine volcanic rocks of the Eastport Quadrangle, Maine. *In*: LUDMAN, A. (ed.) *Guidebook for Field Trips in Southeastern Maine and Southwestern New Brunswick. NEIGC 70th Annual Meeting*, pp. 1–16.

GRAHAM, J. R. 1981. The "Old Red Sandstone" of Co Mayo, NW Ireland. *Geological Journal*, **16**, 157–73.

GREEN, J. C. & GUIDOTTI, C. V. 1968. The Boundary Mountain Anticlinorium in northern New Hampshire and northwestern Maine. *In*: ZEN, E-AN, WHITE, W. S., HADLEY, J. B. & THOMPSON, J. B. (eds) *Studies of Appalachian Geology, Northern and Maritime*, pp. 255–66, Wiley-Interscience, New York.

HALLER, J. 1971. *Geology of the East Greenland Caledonides*, Wiley, New York.

HANCOCK, N. J. 1982. Stratigraphy, palaeogeography and structure of the East Mendip Silurian inlier. *Proceedings of the Geologists' Association*, **93**, 247–61.

HAWKESWORTH, C. J. & POWELL, B. M. 1980. Magma genesis in the Lesser Antilles island arc. *Earth and Planetary Science Letters*, **51**, 297–308.

HEPBURN, J. C. 1981. Rare earth abundances in Siluro-Devonian metavolcanics, eastern Vermont and adjacent Massachusetts. *Geological Society of America, Abstracts with Programs*, **13**, 137.

HON, R. & ROY, D. C. 1981. Magmatectonic and stratigraphic constraints on Acadian tectonism in Maine. *Geological Society of America, Abstracts with Programs*, **13**, 138.

——, ACHESON, D., III & SCULMAN, J. 1981. Geochemical and petrological correlation of Acadian magmatic rocks in northwest and northcentral Maine. *Geological Society of America, Abstracts with Programs*, **13**, 138.

KAYE, C. A. & ZARTMAN, R. E. 1980. A Late Proterozoic to Cambrian age for the stratified rocks of the Boston Basin, Massachusetts, U.S.A. *In*: WONES, D. R. (ed.) *The Caledonides in the USA, Proceedings of the International Geological Correlation Program—Caledonide Orogen Project 27, Blacksburg, VA. Department of Geological Sciences, Virginia Polytechnic Institute and State University, Memoir No. 2*, pp. 257–61.

KEAN, B. F., DEAN, P. L. & STRONG, D. F. 1981. Regional geology of the Central Volcanic Belt of Newfoundland. *Geological Association of Canada Special Paper No. 16*, pp. 65–78.

KEPPIE, J. D. 1979. *Geological Map of the Province of Nova Scotia*. Department of Mines and Energy, Nova Scotia.

LEGGETT, J. K., McKERROW, W. S. & EALES, M. H. 1979. The Southern Uplands of Scotland: a Lower Palaeozoic accretionary prism. *Journal of the Geological Society, London*, **136**, 755–70.

LOESCHKE, J. 1973. Petrochemistry of Palaeozoic spilites of the eastern Alps (Austria). *Geological Magazine*, **110**, 188–218.

McKERROW, W. S., LAMBERT, R. ST. J. & CHAMBERLAIN, V. 1980. The Ordovician, Silurian and Devonian time scales. *Earth and Planetary Science Letters*, **51**, 1–8.

——, —— & COCKS, L. R. M. 1985. The Ordovician, Silurian and Devonian periods. *In*: SNELLING, N. J. (ed.) *The Chronology of the Geological Record. Memoir of the Geological Society of London No. 10*, pp. 73–80.

MYKURA, W. 1976. *Orkney and Shetland: British Regional Geology*, Her Majesty's Stationery Office, London.

—— & PHEMISTER, J. 1976. The geology of western Shetland. *Memoirs of the Geological Survey of Great Britain*.

O'HARA, M. J. & MATHEWS, R. E. 1981. Geochemical evolution in an advancing, periodically tapped, continuously fractionated magma chamber. *Journal of the Geological Society, London*, **138**, 237–77.

PEARCE, J. A. 1975. Basalt geochemistry used to investigate past tectonic environments on Cyprus. *Tectonophysics*, **25**, 41–68.

—— 1983. Role of the sub-continental lithosphere in magma genesis at active continental margins. *In*: HAWKESWORTH, C. J. & NORRY, M. J. (eds) *Continental Basalts and Mantle Xenoliths*, Shiva, Nantwich, pp. 230–49.

—— & CANN, J. R. 1973. Tectonic setting of basic volcanic rocks determined using trace element analyses. *Earth and Planetary Science Letters*, **19**, 290–300.

PHILLIPS, W. E. A. 1974. The stratigraphy, sedimentary environments and palaeogeography of the Silurian strata of Clare Island, Co. Mayo, Ireland. *Journal of the Geological Society of London*, **130**, 19–42.

PONSFORD, D. R. R. 1970. Silurian volcanic rocks of the Mendip Hills, Somerset. *Geological Magazine*, **107**, 561.

RANKIN, D. W. 1968. Volcanism related to tectonism

in the Piscataquis volcanic belt, an island arc of Early Devonian age in north-central Maine. *In:* ZEN, E-AN, WHITE, W. S., HADLEY, J. B. & THOMSON, J. B. (eds) *Studies in Appalachian Geology: Northern and Maritime*, pp. 355–69, Wiley-Interscience, New York.

—— 1980. The Traveler rhyolite and its Devonian setting, Traveler Mountain area, Maine. *In:* ROY, D. C. & NAYLOR, R. S. (eds) *A Guidebook to the Geology of Northeastern Maine and Neighboring New Brunswick. NEIGC 72nd Annual Meeting*, pp. 98–104.

RICHARDSON, J. B., FORD, J. H. & PARKER, F. 1984. Miospores, correlation and age of some Scottish Lower Old Red Sandstone sediments from the Strathmore region (Fife and Angus). *Journal of Micropalaeontology*, 3, 109–24.

SAUNDERS, A. D., TARNEY, J. & WEAVER, S. D. 1980. Transverse geochemical variations across the Antarctic Peninsula: implications for the genesis of calc-alkaline magmas. *Earth and Planetary Science Letters*, 46, 344–60.

SARGENT, S. L., HON, R. & ROY, D. C. 1981. Dockendorff Group—Early Devonian calc-alkaline volcanism of 'Andean type' in northeastern Maine. *Geological Society of America, Abstracts with Programs*, 13, 174.

SHRIDE, A. 1976. Stratigraphy and correlation of the Newbury Volcanic Complex. *Geological Society of America Memoir*, 148, 147–78.

SPARIOSU, D. J. & KENT, D. V. 1983. Palaeomagnetism of the Lower Devonian Traveler Felsite and the Acadian orogeny in the New England Appalachians. *Geological Society of America Bulletin*, 94, 1319–28.

STEIGER, R. H. & JAEGER, E. 1977. Submission on geochronology: convention on the use of decay constants in geo- and cosmochronology. *Earth and Planetary Science Letters*, 36, 359–62.

STILLMAN, C. J. 1981. Caledonian igneous activity. *In:* HOLLAND, C. H. (ed.) *A Geology of Ireland*, pp. 83–106, Scottish Academic Press, Edinburgh.

STRONG, D. F. 1977. Volcanic regimes of the Newfoundland Appalachians. *Geological Association of Canada Special Paper No. 16*, pp. 61–90.

SUN, S.-S. 1980. Lead isotopic study of young volcanic rocks from mid-ocean ridges, oceanic islands and island arcs. *Philosophical Transactions of the Royal Society of London, Series A*, 297, 409–45.

THIRLWALL, M. F. 1979. *The petrochemistry of the British Old Red Sandstone volcanic province. Ph.D. Thesis* (unpublished), University of Edinburgh.

—— 1981. Implications for Caledonian plate tectonic models of chemical data from volcanic rocks of the British Old Red Sandstone. *Journal of the Geological Society, London*, 138, 123–38.

—— 1982. Systematic variation in chemistry and Nd–Sr isotopes across a Caledonian calc-alkaline volcanic arc: implications for source materials. *Earth and Planetary Science Letters*, 58, 27–50.

—— 1983a. Isotope geochemistry and origin of calc-alkaline lavas from a Caledonian continental margin volcanic arc. *Journal of Volcanology and Geothermal Research*, 18, 589–631.

—— 1983b. Discussion on implications for Caledonian plate tectonic models of chemical data from volcanic rocks of the British Old Red Sandstone: reply to Dr T. R. Astin. *Journal of the Geological Society, London*, 140, 315–18.

—— 1986. Lead isotope evidence for the nature of the mantle beneath Caledonian Scotland. *Earth and Planetary Science Letters*, 80, 55–70.

—— & BLUCK, B. J. 1984. Sr–Nd isotope and chemical evidence that the Ballantrae 'ophiolite', SW Scotland, is polygenetic. *In:* GASS, I. G., LIPPARD, S. J. & SHELTON, A. W. (eds) *Ophiolites and Oceanic Lithosphere. Special Paper of the Geological Society of London No. 13*, 215–30.

—— & GRAHAM, A. M. 1984. Evolution of high-Ca, high-Sr C-series basalts from Grenada, Lesser Antilles: the effects of intra-crustal contamination. *Journal of the Geological Society, London*, 141, 427–45.

—— & JONES, N. W. 1983. Isotope geochemistry and contamination mechanics of Tertiary lavas from Skye, Northwest Scotland. *In:* HAWKESWORTH, C. J. & NORRY, M. J. (eds) *Continental Basalts and Mantle Xenoliths*, pp. 186–208, Shiva, Nantwich.

THOMPSON, R. N., MORRISON, M. A., HENDRY, G. L. & PARRY, S. J. 1984. An assessment of the relative roles of crust and mantle in magma genesis: an elemental approach. *Philosophical Transactions of the Royal Society of London, Series A*, 310, 549–90.

TULL, J. F. & STOW, S. H. 1980. The Hillabee Greenstone: a mafic volcanic complex in the Appalachian Piedmont of Alabama. *Geological Society of America Bulletin*, 91, 27–36.

VAN DE KAMP, P. C. 1969. The Silurian volcanic rocks of the Mendip Hills, Somerset; and the Tortworth area, Gloucestershire, England. *Geological Magazine*, 106, 542–53.

WOOD, D. A. 1980. The application of a Th–Hf–Ta diagram to problems of tectonomagmatic classification and to establishing the nature of crustal contamination of basaltic lavas of the British Tertiary Volcanic Province. *Earth and Planetary Science Letters*, 50, 11–30.

——, JORON, J. L. & TREUIL, M. 1979. A re-appraisal of the use of trace elements to classify and discriminate between magma series erupted in different tectonic settings. *Earth and Planetary Science Letters*, 45, 326–36.

YORK, D. 1969. Least squares fitting of a straight line with correlated errors. *Earth and Planetary Science Letters*, 5, 320–4.

M. F. THIRLWALL, Department of Geology, Royal Holloway and Bedford New College, Egham Hill, Egham, Surrey TW20 0EX, UK.

Timing of Silurian to middle Devonian deformation in the Caledonides of Scandinavia, Svalbard and E Greenland

David Roberts

SUMMARY: Polyphase orogenic deformation in Scandinavia during the period from early Silurian to middle Devonian time is concentrated in the time-range late Llandovery to early Devonian—the Scandian orogenic event. Deformation and metamorphism began earliest in the western internal parts of the orogen and shifted progressively eastwards to southeastwards towards the external foreland. Early SE-directed high-temperature ductile thrusting was succeeded by imbrication in several areas. In Svalbard the principal tectonothermal event is of middle to late Silurian age. Stratigraphical and isotopic evidence from the E Greenland Caledonides favours a latest Ordovician deformation and metamorphism in central regions, whereas the main deformation and thrusting in the extreme NE occurred during the middle Silurian.

As in the case of the N American and British–Irish segments of the orogen, evidence for timing of tectonic deformation during the Siluro-Devonian period in the now separated Scandinavian, Svalbard and E Greenland parts of the Caledonian fold belt relies principally on biostratigraphic control and radiometric dating. In recent years isotopic age-determination data have proved invaluable in allowing a more comprehensive assessment of the tectonothermal evolution of the orogen, particularly in Scandinavia. There, increasing recognition has been given to the important late Cambrian to early Ordovician Finnmarkian deformation event (Hall & Roberts 1988), but the present disposition of the major nappe complexes is by and large a result of Silurian orogenesis arising from collision of the continents Laurentia and Baltica. In addition it is possible to recognize an orogen-transverse diachronism of Siluro-Devonian deformation from NW to SE. For Svalbard and much of E Greenland, constraints on the timing of Silurian deformation in particular are less precise.

Scandinavia

Evidence bearing on the tectonometamorphic evolution of the Scandinavian Caledonides during Siluro-Devonian time has previously been presented in review articles by Gee & Roberts (1983) and Roberts & Gee (1985). In this synthesis, attention is given to the principal features of the stratigraphic record coupled with the most relevant, and some of the newest, isotopic-dating constraints. For Scandinavia it is convenient to view the orogen in terms of its major tectonostratigraphic divisions: the autochthon and parautochthon, the lower, middle,

upper and uppermost allochthons, and the suprajacent Old Red Sandstone (ORS) molasse sediments (Fig. 1) (Roberts & Gee 1985). With this common thread, descriptions of timing of deformation in the different regions can be assessed more readily and the significance of diachronism in orogenic evolution is at once appreciated (Fig. 2).

In general terms the rock record shows that the period from middle Ordovician to early Silurian was one of relative tectonic quiescence, with accumulation of sedimentary and volcanic rocks in a variety of depositional environments ranging from continental and near-shore milieux to fault-controlled basins and mature volcanic arcs (Roberts et al. 1985). Major orogenic activity began in Wenlock or even late Llandovery time and continued, in southeastern districts at least, into earliest Devonian. This period of orogenesis is termed the Scandian (Gee 1975).

In N Norway, embracing the counties of Finnmark and Troms, biostratigraphic control for Scandian deformation is confined to the upper allochthon in three widely separated areas: on Magerøy and at Balsfjord-Sagelvvatn and Guolasjav'ri (Fig. 1). Fauna in the Magerøy Supergroup metasediments in the Magerøy Nappe denote an early to middle Llandovery age (Andersen 1981, 1984, Bassett 1985) for part of the sequence, and this is succeeded by proximal turbidites which are considered by Andersen (1981) to reflect incipient Scandian tectonism further W. A synorogenic granite, the Finnvik granite, cutting Scandian D1 folds but itself affected by D2 structures, has yielded an Rb–Sr isochron age of 411 Ma (Andersen et al. 1982). In Troms the lithostratigraphic sequence in the Lyngen Nappe of the Balsfjord-Sagelvvatn district contains fossil-bearing platform carbonates

From HARRIS, A. L. & FETTES, D. J. (eds), 1988, *The Caledonian–Appalachian Orogen,*
Geological Society Special Publication No. 38, pp. 429–435.

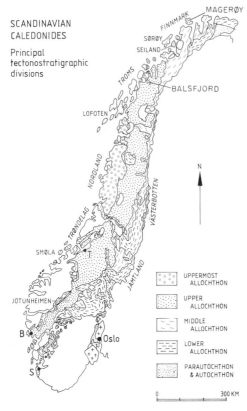

SCANDINAVIAN
CALEDONIDES

Principal
tectonostratigraphic
divisions

MAGERØY
FINNMARK
SØRØY
SEILAND
BALSFJORD
TROMS
LOFOTEN
NORDLAND
TRØNDELAG
SMØLA   T
JÄMTLAND
VÄSTERBOTTEN
JOTUNHEIMEN
B
Oslo
S

N

	UPPERMOST ALLOCHTHON
	UPPER ALLOCHTHON
	MIDDLE ALLOCHTHON
	LOWER ALLOCHTHON
	PARAUTOCHTHON & AUTOCHTHON

0   300 KM

FIG. 1. Simplified map showing the principal tectonostratigraphic divisions of the Caledonides in Scandinavia: crosses near Oslo represent Permian igneous rocks; B, Bergen; S, Stavanger; T, Trondheim. The non-ornamented areas are those of the crystalline autochthon in the E, and parautochthonous and allochthonous Precambrian units and tectonic windows within and to the W of the main Caledonian nappes.

of middle or late Llandovery age (Olaussen 1976) which, according to Bassett (1985), are succeeded by a progradation of fluvial deposits. At Guolas-jav'ri in the Vaddas Nappe the age assignment of the fauna (Binns & Gayer 1980) is less definitive: late Ordovician to early Silurian. Both these successions in Troms are polyphasally deformed and metamorphosed in greenschist facies, and a late Silurian age has generally been assumed for this event (Bjørlykke & Olaussen 1981, Andresen *et al.* 1985). No radiometric data confirming this timing are yet available. It should be noted that no post-Scandian molasse sediments are exposed anywhere in northern Scandinavia.

In Finnmark, although the parautochthon and lower and middle allochthons were initially deformed and thrust-emplaced during the Finn-

markian orogenic event, there are indications (Roberts 1985) that higher parts of the middle allochthon, the Kalak Nappe Complex, were also affected by Scandian movements and thermal overprint (Sturt *et al.* 1975, Ramsay *et al.* 1985). K–Ar mineral ages of 428–392 Ma (Sturt *et al.* 1967, recalculated) and an Rb–Sr isochron (high i.r.) of 410 Ma for migmatites (Andersen *et al.* 1982) lend support to this view, which is further corroborated by $^{40}Ar-^{39}Ar$ plateau dates for muscovites of 435–429 Ma (Dallmeyer 1988). Samples of Karelian slates from tectonic windows subjacent to the Kalak thrust also record this Scandian thermal overprint (430–420 Ma, $^{40}Ar-^{39}Ar$ (Dallmeyer 1988)). In Troms, radiometric evidence for Scandian metamorphism is seen in an Rb–Sr isochron age of 433 Ma for an orthogneiss in the Tromsø Nappe Complex and K–Ar hornblende dates of 430–420 Ma from anorthosite dykes (Andresen *et al.* 1985), as well as $^{40}Ar-^{39}Ar$ plateau dates of 390–380 Ma, representing cooling, for muscovites from Senja (Dallmeyer 1988).

Another feature of the Scandian orogenesis in these northern areas is that the initial high-temperature ductile thrusting was succeeded by lower-temperature imbrication tectonics in which slices of Finnmarkian-deformed rocks were incorporated in the Scandian nappe pile (Zwaan & Roberts 1978, Andersen 1981).

In N Central Scandinavia, which has been reviewed by Stephens *et al.* (1985), the youngest fauna occur in the lower Köli Nappes of the upper allochthon and are of middle to late Llandovery age. These rocks are succeeded by barren metagreywackes. As in Troms, these lithostratigraphic sequences were polyphasally deformed, metamorphosed and thrust-emplaced, but again we have no upper biostratigraphic constraints. It is reasonable to argue, however, that the turbiditic greywackes probably herald the onset of orogenic movements such that a Scandian tectonothermal event would be placed in the middle to late Silurian time-period.

Radiometric controls are unfortunately not too good in this part of the fold belt and until recently have consisted largely of K–Ar mineral ages from widely scattered areas (Tull 1978, Cribb 1981, Brattli *et al.* 1982); these range from 420 to 330 Ma. There is reason for believing that with such an age range these dates may be recording cooling related to both Scandian and subsequent late Caledonian tectonothermal events. Wilson (1981) reported three Rb–Sr isochron dates of 418, 422 and 424 Ma for syntectonic granitic rocks in the upper Köli Nappes. Of these, the 424 date for the Furuland granite is interesting as the body post-dates D1 folds and thrust emplacement

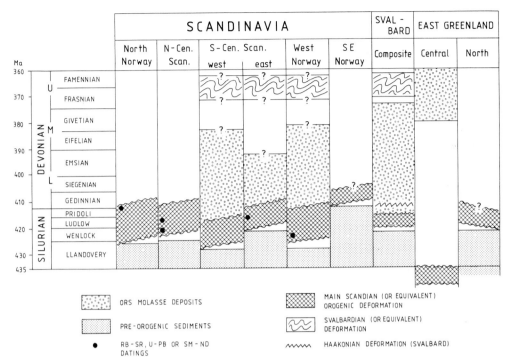

FIG. 2. Chart showing the timing of Siluro-Devonian deformation in the Caledonides of Scandinavia, Svalbard and E Greenland. The sloping belts of deformation for Scandinavian areas signify W (left) to E (right) diachronism of deformation. An E–W diachronism is indicated for E Greenland, but this has not been proved. The column for Svalbard is a composite assembled from the three main terranes (see text for details).

of the Gasak Nappe. $^{40}Ar–^{39}Ar$ mineral ages from lower Köli Nappe rocks fall in the range 435–417 Ma (Dallmeyer 1988).

The S Central segment of the Caledonides in Scandinavia (reviewed by Gee *et al.* 1985) includes ORS molasse sediments in two separate districts in Norway (Steel *et al.* 1985). In the lower allochthon in Jämtland, Sweden, early Wenlock graptolitic rocks are followed conformably by continental-facies sandstones (Bassett *et al.* 1982) signifying derivation from a rising mountain chain. In eastern Trøndelag, Norway, in the upper allochthon, the youngest fossiliferous metasediments involved in the polyphase Scandian deformation are of middle Llandovery age (Bassett 1985). Caradoc–Ashgill sediments occur below sandstones of presumed Llandovery age in western areas of the Trondheim region. These Ordo-Silurian sequences in the Trondheim Nappe Complex were then polyphasally deformed, probably during Wenlock time (Roberts 1967, Gee & Wilson 1974). In coastal areas of this region the oldest post-Scandian ORS molasse sediments are of Pridoli (Downton) and possibly Ludlow age (Fig. 2), although Bassett (1985) has

presented evidence suggesting that they may extend back as far as Wenlock or even latest Llandovery time. If this is the case, post-Scandian molasse deposition was occurring in westernmost internal parts of the orogen at the same time as pre-Scandian sedimentation was terminating with a regressive non-marine sequence in the E.

With so much biostratigraphic control in this region, radiometric dating is less critically important in terms of placing an age on the Scandian orogenesis than it is in areas further N (for a bibliography see Gee & Roberts (1983) and Gee *et al.* (1985)). Of particular interest is the work of Claesson (1981) on one of the Seve Nappes of the upper allochthon in Jämtland: ages obtained using Rb–Sr and U–Pb (zircon and monazite) techniques range from 414 to 390 Ma, with the high-grade metamorphic peak in these rocks occurring at or before 414 Ma. Another important dating study is that of Dallmeyer *et al.* (1985) and Dallmeyer (1988) who employed the $^{40}Ar–^{39}Ar$ method. Plateau ages for hornblendes have revealed a significant Ordovician tectonothermal record in parts of the Köli and Seve Nappes (see also Hall & Roberts 1988), while muscovite and biotite show fairly consistent Scandian cooling ages between 425 and 410 Ma in eastern and central areas and 410–395 Ma in the W. In western Trøndelag, U–Pb dating of zircons and sphenes from basement gneisses have placed the Scandian orogenesis in the time-range 423–396 Ma (Tucker *et al.* 1986).

The work of Dallmeyer *et al.* (1985) has shown that, as in northern Norway, the upper allochthon contains imbricated slices of polydeformed rocks carrying an early Caledonian thermal history. Again, this favours a two-stage development of the Scandian orogeny with early ductile thrusting succeeded by later imbrications.

In W Norway, including the extensive Western Gneiss Region, faunal evidence in two parts of the upper allochthon in the Bergen arcs shows that the Ordo-Silurian stratigraphic successions extend up at least into the middle Llandovery (Ryan & Skevington 1976, Bryhni & Sturt 1985). A minimum age for the Scandian event in this region is set by the lower to middle Devonian molasse sediments occurring in several areas N of Bergen (Steel *et al.* 1985).

Radiometric dating bearing on the Scandian stage of orogenic development is sparse in the Bergen arcs, but in western Norway as a whole there are many Rb–Sr, K–Ar and ^{40}Ar–^{39}Ar mineral ages which fall at around 410–390 Ma (Brueckner 1972, Lux 1985, Kullerud *et al.* 1986) and some in the 390–360 range. More interesting are the U–Pb (zircon) and Sm–Nd mineral ages of 410–400 Ma and about 425 Ma respectively (Krogh *et al.* 1974, Griffin & Brueckner 1980) from the Western Gneiss Region which indicates that Scandian eclogite-facies metamorphism occurred at or around 425 Ma, i.e. approximately early Wenlock time. Cooling and uplift then occurred through late Silurian and well into the Devonian period simultaneously with ORS sedimentation in intermontane basins. Some mineral ages and pegmatite whole-rock ages in the 375–360 Ma bracket may relate to late Devonian deformation and reheating of basement gneisses rather than to cooling following the middle Silurian high-grade metamorphism.

In SE Norway the lithostratigraphic succession in the lower allochthon extends up into the early Wenlock, but in the parautochthon of the Oslo region the sequence passes up from Wenlock carbonates through estuarine deposits into latest Wenlock to lower Downtonian continental sandstones (Worsley *et al.* 1983, Bockelie & Nystuen 1985). These continental sediments were clearly derived from the elevated front of the advancing Scandian nappes (Gee & Roberts 1983). Thus Scandian deformation, represented in the Oslo succession by a décollement type of folding and

thrusting (Bockelie & Nystuen 1985), did not affect the southeastern frontal parts of the orogen until latest Silurian to earliest Devonian time.

The evidence from Scandinavia can be summarized as follows. Scandian deformation and metamorphism began in internal and tectonostratigraphically higher parts of the orogen, probably in late Llandovery time, and progressively shifted eastwards to southeastwards, ultimately affecting the thin sedimentary successions of the mountain front in late Silurian to early Devonian time. Post-Scandian ORS molasse sedimentation is recorded in one area in western Central Norway from Downton or Ludlow time and possibly as early as Wenlock. Thus the Scandian-deformed nappe pile was already uplifted and being eroded far to the 'W' at the same time as marine to estuarine sedimentation was occurring in southeastern marginal parts of the orogen. The wide range of mineral ages recorded by different isotopic dating methods from several areas within both Norway and Sweden indicate that uplift and post-metamorphic cooling continued into early and middle Devonian time. Indications of these late Scandian effects are reflected in the character of the ORS sedimentation with its tectonic controls on cyclicity of deposition in the several molasse basinal areas (Steel *et al.* 1985). Younger mineral ages, latest Devonian to earliest Carboniferous, may relate to late Devonian deformation and metamorphism (Roberts 1983), during which time many of the ORS basinal successions were thrust emplaced, some with attached Scandian-deformed 'basement', to their present locations in the mountain belt.

Although there was a general W–E diachronism of deformation and metamorphism during the Scandian, such tectogenesis is unlikely to have been contemporaneous along the length of the orogen. Ductile deformation structures in one area may not necessarily be strictly time equivalent to similar structures in another region. The Ordovician period was characterized by an extremely diverse palaeogeography involving volcanic arcs, marginal basins and possible elongate microcontinental islands, an irregularity which would have had consequences for timing of deformation during the collision between Laurentia and Baltica.

Svalbard

The archipelago of Svalbard consists of three markedly different tectonic provinces or terranes, considered by Harland (1972, 1985) to be juxtaposed by substantial late Devonian strike-slip movement along major crustal fractures. Torsvik *et al.* (1986), however, have rejected this latter hypothesis. As in Scandinavia, there are ORS molasse-facies sediments lying unconformably upon deformed and metamorphosed lower Palaeozoic rocks, but the critical biostratigraphic controls are not ubiquitous; Devonian molasse sediments, for example, are confined to the Central Province.

In the Eastern Province the youngest strata affected by Caledonian tectogenesis are of Llanvirn age and the oldest post-Caledonian sediments are earliest Carboniferous. Radiometric evidence here is confined to K–Ar ages of 444–372 Ma, which is regarded as 'dating' the main metamorphism (Harland 1985), and late- to post-tectonic granites have yielded dates of about 410–390 Ma. The main tectonothermal event, called the Ny Friesland orogenic phase, has been considered to be of approximately middle to late Silurian age. Even so, the possibility that Ordovician or Devonian deformations have affected the pre-Tournaisian rocks of this province cannot be excluded.

The Central Province exposes an ORS molasse sequence several kilometres thick, which may extend down to latest Silurian (Harland 1985). The youngest pre-ORS rocks, in southern areas, are of early Ordovician age (Birkenmajer 1975), although latest middle Ordovician sediments crop out on Bjørnøya (Bear Island) further S. Isotopic data from this province are not very helpful, with K–Ar cooling ages ranging from 460 to 390 Ma, yet the main Caledonian metamorphism is considered to be of Silurian age, pre-dating the ORS deposition. In this region of Svalbard, on Spitsbergen, the oldest ORS rocks, the Siktefjellet Group, were folded and thrust in a latest Silurian to earliest Devonian diastrophic event known as the Haakonian (Gee 1972). Succeeding ORS sediments of Gedinnian to Givetian age were subsequently affected by the late Devonian Svalbardian deformation.

The Western Province, in W Spitsbergen, provides good evidence of middle Ordovician deformation and high-pressure metamorphism (Ohta *et al.* 1983, Hall & Roberts 1988), with the unconformably overlying sedimentary sequence extending up into the Wenlock. While there are no Devonian strata known from this western province, comparison with neighbouring areas has led to the assumption that the second Caledonian tectonothermal event occurred in the period late Wenlock to Pridoli (Harland 1985). However, Harland has entertained the possibility that this deformation may be younger and could be time equivalent to the middle Devonian to Carboniferous Ellesmerian orogeny of the N Greenland fold belt.

In summary, there is stratigraphic evidence in Svalbard for an approximately middle to late Silurian tectonometamorphic event (Fig. 2) as well as a separate minor diastrophic phase at the Silurian–Devonian transition. A late Devonian fold-and-thrust deformation event is also firmly established. Radiometric dating evidence is not particularly satisfactory as yet, although K–Ar cooling ages support the notion of there having been a Silurian metamorphic event.

E Greenland

The Caledonian geology of E Greenland has been treated comprehensively in recent reviews (Haller 1985, Henriksen 1985, Hurst *et al.* 1985). From the data currently available, it is clear that there are differences in the timing of the main Caledonian event, or events, from N to S. In the most extensively documented central E Greenland segment the youngest sediments affected by Caledonide deformation are of middle Ordovician age. Above these, the ORS molasse commences with middle Devonian (Givetian) deposits (Fig. 2). Radiometric dating has helped to narrow this wide time gap, and a minimum age for the main Caledonian deformation has been provided by an Rb–Sr isochron age of 445 Ma on a post-tectonic granite which clearly truncates folded Ordovician sediments (Rex & Gledhill 1981). This places the deformation approximately in Caradoc time in the rocks of this particular area. However, there are many datings of Caledonian granites ranging from 560 to 380 Ma, though with most between 480 and 430 Ma (Henriksen 1985), so that deformation may well have continued into latest Ordovician or earliest Silurian time in some areas. Rb–Sr and K–Ar mineral dates, representing cooling and uplift, are generally in the range 440–365 Ma with the youngest dates coming from deep-seated infracrustal units (Rex & Higgins 1985).

In northernmost E Greenland biostratigraphic evidence shows that the sedimentary record on the platform prior to deformation extends into the Silurian. There, Llandovery to middle Wenlock turbidites are affected by westward-emplaced nappes (Hurst *et al.* 1985), such that the main Caledonian diastrophism started in late Wenlock time, or perhaps earlier in eastern internal parts of the orogen if the turbidites are indicating derivation from a rising mountain chain. Interestingly, there is no hiatus in the foreland lithostratigraphy of this northern region which would correspond to the late Ordovician tectonometamorphic event in central E Greenland. No Devonian sediments are known from this part of Greenland; the oldest post-Caledonian sediments are of Carboniferous age. The only radiometric data so far available, U–Pb on zircons from a crystalline basement gneiss, indicate isotopic disturbance at about 400 Ma.

In summary, there are differences in the timing of the main Caledonian deformation from late Ordovician in the nappes of central E Greenland to middle Silurian in the foreland sediments of the extreme N. Whether this represents one lengthy wave of diachronous deformation along the orogen or two separate events is uncertain with our present state of knowledge.

References

ANDERSEN, T. B. 1981. The structure of the Magerøy Nappe, Finnmark, North Norway. *Norges Geologiske Undersøkelse*, **363**, 1–23.

—— 1984. The stratigraphy of the Magerøy Supergroup, Finnmark, North Norway. *Norges Geologiske Undersøkelse Bulletin*, **395**, 26–37.

——, AUSTRHEIM, H., STURT, B. A., PEDERSEN, S. & KJÆRSRUD, K. 1982. Rb–Sr whole rock ages from Magerøy, North Norwegian Caledonides. *Norsk Geologsk Tidsskrift*, **62**, 79–85.

ANDRESEN, A., FARETH, E., BERGH, S., KRISTENSEN, S. E. & KROGH, E. 1985. Review of lithotectonic units in Troms, North Norway. *In*: GEE, D. G. & STURT, B. A. (eds) *The Caledonian Orogen–Scandinavia and Related Areas*, pp. 569–78, Wiley, Chichester.

BASSETT, M. G. 1985. Silurian stratigraphy and facies development in Scandinavia. *In*: GEE, D. G. & STURT, B. A. (eds) *The Caledonian Orogen—Scandinavia and Related Areas*, pp. 283–92, Wiley, Chichester.

——, CHERNS, L. & KARIS, L. 1982. The Röde Formation: early Old Red Sandstone facies in the Silurian of Jämtland, Sweden. *Sveriges Geologiska Undersökning, Serie C*, **793**, 1–24.

BINNS, R. E. & GAYER, R. A. 1980. Silurian or Upper Ordovician fossils at Guolasjav'ri, Troms, Norway. *Nature, London*, **284**, 53–55.

BIRKENMAJER, K. 1975. Caledonides of Svalbard and plate tectonics. *Bulletin of the Geological Society of Denmark*, **24**, 1–19.

BJØRLYKKE, A. & OLAUSSEN, S. 1981. Silurian sediments, volcanics and mineral deposits in the Sagelvvatn area, Troms, North Norway. *Norges Geologiske Undersøkelse*, **365**, 1–38.

BOCKELIE, J. F. & NYSTUEN, J. P. 1985. The southeastern part of the Scandinavian Caledonides. *In*: GEE, D. G. & STURT, B. A. (eds) *The Caledonide Orogen—Scandinavia and Related Areas*, pp. 69–88, Wiley, Chichester.

BRATTLI, B., TØRUDBAKKEN, B. O. & RAMBERG, I. B. 1982. Resetting of a Rb–Sr total rock system in the Rødingfjellet Nappe Complex, Nordland, North Norway. *Norsk Geologisk Tidsskrift*, **62**, 219–24.

BRUECKNER, H. K. 1972. Interpretation of Rb–Sr ages from the Precambrian and Paleozoic rocks of southern Norway. *American Journal of Science*, **272**, 334–58.

BRYHNI, I. & STURT, B. A. 1985. Caledonides of southwestern Norway. *In*: GEE, D. G. & STURT, B. A. (eds) *The Caledonide Orogen–Scandinavia and Related Areas*, pp. 89–107, Wiley, Chichester.

CLAESSON, S. 1981. Caledonian metamorphism of Proterozoic Seve rocks on Mt. Åreskutan, southern Swedish Caledonides. *Geologiska Föreningens i Stockholm Förhandlingar*, **103**, 291–304.

CRIBB, S. J. 1981. Rb–Sr geochronological evidence suggesting a reinterpretation of part of the North Norwegian Caledonides. *Norsk Geologisk Tidsskrift*, **61**, 97–110.

DALLMEYER, R. D. 1988. Polyphase tectonothermal evolution of the Scandinavian Caledonides. *This volume*.

——, GEE, D. G. & BECKHOLMEN, M. 1985. ^{40}Ar–^{39}Ar mineral age record of early Caledonian tectonothermal activity in the Baltoscandian miogeocline. *American Journal of Science*, **285**, 532–68.

GEE, D. G. 1972. Late Caledonian (Haakonian) movements in northern Spitsbergen. *Norsk Polarinstitutt, Årbok*, **1970**, 92–101.

—— 1975. A tectonic model for the central part of the Scandinavian Caledonides. *American Journal of Science*, **275a**, 468–515.

—— & ROBERTS, D. 1983. Timing of deformation in the Scandinavian Caledonides. *In*: SCHENK, P. E. (ed.) *Regional Trends in the Geology of the Appalachian–Caledonian–Hercynian–Mauritanide Orogen*, pp. 279–92, Reidel, Dordrecht.

—— & WILSON, M. R. 1974. The age of orogenic deformation in the Swedish Caledonides. *American Journal of Science*, **274**, 1–9.

——, GUEZOU, J. C., ROBERTS, D. & WOLFF, F. C. 1985. The central-southern part of the Scandinavian Caledonides. *In*: GEE, D. G. & STURT, B. A. (eds) *The Caledonide Orogen—Scandinavia and Related Areas*, pp. 109–33, Wiley, Chichester.

GRIFFIN, W. L. & BRUECKNER, H. K. 1980. Caledonian Sm–Nd ages and a crustal origin for Norwegian eclogites. *Nature, London*, **285**, 319–21.

HALL, L. M. & ROBERTS, D. 1988. Timing of Ordovician deformation in the Caledonian–Appalachian orogen. *This volume*.

HALLER, J. 1985. The East Greenland Caledonides—reviewed. *In*: GEE, D. G. & STURT, B. A. (eds) *The Caledonide Orogen—Scandinavia and Related Areas*, pp. 1031–46, Wiley, Chichester.

HARLAND, W. B. 1972. Early Palaeozoic faults as margins of Arctic plates in Svalbard. *24th International Geological Congress*, Vol. 3, pp. 230–7.

—— 1985. Caledonide Svalbard. *In*: GEE, D. G. & STURT, B. A. (eds) *The Caledonide Orogen—Scandinavia and Related Areas*, pp. 999–1016, Wiley, Chichester.

HENRIKSEN, N. 1985. The Caledonides of central East

Greenland 70°–76°N. *In*: GEE, D. G. & STURT, B. A. (eds) *The Caledonide Orogen—Scandinavia and Related Areas*, pp. 1095–113, Wiley, Chichester.

HURST, J. M., JEPSEN, H. F., KALSBECK, F., MC-KERROW, W. S. & PEEL, J. S. 1985. The geology of the northern extremity of the East Greenland Caledonides. *In*: GEE, D. G. & STURT, B. A. (eds) *The Caledonide Orogen—Scandinavia and Related Areas*, pp. 1047–63, Wiley, Chichester.

KROGH, T. E., MYSEN, B. O. & DAVIS, G. L. 1974. A Paleozoic age for the primary minerals of a Norwegian eclogite. *Annual Report of the Geophysical Laboratory, Carnegie Institute, Washington*, **73**, 575–6.

KULLERUD, L., TØRUDBAKKEN, B. O. & ILEBEKK, S. 1986. A compilation of radiometric age determinations from the Western Gneiss Region, South Norway. *Norges Geologiske Undersøkelse Bulletin*, **406**, 17–42.

LUX, D. R. 1985. K/Ar ages from the Basal Gneiss Region, Stadlandet area, Western Norway. *Norsk Geologisk Tidsskrift*, **65**, 277–86.

OHTA, Y., HIROI, Y. & HIRAJIMA, T. 1983. Additional evidence of pre-Silurian high-pressure metamorphic rocks in Spitsbergen. *Polar Research*, **1**, 215–8.

OLAUSSEN, S. 1976. Paleozoic fossils from Troms, Norway. *Norsk Geologisk Tidsskrift*, **56**, 457–9.

RAMSAY, D. M., STURT, B. A., ZWAAN, K. B. & ROBERTS, D. 1985. Caledonides of northern Norway. *In*: GEE, D. G. & STURT, B. A. (eds) *The Caledonide Orogen—Scandinavia and Related Areas*, pp. 163–84, Wiley, Chichester.

REX, D. C. & GLEDHILL, A. R. 1981. Isotopic studies in the East Greenland Caledonides (72°–74°N)—Precambrian and Caledonian ages. *Rapport Grønlandes Geologiske Undersøkelse*, **104**, 47–72.

—— & HIGGINS, A. K. 1985. Potassium–argon mineral ages from the East Greenland Caledonides between 72° and 74°N. *In*: GEE, D. G. & STURT, B. A. (eds) *The Caledonide Orogen—Scandinavia and Related Areas*, pp. 1115–24, Wiley, Chichester.

ROBERTS, D. 1967. Structural observations from the Kopperå–Riksgrense area and discussion of the tectonics of Stjørdalen and the NE Trondheim region. *Norges Geologiske Undersøkelse*, **245**, 64–122.

—— 1983. Devonian tectonic deformation in the Norwegian Caledonides and its regional perspectives. *Norges Geologiske Undersøkelse*, **380**, 85–96.

—— 1985. The Caledonian fold belt in Finnmark: a synopsis. *Norges Geologiske Undersøkelse Bulletin*, **403**, 161–78.

—— & GEE, D. G. 1985. An introduction to the structure of the Scandinavian Caledonides. *In*: GEE, D. G. & STURT, B. A. (eds) *The Caledonide Orogen—Scandinavia and related areas*, pp. 55–68, Wiley, Chichester.

——, STURT, B. A. & FURNES, H. 1985. Volcanite assemblages and environments in the Scandinavian Caledonides and the sequential development history of the mountain belt. *In*: GEE, D. G. & STURT, B. A. (eds) *The Caledonide Orogen—Scandinavia and Related Areas*, pp. 919–30, Wiley, Chichester.

RYAN, P. D. & SKEVINGTON, D. 1976. A re-interpretation of the late Ordovician–early Silurian stratigraphy of the Dyvikvågen and Ulven–Vaktdal areas, Hordaland, Western Norway. *Norges Geologiske Undersøkelse*, **324**, 1–29.

STEEL, R., SIEDLECKA, A. & ROBERTS, D. 1985. The Old Red Sandstone basins of Norway and their deformation: a review. *In*: GEE, D. G. & STURT, B. A. (eds) *The Caledonide Orogen—Scandinavia and Related Areas*, pp. 293–315, Wiley, Chichester.

STEPHENS, M. B., GUSTAVSON, M., RAMBERG, I. B. & ZACHRISSON, E. 1985. The Caledonides of central-north Scandinavia—a tectonostratigraphic overview. *In*: GEE, D. G. & STURT, B. A. (eds) *The Caledonide Orogen—Scandinavia and Related Areas*, pp. 135–62, Wiley, Chichester.

STURT, B. A., MILLER, J. A. & FITCH, F. J. 1967. The age of alkaline rocks from West Finnmark, northern Norway, and the timing of orogenic deformation and metamorphism. *Norsk Geologisk Tidsskrift*, **47**, 255–73.

——, SKARPENES, O., OHANIAN, H. T. & PRINGLE, I. R. 1975. Reconnaissance Rb–Sr isochron study in the Bergen Arc System and regional implications. *Nature, London*, **253**, 595–9.

TORSVIK, T. H., LØVLIE, R. & STURT, B. A. 1986. Palaeomagnetic argument for a stationary Spitsbergen relative to the British Isles (Western Europe) since late Devonian and its bearing on North Atlantic reconstruction. *Earth and Planetary Science Letters*, **75**, 278–88.

TUCKER, R. D., RÅHEIM, A., KROGH, T. E. & CORFU, F. 1986. Uranium–lead zircon and titanite ages from the northern portion of the Western Gneiss Region, South-Central Norway. *Earth and Planetary Science Letters*, **81**, 203–11.

TULL, J. F. 1978. Geology and structure of Vestvågøy, Lofoten, North Norway. *Norges Geologiske Undersøkelse*, **333**, 1–59.

WILSON, M. R. 1981. Geochronological results from Sulitjelma, Norway. *Terra Cognita*, **1**, 82 (abstract).

WORSLEY, D., AARHUS, N., BASSETT, M. G., HOWE, M. P. A., MØRK, A. & OLAUSSEN, S. 1983. The Silurian succession of the Oslo Region. *Norges Geologiske Undersøkelse*, **384**, 1–57.

ZWAAN, K. B. & ROBERTS, D. 1978. Tectonostratigraphy succession of the Finnmarkian nappe sequence, North Norway. *Norges Geologiske Undersøkelse*, **343**, 55–71.

D. ROBERTS, Norges Geologiske Undersøkelse, Postboks 3006, 7001 Trondheim, Norway.

Wenlock to Givetian deformation in the British Isles and the Canadian Appalachians

W. S. McKerrow

SUMMARY: A combination of stratigraphic evidence and dates on igneous rocks suggests that the climax of Caledonian deformation in the British Isles and of Acadian deformation in the Canadian Appalachians both occurred during the middle to late Emsian stage, or about 397 to 390 Ma ago. In addition to this event, many small regions show uplift and/or deformation spasmodically throughout Silurian and Devonian time, both before and after the Emsian.

Deformation in Britain and eastern Canada occurred at intervals throughout the closing stages of the Iapetus Ocean, but a major widespread event took place during the Emsian stage. The times of deformation can be derived from unconformities, where the age limits can be directly determined stratigraphically. Many of the longer stratigraphic breaks include periods of igneous activity, and where these intrusive rocks have been dated they can be used to narrow the time intervals when deformation is known to occur. Some additional information on the times of deformation can be obtained from the appearance of coarse clastic sediments which indicate uplift in the source areas.

Unconformities, major igneous intrusions and terranes providing coarse sediments thus form the basis for this summary of the closing stages of the Caledonian orogeny in Britain and the Acadian orogeny in Canada. The reconstruction of Wenlock palaeogeography (Fig. 1) is discussed elsewhere (McKerrow 1988). It is probable that, by the Wenlock, the Iapetus Ocean had closed completely between Scotland and Norway but that a small remnant of oceanic crust was still present between Laurentia (i.e. Palaeozoic N America) on the one hand and England, Wales and Avalon (Avalonia) on the other hand. There are thus some general grounds for Stille's (1924) concept of a Caledonian orogeny in the late Silurian and an Acadian orogeny in the middle Devonian, but whereas the modern evidence from Canada still supports a widespread Devonian Acadian orogeny (though Emsian rather than middle Devonian) the British evidence now also suggests a climax in the Emsian rather than at the end of the Ludlow.

Unconformities, major igneous intrusions and coarse clastic sediments are shown for selected areas in England and Wales (Fig. 2, columns 1–6), Ireland (columns 7 and 8), Scotland (columns 9–13), New Brunswick, Nova Scotia and Quebec (Fig. 3, columns 14–18) and Newfoundland (columns 19 and 20). The regions will be discussed in geographic sequence from S to N in the British Isles, and from SW to NE in the Canadian Appalachians.

The British Isles

SW England

In S Devon (Fig. 2, column 1) the lower Devonian sediments consist of the fluvial Dartmouth Beds followed by the marine Bovisand Beds and

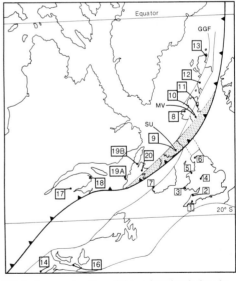

FIG. 1. A reconstruction of the regions bordering the Iapetus Ocean during the Wenlock (after McKerrow 1987): GGF, Great Glen Fault; MV, Midland Valley of Scotland; SU, Southern Uplands of Scotland. The numbers refer to the columns in Figs 2–4, but column 15, representing the Meguma terrane of southern Nova Scotia, is not on the map.

From HARRIS, A. L. & FETTES, D. J. (eds), 1988, *The Caledonian–Appalachian Orogen*, Geological Society Special Publication No. 38 pp. 437–448.

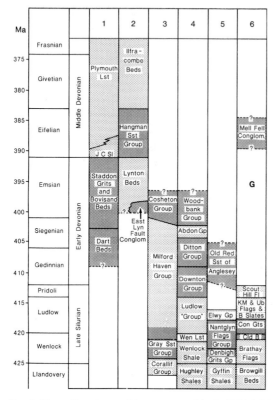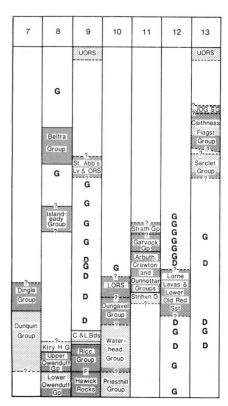

FIG. 2. The sedimentary and igneous record in the British Isles: D, dated dyke-swarms; G, dated granitoid plutons. The locations of the columns are shown in Fig. 1. Darker shading indicates coarser clastic sediments. Column 1: JCSl, Jenny Cliff Slates; Dart, Dartmouth. Column 3: Corallif, Coralliferous. Column 4: Wen, Wenlock. Column 6: Fl, Flags; KM & Ub, Kirkby Moor and Underbarrow; B, Bannisdale; Con Gts, Coniston Grits; Cld B, Coldwell Beds. Column 8: Klry HG, Killary Harbour Group. Column 9: UORS, upper Old Red Sandstone; Lv & ORS, lavas and Old Red Sandstone; C. & L. Bds, Coldingham and Linkim Beds; Ricc, Riccarton; F, fault contact. Column 10: LORS, lower Old Red Sandstone. Column 11: Strath Gp, Strathmore Group; Arbuth, Arbuthnott; Stnhvn G, Stonehaven Group. Column 13: UORS, upper Old Red Sandstone; JOGSG, John O'Groats Sandstone Group. The time-scale is from McKerrow et al. (1985).

Staddon Grits (House et al. 1977). Both include coarse detritus probably derived from the rising landmass of Wales (oddly termed St George's Land by many English workers) and the Bristol Channel. In N Devon (Fig. 2, column 2) and the Bristol Channel area several Emsian and middle Devonian conglomerate and sandstone formations have been related to pulsatory uplift of a Bristol Channel–S Carmarthen landmass (Tunbridge 1986), but in Devon itself sedimentation was continuous throughout the middle Devonian.

In S Cornwall, a southerly source for the early to middle Devonian turbidites of the Portscatho Formation may indicate that northward-moving 'Hercynian' nappes were starting to develop S of England by this time (Holder & Leveridge 1986). However, these would have been related to closure of the Rheic Ocean (McKerrow & Ziegler

1972) and probably had no direct relationships with the Caledonian orogen and the Iapetus Ocean. It should be noted that, if orogenies are defined purely by time, there would be overlap between 'Caledonian' and 'Hercynian'; this observation supports the conclusion (McKerrow 1962) that the definition of the Caledonian orogeny should be limited in space as well as in time. I now suggest that the Caledonian orogeny should be limited to the events along the margins of the Iapetus Ocean between the Ordovician and the middle Devonian.

Wales and the Welsh Border

In SW Wales (Fig. 2, column 3) the development of Hercynian thrusts has brought several different Silurian successions, originally widely separated,

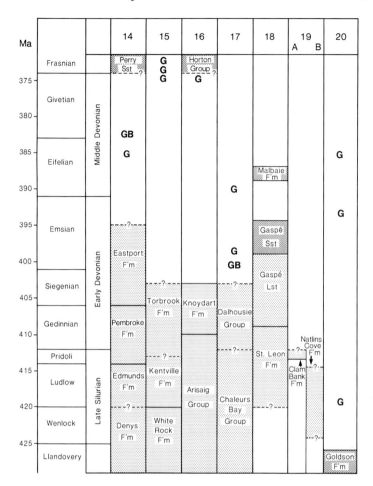

FIG. 3. The sedimentary and igneous record in the Canadian Appalachians: G, dated granitoid and related plutons; GB, Gabbro plutons; F'm, formation. Darker shading indicates coarser sediments. The locations of the columns are shown in Fig. 1 (except for column 15 which represents the Meguma terrane of southern Nova Scotia). The time-scale is from McKerrow *et al.* (1985).

into close proximity. Some of these successions show a major break between Silurian and lower Old Red Sandstone beds, but at Marloes Sands marine beds of Wenlock age pass conformably up into fluvial deposits of the Milford Haven Group (Walmsley & Bassett 1976, Hurst *et al.* 1978, Allen *et al.* 1981); therefore it is concluded that locally the Old Red Sandstone facies begins as early as the Wenlock and that the stratigraphic breaks present in some successions are only of local extent. At Marloes Sands the lower Old Red Sandstone succession is continuous up into the Cosheton Group which is of Siegenian age in part and may extend into Emsian time (Allen *et al.* 1981). The evidence from S Wales is that, while there were local episodes of uplift and

folding during the Silurian and early Devonian, there cannot have been any widespread episode of folding until after the Siegenian stage. Coarse detritus in the Cosheton Group may be related to uplift of the Irish Sea landmass during the early Devonian but other conglomerates in S Wales were derived from the S, confirming the evidence from Devon of an active Bristol Channel source area (Tunbridge 1986).

Eastern Wales and the Welsh Border provide numerous sections (e.g. Fig. 2, column 4) showing continuous deposition from marine Wenlock and Ludlow beds through a variety of coastal facies in the Pridoli (Downton Group) to fluvial environments in the early Devonian. In this area deposition continued until the Woodbank Group, which is possibly of Emsian age (House *et al.* 1977). The conglomerates in this group include tuffs, lavas and greywackes similar to those now exposed in the Ordovician and Silurian of N Wales (Allen 1974); thus, although the stratigraphy of eastern Wales and Shropshire indicate that the major Caledonian deformation occurred in the Emsian or middle Devonian, there was some earlier Devonian (i.e. pre-Emsian) uplift of a terrane identical with N Wales situated to the N or NW of Shropshire.

The break in sedimentation above the lower Old Red Sandstone in Wales led Jones (1956, p. 338) to conclude that 'the great earth-movements to which the name Caledonian has usually been applied occurred after the deposition of all known Lower Old Red Sandstone' in Wales and the adjoining regions. It is significant that in the type area of the Silurian system (the Welsh Border and eastern Wales) the Caledonian orogeny had its climax in the Emsian or the middle Devonian. The rocks above the break in Shropshire are probably of very late Devonian (Famennian) age.

In NE Wales (Fig. 2, column 5) the Silurian succession is continuous from the Llandovery to the Ludlow (Warren *et al.* 1984). Although all the beds are deep-water deposits, it is thought that the Wenlock Denbigh Grits Group was deposited within a few miles of a landmass to the SW of Llanrwst (Warren *et al.* 1984, p. 36), i.e. in the heart of Snowdonia, N Wales; similar conclusions were reached by Cummins (1957). Hurst *et al.* (1978) used these sedimentological data, together with the evidence of K–Ar cooling dates, to suggest that the Irish Sea landmass was present to the W of Wales during the Wenlock and that it continued to act as a source of sediments to eastern Wales and the Welsh Border throughout the later Silurian and early Devonian. This uplift is clearly earlier than, and independent of, the Emsian or later deformation which affected all Wales.

Allen (1965) gave reasons for thinking that the non-fossiliferous Old Red Sandstone deposits on Anglesey were early Devonian, but Hurst *et al.* (1979) considered that they were more probably middle Devonian; however, as they appear to have suffered the same deformation cleavage as the lower Palaeozoic rocks (see Greenly 1919, p. 598), the Old Red Sandstone of Anglesey must pre-date the main Caledonian deformation of Wales. N Wales and Anglesey provide evidence for the late Silurian uplift of the Irish Sea landmass, but it is southern and eastern Wales and the Welsh Border which show that the main Caledonian deformation was after the Siegenian in this region.

Northern England

In the Lake District (Fig. 2, column 6) all the Llandovery and much of the Wenlock consist of fine-grained deep-water deposits, but turbidites appear in the latest Wenlock and Ludlow (Rickards, in Moseley 1978, p. 140). The current directions and sedimentology of these beds suggest erosion of a sedimentary terrane to the N. It has been postulated (Leggett *et al.* 1983) that, when accretion ceased in the Southern Uplands, subduction of (English) continental crust below southern Scotland was responsible for uplift of that area (see below). The turbidite succession in northern England continues until the very end of the Silurian (Pridoli Series). Subsequently the lower Palaeozoic rocks were folded and cleaved. This deformation appears to have formed concurrently with the intrusion of the Shap and Skiddaw granites (Soper & Moseley, in Moseley 1978, p. 53), where some features of the metamorphic aureoles appear to be before, and others after, the development of cleavage. The firmest date on these granites is an Rb–Sr isochron yielding an age of 394 ± 3 Ma for the Shap Granite (Wadge *et al.* 1978), which correlates with the Emsian Stage (McKerrow *et al.* 1985). This is compatible with the stratigraphic dates from Wales and the Welsh Border; the climax of Caledonian deformation throughout England and Wales could be synchronous if it was Emsian in age.

The non-fossiliferous Mell Fell Conglomerate post-dates these movements (Moseley 1978, p. 164) and it is probably of middle or late Devonian age.

Ireland

In much of Ireland the Old Red Sandstone is only represented by late Devonian sediments, but some older fluvial beds are present in the W and N. The Dingle Group (Fig. 2, column 7) of County Kerry is non-fossiliferous, but it is considered (House *et al.* 1977, p. 56) to follow the Ludlow beds at the top of the Dunquin Group gradationally and to extend through the Pridoli Series into the early Devonian. It has clearly been deformed along with the underlying Silurian. The remaining outcrops of lower Old Red Sandstone in Ireland (in the Curlew Mountains and Ulster) have not yet provided any stratigraphic control of times of deformation.

In County Mayo (Fig. 2, column 8) the Islandeady Group has yielded Siegenian or early Emsian spores, and the nearby Beltra Group contains Eifelian spores (Graham *et al.* 1983). The earlier group is more tightly folded, showing that in this part of western Ireland there were two episodes of folding, one in the early Devonian and the other in the late Devonian (Phillips *et al.* 1969). The earlier phase may correspond in time to the emplacement of the Galway Granite 60 km to the S at 398 ± 12 Ma (Max *et al.* 1978); other granites in Mayo have slightly younger ages of 383 ± 10 and 381 ± 19 Ma (Stillman 1981).

The evidence from Ireland, therefore, is consistent with the widespread Emsian event seen in England and Wales, but in addition there has been some folding in Mayo between the Eifelian and the Carboniferous.

The Southern Uplands of Scotland

The northward subduction of the Iapetus Ocean from a trench containing thick sequences of turbidites above graptolitic shales is thought to have led to the accretion of the Southern Uplands (Fig. 2, column 9) (Leggett *et al.* 1982). In the light of this model the oldest stratigraphic sequence (where turbidites occur above Llandeilo shales) is likely to have been accreted in the Caradoc, and the youngest sequence (which contains late Wenlock graptolites) close to the end of the Wenlock; it is probable that tectonic underplating of trench sediments developed more or less continuously during this time interval. As accretion advanced, the trench slope break (known as Cockburnland) would have been elevated, and there is some sedimentary evidence (in both the Midland Valley and the younger parts of the Southern Uplands) of erosion of a sedimentary terrane S of the Southern Upland Fault during the Llandovery and Wenlock (McKerrow 1986).

On the Berwickshire coast the broken and slumped Coldingham and Linkim Beds are now thought to be of Wenlock or Ludlow age, and have been interpreted as trench slope basin deposits lying unconformably on the rising prism (Oliver *et al.* 1984). Their structural complexity may be due to pre-lithification deformation during gravity sliding as the accretionary prism was uplifted.

Although other interpretations of the tectonic history of the Southern Uplands have been proposed (Murphy & Hutton 1986), I consider that the accretionary prism model still stands, although perhaps in a more complicated form than that originally suggested (Mitchell & McKerrow 1975, McKerrow *et al.* 1977). If this model is accepted, it follows that deformation was continuous until accretion ended in the late Wenlock.

Widespread dyke-swarms affected most of Scotland in the late Silurian and early Devonian (Richey 1939). Dates of 418–395 Ma have recently been reported for these dykes in the Southern Uplands (Barnes *et al.* 1986), suggesting that they range in age from late Silurian to Emsian times; their petrology indicates that, by the time of emplacement, the igneous activity was not related to subduction of oceanic crust. Perhaps the northerly extension of the English continent was subducted below Scotland through part of this time interval (Leggett *et al.* 1983). During the later part of this interval (408–391 Ma) plutons (Cairnsmore of Carsphairn, Loch Doon, Cairnsmore of Fleet, Criffell, Priestlaw and Cockburn Law) were also intruded in the Southern Uplands (Brown *et al.* 1985); there is thus no doubt (whichever tectonic model is preferred) that uplift of the Southern Uplands occurred in the late Silurian and early Devonian.

The Southern Uplands are overlain by lower Old Red Sandstone sediments and lavas at St Abb's in Berwickshire. These contain the early Devonian eurypterid *Pterygotus*, but are relatively undeformed. The lavas are distinct from those of the Midland Valley and northern Scotland but similar to those of the Cheviot lavas, which are also undeformed and have an age of 389–383 Ma (Thirlwall 1981, 1983). If the St Abb's lavas have a similar (late Emsian) age, they could still be early Devonian (as suggested by the eurypterid) and yet later than the (pre-394 ± 3 Ma) Emsian event seen in northern England, which may also have extended to Scotland (see below).

Some later Devonian uplift and faulting occurred in the Southern Uplands. The upper Old Red Sandstone appears to be conformable below the Carboniferous where exposure shows the relationships, yet some considerable faulting is present in the St Abb's area prior to the Carboniferous.

The Midland Valley

The Silurian inliers along the southern margin of the Midland Valley (from Craighead to the Pentlands) show marine Llandovery and early Wenlock successions passing up into non-marine sediments which have not been easy to date accurately, although some fossils are present (Walton 1983). The late Silurian regression in the Midland Valley is marked by the appearance of conglomerates and sandstones which have been derived from the S and deposited in fluvial and deltaic environments (Bluck 1983). As Bluck points out, there are problems explaining how Wenlock conglomerates with clasts of lavas, porphyries, plutonic rocks, vein quartz and quartzite can be derived from the Southern Uplands; some post-Wenlock tectonic movements are clearly evident, though whether these are simply strike-slip movements along the Southern Upland Fault (McKerrow 1986, 1987) or N-directed thrusts transporting the Southern Uplands from the S (Bluck 1983) is still uncertain.

In the Pentland Hills the lower Old Red Sandstone consists of conglomerates and lavas which rest with marked unconformity on folded Silurian, but this late Silurian deformation is confined to the eastern parts of the Midland Valley, for at Lesmahagow (Fig. 2, column 10) and other western parts of the Midland Valley there is a complete lack of angular discordance (Mykura 1983). It should be noted that, like the uppermost Silurian, the earliest Old Red Sandstone in the southern part of the Midland Valley is not at all accurately dated; Thirlwall (1983) interprets some isotopic dates on lower Old Red Sandstone lavas from Fife as indicating a Silurian age, but the only fossils present in the southern Midland Valley are early Devonian (House *et al.* 1977, p. 73). An upper limit on the lower Old Red Sandstone of eastern Ayrshire is provided by the Rb–Sr date of 408 ± 6 Ma (Brown *et al.* 1985) corresponding to the Gedinnian on the Distinkhorn granodiorite which intrudes the local lower Old Red Sandstone (Sutherland 1982, p. 170).

In the northeastern part of the Midland Valley (Fig. 2, column 11) the lower Old Red Sandstone sequence commences in the Pridoli and continues until the late Siegenian or Emsian (House *et al.* 1977, pp. 72–3); it forms a remarkably thick sequence, reaching a maximum of around 8.5 km along the E coast (Mykura 1983). Although palaeontological control is quite good in the NE, 2.4 km of lavas occur in the Ochil Hills below any reported fish beds so that the age of the oldest lavas here is uncertain; Thirlwall (1981, 1983) suggests that some may be Silurian.

In the Midland Valley the upper Old Red Sandstone is probably all of Famennian age (House *et al.* 1977). Movements on the Southern Upland Fault and the Highland Boundary Fault have produced marked unconformities between the lower and upper Old Red Sandstone along both margins of the Midland Valley; a large unconformity is also evident in Fife, but the break is less marked in the W and there is no conclusive evidence of an unconformity in Arran (Friend *et al.* 1963). However, as Mykura (1983, p. 206) points out, the Midland Valley received little or no sediment during the middle Devonian (and perhaps none between the Emsian and the Frasnian, an interval of over 30 Ma); it was

perhaps raised to an upland or highland area during this time.

The Grampian Highlands

The late Proterozoic to Cambrian Dalradian rocks were deformed and metamorphosed in the early Ordovician Grampian orogeny; subsequently, at least a dozen plutons have been emplaced, dated at intervals from 490 to 420 Ma (Pankhurst 1982), followed by a peak of plutons dated between 420 and 400 Ma. There is no doubt that much of the Grampian Highlands (in both Scotland and Ireland) were uplifted continuously between the Ordovician and the early Devonian; the study of radiometric age patterns (Dewey & Pankhurst 1970, Dewey *et al.* 1970) supports the evidence from the plutons.

The interval from 490 to 400 Ma (Arenig to basal Emsian) naturally saw few deposits in the Grampian terrane, but early Devonian (and possibly latest Silurian) sediments are present in places. The Crawton, Arbuthnott and Garvock Groups of Angus overlap the Highland Boundary Fault (Mykura 1983), and these Gedinnian sediments have been traced southwestwards to the Firth of Clyde and Kintyre (Morton 1979). In Lorne (Fig. 2, column 12), on the W coast of Scotland, a series of sandstones and lavas yield Gedinnian fish and an Rb–Sr age of 415 ± 7 Ma (Mykura 1983), which is late Silurian or Gedinnian on the time-scale of McKerrow *et al.* (1985), and suggests that the sequence here is close to the Silurian–Devonian boundary. In the NE of the Grampians the outlier at Rhynie (which contains some of the earliest vascular plant remains) is probably of Siegenian age, and the lower Old Red Sandstone at Turriff is possibly Siegenian or Emsian (Mykura 1983). It thus follows that the widespread uplift of the Grampian terrane ceased sufficiently during the early Devonian for many small sedimentary basins to develop. Two suites of 'Caledonian' dykes are present on both sides of the Great Glen Fault: an older microdiorite suite associated with granites dated at around 420 Ma (Brown 1983, Brown *et al.* 1985) and a younger minette suite. Like the sedimentary basins, these also suggest tensional tectonic regimes in the Grampians during the late Silurian and early Devonian.

The Northern Highlands

In contrast with the Grampian Highlands, the first Palaeozoic metamorphism and deformation to the NW of the Great Glen Fault occurred between 460 and 450 Ma (Llandeilo and Caradoc); this was then followed by a long interval of cooling from 453 to 405 Ma (Powell & Phillips 1985). The later part of this interval (from 435 Ma) saw the emplacement of several plutons (Pankhurst 1982); the dyke-swarms of the Grampians at 420 Ma and later (see section above) are also present to the NW of the Great Glen Fault. It is thus likely that the Northern Highlands were uplifted from 460 to 405 Ma (Llandeilo to Siegenian), with regional tension developing after 420 Ma (Ludlow).

Along the E coast of the Northern Highlands there are extensive outcrops of Old Red Sandstone (Fig. 2, column 13). The oldest beds (the Sarclet Group and its equivalents) have yielded spores and fish scales in a few localities, suggesting that sedimentation began in the late Emsian or early Eifelian (Mykura 1983, p. 222). These 'lower Old Red Sandstone' beds were folded before deposition of the middle Old Red Sandstone, the Caithness Flagstone Group and the succeeding John O'Groats Sandstone Group, which are considered to be of Eifelian–Givetian age (Donovan *et al.* 1974); thus this folding probably occurred during the Eifelian. Further folding developed locally before the upper Old Red Sandstone, which is probably Frasnian in age from both the fish remains and a 370 Ma date for the Hoy Lavas of Orkney (Mykura 1983, p. 242). Thus, in the N of Scotland, where the Devonian stratigraphical record is most complete, we have evidence of uplift until the Siegenian, but with regional tension developing after the Ludlow, followed by two discrete periods of folding in the Eifelian and near the Givetian–Frasnian boundary. Similar episodes of deformation could have existed further S, but as yet they have not been recognized.

The Canadian Appalachians

Southern New Brunswick

Along the S coast of New Brunswick (and adjacent parts of Maine) sedimentation appears to have been more or less continuous, although there are several volcanic episodes, from the Llandovery until the Siegenian (Fig. 3, column 14) (Boucot 1968, Berry & Boucot 1970). Subsequently, the region was intruded by several granite and gabbro plutons (Gates 1969). The most accurately dated of these intrusions (Pajari *et al.* 1974) is the Red Beach Granite, which (with a decay constant corrected to 1.42) gives an Rb–Sr isochron of 385 ± 6 Ma (Spooner & Fairbairn 1970); on the time-scale of McKerrow *et al.*

(1985) this date (with the error) falls in the Eifelian or early Givetian, i.e. close to the middle of the middle Devonian. Both the Red Beach Granite and the folded and deformed early Devonian sediments and lavas are overlain unconformably by the late Devonian Perry Sandstone (Spooner & Fairbairn 1970). As the plutons close to the New Brunswick–Maine border are undeformed (Pajari *et al.* 1974), the Acadian orogeny in this region appears to consist of deformation in the Emsian followed by plutonism in the Eifelian and Givetian prior to the deposition of the late Devonian sediments.

Nova Scotia

In Nova Scotia there are two distinct groups of terranes on the Avalon margin of Iapetus: the Meguma terrane, to the S of the Chedabucto Fault, has a very different pre-Devonian history from the terranes to the N (Keppie 1985).

In the Annapolis Valley the thick turbidite and slate sequences of the Meguma Group are overlain by a thin Silurian and Devonian sequence (Fig. 3, column 15) (Smitheringdale 1973) which terminates at the top of the Torbrook Formation during the Siegenian or possibly Emsian (Jensen 1976). The abundant granite plutons in this belt cut the Torbrook Formation and are therefore likely to be Emsian or younger in age.

Age studies on slates of the Meguma Group (Reynolds & Muecke 1978) suggest a minimum value of 415–400 Ma for the time of initiation of the Acadian orogeny in this terrane followed by post-deformational intrusions at 380–370 Ma; on the time-scale of McKerrow *et al.* (1985) these two events would have occurred in the early Devonian (from the stratigraphic evidence this would have been in the Emsian) and the Givetian–Frasnian interval respectively. The Meguma terrane thus appears to have been deformed in the Emsian and to have had emplacement of plutons towards the end of the middle Devonian accompanied by some further deformation.

In Nova Scotia to the N of the Chedabucto Fault (Fig. 3, column 16) the continuous Silurian to late Gedinnian sequence of the Arisaig Group (Boucot *et al.* 1974) has also been deformed prior to the deposition of the overlying late Devonian and Carboniferous. The plutons in northern Nova Scotia show a wide range of dates, but those in the Devonian with errors less than 12 Ma give (recalculated) dates of 370 ± 12 Ma and 376 ± 10 Ma (Clarke *et al.* 1980) for post-tectonic plutons in this terrane, which confirm deformation prior to late Devonian.

Northern New Brunswick and Gaspé Peninsula

The Chaleurs Bay Group is followed conformably, though perhaps with some local nonsequences, by the early Devonian Dalhousie Group (Fig. 3, column 17) (Skinner 1974). These Silurian and Devonian rocks are intruded by gabbro which, in turn, is intruded by granite plutons with K–Ar ages of 392 and 398 Ma (Skinner 1974, p. 67), suggesting an Emsian (or slightly later) age for both the plutons and the deformation in this region which lies clearly on the N American side of the Iapetus suture (McKerrow & Ziegler 1971).

In eastern Gaspé (Fig. 3, column 18), further from the suture, the Devonian stratigraphic record is more complete. The St Leon Formation, which straddles the Silurian–Devonian boundary, is followed conformably by the Gaspé Limestone and the Gaspé Sandstone, which extends up to include the *Etymothyris* brachiopod zone (Lespérance 1980), equivalent to the early Emsian (Johnson 1979). In the Pte-St-Pierre region this early Devonian sequence appears to be overlain unconformably by the middle Devonian Malbaie Formation, which in turn was folded prior to the Carboniferous (Rust 1976). Both Emsian and Givetian (or slightly later) movements are thus distinguished in eastern Gaspé.

Newfoundland

In Western Newfoundland (Fig. 3, column 19) the Natlins Cove Formation at Sops Arm is very poorly dated (Lock 1969), but may be Wenlock or Ludlow in age. On the W coast, at Clam Bank, another succession is of Pridoli age (Berry & Boucot 1970). The Sops Arm rocks are intruded by a granite which may be of Devonian age.

In Central Newfoundland, around Notre Dame Bay (Fig. 3, column 20), the youngest preAcadian sediments are of Llandovery age (Arnott et al. 1985). The late Caradoc to Llandovery sediments of this region indicate contemporary fault movements associated with local uplift and deformation (Arnott 1983, Arnott et al. 1985). To the S, these sediments are intruded by the Topsails Igneous Complex, which consists of peralkaline granites dated at 419 ± 5 Ma and peraluminous granites at 386 ± 9 Ma (Taylor et al. 1980). The area S of Notre Dame Bay was thus uplifted in the late Silurian, and again when plutonism was renewed in the middle Devonian.

To the E of the Reach Fault, which is thought (McKerrow & Cocks 1977) to form the suture where the Iapetus Ocean closed in the Devonian (as opposed to the earlier closure further W in Newfoundland related to the Llandeilo Humber-

ian orogeny), the Botwood Group is largely Llandovery in age but may extend into the upper Silurian; it is intruded by the Mount Peyton pluton which has an approximate age of 393 ± 30 Ma (Bell et al. 1977) and may thus be of Devonian age.

Further E in Newfoundland, the youngest sediments affected by the Acadian orogeny are Ordovician or earlier. A summary of Silurian and Devonian plutonism in the Gander and Avalon zones (Dallmeyer et al. 1981) shows granites with Rb–Sr ages ranging from 432 ± 22 and 411 ± 5 Ma to 355 ± 5 Ma; in the same paper Dallmeyer et al. also report widely distributed $^{40}Ar–^{40}Ar$ plateau ages of 383–365 Ma which they interpret as the period of regional post-metamorphic cooling in the Bonavista Bay area. On the timescale of McKerrow et al. (1985) this would indicate uplift from Givetian times until the end of the Devonian. The earlier ages of some plutons suggest that plutonism may have started in the Silurian, and Dallmeyer et al. (1981) proposed that a 460 ± 20 Ma zircon age on the Lockers Bay Granite pre-dates a regional mylonitic foliation which occurred between 420 and 400 Ma when the Gander and Avalon terranes were brought together along the Dover Fault.

The evidence from Newfoundland is that plutonism commenced in the Silurian; this was perhaps accompanied by uplift and cooling over a considerable period both before and after the Acadian deformation. The date of the deformation has not yet been defined with any precision, but it could well be Emsian as in the rest of the Canadian Appalachians.

Summarizing comments and conclusions

In southern England and the British Channel area local tectonism persisted through much of the Devonian, but regional deformation is restricted to Wales N of a Bristol Channel landmass, where it can be dated stratigraphically as post-Siegenian (Fig. 4, columns 1–5). At the same time much of NW Wales had been uplifted from Wenlock times onwards as part of a large Irish Sea landmass.

In northern England (Fig. 4, column 6) Pridoli and older beds are intruded by the 394 ± 3 Ma Shap Granite which is straddled by the Caledonian deformation in the region. This date corresponds to the middle and late Emsian Stage. If the Devonian deformation in England and Wales was synchronous, this would be the time of the main Caledonian orogeny. However, if it were

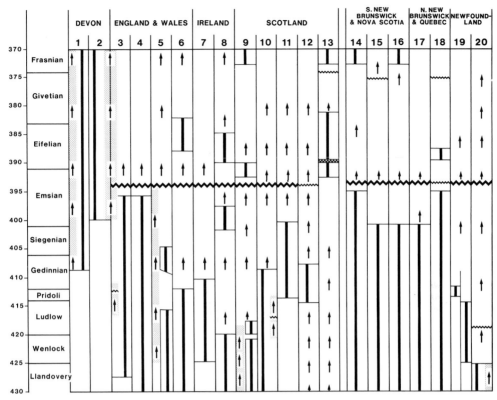

FIG. 4. A summary of deformational events (undulating lines) and times of uplift (vertical arrows) in the British Isles and the Canadian Appalachians. Columns numbered as in Figs 1–3. Thick vertical lines indicate times of sedimentation (for details see Figs 2 and 3 and text). Uplift in areas adjacent to those receiving sediment is indicated (by shaded ornamentation) as follows: column 1, Devonian uplift in S Cornwall; columns 2 and 3, Devonian uplift of the Bristol Channel landmass; column 3, late Silurian uplift locally in SW Wales; column 5, Silurian and early Devonian uplift of NW Wales; column 9, Silurian uplift of Cockburnland in the northern Southern Uplands; column 10, late Silurian folding in the SE of the Midland Valley; column 20, early Silurian faulting accompanying sedimentation in Notre Dame Bay, Newfoundland. Note the widespread middle and late Emsian deformation, and the relative amount of pre-Emsian uplift in much of the British Isles and Newfoundland compared with southern Britain and the Appalachians of the Canadian mainland. See text for constraints on dating events.

not synchronous, the deformation could have been later in Wales than in northern England. It could not have been earlier, and there is no possibility of widespread Caledonian folding occurring at the end of the Silurian in either England or Wales.

The evidence of the timing of deformation in Ireland is less precise (Fig. 4, columns 7 and 8), though the presence of middle Devonian sediments in Mayo does indicate some Eifelian or later folding in addition to the Emsian event.

In Scotland (Fig. 4, columns 9–13) continuous Caradoc to Wenlock development of the Southern Uplands was followed by post-Wenlock uplift and deformation prior to the St Abb's Old Red Sandstone. In the Midland Valley local folding

occurred in the E prior to deposition of the lower Devonian; sedimentation in the S ceased before the end of the Gedinnian but continued through much of the Siegenian in the NE. Thus the Emsian deformation seen in England could also have occurred over much of Scotland S of the Highlands; there is no direct evidence, however, of deformation at this time in the Scottish Highlands. All the Caithness Old Red Sandstone may have been deposited after the middle Emsian. All the Highlands show uplift through much of Silurian and Devonian time, with local episodes of tension permitting ephemeral sedimentary basins.

In the Canadian Appalachians (Fig. 4, columns 14–20), post-Siegenian deformation occurred on both sides of the Iapetus suture over wide areas of New Brunswick and Nova Scotia, with some earlier uplift (early Emsian) in northern New Brunswick and later local deformation in places. Plutons with a late Emsian or Eifelian age postdate the main deformation in southern New Brunswick. The timing of the Acadian orogeny in Newfoundland is still poorly constrained, but it is definitely Emsian in parts of New Brunswick and Nova Scotia.

From this evidence it seems probable that much of the Silurian and Devonian deformation was (or could well have been) restricted to the middle and late Emsian Stage; the duration of this interval was possibly around 7 Ma, from 397 to 390 Ma. In addition, local uplift and/or deformation (often accompanied by plutonism) was present in many areas both before and after the Emsian. The presence of abundant calc-alkaline igneous rocks to the NW of the Iapetus suture until the Emsian deformation indicates that subduction of oceanic crust was occurring throughout both Britain and eastern Canada until this time. This Emsian event thus seems to mark the final closure of the Iapetus Ocean.

References

ALLEN, J. R. L. 1965. The sedimentation and palaeogeography of the Old Red Sandstone of Anglesey, North Wales. *Proceedings of the Yorkshire Geological Society*, **35**, 139–85.

—— 1974. Sedimentology of the Old Red Sandstone (Siluro-Devonian) in the Clee Hills area, Shropshire, England. *Sedimentary Geology*, **12**, 73–167.

——, THOMAS, R. G. & WILLIAMS, B. J. P. 1981. Field Meeting: The facies of the Lower Old Red Sandstone, north of Milford Haven, southwest Dyfed, Wales. *Proceedings of the Geologists Association*, **92**, 251–67.

ARNOTT, R. J. 1983. Sedimentology of Upper Ordovician–Silurian sequences on New World Island, Newfoundland: separate fault controlled basins? *Canadian Journal of Earth Sciences*, **20**, 345–54.

——, McKERROW, W. S. & COCKS, L. R. M. 1985. The tectonics and depositional history of the Ordovician and Silurian rocks of Notre Dame Bay, Newfoundland. *Canadian Journal of Earth Sciences*, **22**, 607–18.

BARNES, R. P., ROCK, N. M. E. & GASKARTH, J. W. 1986. Late Caledonian dyke-swarms in Southern Scotland: new field, petrological and geochemical data for the Wigtown Peninsula, Galloway. *Geological Journal*, **21**, 101–25.

BELL, K., BLENKINSOP, J. & STRONG, D. F. 1977. The geochronology of some granitic bodies from eastern Newfoundland and its bearing on Appalachian evolution. *Canadian Journal of Earth Sciences*, **14**, 456–76.

BERRY, W. B. N. & BOUCOT, A. J. 1970. Correlation of the North American Silurian rocks. *Geological Society of America, Special Paper No. 102*, 289 pp.

BLUCK, B. J. 1983. Role of the Midland Valley of Scotland in the Caledonian Orogeny. *Transactions of the Royal Society of Edinburgh, Earth Sciences*, **74**, 119–36.

BOUCOT, A. J. 1968. Silurian and Devonian of the Northern Appalachians. *In:* ZEN, E-AN, WHITE, W. S. & HADLEY, J. B. (eds) *Studies of Appalachian Geology: Northern and Maritime*, pp. 83–94, Wiley-Interscience, New York.

——, DEWEY, J. F., DINELEY, D. L., FLETCHER, R., FYSON, W. K., GRIFFIN, J. G., HICKOX, C. F.,

McKERROW, W. S. & ZIEGLER, A. M. 1974. Geology of the Arisaig area, Antigonish County, Nova Scotia. *Geological Society of America, Special Paper No. 139*, 191 pp.

BROWN, G. C., FRANCIS, E. H., KENNAN, P. & STILLMAN, C. J. 1985. Caledonian igneous rocks of Britain and Ireland. *In:* HARRIS, A. L. (ed.) *The Nature and Timing of Orogenic Activity in the Caledonian Rocks of the British Isles, Geological Society of London, Memoir No. 9*, pp. 1–15.

BROWN, P. E. 1983. Caledonian and earlier magmatism. *In:* CRAIG, G. Y. (ed.) *Geology of Scotland*, pp. 167–204, Scottish Academic Press, Edinburgh.

CLARKE, D. B., BARR, S. M. & DONOHOE, H. V. 1980. Granitoid and other plutonic rocks of Nova Scotia. *In:* WONES, D. R. (ed.) *The Caledonides in the USA. Proceedings of the International Geological Correlation Project 27, Blacksburg, VA. Department of Geological Sciences, Virginia Polytechnic Institute and State University, Memoir No. 2*, pp. 107–16.

CUMMINS, W. A. 1957. The Denbigh Grits: Wenlock greywackes in Wales. *Geological Magazine*, **94**, 437–51.

DALLMEYER, R. D., BLACKWOOD, R. F. & ODOM, A. L. 1981. Age and origin of the Dover Fault: tectonic boundary between Gander and Avalon Zones of the northeastern Newfoundland Appalachians. *Canadian Journal of Earth Sciences*, **18**, 1431–42.

DEWEY, J. F., McKERROW, W. S. & MOORBATH, S. 1970. The relationship between isotopic ages, uplift and sedimentation during Ordovician times in Western Ireland. *Scottish Journal of Geology*, **6**, 133–45.

—— & PANKHURST, R. J. 1970. Evolution of the Scottish Highlands and their radiometric age pattern. *Transactions of the Royal Society of Edinburgh*, **68**, 361–89.

DONOVAN, R. N., FOSTER, R. J. & WESTOLL, T. S. 1974. A stratigraphical revision of the Old Red Sandstone of Northern Caithness. *Transactions of the Royal Society of Edinburgh*, **69**, 167–201.

FRIEND, P. F., HARLAND, W. B. & HUDSON, J. D. 1963. The Old Red Sandstone and the Highland Boundary in Arran, Scotland. *Transactions of the Edinburgh Geological Society*, **19**, 363–425.

GATES, O. 1969. Lower Silurian–lower Devonian volcanic rocks of New England coast and southern New Brunswick. *In:* KAY, M. (ed.) *American Association of Petroleum Geologists, Memoir No. 12*, pp. 484–503.

GRAHAM, J. R., RICHARDSON, J. B. & CLAYTON, G. 1983. Age and significance of the Old Red Sandstone around Clew Bay, NW Ireland. *Transactions of the Royal Society of Edinburgh, Earth Sciences*, **73**, 245–9.

GREENLY, E. 1919. The geology of Angelsey. *Memoir of the Geological Survey*, 980 pp.

HOLDER, M. T. & LEVERIDGE, B. E. 1986. A model for the tectonic evolution of Cornwall. *Journal of the Geological Society of London*, **143**, 125–34.

HOUSE, M. R., RICHARDSON, J. B., CHALONER, W. G., ALLEN, J. R. L., HOLLAND, C. H. & WESTOLL, T. S. 1977. A correlation of Devonian rocks of the British Isles. *Special Report of the Geological Society of London No. 7*.

HURST, J. M., HANCOCK, N. J. & MCKERROW, W. S. 1978. Wenlock stratigraphy and palaeogeography of Wales and the Welsh Borderland. *Proceedings of the Geologists Association*, **89**, 197–226.

——, —— & —— 1979. Old Red Sandstone facies and Wenlock stratigraphy and palaeogeography in Wales and the Welsh Borderland: reply by the authors. *Proceedings of the Geologists Association*, **90**, 231–2.

JENSEN, L. R. 1976. The Torbrook Formation (Lower Devonian, Nova Scotia). *Maritime Sediments*, **12**, 107–18.

JOHNSON, J. G. 1979. Devonian brachiopod biostratigraphy. *Special Paper in Palaeontology*, **23**, 291–306.

JONES, O. T. 1956. The geological evolution of Wales and adjacent regions. *Quarterly Journal of the Geological Society of London*, **111**, 323–51.

KEPPIE, J. D. 1985. The Appalachian collage. *In:* GEE, D. G. & STURT, B. A. (eds) *The Caledonide Orogen—Scandinavia and Related Areas*, pp. 1217–26, Wiley, Chichester.

LEGGETT, J. K., MCKERROW, W. S. & CASEY, D. M. 1982. The anatomy of a Lower Palaeozoic accretionary forearc: the Southern Uplands of Scotland. *In:* LEGGETT, J. K. (ed.) *Trench–Forearc Geology, Special Publication of the Geological Society of London No. 10*, pp. 494–520.

——, —— & SOPER, N. J. 1983. A model for the crustal evolution of Southern Scotland. *Tectonics*, **2**, 187–210.

LESPÉRANCE, P. J. 1980. Les Calcaires Superieurs de Gaspé (Dévonien Inférieur) dans le nord-est de la Gaspésie. *Rapport DPV-751*, Ministère de l'Energie et des Ressources, Québec, 35 pp.

LOCK, B. E. 1969. Silurian rocks of west White Bay area, Newfoundland. *In:* KAY, M. (ed.) *American Association of Petroleum Geologists, Memoir No. 12*, pp. 433–42.

MAX, M. D., LONG, C. B. & GEOGHEGAN, M. A. 1978. The Galway Granite. *Bulletin of the Geological Survey of Ireland*, **2**, 223–33.

MCKERROW, W. S. 1962. The chronology of Caledonian folding in the British Isles. *Proceedings of the*

National Academy of Sciences of the USA, **48**, 1905–13.

—— 1987. The tectonic setting of the Southern Uplands. *In:* FETTES, D. J. & HARRIS, A. L. (eds) *Synthesis of the Caledonian Rocks of Britain*, pp. 207–20, Reidel, Dordrecht.

—— 1988. The development of the Iapetus Ocean from the Arenig to the Wenlock. *This volume.*

—— & COCKS, L. R. M. 1977. The location of the Iapetus Ocean suture in Newfoundland. *Canadian Journal of Earth Sciences*, **14**, 488–95.

——, LAMBERT, R. ST. J. & COCKS, L. R. M. 1985. The Ordovician, Silurian and Devonian periods. *In:* SNELLING, N. J. (ed.) *Geochronology and the Geological Record, Geological Society of London Memoir No. 10*, pp. 73–80.

——, LEGGETT, J. K. & EALES, M. H. 1977. Imbricate thrust model of the Southern Uplands of Scotland. *Nature, London*, **267**, 237–9.

—— & ZIEGLER, A. M. 1971. The Lower Silurian palaeogeography of New Brunswick and adjoining areas. *Journal of Geology*, **79**, 635–46.

—— & —— 1972. Palaeozoic oceans. *Nature, London, Physical Science*, **240**, 92–4.

MITCHELL, A. H. G. & MCKERROW, W. S. 1975. Analogous evolution of the Burma orogen and the Scottish Caledonides. *Geological Society of America Bulletin*, **86**, 305–15.

MORTON, D. J. 1979. Palaeogeographical evolution of the Lower Old Red Sandstone basin in the western Midland Valley. *Scottish Journal of Geology*, **15**, 97–116.

MOSELEY, F. (ed.) 1978. The geology of the Lake District. *Yorkshire Geological Society, Occasional Publication No. 3*, 284 pp.

MURPHY, F. C. & HUTTON, D. H. W. 1986. Is the Southern Uplands of Scotland really an accretionary prism? *Geology*, **14**, 354–8.

MYKURA, W. 1983. Old Red Sandstone. *In:* CRAIG, G. Y. (ed.) *Geology of Scotland*, pp. 205–51, Scottish Academic Press, Edinburgh.

OLIVER, G. J. H., SMELLIE, J. L., THOMAS, L. J., CASEY, D. M., KEMP, A. E. S., EVANS, L. J., BALDWIN, J. R. & HEPWORTH, B. C. 1984. Early Palaeozoic history of the Midland Valley, Southern Uplands–Longford Down massif and the Lake District, British Isles. *Transactions of the Royal Society of Edinburgh, Earth Sciences*, **75**, 245–58.

PAJARI, G. E., TREMBATH, L. T., CORMIER, R. F. & FYFFE, L. R. 1974. The age of the Acadian deformation in southwestern New Brunswick. *Canadian Journal of Earth Sciences*, **11**, 1309–13.

PANKHURST, R. J. 1982. Geochronological tables for British igneous rocks. *In:* SUTHERLAND, D. S. (ed.) *Igneous Rocks of the British Isles*, pp. 575–81, Wiley, Chichester.

PHILLIPS, W. E. A., KENNEDY, M. J. & DUNLOP, G. M. 1969. Geologic comparison of western Ireland and northeastern Newfoundland. *In:* KAY, M. (ed.) *American Association of Petroleum Geologists, Memoir No. 12*, pp. 194–211.

POWELL, D. & PHILLIPS, W. E. A. 1985. Time of deformation in the Caledonide Orogen of Britain and Ireland. *In:* HARRIS, A. L. (ed.) *Geological Society of London, Memoir No. 9,* 17–39.

REYNOLDS, P. H. & MUECKE, G. K. 1978. Studies on slates: applicability of the ^{40}Ar/^{39}Ar stepwise outgassing method. *Earth and Planetary Science Letters,* **40,** 111–8.

RICHEY, J. E. 1939. The dykes of Scotland. *Transactions of the Edinburgh Geological Society,* **13,** 393–435.

RUST, B. R. 1976. Stratigraphic relationships of the Malbaie Formation (Devonian), Gaspé, Quebec. *Canadian Journal of Earth Sciences,* **13,** 1556–9.

SKINNER, R. 1974. Geology of Tetagouche Lakes, Bathurst and Nepisiguit Falls map-areas, New Brunswick. *Geological Survey of Canada, Memoir No. 371,* 133 pp.

SMITHERINGDALE, W. G. 1973. Geology of parts of Digby, Bridgetown and Gaspereau Lake map-areas, Nova Scotia. *Geological Survey of Canada, Memoir No. 375,* 78 pp.

SPOONER, C. M. & FAIRBAIRN, H. W. 1970. Relation of radiometric age of granitic rocks near Calais, Maine, to the time of Acadian Orogeny. *Geological Society of America Bulletin,* **81,** 3663–70.

STILLE, H. 1924. *Grundfragen der verleichenden Tektonik.* Borntraeger, Berlin.

STILLMAN, C. J. 1981. Caledonian igneous activity. *In:* HOLLAND, C. H. (ed.) *A Geology of Ireland,* pp. 83–106, Scottish Academic Press, Edinburgh.

SUTHERLAND, D. S. (ed.) 1982. *Igneous Rocks of the British Isles.* Wiley, Chichester, 645 pp.

TAYLOR, R. P., STRONG, D. F. & KEAN, B. F. 1980. The Topsails Igneous Complex: Silurian–Devonian

peralkaline magmatism in western Newfoundland. *Canadian Journal of Earth Sciences,* **17,** 425–39.

THIRLWALL, M. 1981. Implications for Caledonian plate tectonic models of chemical data from volcanic rocks of the British Old Red Sandstone. *Journal of the Geological Society, London,* **138,** 123–38.

—— 1983. Discussion on Implications for Caledonian plate tectonic models of chemical data from volcanic rocks of the British Old Red Sandstone. *Journal of the Geological Society, London,* **140,** 315–8.

TUNBRIDGE, I. P. 1986. Mid-Devonian tectonics and sedimentation in the Bristol Channel area. *Journal of the Geological Society, London,* **143,** 107–15.

WADGE, A. J., GALE, N. H., BECKINSALE, R. D. & RUNDLE, C. C. 1978. A Rb–Sr isochron for the Shap Granite. *Proceedings of the Yorkshire Geological Society,* **42,** 297–305.

WALMSLEY, V. G. & BASSETT, M. G. 1976. Biostratigraphy and correlation of the Coralliferous Group and Gray Sandstone Group (Silurian) of Pembrokeshire, Wales. *Proceedings of the Geologists Association,* **87,** 191–220.

WALTON, E. K. 1983. Lower Palaeozoic—stratigraphy. *In:* CRAIG, G. Y. (ed.) *Geology of Scotland,* pp. 105–37, Scottish Academic Press, Edinburgh.

WARREN, P. T., PRICE, D., NUTT, M. J. C. & SMITH, E. G. 1984. Geology of the country around Rhyl and Denbigh. *British Geological Survey Memoir,* 217 pp.

W. S. McKERROW, Department of Earth Sciences, Parks Road, Oxford OX1 3PR, UK.

Silurian to Lower Carboniferous tectonism in the Appalachians of the USA

P. H. Osberg

SUMMARY: In New England highly deformed Silurian and lower Devonian beds are overlain unconformably by middle Devonian sediments. Early structures include westward-verging recumbent folds and thrusts, while younger features include local development of back-folding and upright folds with a NE trend. In the central and southern Appalachians the recognition of Acadian structures is not clearly documented, except for the Talladega Belt. Middle and upper Devonian molasse occurs to the W of the central Appalachians.

New England Appalachians

Silurian sequences in New England belong to two facies: a western shelf and a more easterly turbidite section. The boundary between these two facies lies just E of the New Hampshire–Vermont border and extends southward into Connecticut and northward into western and northern Maine. The turbidite facies represents a continental margin deposit. Pridoli to Gedinnian volcanics occupy a belt extending from western into northern Maine, and Silurian to Gedinnian volcanics occupy a belt located along coastal Maine extending into northeastern Massachusetts. These volcanic rocks consist of basalts, andesites, dacites, rhyolites and abundant volcaniclastics, and represent arc volcanics. Lower Devonian flysch was probably deposited in front of an advancing tectonic front.

Acadian (late Caledonian) structures can be shown to be widespread E of longitude about 72°30′ W (Maine, New Hampshire and eastern Massachusetts). Acadian deformation exists W of this longitude, but its character and limits are somewhat uncertain because appropriate cover rocks have been eroded. The eastern margin of Acadian deformation is seaward of New England.

Stratigraphic sections, which include late Ordovician to early Devonian rocks, contain Acadian structures over much of New England. Older structural features in pre-late Ordovician sections lying approximately E of longitude 72°30′ W are difficult to identify. In northern Maine, Arenig to Caradoc sections are no more deformed than Silurian and lower Devonian sections. To the S, where deformation is more intense, structural features in pre-Ashgill rocks are essentially parallel to those in adjacent Silurian–lower Devonian sections, but because of the intense deformation the presence of pre-Acadian structural features is possible.

A large amount of shortening across the Acadian orogen in southern New England has produced alpine-style structures and exposes a deep structural level. Northward, shortening across the orogen is less and structures are less extreme and at higher structural level.

Early formed Acadian structures include recumbent folds (Thompson et al. 1968) and thrusts with westward transport (Osberg et al., in press). An important back-folding stage (Robinson & Hall 1980) affects these structures, imposing large E-facing folds on them and producing W-dipping thrusts. These structures are overprinted regionally by nearly upright folds with NE trends and an associated penetrative cleavage (Osberg 1968). The latter folds determine the tectonic grain. Younger structural features include local development of E–W folds and lineations (Robinson et al. 1982), N-trending folds and associated cleavage (Osberg 1968) and gneiss domes (Thompson et al. 1968) in southern New England where they are localized along the NE-trending antiforms.

These structures are interpreted to have been produced by a collision joining Avalonia with N America along a suture, much complicated by thrusting and later high-angle faulting, whose traces run through southeastern New England and along the coast of northern New England. Initial continental collision is thought to have developed a tectonic lid by thrusting rocks of the eastern plate westwards and generating general W-verging nappes, thrusts and folds throughout the orogen. Later the operative strain mechanisms could not accommodate the stress, and the crust of the eastern continent broke and was thrust under the western plate to produce the back-folding and much of the current physical relations of the suture in coastal New England. These features were refolded, owing to tightening of the orogen, giving rise to the dominant NE trends. Other superimposed structures were due

From HARRIS, A. L. & FETTES, D. J. (eds), 1988, *The Caledonian–Appalachian Orogen,*
Geological Society Special Publication No. 38, pp. 449–452.

to adjustments as under-thrusting continued and the width of the orogen was shortened. This sequence of structural events may have doubled the thickness of the crust beneath the orogen in southern New England and juxtaposed a volcanic terrane of the eastern plate against the passive margin of the western continent.

Plutons that are considered to be related to the Acadian orogeny belong to three groups: early plutons ranging in age from about 415 to about 400 Ma, widely distributed plutons with ages between about 395 and about 320 Ma, and mildly alkalic plutons that span approximately the same range of ages as does the second group. The early plutons are calc-alkaline and consist of granites to granodiorites. They occupy a belt that is nearly coincident with the volcanic belt of northern Maine and extend southward through New Hampshire into Massachusetts. These plutons are highly deformed in the southern part of the belt but show less deformation toward the N. Hon (1980) has linked the compositions of plutons in the northern part of this belt with those of the nearby volcanics. The widely distributed plutons that belong to the second group have a large range of composition, gabbro to granite. Many have S-type characteristics. The magmas of these plutons are thought to have been generated by partial melting of a tectonically thickened crust 30–70 Ma after continental collision. The mildly alkalic plutons are situated along coastal New England. They are thought to have an origin similar to that of the second group, but these bear the chemical signature of the eastern continent.

Stratigraphic constraint for the timing of Acadian deformation comes principally from northern New England (Naylor 1971, Osberg 1983) where slightly deformed middle Devonian beds lie across highly deformed Silurian–lower Devonian sections (Boucot *et al.* 1964). The folds in the middle Devonian rocks are probably due to Alleghanian structural adjustments. Somewhat similar relations occur in northeastern New England where slightly deformed upper Devonian red beds rest on a more deformed Silurian–lower Devonian section (Schluger 1973); here again the slight folding in the upper Devonian sections is probably Alleghanian (Hercynian).

Plutonic rocks that cross-cut Acadian structures have been dated as 400–360 Ma (Brookings 1976; Lyons 1979, Dallmeyer & Van Breeman 1981). These plutons cut the prominent NE-trending upright folds throughout New England, but Ashwal *et al.* (1979) have suggested that plutons dated at 380 Ma are involved in doming which is associated with the youngest Acadian fold phase.

The stratigraphic and radiometric controls indicate that continental collision occurred in latest lower Devonian time and that the deformation process was rapid. Minor readjustments occurred until the end of the Devonian. The thermal effects were of much longer duration.

Central and southern Appalachians

The widespread removal of Silurian–lower Devonian cover sequences in the central and southern Appalachians has made the recognition of Acadian structures difficult. Moreover, Alleghanian thrusts with large displacements have redistributed any Acadian relationships, further complicating an understanding of the Acadian for this part of the orogen. Acadian structures are not present in the Valley and Ridge province where the Silurian–Devonian sections exhibit the same degree of folding as the Carboniferous rocks. Glover *et al.* (1983) have presented relationships supporting a widespread Acadian ductile deformation to the E, but few specific occurrences of Acadian structural features have been documented. One of the best of these is in the southwestern extremity of the mountain belt (Talladega belt) where Tull (1982) described tight to isoclinal folds and associated cleavage in a palaeontologically dated lower Devonian sequence. Whole-rock K–Ar fusion dates from folded phyllites (sub-biotite metamorphic zone) of this sequence exhibit a thermal maximum at 390 Ma, demonstrating the Acadian age of these structures. A second well-documented locality is in the southern part of the central Appalachians where Pavlides (1980) has shown that a foliated pluton dated at 415 Ma has been deformed by early almost recumbent folds and later upright folds. These folds also occur in Cambrian–Ordovician sections which are in turn intruded by a relatively undeformed Carboniferous granite. Acadian folds must have a wide distribution, but their identification is made difficult by the lack of critical geological constraints.

A few Acadian faults have been identified. Glover *et al.* (1983) have described an E-dipping thrust (Ridgeway) that cuts previously deformed rocks in the southern part of the central Appalachians, and Acadian motion on steep ductile faults (Brevard, Towalaga, Gold Hill) has been dated in the southern Appalachians (Bond & Fullagar 1974, Russell 1978, Glover *et al.* 1983). Presumably, some of these faults have had a long history of recurring movement.

Middle and upper Devonian molasse occurs along the W margin of the central Appalachians. These deposits are the erosion products of mountainous terrane to the E, and therefore mountain building processes must have been operative just prior to and during(?) the time of deposition (Faill 1985).

Devonian and Carboniferous plutons are scattered through the central and southern Appalachians and may be related to the Acadian orogeny (Osberg *et al.*, in press). Their compositions include gabbro, syenite, granite and granodiorite. A few Devonian plutons are intensely deformed; the rest, including most Devonian and all Carboniferous plutons, are only slightly deformed, presumably by Alleghanian events. The tectonic significance of these plutons has not been completely explained. Most workers in the southern Appalachians have interpreted the Carboniferous plutons as being related to the Alleghanian, but alternatively they, together with many or all of the Devonian plutons, could by derived from partial fusion of crustal and mantle material during Acadian tectonic thickening processes. The time frame is of approximately the right order.

References

ASHWAL, L. D., LEO, G. W., ROBINSON, P, ZARTMAN, R. E. & HALL, D. J. 1979. The Belchertown Quartz Monzodiorite pluton, west-central Massachusetts, a syntectonic Acadian intrusion. *American Journal of Science*, **279**, 936–69.

BOND, P. A. & FULLAGAR, P. D. 1974. Origin and age of the Henderson augen gneiss and associated cataclastic rocks in southwestern North Carolina. *Geological Society of America, Abstracts with Programs*, **6**, 336.

BOUCOT, A. J., FIELD, M. T., FLETCHER, R., FORBES, W. H., NAYLOR, R. S. & PAVLIDES, L. 1964. Reconnaissance bedrock geology of the Presque Isle quadrangle, Maine. *Maine Geological Survey Quadrangle Map Series No. 2*, 123 pp.

BROOKINGS, D. G. 1976. Geochronologic contributions to stratigraphic interpretation and correlation in the Penobscot Bay area, eastern Maine. *In: Geological Society of America Memoir No. 148*, pp. 129–45.

DALLMEYER, R. D. & VAN BREEMAN, O. 1981. Rb-Sr whole rock and ^{40}Ar/^{39}Ar mineral ages of the Togue and Hallowell quartz-monzonite and Three Mile Pond granodiorite plutons, south-central Maine: their bearing on post Acadian cooling history. *Contributions to Mineralogy and Petrology*, **78**, 61–73.

FAILL, R. T. 1985. The Acadian orogeny and the Catskill Delta. *In: WOODROW, D. L. & SEVON, W. D. (eds) The Catskill Delta. Geological Society of America Special Paper No. 201*, pp. 15–37.

GLOVER, L., III, SPEER, J. A., RUSSELL, G. S. & FARRAR, S. S. 1983. Ages of regional metamorphism and ductile deformation in the central and southern Appalachians. *Lithos*, **16**, 224–45.

HON, R. 1980. Geology and petrology of igneous bodies within the Katahdin pluton. *In: ROY, D. C. & NAYLOR, R. S. (eds) Guidebook to the Geology of Northeastern Maine and Neighboring New Brunswick. 72nd Annual Meeting, New England Intercollegiate Geological Conference, Presque Isle, ME*, pp. 65–79.

LYONS, J. B. 1979. Stratigraphy, structure, and plutonism east of the Bronson Hill anticlinorium, New Hampshire. *In: SKEHAN, J. W., S. J. & OSBERG, P. H. (eds) The Caledonides in the U.S.A.: Geological Excursions in the Northeast Appalachians*, pp. 73–92, Weston Observatory, Weston, MA.

NAYLOR, R. S. 1971. Acadian orogeny—an abrupt and brief event. *Science*, **172**, 558–60.

OSBERG, P. H. 1968. Stratigraphy, structural geology, and metamorphism of the Waterville–Vassalboro area, Maine. *Maine Geological Survey, Bulletin No. 20*, 64 pp.

—— 1983. Timing of orogenic events in the U.S. Appalachians. *In: SCHENK, P. E. (ed.) Regional Trends in the Geology of the Appalachian–Caledonian–Hercynian–Mauritanide Orogen*, pp. 315–37, Reidel, Dordrecht.

——, TULL, J. F., ROBINSON, P., HON, R. & BUTLER, J. R. The Acadian orogeny. *In: HATCHER, R. D., JR., VIELE, G. W. & THOMAS, W. A. (eds) The Appalachian/Ouachita Regions: U.S. Geological Society of America D.N.A.G. Volume*, in press.

PAVLIDES, L. 1980. Revised nomenclature and stratigraphic relationships of the Fredericksburg complex and Quantico Formation of the Virginia Piedmont. *U.S. Geological Survey Professional Paper No. 1146*, 29 pp.

ROBINSON, P. & HALL, L. M. 1980. Tectonic synthesis of southern New England. *In: WONES, D. R. (ed.) The Caledonides in the USA. Proceedings of the International Geological Correlation Program—Caledonide Orogen Project 27, Blacksburg, VA. Department of Geological Sciences, Virginia Polytechnic Institute and State University, Memoir No. 2*, pp. 73–82.

——, FIELD, M. T. & TUCKER, R. D. 1982. Stratigraphy and structure of the Ware–Barre area, central Massachusetts. *In: JOESTEN, R. & QUARRIER, S. S. (eds) Guidebook for Field Trips in Connecticut and South-central Massachusetts, 74th Annual Meeting, New England Intercollegiate Geological Conference, Storrs, CT*, pp. 341–73.

RUSSELL, G. S. 1978. U–Pb, Rh–Sr and K–Ar isotopic studies bearing on the tectonic development of the southernmost Appalachian orogen, Alabama.

Ph.D. Thesis, Florida State University, Tallahassee, FL, 197 pp.

SCHLUGER, P. R. 1973. Stratigraphy and sedimentary environments of the Devonian Perry Formation, New Brunswick, Canada and Maine, U.S.A. *Geological Society of America Bulletin*, **84**, 2533–48.

THOMPSON, J. B., JR., ROBINSON, P., CLIFFORD, T. N. & TRASK, N. J., JR. 1968. Nappes and gneiss domes in west-central New England. *In*: ZEN, E-AN, WHITE, W. S., HADLEY, J. B. & THOMPSON, J. B., JR. (eds) *Studies of Appalachian Geology: Northern and Maritime*, pp. 203–18, Wiley-Interscience, New York.

TULL, J. F. 1982. Stratigraphic framework of the Talladega belt, Alabama Appalachians. *In*: BEARCE, D. N., BLACK, W. W., KISH, S. A. & TULL, J. F. (eds) *Tectonic Studies in the Talladega and Carolina Slate Belts, Southern Appalachian Orogen. Geological Society of America Special Paper No. 191*.

P. H. OSBERG, Department of Geological Sciences, University of Maine, Orono, ME 04469, USA.

Scandian–Acadian–Caledonian *sensu strictu* metamorphism in the age range 430–360 Ma

Peter Robinson, R. J. Tracy, D. S. Santallier, P.-G. Andreasson & J. I. Gil-Ibarguchi

SUMMARY: Metamorphism in the age range Wenlock to mid-Devonian, when it can be recognized, appears to have accompanied some of the most intense phases of convergent tectonics in the orogen. Very different styles of metamorphism in different regions suggest different tectonic settings. In Scandinavia deep subduction and imbrication of the Baltic continental margin beneath N America (?), with little or no plutonism, produced a regional pattern leading to high temperature eclogites and granulites. In the British Isles, Canada and Maine, broad greenschist, prehnite–pumpellyite and lower-grade metamorphism accompanied the closure of Iapetus, with local higher-grade punctuations associated with widespread plutonic activity. In France, locally in Newfoundland, in southern New England and in part of the southern Appalachians both plutonic heating and intense deformation were involved in metamorphism to the amphibolite and locally the granulite facies, complicated in France by eclogites and locally by glaucophane schists.

Introduction

Regional metamorphism in the age range 430–360 Ma accompanied the most intense and culminating phases of deformation in much of the orogen. This is particularly true in Scandinavia and the northern Appalachians. In the British Isles this was the period of final closure of the Iapetus Ocean, accompanied by plutonism and very mild metamorphism in the so-called 'paratectonic' Caledonides, but modern geochronological data have shown that most of the more intense metamorphism in Caledonia (i.e. Scotland) is late Cambrian–early Ordovician or older. Thus we have the irony that metamorphism in Caledonia is not Caledonian (i.e. late Silurian) in the strict sense.

In France areas of earlier Silurian high-pressure metamorphism and later Devonian Barrovian metamorphism have been identified within areas of extensive late Palaeozoic deformation. The high-pressure metamorphism is also tentatively identified within late Palaeozoic (Hercynide) deformed areas of Iberia, and the Barrovian metamorphism in a tiny patch in the eastern Meseta of Morocco. At this time it is not clear whether any of the late Devonian–early Carboniferous deformation of the Mauritanides (Le-Corche 1983) relates to metamorphism within the bounds of this paper.

In the southern Appalachians rather extensive areas of late Silurian or Devonian metamorphism have been recognized, for the most part superimposed on Taconian or earlier metamorphism. The whole Acadian–Taconian metamorphic assemblage, however, was cut and transported westward by extensive late Palaeozoic thrusts.

The distribution of areas of Scandian–Acadian metamorphism is given for the entire orogen in Fig. 1. The boundaries of these areas are strongly dependent on the mapping system adopted by the IGCP Project 27 Caledonide Metamorphism Working Group. In this system the metamorphic grade assigned is the highest attained during a Phanerozoic metamorphism, and the assignment of age of metamorphism is based on the best evidence from palaeontological, geochronological and structural data. Thus the boundaries of areas showing Scandian–Acadian metamorphism are of four different types: A, where Scandian–Acadian metamorphism laps onto areas of older Phanerozoic metamorphism of equal or higher grade; B, where it grades into areas of unmetamorphosed sedimentary rocks; C, where it is overprinted by younger higher-grade metamorphism; D, where it is unconformably overlain by younger sedimentary rocks or lower-grade metamorphic rocks. When these criteria are adopted extensive areas where lower-grade Scandian–Acadian metamorphism is superimposed on older higher-grade rocks are not shown, except where the older metamorphism was Precambrian. In general the metamorphism shown is only rather broad regional metamorphism; contact aureoles are usually too thin to show. The symbols in Fig. 1 referring to very generalized different styles of metamorphism are discussed in a later section. The metamorphic zones shown in Figs 2, 4 and 6 are those defined by the Metamorphism Working Group, and are explained in detail elsewhere and in brief in the captions.

From HARRIS, A. L. & FETTES, D. J. (eds), 1988, *The Caledonian–Appalachian Orogen,* Geological Society Special Publication No. 38, pp. 453–467.

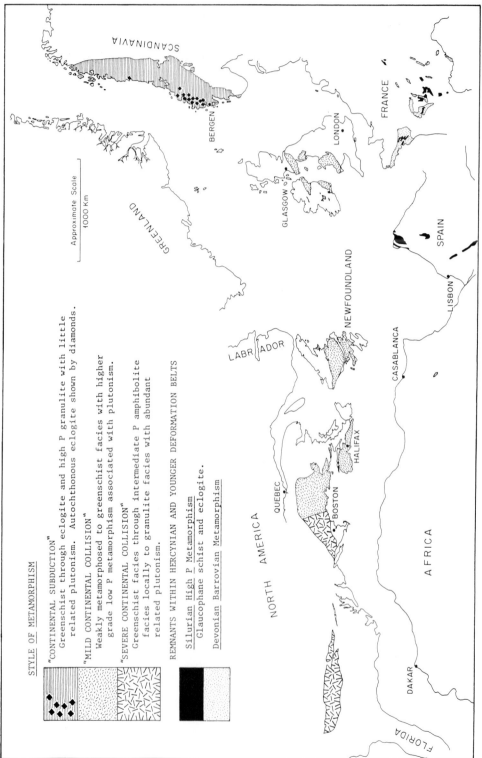

Fig. 1. Map of Scandian–Acadian metamorphism in the entire Caledonian orogen, showing the varying generalized styles of metamorphism.

Scandinavia

The Scandinavian Caledonides (Fig. 2) include terranes metamorphosed under high-, intermediate- and low-pressure conditions. Large-scale thrusting, rapid uplift and the near absence of Scandian plutonism resulted in regional and vertical metamorphic patterns which are markedly different from those of other segments of the orogen. For instance, whereas plutonic heating

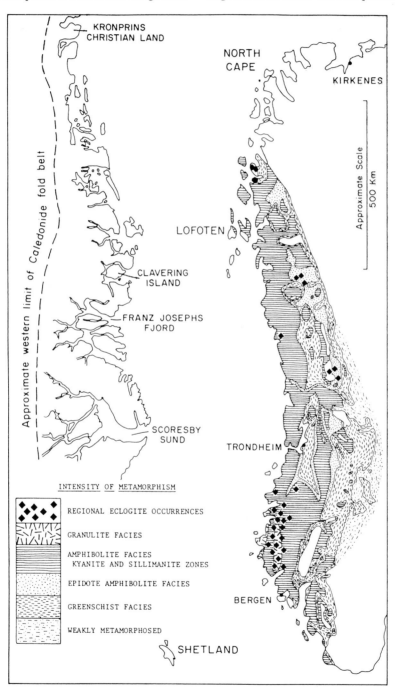

FIG. 2. Map of Scandian–Acadian metamorphism in Scandinavia and E Greenland.

contributed significantly to regional metamorphic patterns in the British and Appalachian segments, it contributed very little to the energy budget of Scandian metamorphism. Apparent disequilibrium is characteristic. Tectonic transport of several hundred kilometres has removed metamorphic zones from their energy sources. Evidence of strain-enhanced metamorphism is widespread. Deep-seated eclogite and granulite zones are difficult to place in a proper tectonic context.

Despite the obvious contrasts with other 'Acadian' terranes, the Scandian metamorphic belt can be fitted into the overall late Silurian–middle Devonian regime of plate convergence, representing various stages of westward-directed subduction of the Baltic Plate and subsequent extensive displacement of nappes onto the Baltic foreland including imbrication of the margin of the down-going plate (Bryhni & Andreasson 1986).

Scandian metamorphism was produced by a sequence of tectonometamorphic events which began in the late Llandovery, culminated in the middle to late Silurian and continued into the Devonian (Gee & Roberts 1982). From Fig. 3 it may seem that the Scandian phase was an isolated and well-defined event; however, current ideas of timing of tectonometamorphism rely heavily on a few scattered geochronological data. With more data, the Scandian event may well appear less distinct. Moreover, Scandian structures and parageneses are not always easily separated from those of older, possibly Finnmarkian, age.

The metamorphic history deduced from Scandian nappe terranes is largely related to events which occurred in various tectonic environments to the W of the present-day orogenic belt. Conventional metamorphic maps, such as Fig. 2, which present the geographic distribution of Scandian metamorphic grades may therefore provide a distorted view of the orogenic evolution of the belt. Figure 3 describes the temporal and spatial (vertical) distribution of Scandian metamorphism in a central and relatively well-investigated portion of the belt with Finnmarkian, Ordovician and Devonian events used as a conceptual framework. As the figure shows, only the uppermost Precambrian basement and the margins of the lower nappes were pervasively metamorphosed.

Scandian ages have been assigned to eclogites, migmatites, granulites, Barrovian amphibolite-facies zones and contact metamorphism, in other words to terranes of strongly contrasting facies series character. Interpretations are based on meagre geochronological evidence, notably with regard to fundamental geotectonic implications

of a Scandian age for regional eclogite-facies metamorphism of crustal rocks in the Western Gneiss Region (Griffin & Brueckner 1980). Eclogites in the upper nappes grade into blueschist-type rocks and may have formed in pre-Scandian time. There is also evidence from recent $^{40}Ar–^{39}Ar$ work that the long-held view of late Silurian metamorphism as the most intense and climactic phase of Caledonian metamorphism may be incorrect, and that this phase is only a low-temperature reworking of Finnmarkian high-grade metamorphism (Dallmeyer *et al.* 1985).

As Fig. 3 shows, no large heat flux (up or down) could have passed through the low-grade or unmetamorphosed nappes of the Scandian nappe pile and its crystalline basement. Recent studies of the thermal structure and evolution of geotherms provide considerable evidence for metamorphic disequilibrium resulting from Scandian nappe displacement. Apparently, Scandian thrusting perturbed geotherms which were not yet completely restored following Finnmarkian thrusting and obduction.

In Scandinavia the development of Siluro–Devonian tectonometamorphic events seems accelerated compared with other orogenic belts. Uplift and deep-seated metamorphism appear to have nearly overlapped each other, as have thrusting at both deep and shallow levels. Such compressed timing can be understood in terms of a collision where uplift occurred not only as late orogenic isostatic rebound but also in response to continuous stacking from beneath the nappe pile achieved by imbrication of the down-going basement and the miogeoclinal wedge. As the pile grew the upper tectonic sheets became gravitationally unstable and collapsed, spreading eastwards. Such a model allows for uplift and thrusting at high levels simultaneously with eclogite formation at depth.

E Greenland

The Caledonian fold belt of E Greenland lies between latitudes 70°N (Scoresby Sund) and 82°N (Kronprins Christian Land) and varies from about 50 to 250 km in width. It exposes the apparent western margin of the Caledonide orogen, as does the NW part of the British Isles (Higgins & Phillips 1979) which lie 600 km to the south in a palaeogeographic reconstruction (Figs 1 and 2).

Relatively little is known in detail about Scandian–Acadian metamorphism in Greenland. As discussed by Haller (1971) and Higgins & Phillips (1979), Caledonian metamorphism

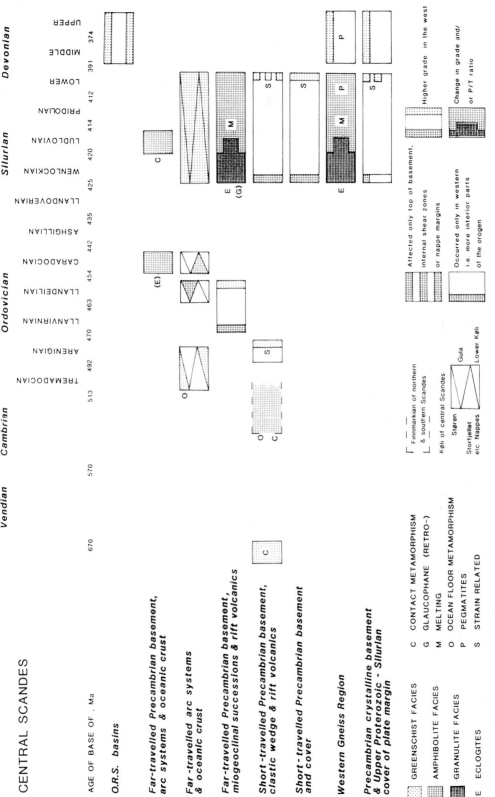

Fig. 3. Chart of Scandian metamorphism in a central segment of the Scandinavian Caledonides. Tectono-stratigraphic groupings, mainly in thrust sheets, are arranged in approximately the present vertical stacking position with the Baltic autochthon and basal (western) gneiss region at the bottom and Old Red Sandstone basins at the top. Time-scale dates are those agreed upon at the IGCP Caledonide Orogen Meeting in Rabat in 1983. Broken boxes and symbols within parentheses refer to northern and southern segments of the belt.

and deformation overprinted one or more pre-Caledonian episodes in rocks ranging from Archaean and Proterozoic gneiss complexes to Cambro–Ordovician sediments, and it is difficult to separate the relative effects of the different episodes. Many of the deeper levels of the fold belt seem to be characterized by amphibolite-facies metamorphism, but the metamorphic grade decreases rapidly upward. Haller (1971) proposed that levels of Caledonian metamorphism lay deeper farther N in the fold belt. There does not seem to be evidence for high-grade metamorphism in the 430–360 Ma time slice; migmatization events have been dated as no younger than about 475 Ma, and some are probably Precambrian.

Metamorphic dating based on Rb–Sr and K–Ar mineral ages shows a range from 445–410 Ma in the Scoresby Sund region (70°N) to 420–375 Ma SW of Clavering Island (74°N) and to 380–320 Ma farther N. Interpretation of these ages is complicated by the possibility that they may be composite from partial resetting of older ages or may represent slow cooling after the documented metamorphic peak in the Ordovician (about 450–475 Ma). An upper limit to Scandian–Acadian metamorphism is set by the development of an unmetamorphosed stratigraphic succession of middle and upper Devonian through Carboniferous non-marine sediments in several molasse basins.

Much of the presently exposed Caledonian metamorphic terrane in the E Greenland fold belt may actually be allochthonous. Higgins & Phillips (1979) have suggested that E Greenland closely approximates a mirror image of the Scandinavian Caledonides, with westward-directed thrusting and imbrication onto an older (Grenvillian) crystalline basement; they noted, however, that this apparent symmetry between E and W margins of the orogen does not seem to continue southward into the British Isles.

British Isles

Scandian–Acadian metamorphism (Fig. 4) affects lower Palaeozoic rocks in the Southern Uplands of Scotland, the Lake District, the Isle of Man, N Wales and Ireland (Fettes 1979). The regional metamorphism is almost uniformly of low grade, ranging from slight recrystallization to greenschist facies locally; one exception is a very small area of intermediate-pressure low amphibolite facies on the Isle of Man. Recent work in the postulated accretionary prism of the Southern Uplands has recognized zeolite-facies metamorphism, and further work on this and

illite crystallinity may help to establish metamorphic patterns in these very low-grade rocks.

A second style of Scandian–Acadian metamorphism, although not necessarily one with orogenic implications, is contact metamorphism accompanying intrusion of the post-metamorphic Newer Granites and Basics during the Scandian–Acadian time slice. It is not shown in the figures (but see Harte (1988) where contact aureoles in the orthotectonic belt of Britain are summarized). A classic example of this metamorphism which has recently been studied is the contact aureole of the Strontian Granite in Scotland (Tyler & Ashworth 1982) where contact assemblages as high grade as sillimanite–orthoclase–garnet–cordierite, accompanied by migmatization, are superimposed on previously regionally metamorphosed rocks of the Moine Series.

France, Iberia and Morocco

Various domains affected by Devonian or pre-Devonian metamorphism are now more or less well-preserved regions in the Carboniferous (Hercynian) orogen (Fig. 5). Timing of events, although often imprecise, is typically based on radiometric dates (Santallier 1983). Two principal events are (1) an Ordovician or Silurian high-pressure metamorphic phase (450–415 Ma) with little evidence of deformation (Lasnier 1977, Godard 1981), and (2) a middle Devonian intermediate-pressure metamorphic phase accompanied by major tectonism which is well developed in France and Morocco but more speculative in Iberia.

France

The early high-pressure facies including eclogites, granulites and blueschists are found mostly in the southern Armorican Massif, the Massif Central and the Vosges (Lasnier *et al.* 1973). These high-pressure rocks, which are found either as small lenses in mesozonal country rocks or on a more regional scale, are associated with the earliest described Palaeozoic deformation.

Eclogites are typically of mafic composition, or much less commonly ultramafic, and occur either in metamorphosed felsic igneous rocks or in sedimentary rocks. The most common primary assemblages include omphacite, garnet and rutile with such other minerals as phengite, quartz, amphibole, zoisite, kyanite and corundum. Estimated pressure and temperature conditions vary between 11 and 20 kbar and between 900 and 1000°C.

Granulites are both felsic and mafic, and of three main types (Marchand 1974, Lasnier 1977):

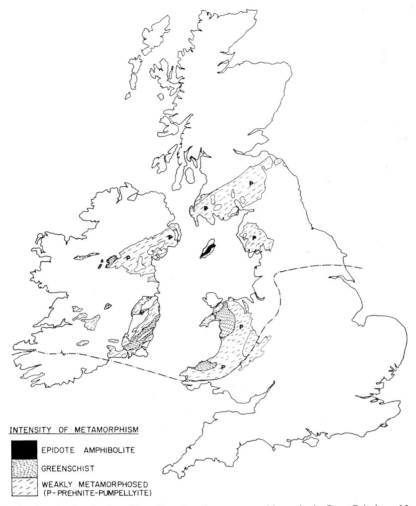

INTENSITY OF METAMORPHISM

■ EPIDOTE AMPHIBOLITE

▨ GREENSCHIST

▨ WEAKLY METAMORPHOSED
(P - PREHNITE-PUMPELLYITE)

FIG. 4. Map showing the distribution of Scandian–Acadian metamorphic grades in Great Britain and Ireland. The broken line is taken from Fettes (1979) and represents the southern extent of Caledonian effects.

(1) metamorphosed felsic igneous rocks, with or without Al-silicates; (2) metabasites such as pyrigarnites, pyriclasites or coronitic gabbros; (3) metamorphosed sedimentary rocks of grey-wacke composition, commonly containing kyanite, K-feldspar, rutile and graphite. These rocks apparently crystallized under rather lower pressures than the eclogites.

Blueschists are known only from the Armorican Massif, and dating shows that they formed between 420 and 375 Ma (Peucat & Cogne 1977) in conjunction with a major tectonic event. This event involved northward obduction onto the old continental margin of S Brittany (LeFort *et al.* 1982).

Devonian metamorphism in France is well documented in the S of the Armorican Massif

(Autran & Cogne 1980) and the W of the Massif Central (Autran & Guillot 1975) with basically the same characteristics everywhere. Recrystallization is contemporaneous with development of a first, and locally second, regional schistosity. The metamorphism is plurifacial and mostly of intermediate-pressure type. In the western Massif Central the zonal succession is complete from the chlorite zone to the sillimanite + K-feldspar zone (Santallier *et al.* 1978). The mean pressure–temperature gradient appears to have been about $25\,^{\circ}C\,km^{-1}$ during early metamorphism, increasing to $30\,^{\circ}C\,km^{-1}$ during the later anatectic phase. In the Armorican Massif weakly metamorphosed rocks are in abrupt, apparently tectonic, contact with high-grade rocks. In the Maures Massif metamorphic zonation is also

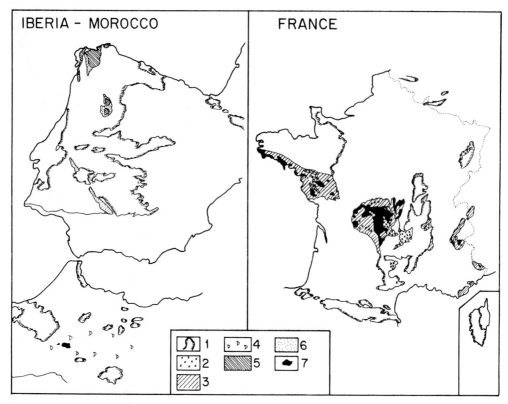

FIG. 5. Map showing the distribution of Scandian–Acadian metamorphic rocks in France, Iberia and Morocco: 1, Palaeozoic orogen domains including Carboniferous; 2, Silurian high-pressure areas in France; 3, mid-Devonian metamorphic phase domains in France and Morocco; 4, possible middle Devonian metamorphic areas in Morocco; 5, pre-upper Devonian metamorphic areas in the Iberian peninsula; 6, doubtful pre-upper Devonian metamorphic areas in the Iberian peninsula; 7, plutonic rocks.

complete but with a slightly higher gradient (about 30 °C km^{-1}) as indicated by the occurrence of both staurolite–andalusite and staurolite–kyanite zones.

Iberia

The northwestern part of the Iberian peninsula exhibits five high-grade metamorphic complexes involved in the later Carboniferous orogen, the best known being the Cabo Ortegal and Malpica–Tuy units. Metamorphism occurred over a wide range of temperatures at intermediate to high pressures, probably during the Silurian. The high-grade complexes are interpreted to be tectonic units overlying a supracrustal sequence of rocks that were themselves involved in Barrovian-type metamorphism of probable late Devonian or early Carboniferous age. The complexes comprise many mafic–ultramafic units (considered at least in part to be an ophiolite sequence) (Iglesias *et al.*

1983) which are associated with metamorphosed felsic igneous and sedimentary rocks (Vogel 1967). Typical granulite- and eclogite-facies assemblages are well represented in mafic rocks at Cabo Ortegal, whereas in the Malpica–Tuy unit high-pressure low-temperature assemblages developed in glaucophane-bearing eclogites and in 460-Ma-old calc-alkaline and peralkaline orthogneisses. Such assemblages are also well preserved in phengite- and omphacite-bearing pelitic and semipelitic rocks. A later, either upper Devonian or lower Carboniferous, retrogression of the high-pressure rocks occurred under intermediate-pressure amphibolite- and greenschist-facies conditions, as in France.

On the basis of available isotopic dating in the Cabo Ortegal and Malpica–Tuy units (van Calsteren *et al.* 1979, Peucat *et al.* 1983) it has been proposed that protoliths were probably of Precambrian or Cambrian age and that they underwent highest-grade metamorphism between lower Ordovician and lower Devonian time. Other Iberian areas may have undergone a similar history, but present knowledge is sketchy.

Morocco

The existence of a Devonian metamorphism (at about 366 Ma) has been proved only in a small area in the eastern Meseta between the High Atlas and Middle Atlas chains (Clauer *et al.* 1980). This metamorphic episode may well be more widely represented in Morocco in association with well-developed tectonism at the same time, but this is still hypothetical. Where Devonian metamorphism has been proved, the rocks are weakly metamorphosed (biotite and garnet zones) and have been intruded by 330-Ma-old postmetamorphic granitoids. The early high-pressure phases seen in France and Iberia are not known here.

Interpretation

In western France Vendian blueschists of the early high-pressure phase are interpreted as oceanic crustal fragments (Peucat *et al.* 1982), whereas to the E in the Massif Central the eclogites have either transitional basaltic compositions or represent back-arc tholeiitic magmatism, depending on their location (Briand & Piboule 1979, Cabanis *et al.* 1983). Farther to the E, mafic rocks in the Maures Massif are either transitional or alkaline. All the above are commonly associated with felsic granulites, suggesting the presence of a thinned lower Palaeozoic continental crust over much of the French domain. The high-pressure metamorphism is linked to the first documented deformation which can be considered to be 'Caledonian' because it is pre-Devonian.

Although less well established in detail, the palaeo-environment in Iberia seems to have been comparable with France, based upon two principal points: (1) the existence of mafic and ultramafic oceanic crustal relicts in the exhumed catazonal complexes, and (2) the occurrence of calc-alkaline and peralkaline plutons suggesting a crustal thinning or rifting episode in the lower Palaeozoic.

The Barrovian metamorphism during the Devonian is linked to the first major tectonic event in the French Palaeozoic orogen and corresponds to a collisional event followed by a main deformation episode. A later metamorphism in the lower Carboniferous was a comparable intermediate-pressure episode. It is not possible at this time to relate the Iberian Barrovian metamorphism to either the Devonian or Carboniferous French episodes. In Morocco the eastern

Meseta may represent a more internal domain than the western Meseta, possibly an old continental margin, suggesting the existence of an oceanic domain farther to the E which closed during the Devonian.

Appalachians

The distribution of Acadian metamorphic zones in the Appalachians (Fig. 6) is based on preliminary versions of the *Metamorphic Map of the U.S. and Canadian Appalachians* (Fisher & Trzcienski, in press). Age assignments were based on data on the U.S. segment of this map, on the data of Glover *et al.* (1983), on the *Structural Map of the Appalachian Orogen in Canada* (Keppie 1982) for New Brunswick and Newfoundland, and on the *Metamorphic Map of Nova Scotia* (Keppie & Muecke 1979).

The image of Caledonian (s.s.)–Acadian metamorphism in Newfoundland has changed very rapidly in recent years as detailed studies have moved away from the populated NE coast into the interior and to the inaccessible SW. It now appears that Acadian greenschist-facies metamorphism is responsible for the peak mineral fabric, not only in most of the Central Mobile Belt but also in late Precambrian and Cambro-Ordovician strata in the western part of the Avalon Zone (O'Brien & King 1982). In the interior amphibolite-facies zones are characterized by kyanite or andalusite and seem to be associated with plutons. The sillimanite zone and environs in the extreme SW are assigned to a late Silurian (i.e. Caledonian) metamorphism rather than to the Acadian of the rest of the island.

Regional metamorphism at the northern end of the mainland Appalachians seems to have been dominated by an early phase with moderately to strongly developed axial-plane cleavage followed by more intense static metamorphism associated with Acadian plutons (Guidotti *et al.* 1983). With a few exceptions, low-amphibolite-grade pelites contain andalusite indicative of low pressure. Apart from two plutonic areas in New Brunswick, the onset of more intense metamorphism forms a remarkably linear front from northernmost Vermont and adjacent Quebec through central and coastal Maine to southernmost Nova Scotia, the type area of the Acadian. This front appears to cut at a sharp angle across all major stratigraphic and structural belts with, however, a data gap in the Gulf of Maine. A complication is that some workers have proposed that southern Nova Scotia did not reach its present position along the linear front until the late Palaeozoic (Keppie 1983, Williams & Hatcher 1983). If this

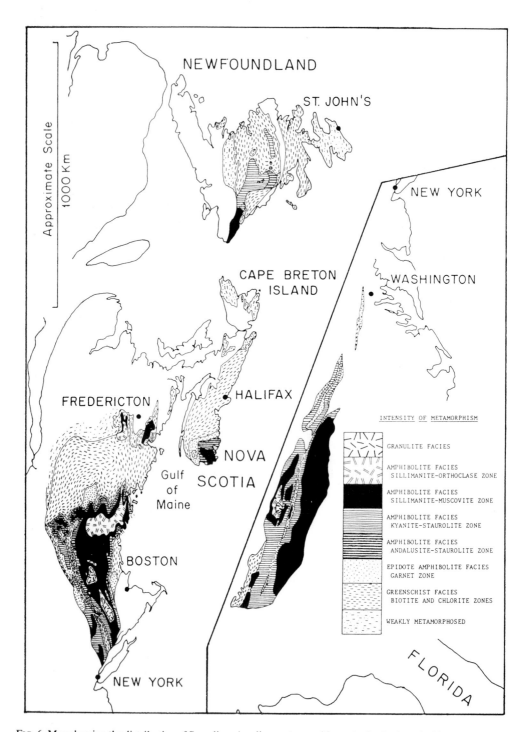

FIG. 6. Map showing the distribution of Scandian–Acadian metamorphic grades in the Appalachians.

is true, we should question why there is Acadian metamorphism in Acadia! An alternative to be explored is that this line represents an unexplained thermal anomaly reaching across most of the width of the orogen. A further complication is the new data (Lux & Guidotti 1985) showing that the region in close proximity to the western lobe of the sillimanite–orthoclase zone in western Maine is related to thermal gradients associated with the recently dated Carboniferous Sebago batholith (Aleinikoff *et al.* 1985).

In western and southern New England the Acadian metamorphism is more distinctly related to stratigraphic–tectonic belts, with two discrete metamorphic highs separated by a narrow metamorphic low (Robinson 1983, 1986). The western high ('Vermont high') reaches kyanite–staurolite grade in Vermont where it is spatially related to a series of gneiss domes (Thompson *et al.* 1986). In western Massachusetts and Connecticut the sillimanite zone is attained, but spatial relations between isograds and domes are less obvious here. Acadian rocks overlap with Taconian metamorphic rocks of equivalent grade everywhere along the western margin of this high, and the boundary has only been located recently by detailed structural and radiometric studies (Laird & Albee 1981, Laird *et al.* 1984, Sutter *et al.* 1985). The greenschist-facies metamorphic low is almost continuous along the Connecticut Valley to Long Island Sound, except where it is locally interrupted by the contact effects of the syn-Acadian Belchertown intrusion. Even in the chlorite zone there is no obvious difference in metamorphic grade between Ordovician and Siluro-Devonian strata, showing that the Connecticut Valley Acadian low lies well E of the zone of intense Taconian metamorphism. The eastern high ('New Hampshire high') has a very broad sillimanite–muscovite grade plateau punctuated by local areas of sillimanite–orthoclase–garnet–cordierite gneisses (Spear & Chamberlain 1986) and, in central Massachusetts, true granulite-facies assemblages of hypersthene–orthoclase (Robinson *et al.* 1986). Characteristic features of much of this area are a varied suite of syntectonic intrusions including abundant biotite tonalites of high-K andesite composition and widespread sillimanite pseudomorphs after andalusite. Both imply early input of a large component of plutonic heat at relatively shallow levels, which was followed by development of the peak metamorphic assemblages at temperatures up to 730 °C and pressures up to 6.5 kbar. Peak metamorphic fabrics are distinctly cut by mylonite zones that are themselves deformed and recrystallized during development of an eastern line of gneiss domes that do not obviously deflect the isograd pattern. Abundant evidence along the western margin of this high indicates that high-grade rocks were transported westward by early Acadian nappes to a position above rocks of the greenschist facies (Spear & Chamberlain 1986, Spear & Rumble 1986). There is also evidence of late eastward overturning along the eastern margin of the high in central Massachusetts (Robinson 1983).

A second distinct metamorphic low of greenschist and epidote amphibolite facies borders the New Hampshire high on the E as far S as southern Massachusetts (Robinson 1983). On its E side this low is in contact with Ordovician metamorphic rocks across the Clinton–Newbury fault zone (Zen *et al.* 1983). The picture is further complicated here by the presence of four outliers of Pennsylvanian strata metamorphosed to chloritoid or garnet grade, suggesting the possibility of an Alleghanian overprint on both Ordovician and Devonian metamorphisms. In northern Connecticut kyanite-grade Acadian rocks are in contact with sillimanite-grade Ordovician rocks to the E, whereas in southernmost Connecticut sillimanite-grade Acadian rocks appear to have been overprinted by an Alleghanian metamorphism of sillimanite grade or higher.

Early Acadian plutons cutting lower Devonian (Emsian) strata in the New Hampshire high yield radiometric ages around 400 Ma. The unmetamorphosed core of the late Acadian Belchertown pluton yields a zircon age of 380 Ma (Ashwal *et al.* 1979), yet its outer parts were converted to hornblende gneiss structurally conformable with features of the gneiss dome stage and yielding K–Ar hornblende ages of about 360 Ma. Thus it appears that Acadian metamorphism and deformation spanned a period of about 40 Ma in southern New England.

Overall, the Acadian metamorphism of New England shows a trend from a broad belt of rocks with associated plutons in the N, with peak metamorphic minerals overprinted on earlier tectonic fabrics, to a much narrower more highly deformed belt in the S, with tectonic fabrics generally overprinted on peak metamorphic minerals. Although peak metamorphic pressures were several kilobars higher in the S than in the N, it would be misleading to think that southern New England gives a representative image of northern New England at a deeper structural level. Rather, the regional map pattern shows that the striking differences are due to much greater collisional convergence in the S. The structural and mineralogical characteristics of Acadian metamorphism in southern New England, however, seem to have superficial parallels to those in the southern Appalachians.

The bulk of 'Acadian' metamorphism in the southern Appalachians is broadly of amphibolite facies and is superimposed on Ordovician and Precambrian metamorphic rocks, as recognized on radiometric grounds. Glover *et al.* (1983) have indicated additional areas of probable Acadian metamorphism where it is difficult to recognize because it was less intense than Ordovician metamorphism. Highest-grade Acadian metamorphic rocks are now situated in four distinctive areas, three to the W in the Blue Ridge thrust sheet, where the grade locally attains granulite, and one large area in the E which is dominantly of sillimanite grade. The western and eastern areas are separated by the middle to late Palaeozoic Brevard fault zone, marked on Fig. 6 by linear patches of epidote amphibolite-facies rocks. SW of Washington the narrow Arvonia belt yields clear evidence of Acadian metamorphism, including late Ordovician fossils in the metamorphosed strata, but it is not known how far this metamorphism extends into older and higher-grade rocks. Unique to the southern Appalachians is the Talladega belt in the extreme SW which consists of a thrust slice of lower Devonian strata metamorphosed to the lower greenschist facies. Reconstruction of the original pattern of Acadian metamorphism in the southern Appalachians depends on detailed unravelling of several generations of late Palaeozoic thrust sheets and on understanding the relations between metamorphism and older stratigraphic–tectonic features. Southern New England, where late Palaeozoic allochthony is not apparent, seems to provide the only useful model.

Comparison of styles of metamorphism

Metamorphic petrology contributes to the study of Caledonian tectonics by providing measures of the intensity of thermal and deformational effects and of heat inputs within the orogen as well as information on the pressure–temperature–time trajectories of individual rock masses. In the very broad survey given here we have attempted to assign large regions of Scandian–Acadian metamorphism to three major styles (Fig. 1), each with attendant tectonic implications. This simplified approach should be treated with caution, particularly because as much as 40% of the metamorphic area produced during this time slice may be hidden beneath continental shelves and coastal plains. Assignment was not attempted for the remnants within Hercynian and younger deformation belts where the spatial arrangements at the time of metamorphism are less clear.

The assignment of the Scandinavian region to a continental subduction regime during late Silurian is based in part on the complex pattern of far-travelled thrust sheets, more particularly on the regional pattern of eclogite-facies metamorphism in the Western Gneiss Region, which has only recently been recognized as Caledonian, and also on the scarcity of plutons contemporaneous with regional metamorphism. The edge of the other continental mass, beneath which the Baltic Shield was evidently subducting and which may have been undergoing contemporary metamorphism and plutonism on the opposite side of this collision zone, is apparently not exposed.

The middle portion of the orogen is assigned to a setting of 'mild' continental collision. Broad areas of regional metamorphism are either 'weakly metamorphosed' or in the greenschist facies ('weakly metamorphosed' is only indicated in Fig. 1 for the British Isles). In the Southern Uplands of Scotland the weak metamorphism is considered to have occurred during development of an accretionary prism in a NW-directed subduction zone, but evidence of high-pressure metamorphism or intense regional metamorphism accompanying collision are unknown. Smaller areas show local higher-grade metamorphism, usually with andalusite in lower amphibolite-facies pelites associated with granite and gabbro plutons indicating abundant magma sources at depth. Commonly, early deformational fabrics are overprinted by more static fabrics associated with plutonic heating.

The southern portion of the orogen is assigned to a setting of severe continental collision. Plutonic rocks including tonalites are abundant in higher-grade regions, but metamorphic isograds are much less clearly related to plutons. Typically, the peak metamorphic textures and widespread migmatites are overprinted by deformational fabrics indicating long-continued metamorphism in an environment of continued high strain. The transition from 'mild collision' to 'severe collision' occurs in middle New England, which is one of the best exposed portions of the Appalachians, and this transition may be directly related to the dramatic narrowing of the Acadian metamorphic belt from northern to southern New England.

Modern oceans and younger rocks cover large areas which are probably underlain by Acadian metamorphic rocks. Across the largest water gap, between Newfoundland and the British Isles, there is a seeming continuity of metamorphic character, whereas the contrast across the shorter gap between Britain and Scandinavia could hardly be greater. Between the S end of the northern Appalachian region and the southern

Appalachians there is not a massive change in the character of exposed metamorphic rocks even though the southern Appalachian rocks occur in thrust slices produced in the Alleghanian orogeny. The position of the autochthonous rocks of the Acadian metamorphic belt in the southern Appalachians is unknown at present.

One of the most dramatic features in the reconstruction of the orogen (Fig. 1) is the angle of nearly 90° between the Scandinavian belt and the belt from the British Isles through the southern Appalachians. In view of the nearly contempor-aneous tectonism and metamorphism in all these regions, is it possible that the dramatic change in style of metamorphism at the bend is directly related to plate-boundary orientations and rela-tive movements during the 'death' of the Iapetus Ocean?

ACKNOWLEDGMENTS: The authors would like to thank I. Bryhni, A. Michard and A. Picque for their collaboration in the preparation of this paper. Reviews by Ben Harte, Robert Hatcher and an anonymous reviewer are gratefully acknowledged. The lettering on Figs 1, 2 and 6 was done by Marie Litterer.

References

ALEINIKOFF, J. N., MOENCH, R. H. & LYONS, J. B. 1985. Carboniferous U–Pb age of the Sebago batholith, southwestern Maine. *Geological Society of America Bulletin*, **96**, 990–6.

ASHWAL, L. D., LEO, G. W., ROBINSON, P., ZARTMAN, R. E. & HALL, D. J. 1979. The Belchertown quartz monzodiorite pluton, west-central Massachusetts: a syntectonic Acadian intrusion. *American Journal of Science*, **279**, 936–69.

AUTRAN, A. & COGNE, J. 1980. La zone interne de l'orogen varisque dans l'Ouest de la France et sa place dans le développement de la chaîne hercy-nienne. *Memoires du Bureau de Recherches Géolo-giques et Minières (France)*, **108**, 90–111.

—— & GUILLOT, P. L. 1975. *Comptes Rendus Hebdo-madaires des Séances de l'Acadamie des Sciences*, *Séne D*, **280**, 1649–52.

BRIAND, B. & PIBOULE, M. 1979. *Bulletin du Bureau de Recherches Géologiques et Minières (France)*, Sec-tion 1, **2**, 131–71.

BRYHNI, I. & ANDREASSON, P.-G. 1986. Metamorphism in the Scandinavian Caledonides. *In:* GEE, D. G. & STURT, B. A. (eds) *The Caledonian Orogen—Scandinavia and Related Areas*, pp. 763–81, Wiley, Chichester.

CABANIS, B. *et al.* 1983. *Bulletin de la Société Géologique de France*, **25**(4), 563–74.

VAN CALSTEREN, P. W. C., BOELRIJK, N. A. I. M., HEBEDA, E. H., PRIEM, H. N. A., DENTEX, E., ERDURMEN, E. A. TH. & VERSCHURE, R. H. 1979. Isotopic dating of older elements (including the Cabo Ortegal mafic-ultramafic complex) in the Hercynian orogen of NW Spain: manifestations of a presumed early Paleozoic mantle-plume. *Chemical Geology*, **24**, 35–56.

CLAUER, N., JEANETTE, D. & TISSERAT, D. 1980. Datation isotopique des crystallins successives d'un socle cristallin et crystophyllien (Haute Mou-louya, moyen Maroc). *Geologisches Rundschau*, **69**, 63–83.

DALLMEYER, R. D., GEE, D. G. & BECKHOLMEN, M. 1985. $^{40}Ar/^{39}Ar$ mineral age record of early Caledonian tectonothermal activity in the Balto-scandian miogeocline, central Scandinavia. *Amer-ican Journal of Science*, **285**, 532–68.

FETTES, D. J. 1979. A metamorphic map of the British and Irish Caledonides. *In:* HARRIS, A. L., HOL-LAND, C. H. & LEAKE, B. E. (eds) *The Caledonides of the British Isles Reviewed. Special Publication of the Geological Society of London No. 8*, pp. 307–22.

FISHER, G. W. & TRZCIENSKI, W. E. *Metamorphic Map of the U.S. and Canadian Appalachians*, in press.

GEE, D. G. & ROBERTS, D. 1982. Timing of deformation in the Scandinavian Caledonides. *In:* SCHENK, P. E. (ed.) *Regional Trends in the Geology of the Appalachian–Caledonian–Hercynian–Mauritanide Orogen*, pp. 279–92, Reidel, Dordrecht.

GLOVER, L., III, SPEER, J. A., RUSSELL, G. S. & FARRAR, S. S. 1983. Ages of regional metamorph-ism and ductile deformation in the central and southern Appalachians. *Lithos*, **16**, 223–45.

GODARD, G. 1981. *Thèse du 3ème Cycle*, Université de Montpellier, 205 pp.

GRIFFIN, W. L. & BRUECKNER, H. K. 1980. Caledonian Sm–Nd ages and a crustal origin for Norwegian eclogites. *Nature, London*, **285**, 319–21.

GUIDOTTI, C. V., TRZCIENSKI, W. E. & HOLDAWAY, M. J. 1983. A northern Appalachian metamorphic transect—eastern townships, Quebec, to the cen-tral Maine coast. *In:* SCHENK, P. E. (ed.) *Regional Trends in the Appalachian–Caledonian–Hercynian–Mauritanide Orogen*, pp. 235–48, Reidel, Dor-drecht.

HALLER, J. 1971. *Geology of the East Greenland Caledonides*. Wiley, New York, 413 pp.

HARTE, B. 1988. Lower Palaeozoic metamorphism in the Moine–Dalradian belt of the British Isles. *This volume*.

HIGGINS, A. K. & PHILLIPS, W. E. A. 1979. East Greenland Caledonides—an extension of the Brit-ish Caledonides. *In:* HARRIS, A. L., HOLLAND, C. H. & LEAKE, B. E. (eds) *The Caledonides of the British Isles Reviewed. Special Publication of the Geological Society of London No. 8*, pp. 19–32.

IGLESIAS, M. *et al.* 1983. Ed. I.G.M.E., Madrid, pp. 459–67.

KEPPIE, J. D. 1982. *Structural Map of the Appalachian Orogen in Canada. Memorial University of New-foundland Map 4.*

—— 1986. The Appalachian collage. *In*: GEE, D. G. & STURT, B. A. (eds) *The Caledonian Orogen—Scandinavia and Related Areas*, pp. 1217–26. Wiley, Chichester.

—— & MUECKE, G. K. 1979. *Metamorphic Map of Nova Scotia (1:1,000,000)*, Nova Scotia Department of Mines and Energy.

LAIRD, J. & ALBEE, A. L. 1981. Pressure, temperature and time indicators in mafic schist; their application to reconstructing the polymetamorphic history of Vermont. *American Journal of Science*, **281**, 127–75.

——, LANPHERE, M. & ALBEE, A. L. 1984. Distribution of Ordovician and Devonian metamorphism in mafic and pelitic schists from northern Vermont. *American Journal of Science*, **284**, 376–413.

LASNIER, B. 1977. *Thèse d'Etat*, Université of Nantes, 351 pp.

——, LEYRELOUP, A. & MARCHAND, J. 1973. Découverte d'un granite "charnockitique" au sein de "gneiss oeillés". Perspectives nouvelles sur l'origine de certaines leptynites du Massif Armoricain Méridional (France). *Contributions to Mineralogy and Petrology*, **41**, 131–44.

LECORCHE, J.-P. 1983. Structure of the Mauritanides. *In*: SCHENK, P. E. (ed.) *Regional Trends in the Geology of the Appalachian–Caledonian–Hercynian–Mauritanide Orogen*, pp. 347–54, Reidel, Dordrecht.

LEFORT, J. P., AUDREN, CL. & MAX, M. D. 1982. The southern part of the Armorican orogeny: a result of crustal shortening related to reactivation of a pre-Hercynian mafic belt during Carboniferous time. *Tectonophysics*, **89**, 359–77.

LUX, D. R. & GUIDOTTI, C. V. 1985. Evidence for extensive Hercynian metamorphism in western Maine. *Geology*, **13**, 696–700.

MARCHAND, J. 1974. *Thèse du 3ème Cycle*, Université de Nantes, 207 pp.

O'BRIEN, S. J. & KING, A. F. 1982. The Avalon Zone of Newfoundland. *In*: KING, A. F. (ed.) *Field Guide for Avalon and Meguma Zones, IGCP Project 27, NATO Advanced Study Institute*, pp. 1–121, Department of Earth Sciences, Memorial University, Newfoundland.

PEUCAT, J. J. & COGNE, J. 1977. Geochronology of some blueschists from the Ile de Groix, France. *Nature, London*, **268**, 131–2.

——, BERNARD-GRIFFITHS, J., IGLESIAS, M. & CORNICHET, J. 1983. Preliminary U–Pb, Sm–Nd and REE data from eclogites of the Iberian peninsula. *Terra Cognita*, **3**, 139.

——, VIDAL, PH., GODARD, G. & POSTAIRE, B. 1982. Precambrian U–Pb zircon ages in eclogites and garnet pyroxenites from South Brittany (France): an old oceanic crust in the West European Hercynian belt? *Earth and Planetary Science Letters*, **60**, 70–8.

ROBINSON, P. 1983. Realms of regional metamorphism in southern New England, with emphasis on the eastern Acadian metamorphic high. *In*: SCHENK, P. E. (ed.) *Regional Trends in the Appalachian–Caledonian–Hercynian–Mauritanide Orogen*, pp. 249–58, Reidel, Dordrecht.

—— 1986. Introduction. *In*: *Guidebook, Regional Metamorphism and Metamorphic Phase Relations in Northwestern and Central New England, Contribution No. 59*, pp. 1–10, Department of Geology and Geography, University of Massachusetts, Amherst, MA.

——, TRACY, R. J., HOLLOCHER, K. T., SCHUMACHER, J. C. & BERRY, H. N., IV 1986. The central Massachusetts metamorphic high. *In*: *Guidebook, Regional Metamorphism and Metamorphic Phase Relations in Northwestern and Central New England, Contribution No. 59*, pp. 195–266, Department of Geology and Geography, University of Massachusetts, Amherst, MA.

SANTALLIER, D. S. 1983. Main metamorphic features of the Paleozoic orogen in France. *In*: SCHENK, P. E. (ed.) *Regional Trends in the Appalachian–Caledonian–Hercynian–Mauritanide Orogen*, pp. 263–74, Reidel, Dordrecht.

——, FLUCK, J.-P. & GUILLOT, P. L. 1978. Quelques aspects du métamorphisme dévonien en Bas-Limousin (Massif central, France). *Bulletin de Minéralogie de Société Française de Minéralogie et Cristallographie*, **101**, 77–88.

SPEAR, F. S. & CHAMBERLAIN, C. P. 1986. Metamorphic and tectonic evolution of the Fall Mountain Nappe complex and adjacent Merrimack synclinorium. *In*: *Guidebook, Regional Metamorphism and Metamorphic Phase Relations in Northwestern and Central New England, Contribution No. 59*, pp. 120–43, Department of Geology and Geography, University of Massachusetts, Amherst, MA.

—— & RUMBLE, D., III 1986. Mineralogy, petrology and *P–T* evolution of the Orfordville area, west-central New Hampshire and east-central Vermont. *In*: *Guidebook, Regional Metamorphism and Metamorphic Phase Relations in Northwestern and Central New England, Contribution No. 59*, pp. 57–93, Department of Geology and Geography, University of Massachusetts, Amherst, MA.

SUTTER, J. F., RATCLIFFE, N. M. & MUKASA, S. B. 1985. ^{40}Ar/^{39}Ar and K–Ar data bearing on the metamorphic and tectonic history of western New England. *Geological Society of America Bulletin*, **96**, 123–36.

THOMPSON, J. B., JR., CHENEY, J. T. & ROBINSON, P. 1986. Metamorphism on the east flank of the Green Mountain massif and Chester dome. *In*: *Guidebook, Regional Metamorphism and Metamorphic Phase Relations in Northwestern and Central New England, Contribution No. 59*, pp. 94–119, Department of Geology and Geography, University of Massachusetts, Amherst, MA.

TYLER, I. M. & ASHWORTH, J. R. 1982. Sillimanite–K-feldspar assemblages in graphitic pelites, Strontian area, Scotland. *Contributions to Mineralogy and Petrology*, **81**, 18–29.

VOGEL, D. E. 1967. Petrology of an eclogite- and pyrigarnite-bearing polymetamorphic rock complex at Cabo Ortegal, NW Spain. *Leidse Geologische Mededelingen*, **40**, 121–214.

WILLIAMS, H. & HATCHER, R. D., JR. 1983. Appalachian suspect terranes. *In*: HATCHER, R. D., JR., WIL-

LIAMS, H. & ZEITZ, I. (eds) *Contributions to the Tectonics and Geophysics of Mountain Chains. Geological Society of America Memoir No. 150*, pp. 33–53.

ZEN, E-AN, GOLDSMITH, R., RATCLIFFE, N. M., ROBINSON, P. & STANLEY, R. S. 1983. *Bedrock Geologic Map of Massachusetts (scale 1:250,000)*, U.S. Geological Survey, Washington, DC.

P. ROBINSON, Department of Geology and Geography, University of Massachusetts, Amherst, MA 01003, USA.

R. J. TRACY, Department of Geological Sciences, Virginia Polytechnic Institute and State University, Blacksburg, VA 24061, USA.

D. S. SANTALLIER, Departement des Sciences de la Terre, Université Claude-Bernard, Lyon 1, 69622 Villeurbanne Cédex, France.

P.-G. ANDREASSON, Department of Mineralogy and Petrology, Lund University, Solvegatan 13, S-22362 Lund, Sweden.

J. I. GIL-IBARGUCHI, Departado de Petrologia, Universidad Autonoma de Barcelona, Bellaterra (Barcelona), Spain.

Silurian–Permian palaeocontinental reconstructions and circum-Atlantic tectonics

D. V. Kent & J. D. Keppie

SUMMARY: On the basis of the palaeomagnetic record, supplemented by constraints provided by faunal and tectonic information, reconstructions involving Laurentia, Baltica, Gondwana and numerous continent-like fragments and terranes within the circum-Atlantic Palaeozoic orogenic belts are made for three critical time intervals, late Silurian, early Carboniferous and late Carboniferous–early Permian, all of which bracket important phases of tectonic activity. The late Caledonian–Scandian–Acadian–Ligerian orogenies are due to the predominantly E–W final closure of Iapetus. This phase was followed in mid-Devonian times by a major sinistral megashear along the orogen which eliminated latitudinal separations and resulted in a Pangea-like assembly by the latest Devonian. The final phase involved a rotation of Gondwana with respect to the assembled Euramerican landmass, expressed as late Variscan–Hercynian dextral shear from central Europe to northeastern N America and culminating in the late Carboniferous–Permian Alleghanian orogeny in the Appalachians from New England S and in the Mauritanides.

The Caledonide–Hercynide–Mauritanide–Appalachian orogenic belts can be considered to be the result of the multistage interaction of three major surrounding cratonic areas (Laurentia, Baltica and Gondwana) and numerous continent-like fragments and terranes (Dewey 1983, Keppie 1984). We concentrate here on the time interval late Silurian to Permian and seek to account for the major tectonic activity in terms of changes in the relative position of these areas as interpreted primarily from the palaeomagnetic record because geological parameters allow too many alternative reconstructions to be useful. Much of the palaeomagnetic data from the Atlantic-bordering land areas are reviewed by Briden *et al.* (1988) and our interpretations generally conform to their assessments of data reliability.

In the sequence of reconstructions outlined below it has been necessary to make a number of simplifications owing to the unequal spatial and temporal distribution of what are believed to be the most reliable data. Documentation of terranes is at an early stage, and since palaeomagnetic data are generally lacking for most individual terranes they have been conservatively placed in their present relative locations although they may eventually be shown to have separate histories. However, it has become evident that some discrepant palaeomagnetic directions are due to previously unrecognized secondary magnetizations. Despite considerable study, there is still a surprising amount of uncertainty in the apparent polar wander (APW) paths of the major cratonic areas, notably Laurentia and Gondwana, and also Baltica if Britain is not included within it. Hence the time progression and amount of total closure across the orogenic belts are known only

in very broad terms. It also follows that the arrangement of terranes that lie within the orogens with respect to the major bordering cratonic areas is imprecisely known.

After having carefully screened the available palaeomagnetic data and using only the best palaeopoles we suggest a working hypothesis for the APW of the Atlantic-bordering continents (except for Gondwana where there are insufficient data). This shows comparatively rapid shifts in palaeopole positions, separating time intervals in which the poles tend to group for the various continental areas. These APW shifts or drift episodes (Briden 1967) roughly correspond to phases of latitudinal adjustments of the landmasses, whereas the apparently static APW intervals allow closure of only longitudinal oceans. Palaeopoles appear to cluster for the intervals late Silurian (Fig. 1), early Carboniferous (Fig. 2) and late Carboniferous–early Permian (Fig. 3). The corresponding reconstructions span the time interval during which the various phases of deformation attributed to the Acadian–late Caledonian and Alleghanian–Hercynian orogenic events took place. Constraints on the relative positions of the landmasses provided by the palaeomagnetic record are supplemented where possible by faunal province and tectonic data.

Constraints on late Silurian reconstruction

We now believe that the late Silurian is the youngest time interval in the Palaeozoic for which large separations or offsets of the constituent

---

From HARRIS, A. L. & FETTES, D. J. (eds), 1988, *The Caledonian–Appalachian Orogen,*
Geological Society Special Publication No. 38, pp. 469–480.

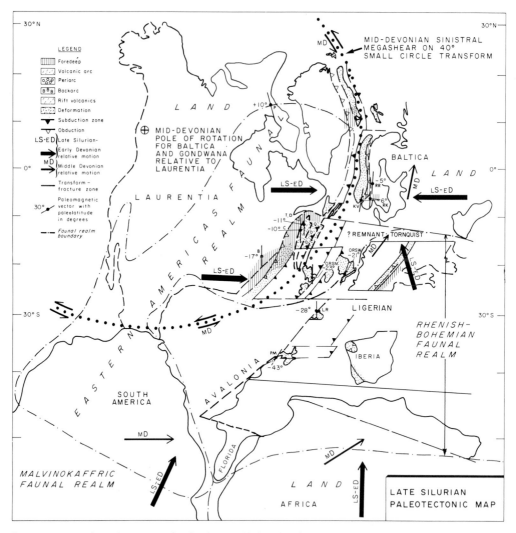

FIG. 1. Palaeocontinental reconstruction for the late Silurian showing the major tectonic elements of the late Caledonian orogen and the distribution of faunal realms (Gray & Boucot 1979). Representative palaeomagnetic data used to constrain the position of the continental areas are as follows. Laurentia: B, Bloomsburg; P, Peel Sound; T, Traveller; C, Compton; D, Dockendorff. Baltica: KV, Kvamshesten; RR, Roragen; RK, Ringerike. Britain: ORSM, Midland Valley Old Red Sandstone lavas; ORSW, lower Old Red Sandstone, Wales/England. Avalon: PM, Pembroke; LR, Lawrenceton. The position of Africa–S America is based on Mereenie sandstone from Australia (Embleton 1972).

components of the circum-Atlantic Pangean assembly (Bullard *et al.* 1965) can be convincingly demonstrated by palaeomagnetic means. Therefore this critical interval, the oldest considered here, sets the stage for the pattern of closure and related major tectonic activity in the subsequent time periods.

Baltica

Baltica is positioned according to consistent but early palaeomagnetic data from Old Red Conti-

nent facies rock units in Norway and Sweden (RK, KV, RR in Fig. 1). However, no field evidence to constrain magnetization age is available for these early results, and because the poles tend to fall on younger parts of the British APW path the magnetizations may be contaminated by secondary components. It is therefore not clear whether, following Briden *et al.* (1973), the palaeomagnetic data from Baltica can be accepted at face value. However, we note that the near-equatorial position for Baltica in the

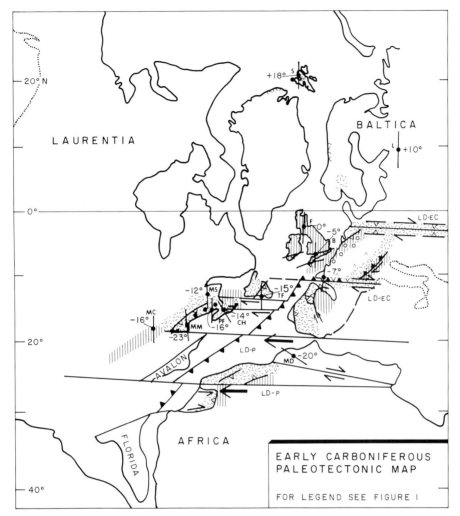

FIG. 2. Early Carboniferous palaeocontinental reconstruction, with representative palaeomagnetic data used to constrain continental positions: MC, Mauch Chunk; MS, Mapleton; PF, Perry sediments and lavas; MM, Massachusetts metavolcanics; TF, Terrenceville; M, Maringoin; CH, Cheverie; S, Svalbard sediments; F, Foyers middle Old Red Sandstone; B, Bristol upper Old Red Sandstone; L, Leningrad; MD, Moroccan sediments and lavas.

Siluro-Devonian suggested by these data is supported by the equatorial-zone Devonian spores recovered from the Old Red Continent facies in southern Scandinavia (McGregor 1979).

Laurentia

The late Silurian–early Devonian palaeolatitudinal position for Laurentia was formerly based only on palaeomagnetic results (normal and reverse polarities and the positive fold test (Roy *et al.* 1967)) from the upper Silurian Bloomsburg Formation (B, Fig. 1). These data are now

generally supported by the most representative results from the lower Devonian Peel Sound Formation (PS, Fig. 1) of Arctic Canada (Dankers 1982) and indirectly by a set of systematically abberrant directions from lower Devonian rock units from what is referred to as the Traveller terrane of the northern Appalachians (T, C, D, Fig. 1). The Traveller directions, which include a positive fold test and reversals, are compatible in palaeolatitude with Laurentia but, because of a significant deviation in declination compared with the Bloomsburg Formation (and also the Peel Sound), are thought to reflect a subsequent

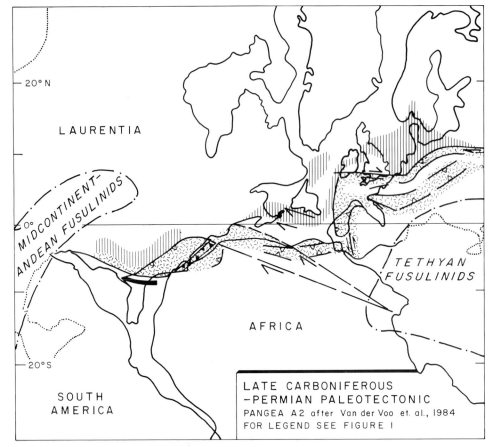

FIG. 3. Late Carboniferous to Permian palaeocontinental reconstructions corresponding to the Pangea A2 model (Van der Voo *et al.* 1984). Fusilinid faunal provinces from Ross (1979).

clockwise tectonic rotation of the Traveller terrane against stable N America (Spariosu & Kent 1983). Together these palaeomagnetic data place Laurentia as straddling the equator and are consistent with the presence of low-latitude upper Silurian–lower Devonian lithologies (such as carbonates and evaporites) and the associated Appohimchi sub-province of the Eastern Americas Faunal Realm (Boucot 1975).

That Laurentia and Baltica were close together at this time cannot be established by palaeomagnetic means because longitude is indeterminant, but a proximal position is indicated by the appearance of similar freshwater vertebrates on both cratons at the end of the Silurian (Young 1981). However, when compared with a conventional Triassic Euramerican reconstruction (Bullard *et al.* 1965), the available palaeomagnetic data from Laurentia and Baltica conflict. This

conflict remains regardless of whether or not the Baltica directions represent later remagnetization because in neither case do they fall on any younger portion of the Laurentia APW path. We resolve the conflict by placing Baltica offset approximately 15°S with respect to Laurentia (Fig. 1).

Gondwana

The position of Gondwana is very poorly constrained owing to inadequate palaeomagnetic data. One of the few results that may pertain to an assembled Gondwana (Smith & Hallam 1970) for this time interval is from the Mereenie Sandstone of central Australia. Although the magnetization history and even the age of the Mereenie is quite uncertain (cited as Silurian?–Devonian by Embleton (1972)), the palaeopole reassuringly falls near the terminus of the better-documented lower Palaeozoic APW path for Gondwana (Embleton *et al.* 1974). A variety of APW paths can be drawn through Silurian and Devonian palaeopoles obtained from southeastern Australia (Schmidt & Morris 1977, Morel & Irving 1978, Goleby 1980), but they may reflect tectonic movements in the Tasman orogen rather than drift of all Gondwana (Embleton *et al.* 1974). In view of the lack of definitive palaeomagnetic data to the contrary, we position Gondwana according to the Mereenie palaeopole constraint with Africa centred over the S pole. This is consistent with the presence of the cold-water Malvinokaffric Faunal Realm in the early Devonian rocks of southern S America and S Africa (Boucot 1975). At the same time the presence of the Amazon–Colombian brachiopod sub-province in northern S America, which has strong affinities with the Appohimchi sub-province (Boucot 1975), suggests proximity between N and S America which is satisfied by the arrangement shown in Fig. 1.

Terranes

Old Red Continent rocks from British terranes tend to give concordant palaeomagnetic results that place them in moderate southerly palaeolatitudes. Representative of the late Silurian–early Devonian palaeopole position for two terranes on either side of the Iapetus suture in Britain are results from the Midland Valley Old Red Sandstone lavas (ORSM) and the lower Old Red Sandstone of Wales/England (ORSW) which suggest palaeolatitudes in the 20–25°S range. These and similar late Silurian and early Devonian palaeomagnetic results from other British terranes (Briden *et al.* 1973, 1984) suggest that there is not much latitudinal separation between them. This is consistent with the conclusions of Bluck (1983) and of Mitchell & McKerrow (1975). However, these British data are not compatible with those taken at face value from either Baltica or Laurentia in a conventional Euramerican assembly. These data show a latitudinal offset of Laurentia on one side and Baltica and southern Britain on the other, and less clearly between Baltica and Britain.

This reconstruction neatly suggests that the Scottish Siluro-Devonian volcanic arc was a continuation of the Traveller volcanic arc terrane (Fig. 1), but this appears to create problems in explaining the location of the Archaean Scourian basement adjacent to the Grenville basement of N America. However, it has been suggested that Baltica lay adjacent to eastern N America during the latest Precambrian (Ueno *et al.* 1975, Patchett & Bylund 1977). Therefore it is possible that the Scourian basement is correlated with the pre-Karelian basement in Baltica and was a fragment left behind in the early Palaeozoic only to be transported later, in the Devonian, to more or less its present position relative to Baltica.

Siluro-Devonian palaeopoles from the Avalon composite terrane in the northeastern Appalachians suggest a location between 28 and 43°S. This is based on palaeomagnetic data from the uppermost Silurian Pembroke Formation (PM, Fig. 1) (cited by Roy & Anderson (1981) as the most reliable result in their study of the Mascarene Group of coastal New Brunswick) and from the Lawrenceton rhyolite of central Newfoundland (LR, Fig. 1) (supported by a positive fold test (Lapointe 1979)). The palaeolatitudinal position of the Avalon composite terrane is therefore consistent with a Siluro-Devonian position relative to Britain as seen in a Pangea fit. The somewhat shallower inclinations (lower palaeolatitudes) obtained from some other Siluro-Devonian rock units in Avalonia may imply that these units have younger (reset?) magnetization ages, whereas the generally much steeper but scattered directions reported from some Devonian igneous intrusions in the northern Appalachians are intrinsically problematical with regard to their tilt correction and may be of only local significance (Kent & Opdyke 1982, Roy 1982).

Southern Britain and Avalonia are thought to be part of a larger continental-like mass, Armorica, which formally includes the Hercynian Massif (Andreeva *et al.* 1965) give a palaeolatitude of about 25°S, which is compatible with this arrangement at least in terms of closely associated tectonic elements. The proximity of these terranes to one another and to adjacent cratons is also suggested by their common impoverished Rhenish–Bohemian fauna which extended onto the marginal areas of N and S America and Africa (Boucot 1975). Thus the Armorica assemblage was probably distributed around a small ocean basin with restricted circulation and high evaporation rates, consistent with the 30°S palaeolatitudinal belt suggested by the palaeomagnetic evidence (Fig. 1).

Constraints on early Carboniferous reconstruction

There is increasing agreement that Euramerica, consisting of Baltica, Laurentia, Britain and other parts of the Armorica mosaic, was essentially assembled by the end of the Devonian. However, the relationship between Euramerica and Gondwana at this time is less certain.

Euramerica

According to late Devonian palaeomagnetic data from the Leningrad area (L, Fig. 2) (summarized by Van der Voo & Scotese 1981), Baltica is placed between the equator and 20°N; a similar position is suggested for the early Carboniferous Svalbard sediments (S, Fig. 2). This location is supported by the presence of the equatorial *Lepidodendropsis* fauna (Chaloner & Lacey 1973) and the restricted distribution of *Archaeoperisaccus* spores to the belt N of the Devonian equator (McGregor 1979).

Formerly, the best palaeomagnetic results (with positive fold tests) from upper Devonian (Catskill Formation (Van der Voo *et al.* 1979)) and lower Carboniferous (Mauch Chunk Formation (Knowles & Opdyke 1968)) rock units from Laurentia placed it in equatorial latitudes, but still offset by about 15° or 2000 km to the N with respect to Baltica and the continental-like Armorica assemblage. However, it can now be shown that the Laurentia reference poles for at least the early Carboniferous on which this interpretation partly rested were not sufficiently demagnetized and thus are partly due to later (Permo–Carboniferous) magnetization overprints (Roy & Morris 1983, Irving & Strong 1984, Kent & Opdyke 1985). The new results (MC and DL, Fig. 2) from complete demagnetization analysis pass the fold test and place Laurentia about 15° farther to the S in the early Carboniferous, a position similar to the late Silurian but which is now in accord with Armorica–Avalon–Britain and Baltica palaeomagnetic data (TF, M, S, B, AM and L, Fig. 2) on a Pangea model. Palaeomagnetic results from the middle and upper Devonian rocks of the Traveller terrane are consistent in both palaeolatitude and meridional orientation with these new early Carboniferous data (Spariosu & Kent 1984). In this light, the Catskill pole is anomalous and, indeed, recent results from a restudy of the Catskill indicate that the reported directions are secondary (Miller & Kent 1985). Furthermore, discordant data from N of the Great Glen Fault, which is considered as evidence for a major (about 2000 km) late Devonian offset across it (Van der Voo & Scotese 1981), are now being interpreted as secondary magnetizations of Permian, Mesozoic or Tertiary age (Briden *et al.* 1984, Cisowski 1984).

Therefore a coherent Euramerica assembly with no major internal offsets, closely resembling the geometrical fit described by Bullard *et al.* (1965), is suggested by this time (Fig. 2). Minor documented exceptions are from Carboniferous directions for the Meguma in southern Nova Scotia (Spariosu *et al.* 1984) and for central Europe (Bachtadse *et al.* 1983) which show evidence of rotations about local vertical axes. The revised early Carboniferous location for Laurentia is consistent with its being part of the Old Red Continent with its cosmopolitan flora such as *Retispore lepidophyta* and its distinct *Archaeoperisaccus* spores confined to Hudson's Bay, southern Greenland and southern Scandinavia (McGregor 1979).

Gondwana

Palaeomagnetic data available from Gondwana at present lend themselves to two different interpretations (Kent *et al.* 1984): either Africa remained centred over the S pole (on the basis of results from the Msissi norite of Morocco) or, according to the remanence directions from Gneiguira sediments from Mauritania, its northern margin had already migrated to moderate southern latitudes by this time. The age and tectonic setting of the Msissi norite is not well described in the report on the palaeomagnetism of the unit (Hailwood 1974). However, no field tests are available to constrain the magnetization age of the hematite remanence of the Gneiguira (Kent *et al.* 1984) and post-Devonian remagnetization cannot be excluded. Hence the interpretation is ambiguous.

The first possibility, based on the Msissi data, implies the development of a large ocean between Gondwana and the more equatorial Euramerican assembly (Jones *et al.* 1979); the large ocean created must then have been rapidly consumed because there is general agreement (Schmidt & Morris 1977, Morel & Irving 1978) that the facing margins of Gondwana (Africa–South America) were already in low palaeolatitudes by the early Carboniferous. The second possibility, suggested by the Gneiguira data, does not require independent Armorican and Gondwana plates but allows them to remain generally contiguous. This requires neither the creation nor the rapid consumption of a large late Devonian ocean. At present we favour the second option (Fig. 2) and note that a proximal position for Gondwana with respect to Euramerica is supported by the dispersal of freshwater vertebrates between these areas during the late Devonian (Young 1981) and the highly cosmopolitan marine fauna when no biogeographic realms can be distinguished (Boucot & Gray 1983).

Constraints on late Carboniferous–Permian reconstruction

The late Carboniferous–Permian reconstruction (Fig. 3) used in this paper is model A2 of Van der Voo *et al.* (1976). We prefer the Pangea A2 model to the Pangea B model of Irving (1977) because, among other factors, the former better satisfies the geographic distribution of Permian fusilinid faunal provinces (Ross 1979). We also consider it more than a coincidence that model A2 is near to the model of closure derived from totally independent evidence from the Atlantic ocean floor and margins (Klitgord & Schouten 1982). Thus we would suppose that Pangea in approximately the A2 configuration persisted essentially from about the late Carboniferous until the opening of the modern Atlantic Ocean in the middle Jurassic. In contrast, the Pangea B model would necessitate a major reorganization, with extravagant relative movements of the order of 3500 km in the Mesozoic for which geological evidence is difficult to find, in order to achieve the Jurassic pre-drift configuration. A full discussion of the palaeomagnetic evidence bearing on these and other Pangea models is given by Van der Voo *et al.* (1984).

Evolution of the orogen

The three palinspastic maps (Figs 1–3) provide bases on which to plot the appropriate palaeotectonic elements, which in turn form the basis for a tectonic model for the orogen between Silurian and Permian times. This method was used by Keppie (1977) and is followed here in historical sequence. The polarity of subduction is derived not only from volcanic arc complexes but also from the polarity of obduction with which it is parallel.

Late Silurian–early Devonian

In order to understand the genesis of the orogen at this time it is necessary to review briefly the earlier movements of the three major cratonic areas: Laurentia, Baltica and Gondwana. During the early Palaeozoic Laurentia and Baltica occupied low palaeolatitudes, in contrast with Gondwana which was located at high palaeolatitudes (Briden *et al.* 1988). Similar late Precambrian–Ordovician APW paths derived for both Armorica and Gondwana imply that these areas were attached or closely associated during this time interval (Hagstrum *et al.* 1980, Perigo *et al.* 1983,

Perroud & Van der Voo 1985). Similar evidence is accumulating that the Avalon, Meguma (at least the Piedmont of Delaware) and peninsular Florida areas of eastern N America were also once part of Armorica and/or Gondwana (Rao & Van der Voo 1980, Johnson *et al.* 1983, Jones *et al.* 1983).

During the Silurian, Gondwana with Armorica (including Avalonia and southern Britain) evidently moved northward. These relative motions between Gondwana, Laurentia and Baltica included the closure of Iapetus. The convergence between Baltica and Laurentia led to the obduction of the Scandinavian and Greenland Caledonide nappes during the Silurian and early Devonian Scandian orogeny with the development of foredeep clastic wedges (Hurst & McKerrow 1981, Gee & Roberts 1983). The direction of obduction suggests that both eastern Greenland and western Scandinavia were on the subducting plate. At first glance this appears contradictory, but it should be noted that these two areas were not opposite one another at this time (Fig. 1). A transform fault between the subduction zones with opposing polarities is therefore inferred.

Farther S along the orogen, in the northern Appalachians, the convergence was marked by the following events: (i) the extensive Siluro–Devonian Acadian overthrusting in central Newfoundland and intermediate pressure metamorphism in the Gander Zone, implying southeasterly obduction (Karlstrom *et al.* 1982, Colman-Sadd & Swinden 1984); (ii) the development of a Siluro-Devonian volcanic arc through eastern Gaspé and northern Maine (Osberg 1978) indicative of northwestward subduction; (iii) intermediate pressure metamorphism associated with northwestward obduction in southern New England; (iv) the Siluro-Devonian peripheral bulge unconformity followed by the late Devonian–early Carboniferous Catskill–Pocono clastic wedge, inferred to have accompanied the northwestward emplacement of nappes in the central Appalachians (Thomas 1977, Quinlan & Beaumont 1984). The opposite polarity between the Gaspé–Maine volcanic arc and the southern New England–central Appalachian region suggests a complex microplate geometry with transform faults separating regions of opposite polarity (Fig. 1).

In the British Isles the convergence is recorded by (i) the late Ordovician–Silurian accretionary wedge in the Southern Uplands of Scotland and the volcanic arc complex in the Midland Valley and Highlands of Scotland (Bluck 1983, McKerrow 1988), implying northwesterly subduction, and (ii) volcanic arc complexes in England,

Wales and SE Ireland, indicating southeasterly subduction (Stillman & Francis 1979). Palaeomagnetic data show that Iapetus was basically closed by the end of the Silurian (Briden *et al.* 1984) (Fig. 1).

In western Europe the effects of convergence are recorded by Siluro-Devonian calc-alkalic volcanism, deformation and metamorphism, although the polarity is rather uncertain at this time and may have involved complex microplate interactions (Bard *et al.* 1980, Matte 1983, Ziegler 1984). In Avalonia, the effects are limited to weak to moderate deformation (Keppie *et al.* 1982).

Mid-Devonian

The collision of Baltica and Laurentia by the early Devonian evidently choked the subduction zone(s) and the E–W component of convergence ceased. Plate motions were reorganized and the northward component of motion of Gondwana and also Baltica became dominant. Comparison of Figs 1 and 2 reveals that, while Laurentia remained essentially stationary, Gondwana, Baltica and the elements of Armorica all moved northward by between 15° and 30°. This motion can be resolved on a sinistral megashear coinciding with a small circle with a centre in northwestern N America (Fig. 1). Evidence for this megashear relies heavily upon palaeomagnetic data for the postulated megashear presumably lies offshore along most of its length. In the light of the discoveries of the effects of secondary magnetizations where they were taken as primary in the upper Devonian and lower Carboniferous rock record of Laurentia and northern Britain, the same reanalysis is probably necessary for the Siluro-Devonian poles. Nevertheless, the most reliable palaeomagnetic data suggest such a sinistral megashear in the mid-Devonian. Geological evidence for mid-Devonian sinistral transcurrent faulting along the trend of the proposed megashear can be found in Svalbard (Harland 1969, 1984) and in the Gander Zone of Newfoundland (Hanmer 1981). Farther S along the Fredericton Trough only dextral motions have been observed (Ludman & Morisi 1984). However, these may be younger and, if superposed on earlier fabrics, may obscure the earlier sense of motion.

The northward movement of Baltica appears to have initiated convergence and subduction along its northeastern margin in the western Urals (Hamilton 1970). Some of the sinistral megashear was taken up by convergence across the Ligerian–Variscan orogens (Cogne & Lefort 1984) and possibly across a remnant Tornquist (Fig. 1).

Late Devonian–Permian

By the late Devonian, Pangea was close to being assembled (Fig. 2) although subduction accompanied by dextral transcurrent faulting (Pique 1983, Francis 1988) and thrusting occurred in the Moldanubian and N African volcanic arcs. After final closure of Armorica against both Baltica and Laurentia, the movement of Gondwana became decoupled from that of Armorica and it rotated and converged against Laurentia with eastward obduction of the Mauritanide nappes. In the late Carboniferous and early Permian (Fig. 3) this motion of Gondwana with respect to Euramerica created dextral shear in the Hercynides and westward-directed Alleghanian thrusting in the central and southern Appalachians (Arthaud & Matte 1977), accompanied by the formation of foredeep clastic wedges (Thomas 1977). The direction of obduction suggests a southeasterly-dipping subduction zone. The local tectonic rotations documented for Meguma and central Europe probably also occurred at this time within the broad Hercynian orogenic belt. The Suwanee basin of Florida was S of a transform boundary and hence suffered little deformation (Nelson *et al.* 1985). In the Ouachitas deposition of flysch preceded nappe emplacement as the northern part of S America converged with this S central part of Laurentia.

Concluding comments

The sequence of palaeocontinental reconstructions we propose for the late Silurian to Permian time interval can be regarded as a rather conservative tectonic framework for the evolution of the late Caledonian and Hercynian orogenies. It involves a minimal number of interacting continental elements and terranes, and assumes the least amount of relative movement consistent with a reasonable interpretation of the best available palaeomagnetic, as well as tectonic and faunal, evidence. The relative simplicity of the model also makes critical aspects readily subject to test, especially by further palaeomagnetic work. Further work in the terranes is necessary to document whether they were separate from or closely associated with major continents during the late Palaeozoic.

Our Devonian assembly model for the main elements of Pangea differs from several recent palaeomagnetic models in several notable respects. A critical difference is that major latitudinal oceans had closed by the early to middle Devonian producing the late Caledonian–Scandian–Acadian–Ligerian orogenic events, whereas some previous interpretations infer the existence of an ocean several thousand kilometres wide separating Euramerica and Gondwana even later in the Devonian (Kent 1982, Van der Voo 1982). The suggested absence of this wide Devonian ocean allows Armorica to remain closely associated with Gondwana throughout the Palaeozoic.

However, a latitudinal offset between Laurentia on the western side and Armorica–Avalon and Baltica on the eastern side is required to explain the late Silurian–early Devonian palaeomagnetic poles (Morris 1976). Until very recently the best available evidence pointed to a Carboniferous age for motion on a sinistral megashear between eastern and western Euramerica. New palaeomagnetic data from Laurentia (Irving & Strong 1984, Kent & Opdyke 1985) now show that there is no major offset in the early Carboniferous and cast serious doubt on its reality for the late Devonian (Irving & Strong 1985, Miller & Kent 1885). Instead, major sinistral motion most probably occurred much earlier in the Devonian. The Variscan–Hercynian and Alleghanian orogenies are then apparently due to predominantly dextral shear and E–W closure respectively as Africa–S America rotated westward with respect to Euramerica. The palaeomagnetic signature of this culminating phase of tectonic activity seems to be minor because relative motion occurred predominantly along lines of latitude or about local vertical axes, while Pangea as a whole migrated northward.

ACKNOWLEDGMENTS: We thank the reviewers for offering constructive comments that allowed us to improve the paper. The work was supported by U.S. National Science Foundation Grants EAR82–12549 and EAR85–07046 to DVK and the Department of Mines and Energy, Nova Scotia. This paper is a Lamont–Doherty Geological Observatory contribution.

References

ANDREEVA, O. L., BUKHA, V. V. & PETROVA, G. N. 1965. Laboratory evaluation of magnetic stability of the Czech Massif. *Izvestia Akademii Nauk SSSR, Seriya Geofizicheskaya*, 54–64.

ARTHAUD, F. & MATTE, P. 1977. Late Paleozoic strike-slip faulting in southern Europe and northern Africa: result of a right-lateral shear zone between the Appalachians and the Urals. *Geological Society of America Bulletin*, **88**, 1305–20.

BACHTADSE, V., HELLER, F. & KRONER, A. 1983. Paleomagnetic investigations in the Hercynian mountain belt of central Europe. *Tectonophysics*, **91**, 185–299.

BARD, J. P., BURG, J. P., MATTE, PH. & RIBEIRO, A. 1980. La chaine hercynienne d'Europe occidentale en termes de tectonique des plaques. *Memoire du Bureau de Recherches Géologiques et Minières*, **108**, 233–46.

BLUCK, B. J. 1983. Role of the Midland Valley of Scotland in the Caledonide Orogeny. *Transactions of the Royal Society of Edinburgh, Earth Sciences*, **74**, 119–36.

BOUCOT, A. J. 1975. *Developments in Paleontology and Stratigraphy*, Vol. 1, *Evolution and Extinction Rate Controls*, Elsevier, Amsterdam, 427 pp.

—— & GRAY, J. 1983. A Paleozoic Pangaea. *Science*, **222**, 571–81.

BRIDEN, J. C. 1967. Recurrent continental drift of Gondwanaland. *Nature, London*, **215**, 1334.

——, KENT, D. V., LAPOINTE, P. L., LIVERMORE, R. A., ROY, J. L., SEGUIN, M. K., SMITH, A. G., VAN DER VOO, R. & WATTS, D. R. 1988. Palaeomagnetic constraints on the evolution of the Caledonian–Appalachian orogen. *This volume*.

——, MORRIS, W. A. & PIPER, J. D. A. 1973. Palaeomagnetic studies in the British Caledonides, VI. Regional and global implications. *Geophysical Journal of the Royal Astronomical Society*, **34**, 107–34.

——, TURNELL, H. B. & WATTS, D. R. 1984. British paleomagnetism, Iapetus Ocean and the Great Glen Fault. *Geology*, **12**, 428–31.

BULLARD, E. C., EVERETT, J. E. & SMITH, A. G. 1965. A symposium on Continental Drift. IV. The fit of the continents around the Atlantic. *Philosophical Transactions of the Royal Society of London, Series A*, **258**, 41–51.

CHALONER, W. G. & LACEY, W. S. 1973. The distribution of Late Palaeozoic floras. *Special Papers in Palaeontology*, **12**, 271–289.

CISOWSKI, S. M. 1984. Evidence for early Tertiary remagnetization of Devonian rocks from the Orcadian, northern Scotland, and associated transcurrent fault motion. *Geology*, **12**, 369–72.

COGNE, J. & LEFORT, J. P. 1985. The Ligerian Orogeny: a proto-Variscan event related to the Siluro-Devonian evolution of the Tethys I Ocean. *In:* GEE, G. D. & STUART, B. (eds) *The Caledonide Orogen: Scandinavia and Related Areas*, 1185–94, Wiley, Chichester.

COLMAN-SADD, S. P. & SWINDEN, H. S. 1984. A tectonic window in central Newfoundland: geological evidence that the Appalachian Dunnage Zone may be allochthonous. *Canadian Journal of Earth Sciences*, **21**, 1349–67.

DANKERS, P. 1982. Implications of early Devonian poles from the Canadian Arctic Archipelago for the North American apparent polar wander path. *Canadian Journal of Earth Sciences*, **19**, 1802–9.

DEWEY, J. F. 1983. Plate tectonics and the evolution of the British Isles. *Journal of the Geological Society, London*, **139**, 371–412.

EMBLETON, B. J. J. 1972. The Palaeomagnetism of some Palaeozoic sediments from central Australia. *Journal and Proceedings of the Royal Society of New South Wales*, **105**, 86–93.

EMBLETON, B. J. J., McELHINNY, M. W., CRAWFORD, A. R. & LUCK, G. R. 1974. Palaeomagnetism and the tectonic evolution of the Tasman orogenic zone. *Journal of the Geological Society of Australia*, **21**, 187–93.

FRANCIS, E. H. 1988. Mid-Devonian to early Permian volcanism: Old World. *This volume*.

GEE, D. G. & ROBERTS, D. 1983. Timing of deformation in the Scandinavian Caledonides. *NATO ASI Series C*, **116**, 279–92.

GOLEBY, B. R. 1980. Early Palaeozoic palaeomagnetism in South East Australia. *Journal of Geomagnetism and Geoelectricity*, **32**, Suppl. SIII, SIII 11, SIII 21.

GRAY, J. & BOUCOT, A. J. (eds) 1979. *Historical Biogeography, Plate Tectonics, and the Changing Environment*, Oregon State University Press, Corvallis, OR.

HAGSTRUM, J. T., VAN DER VOO, R., AUVRAY, B. & BONHOMMET, N. 1980. Eocambrian–Cambrian palaeomagnetism of the Armorican Massif, France. *Geophysical Journal of the Royal Astronomical Society*, **61**, 489–517.

HAILWOOD, E. A. 1974. Paleomagnetism of the Msissi Norite (Morocco) and the Paleozoic Reconstruction of Gondwanaland. *Earth and Planetary Science Letters*, **23**, 376–86.

HAMILTON, W. 1970. The Uralides and the motion of the Russian and Siberian Platforms. *Geological Society of America Bulletin*, **81**, 2553–76.

HANMER, S. 1981. Tectonic significance of the northeastern Gander Zone, Newfoundland: an Acadian ductile shear zone. *Canadian Journal of Earth Sciences*, **18**, 120–35.

HARLAND, W. B. 1969. Contribution of Spitsbergen to understanding of tectonic evolution of North Atlantic Region. *In:* KAY, H. (ed.) *North Atlantic—Geology and Continental Drift*, pp. 234–5, American Association of Petroleum Geologists, Tulsa, OK.

—— 1985. Caledonide Svalbard. *In:* GEE, D. G. & STURT, B. A. (eds) *The Caledonide Orogen, Scandinavia and Related Areas*, pp. 999–1016, Wiley, Chichester.

HURST, J. M. & McKERROW, W. S. 1981. The Caledonian nappes of Kronprins Christian Land, Eastern North Greenland. *Rapport Grønlands Geologiske Undersøkelse*, **106**, 15–19.

IRVING, E. 1977. Drift of the major continental blocks since the Devonian. *Nature, London*, **270**, 304–9.

—— & STRONG, D. F. 1984. Paleomagnetism of the Early Carboniferous Deer Lake Group, western Newfoundland: no evidence for Carboniferous displacement of "Acadia". *Earth and Planetary Science Letters*, **69**, 379–90.

—— & —— 1985. Paleomagnetism of rocks from Burin Peninsula, Newfoundland: hypothesis of Late Devonian displacement of Acadia criticized. *Journal of Geophysical Research*, **90**, 1949–62.

JOHNSON, R. J., VAN DER VOO, R. & KEPPIE, D. 1983. The Paleozoic drift of the Avalon basement terrane of Nova Scotia. *EOS*, **64**, 690 (abstract).

JONES, D. S., MACFADDEN, B. J., OPDYKE, N. D. & SMITH, D. L. 1983. Paleomagnetism of lower Paleozoic rocks of the Florida basement. *EOS*, **64**, 690.

JONES, M., VAN DER VOO, R. & BONHOMMET, N. 1979. Late Devonian to early Carboniferous palaeomagnetic poles from the Armorican Massif, France. *Geophysical Journal of the Royal Astronomical Society*, **58**, 287–308.

KARLSTROM, D. E., VAN DER PLUIJM, B. A. & WILLIAMS, P. F. 1982. Structural interpretation of the eastern Notre Dame Bay area, Newfoundland: regional post-middle Silurian thrusting and asymmetrical folding. *Canadian Journal of Earth Sciences*, **19**, 2325–41.

KENT, D. V. 1982. Paleomagnetic evidence for post-Devonian displacement of the Avalon Platform (Newfoundland). *Journal of Geophysical Research*, **87**, 8709–16.

—— & OPDYKE, N. D. 1982. Paleomagnetism of Siluro-Devonian rocks from eastern Maine: Reply. *Canadian Journal of Earth Sciences*, **19**, 232–7.

—— & —— 1985. Revised paleomagnetic directions for the lower Carboniferous Mauch Chunk Formation of the central Appalachians and their tectonic implications. *Journal of Geophysical Research*, **90**, 5371–83.

——, DIA, O. & SOUGY, J. M. A. 1984. Paleomagnetism of lower-middle Devonian and upper Proterozoic-Cambrian(?) rocks from Mejeria (Mauritania, West Africa). *In:* VAN DER VOO, R. *et al.* (eds) *Plate Reconstruction from Paleozoic Paleomagnetism, Geodynamic Series*, Vol. 12, pp. 99–115, American Geophysical Union, Washington, DC.

KEPPIE, J. D. 1977. Plate tectonic interpretation of Paleozoic world maps. *Nova Scotia Department of Mines and Energy Paper 77–3*, 41 pp.

—— 1985. The Appalachian collage. *In:* GEE, D. G. & STURT, B. (eds) *The Caledonide Orogen, Scandinavia and Related Areas*, pp 1217–26, Wiley, Chichester.

——, ST JULIEN, P., HUBERT, C., BELAND, J., SKIDMORE, B., RINTENBERG, A. A., FYFFE, L. R., McCUTCHEON, S. R., WILLIAMS, H. & BURSNALL, J. 1982. Structural map of the Canadian Appalachians. *Memorial University of Newfoundland Map No. 4*, Scale 1 : 1,000,000.

KLITGARD, K. D. & SCHOUTEN, H. 1982. Early Mesozoic Atlantic reconstructions from seafloor-spreading data. *EOS*, **63**, 307 (abstract).

KNOWLES, R. R. & OPDYKE, N. D. 1968. Paleomagnetic results from the Mauch Chunk Formation: a test of the origin of curvature in the folded Appalachians of Pennsylvania. *Journal of Geophysical Research*, **73**, 6515–26.

LAPOINTE, P. L. 1979. Paleomagnetism and orogenic history of the Botwood Group and Mount Peyton Batholith, Central Mobile Belt, Newfoundland. *Canadian Journal of Earth Sciences*, **16**, 866–76.

LUDMAN, A. & MORISI, L. 1984. Stratigraphic and structural control in eastern Maine. *Geological Society of America, Abstracts with Programs*, **16**, 48.

MATTE, P. 1983. Two geotraverses across the Ibero-Amorican Variscan of Western Europe. *In: Geodynamic Series*, Vol. 10, pp. 53–82, American Geophysical Union, Washington, DC.

McGREGOR, D. C. 1979. Spores in Devonian stratigraphical correlations. *Special Papers in Palaeontology*, **23**, 163–84.

McKERROW, W. S. 1988. Wenlock to Givetian deformation in the British Isles and the Canadian Appalachians. *This volume.*

MILLER, J. D. & KENT, D. V. 1985. Another look at the Catskill. *EOS*, **66**, 257 (abstract).

MITCHELL, A. H. G. & McKERROW, W. S. 1975. Analogous evolution of the Burma orogen and the Scottish Caledonides. *Geological Society of America Bulletin*, **86**, 305–15.

MOREL, P. & IRVING, E. 1978. Tentative paleocontinental maps for the early Phanerozoic and Proterozoic. *Journal of Geology*, **86**, 535–61.

MORRIS, W. A. 1976. Transcurrent motion determined paleomagnetically in the northern Appalachians and Caledonides and the Acadian orogeny. *Canadian Journal of Earth Sciences*, **13**, 1236–43.

NELSON, D. D., ARNOW, J. A., McBRIDE, J. H., WILLEMIN, J. H., HUANG, J., ZHENG, L., OLIVER, J. E., BROWN, L. D. & KAUFMAN, S. 1985. New COCORP profiling in the southeastern United States, Part 1, Late Paleozoic suture and Mesozoic rift basin. *Geology*, **13**, 714–18.

OSBERG, P. H. 1978. Synthesis of the geology of the northern Appalachians, U.S.A. *Geological Survey of Canada Paper No. 78–13*, pp. 127–47.

PATCHETT, P. J. & BYLUND, G. 1977. Age of Grenville Belt magnetisation: Rb–Sr and palaeomagnetic evidence from Swedish dolerites. *Earth and Planetary Science Letters*, **35**, 92–104.

PERIGO, R., VAN DER VOO, R., AUVRAY, B. & BONHOMMET, N. 1983. Palaeomagnetism of late Precambrian–Cambrian volcanics and intrusives from the Armorican Massif, France. *Geophysical Journal of the Royal Astronomical Society*, **75**, 235–60.

PERROUD, H. & VAN DER VOO, R. 1985. Paleomagnetism of the late Ordovician Thouars Massif. Vendee Province, France. *Journal of Geophysical Research*, **90**, 4611–25.

PIQUE, A. 1983. Structural domains of the Hercynian belt in Morocco. *NATO ASI Series C*, **116**, 339–46.

QUINLAN, G. H. & BEAUMONT, C. 1984. Appalachian thrusting, lithospheric flexure and the Paleozoic stratigraphy of the Eastern interior of North America. *Canadian Journal of Earth Sciences*, **21**, 973–96.

RAO, R. V. & VAN DER VOO, R. 1980. Paleomagnetism of a Paleozoic anorthosite from the Appalachian Piedmont, Northern Delaware: possible tectonic implications. *Earth and Planetary Science Letters*, **47**, 113–20.

ROSS, C. A. 1979. Late Paleozoic collision of North and South America. *Geology*, **7**, 41–4.

ROY, J. L. 1982. Paleomagnetism of Siluro-Devonian rocks from eastern Maine: Discussion. *Canadian Journal of Earth Sciences*, **19**, 225–32.

—— & ANDERSON, P. 1981. An investigation of the remanence characteristics of three sedimentary units of the Silurian Mascarene Group of New Brunswick, Canada. *Journal of Geophysical Research*, **86**, 6351–68.

—— & MORRIS, W. A. 1983. A review of paleomagnetic results from the Carboniferous of North America; the concept of Carboniferous geomagnetic field horizon markers. *Earth and Planetary Science Letters*, **65**, 167–81.

——, OPDYKE, N. D. & IRVING, E. 1967. Further paleomagnetic results from the Bloomsburg formation. *Journal of Geophysical Research*, **72**, 5075–86.

SCHMIDT, P. W. & MORRIS, W. A. 1977. An alternate view of the Gondwana Paleozoic apparent polar wander path. *Canadian Journal of the Earth Sciences*, **14**, 1674–8.

SMITH, A. G. & HALLAM, A. 1970. The fit of the southern continents. *Nature, London*, **225**, 139–44.

SPARIOSU, D. J. & KENT, D. V. 1983. Paleomagnetism of the Lower Devonian Traveler Felsite and the Acadian orogeny in the New England Appalachians. *Geological Society of America Bulletin*, **94**, 1319–28.

—— & KENT, D. V. 1984. Devonian APW for North America. Suspect terranes, and the remagnetization hypothesis. *EOS*, **65**, 197 (abstract).

——, —— & KEPPIE, J. D. 1984. Late Paleozoic motions of the Meguma Terrane, Nova Scotia: new Paleomagnetic evidence. *In: VAN DER VOO, R. et al. (eds) Plate Reconstruction from Paleozoic Paleomagnetism. Geodynamics Series*, Vol. 12, pp. 82–98, American Geophysical Union, Washington, DC.

STILLMAN, C. R. & FRANCIS, E. H. 1979. Caledonide volcanism in Britain and Ireland. *In: HARRIS, A. L., HOLLAND, C. H. & LEAKE, B. E. (eds) The Caledonides of the British Isles Reviewed. Special Publication of the Geological Society of London No. 8*, p. 557.

THOMAS, W. A. 1977. Evolution of Appalachian–Ouachita: salients and recesses from reentrants and promontories in the continental margins. *American Journal of Science*, **277**, 1233–78.

UENO, H., IRVING, E. & McNUTT, R. H. 1975. Paleomagnetism of the Whitestone anarthosite and diorite, the Grenville polar track, and relative motions of the Laurentian and Baltic Shields. *Canadian Journal of Earth Sciences*, **12**, 209–26.

VAN DER VOO, R. 1979. Paleozoic assembly of Pangea: a new plate tectonic model for the Tactonic, Caledonian, and Hercynian orogenies. *EOS*, **60**, 241.

—— 1982. Pre-Mesozoic Paleomagnetism and plate tectonics. *Annual Review of Earth and Planetary Sciences*, **10**, 191–220.

—— & SCOTESE, C. 1981. Paleomagnetic evidence for a large (2000 km) sinistral offset along the Great Glen fault during Carboniferous time. *Geology*, **9**, 583–9.

——, FRENCH, A. N. & FRENCH, R. B. 1979. A palaeomagnetic pole position from the folded Upper Devonian Catskill redbeds, and its tectonic implications. *Geology*, **7**, 345–48.

——, MAUK, F. J. & FRENCH, R. B. 1976. Permian–Triassic continental configurations and the origin of the Gulf of Mexico. *Geology*, **4**, 177–80.

——, PEINADO, J. & SCOTESE, C. R. 1984. A Paleomagnetic reevaluation of Pangea reconstructions. *In:* VAN DER VOO, R. *et al.* (eds) *Plate Reconstruction from Paleozoic Paleomagnetism. Geodynamics Se-*

ries, Vol. 12, pp. 11–26, American Geophysical Union, Washington, D.C.

YOUNG, G. C. 1981. Biogeography of Devonian vertebrates. *Alcheringa*, **5**, 225–43.

ZIEGLER, P. A. 1984. Caledonian and Hercynian crustal consolidation of Western and Central Europe—a working hypothesis. *Geologie en Mijnbouw*, **63**, 93–108.

D. V. KENT, Lamont-Doherty Geological Observatory and Department of Geological Sciences, Columbia University, Palisades, NY 10964, USA.

J. D. KEPPIE, Department of Mines and Energy, Halifax, Nova Scotia B3J 2XI, Canada.

Note added in proof

Since this paper was presented in Glasgow in September 1984, and revised copy accepted for publication in January 1986, new data have become available that in some cases do, but in other cases do not, support the tectonic syntheses presented here. New palaeomagnetic results from Lower Devonian redbeds in the Appalachians place America approximately 15° farther south than shown in Fig. 1, reducing the latitudinal offset between N America on one side and Baltica as well as Armorica on the other; thus a Pangea B-like assembly may have been approached by early Devonian time with northwestern S America against eastern N America (Miller & Kent 1987), similar to the configuration suggested previously by McKerrow & Ziegler (1972), Keppie (1977) and Morel & Irving (1978). For the late Devonian, the secondary nature of the magnetizations originally reported from the Upper Devonian Catskill redbeds has been confirmed (Miller & Kent 1986a, b). Nevertheless, palaeomagnetic results from Upper Devonian rocks from western Australia strongly suggest that a wide ocean existed between Gondwana and Euramerica in the late Devonian (Hurley & Van der Voo 1987); thus Fig. 2 refers more appropriately only to the early Carboniferous. Taken at face value, the palaeomagnetic evidence would now seem to suggest that the Devonian encompassed an interval of ocean closure followed by opening between Gondwana and Euramerica.

References

HURLEY, N. F. & VAN DER VOO, R. 1987. Paleomagnetism of Upper Devonian reefal limestones, Canning basin, Western Australia. *Geological Society of America Bulletin*, **98**, 138–46.

McKERROW, W. S. & ZIEGLER, A. M. 1972. Palaeozoic oceans. *Nature*, **240**, 92–4.

MILLER, J. D. & KENT D. V. 1986a. Paleomagnetism of the Upper Devonian Catskill Formation from the Southern Limb of the Pennsylvania Salient: Possible evidence of oroclinal rotation. *Geophysical*

Research Letters, **13**, 1173–6.

—— & —— 1986b. Synfolding and prefolding magnetizations in the Upper Devonian Catskill formation of eastern Pennsylvania: Implications for the tectonic history of Acadia. *Journal of Geophysical Research*, **91**, 12, 791–803.

—— & —— 1987. Synfolding and prefolding magnetizations of the lower Devonian Andreas Redbeds, Andreas, PA. *EOS*, **68**, 292.

Timing and geometry of collision, terrane accretion and sinistral strike-slip events in the British Caledonides

N. J. Soper

SUMMARY: Recent geotectonic interpretations of the British Caledonides invoked E–W closure between two plates, Laurentia and 'Europe', to produce the N–S striking N Atlantic Caledonides and dextral strike-slip along the NE–SW-oriented British sector of the Iapetus suture. However, this model does not satisfy the following important new lines of evidence: the provinciality of Cambro-Ordovician shelf fauna, which indicates oceanic separation between Laurentia, Baltica and a third plate or terrane ('Cadomia') of which S Britain forms a part; the Y-shaped configuration of the orogen comprising the Appalachians, N Atlantic Caledonides and the N German–Polish zone which marks collision sutures between three plates rather than two; the evidence of sinistral, not dextral, transpressive displacements in both the orthotectonic Caledonides and the slate belts of Britain.

The 'three-plate' model for the British Caledonides which was proposed to accommodate these lines of evidence is developed further in terms of terrane accretion: Ordovician to mid-Silurian accretion events affected the Laurentian margin before the closure of Iapetus and produced the orthotectonic Caledonides of Scotland and Ireland; the Laurentia–Baltica collision closed the northern arm of Iapetus in the late Silurian and produced the Scandian orogeny; early Devonian northward accretion of a Gondwana-derived terrane induced sinistral transpression across the British slate belts and segmented the Scottish Highlands by sinistral strike-slip.

Since publication of the synthesis of British Caledonide geotectonics by Phillips *et al.* (1976) a two-plate configuration has generally been accepted for the terminal phase of the Caledonian orogeny, and the Grampian orogeny has been recognized as an earlier unrelated event (Lambert & McKerrow 1976). In the two-plate model approximately E–W convergence of a N American (Laurentian) plate and a European plate produced N–S-striking Scandinavian and E Greenland Caledonides and induced dextral transpressive strain along the NE–SW-oriented sector of the Iapetus suture (Dewey 1982, McKerrow 1982).

However, this model does not satisfy three important lines of evidence.

1 The provinciality of Cambro-Ordovician shelf fauna is well established and implies that there was wide oceanic separation in the early Palaeozoic between Laurentia, Baltica and a third plate, of Gondwanan affinity, of which S Britain is a part (Cocks & Fortey 1982). The establishment of cosmopolitan fauna in the late Ordovician, while indicating that the oceans were no longer effective barriers to dispersal, does not necessarily date the onset of collision-induced orogeny.

2 In addition to the Appalachians and the N Atlantic Caledonides of Britain, Scandinavia and E Greenland, there is a third Caledonian deformation zone which extends eastwards through central Europe (Fig. 1). Although the lower Palaeozoic rocks of this zone are poorly exposed and the Caledonian structures are frequently masked by Hercynian overprinting, two distinct deformation belts have been recognized (Ziegler 1982): the N German–Polish Caledonides and the mid-European Caledonides (Fig. 2). The orogen thus has a Y-shaped configuration whose arms, which intersect near Britain in the N Sea, mark collision sutures between elements derived from three continental plates: Laurentia, Baltica and Gondwana (Fig. 1).

3 The late Caledonian structures of the Scottish Highlands and the slate belts of central Britain indicate sinistral, not dextral, transpressive strains.

Soper & Hutton (1984) synthesized these lines of evidence to produce a 'three-plate' model for the British Caledonides. In the present paper the model is developed in terms of current concepts of terrane accretion, with particular attention being paid to the timing and geometry of the late Caledonian accretion-related deformations.

Orogenic events in the orthotectonic Caledonides

The orthotectonic or metamorphic Caledonides of Scotland and Ireland (Fig. 3) carry the imprint of several distinct orogenic events of early Palaeozoic age.

From HARRIS, A. L. & FETTES, D. J. (eds), 1988, *The Caledonian–Appalachian Orogen*, Geological Society Special Publication No. 38, pp. 481–492.

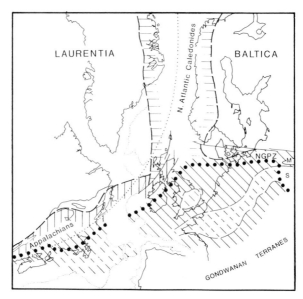

FIG. 1. Pre-Atlantic reconstruction showing the Y-shaped configuration of the Caledonian–Appalachian orogen: horizontal shading, N Atlantic Caledonides; vertical shading, limit of Appalachian accreted terranes; diagonal shading, late Caledonian and Acadian deformation; small dots, possible locus of major mid-Palaeozoic sinistral strike-slip; large dots, northern limit of Gondwana-derived terranes. Terranes with Baltic faunas: M. Malopolska massif; S. E Silesian massif; NGPZ. North German–Polish Caledonide zone.

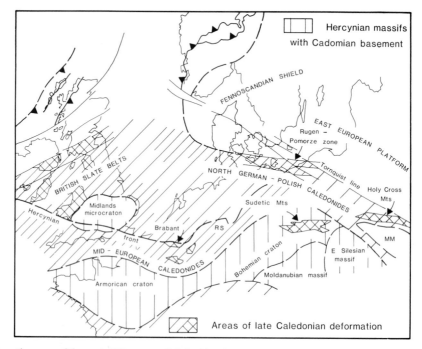

FIG. 2. Location map of the central European Caledonides: MM, Malopolska massif; RS, Rhenish Schiefergebirge. (Mainly after Ziegler 1982, 1984, Pegrum 1984, Chaloupský 1988.)

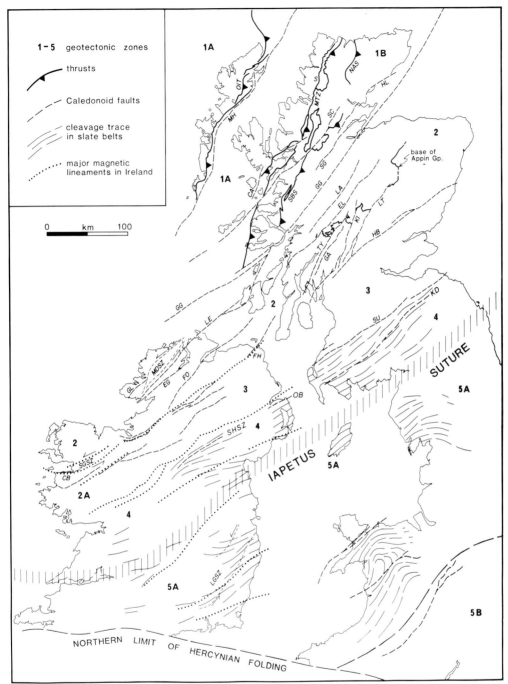

FIG. 3. Some Caledonian structures of the British Isles. Faults, mainly with proven or inferred sinistral displacements: CB, Clew Bay; EG, Eglish; EL, Ericht–Laidon; FO, Foyle; GA, Garabal; GG, Great Glen; GL, Glengesh; HB, Highland Border; HL, Helmsdale; KD, Kingledores; KI, Killin; LA, Laggan; LE, Lennan; LT, Loch Tay; MH, Minch; OB, Orlock Bridge; SC, Strathconon; SG, Strath Glass; SU, Southern Upland; TY, Tyndrum. Thrusts in Northern Scotland: MTZ, Moine Thrust Zone; NAS, Naver slide; OIT, Outer Isles thrust; SBS, Sgurr Beag slide. Sinistral shear zones; LGSZ, Leinster granite; MDSZ, Main Donegal; SGSZ, Slieve Gamph; SHSZ, Slieve Glah. Geotectonic zones of the British Caledonides: 1, Northern Highlands imbricate fan (1A, external zone; 1B, internal zone); 2, Grampian orogen (2A, Connemara terrane); 3, Midland Valley terrane; 4, Southern Uplands–Longford–Down accretionary complex; 5, Cadomian–Avalonian terrane (5A, deformed; 5B, undeformed Midlands microcraton). Zones 1 and 2 constitute the orthotectonic or metamorphic Caledonides; zones 4 and 5A constitute the paratectonic Caledonides or slate belts. (Magnetic lineaments in Ireland after Max & Inamdar 1983.)

The Grampian orogeny

The earliest of these events, the Grampian orogeny, affected the Dalradian Supergroup, a thick late Proterozoic–early Cambrian clastic sequence, in Tremadocian time (Bradbury *et al.* 1976, Lambert & McKerrow 1976). Although commonly regarded as an ensialic deposit, its great cumulative thickness (25 km according to Harris *et al.* (1978)) suggests that the Dalradian prograded onto oceanic crust as a prodigious continental margin clastic wedge. The Grampian orogeny took place long before collision between the Laurentian and Baltic cratons. It may represent the earliest of a series of terrane-accretion events which affected the southern Laurentian margin in Cambrian to Carboniferous time (Williams & Hatcher 1982). By analogy with models developed for Newfoundland, Dewey & Shackleton (1984) have argued that the event involved ophiolite obduction and that convergence was notably oblique.

The Grampian zone is suspiciously narrow—75 km at its narrowest in the SW Highlands (Fig. 3)—and was evidently truncated by the later Caledonian strike-slip event which is discussed below. In Scotland, the southern margin is the Highland Border Fault (HBF) along which are strung out the dismembered fragments of an exotic Ordovician basinal sequence, the Highland Border Complex (Curry *et al.* 1984 and references cited therein). S of the HBF is the Midland Valley terrane, whose basement, sampled as xenoliths, shows no evidence of pervasive reworking during the Grampian orogeny (Halliday *et al.* 1984) and which did not dock into its present position with respect to the Highlands until the early Devonian. In Ireland, Dalradian rocks occur on both sides of the Highland Border continuation (Fig. 3) and the Connemara massif should perhaps be recognized as a small allochthonous terrane of the Dalradian assemblage.

The northern margin of the Grampian zone, the Great Glen Fault (GGF), is not a Caledonian terrane boundary; as argued below, post-Ordovician sinistral displacement is unlikely to be more than about 200 km. Nonetheless, the Caledonide segment to the N of the GGF, the Northern Highlands, has a tectonic history distinct from that of the Grampians, with no evidence of Grampian tectono-metamorphism, and the NW Grampian 'front' seems to be obscured by the GGF.

The main Caledonides of the Northern Highlands

The Caledonian structures of the Northern Highlands and W Shetland shelf have a more northerly trend than the NE–SW grain typical of more southerly parts of the British Caledonides, but roughly parallel to that of the Scandinavian and E Greenland Caledonides. The gross structure is that of a stack of westward-directed thrust sheets. The best known of the thrust detachments, the Moine Thrust Zone (MTZ), is traditionally regarded as the NW Caledonian front and marks the NW limit of pervasive deformation at the present erosion level. NW of the MTZ the Laurentian craton is segmented by a number of major thrusts, perhaps as far W as the present continental margin, but is not pervasively deformed (the external zone of Fig. 3). SE of the MTZ the metamorphic internal zone is cut by a number of slides or ductile thrusts, of which the Sgurr Beag Slide (SBS, Fig. 3) (Tanner 1971, Powell 1974) is the best documented. These internal slide zones are 'syn-metamorphic' (Powell *et al.* 1981), but the ages of the metamorphic peak (467 ± 20 Ma (Brewer *et al.* 1979)) and the SBS (before about 456 Ma, the age of the Glen Dessary syenite (van Breemen *et al.* 1979, Roberts *et al.* 1984)) are constrained only as broadly mid-Ordovician. It is clear, however, that these events pre-date the evolution of the MTZ (Kelly & Powell 1985), which in Assynt spans the time of emplacement of the Borrolan intrusion (about 430 Ma, early Silurian (van Breemen *et al.* 1979)), and was completed by about 425 Ma (Johnson *et al.* 1985). No direct evidence exists for the age of compressional movements on the Outer Isles and Flannan thrusts, but if they belong to the same linked imbricate system the relatively small displacements were probably completed by mid-Silurian time (Watson 1984). Late, perhaps extensional, 'out-of-sequence' displacements in the MTZ (Coward 1983) ceased before emplacement of the Ross of Mull granite (Harris 1983) at about 414 Ma (late Silurian (Halliday *et al.* 1979)). The main Caledonian orogeny of NW Scotland thus spanned the period from mid-Ordovician to mid-Silurian, and numerous K–Ar ages of around 420–430 Ma on metamorphic micas show that erosion and cooling of the orogen were well advanced by the middle of the Silurian.

From the geotectonic viewpoint, the main question regarding the orthotectonic Caledonides is whether the Grampian, 'Sgurr Beag' and 'Moine Thrust' phases represent components of a single foreland (i.e. inboard) propagating 'upper lithosphere imbricate fan' system, as proposed by Dewey & Shackleton (1984, fig. 3(a)) and Bradbury (1985, fig. 4), or whether they relate to three separate collision events. There is a 30° strike disparity between the Grampians and Northern Highlands and a 40–50 Ma time gap between their metamorphic maxima, suggesting two distinct causes of orogeny. Similarly, there was delay of some 30 Ma between the Sgurr Beag and Moine Thrust deformations. In addition, the thrust systems in NW Scotland do not possess the geometry of a classical imbricate fan on the largest scale: the more westerly detachments cut progressively more deeply into the lithosphere (Blundell *et al.* 1985). However, if three distinct collisions are involved, the terranes which were accreted at each period are no longer present in the British region. The rocks of the Grampians and N Highlands are not exotic; the Moine and Dalradian sequences comprise two large clastic wedges which were deposited on the Laurentian margin and subsequently stacked back onto the cratonic interior. The thrusts on which this stacking was achieved have a cumulative displacement of several hundred kilometres (Butler 1986), so that the whole Caledonide zone N of the Highland Border is allochthonous in the classical sense but not exotic. The situation is quite different from that of the Appalachians where exotic terranes, i.e. the 'doubly-allochthonous' terranes described by Zen (1981), are thought to have been accreted in sequence so that the inboard deformations are oldest.

Regardless of the cause of the Grampian, Sgurr Beag and Moine Thrust tectono-metamorphic phases, it is clear that all three took place before the final closure of the northern arms of Iapetus. As outlined below, the terminal collision between Laurentia and Baltica, which produced the Scandian orogeny, did not take place until later Silurian time.

Late Caledonian strike-slip displacements

Johnson & Frost (1977) described the pattern of fractures and photo-lineaments which cut the metamorphic rocks of the Grampians. Watson (1984) has considered the age of these fractures through the Highlands generally and drawn attention to their relationship to the emplacement of the Newer Granites. N of the HBF, which trends ENE (about 055°), these workers recognize NE, NW and E–W sets. Of those with significant late Caledonian displacement the NE–SW set (termed the 'Great Glen set' by Watson) predominates, with sinistral strike–slip displacement and often downthrow to the SE.

Figure 3 shows the principal faults of the Great Glen set. Six major faults are present in the Grampians (Loch Tay, Killin, Garabal, Tyndrum, Ericht–Laidon and Laggan), trending between 025° and 040° with an average azimuth of about 035° parallel to the mainland sector of the GGF. To the N the Strath Glass, Strathconan

and Loch Kishorn faults are similarly oriented. All faults of the Great Glen set have either proven or inferred sinistral displacements, usually less than 10 km, suggesting that the GGF itself also has a component of sinistral offset. Adopting a simplified version of Johnson & Frost's interpretation, we regard the whole set, including the Great Glen, as first-order Riedel shears at about 15° to the HBF. This implies that the HBF is itself a major sinistral wrench fault. It is an important terrane boundary, separating Laurentian continental margin rocks to the N from the exotic Highland Border and Midland Valley terranes to the S, and is likely to have suffered a very large displacement during the Ordovician.

As discussed by Harris (1983) and Watson (1984) the HBF was also active late in the Caledonian orogeny, when the major displacement took place in the Great Glen set. Early movement on certain of these faults (Loch Tay, Strathconon) was linked to the later stages of ductile deformation, partly replacing late fold limbs. Watson has emphasized the close association in time between the Scottish Newer Granite suite of late Caledonian intrusives and the wrench faulting; certain granite bodies were emplaced along existing faults, and many others are fractured and offset by them.

The best example comes from Ireland. Hutton (1982) has shown that the elongate main Donegal granite lay in a NE–SW trending sinistral shear zone 80 km long on the NW seaboard of Ireland. The deformation in the pluton was approximately synchronous with its emplacement and crystallization at around 400 Ma (Halliday *et al.* 1980, O'Connor *et al.* 1982). The Lennan fault in NW Donegal cuts Dalradian rocks and has a sinistral displacement of at least 40 km with a southerly downthrow of several kilometres. Movement on it was coeval with the deposition of lower Devonian red beds with locally derived clasts which lie in a small isolated graben in the fault zone in NE Donegal. Further W in Ireland the Silurian rocks of the S Mayo Trough were deformed at about this time by sinistral transpressive deformation associated with the Clew Bay fault zone.

In Scotland, Watson (1984) has argued that the sinistral wrench faulting post-dated movement in the MTZ. A suite of felsites crosses the MTZ in the Glenelg area and shows small sinistral displacements on faults parallel to the Strathconon fault. The thrust and wrench episodes are evidently responses to separate tectonic regimes; the wrench faults are oriented about 75° oblique to the MTZ slip direction, and so the two sets of structures cannot be linked in the way suggested by Phillips *et al.* (1976).

It has been established on both palaeomagnetic (Briden *et al.* 1982, Tarling 1985) and geological (Smith & Watson 1983) grounds that displacement on the GGF must fall far short of the 2000 km proposed by Van der Voo & Scotese (1981). Despite suggestions of net dextral displacement (Garson & Plant 1972, Thirwall 1981), the association of the GGF with faults of proven sinistral displacement indicates the strong probability of sinistral movement in pre-middle Devonian time followed by smaller post-Devonian dextral movement to leave a net sinistral shift. Two recent estimates have been made. Winchester (1973) suggested a sinistral offset of 160 km to align the regional metamorphic zonal pattern of the Highlands across the Great Glen. van Breemen & Piasecki (1983) suggested a 200 km sinistral offset to align the Glenfinnan and Locheil Moines and the Loch Quoich line N of the fault with the Central Highland and Grampian Moines and Grampian slide respectively to the S. For reasons which need not be elaborated here (Harris *et al.* 1983, Roberts & Harris 1983) these correlations are untenable in detail, but the probability remains that a palaeomagnetically undetectable sinistral displacement of some 200 km occurred on the CGF late in the Caledonian cycle.

In summary, an important phase of sinistral strike-slip displacement affected the cooling and eroding metamorphic rocks of the orthotectonic Caledonides of Britain in mid-Silurian to early Devonian time. The total on-land displacement N of the HBF is difficult to evaluate, but must be several hundred kilometres. This places N Scotland opposite S Norway in pre-Silurian time.

We now turn to the paratectonic Caledonides and show that their main tectonic evolution took place at the same time and also involved sinistral displacements.

Late Caledonian deformation in the slate belts

The paratectonic Caledonides or slate belts of Britain consist largely of turbiditic sediments and arc volcanics which are strongly deformed but at a regional metamorphic grade which rarely exceeds prehnite–pumpellyite facies at the present surface (Oliver *et al.* 1984). The region is divided by the Solway–Navan–Silvermines line which is widely regarded as the Iapetus suture (Fig. 3). Since the suture is defined regionally on the provinciality of Ordovician fauna but is located in a region where Silurian turbidites were being deposited during final closure of the ocean,

the position of its surface trace cannot be precisely located.

N of the suture in the Southern Uplands–Longford–Down Zone (Fig. 3) the slate belt structure is widely regarded as that of an accretionary complex (McKerrow *et al.* 1977, Anderson & Cameron 1979, Leggett *et al.* 1979) developed by subduction of Iapetus oceanic lithosphere beneath the southern margin of Laurentia in Ordovician to mid-Silurian or later time. Recognition of the importance of sinistral displacements along the Laurentian margin means that the accretionary complex was not developed adjacent to the Highlands but some considerable distance to the SW, and the identification of large sinistral displacements on faults within the complex (e.g. the Orlock Bridge–Kingledores fault (Fig. 3) (Anderson & Oliver 1986)) implies that the northern (mainly Ordovician) and central southern (Silurian) parts of the complex, now juxtaposed, were once widely separated.

Ductile deformation in the accretionary complex is dominated by upright folds which face up to the S and are accompanied by a single cleavage of the pressure-solution type. The main folds and cleavage are thought to have been developed sequentially in each package during accretion, overlapping in time the reverse faulting which detached the package.

S of the suture in the Lake District, Wales and SE Ireland, accretionary structures are not developed. The Silurian sediments tend to show a single set of upright folds and a single cleavage. These structures are thought to have been produced during the final collision event.

Current interpretations thus attribute the major structural evolution of the slate belts N and S of the suture to accretion and collision respectively. However, a unifying characteristic exists. This is the non-axial planar nature of the cleavage which transects the fold axes at a small angle (usually less than 10°), almost always in a clockwise sense. This relationship holds throughout the Silurian rocks of NW England (Moseley 1968, 1972), the Southern Uplands (Leggett *et al.* 1979, Stringer & Treagus 1980, 1981), Ireland on both sides of the suture (Phillips *et al.* 1976, Soper & Hutton 1984, Murphy 1985), Wales (N. H. Woodcock, personal communication) and indeed Newfoundland (W. S. McKerrow, personal communication).

Transecting cleavage can, in principle, be produced either by coaxial strains imposed on bedding not orthogonal to the strain axes (Treagus & Treagus 1981) or by transpressive non-coaxial strains. The latter mechanism seems more appropriate to the regionally developed feature described above, particularly in the context of continental margin deformation which, as shown, involves strike-slip. Sanderson *et al.* (1980) have explored the geometry of cleavage transection in superimposed shear zones and showed that the achievement of clockwise fold-axis transection by dextral shear, as demanded by the model of Phillips *et al.*, requires the fold axes to be initially oriented at an improbably large angle to the shear zone. Murphy (1985) showed that clockwise transecting cleavage is associated with sub-horizontal stretching lineations in a zone which extends about 50 km on each side of the Solway line in E Ireland. He attributed this to the superimposition of sinistral transpression (Sanderson & Marchini 1984) on a more orthogonal regional strain pattern. Elsewhere in the slate belts, clockwise transection occurs frequently in Silurian rocks which show no evidence of strike-parallel stretching, but in association with other structures such as wrench faults and shear zones which indicate sinistral transpression (Soper & Hutton 1984).

The age of the cleavage-forming episode is constrained S of the suture in the Lake District and in Wales. In the Lake District (Soper & Moseley 1978) it post-dates Pridoli sedimentation (Scout Hill Flags) and predates the Shap granite (394 Ma (Emsian)) (Wadge *et al.* 1978), and is therefore of lower Devonian age. In the Myddfai steep belt in SE Wales a continuous sequence from lower Silurian to Emsian is involved in a SE-facing monocline. Only the marine Silurian rocks show cleavage, which dies out up-section, but it is evident that the deformation took place late in the lower Devonian. The only example of cleaved Old Red Sandstone facies sediments in Britain appear to be those of Anglesey, which are presumed to be of lower Devonian age (Allen 1965). It is evident that the regional late Caledonian episode of folding and cleavage, long regarded as the 'end-Silurian collision event' is in reality late lower Devonian (Soper *et al.*, in press). McKerrow (1988) has assembled further stratigraphic evidence in support of this view and has also shown that the Acadian orogeny of the NE Appalachians took place at much the same time. The term 'collision' is not entirely appropriate for this event: it marks the termination of convergence (under-thrusting) across the suture zone and may post-date by 10 or 20 Ma the elimination of oceanic crust and destruction of the trench (Leggett *et al.* 1983, Murphy & Hutton 1986).

This interpretation of the regional structure of the slate belts thus involves sinistral transpression during final closure of Iapetus and is directly opposed to earlier dextral models, requiring a roughly N–S rather than E–W plate displacement

vector. The model is consistent with the evidence of sinistral displacements in the orthotectonic Caledonides which, as shown above, were taking place synchronously with convergence across the slate belts. It leaves open the question of how the observed structures in the accretionary complex should be apportioned between the accretion and collision phases.

Deformations on the margins of Baltica

Leaving aside the Grampian orogeny, it is clear that in Britain we see the tectono-metamorphic effects of two distinct Caledonian convergence regimes: the main Caledonian orogeny of the NW Highlands (Sgurr Beag and Moine Thrust events) and the late Caledonian transpression event. Let us examine briefly the geometry and timing of equivalent deformations on the opposing margins of Baltica.

The Scandian Caledonides

Restoration of a minimum 300 km sinistral displacement within mainland Britain places the Northern Highlands opposite southern Norway where Scandian structures have a similar trend and take the form of an even larger-scale imbricate fan, but with opposed (easterly) vergence. The gross structure of the Scandinavian Caledonides, as synthesized by Hossack & Cooper (1986), consists of four major groups of thrust sheets. From W to E these comprise the exotic nappe complex (largely derived from Laurentia), the oceanic thrust sheets (marking the Iapetus suture zone) and the crystalline and Baltic cover sheets (derived from Baltica). Lateral ramps, lateral branch lines and stretching lineations (Hossack 1983, Shackleton & Ries 1984) indicate ESE–WNW convergence (Fig. 4). The fact that Laurentia-derived thrust sheets were stacked onto the Baltic craton shows that the Scandian orogeny must be interpreted as the result of full continent–continent collision between Laurentia and Baltica.

The Scandian orogeny took place in mid- to end-Silurian time (Barker & Gayer 1985). It is evident that the main tectono-metamorphic evolution of N Scotland and Scandinavia did not take place synchronously, as proposed by Soper & Hutton (1984). The Scandian thrusting post-dates the Moine Thrust episode and is coeval with the phase of strike-slip segmentation of the Scottish Highlands described above. By earliest Devonian time Laurentia and Baltica were

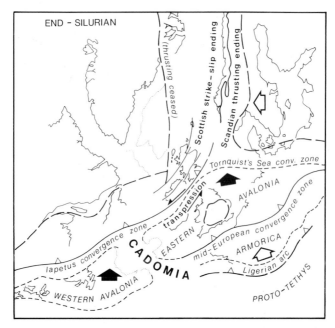

FIG. 4. Reconstruction of the Caledonides at about the Siluro-Devonian boundary (410 Ma). Closure between Laurentia and Baltica is ending, the leading edge of E Avalonia is under-thrusting the Laurentian margin in Britain and sinistral transpression is starting to affect the British slate belts. Closure continues across the remnant of Tornquist's Sea and collision is taking place across the mid-European convergence zone. W Avalonia has not yet collided with the northern Appalachians. Note that an alternative reconstruction would have a widening Rheic Ocean in the position of the mid-European convergence zone.

sutured together to form part of the 'Old Red' supercontinent.

The N German–Polish Caledonides

Cocks & Fortey (1982) have shown that, by the Ashgill, Britain and Scandinavia had similar shelf fauna, even at specific level. Many workers have therefore inferred that convergence across the Tornquist's Sea suture had ceased by the end of the Ordovician. This is the essence of the two-plate dextral model for the late Caledonides of Britain. Yet clearly it is not possible to combine northward convergence between 'Cadomia' (S Britain and elsewhere) and Laurentia, which is necessary to produce sinistral transpression in the British region, with E–W closure between Laurentia and Baltica unless convergence also took place between Baltica and Cadomia. Strike-slip displacement on the Tornquist line (Fig. 2) without convergence is not enough; compare Fig. 4 with figs 8 and 9 of Barker & Gayer (1985).

Faunal provinciality between Laurentia and Baltica likewise became insignificant in the late Ordovician but, as outlined above, the tectonic and stratigraphic evidence show that final colli-

sion between those continents did not take place until the late Silurian. Evidently, oceans may become insignificant in terms of faunal provinciality long before convergence between their bordering continents ceases. A modern example is provided by India, which began to collide with Asia 45 Ma ago but continues to under-thrust Tibet at some 5 cm a^{-1} (Tapponier & Molnar 1976, Allegre *et al.* 1984).

Ziegler (1982) has shown that the poorly exposed N German–Polish Caledonides (Fig. 2) provide evidence that convergence between Baltica and Cadomia continued into the lower Devonian. Several wells drilled in the North Sea W of Denmark penetrate metamorphic basement which has yielded radiometric ages in the range 410–440 Ma. These rocks are thought to represent the metamorphic internides of the N German Caledonian deformation belt, and their existence disproves earlier suggestions of a connection between the Baltic Shield and the London Platform. The position of the Caledonian front is adequately controlled by boreholes in S Denmark and Pomerania; in the latter area deformation of the lower Palaeozoic flysch sequence is strati-graphically dated as post-Wenlock and pre-

Downtonian. Further SE in the Holy Cross mountains of Poland marine flysch was deposited until early Devonian time and Old Red Sandstone facies sedimentation commenced in the Siegenian.

Synchroneity of deformation in the N German–Polish Caledonides and the late Caledonides of Britain suggests a single collision event as the cause. Ziegler (1982) and Soper & Hutton (1984) proposed that a terrane of Gondwanan origin—'Cadomia'—was accreted onto the southern margin of Laurentia–Baltica in early Devonian time.

Late Caledonian terrane-accretion events

Cadomia is one of several microcontinental fragments recognized by Ziegler (1982, 1984) as forming the pre-Hercynian framework of Europe. It is shown in Fig. 4 as comprising two terranes—'Eastern Avalonia' and 'Armorica'—whose time of amalgamation is discussed below. It is bounded to the NW by the British slate belts which mark the Iapetus suture, to the NE by the N German–Polish zone (Tornquist's Sea suture) and to the S by the Ligerian magmatic arc (Fig. 4).

Cadomia has a pre-Caledonian geological history distinct from that of adjacent parts of Laurentia and Baltica. It is characterized by thick late Proterozoic clastic and volcanic sequences, partly built on early Proterozoic (Pentevrian) continental basement but in Britain composed of continental margin and magmatic arc material no older than 900 Ma (Le Bas 1982, Thorpe *et al.* 1984). These elements are thought to have been amalgamated during the end-Proterozoic Cadomian orogeny (Cogne & Wright 1980). This took place before Cadomia was detached from Gondwana, and the Cadomian orogeny can thus be regarded as part of the pan-African orogenic system.

Cadomia has much in common with the Avalonian terrane of E Newfoundland and maritime Canada, whose accretion onto the Laurentian margin produced the Acadian orogeny of late lower Devonian to earliest Middle Devonian age (Williams & Hatcher 1982, O'Brien *et al.* 1983, McKerrow 1988).

The geometry of the Cadomia accretion is depicted in Fig. 4. A northward displacement vector is inferred. The cooling and eroding metamorphic rocks of the Highlands responded by strike-slip faulting, whereas the turbidite wedges and volcanic piles to the S were folded and cleaved to produce the slate belts athwart the Iapetus suture. Strike-slip segmentation of the

Highlands effectively ceased with the ending of the Scandian thrusting in the early Devonian, suggesting that the active thrusts provided detachments necessary to accommodate the wrench displacements. Transpression in the slate belts continued until convergence between Cadomia and Laurentia ceased in later lower Devonian time.

The configuration of the terranes which comprise Cadomia and their amalgamation history are poorly understood. As synthesized by Ziegler (1982, 1984), Cadomia contains a number of cratons (the Irish Sea horst, the London Platform, the Armorican craton, the Bohemian craton) of Gondwanan origin surrounded by late Caledonian deformation belts. If the cratons represent distinct allochthonous terranes which were detached from Gondwana in the early Palaeozoic and if these terranes were separated by small ocean basins, some of the deformation belts must hide subduction sutures which mark the closure of these basins in late Caledonian time. An important deformation zone, the mid-European Caledonides (Fig. 2), separates Cadomia into two terranes, themselves composite, which are labelled Eastern Avalonia and Armorica in Fig. 4. Attention is focused on these because some of the outstanding problems of mid-Palaeozoic European geotectonics centre on their inter-relationship.

The mid-European Caledonides are known mainly from sub-surface information in a zone from SE England to the Rhenish Schiefergebirge (Krebs 1978) but have limited exposure in the Brabant Massif where folds and thrusts affect sediments of Gedinnian age and verge S (Michot 1980). An interpretation in terms of terrane accretion is that the deformation belt marks a northwardly inclined subduction suture between Armorica and E Avalonia—the mid-European convergence zone (Fig. 4)—and that these two terranes were amalgamated by collision in the early Devonian to form the composite Cadomian terrane which was then accreted onto the Laurasian margin. The possibility of northward oceanic subduction beneath S Britain has some interesting implications; it might account for the voluminous and hitherto unexplained Siluro-Devonian granite magmatism in the British slate belts (Soper 1986).

However, palaeontological evidence (Cocks & Fortey 1982) requires an opening rather than a closing ocean between E Avalonia and Armorica from Wenlock time onwards. This, the Rheic Ocean, is thought to have been faunally important until Westphalian time. Palaeoclimatological evidence, such as the earlier appearance of warmwater limestones in E Avalonia than in Armorica, tends to support the Rheic Ocean concept (W. S. McKerrow, personal communication). Palaeomagnetic evidence, however, suggests that Armorica had moved to low latitudes and had been accreted onto Laurentia–Baltica by mid-Devonian time (Perroud *et al.* 1984). It is beyond the scope of this paper to review these conflicting lines of evidence, but until the Rheic Ocean problem has been resolved and a better understanding of Hercynian displacements achieved it is not possible to make much further progress in defining the boundaries and accretion histories of the European Caledonide terranes.

The broad implication of the model proposed here, and indeed of many of the contributions to this volume, follows from any view of geotectonics which accepts the importance of terrane accretion as a cause of orogeny, with its corollary that strike-slip displacements are always likely to be important in orogenic belts. The main segments of the British Caledonides shown in Fig. 3 were not assembled in their present relative positions until the early Devonian. Displacements along the Highland Border Fault, Solway line and other faults may have been very substantial. 'Orthogonal' plate-tectonic models, which attempt to relate pre-Devonian events along a present-day line of section, are suspect.

References

ALLEGRE, C. J. *et al.* 1984. Structure and evolution of the Himalaya–Tibet orogenic belt. *Nature, London,* **307**, 17–22.

ALLEN, J. R. L. 1965. Sedimentation and palaeogeography of the Old Red Sandstone of Anglesey, North Wales. *Proceedings of the Yorkshire Geological Society,* **35**, 139–85.

ANDERSON, T. B. & CAMERON, T. D. 1979. A structural profile of Caledonian deformation in Down. *In:* HARRIS, A. L., HOLLAND, C. W. & LEAKE, B. E. (eds) *The Caledonides of the British Isles Reviewed. Special Publication of the Geological Society of London No. 8*, pp. 263–7.

ANDERSON, T. B. & OLIVER, G. J. H. 1986. The Orlock Bridge fault: a major late Caledonian sinistral fault in the Southern Uplands terrane, British Isles. *Transactions of the Royal Society of Edinburgh Earth Sciences,* **77**, 203–22.

BARKER, A. J. & GAYER, R. A. 1985. Caledonide–Appalachian tectonic analysis and evolution of related oceans. *In:* GAYER, R. A. (ed.) *The Tectonic Evolution of the Caledonide–Appalachian Orogen,* pp. 126–65, Vieweg, Braunschweig.

BLUNDELL, D. J., HURICH, C. A. & SMITHSON, S. B. 1985. A model for the MOIST seismic reflection profile, N Scotland. *Journal of the Geological Society, London,* **142**, 245–58.

VAN BREEMEN, O. & PIASECKI, M. A. J. 1983. The Glen Kyllachy Granite and its bearing on the nature of the Caledonian Orogeny in Scotland. *Journal of the Geological Society, London,* **130**, 493–507.

——, AFTALION, M. & JOHNSON, M. R. W. 1979. Age of the Loch Borrolan Complex, Assynt, and late movements along the Moine Thrust Zone. *Journal of the Geological Society, London,* **136**, 489–95.

BRADBURY, H. J. 1985. The Caledonian metamorphic core: an Alpine model. *Journal of the Geological Society, London,* **142**, 129–36.

——, SMITH, R. A. & HARRIS, A. L. 1976. 'Older' granites as time-markers in Dalradian evolution. *Journal of the Geological Society, London,* **132**, 677–84.

BREWER, M. S., BROOK, M. & POWELL, D. 1979. Dating of the tectono-metamorphic history of the southwestern Moine, Scotland. *In:* HARRIS, A. L.,

HOLLAND, C. W. & LEAKE, B. E. (eds) *The Caledonides of the British Isles Reviewed. Special Publication of the Geological Society of London No. 8*, pp. 129–38.

BRIDEN, J. C., TURNELL, H. B., WATTS, D. R., McCLELLAND BROWN, E. & EVERETT, S. 1982. Palaeomagnetism of the Scottish Highlands and the question of magnitude of displacement on the Great Glen Fault. *European Geophysical Society and European Seismological Commission Symposium, Leeds* (abstract).

BUTLER, R. H. W. 1986. Structural evolution of the Moine in northwest Scotland: a Caledonian linked thrust system? *Geological Magazine,* **123**, 1–11.

CHALOUPSKÝ, J. 1988. Caledonian folding in the Bohemian Massif. *This volume.*

COCKS, L. R. M. & FORTEY, R. A. 1982. Faunal evidence for oceanic separations in the Palaeozoic of Britain. *Journal of the Geological Society, London,* **138**, 467–80.

COGNE, J. & WRIGHT, A. E. 1980. L'Orogene cadomien. *26th International Geological Congress, Paris,* Vol. 6, pp. 29–55.

COWARD, M. P. 1983. The thrust and shear zones of the Moine thrust zone and the NW Scottish Caledonides. *Journal of the Geological Society, London,* **140**, 795–812.

CURRY, G. B., BLUCK, B. J., BURTON, C. J., INGHAM, J. K., SIVETER, D. J. & WILLIAMS, A. 1984. Age, evolution and tectonic history of the Highland Border Complex, Scotland. *Transactions of the Royal Society of Edinburgh, Earth Sciences,* **75**, 113–34.

DEWEY, J. F. 1982. Plate tectonics and the evolution of the British Isles. *Journal of the Geological Society, London,* **139**, 371–412.

—— & SHACKLETON, R. M. 1984. A model for the evolution of the Grampian tract in the early Caledonides and Appalachians. *Nature, London,* **312**, 115–21.

GARSON, M. S. & PLANT, J. 1972. Possible dextral movements on the Great Glen and Minch faults, Scotland. *Nature, London, Physical Science,* **240**, 31–2.

HALLIDAY, A. N., AFTALION, M., VAN BREEMEN, O. & JOCELYN, J. 1979. Petrogenetic significance of Rb–Sr and U–Pb isotopic systems in the *c*. 400 My old British Isles granitoids and their hosts. *In:* HARRIS, A. L., HOLLAND, C. W. & LEAKE, B. E. (eds) *The Caledonides of the British Isles Reviewed. Special Publication of the Geological Society of London No. 8*, pp. 653–61.

——, —— & LEAKE, B. E. 1980. A revised age for the Donegal granites. *Nature, London*, **284**, 542–3.

——, UPTON, B. G. J., ASPEN, P. & JOCELYN, J. 1984. U–Pb isotopic ages from a granulite-facies xenolith from Partan Craig in the Midland Valley of Scotland. *Transactions of the Royal Society of Edinburgh, Earth Sciences*, **75**, 71–4.

HARRIS, A. L. 1983. The growth and structure of Scotland. *In:* CRAIG, G. Y. (ed.) *Geology of Scotland*, pp. 1–22, Scottish Academic Press, Edinburgh.

——, BALDWIN, C. T., BRADBURY, H. J., JOHNSON, H. D. & SMITH, R. A. 1978. Ensialic basin sedimentation: the Dalradian Supergroup. *In:* BOWES, D. R. & LEAKE, B. E. (eds) *Crustal Evolution in Northwestern Britain and Adjacent Regions*, pp. 115–38, Seel House Press, Liverpool.

——, HIGHTON, A. J., ROBERTS, A. M. & STOKER, M. S. 1983. Discussion on the Glen Kyllachy Granite and its bearing on the nature of the Caledonian Orogeny in Scotland. *Journal of the Geological Society, London*, **140**, 961–3.

HOSSACK, J. R. 1983. A cross-section through the Scandinavian Caledonides constructed with the aid of branch-line maps. *Journal of Structural Geology*, **5**, 103–12.

—— & COOPER, M. A. 1986. Collision tectonics in the Scandinavian Caledonides. *In:* COWARD, M. P. & RIES, A. C. (eds) *Collision Tectonics. Special Publication of the Geological Society of London No. 19*, 287–304.

HUTTON, D. H. W. 1982. A tectonic model for the emplacement of the main Donegal granite, N. W. Ireland. *Journal of the Geological Society, London*, **139**, 615–32.

JOHNSON, M. R. W. & FROST, R. T. C. 1977. Fault and lineament patterns in the southern Highlands of Scotland. *Geologie en Mijnbouw*, **56**, 287–94.

——, KELLEY, S. P., OLIVER, G. J. H. & WINTER, D. A. 1985. Thermal effects and timing of thrusting in the Moine thrust zone. *Journal of the Geological Society, London*, **142**, 863–73.

KELLY, S. P. & POWELL, D. 1985. Relationships between marginal thrusting and movement on major internal shear zones in the Northern Highland Caledonides, Scotland. *Journal of Structural Geology*, **7**, 161–74.

KREBS, W. 1978. Die Kaledoniden im nordlichen Mitteleuropa. *Zeitschrift für Deutsches Geologisches Gesellschaft*, **129**, 403–22.

LAMBERT, R. St. J. & McKERROW, W. S. 1976. The Grampian orogeny. *Scottish Journal of Geology*, **12**, 271–92.

LE BAS, M. J. 1982. Geological evidence from Leicestershire on the crust of southern Britain. *Transac-tions of the Leicester Literary and Philosophical Society*, **76**, 54–67.

LEGGETT, J. K., McKERROW, W. S., MORRIS, J. H., OLIVER, G. J. H. & PHILLIPS, W. E. A. 1979. The northwestern margin of the Iapetus Ocean. *In:* HARRIS, A. L., HOLLAND, C. W. & LEAKE, B. E. (eds) *The Caledonides of the British Isles Reviewed. Special Publication of the Geological Society of London No. 8*, 499–511.

——, —— & SOPER, N. J. 1983. A model for the crustal evolution of southern Scotland. *Tectonics*, **2**, 187–210.

MAX, M. D. & INAMDAR, D. D. 1983. Detailed compilation magnetic map of Ireland and a summary of its deep geology. *Geological Survey of Ireland Report Series 83/1*.

McKERROW, W. S. 1982. The northwest margin of the Iapetus Ocean during the early Palaeozoic. *Memoir, American Association of Petroleum Geologists*, **34**, 521–33.

—— 1988. Wenlock to Givetian deformation in the British Isles and the Canadian Appalachians. *This volume.*

——, LEGGETT, J. K. & EALES, M. H. 1977. Imbricate thrust model of the Southern Uplands of Scotland. *Nature, London*, **267**, 237–9.

MICHOT, P. 1980. Le segment tectogenique caledonien belge. *Académie Royale de Belgique, Memoires de la Classe des Sciences*, **43**, 1–61.

MOSELEY, F. 1968. Joints and other structures in the Silurian rocks of the southern Shap Fells, Westmorland. *Geological Journal*, **4**, 127–42.

—— 1972. A tectonic history of north-west England. *Journal of the Geological Society, London*, **128**, 561–98.

MURPHY, F. C. 1985. Non-axial planar cleavage and Caledonian sinistral transpression in eastern Ireland. *Geological Journal*, **20**, 257–79.

—— & HUTTON, D. H. W. 1986. Is the Southern Uplands of Scotland really an accretionary prism? *Geology*, **4**, 354–7.

O'BRIEN, S. J., WARDLE, R. J. & KING, A. F. 1983. The Avalon Zone: a Pan-African terrane in the Appalachian orogen of Canada. *Geological Journal*, **18**, 195–222.

O'CONNOR, P. J., LONG, C. B., KENNAN, P. S., HALLIDAY, A. N., MAX, M. D. & RODDICK, J. C. 1982. Rb–Sr isochron study of the Thorr and Main Donegal granites. *Geological Journal*, **17**, 279–95.

OLIVER, G. J. H., SMELLIE, J. L., THOMAS, L. J., CASEY, D. M., KEMP, A. E. S., EVANS, L. J., BALDWIN, J. R. & HEPWORTH, B. C. 1984. Early Palaeozoic metamorphic history of the Midland Valley, Southern Uplands–Longford–Down Massif and the Lake District, British Isles. *Transactions of the Royal Society of Edinburgh, Earth Sciences*, **75**, 245–58.

PEGRUM, R. M. 1984. The extension of the Tornquist Zone in the Norwegian North Sea. *Norsk Geologisk Tidsskrift*, **64**, 39–68.

PERROUD, H., VAN DER VOO, R. & BONHOMMET, N. 1984. Palaeozoic evolution of the Armorica plate on the basis of palaeomagnetic data. *Geology*, **12**, 579–82.

PHILLIPS, W. E. A., STILLMAN, C. J. & MURPHY, T. 1976. A Caledonian plate tectonic model. *Journal of the Geological Society, London,* **132**, 579–609.

POWELL, D. 1974. Stratigraphy and structures of the western Moine and the problem of Moine orogenesis. *Journal of the Geological Society, London,* **130**, 575–93.

——, BAIRD, A. W., CHARNLEY, N. R. & JORDAN, P. J. 1981. The metamorphic environment of the Sgurr Beag Slide; a major crustal displacement zone in Proterozoic, Moine rocks of Scotland. *Journal of the Geological Society, London,* **138**, 661–73.

ROBERTS, A. M. & HARRIS, A. L. 1983. The Loch Quoich Line—a limit of early Palaeozoic crustal reworking in the Moine of the Northern Highlands of Scotland. *Journal of the Geological Society, London,* **140**, 883–92.

——, SMITH, D. I. & HARRIS, A. L. 1984. The structural setting and tectonic significance of the Glen Dessary Syenite, Inverness-shire. *Journal of the Geological Society, London,* **141**, 1033–42.

SANDERSON, D. J. & MARCHINI, D. 1984. Transpression. *Journal of Structural Geology,* **6**, 449–58.

——, ANDREWS, J. R., PHILLIPS, W. E. A. & HUTTON, D. H. W. 1980. Deformation studies in the Irish Caledonides. *Journal of the Geological Society, London,* **137**, 289–302.

SHACKLETON, R. M. & RIES, A. C. 1984. The relation between regionally consistent stretching lineations and plate motions. *Journal of Structural Geology,* **6**, 111–20.

SMITH, D. I. & WATSON, J. V. 1983. Scale and timing of movements on the Great Glen fault, Scotland. *Geology,* **11**, 523–6.

SOPER, N. J. 1986. The Newer Granite problem: a geotectonic view. *Geological Magazine,* **123**, 227–36.

—— & HUTTON, D. W. H. 1984. Late Caledonian sinistral displacements in Britain: implications for a three-plate collision model. *Tectonics,* **3**, 781–94.

—— & MOSELEY, F. 1978. Structure. *In:* MOSELEY, F. (ed.) *The Geology of the Lake District. Yorkshire Geological Society Occasional Publication No. 3,* pp. 45–67.

——, WEBB, B. C. & WOODCOCK, N. H. Late Caledonian transpression in North West England: timing, geometry and geotectonic significance. *Proceedings of the Yorkshire Geological Society,* in press.

STRINGER, P. & TREAGUS, J. E. 1980. Non-axial planar S_1 cleavage in the Hawick Rocks of the Galloway area, Southern Uplands, Scotland. *Journal of Structural Geology,* **2**, 317–31.

—— & —— 1981. Asymmetrical folding in the Hawick Rocks of the Galloway area, Southern Uplands. *Scottish Journal of Geology,* **17**, 129–48.

TANNER, P. W. G. 1971. The Sgurr Beag Slide—a major tectonic break within the Moinian of the Western Highlands of Scotland. *Quarterly Journal of the Geological Society of London,* **126**, 435–63.

TAPPONIER, P. & MOLNAR, P. 1976. Slip-line field theory and large-scale continental tectonics. *Nature, London,* **264**, 319–24.

TARLING, D. H. 1985. Palaeomagnetic studies of the Orcadian Basin. *Scottish Journal of Geology,* **21**, 261–73.

THIRLWALL, M. F. 1981. Implications for Caledonian plate tectonic models of chemical data from volcanic rocks of the British Old Red Sandstone. *Journal of the Geological Society, London,* **138**, 123–38.

THORPE, R. S., BECKINSALE, R. D., PATCHETT, P. J., PIPER, J. D. A., DAVIES, G. R. & EVANS, J. A. 1984. Crustal growth and late Precambrian–early Palaeozoic plate tectonic evolution of England and Wales. *Journal of the Geological Society, London,* **141**, 521–36.

TREAGUS, J. E. & TREAGUS, S. H. 1981. Folds and the strain ellipsoid: a general model. *Journal of Structural Geology,* **3**, 1–18.

VAN DER VOO, R. & SCOTESE, C. R. 1981. Palaeomagnetic evidence for a large (~ 2000 km) sinistral offset along the Great Glen fault during Carboniferous time. *Geology,* **9**, 583–9.

WADGE, A. J., GALE, N. H., BECKINSALE, R. D. & RUNDLE, C. C. 1978. A Rb–Sr isochron for the Shap granite. *Proceedings of the Yorkshire Geological Society,* **42**, 297–305.

WATSON, J. V. 1984. The ending of the Caledonian Orogeny in Scotland. *Journal of the Geological Society, London,* **141**, 193–214.

WILLIAMS, H. & HATCHER, R. D. 1982. Suspect terranes and accretionary history of the Appalachian region. *Geology,* **10**, 530–6.

WINCHESTER, J. A. 1973. Pattern of regional metamorphism suggests a sinistral displacement of 160 km along the Great Glen fault. *Nature, London, Physical Sciences,* **246**, 81–4.

ZEN, E-AN. 1981. An alternative model for the development of the allochthonous southern Appalachian piedmont. *American Journal of Science,* **281**, 1153–63.

ZIEGLER, P. A. 1982. *Geological Atlas of Central and Western Europe,* Elsevier, Amsterdam.

—— 1984. Caledonian and Hercynian crustal consolidation of western and central Europe—a working hypothesis. *Geologie en Mijnbouw,* **63**, 93–108.

N. J. SOPER, Department of Geology, Mappin Street, University of Sheffield, Sheffield S1 3JD, UK.

Caledonian folding in the Bohemian Massif

J. Chaloupský

SUMMARY: The Bohemian Massif was formed by metamorphic and tectonic processes during a long period which began about 800–900 Ma ago with the break-up of the ancient continental crust and Brioverian rift sedimentation and ended at the close of the Palaeozoic by transition to the platform-development stage. Caledonian folding has been evidenced in the NE part of the Massif.

Precambrian

Most of the relict blocks of Middle to Lower? Proterozoic Moldanubian crust in the Bohemian Massif were affected by Dalslandian regeneration (Fig. 1). The eastern boundary of the Dalslandian regeneration area runs along the eastern margin of the massif forming a significant tectonic zone of a composite imbricate structure. This zone probably represents the southern continuation of the Vättern Tectonic Zone of South Sweden. To the E of the imbrication zone the Bruno-Vistulicum area (Dudek 1980) displays the characteristic features of E European Platform basement.

The ancient Moldanubian blocks are welded together by thick Brioverian (Upper Proterozoic) sequences (Fig. 2). Both Moldanubian and Brio-

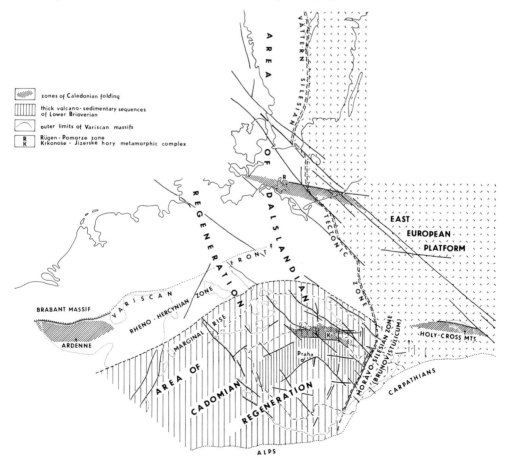

FIG. 1. Mobile zones in central Europe.

From HARRIS, A. L. & FETTES, D. J. (eds), 1988, *The Caledonian–Appalachian Orogen,* Geological Society Special Publication No. 38, pp. 493–498.

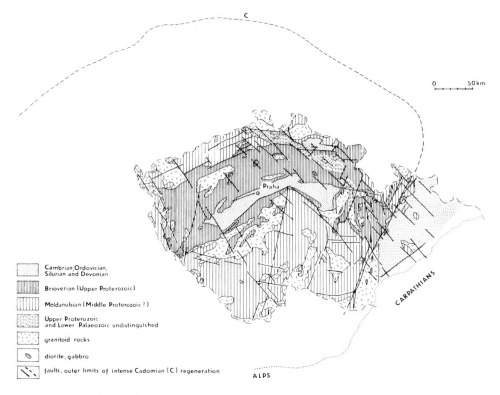

FIG. 2. Distribution of Precambrian and early Palaeozoic rocks in Czech territory (platform sediments removed). The distribution of these rocks in the entire Bohemian Massif has been shown by Chaloupský (1978).

verian rocks were intensely folded and metamorphosed during the Cadomian (Assyntian, Baikalian) orogeny. The initial closure of the Brioverian basin and the maximum metamorphic activity of the Cadomian cycle can be placed at about 650 Ma ago (the lower–upper Brioverian boundary). The final phases of deformation and emplacement of granites fall near the Proterozoic–Cambrian boundary.

Palaeozoic

Cadomian tectonics strongly reactivated the earlier systems of crustal weakness: deep-seated fault zones trending E–W, NE–SW, N–S and NW–SE. Palaeozoic basins developed along these zones, often near the Moldanubian–Brioverian boundary.

In the area of intense Cadomian regeneration, which encompasses the greater part of the Bohemian Massif (Variscan Internides), the Palaeozoic basins are relatively narrow and trend in various directions. In contrast, in the tectonic zones of the Cadomian foreland (Variscan Externides (Rheno–Hercynian and Moravo–Silesian zones)) the Palaeozoic basins are much larger with distinct polarity (Aubouin 1965, Dvořák 1968).

During the Variscan orogeny the sedimentary fill of the Palaeozoic basins was variably folded and in parts underwent regional metamorphism, mostly in greenschist-facies conditions. Variscan plutonic rocks underlie much of the elevated zone.

Caledonian folding

Caledonian events appear in the Bohemian Massif as a minor episode between the two main orogenic cycles—the Cadomian and the Variscan. The early Caledonian phase, roughly at the Cambrian–Ordovician boundary, is generally regarded as the last manifestation of the Cadomian orogeny, and the late Caledonian phase at the close of the Silurian to the middle Devonian is regarded as the onset of the Variscan orogeny.

It has been suggested that the NE part of the Bohemian Massif (Lugicum) represents an area of intense Caledonian metamorphism, folding and final consolidation (Kodym & Svoboda 1948, Stille 1951). This area was thought to be a part of the wide Caledonian orogenic belt stretching from the western margin of the E European Platform to the Scottish and Norwegian Caledonides. Most workers believe that the Lugicum is similar to the rest of the Bohemian Massif, i.e. an area where the Variscan orogeny was of primary importance and the Caledonian events involved mainly epeirogenic movements which resulted in hiatuses and facies changes. Caledonian radiometric changes obtained from polymetamorphic rocks are thought to give problematic mixed ages for which complete stratigraphic evidence is lacking (Mísař *et al.* 1982, Suk *et al.* 1984).

Slight early Caledonian deformation within the Bohemian Massif has been proved to be present in the early Palaeozoic basins of the Barrandian region, the Železné Hory Mountains, Lusatia and the Krkonoše Mountains (Svoboda *et al.* 1966, Havlíček 1981). Evidence of intense late Caledonian deformation associated with low-grade metamorphism has been found in the Krkonoše Mountains.

The Krkonoše Mountains

The Krkonoše Mountains (more accurately the Krkonoše–Jizerské Hory Mountains crystalline complex) lie in the NE part of the Bohemian Massif (Lugicum). The upper to middle? Brioverian and Lower and Middle Cambrian metasediments and greenschists, as well as the more abundant Upper Ordovician quartzites and fossiliferous Silurian phyllites with crystalline limestones, largely fill and cover the tectonic zone between the two higher-grade metamorphic Precambrian complexes, i.e. the Moldanubian and the lower Broverian (Figs 3 and 6). The preceding

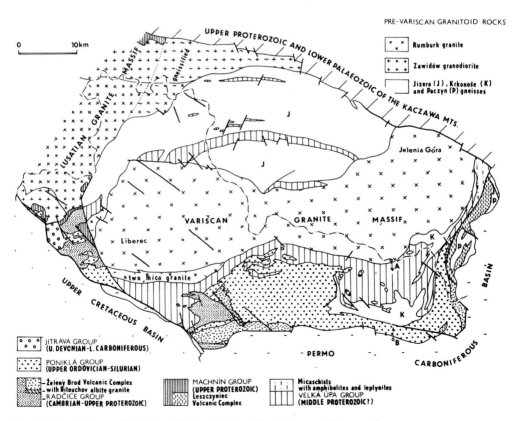

FIG. 3. Geological map of the Krkonoše–Jizerské Hory Mountains crystalline complex.

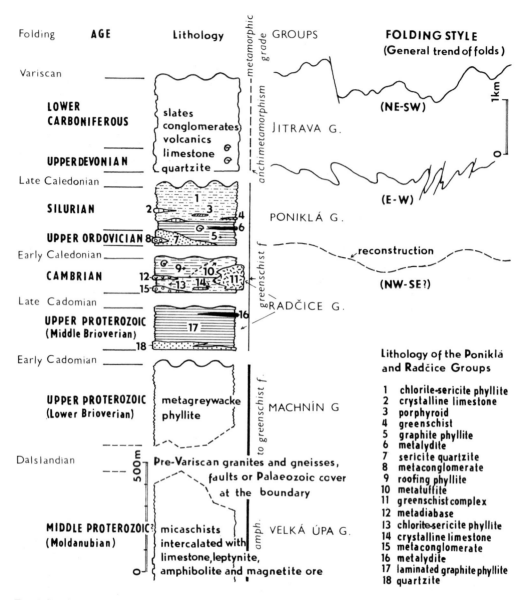

FIG. 4. Stratigraphic column for the Krkonoše–Jizerské Hory Mountains crystalline complex.

early Caledonian phase, between the Middle Cambrian and the Upper Ordovician, was responsible for only slight deformation. After deposition of Late Devonian–Early Carboniferous formations, final anchimetamorphic Variscan folding took place and a post-tectonic granite intruded into the core of the metamorphic complex (Fig. 5).

Two episodes of late Caledonian deformation have been distinguished in the Krkonoše Mountains area. Both occurred under greenschist-facies (mostly chlorite-grade) conditions.

The regional schistosity (axial planar to tight to isoclinal large folds) developed during the first deformation episode D_1 at the end of the Silurian or in the Lower Devonian. The orientation of the axes of the D_1 folds varies. It is partly influenced by right-lateral movements along the E–W to ESE–WNW trending deep-seated fault zones in the Precambrian basement. Similar zones of the

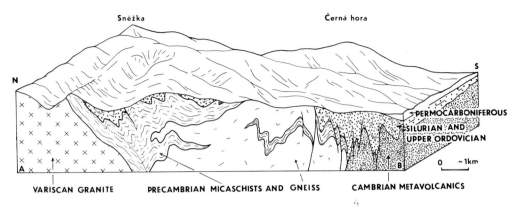

FIG. 5. Geological section of the Krkonoše Mountains.

established Caledonian deformation in other parts of Central Europe (the Ardennes, the Holy Cross Mountains and the Rügen-Pomorze zone (Fig. 1)) as well as in the Krkonoše Mountains can be correlated with the transform fault system of the Scottish and Norwegian Caledonides.

The regional schistosity was folded during the subsequent middle Devonian? D_2 deformation episode. The most common crenulation was almost invariably of E–W to ESE–WNW orientation (Fig. 6). The D_2 deformation episode ended before the regional blastesis of albite.

Both the D_2 deformation and the subsequent Variscan (Carboniferous) D_3 deformation may be predominantly products of the compression caused by the interacting Gondwana and already sutured Laurasia continents and minor blocks between them.

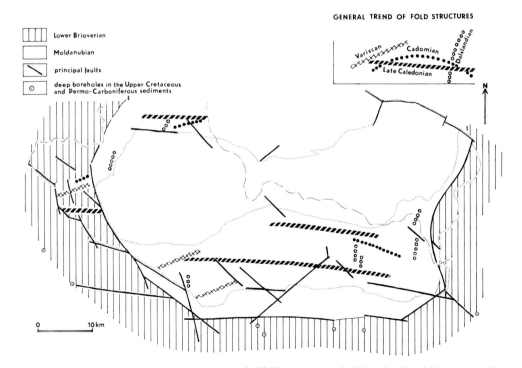

FIG. 6. Precambrian basement and the general trend of fold structures in the Krknoše–Jizerské Hory crystalline complex.

References

AUBOUIN, J. 1965. *Geosynclines*, Elsevier, Amsterdam.

CHALOUPSKÝ, J. 1978. The Precambrian tectogenesis in the Bohemian Massif. *Geologische Rundschau*, **67** (1), 72–90.

DUDEK, A. 1980. The crystalline basement block of the Outer Carpathians in Moravia: Bruno-Vistulicum. *Rozpravy Ceskoslovenske Akadamie Ved, Rada Matematickych a Prirodnich Ved*, **90** (8), 1–85.

DVOŘÁK, J. 1968. Tectogenesis of the Central European Variscides. *Vestnik Ustredniho Ustavu Geologickeho*, **43** (6), 465–71.

HAVLÍČEK, V. 1981. Development of a linear sedimentary depression exemplified by the Prague Basin (Ordovician–middle Devonian, Barrandian area—Central Bohemia). *Sbornik Geologickych Ved, Geologie*, **35**, 7–43.

KODYM, O. & SVOBODA, J. 1948. Kaledonská příkrovová stavba Krkonoš a Jizerských hor. *Sbornik Statniho Geologickeho Ustavu Ceskoslovenske Republiky*, **15**, 109–60.

MÍSAŘ, Z. *et al.* 1982. Regionální geologie Československa. *In*: *Geologie Českého Masivu*, Stát.pedagog. nakl., Prague.

STILLE, H. 1951. Das Mitteleuropaische variszische Grundgebirge im Bilde des gesamteuropaischen. *Geologisches Jahrbuch, Beihefte*, **2**, 138.

SUK, M. *et al.* 1984. Geological history of the territory of the Czech Socialist Republic. *Ustrednio Ustav Geologický*, Akademia, Prague.

SVOBODA, J. *et al.* 1966. Regional geology of Czechoslovakia, Part I, The Bohemian Massif. *Ustrednio Ustav Geologický*, Akademia, Prague.

J. CHALOUPSKÝ, Geological Survey of Czechoslovakia, Prague 1, Malostranské nám. 19, Czechoslovakia.

The third synthesis: Wenlock to mid-Devonian (end of Acadian orogeny)

Robert D. Hatcher Jr

SUMMARY: Major deformational–thermal events occurring during the Wenlock to mid-Devonian interval include the Acadian (N America, France, Spain) and the Scandian. These events are possibly related to the closing of the Iapetos Ocean between Laurentia and Baltica and the suturing of the Avalon microcontinent and other smaller terranes to N America. Metamorphism, plutonism and deformation during this interval resulted from the convergence events. Metamorphic grade and intensity of deformation vary spatially throughout the orogen. Both felsic (I-, S- and A-type granites) and mafic plutonism were abundant in N America in the Acadian, but Scandian metamorphism produced relatively little plutonism, most of which was felsic (I-type granites). Volcanic activity was restricted during this time, occurring in Scotland with substantial amounts in E Greenland, the Canadian Maritimes and New England with minor marine tholeiitic volcanism in SW England, France and Germany.

This paper consists of a summary of the events occurring in the Atlantic region from the Wenlock to mid-Devonian or the end of the Acadian orogeny (Fig. 1). This constitutes the mid-Palaeozoic series of events culminating in the Acadian and Scandian orogenies affecting N America and western Europe.

The purpose here is to present a summary of the different events affecting the mid-Atlantic region during middle Palaeozoic time which culminated with closing of the Iapetos Ocean and resulted in the formation of extensive mountain chains in Scandinavia in Early to Late Silurian time (the Scandes) and the Acadian mountains in eastern N America, the late Caledonian Mountains in Britain and their equivalents in western Europe (France, Iberia) during the Devonian (Fig. 2).

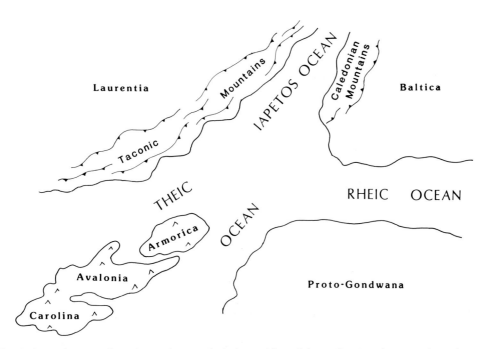

FIG. 1. Approximate configurations and assumed relative positions of the continents and oceans prior to the middle Palaeozoic events.

From HARRIS, A. L. & FETTES, D. J. (eds), 1988, *The Caledonian–Appalachian Orogen,*
Geological Society Special Publication No. 38, pp. 499–504.

499

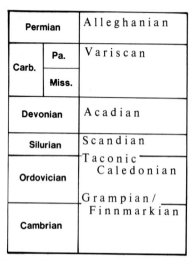

Permian		Alleghanian
Carb.	Pa.	Variscan
	Miss.	
Devonian		Acadian
Silurian		Scandian
Ordovician		Taconic ⎯⎯⎯ Caledonian
Cambrian		Grampian/ ⎯⎯ Finnmarkian

FIG. 2. Approximate times of occurrence of major orogenic events in the Appalachian–Caledonide–Variscan orogenic system during the Palaeozoic.

Attributes of mid-Palaeozoic orogenesis

The different elements which contribute to any summary of middle Palaeozoic orogenesis in the Atlantic region and provide the basis for interpretation should be summarized. Many of the data relating to this summary have been drawn from Thirwall, Robinson et al., Kent & Keppie, and Dallmeyer whose articles appear in this volume. Consequently, this synthesis has drawn extensively from information presented elsewhere in this volume, since it constitutes syntheses of more specific data and major ideas throughout the orogen.

Both the style and timing of deformation vary lengthwise along the orogenic belts. The style of deformation produced during the Scandian events in Scandinavia and E Greenland consists of continentward-vergent thrust faults carrying rocks of the internal portions of the orogen over rocks of the foreland (Haller 1971, Escher & Watt 1976, Gee & Wolff 1981). In many places, particularly in Scandinavia, basement rocks from the edge of the Precambrian continent were removed and transported inland as elements of thrust sheets directed toward the interiors of the continents. Transport ranges from relatively small amounts along the most continentward portions of the foreland to possibly hundreds of kilometres for the more internal thrusts (Gee 1978). Likewise, farther S during the Acadian orogeny, deformation occurred predominantly as thrusts and fold nappes and by strike-slip faulting

in southeastern New England and France. Deformation was brittle in a few areas, particularly those more proximal to the continental interior, and ductile towards the interior parts of the orogenic belt accompanying the increasing metamorphic grade (Hall & Robinson 1982).

Metamorphism was dominantly Barrovian over both the Scandian and Acadian orogens. However, there were areas where regional high temperature (Buchan) metamorphism has been identified locally in New England (Hall & Robinson 1982). Metamorphic grade varied considerably along strike in the Acadian orogen in N America from very low grade in northern New England to very high grade granulite facies in southern New England. In the southern and central Appalachians it is uncertain to what degree high-grade metamorphism can be attributed to the Acadian event (Glover et al. 1983), although some believe that the major event in the southern and central Appalachians may be Acadian (e.g. Odom et al. 1982). Scandian metamorphism was dominantly Barrovian but eclogite-facies assemblages occur along the westernmost edge of the exposed part of the orogen (Lappin & Smith 1978, Griffin & Brueckner 1980, Santallier 1983).

Both felsic and mafic plutonism were abundant in N America during the Acadian orogeny (Page 1968, Fullagar 1971, Clarke et al. 1980, Loiselle & Ayuso 1980). All types of granites are included as well as some intermediate and mafic rocks. Most of the relatively few Scandian plutons occur in Greenland and Scandinavia and are felsic I-type granites (Size 1979, Furnes et al. 1981). The latter may relate to the amount of orogen which is presently exposed in Scandinavia, whereas much more of the Acadian orogen in N America is exposed. It can be argued that Acadian plutonism and metamorphism both occur in the exposed portions of the orogen in Britain, Ireland and France. In Britain and Ireland, plutonism is I type N of the Iapetos suture, while it is dominantly S type S of the suture. High-grade metamorphism affected the rocks in the Massif Central and Vendee (Ters 1979, Santallier 1983) in France, in Iberia (Iglesias et al. 1983, Martinez-Garcia 1983) and in the Rhenohercynian massifs of Germany (Weber & Behr 1983).

Volcanic activity, most of which was calc-alkalic, was abundant in Scotland during this time-period (Thirlwall 1981). Apparently, this volcanism was related to subduction along the NW margin of the Iapetos Ocean. Volcanism also occurred in greater amounts in New England as the Traveller Rhyolite (Rankin 1968), in the Canadian Maritimes, and in smaller amounts in parts of western Europe (Thirlwall 1988).

Stratigraphic and faunal data provide abundant evidence of the appearance of a land mass, the Old Red Continent, in western Europe during the late Middle Devonian. Part of the evidence for this land mass is the extensive drainage system which existed along the southern margin of the Caledonian Mountains (Simon & Bluck 1982). A land mass also appeared at about the same time in central-eastern N America as a result of the Acadian orogeny, producing the extensive Catskill delta. Portions of the Old Red Sandstone in Norway were metamorphosed to greenschist-facies conditions indicating that sediments accumulated rapidly to considerable depths while the crust was still experiencing moderate to high heat flow conditions. Burial must have occurred very rapidly so that available heat could be utilized for metamorphism. The elevation of land masses above sea level provides evidence for the final closing of the Iapetos Ocean producing a much larger land area than had existed before during Phanerozoic time.

Results of mid-Palaeozoic orogeny

The Old Red Continent and the appearance of the Catskill delta in N America provided evidence for closing of the Iapetos Ocean and collision of N America with the Baltic continent to produce the supercontinent Laurussia (Fig. 3). Preceding collision was the final docking of Avalon to N America either in segments or as a single block. Uplift data from ^{40}Ar–^{39}Ar studies (Dallmeyer 1988) indicate that the closing of the Iapetos Ocean was diachronous since cooling ages systematically change, becoming younger from N to S. Timing of deformation and metamorphism may also support this conclusion.

The abrupt change in metamorphic grade in New England and in parts of the Canadian Maritimes from greenschist towards the N to very high-grade amphibolite- and granulite-facies assemblages farther S may reflect changes in the character of collision during the closing of the Iapetos Ocean. Closing may have occurred as a head-on collision process in southern New England, whereas in the Maritimes, except at the SW end of Nova Scotia and in northern New England, closing of the Ocean may have taken place by oblique collision (transpression). This event has also been used to explain the weak metamorphism in Britain (Thirlwall 1981). Evidence from metamorphism in France, Iberia and Africa is less conclusive of either direct or oblique collision. France and the rest of continental Europe may

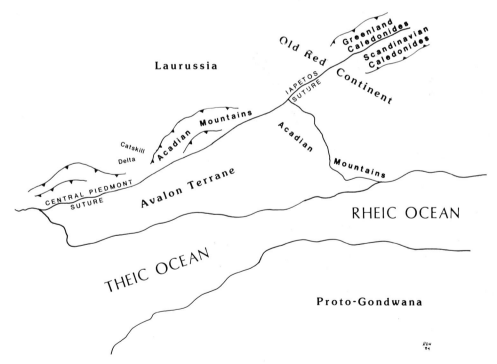

FIG. 3. Assumed configurations and relative positions of the continents following the Scandian and Acadian events.

have been a continental terrane at this time with the oceanic terranes located farther to the W.

Scandian collisional events in E Greenland and Scandinavia joined the northernmost parts of the Laurentian and Baltic cratons during the Late Silurian. The net result of later collision and final closing of Iapetos was the supercontinent Laurussia composed of European, African and N American elements. These may have experienced some readjustments following collision by strike-slip motion on major boundaries (Kent & Keppie 1988). It is uncertain whether major strike-slip motion occurred on particular boundaries in the southern Appalachian Piedmont because they formed early and were overprinted by metamorphism. If this metamorphism is Acadian, as some have speculated, the collision process would have terminated very early.

The mid-Palaeozoic history of the Avalon terrane provides some interesting constraints on the relative positions of the continents at this time. Kent & Opdyke (1978) and Kent (1982) suggested that the Avalon terrane had moved northward from 1 to 2000 km to the S and was accreted to N America during the Devonian or Early Carboniferous. Rocks and faunas of Avalonian affinities also occur in Wales, Brittany, Spain and Morocco (Fig. 4). Accretion of Avalonian elements to Africa and Europe may have occurred during the Carboniferous, but deformational overprinting relationships indicate that they too may have been accreted earlier (Rast & Skehan 1983). Without additional data we are left with a kind of paradox between an obvious exotic terrane of large proportions, palaeomagnetic data which indicate that Avalon had been transported from the S for thousands of kilometres and geological data which constrain the timing of accretion to an earlier period than that indicated by palaeomagnetic data. It is likely that

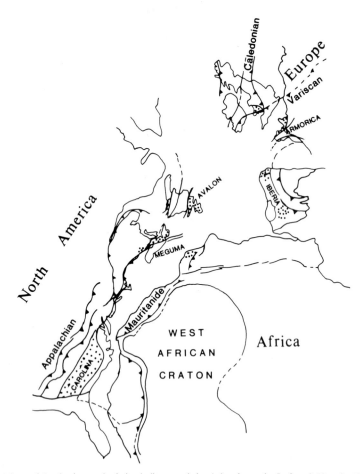

Fig. 4. Distributions of Avalonian rocks (stippled) around the Atlantic on the Lefort & Van der Voo (1979) reconstruction.

subduction followed by collision of Avalon with N America and parts of Europe is the ultimate cause of the Acadian orogeny, as suggested previously by Osberg (1978) and Hall & Robinson (1982). This paradox may further indicate that Avalon was not a single microcontinent but a collection of small volcanic arcs and continental fragments that formed at the same time but were accreted independently on both sides of the Atlantic.

There are fundamental differences between the Acadian and Scandian orogens. The Acadian orogen in N America is characterized by large-scale ductile folding and low- to high-grade metamorphism. It was accompanied by emplacement of many plutons throughout its length. Although it is not certain from present knowledge, the Acadian orogen in France and Iberia may exhibit many of the same characteristics. In contrast, the Scandian orogen is dominated by large far-travelled thrust sheets (which add to the Late Cambrian–Early Ordovician Finnmarkian stack). Few plutons were emplaced at this time and the metamorphic overprint may mark the only real principal similarity to the Acadian event, along with the early Acadian deformational phase.

Conclusions

1   The Wenlock to mid-Devonian, or slightly later, was a time of collision of a major composite exotic terrane and emergence of the continents in the Atlantic region.

2   The Acadian, like the Taconic and later Alleghanian–Variscan events, was a strongly diachronous event.

3   Contrasting orogenic styles are represented in the Acadian and Scandian orogens, indicating that somewhat different processes probably formed each orogen and that they were separated by significant distances when each event took place.

ACKNOWLEDGMENTS: Research related to the subject of this paper in the Appalachians has been supported by U.S. National Science Foundation Grants EAR-7911802, EAR 81-0852, EAR 82-06949 and EAR 84-12875. The IGCP-Caledonide Orogen Project (No. 27) has provided me with the opportunity to observe other segments of the Caledonide orogen and to meet many of those who have solved many of the problems, for which I will remain eternally grateful. The manuscript was improved by the comments of P. G. Andreasson, D. G. Gee, D. Santallier and M. F. Thirlwall. However, I remain responsible for any errors of fact or interpretation.

References

CLARKE, D. B., BARR, S. M. & DONOHOE, H. 1980. Granitoid and other plutonic rocks of Nova Scotia. *In*: WONES, D. R. (ed.) *The Caledonides in the USA: Proceedings of the International Geological Correlation Program–Caledonide Orogen Project 27, Blacksburg, VA. Department of Geological Sciences, Virginia Polytechnic Institute and State University, Memoir No. 2*, pp. 107–16.

DALLMEYER, R. D. 1988. Polyphase tectonothermal evolution of the Scandinavian Caledonides. *This volume.*

ESCHER, A. & WATT, W. S. 1976. *Geology of Greenland*, Geological Survey of Greenland, Copenhagen, 603 pp.

FULLAGAR, P. D. 1971. Age and origin of plutonic intrusions in the Piedmont of the southeastern Appalachians. *Geological Society of America Bulletin*, **82**, 2845–62.

FURNES, H., ROBINS, B., STEPHENS, M. B. & STURT, B. A. 1981. Igneous activity within the Scandinavian Caledonides. *Terra Cognita*, **1**, 43 (abstract).

GEE, D. G. 1978. Nappe displacement in the Scandinavian Caledonides. *Tectonophysics*, **47**, 393–419.

—— & WOLFF, F. C. 1981. Central Scandinavian Caledonides—Ostersund to Trondheim. *International Geological Correlation Program—Caledonide Orogen Project 27, Uppsala Caledonide Symposium, Excursion A2 Guidebook*, 85 pp. Geological Survey of Sweden.

GLOVER, LYNN, III, SPEER, ALEXANDER, RUSSELL, G. S. & FARRAR, S. S., 1983. Ages of regional metamorphism and ductile deformation in the central and southern Appalachians. *Lithos*, **16**, 223–45.

GRIFFIN, W. L. & BRUECKNER, H. K. 1980. Caledonian Sm–Nd ages and a crustal origin for Norwegian eclogites. *Nature, London*, **285**, 319–21.

HALL, L. M. & ROBINSON, P. 1982. Stratigraphic–tectonic subdivisions of southern New England. *In*: ST. JULIEN, P. & BELAND, J. (eds) *Major Structural Zones of the Northern Appalachians. Geological Association of Canada Special Paper No. 24*, pp. 15–41.

HALLER, J. 1971. *Geology of the East Greenland Caledonides*, Wiley-Interscience, New York, 413 pp.

IGLESIAS, M., RIBEIRO, M. L. & RIBEIRO, A. 1983. La interpretacion aloctonista de la estructura del Noroeste peninsula. *In: Geologia de Espana*, pp. 459–67, IGME, Madrid.

KENT, D. V. 1982. Paleomagnetic evidence for post-Devonian displacement of the Avalon platform (Newfoundland). *Journal of Geophysical Research*, **87**, 8709–16.

—— & KEPPIE, J. D. 1988. Silurian–Permian palaeocontinental reconstructions and circum-Atlantic tectonics. *This volume.*

—— & OPDYKE, N. D. 1978. Paleomagnetism of the

Devonian Catskill red beds: evidence for motion of the coastal New England–Canadian Maritime region relative to cratonic North America. *Journal of Geophysical Research*, **83**, 4441–50.

LAPPIN, M. A. & SMITH, D. C. 1978. Mantle-equilibrated orthopyroxene eclogite pods from the basal gneisses in the Selje district, western Norway. *Journal of Petrology*, **19**, 530–84.

LEFORT, J. P. & VAN DER VOO, R. 1979. A kinematic model for the collision and complete suturing between Gondwanaland and Laurussia in the Carboniferous. *Journal of Geology*, **89**, 537–50.

LOISELLE, M. C. & AYUSO, R. A. 1980. Geochemical characteristics of granitoids across the Merrimack synclinorium, eastern and central Maine. *In*: WONES, D. R. (ed.) *The Caledonides in the USA. Proceedings of the International Geological Correlation Program–Caledonide Orogen Project 27, Blacksburg, VA. Department of Geological Sciences, Virginia Polytechnic Institute and State University, Memoir No. 2*, pp. 117–21.

MARTINEZ-GARCIA, E. 1983. Pre-Hercynian tectonic events and geological evolution of the northwestern Iberian Penninsula. *International Geological Correlation Program–Caledonide Orogen Project 27, Symposium de Rabat Resumé des Communications*, p. 32, Service Géologique du Maroc.

ODOM, A. L., HATCHER, R. D. & HOOPER, R. J. 1982. A pre-metamorphic tectonic boundary between contrasting Appalachian basements, southern Georgia Piedmont. *Geological Society of America Abstracts with Programs*, **14**, 579.

OSBERG, P. H. 1978. Synthesis of the geology of the northeastern Appalachians, U.S.A. *In*: TOZER, E. T. & SCHENK, P. E. (eds) *Geological Survey of Canada Paper 78-13*, pp. 137–48.

PAGE, L. R. 1968. Devonian plutonic rocks in New England. *In*: ZEN, E-AN, WHITE, W. S., HADLEY, J. B. & THOMPSON, J. R. Jr. (eds) *Studies in Appalachian Geology: Northern and Maritime*, pp. 371–83, Wiley-Interscience, New York.

RANKIN, D. W. 1968. Volcanism related to tectonism in the Piscataquis volcanic belt: an island arc of early Devonian age in North-central Maine. *In*: ZEN, E-AN, WHITE, W. S., HADLEY, J. B. & THOMPSON, J. B., Jr. (eds) *Studies in Appalachian Geology: Northern and Maritime*, pp. 355–83, Wiley-Interscience, New York.

RAST, N. & SKEHAN, J. W. 1983. The evolution of the Avalonian plate. *Tectonophysics*, **100**, 257–86.

SANTALLIER, D. S. 1983. Main metamorphic features of the Paleozoic orogen in France. *In*: SCHENK, P. E. (ed.) *Regional Trends in the Geology of the Appalachian–Caledonian–Hercynian–Mauritanide Orogen. NATO-ASI Series C Mathematics and Physical Science*, Vol. 116, pp. 263–74, Reidel, Dordrecht.

SIMON, J. B. & BLUCK, B. J. 1982. Paleodrainage of the southern margin of the Caledonian mountain chain in the northern British Isles. *Transactions of the Royal Society of Edinburgh, Earth Sciences*, **73**, 11–15.

SIZE, W. B. 1979. Petrology, geochemistry and genesis of the type area trondhjemite in the Trondheim region, central Norwegian Caledonides. *Norges Geologiske Undersökelse Bulletin*, **51**, 51–7.

TERS, M. 1979. Les synclinoriums paléozoiques et le Précambrien sur la façade occidentale du Massif vendeen stratigraphie et structure. *Bulletin BRGM (2nd Series), Section 1, No. 4*, pp. 293–301.

THIRLWALL, M. F. 1981. Implications for Caledonian plate tectonic models of chemical data from volcanic rocks of the British Old Red sandstone. *Journal of the Geological Society, London*, **138**, 123–38.

—— 1988. Wenlock to mid-Devonian volcanism of the Caledonian–Appalachian orogen. *This volume*.

WEBER, K. & BEHR, H.-J. 1983. Geodynamic interpretation of the mid-European Variscides. *In*: MARTIN, H. & EDEN, F. W. (eds) *Intracontinental Fold Belts: Case Studies in the Variscan Belt of Europe and the Damara Belt in Namibia*, pp. 427–68, Springer, Berlin.

R. D. HATCHER JR, Department of Geological Sciences, University of Tennessee, Knoxville, TN 37996–0140, USA.

Mid-Devonian–Permian Activity in the Caledonian–Appalachian Orogen

CONVENOR
JOHN RODGERS
Yale University

Basement–cover relationships in the Appalachian–Caledonian–Variscan orogen: mid-Devonian (end of Acadian orogeny) to end of Permian

Robert D. Hatcher Jr

SUMMARY: The Alleghanian–Variscan orogen was, in part, superimposed upon continental crust produced by earlier Palaeozoic orogenies from continental platform and slope and rise sediments volcanic rocks, together with island arcs, rift volcanic rocks and sediments from diverse sources and older Precambrian basement. The effects of the Alleghanian–Variscan orogeny are particularly marked in the southern half of the Palaeozoic mountain chains of N American and western Europe. The Alleghanian–Variscan event(s) produced both ductile and brittle deformation involving folding and faulting (both thrust and strike-slip). Movement along many of these faults produced large displacements of the order of tens to hundreds of kilometres. Large-scale transport on thrusts in the southern and central Appalachians and NW and W Africa (Mauritanides) probably resulted from collision related to final closing of the Theic Ocean. Dominant thrust transport in the southern and central Appalachians contrasts with dominant large-scale strike-slip motion in the Maritime Appalachians of Canada and transpressive motion in the Variscides of western Europe. The character of Variscan deformation in Europe suggests that the orientation of boundary stresses there was somewhat different from those in N America. Late Palaeozoic thrusting in southeastern N America and northwestern Africa suggests that collision was normal there but it may have been oblique in western Europe. However, thrusting occurs along both the northern (Ireland, Wales, Belgium) and southern (France, Iberia) flanks of the Variscan orogen in western Europe. Large-scale over-thrusting of basement and cover rocks in the Rheinisches Schiefergebirge has also been suggested. The basement appears to have responded homogeneously in large domains with major differences in style related in part to stress orientation.

One of the products of the orogenic process is an increase in the amount of continental crust, resulting through time in an areal increase in the sizes of continents. The process is accomplished by accretion of island arcs, oceanic debris and other exotic fragments, so that 'cratonization' occurs by intrusion of mostly granitoid plutons, metamorphism and deformation of non-continental materials. Continental basement from previous cycles may also be reactivated and incorporated into new orogenic cycles. The earlier Taconic and Acadian orogenies in the Appalachians converted a large volume of continental platform, slope and rise sediments/volcanic rocks, and other volcanic materials and diverse sediments into sialic crust through deformation and metamorphism. These were intruded by numerous S- and I-type plutons. Both the Taconic and Acadian events, along with the Alleghanian–Variscan, reactivated and incorporated masses of older Precambrian basement into the deforming orogen along with younger materials which had been formed during the earlier orogenies.

The purpose of this paper is to examine the effects of the process of cratonization as it was manifested in the late Palaeozoic orogenies affecting the rocks and continents on each side of the present Atlantic Ocean. It is appropriate to consider this process here because the result of cratonization was the largest known supercontinent, Pangaea, which formed in the late Palaeozoic as a result of plate motion, accretion and continent–continent collision. The presumed collisional events which resulted in the Alleghanian and Variscan–Hercynian orogenies were produced by the closing of the Theic–Rheic Ocean and the collision of Gondwana with Laurussia resulting in assembling of the supercontinent of Pangaea (Fig. 1).

Character of Alleghanian–Variscan deformation and basement involvement

Alleghanian medium- to high-grade metamorphism, penetrative deformation and plutonism in N America were largely restricted to the eastern exposed margin of the Appalachian orogen. However, Alleghanian brittle deformation (possibly produced by collision between N America

From HARRIS, A. L. & FETTES, D. J. (eds), 1988, *The Caledonian–Appalachian Orogen,* Geological Society Special Publication No. 38, pp. 507–514.

A. PERMIAN   B. LATE DEVONIAN   C. EARLY SILURIAN

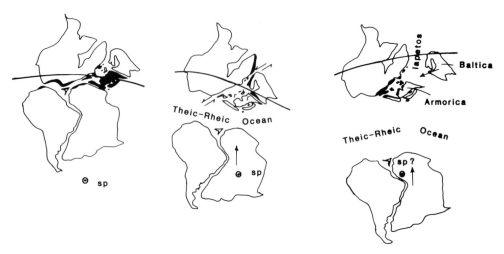

F IG. 1. Configurations of the continents in the Atlantic region through the mid to late Palaeozoic: black areas indicate orogenic terranes; sp, S pole. (Modified from Van der Voo 1983.)

and Africa) produced a detachment in the southern and central Appalachians that propagated through the crust which had been formed during earlier orogenies and into the foreland cover as a large complex wedge of thin-skinned crystalline and foreland thrusts (Fig. 2). Differences in interpretation exist regarding the eastward extent of this thrust complex (Hatcher & Zietz 1978, 1980, Cook *et al.* 1979, Harris & Bayer 1979, Iverson & Smithson 1982).

In the southern and central Appalachian Blue Ridge, Alleghanian and older crystalline/cover thrusts merge at depth with the main detachment and transport internal zone rocks over the largely unmetamorphosed cover of the Valley and Ridge. Farther E, the Brevard fault zone was reactivated as an Alleghanian brittle structure. Brevard faults cut earlier possible Alleghanian thrusts in the Piedmont and eastern Blue Ridge as indicated by preliminary results of ^{40}Ar/^{39}Ar studies (Dall-meyer & Hatcher 1985).

Large ductile faults, including the Modoc–Nutbush Creek, Augusta, and Hylas in the eastern Piedmont, with small to moderate displacements cut through the Piedmont block on the flanks of the Kiokee–Raleigh high-grade metamorphic core of Alleghanian deformation in the southern and central Appalachians (Hatcher *et al.* 1977, Bobyarchick & Glover 1979, Snoke *et al.* 1980).

The Narrangansett Basin in New England (Fig. 3) developed initially as a rhombochasm

(Mosher 1983) and then was penetratively deformed and metamorphosed in a larger transpressional realm where southwestward-directed compression gave way to dextral strike-slip faults farther N (involving the Cobequid, Chedabucto and Cabot faults). The latter reflect transition from head-on to oblique or rotating collision from S to N, and to some degree reflect the transition from a more characteristic western European strike-slip style of deformation to the southeastern N American compressional style, no doubt reflecting oblique to head-on collision. Recent geochronological studies (O'Hara & Gromet 1983) suggest that the Lake Char–Honey Hill fault in southeastern New England is also an Alleghanian structure. It may have been an E vergent normal despite its gentle W dip (Goldstein 1982). Rast & Grant (1973) concluded that the Variscan front in southern New Brunswick is a compressional feature resulting from dip-slip transport towards the continental interior.

In western Europe and northwestern Africa the style of deformation varied considerably during the Variscan event (Fig. 4). Large-scale strike-slip displacements occur in the southern and central parts of western Europe in the S Armorican fault zone, the Bay of Biscay fault and the Agadir (Sud Atlas) fault in Morocco. All may have formed at this time as major strike-slip features. However, along the northern flank of the Variscan fold belt in southern Ireland, Britain and northwestern central Europe, the rocks have

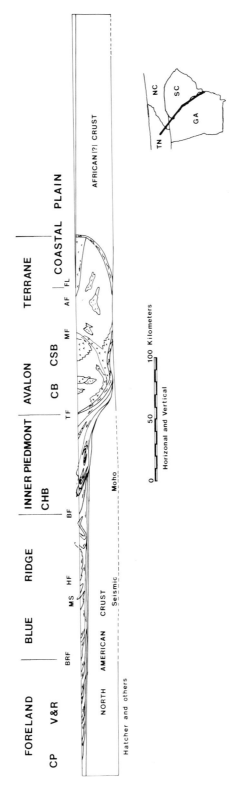

FIG. 2. Cross-section through the southern Appalachians showing the large detachment and major boundaries within the thrust sheet: CP, Cumberland Plateau; V&R, Valley and Ridge; BRF, Blue Ridge fault; MS, Murphy syncline; HF, Hayesville fault; BF, Brevard fault; CHB, Chauga belt; TF, Towaliga fault; CB, Charlotte belt; CSB, Carolina State belt; MF, Modoc fault; AF, Augusta fault; FL, Fall line.

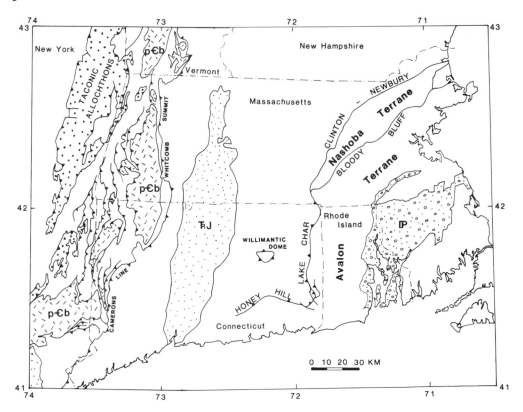

FIG. 3. Map of southern New England showing the distribution of major faults: **p-€b**, Grenville basement; **℗**, Pennsylvanian sedimentary rocks of the Narragansett Basin; **ℝJ**, Triassic–Jurassic sedimentary rocks.

been overthrust and folded, indicating direct compression (Ziegler 1979). Thrusting also occurred along the northern edge in the Rheinisches Schiefergebirge (Weber & Behr 1983) and is present in northern France and southwestern Portugal. Thrusting also occurs along the southern flanks of the Hercynian orogen in western Europe (France and Spain) (Ziegler 1979).

Basement involvement in the Massif Central in France resulted in S–SW-directed emplacement by thrusting of about 540 Ma old upper-amphibolite- and granulite-facies lower palaeozoic rocks onto the platform rocks of southern Europe which were metamorphosed to amphibolite-facies conditions during the Variscan events (Burg et al. 1984). In contrast, NW-directed thrusting and basement reactivation occurred in the Rheinisches Schiefergebirge during the Variscan events where metamorphism of late Precambrian? to Ordovician sedimentary rocks produced greenschist- to lower-amphibolite-grade assemblages, where in the Saxothurin-gian and Moldanubian zones higher-grade conditions, resulting in basement reactivation and even anatectic melting, were reached (Weber 1984).

Metamorphism and plutonism (described in other papers in this book) accompanied the Variscan deformation. Alleghanian plutons are abundant and well preserved in both the southern and central Appalachians and New England. They are also well known in NW Africa and the Variscan domain in western central Europe. Metamorphism related to the Alleghanian–Variscan orogeny is more restricted in N America, being confined to the eastern part of the Piedmont in the Kiokee–Raleigh belt and to small areas in southeastern New England and southern New Brunswick. It is more widespread in western Europe where high- or medium-grade metamorphic rocks have been identified. However, much of the metamorphism previously associated with the Variscan event in western France may actually be Acadian (Ters 1979).

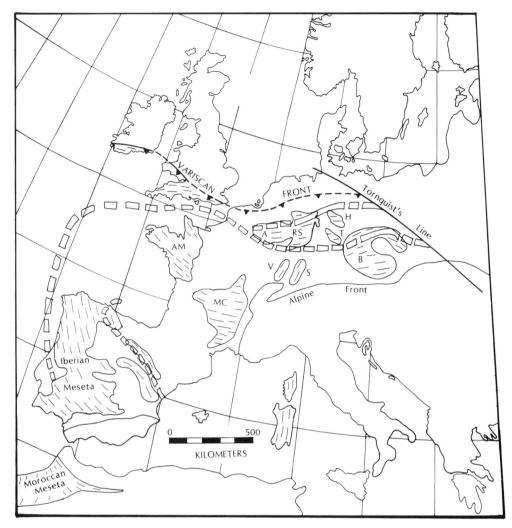

FIG. 4. Distribution of Variscan elements in western Europe and NW Morocco (lines indicate approximate dominant structural trends): AM, Armorican Massif; MC, Massif Central; V, Vosges Massif; S, Schwarzwald; B, Bohemian Massif; A, Ardennes; R, Rheinisches Shiefergebirge; H, Harz Massif; T, Thuringian Massif. (Modified from Ziegler 1979, Engel & Franke 1984.)

Basement involvement

The character of basement involvement varies from place to place within the Alleghanian–Variscan orogen. Large-scale overthrusting of basement and cover rocks occurs in the southern and central Appalachians and in parts of the Variscan orogen in Europe. In other parts of the orogen, such as New England, the Canadian Maritimes and parts of France and Iberia, the character of basement interaction is quite different and involves the development of strike-slip faults.

The nature of basement and basement–cover interaction throughout the Alleghanian–Variscan orogen appears to be only partially related to the character of the basement, the thickness and character of cover materials, and the orientations of boundary stresses which produced the deformation. Moreover, the amount of transport on both thrust and strike-slip faults appears to be primarily related to the shapes of the colliding blocks and the amount of displacement taken up in penetrative strain within the different blocks. An even more inaccessible quantity is the relationship of displacement on faults and basement interaction to the amount of absolute plate motion.

Palaeozoic cratonization process

The assembly of the supercontinent of Pangaea resulted from closure of the various Palaeozoic oceans during the consequent suturing of America, Eurasia and Africa. Nevertheless, attempts to reassemble the continents around the Atlantic into a supercontinent such as Pangaea (Lefort & Van der Voo 1979, Morel & Irving 1981, Van der Voo 1983) produce several inconsistencies, which is evidence of our fragmentary knowledge of the history of the orogens that record this history.

Even so, several facts regarding continental evolution during the Palaeozoic are clear. The process of cratonization through the generation, remobilization, transfer and accretion of continental crust occurred episodically throughout the Palaeozoic, as it had earlier during the Proterozoic. Gastil (1960) first recognized this in N America and suggested that continental growth had occurred by the addition of successively younger orogens to the continental margins. Osberg (1978) suggested that 'basement' terranes of different types were accreted to the N American margin in New England during the Taconic and Acadian orogenies. The evolution of basement massifs in the Appalachians was considered by Hatcher (1983). The process of cratonization

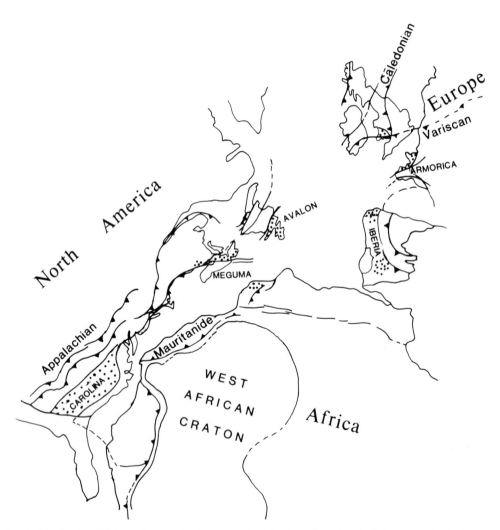

FIG. 5. Distribution of Palaeozoic orogenic elements in the Atlantic region: the stippled areas are Avalonian rocks. (Modified from Lefort & Van der Voo 1979.)

resulted in the addition of some new material, perhaps as much as a crustal zone 400–500 km wide added to eastern N America during the Palaeozoic orogenies (Fig. 5). Comparable amounts of new continental crust were probably added to Europe. While the net result of cratonization appears simple, the paths by which this is accomplished are difficult and complex. The Palaeozoic orogens serve as excellent examples to illustrate the complexity of the process. Thermally and mechanically driven processes produced an asemblage of ductile and brittle structures, metamorphism and plutonism, with attendant basement reactivation from each previous cycle. During this process at least three oceans (Iapetos, the Theic and the Rheic) were generated and then closed, and any intervening fragments were swept into the accreting mass. The final result was the supercontinent Pangaea which, perhaps because of its size, soon began to break apart in the later Triassic as the present Atlantic Ocean began to form, producing orogenic activity on the leading distal margins of the continents.

Conclusions

1 'Basement' materials from the earlier Palaeozoic orogenies were reactivated during the Alleghanian–Variscan orogeny as elements in the different kinds of ductile and brittle deformation that produced both dip-slip and strike-slip displacements of tens to hundreds of kilometres.
2 The character of deformation that dominated in northwestern Europe (strike-slip) compared with that in central and southern N America and central W Africa (thrust) suggests that oblique collision occurred in the N and head-on collision occurred in the S.
3 The crust within large domains reacted homogeneously with respect to boundary-stress orientations during the Alleghanian–Variscan without regard for pre-existing structures of any size.
4 The process of basement reactivation was accompanied by metamorphism and plutonic activity in each major segment of the Alleghanian–Variscan orogen. However, these phenomena were not pervasive throughout each segment.
5 Basement reactivation associated with the process of cratonization is a complex process despite its seeming simplicity.

ACKNOWLEDGMENTS: Research support for study of basement reactivation processes has been provided by the U.S. National Science Foundation (Grants EAR-8018507, EAR-810852 and EAR 8206949). Considerable improvement in the manuscript resulted from review and comments by P. H. Osberg, John Rodgers and an anonymous reviewer. However, I remain responsible for all errors of fact or interpretation.

References

BOBYARCHICK, A. R. & GLOVER, L. III 1979. Deformation and metamorphism in the Hylas zone and adjacent parts of the eastern Piedmont in Virginia. *Geological Society of America Bulletin,* **90**, 739–52.

BURG, J. P., LEYRELOUP, A., MARCHAND, J. & MATTE, PH. 1984. Inverted metamorphic zonation and large-scale thrusting in the Variscan belt: an example in the French Massif Central. *In:* HUTTON D. W. H. & SANDERSON, D. J. (eds) *Variscan Tectonics of the North Atlantic. Special Publication of the Geological Society of London No. 14,* pp. 47–61.

COOK, F. A., ALBAUGH, D. S., BROWN, L. D., KAUFMAN, S., OLIVER, J. E. & HATCHER, R. D. 1979. Thin-skinned tectonics in the crystalline southern Appalachians: COCORP seismic-reflection profiling of the Blue Ridge and Piedmont. *Geology,* **7**, 563–7.

DALLMEYER, R. D. & HATCHER, R. D., JR 1985. The Alto allochthon: Part 2, Geochronological constraints on tectonothermal evolution. *Geological Society of America Abstracts with Programs,* **17**, 86.

ENGEL, W. & FRANKE, W. 1984. Flysch sedimentation: its relation to tectonism in the European Variscides. *In:* MARTIN, H. & EDER, F. W. (eds) *Intracontinental Foldbelts,* pp. 289–321, Springer-Verlag, Berlin.

GASTIL, G. 1960. The distribution of mineral dates in space and time. *American Journal of Science,* **258**, 1–35.

GOLDSTEIN, A. G. 1982. Geometry and kinematics of ductile faulting in a portion of the Lake Char mylonite zones, Massachusetts and Connecticut. *American Journal of Science,* **282**, 1378–405.

HARRIS, L. D. & BAYER, K. C. 1979. Sequential development of the Appalachian orogen above a master decollement—a hypothesis. *Geology,* **7**, 568–72.

HATCHER, R. D., JR 1983. Basement massifs in the Appalachians: their role in deformation during the Appalachian orogenies. *Geological Journal,* **18**, 255–65.

—— & ZIETZ, I. 1978. Thin crystalline thrust sheets in the southern Appalachian Inner Piedmont and Blue Ridge: interpretation based upon regional aeromagnetic data. *Geological Society of America Abstracts with Programs,* **10**, 417.

—— & —— 1980. Tectonic implications of regional

aeromagnetic and gravity data from the southern Appalachians. *In:* WONES, D. R. (ed) *The Caledonides in the USA: Proceedings of the International Geological Correlation Program—Caledonide Orogen Project 27, Blacksburg, VA. Department of Geological Sciences, Virginia Polytechnic Institute and State University, Memoir No. 2,* pp. 235–44.

——, HOWELL, D. E., TALWANI, P. & ZIETZ, I. 1977. Eastern Piedmont fault system: some speculations on its extent. *Geology,* **5,** 636–40.

IVERSON, W. P. & SMITHSON, J. B. 1982. Master decollement root zone beneath southern Appalachians and crustal balance. *Geology,* **10,** 241–5.

LEFORT, J. P. & VAN DER VOO, R. 1979. A kinematic model for the collision and complete suturing between Gondwanaland and Laurussia in the Carboniferous. *Journal of Geology,* **89,** 537–50.

MOREL, P. & IRVING, E. 1981. Palaeomagnetism and the evolution of Pangaea. *Journal of Geophysical Research,* **86,** 1858–72.

MOSHER, S. 1983. Kinematic history of the Narragansett Basin, Massachusetts and Rhode Island: constraints on late Paleozoic plate reconstruction. *Tectonics,* **2,** 327–44.

O'HARA, K. D. & GROMET, P. L. 1983. Textural and Rb–Sr isotopic evidence for late Paleozoic mylonitization within the Honey Hill fault zone, southeastern Connecticut. *American Journal of Science,* **283,** 762–99.

OSBERG, P. H. 1978. Synthesis of the geology of the northeastern Appalachians, U.S.A. *In:* TOZER, E. T. & SCHENK, P. E. (eds) *Geological Survey of Canada Paper No. 78-13,* pp. 137–48.

RAST, N. & GRANT, R. 1973. Transatlantic correlation of the Variscan–Appalachian orogen. *American Journal of Science,* **273,** 572–9.

SNOKE, A. W., KISH, S. A. & SECOR, D. T., JR 1980. Deformed Hercynian granitic rocks from the Piedmont of South Carolina. *American Journal of Science,* **280,** 1019–34.

TERS, M. 1979. Les synclinoriums Paléozoiques et le Précambrien sur la façade occidentale du Massif vendéen: Stratigraphie et structure. *Bulletin du Bureau de Recherches Géologiques et Minières (France), Section 1,* No. 4, 292–301.

VAN DER VOO, R. 1983. A plate tectonic model for the Paleozoic assembly of Pangaea based on paleomagnetic data. *In:* HATCHER, R. D., JR, WILLIAMS, H. & ZIETZ, I. (eds) *Contributions to the Tectonics and Geophysics of Mountain Chains. Geological Society of America Memoir No. 158,* pp. 19–23.

WEBER, K. 1984. Variscan events: early Palaeozoic continental rift metamorphism and late Palaeozoic crustal shortening. *In:* HUTTON, D. W. H. & SANDERSON, D. J. (eds) *Variscan Tectonics of the North Atlantic Region. Geological Society of London Special Publication No. 14,* pp. 3–22.

—— & BEHR, H.-J. 1983. Geodynamic interpretation of the mid-European Variscides. *In:* MARTIN, H. & EDER F. W. (eds) *Intracontinental Fold Belts: Case Studies in the Variscan Belt of Europe and the Damara Belt in Namibia,* pp. 427–68, Springer-Verlag, New York.

ZIEGLER, P. A. 1979. Northwestern Europe: tectonics and basin development. *Geologie en Mijnbouw,* **57,** 589–626.

R. D. HATCHER, JR, Department of Geology, University of South Carolina, Columbia, SC 29208, USA. *Present address:* Department of Geological Sciences, University of Tennessee, Knoxville, TN 37996-0140, USA.

Late Palaeozoic sedimentation along the Appalachian orogen

William A. Thomas & Paul E. Schenk

SUMMARY: The sedimentological framework of post-Early Devonian strata in the Appalachians includes two different domains. S of the New York recess in the foreland fold–thrust belt, clastic wedges of two different ages (Devonian–Early Mississippian and Late Mississippian–Pennsylvanian) constitute the sedimentological record of the Acadian and Alleghanian orogenies. The widespread semicircular clastic wedges prograded cratonward across broad foreland basins from orogenic provenances. Distribution of siliciclastic sediments suggests a genetic relation to large-scale curves (salients and recesses) of the orogenic belt and indicates variation in time of orogeny along strike. N of the New York recess in the more interior part of the orogen, Devonian to Permian siliciclastic sediments derived from local fault-block uplifts filled and overflowed pull-apart basins associated with mainly dextral wrench faults. The history of sediment supply and deposition varies from basin to basin. Parts of the northern domain are covered by more widespread siliciclastic sediments. Differences in the two domains reflect not only variation along strike in time of orogeny but also a range of structural style from large-scale cratonward thrusting in the S to wrench faulting in the N.

Clastic sedimentary rocks of Devonian to Permian ages record the Acadian and Alleghanian phases of Appalachian orogenic history. Studies of thickness, composition, dispersal patterns and depositional systems provide for interpretation of location and tectonic setting of sediment sources and depositional basins. Evolution of the tectonic elements is recorded in the ages of sedimentary units.

The trace of the Appalachian orogenic belt describes a series of large-scale sinuous curves: salients, which are convex toward the craton; and recesses, which are concave toward the craton (Fig. 1). In foreland basins on the eastern part of the N American craton and within the foreland fold–thrust belt S of the New York recess the sedimentological record of the Acadian and Alleghanian orogenies is contained in large-scale clastic wedges of sediment derived from orogenic provenances. Clastic wedges, broadly semicircular in shape, thin and in part grade to carbonate facies both toward the craton and along Appalachian strike (King 1959, Thomas 1977). N of the New York recess, where no late Palaeozoic clastic wedges are preserved in the Appalachian foreland, fault-bounded basins within the orogenic belt are filled with late Palaeozoic clastic sediments.

Appalachian clastic wedges

Catskill–Pocono clastic wedge

The Devonian–Mississippian Catskill–Pocono clastic wedge ranges in age from Siegenian to Viséan. Regional thickness and facies distribution patterns are semicircular and are centred on the Pennsylvania salient (Figs 2 and 3). Local variations reflect syn-sedimentary structures and separate delta lobes (Cooper 1964, Dennison 1985).

The Devonian succession, the classic 'Catskill delta' (see summary volume edited by Woodrow & Sevon (1985)), grades upward from deep-water black shales, through shallow-marine sandstones and shales to deltaic and fluvial red beds (Fig. 2) (Oliver et al. 1967, McIver 1970, Meckel 1970, Dennison 1985). These facies prograde both northwestward towards the craton and southwestward along structural strike. Palaeocurrent data indicate transport from the ESE and from the ENE in the northern part of the wedge (Fig. 3) (Burtner 1963). Clastic sediment distribution and separate delta lobes (Fig. 3) (Willard 1934) indicate a southwestward shift to younger sites of sediment input as a result of along-strike diachroneity of orogeny in the provenance (Dennison 1985, Ettensohn 1985). Distributions of thickness and facies suggest a dominant sediment supply from SE of the Pennsylvania salient and a secondary supply from the NE (Fig. 3). Sediment composition indicates a source terrain of low-grade metamorphic rocks as well as sedimentary and volcanic rocks (Allen & Friend 1968, Sevon 1985).

For the Mississippian rocks in the Pennsylvania salient, palaeocurrent data, pebble-size distribution and sand-to-shale ratio mapping indicate dispersal to the NW and W (Fig. 3), and sandstone petrography indicates a source terrain of sedimentary and low-grade metamorphic rocks (Pel-

From HARRIS, A. L. & FETTES, D. J. (eds), 1988, *The Caledonian–Appalachian Orogen,*
Geological Society Special Publication No. 38, pp. 515–530.

515

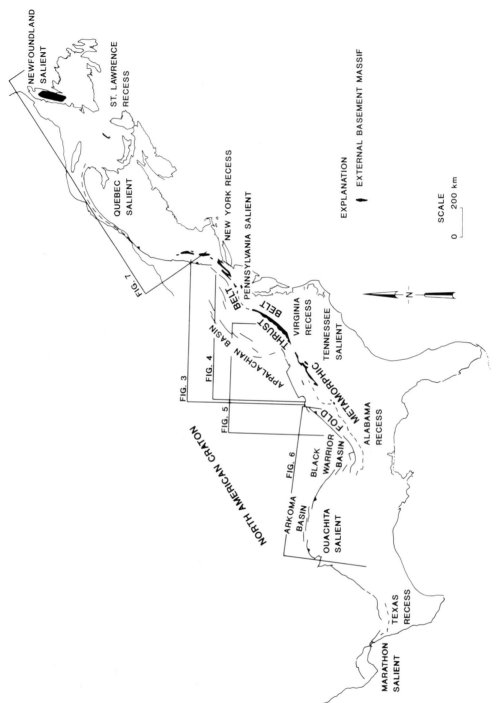

FIG. 1. Map of Appalachian orogen in N America. Location map of Figs 3–7.

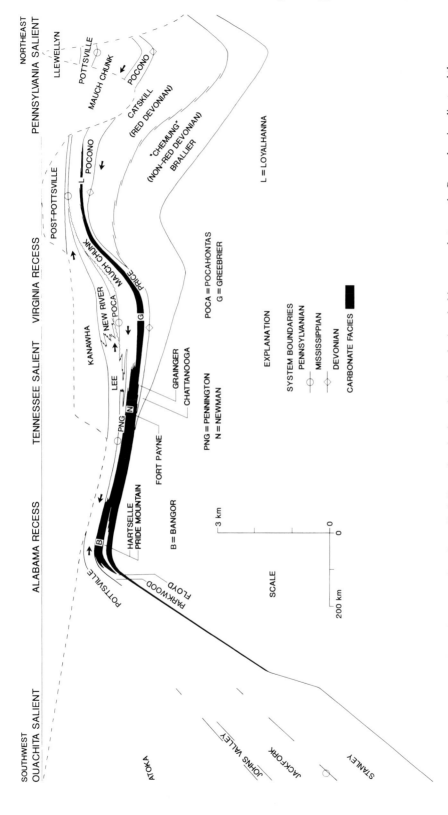

FIG. 2. Diagrammatic stratigraphic cross section of post-Early Devonian clastic wedges along the Appalachian orogen between the Pennsylvania salient and the Ouachita salient. The broken line at the top of the cross section shows the level of post-Palaeozoic erosion. The arrows show the direction of progradation within clastic facies.

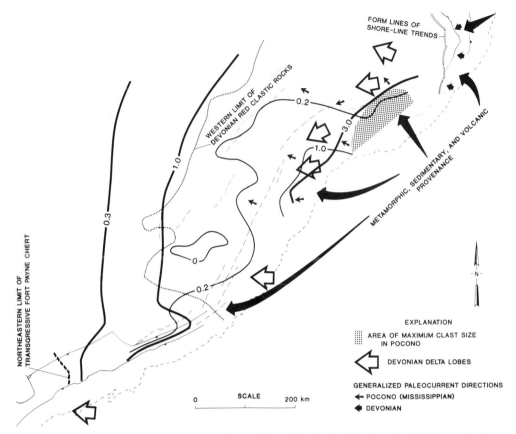

FIG. 3. Stratigraphic map of the Catskill–Pocono (Devonian–Mississippian) clastic wedge in the Pennsylvania salient. Isopach maps of Devonian clastic units (bold lines) and Mississippian clastic units (light lines) (contour values in kilometres). Compiled from Willard (1934), Thomas (1977), Dennison (1985) and references cited therein. The location of the map area is shown in Fig. 1.

letier 1958). Southwestward along strike in the Virginia recess, deltaic to shallow-marine sediments were derived from a similar source (Kreisa & Bambach 1973). An area of no sandstone (Fig. 3) (Arkle 1974, Arkle et al. 1979, Donaldson & Shumaker 1981) in the southern part of the Pennsylvania salient may mark a divide between two Early Mississippian delta systems dispersed either from one provenance SE of the Pennsylvania salient or from two separate sources along the orogen. The deltaic sediments grade westward into bayfill facies (Pepper et al. 1954), and farther SW the clastic facies grades southwestward into a shallow-marine chert and carbonate (Fort Payne Chert) facies (Fig. 3) (Rodgers 1953, Englund 1968).

A regionally extensive transgressive carbonate facies (Loyalhanna Limestone and related carbonate units (Fig. 2)) overlaps the southwestern part of the Catskill–Pocono clastic wedge (Adams 1970). The limestone tongue pinches out eastward

(Fig. 4); and, in the central part of the salient, the Catskill–Pocono clastic wedge is directly overlain by the Mauch Chunk–Pottsville clastic wedge (Meckel 1970).

Mauch Chunk–Pottsville clastic wedge

The youngest clastic wedge in the Pennsylvania salient, the Mississippian–Pennsylvanian Mauch Chunk–Pottsville clastic wedge (Fig. 2), ranges in age from Viséan to Stephanian. Although erosion has been extensive, preserved units are thickest in the eastern part of the Pennsylvania salient and are thinner to the W and SW (Fig. 4) (Meckel 1970, Arkle 1974). An anomalous local thickness is associated with a syn-sedimentary structure in the Virginia recess (Thomas 1966).

The Mauch Chunk red bed facies prograles southwestward over Mississippian limestone (Figs 2 and 4). Much of the Mauch Chunk is alluvial and delta-plain sediment, but on the SW

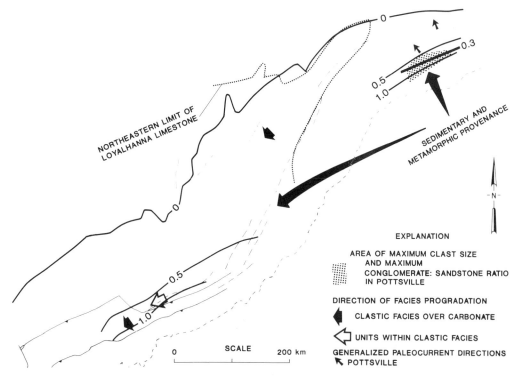

FIG. 4. Stratigraphic map of the Mauch Chunk–Pottsville (Mississippian–Pennsylvanian) clastic wedge in the Pennsylvania salient. Isopach maps of Mauch Chunk (light lines) and Pottsville (bold lines) (contour values in kilometres). Compiled from Dennison & Wheeler (1975), Thomas (1977), Donaldson & Shumaker (1981) and references cited therein. The location of the map area is shown in Fig. 1.

it includes marine facies (Donaldson & Shumaker 1981). The southwestern part of the Mauch Chunk includes barrier sandstones, marine mudstones and limestones, lagoonal to marsh mudstones and thin coals, and deltaic sandstones (Miller 1974, Englund 1979); barrier sandstones prograde westward or southwestward.

The Pennsylvanian (Pottsville and Llewellyn) part of the clastic wedge includes conglomerate, sandstone, shale and coal. Palaeocurrent data, pebble-size distribution, conglomerate-to-sandstone ratios and thickness distribution indicate Pottsville sediment dispersal northward and northwestward from a source SE of the Pennsylvania salient (Meckel 1967). Sandstone petrography demonstrates a provenance of sedimentary and metamorphic rocks (Meckel 1967).

Pennington–Lee clastic wedge

The Mississippian–Pennsylvanian Pennington–Lee clastic wedge is centred on the Tennessee salient (Figs 2 and 5), but extensive erosion has obscured much of the original distribution. The

oldest possible remnant of the clastic wedge on the SE is a structurally isolated unit of limestone, sandstone and shale (Greasy Cove Formation of Neuman & Wilson 1960) of probable Viséan age (Milici *et al.* 1979). The youngest preserved strata in the Tennessee salient are Westphalian (Milici *et al.* 1979), but the northern fringe of the clastic wedge includes Early Permian strata (Fig. 2) (Arkle 1974, Donaldson & Shumaker 1981).

In the central part of the Tennessee salient the Pennington (sandstone and shale) thins northwestward from a maximum of more than 400 m (Cooper 1948). Marine fine-grained clastic rocks of the upper Pennington intertongue with conglomeratic quartzose sandstones (Lee Formation) that prograde both NE and SW along structural strike (Fig. 2) as well as across strike to the NW (Englund 1964, 1968, Englund & DeLaney 1966).

In the southwestern part of the clastic wedge, siliciclastic tongues as old as Viséan pinch out westward into the Mississippian carbonate sequence (Fig. 5) (Rich 1983). Further W and SW, younger Pennington clastic rocks (Namurian) grade westward into the Mississippian carbonate

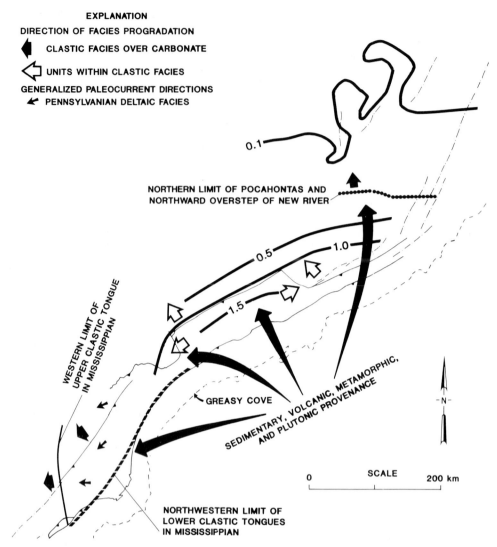

FIG. 5. Stratigraphic map of the Pennington–Lee (Mississippian–Pennsylvanian) clastic wedge in the Tennessee salient. Isopach map of Lee and Kanawha and equivalent clastic units (contour values in kilometres). Compiled from Dennison & Wheeler (1975), Thomas (1977), Donaldson & Shumaker (1981) and references cited therein. The location of the map area is shown in Fig. 1.

facies, and Lee-equivalent massive sandstones prograde over the Mississippian limestones (Figs 2 and 5) (Thomas 1972, 1974).

Northeastward along strike in the Virginia recess, Pennington clastic rocks merge with the southwestward-prograding Mauch Chunk clastic facies (Fig. 2). Towards the NE, quartz-pebble conglomerates of the upper part of the Lee overlap the Pocahontas Formation and intertongue with sandstone, mudstone and coal of the New River Formation (Fig. 2) (Englund 1979). The section thins northeastward in part because

of overstep of the older units (Figs 2 and 5) (Arkle 1974, Dennison & Wheeler 1975). Distribution of Pocahontas deltaic and barrier sandstones indicates northwestward progradation from a source on the SE (Englund 1974), and younger deltaic sandstones prograded northward across the Appalachian basin N of the Virginia recess from Middle Pennsylvanian to Early Permian (Donaldson 1974).

A single source SE of the Tennessee salient possibly supplied all the sediment of the Pennington–Lee clastic wedge (Fig. 5), or alternatively a chain of more local sources may have extended from SE of the Virginia recess to SE of the Tennessee salient. Petrography of Pennsylvanian clastic-wedge sandstones N of the Virginia recess indicates unroofing of a sediment source that included a cover of sedimentary, volcanic and low-grade metamorphic rocks and a core of higher grade metamorphic and plutonic rocks (Davis & Ehrlich 1974).

Ouachita clastic wedge

The Mississippian–Pennsylvanian clastic wedge in the Ouachita salient is a deep-water turbidite succession more than 9 km thick (Figs 2 and 6) dominated by mudstone in the lower part and sandstone and mudstone in the upper part (Cline 1970, Morris 1974). Volcanic tuff units were derived from S of the Ouachita salient (Niem 1977). Palaeocurrent data indicate generally northwesterly and westerly flow of turbidity currents (Fig. 6) (Morris 1974). In the Arkoma foreland basin the Mississippian–Pennsylvanian succession is much thinner and consists of shallow-marine and deltaic sandstones, shales and limestones.

E of the Ouachita salient the clastic wedge thins northeastward to less than 3 km in the Black Warrior foreland basin and Alabama Appalachian recess (Figs 1, 2 and 6) where the succession consists of deltaic and shallow-marine strata (Thomas 1974, 1977). The Mississippian part of the clastic wedge grades northeastward into a shelf-carbonate facies in Alabama (Thomas 1972, 1974), and the clastic facies intertongues with carbonate units (Figs 2 and 6). A northeastward-prograding delta system (Fig. 6) is indicated by distribution of the clastic facies and by palaeogeographic reconstructions based on sand-body geometry, sedimentary structures and vertical sequences (Thomas 1972, 1979, Thomas & Mack 1982). One delta lobe was initiated during the Viséan in the Black Warrior basin and another further SE during the Namurian. The northeastward-prograding Mississippian clastic facies extends furthest NE along syn-sedimentary depressions in the Alabama recess (Thomas 1974).

The Pennsylvanian part of the Ouachita clastic wedge (Pottsville) in the Black Warrior basin and the Alabama recess includes deltaic to shallow-marine mudstones, barrier and deltaic sandstones, and coals. The Pennsylvanian clastic facies progrades northeastward over the stratigraphically highest part of the Mississippian carbonate facies in the Alabama recess and evidently merges with southwestward-prograding clastic sediments (Pennington–Lee clastic wedge) above the Mississippian limestone (Fig. 2) (Hobday 1974, Thomas 1974).

Sediment-dispersal patterns indicate a provenance SW of the Black Warrior foreland basin

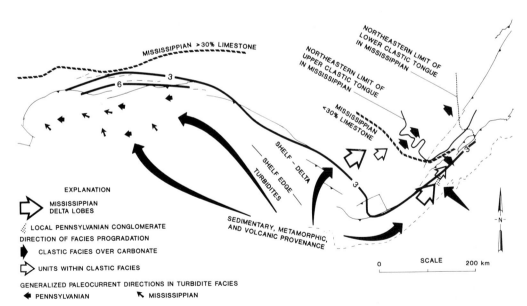

FIG. 6. Stratigraphic map of the Mississippian–Pennsylvanian clastic wedge in the Ouachita salient. Composite isopach map of the clastic wedge (contour values in kilometres). Compiled from Morris (1974), Thomas (1977) and references cited therein. The location of the map area is shown in Fig. 1.

and the Alabama recess (Fig. 6). Locally preserved Pennsylvanian conglomerate (Fig. 6) indicates initiation during Early Pennsylvanian time of an additional minor supply of clastic sediment from SE of the Alabama recess (Horsey 1981). The dominant pattern of northeastward progradation of clastic sediments persisted from Viséan at least through early Westphalian (the youngest preserved sediments). Sandstone composition indicates a source terrain of sedimentary, low-grade metamorphic and volcanic rocks, and the provenance is interpreted to be the result of arc–continent collision (Mack *et al.* 1983). Populations of lithic grains in sandstones of the Alabama Pottsville and equivalent sandstones in the Ouachita salient are essentially indistinguishable, indicating derivation from the same source rocks (Graham *et al.* 1976). The tectonic–sedimentological setting of the shelf and deltaic facies in the Black Warrior basin and the Alabama recess on the E contrasts with that of the deep-water turbidites in the Ouachita salient on the W, indicating that the collision orogen intersected the N American shelf edge obliquely (Fig. 6).

Fault-bounded basins

Middle Devonian to Permian red siliciclastic rocks and minor carbonates and evaporites are now exposed in fault-bounded basins from the Narragansett basin in the interior of the New York recess northeastward to the Newfoundland salient (Fig. 1). Although the outcrop belt is widest within the Quebec salient, the depocentre is the Magdalen basin within the St. Lawrence recess (Fig. 7). These sediments and some associated volcanics were deposited in a system of fault-block basins, the central part of which has been called the Fundy Basin rift (Belt 1968). NE-trending faults separate the rift from platform areas to the NW and SE and also divide the rift internally into a number of smaller horsts and grabens. In general, the horsts were sporadically active local uplifts that supplied siliciclastic sediments to adjacent partially interconnected grabens and half-grabens (Bell 1958). The platform areas contributed little sediment. However, units have been traced from one 'basin' to another, thereby questioning the complexity of the structure (van de Poll 1972, Giles 1981, Schenk, in McCabe & Schenk 1982). In the Late Carboniferous and Permian, most of the sediment came from far to the W, outside the region of fault-bounded basins.

Stratigraphy

Stratigraphic successions vary from graben to graben in preserved thickness, lithology, age, internal unconformities and comprehension (Table 1). Although the sum of unit thicknesses within a basin may be great (e.g. 10.5 km in the Cumberland basin), as in most strike-slip basins, the total thickness at any point is probably much less because of migration of the locus of sedimentation during strike-slip motion (Reading 1980). Post-Palaeozoic erosion has removed great masses of the late Palaeozoic cover from the region as a result of thermal doming preceding Triassic rifting.

Middle(?) and Upper Devonian strata are exposed in the Perry, Cumberland, Mabou and Terrenceville basins, and are suspected in others (Fig. 7 and Table 1). The section consists mainly of volcanic and coarse-grained red siliciclastic rocks. In the Mabou basin the volcanics are of bimodal basalt–rhyolite suites which are apparently tholeiitic (Blanchard *et al.* 1984). The sedimentary environments have been interpreted primarily as alluvial fans, as well as fluvial and some lacustrine systems (Schluger 1973, Fralick & Schenk 1981).

In general, the Carboniferous System consists of three fining-upward sequences, which in order of age are Tournaisian (or Late Devonian) through Namurian, Westphalian, and late Westphalian to Early Permian (Fralick & Schenk 1981). In the Lower Carboniferous (Tournaisian and Viséan) volcanic rocks abruptly decrease upwards in abundance, and the siliciclastic rocks are generally finer grained than in the Devonian. Coarse alluvial fans are generally restricted to basin margins, and lacustrine deposits are common within the basins. The Viséan Windsor Group is distinctive within the entire basin-filling succession because of a dominance of carbonate and evaporite strata. A basal thin laminite interpreted as a tidal deposit (Schenk 1967) may or may not be equivalent to thick metalliferous mud mounds (Giles *et al.* 1979, Schenk & Hatt 1984). An overlying thick anhydrite may be a replacement of a carbonate precursor (Schenk 1984) and underlies 300 m of halite and some potash salt. The upper half of the Windsor Group consists of many thick carbonate–sulphate–red bed cycles (Bell 1958) of marine to marginal and inland sabkha facies (Schenk 1969).

Upper Carboniferous rocks (Namurian, Westphalian and Stephanian) are the most widespread in the Fundy Basin rift. Everywhere, the section is characterized by coarse- to fine-grained fluvial and lacustrine siliciclastic rocks, coal and minor volcanic rocks. During the Late Carboniferous,

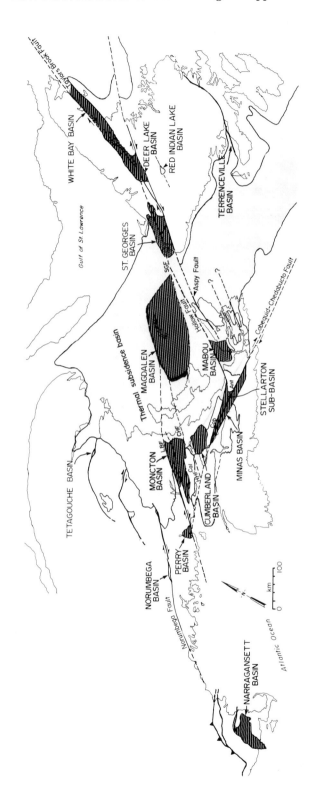

FIG. 7. Late Palaeozoic basins and faults in the northern and Canadian Appalachians (after Bradley 1982): dark shading, pull-apart basins of rifting phase; lighter shading later thermal subsidence enlargement; Ant, Antigonish uplift; Cal, Caledonian uplift; Cob, Cobequid uplift; CHF, Clover Hill–Pollet River fault; HHF, Harvey–Hopewell fault; LBF, Lubec–Belle Isle fault; SGF, St Georges fault. Many other faults are not shown. The location of the map area is shown in Fig. 1.

TABLE 1. *Late Palaeozoic fault-bounded basins: northern and Canadian Appalachians*

Basin	Age	Area ($\times 1000$ km^2)	Basin fill	Volcanism
White Bay	Tournaisian	3	Alluvial fan to lacustrine 1.5 km	None known
Deer Lake	1 Tournaisian 2 Late Viséan–Namurian	2	1 Alluvial, fluvial 2 Fluvial, lacustrine 8 km	Late Viséan basalt
St Georges	1 Tournaisian 2 Late Viséan–Namurian	4	1 Alluvial, fluvial 2 Salt pan, alluvial, fluvial 8 km	None known
Magdalen	1 Late Devonian?–Tournaisian 2 Viséan 3 Permian	25	1 Alluvial 2 Fluvial, marine, salt flat 3 Aeolian 9 km	Viséan, much basalt to rhyolite
Sydney	1 Tournaisian 2 Viséan 3 Westphalian–Stephanian		1 Alluvial 2 Alluvial, marine, salt pan, lacustrine 3 Paludal, fluvial, lacustrine	None known
Mabou	1 Late Devonian 2 Tournaisian–Westphalian	1.5	1 Alluvial 2 Alluvial, fluvial; Viséan marine, salt flat, lacustrine, fluvial 10 km	Late Devonian, Tournaisian basalt and rhyolite
Stellarton	1 Viséan 2 Westphalian	0.2	1 Alluvial, fluvial, lacustrine, marine 2 Fluvial, lacustrine 8 km	None known
Minas	1 Tournaisian 2 Viséan 3 Westphalian	0.6	1 Alluvial, fluvial 2 Marine, salt flat 3 Alluvial, fluvial 4 km	None known
Cumberland	1 Late Devonian 2 Tournaisian 3 Viséan 4 Westphalian 5 Namurian	2.5	1 Alluvial, fluvial 2 Lacustrine 3 Alluvial, fluvial, marine 4 Lacustrine, fluvial, deltaic 5 Fluvial, deltaic 10.5 km	Devonian basalt
Moncton	1 Mississippian 2 Pennsylvanian		1 Fluvial, paludal 2 Alluvial	
Perry	Late Devonian		Alluvial, fluvial, lacustrine 1.2 km	Much basalt
Narragansett	Westphalian–Permian	2.5	Alluvial, fluvial 4 km	Basalt and rhyolite

Modified from Bradley (1982); for references see Bradley (1982).

the basins received sediment not only from the local horsts but also more importantly from sources to the W, NW, and SW, well outside the area of fault-bounded basins (Fralick & Schenk 1981, McCabe, in McCabe & Schenk 1982). The regional sediment dispersal was probably a result in part of a more humid climate and in part of broad regional uplift (Fralick & Schenk 1981). After the arid climate and partially marine environment represented by the Windsor Group, the younger Mabou Group records a return to earlier depositional regimes of lakes in low areas and alluvial fans along basin margins (Belt 1965, McCabe, in McCabe & Schenk 1982). A major event of possible inter-regional significance occurred in the early Westphalian, when horsts were reactivated as reflected in a widespread fining-upward succession (Fralick & Schenk 1981). This was succeeded by regional eastward dispersal of fluvial-deltaic complexes of the late Westphalian to Early Permian Pictou Group which eventually blanketed the area (van de Poll 1966, 1972).

Permian strata occur in the Magdalen basin and change upward from deltaic–lacustrine to floodplain–alluvial fan and at the top to fluvial. Again, the source area was distant and probably to the SW (Frankel & Crowl 1970). Aeolian dune deposits are common. In general a drier climate returned and semi-arid conditions persisted into the Mesozoic.

Sedimentary tectonics

The considerable variation in the basin fills reflects continuing episodic fault movement through Devonian and Carboniferous time. Local effects decreased rapidly in frequency and magnitude in the later Carboniferous and Permian. Distribution of alluvial and fluvial sediments in both time and space documents frequent shifts in dispersal systems at basin margins. Lacustrine, paludal and at times marine environments existed in basin centres. Lava flows and coarse volcaniclastic rocks are locally important and may represent fissure eruptions from border faults.

Fault movement during the Carboniferous is indicated by alluvial fan sediments around blocks (Belt 1965, 1968), laterally offset facies (Belt 1968), syn-sedimentary folds (Fyson 1964) and the large apparent thicknesses of sediments within the basins (McCabe & Schenk 1982). In addition to syn-sedimentary fault movement, post-sedimentary deformation of the basin-fill sediment is reflected in faults, folds and metamorphism. Thrust faults are documented in some basins, but no regionally pervasive thrust faults have been recognized. Some of the deformation

is a result of halokinesis, e.g. salt diapirs in the Magdalen basin.

The pattern of faults suggests a wrench system along which uplifted blocks and intervening basins resulted from alternate compression and subsidence at bends in the system (Schenk 1978, McCabe & Schenk 1982). In general, these *en échelon* basins are interpreted as pull-aparts which followed a classical pattern of basement fragmentation such as (1) stretching of the lithosphere, (2) sagging along the pull-apart walls, (3) erosion of horst blocks and consequent rapid deposition in the subsiding basin and (4) simultaneous extrusion of volcanic rocks along the faults (Fralick & Schenk 1981, after Crowell 1974). Bradley (1982) suggested that the lithosphere was stretched and thinned over an intra-continental transform boundary. Subsidence would have been rapid, fault controlled and generally accompanied by volcanism. During gradual thermal subsidence in middle and late Carboniferous time, the depocentre expanded out of the Magdalen basin *sensu stricto* to bury the earlier border faults, and progressively younger sedimentary units lapped onto platforms to the SE and NW (Fig. 7). In western Cape Breton, bimodal volcanics of Late Devonian age are mainly tholeiitic and may be related to crustal thinning in an extensional regime (Blanchard *et al.* 1984). Regionally, the age of such volcanics ranges into the Mississippian and appears to be younger towards the centre of the Magdalen basin, thus supporting a pull-apart mechanism in a 'within-plate' tectonic setting as advocated by Bradley (1982). However, palaeomagnetic data suggest regional convergence such that the Theic Ocean (between Euramerica and Gondwana) was narrow during Devonian time, very narrow in the Mississippian and closed in the Early Permian (Kent & Opdyke 1985). In contrast, micro-palaeontological data indicate that, at least during Mississippian time, this seaway was quite broad (Jansa *et al.* 1978).

The direction and magnitude of slip on the faults is of great importance for palinspastic models and transatlantic earlier Palaeozoic correlations. Some palaeomagnetic data suggest that very large-scale (possibly 1000–2000 km) sinistral slip along these faults moved the southeastern parts of New England, Atlantic Canada and Britain as a block along the Atlantic seaboard from a position near Georgia (Morris 1976, Kent & Opdyke 1978, Van der Voo *et al.* 1979). The resulting wrench faulting and basement fragmentation could have produced the difference between the late Palaeozoic record of the southern and northern Appalachians in the sedimentary tectonics surveyed in this paper. A more recent analogue would be the northward shift of Baja and southern California along the western seaboard of the continent, accompanied by consequential growth of similar pull-apart basins (Fralick & Schenk 1981). However, more recent palaeomagnetic data suggest that the apparent discrepancy between the palaeolatitudes of cratonic N America and 'Acadia' are a result of overprinting of cratonic palaeopoles in the latest Carboniferous (Irving & Strong 1984) or of Permian lateritic weathering or even of Hercynian metamorphism (Morris 1983). Further palaeomagnetic analysis refutes the proposed latitudinal offset (Kent & Opdyke 1985). Although some sinistral slip on the faults can be documented, field evidence indicates mainly dextral slip measured in terms of a few hundred kilometres at maximum (Belt 1968, 1969, Webb 1969, McMaster *et al.* 1980, Ludman 1981, Bradley 1982, McCabe & Schenk 1982, Johnson & Wones 1984). In order to explain the contradictory strike-slip displacements within the Fundy Basin rift, Rust (1981) suggests that faulting resulted from interaction between a shallow subduction zone and one or more transform faults along a spreading axis, similar to the present configuration in western N America, i.e. the ancient N American continent overrode a subduction zone as well as a spreading axis and a number of transform faults. Subsequent motion within the continental plate occurred along these faults to create the complexities of the Fundy Basin rift.

Although local variation within the many basins in the Fundy Basin rift is great, perhaps some speculation is allowed concerning the perceived large-scale regional sedimentary rhythms and possible correlations S of the New York recess. Three fining-upward sequences are apparent in some basins in Atlantic Canada (Fralick & Schenk 1981). The first, from Late Devonian through Namurian in age, reflects continental collision (the Acadian orogeny) because of closure of the Iapetus Ocean. This sequence is in part equivalent to the Catskill–Pocono clastic wedge in the Pennsylvania salient. In the late Viséan, during deposition of the upper part of the first sequence, the Canadian Appalachians were repeatedly flooded by vestiges of the rapidly closing Theic Ocean. The Loyalhanna Limestone and related marine units S of the Pennsylvania salient also record widespread transgression at this time (Fig. 2). The second sequence is early through middle Westphalian in age, and therefore is younger than the earliest parts of the Alleghanian clastic wedges S of the New York recess. Presumably the sources of these thick sedimentary units were produced by

collisions along the irregularly shaped continental margins of Euramerica and Gondwana as the Theic Ocean closed. The third sequence is a late Westphalian to Early Permian clastic blanket that prograded from the W. The source area must have been along the Alleghanian collision orogen within the new supercontinent Pangaea.

Conclusions

The late Palaeozoic sedimentological record along the Appalachian orogen belongs to two separate domains which are coincident with structural domains. Southward from the New York recess, a domain of clastic wedges extends along the frontal part of the foreland fold–thrust belt and adjacent foreland basins. In the interior part of the orogen northward from the New York recess, basin-fill clastic sequences are coincident with a mainly dextral wrench-fault system.

The Devonian–Mississippian Catskill–Pocono clastic wedge provides a record in the Appalachian foreland of the Acadian orogeny. Dispersal systems indicate orogenic uplifts extending at least from the New York recess to the northern part of the Virginia recess and reflect southwestward migration of delta-lobe progradation through time. The southern extent of orogenic activity is problematic because of a lack of thick clastic sediments in the foreland S of the Tennessee salient.

In the Upper Mississippian and Pennsylvanian, an array of three laterally overlapping foreland clastic wedges records Alleghanian orogenic events and reflects orogenic provenances from the Pennsylvania salient to the Ouachita salient. Differences in the ages of the large-scale clastic wedges, as well as internal stratigraphic details, reflect diachroneity of orogeny along the orogen. The clastic-wedge sediments are displaced by cratonward-directed Alleghanian thrust faults, and thus the terminal orogenic events of the Alleghanian post-date the youngest preserved syn-orogenic sediments. Previously existing clastic wedges may have been entirely eroded from the foreland N of the New York recess, as suggested by a xenolith of Middle Devonian mudstone (equivalent to the lower part of the Catskill–Pocono clastic wedge) in a Cretaceous pluton near Montreal (Boucot & Johnson 1967, as noted by Bradley 1983). However, the well preserved clastic wedges in Appalachian foreland basins front the region of Alleghanian foreland thrusting. Northward from the New York recess, preserved Appalachian frontal thrust faults record Taconic (Ordovician) rather than Alleghanian thrusting.

Late Palaeozoic clastic wedges S of the New York recess provide a record of tectonic activity within the orogenic belt and sedimentation on the foreland. In contrast, northward from the New York recess, late Palaeozoic strata record both tectonism and sedimentation within the orogenic belt. The latter record is an erosional remnant; perhaps similar fault-bounded deposits further S have been entirely eroded. Nevertheless, a distinctive domain of wrench-fault basins and associated basin-fill sediments is preserved in the interior structures from the New York recess to the Newfoundland salient. Late Palaeozoic sediments were deposited in fault-bounded basins within a strike-slip regime, and some fault movement occurred after deposition of the youngest preserved stratigraphic units.

The late Palaeozoic sedimentary record indicates that orogenic compression and cratonward thrusting S of the New York recess were synchronous with wrench-fault movement further N. The distribution of fault types and sedimentary basin types suggests a transpressional margin from the Newfoundland salient to the New York recess and a convergent collisional margin further S. The implied plate motion requires dextral transpression, consistent with interpreted dextral fault movement. The change in kinematic regime along strike of the sinuous orogenic belt is consistent with collision at an irregularly shaped continental margin. Early Palaeozoic facies distribution outlines a zigzag continental margin along which large-scale embayments and promontories were defined by transform offsets of a late Precambrian rift (Thomas 1977). The shape of the margin was modified by Taconic orogenic events, possibly including terrane accretion. However, these events presumably left an irregularly sinuous or zigzag continental margin because Taconic structural strike, where it can be recognized, mimics the shape of the early Palaeozoic rifted margin. Thus the sedimentological-structural domains of the Acadian and Alleghanian orogenies can be interpreted in the context of plate convergence at an irregularly shaped margin, transpressional along some segments and collisional along others, so that the regional trace of the Alleghanian structural system reflects the shape of the earlier continental margin.

References

ADAMS, R. W. 1970. Loyalhanna Limestone—cross-bedding and provenance. *In*: FISHER, G. W., PETTIJOHN, F. J., REED, J. C., JR & WEAVER, K. N. (eds) *Studies of Appalachian Geology: Central and Southern*, pp. 83–100, Wiley-Interscience, New York.

ALLEN, J. R. L. & FRIEND, P. F. 1968. Deposition of the Catskill facies, Appalachian region: with notes on some other Old Red Sandstone basins. *In*: KLEIN, G. de V. (ed.) *Late Palaeozoic and Mesozoic Continental Sedimentation, Northeastern North America. Geological Society of America Special Paper No. 106*, pp. 21–74.

ARKLE, T., JR 1974. Stratigraphy of the Pennsylvanian and Permian Systems of the central Appalachians. *In*: BRIGGS, G. (ed.) *Carboniferous of the Southeastern United States. Geological Society of America Special Paper No. 148*, pp. 5–29.

——, BEISSEL, D. R., LARESE, R. E., NUHFER, E. B., PATCHEN, D. G., SMOSNA, R. A., GILLESPIE, W. H., LUND, R., NORTON, C. W. & PFEFFERKORN, H. W. 1979. The Mississippian and Pennsylvanian (Carboniferous) Systems in the United States— West Virginia and Maryland. *United States Geological Survey Professional Paper No. 1110-D*, 35 pp.

BELL, W. A. 1958. Possibilities for the occurrence of petroleum reservoirs in Nova Scotia. *Nova Scotia Department of Mines Report*, 177 pp.

BELT, E. S. 1965. Stratigraphy and paleogeography of Mabou Group and related middle Carboniferous facies, Nova Scotia, Canada. *Geological Society of America Bulletin*, **76**, 777–802.

—— 1968. Post-Acadian rifts and related facies, eastern Canada. *In*: ZEN, E-AN, WHITE, W. S., HADLEY, J. B. & THOMPSON, J. B., JR (eds) *Studies of Appalachian Geology: Northern and Maritime*, pp. 95–113, Wiley-Interscience, New York.

—— 1969. Newfoundland Carboniferous stratigraphy and its relation to the Maritimes and Ireland. *American Association of Petroleum Geologists Memoir No. 12*, pp. 734–53.

BLANCHARD, M.-C., JAMIESON, R. A. & MORE, E. B. 1984. Late Devonian–Early Carboniferous volcanism in western Cape Breton Island, Nova Scotia. *Canadian Journal of Earth Sciences*, **21**, 762–74.

BOUCOT, A. J. & JOHNSON, J. G. 1967. Paleogeography and correlation of Appalachian province sedimentary rocks. *Tulsa Geological Society Digest*, **35**, 35–87.

BRADLEY, D. C. 1982. Subsidence in late Paleozoic basins in the northern Appalachians. *Tectonics*, **1**, 107–23.

—— 1983. Tectonics of the Acadian orogeny in New England and adjacent Canada. *Journal of Geology*, **91**, 381–400.

BURTNER, R. L. 1963. Sediment dispersal patterns within the Catskill facies of southeastern New York and northeastern Pennsylvania. *Pennsylvania Geological Survey Bulletin No. G39*, pp. 7–23.

CLINE, L. M. 1970. Sedimentary features of late Paleozoic flysch, Ouachita Mountains, Oklahoma. *In*: LAJOIE, J. (ed.) *Flysch Sedimentology in North America. Geological Association of Canada Special Paper No. 7*, pp. 85–101.

COOPER, B. N. 1948. Status of Mississippian stratigraphy in the central and northern Appalachian region. *Journal of Geology*, **56**, 255–63.

—— 1964. Relation of stratigraphy to structure in the southern Appalachians. *In*: LOWRY, W. D. (ed.) *Tectonics of the Southern Appalachians. Virginia Polytechnic Institute Department of Geological Sciences Memoir 1*, pp. 81–114.

CROWELL, J. C. 1974. Origin of late Cenozoic basins in southern California. *In*: DICKINSON, W. R. (ed.) *Tectonics and Sedimentation. Society of Economic Paleontologists and Mineralogists Special Publication No. 22*, pp. 190–204.

DAVIS, M. W. & EHRLICH, R. 1974. Late Paleozoic crustal composition and dynamics in the southeastern United States. *In*: BRIGGS, G. (ed.) *Carboniferous of the Southeastern United States. Geological Society of America Special Paper No. 148*, pp. 171–85.

DENNISON, J. M. 1985. Catskill delta shallow marine strata. *In*: WOODROW, D. L. & SEVON, W. D. (eds) *The Catskill Delta. Geological Society of America Special Paper No. 201*, pp. 91–106.

—— & WHEELER, W. H. 1975. Stratigraphy of Precambrian through Cretaceous strata of probable fluvial origin in southeastern United States and their potential as uranium host rocks. *Southeastern Geology Special Publication No. 5*, 210 pp.

DONALDSON, A. C. 1974. Pennsylvanian sedimentation of central Appalachians. *In*: BRIGGS, G. (ed.) *Carboniferous of the Southeastern United States. Geological Society of America Special Paper No. 148*, pp. 47–118.

—— & SHUMAKER, R. C. 1981. Late Paleozoic molasse of central Appalachians. *In*: MIALL, A. D. (ed.) *Sedimentation and Tectonics in Alluvial Basins. Geological Association of Canada Special Paper No. 23*, pp. 99–124.

ENGLUND, K. J. 1964. In the Cumberland Mountains of southeastern Kentucky, stratigraphy of the Lee Formation. *In: Geological Survey Research 1964. United States Geological Survey Professional Paper No. 501-B*, pp. B30–B38.

—— 1968. Geology and coal resources of the Elk Valley area, Tennessee and Kentucky. *United States Geological Survey Professional Paper No. 572*, 59 pp.

—— 1974. Sandstone distribution patterns in the Pocahontas Formation of southwest Virginia and southern West Virginia. *In*: BRIGGS, G. (ed.) *Carboniferous of the Southeastern United States. Geological Society of America Special Paper No. 148*, pp. 31–45.

—— 1979. The Mississippian and Pennsylvanian (Carboniferous) Systems in the United States— Virginia. *United States Geological Survey Professional Paper No. 1110-C*, 21 pp.

—— & DeLANEY, A. O. 1966. Intertonguing relations of the Lee Formation in southwestern Virginia. *In: Geological Survey research 1966. United States Geological Survey Professional Paper No. 550-D*, pp. D47–D52.

ETTENSOHN, F. R. 1985. The Catskill delta complex and the Acadian orogeny: a model. *In*: WOODROW, D. L. & SEVON, W. D. (eds) *The Catskill Delta. Geological Society of America Special Paper No. 201*, pp. 39–49.

FRALICK, P. W. & SCHENK, P. E. 1981. Molasse deposition and basin evolution in a wrench tectonic setting: the late Paleozoic, eastern Cumberland basin, Maritime Canada. *In*: MIALL, A. D. (ed.) *Sedimentation and Tectonics in Alluvial Basins. Geological Association of Canada Special Paper No. 23*, pp. 77–97.

FRANKEL, L. & CROWL, G. H. 1970. Permo-Carboniferous stratigraphy and structure of central Prince Edward Island. *Geological Survey of Canada Paper No. 69-17*, 26 pp.

FYSON, W. K. 1964. Folds in the Carboniferous rocks near Walton, Nova Scotia. *American Journal of Science*, **262**, 513–22.

GILES, P. S. 1981. Major transgressive–regressive cycles in middle to late Viséan rocks of Nova Scotia. *Nova Scotia Department of Mines and Energy Paper No. 81-2*, 27 pp.

——, BOEHNER, R. C. & RYAN, R. J. 1979. Carbonate banks of the Gays River Formation in central Nova Scotia. *Nova Scotia Department of Mines and Energy Paper No. 78-7*, 57 pp.

GRAHAM, S. A., INGERSOLL, R. V. & DICKINSON, W. R. 1976. Common provenance for lithic grains in Carboniferous sandstones from Ouachita Mountains and Black Warrior basin. *Journal of Sedimentary Petrology*, **46**, 620–32.

HOBDAY, D. K. 1974. Beach- and barrier-island facies in the upper Carboniferous of northern Alabama. *In*: BRIGGS, G. (ed.) *Carboniferous of the Southeastern United States. Geological Society of America Special Paper No. 148*, pp. 209–23.

HORSEY, C. A. 1981. Depositional environments of the Pennsylvanian Pottsville Formation in the Black Warrior basin of Alabama. *Journal of Sedimentary Petrology*, **51**, 799–806.

IRVING, E. & STRONG, D. F. 1984. Palaeomagnetism of the Early Carboniferous Deer Lake Group, western Newfoundland: no evidence for mid-Carboniferous displacement of "Acadia". *Earth and Planetary Science Letters*, **69**, 379–90.

JANSA, L. F., MAMET, B. & ROUX, A. 1978. Viséan limestones from the Newfoundland shelf. *Canadian Journal of Earth Sciences*, **15**, 1422–36.

JOHNSON, T. D. & WONES, D. R. 1984. Sense and mode of shearing along the Norumbega fault zone, eastern Maine. *Geological Society of America Abstracts with Programs*, **16**, 27.

KENT, D. V. & OPDYKE, N. D. 1978. Paleomagnetism of the Catskill red beds: evidence for motion of the coastal New England–Canadian Maritime region relative to cratonic North America. *Journal of Geophysical Research*, **83**, 4441–50.

—— & —— 1985. Multicomponent magnetizations from the Mississippian Mauch Chunk Formation of the central Appalachians and their tectonic implications. *Journal of Geophysical Research*, **90**, 5371–83.

KING, P. B. 1959. *The Evolution of North America*, Princeton University Press, Princeton, NJ, 189 pp.

KREISA, R. D. & BAMBACH, R. K. 1973. Environments of deposition of the Price Formation (Lower

Mississippian) in its type area, southwestern Virginia. *American Journal of Science (Cooper Volume)*, **273A**, 326–42.

LUDMAN, A. 1981. Significance of transcurrent faulting in eastern Maine and location of the suture between Avalonia and North America. *American Journal of Science*, **281**, 463–83.

MACK, G. H., THOMAS, W. A. & HORSEY, C. A. 1983. Composition of Carboniferous sandstones and tectonic framework of southern Appalachian–Ouachita orogen. *Journal of Sedimentary Petrology*, **53**, 931–46.

McCABE, P. J. & SCHENK, P. E. 1982. From sabkha to coal swamp—the Carboniferous sediments of Nova Scotia and southern New Brunswick. *International Association of Sedimentologists, Field Excursion 4A Guidebook*, 169 pp.

McIVER, N. L. 1970. Appalachian turbidites. *In*: FISHER, G. W., PETTIJOHN, F. J., REED, J. C., JR & WEAVER, K. N. (eds) *Studies of Appalachian Geology: Central and Southern*, pp. 69–81, Wiley-Interscience, New York.

McMASTER, R. L., DE BOER, J. & COLLINS, B. P. 1980. Tectonic development of southern Narragansett Bay and offshore Rhode Island. *Geology*, **8**, 496–500.

MECKEL, L. D. 1967. Origin of Pottsville conglomerates (Pennsylvanian) in the central Appalachians. *Geological Society of America Bulletin*, **78**, 223–58.

—— 1970. Paleozoic alluvial deposition in the central Appalachians: a summary. *In*: FISHER, G. W., PETTIJOHN, F. J., REED, J. C., JR & WEAVER, K. N. (eds) *Studies of Appalachian Geology: Central and Southern*, pp. 49–67, Wiley-Interscience, New York.

MILICI, R. C., BRIGGS, G., KNOX, L. M., SITTERLY, P. D. & STATLER, A. T. 1979. The Mississippian and Pennsylvanian (Carboniferous) Systems in the United States—Tennessee. *United States Geological Survey Professional Paper No. 1110-G*, 38 pp.

MILLER, M. S. 1974. Stratigraphy and coal beds of Upper Mississippian and Lower Pennsylvanian rocks in southwestern Virginia. *Virginia Division of Mineral Resources Bulletin No. 84*, 211 pp.

MORRIS, R. C. 1974. Sedimentary and tectonic history of the Ouachita Mountains. *In*: DICKINSON, W. R. (ed.) *Tectonics and Sedimentation. Society of Economic Paleontologists and Mineralogists Special Publication No. 22*, pp. 120–42.

MORRIS, W. A. 1976. Transcurrent motion determined paleomagnetically in the northern Appalachians and Caledonides and the Acadian orogeny. *Canadian Journal of Earth Sciences*, **13**, 1236–43.

—— 1983. Appalachian paleomagnetism—transcurrent motion, or metamorphic remagnetization—some evidence from the Fournier Complex, New Brunswick. *In*: *Evolution of the Ancient Continental Margin of Western Newfoundland. Newfoundland Section, Geological Association of Canada, Spring Meeting, Program with Abstracts.*

NEUMAN, R. B. & WILSON, R. L. 1960. Geology of the Blockhouse quadrangle, Tennessee. *United States Geological Survey Map GQ-131*.

NIEM, A. R. 1977. Mississippian pyroclastic flow and ash-fall deposits in the deep-marine Ouachita flysch basin, Oklahoma and Arkansas. *Geological Society of America Bulletin*, **88**, 49–61.

OLIVER, W. A., JR, DE WITT, W., JR, DENNISON, J. M., HOSKINS, D. M. & HUDDLE, J. W. 1967. Devonian of the Appalachian basin, United States. *In*: OSWALD, D. H. (ed.) *International Symposium on the Devonian System*, Vol. 1, pp. 1001–40, Alberta Society of Petroleum Geologists.

PELLETIER, B. R. 1958. Pocono paleocurrents in Pennsylvania and Maryland. *Geological Society of America Bulletin*, **69**, 1033–64.

PEPPER, J. F., DE WITT, W., JR & DEMAREST, D. F. 1954. Geology of the Bedford Shale and Berea Sandstone in the Appalachian basin. *United States Geological Survey Professional Paper No. 259*, 111 pp.

READING, H. G. 1980. Characteristics and recognition of strike-slip fault systems. *In*: BALLANCE, P. F. & READING, H. G. (eds) *Sedimentation in Oblique-Slip Mobile Zones. International Association of Sedimentologists Special Publication No. 4*, pp. 7–26.

RICH, M. 1983. Stratigraphy of the Floyd Formation (Meramecian–Chesterian) in the Rome area, Georgia. *Georgia Geological Society 18th Annual Field Trip Guidebook*, pp. 16–29.

RODGERS, J. 1953. Geologic map of east Tennessee with explanatory text. *Tennessee Division of Geology Bulletin No. 58*, Part 2, 168 pp.

RUST, B. R. 1981. Alluvial deposits and tectonic style: Devonian and Carboniferous successions in eastern Gaspé. *In*: MIALL, A. D. (ed.) *Sedimentation and Tectonics in Alluvial Basins. Geological Association of Canada Special Paper No. 23*, pp. 49–76.

SCHENK, P. E. 1967. The Macumber Formation of the Maritime Provinces—a Mississippian analogue to Recent strand-line carbonates of the Persian Gulf. *Journal of Sedimentary Petrology*, **37**, 365–76.

—— 1969. Carbonate–sulfate–redbed facies and cyclic sedimentation of the Windsorian Stage (middle Carboniferous), Maritime Provinces. *Canadian Journal of Earth Sciences*, **6**, 1037–66.

—— 1978. Synthesis of the Canadian Appalachians. *In*: TOZER, E. T. & SCHENK, P. E. (eds) *Caledonian–Appalachian Orogen of the North Atlantic Region. Geological Survey of Canada Paper No. 78-13*, pp. 111–36.

—— 1984. Carbonate–sulphate facies relations in the Windsor Group, central Nova Scotia, Canada. *Comptes Rendus 9ème Congrès International du Stratigraphie et Géologie de Caronifère*, Vol. 3, pp. 143–62.

—— & HATT, B. L. 1984. Depositional environment of the Gays River Reef, Nova Scotia, Canada. *Comptes Rendus 9ème Congrès International du Stratigraphie et Géologie de Caronifère*, Vol. 3, pp. 117–30.

SCHLUGER, P. R. 1973. Stratigraphy and sedimentary environments of the Devonian Perry Formation, New Brunswick, Canada, and Maine, U.S.A. *Geological Society of America Bulletin*, **84**, 2533–48.

SEVON, W. D. 1985. Nonmarine facies of the Middle and Late Devonian Catskill coastal alluvial plain.

In: WOODROW, D. L. & SEVON, W. D. (eds) *The Catskill Delta. Geological Society of America Special Paper No. 201*, pp. 79–90.

THOMAS, W. A. 1966. Late Mississippian folding of a syncline in the western Appalachians, West Virginia and Virginia. *Geological Society of America Bulletin*, **77**, 473–94.

—— 1972. Mississippian stratigraphy of Alabama. *Alabama Geological Survey Monograph No. 12*, 121 pp.

—— 1974. Converging clastic wedges in the Mississippian of Alabama. *In*: BRIGGS, G. (ed.) *Carboniferous of the Southeastern United States. Geological Society of America Special Paper No. 148*, pp. 187–207.

—— 1977. Evolution of Appalachian–Ouachita salients and recesses from reentrants and promontories in the continental margin. *American Journal of Science*, **277**, 1233–78.

—— 1979. Mississippian stratigraphy of Alabama. *In*: *The Mississippian and Pennsylvanian (Carboniferous) Systems in the United States—Alabama and Mississippi. United States Geological Survey Professional Paper No. 1110-I*, pp. I1–I22.

—— & MACK, G. H. 1982. Paleogeographic relationship of a Mississippian barrier-island and shelf-bar system (Hartselle Sandstone) in Alabama to the Appalachian–Ouachita orogenic belt. *Geological Society of America Bulletin*, **93**, 6–19.

VAN DE POLL, H. W. 1966. Sedimentation and paleocurrents during Pennsylvanian time in the Moncton basin, New Brunswick. *Report of Investigation 1*, Mines Division, Department of Natural Resources, New Brunswick, 33 pp.

—— 1972. Stratigraphy and economic geology of Carboniferous basins in the Maritime provinces. *In*: GLASS, D. J. (ed.) *Field Excursion A60 Guidebook. International Geological Congress*, pp. 1–32.

VAN DER VOO, R., FRENCH, A. N. & FRENCH, R. B. 1979. A paleomagnetic pole position from the Upper Devonian Catskill red beds and its tectonic implications. *Geology*, **7**, 345.

WEBB, G. W. 1969. Paleozoic wrench faults in Canadian Appalachians. *In*: KAY, M. (ed.) *Geology and Continental Drift. American Association of Petroleum Geologists Memoir 12*, pp. 754–86.

WILLARD, B. 1934. Early Chemung shore line in Pennsylvania. *Geological Society of America Bulletin*, **45**, 897–908.

WOODROW, D. L. & SEVON, W. D. (eds) 1985. *The Catskill Delta. Geological Society of America Special Paper No. 201*, 246 pp.

W. A. THOMAS, Department of Geology, University of Alabama, Tuscaloosa, Alabama Al 35487, USA.

P. E. SCHENK, Department of Geology, Dalhousie University, Halifax, Nova Scotia B3H 3J5, Canada.

Mid-Devonian to mid-Permian floral and faunal regions and provinces

K. C. Allen & D. L. Dineley

SUMMARY: The middle to late Palaeozoic biota in seas adjacent to the Caledonide–Appalachian orogen included an abundant generally cosmopolitan benthos in both carbonate and clastic environments. Where low clastic sediment input permitted, organic reefs and build-ups were characteristic of this tropical area. Early Devonian biogeographic provinces did not persist into later times. The pelagic fauna, dominated by ammonoidea, bivalvia, conodonts and vertebrates, was rich, rapidly evolving and, again, cosmopolitan. Vertebrates and conodonts in particular were wide ranging.

Among the land plants heterospory and arborescence evolved during the middle and late Devonian in a number of classes, particularly the Lycopsida and Progymnospermopsida. Genera were largely cosmopolitan during this time, and only one floristic region can be recognized worldwide, although there is some evidence for slight provincial floral variation outside Laurussia.

During the early Carboniferous arborescent Lycopsida were abundant. Three floristic regions can be identified worldwide, of which one is the Circum-Tethyan Region including Laurussia, Kazakhstania and China. Two floral provinces are recognized within the Laurussian part of this region.

In late Carboniferous and early Permian times, when gymnosperms replaced the pteridophytes as the dominant forms, there is a more clear-cut separation of floral regions, and by early Permian two floral regions are recognized within Laurussia which are clearly different from those away from this land mass.

Non-marine bivalvia and vertebrates were highly cosmopolitan from mid-Devonian time onwards, with amphibia appearing in Greenland in the late Devonian and reptiles appearing in eastern Canada and western Europe in Westphalian A time.

Many palaeogeographical representations of the distribution of the continental blocks and oceanic basins within late Palaeozoic times are now available (Ziegler et al. 1977, 1981, Bambach et al. 1980, Smith et al. 1981, Scotese 1984). Palaeoclimatic signals within the stratigraphic record are common, and there is a broad consensus of view that the Caledonian orogen during mid-Devonian to end Carboniferous times was an intra-continental area extending generally northeastwards from just S of the equator to about 30°N. The region was bounded to the S by an oceanic seaway until mid-Carboniferous time. Thereafter it became increasingly remote from the ocean, with attendant consequences for its climate and biology. Throughout this span of some 100 Ma earth movements were almost continually affecting the orogen itself and the southern margins of the continental forelands on each side. Volcanism, erosion and sedimentation were vigorous. Conditions were right for significant developments and changes in the marine, freshwater and terrestrial environments and their biotas, especially as the continents drew together into Pangaea (Fig. 1).

Boucot & Gray (1979, 1983) have advanced the argument for a pangaeic (rather than dispersed) configuration of landmasses during Pa-laeozoic time. They intentionally disregarded palaeomagnetic data and concentrated on biogeographic evidence. Amongst the features they saw as requiring explanation are the relatively high level of cosmopolitanism of the late Devonian and the subsequent rise of provincialism to a culmination in the middle Permian. The seas between Gondwana and Laurussia, which were latitudinal and tropical, probably experienced a persistent major westward surface current. Innovations in the marine biota at the eastern end of this seaway would be distributed westwards comparatively rapidly. Most workers discussing late Palaeozoic palaeogeographies comment on the conspicuous cyclic nature of the strata and its implications of frequent changes of eustatic level and of local tectonic/isostatic adjustment. Climatic cycles were perhaps also related to sea-level changes and atmospheric if not extraterrestrial cycles as well (Hailwood 1974).

A very low temperature gradient throughout these seas was a major influence in maintaining a relatively stable level of taxonomic diversity during mid-Devonian to mid-Carboniferous times. In conformity with the modern pattern, the ocean surface currents are thought to have followed a constant westward direction along a predominantly E–W coastline (Heckel & Witzke

From HARRIS, A. L. & FETTES, D. J. (eds), 1988, *The Caledonian–Appalachian Orogen,* Geological Society Special Publication No. 38, pp. 531–548.

1979, Klapper & Johnson 1980). Local disturbances of this may have resulted from changes of relief through diastrophism and deposition on a relatively small scale. Movement of species in the opposite direction may have been possible in ocean-current eddies and island-bound channels between continental coastline and open ocean. By late Carboniferous time this seaway became closed to the W and the tropical–sub-tropical current system was no longer effective. At this point relatively high provincial differentiation began to affect both terrestrial and marine environments, and climatic differentiation also became conspicuous. The onset of cooler conditions in the boreal latitudes and continental glaciation in the southern hemisphere had marked consequences for the terrestrial vegetation and its dependent ecologies.

During the mid-Devonian to early Permian time-span the Caledonide Orogen provided a wide range of tropical marine and continental environments with climates becoming progressively more 'continental'. Biotas from lowland, brackish-water and marine habitats are widely represented and some are known in considerable detail. Many palaeobiogeographic, palaeo-ecological and evolutionary studies in recent years (Carroll *et al.* 1972, Hodson & Ramsbottom 1973, Woodrow *et al.* 1973, House 1975, Johnson 1981) show that a monsoonal climate prevailed during the later half of the Devonian period and much of the Carboniferous and that in the lowlands widespread vascular floras extended their cover of the land. Towards the end of Carboniferous times drier climates halted the spread of land vegetation. A two-stage decrease in rainfall is indicated (Phillips & Peppars 1984, Dimichele *et al.* 1985). Desertification took place as maritime climatic influence waned, and the uplift of terrane began. The changing positions of the landmasses and the rise of the Variscan fold belts exerted a climatic influence which led to the greater aridity of Permian times and the accompanying widespread marine regression. As the arid climate spread there were corresponding effects on the terrestrial biotas.

While the end of Palaeozoic time is marked by a major crisis in the history of life, it must be noted that significant extinctions of marine invertebrates and perhaps other animals took place at the Frasnian–Famennian boundary and again at the end of the Devonian Period. The reasons for these are perhaps many and are certainly elusive, but McLaren (1970, 1982, 1983) has suggested that a meteoritic impact (bolide) may have occurred with catastrophic results for corals and other marine life in the tropical realms. This would have influenced the existing biogeographic provinces and, as Schopf (1979) has pointed out, faunal diversity and provinces are related throughout geological time. Little evidence of the effect of such an impact on terrestrial communities is available. Faunal (marine) provinces are primarily dependent upon latitude and major oceanic currents which are themselves dependent upon the positions of the continents. Changes in continental positions, taking place over millions of years, affect ocean currents equally slowly. However, the size of individual provinces may be changed significantly over a few thousand years as the sea level rises or falls. Schopf (1979) sees both influences in the pattern of extinctions and origins during the Permo-Triassic interval.

Marine faunas

Neritic benthos

The relatively well-known fossil record of shallow marine environments of the mid-Devonian to mid-Permian time-slice contains a number of fossil associations representing benthonic communities in both clastic and carbonate deposits. Those of the clastic lithofacies underwent relatively little change during this time but were distinctly different from those of the early Palaeozoic. The epifaunal brachiopod-dominated faunas were modified by the advent of the productids in the second half of the Devonian period; other brachiopod groups declined. Muddy environments supported predominantly suspension-feeding faunas; sandy-shelf environments maintained more diverse faunas including infaunal elements.

Carbonate deposition was widespread where clastic sedimentary input from upland areas was not vigorous. Build-ups and reefs were of many kinds, especially in late Devonian and early Carboniferous times (Burchette 1981, Toomey 1981). At the Frasnian–Famennian boundary, however, there is a widespread hiatus and, as noted, an extinction of Frasnian corals and other marine elements. Early Carboniferous carbonate environments were even more widely distributed and the period was also one of extensive evaporite deposition. These environments were extinguished by the influx of clastic sediments from the uplands throughout later Carboniferous and early Permian times.

The general categories of benthonic environments with characteristic marine invertebrate communities within the region were as follows: (1) coastal, deltaic and inshore; (2) sandy shelf; (3) muddy shelf; (4) carbonate banks and off-

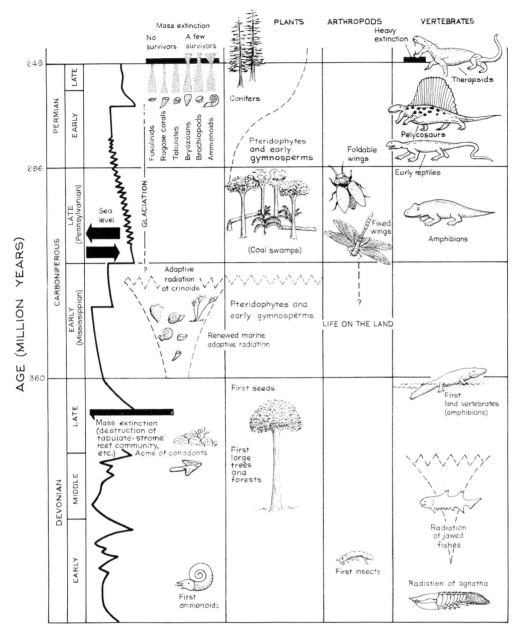

FIG. 1. Synopsis of palaeobiological progress throughout middle to late Palaeozoic times as apparent in the region of the Caledonide orogen (after Stanley 1985).

reef; (5) carbonate organic reefs and associated types; (6) basinal (largely dominated by pelagic and nektonic organisms). An account of these or similar communities in Britain is given by McKerrow (1978), of those in Germany by Goldring & Langenstrassen (1979), and of those in the U.S.A. by Sutton *et al.* (1970), Bowen *et al.* (1974), Thayer (1974), McGhee (1976) and McGhee & Sutton (1981) to name but a few.

In each community there are dominant or most-abundant species, characteristically the brachiopods by which it is distinguished. There is an overall similarity to be found in contemporaneous communities throughout the European and east-

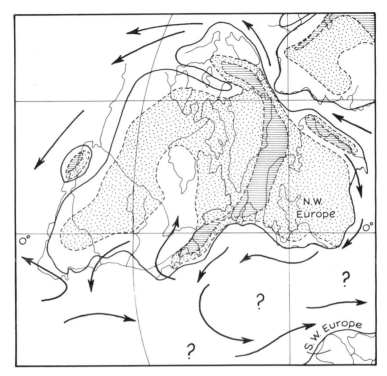

FIG. 2. Middle to late Devonian geography of Laurussia: shaded areas, mountains; stippled areas, platforms with continental–epeiric seas; unshaded areas, shallow relatively permanent sea and ocean; bold lines, edges of continents; arrows, ocean currents. (From many sources.)

ern American areas where these middle to late Palaeozoic rocks occur. Many of these communities are found in similar relationships to their neighbours in both Europe and N America, indicating a general common pattern of biotopes throughout. This is supported by the wide geographical ranges of the dominant genera of brachiopods, mollusca, arthropods, bryozoa, coelenterata and echinodermata. Differences 'along strike' but within ecological zones are common enough at species level, but at generic level and higher the continuity of faunal associations and ranges is probably very high. It must nevertheless be admitted that this seeming uniformity is so far only apparent and, to our knowledge, has not yet been proved by detailed regional analysis. Bailey (1978) has noted that the middle Devonian bivalvia of eastern USA are virtually identical with groups of species in the lower Devonian of central Europe, a distribution which is attributed to slow westward migration.

Certain groups of fossils, corals and brachiopods for example have been studied in this connection. These are particularly common in carbonate facies, but there is little reason to believe that what can be said of dispersal within

carbonate environments may not be said equally or perhaps more truly about the biotas of the neritic clastic environments. In short, the pattern of neritic benthonic associations and communities if not actual faunas seems remarkably constant throughout the region. Cosmopolitanism was widespread in these marine faunas, even though there must have been (minor) local distinctions between them.

Thus, within the early Devonian two major marine palaeobiogeographical realms appear in the study region—the Old World Realm and the Eastern Americas Realm (Boucot 1975, Oliver 1976, 1977) based on benthos. There are several local provinces distinguished within these, especially in the former realm, and the distinctions between Rhenish and Bohemian (or Hercynian) magnafacies have long been known (Erben 1964). These distinctive geographical entities were rapidly subsumed by wide cosmopolitanism in the benthonic faunas during the mid-Devonian. They did not reappear, presumably because the narrow equatorial ocean of the time was free of barriers to migration and possessed relatively uniform conditions throughout each depth zone. High sea levels in late Devonian time dropped intermittently during the later Palaeozoic. This restricted and adversely affected the evolution and diversification of marine invertebrates but was advantageous for the migration of terrestrial vertebrates. After late Devonian time the gathering of continents into Pangaea ensured a growing uniformity of conditions on land and progressive size reduction of marine areas.

Throughout the ensuing time the benthos was generally cosmopolitan. Hill (1973), however, noted that the lower Carboniferous of Nova Scotia, Europe and NW Africa possesses coral faunas rather distinct from those elsewhere. As the Tournaisian transgression took place the coral fauna became enriched. Numerous Tabulata appeared and in the Viséan there were some differences at the coral generic level between this region and eastern Europe. Although the Namurian faunas show that many Viséan forms had disappeared, on the basis of corals the western European region was still somewhat distinct from that to the E.

Carboniferous foraminifera also appear to have been broadly cosmopolitan during this time. Ross (1973) distinguished a Eurasian–Arctic early Carboniferous foraminiferid province in which a European sub-province showed great species diversity and minor differences in species distribution from N to S. Late Carboniferous foraminiferal assemblages are markedly different from earlier ones but biogeographical provinces are no more obvious.

A study of both the microfossils and macrofossils of the Aegir Marine Band and its equivalents (Westphalian C) in northwestern Europe by Bless & Winkler-Prins (1972) indicated free migration between there and NW Spain, with further possible links with SW Russia and eastern N America. N of the Wales–Brabant massif migration of microfaunal elements seems to have been from the NE and links to the S and W were weaker (see also Calver 1968). The influence of the growing Variscan chains in this connection is well illustrated in the palaeogeographical and facies maps of Ziegler (1982).

Pelagic forms

That late Palaeozoic seas and oceans supported a diverse biota of planktonic and nektonic forms is not to be doubted. The Devonian and Carboniferous record indicates a large biota of microorganisms and a rapidly-evolving biota of cephalopods, particularly the ammonoids, bivalvia, arthropods and conodont animals (Raup 1976). Vertebrates included agnatha, chrondreichthyes, placoderms and osteichthyes. At the end of the early Devonian the graptoloids and dacryoconarids had become extinct.

The most important macrofossils amongst the pelagic forms, the ammonoids, became widespread during middle Devonian time. They may have originated in seas adjacent to the orogen in the early Devonian but became diverse and more widely distributed in the following two epochs. The best Eifelian record is that of western Europe and NW Africa; the Givetian record is more widespread with records from eastern and western N America, the Urals and China. Frasnian ammonoids are again most abundant in Europe and NW Africa, and the *Manticoceras* fauna occurs in many parts of the world. *Cheiloceras* and clymeniids are also widespread. The studies of House (1971, 1973) indicate that the western European area contains the fullest record of all Devonian ammonoid faunas and that it was the prime site of their origin, diversification and survival. Carboniferous ammonoids are known from the same general regions across the world as are those of the late Devonian. The earliest Carboniferous forms occur in western Europe and NW Africa, the eastern USSR and N America. Europe provides a very complete record of the (Carboniferous) evolution of the group. Throughout late Devonian–early Carboniferous time there is little sign of provincialism amongst ammonoid faunas, but Hodson & Ramsbottom (1973) point out that, with the advent of the Neoglyphioceratidae, provincialism makes its mark and becomes conspicuous in the late Carboniferous ammonoid faunas. During this time the NW European faunas are different from those elsewhere to the E and the W. Barriers to migration were perhaps a Sudetic ridge between the northern marginal waters and those of more central 'proto-Tethyan' ocean arcs separating the eastern marginal seas of the N American craton from those to the W (Fig. 2).

To what extent other less numerous cephalopoda were similarly distributed throughout the middle to late Palaeozoic world is problematic, and hence the retrieval of information from them is more difficult. The pelagic bivalvia such as *Buchiola* and *Posidonia* are known from many formations in western Europe and NW Africa, and were probably distributed much as were the cephalopods.

Conodonts from the Devonian and Carboniferous are so widely distributed and occur across such a range of lithologies that 'either neritic pelagic or nektobenthic species could have been responsible for these distributions' (Klapper & Barrick 1977). Telford (1972) noted Europe as one of four biogeographic (conodont) provinces and Fahreus (1976) noted it as one of two, of which the Aurelian included Europe to the S and E of the Caledonide orogen. Klapper & Johnson (1980), with more information, maintain that most Devonian genera were not endemic. They show that some endemism occurred in near-shore facies, but that widespread and cosmopolitan species occur primarily in the offshore biofacies. Most conodont genera have a uniform distribution in pan-tropical areas of the Devonian and very probably of the Carboniferous as well.

In near-shore facies in northern Britain crustaceans and fish have been found together and in unexpected numbers. Well-preserved 'shrimps' from Scotland have recently been described by Briggs & Clarkson (1983), and similar forms are known in N America.

Marine vertebrates

Devonian marine placoderms, acanthodians, osteichthyes and chondriechthyes are well known in Europe and N America, but no Devonian placoderm survived into the Carboniferous. They are predominantly mobile nektonic carnivores. Signor & Brett (1984) note that a rapid radiation of vigorous predators, which included not only placoderm and chondriechthyan fishes but also plyllocaidd and eumalacostracan arthropods, began in mid-Devonian times. Coincident predation-resistant features seem to have been developed in, amongst others, brachiopods, ammonoids and crinoids. The late Devonian arthrodires of eastern N America include *Dinichthys* and other genera of very large size; similar giants are known from the Baltic area and N Africa. The shark lineage can be traced to the most primitive known—*Cladoselache*, which is a small form very common in the late Devonian Cleveland shale of Ohio. Amongst osteichthyes the acanthodians reached their acme: the three great groups actinopterygii, crossopterygii and dipnoi had appeared before mid-Devonian time and now set out on an evolutionary radiation of great importance. All are known from both marine and freshwater facies, but far fewer Devonian species are known from marine environments than from freshwater. If marine vertebrates were affected by the extinctions experienced by the invertebrates towards the end of the Devonian, little sign of it is present in the record. Recent discoveries (Janvier & Lund 1983) in the Carboniferous (Namurian) Bear Gulch limestone in Montana indicate that lampreys had evolved by that time and were, at least for part of their life cycle, marine as they are today. Previously lampreys have been recorded from the mid-Pennsylvanian of Illinois (Bardack & Zangerl 1971, Bardack & Richardson 1977).

In Carboniferous times the principal actinopterygians were palaeoniscoids. White (1927) described palaeoniscoids from the near-shore facies of the lower Carboniferous of Berwickshire, and other palaeoniscoid fish faunas are known from eastern Canada (Gardiner 1966). Detailed studies of Pennsylvanian fishes in the American mid-continent indicate a remarkable abundance and variety of palaeoniscoid and chondreichthyan fishes in lagoons and swamp pools (Zangerl & Richardson 1963); the dipnoi steadily declined while the crossopterygians diversified as rhipidistians and coelacanths. Nevertheless, the Carboniferous dipnoi were very widespread in Europe and N America. The diversity of aquatic habitats within and around the equatorial seaway to the S of the Caledonides must have been a prime factor in this evolutionary episode. At Bearsden, near Glasgow, spectacularly well-preserved sharks and at least six other fishes in the lowest Namurian reveal close affinities to those of the Bear Gulch limestone (Wood 1982). The abundance of shelly benthos seems likely to have led to the evolution of shell-crushing sharks within the early Carboniferous. At the same time other sharks entered the freshwaters. The ability of all these forms to migrate rapidly and to adapt to the predatory mode of life must have ensured their rapid spread throughout the warmer seas of the world. However, our knowledge of the animals themselves is poor. For example, Lund (1983) notes 19 nominal species of the chondriechthyan *Polyrhizodus* from N America and six from the Carboniferous limestone of Great Britain. Most are known virtually from their detention only, and some, in addition, are known from fin spines.

Continental faunas

The origins of air-breathing animals in both the Laurentian and Baltic regions appear to extend back into Silurian non-marine habitats (Rolfe 1980, 1982, Chaloner & Lawson 1985). Similar phenomena are found in continental areas (e.g. Australia) (Young 1981). The continental biota of the Devonian and Carboniferous world has been reviewed by Panchen (1980). Although the air-breathing abilities of the arthropoda and vertebrates were of prime importance, they are relatively poorly documented. The purely aquatic forms such as molluscs and fish were more abundant. The distribution of all these forms except the bivalvia is poorly known, although the controlling factors are apparent (Fig. 3).

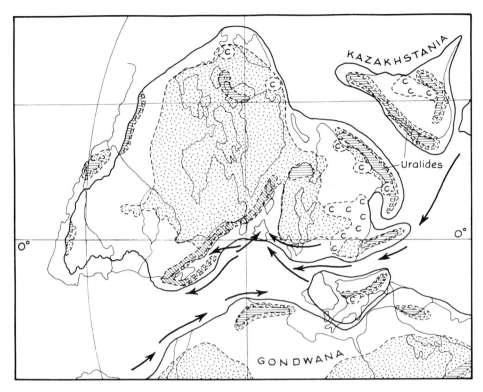

FIG. 3. Early Carboniferous geography of the Laurussian continent and adjacent landmasses. Key as for Fig. 2; C, coal-swamp areas.

Non-marine bivalve faunas

Devonian non-marine bivalvia are well known from the regions around the orogen in both N America and Europe. Their marine relatives showed an Old World Province affinity in early Devonian times, but almost all were cosmopolitan in the late Devonian (Kříž 1979).

Late Carboniferous, especially Westphalian, non-marine formations are characterized by bivalve faunas (Eagar 1961) that have become the basis for a zonal scheme broadly applicable from Appalachia to eastern Europe. The fossils are clearly facies related to a high degree, and their distribution reflects the wide range of freshwater aquatic environments along the southern flank of the Laurussian landmass and perhaps also along the coastal margins of the European Variscan 'highs' and other uplifts in the Appalachian region. The easternmost provinces of Canada in particular possess a succession of forms closely akin to that in western Europe.

Vertebrates

Devonian

The five faunal provinces distinguished by Young (1981) for the vertebrates of the early Devonian were regions in which certain major groups had invaded the freshwater environments and thereafter differentiated in relative isolation. The Caledonide orogen lay within the Euramerica or Cephalaspid Province; the other provinces were the Amphiaspid (Siberia), Tanuaspid (Tuva), Galeaspid–Yunnanolepid (S China) and Wuttagoonaspid–Phyllolepid (E Gondwana). Dispersal of placoderms and osteichthyes was to take place between Euramerica and E Gondwana during the late Devonian. The euarthrodires may have originated in Euramerica, while the antiarchs seem to appear first in S China; *Phyllolepis*, a cosmopolitan placoderm genus, occurs in rocks older in Gondwana than elsewhere. Thus during the early part of the time-span examined here vertebrate migration between Euramerica, S China and E Gondwana at least was taking place. Nevertheless, certain elements of the Euramerican Province remained endemic. The anaspids and the cephalaspids became virtually extinct by the end of the early Devonian, but persisted in one locality (Escuminac, E Canada) until Frasnian time. They are unknown elsewhere, and there was a sudden, universal and conspicuous decline of agnatha at the end of the early Devonian. The placoderms and osteichthyes, however, were ascendant. The Euramerican Province retained a rich vertebrate freshwater fauna throughout middle and late Devonian times (Gross 1950, Dineley & Loeffler 1979, Lyarskaya 1981, Sokolov *et al.* 1981). Antiarchi are conspicuous but include only a few endemic species. Arthrodires are less frequent and less diverse than in the rest of the world where cosmopolitan groups were common. The osteichthyes, which are the most vigorous group of all, are remarkably cosmopolitan. Migration by one means or another, assisted by changing geographies and a spread of suitable habitats as vascular plant evolution proceeded, seems to have become relatively easy. Thus towards the end of Devonian time the freshwater vertebrate faunas were relatively cosmopolitan and well established throughout this tropical belt. Locally there may have been isolated refugia. The exceptional fauna of the Escuminac Formation of Quebec, for example, may have its origins in the late recolonization of an intermontane habitat that had been relatively isolated since the end of early Devonian time. Continuing orogenic activity (Acadian) throughout the middle Devonian may have been significant in keeping local freshwater basins relatively isolated from water systems elsewhere. Only after a long period of isolation of this habitat did more recently evolved forms (arthrodire, antiarch, acanthodian and osteichthyan) invade it.

Early Devonian vertebrate occurrences are largely in fluvial and neritic marine facies; the middle and late Devonian freshwater faunas are also extensive in lacustrine deposits (e.g. Caithness flagstone series). The faunas in the lakes were abundant and diverse. Lung fish appeared in number and the (perhaps seasonally) changing environments of the lakes brought about adaptive responses in the vertebrates. Although some forms were clearly carnivorous, it is not clear what their prey was. Aquatic invertebrates are remarkably rare in these sediments.

Nevertheless it was from one group of active predatory osteichthyids that the earliest known tetrapods seem to have evolved. Tetrapod footprints, which may be middle Devonian, and a further primitive late Devonian amphibian are known from scant evidence in Australia (Campbell & Bell 1977). The ichthyostegids of E Greenland occur in fluvial sediments at the top of the Devonian system (Säve-Söderbergh 1932, Jarvik 1948).

Greiner (1978) suggested that an 'Acadian Divide' within the orogen is indicated by westward-flowing drainage systems in N America and easterly flowing streams on the European–African side of the orogen. The evidence for this needs to be examined in detail, but Greiner believed that the ichthyostegids and the problematic *Elpistostega* (of Escuminac) were confined to the W of the Divide whereas the Devonian osteolepid *Latvius* was confined to the E. In view of the minimal number of ichthyostegid localities the apparent distribution may reflect only the shortage of data (Rayner 1971).

Carboniferous

It is well known that the marine transgressions of late Devonian time extended into the early Carboniferous, and it should be noted that late Devonian non-marine habitats also persisted into the Carboniferous. Nevertheless there seems to have been a marked local diminution in the distribution, abundance and variety of the freshwater vertebrates at the end of the Frasnian and the end of the Famennian. Thus early Carboniferous freshwater vertebrates are rare in the Caledonide region. Fish are limited to acanthodians, palaeoniscoids, dipnoi, osteolepiformes and chondreichthyes in eastern Canada and mainland Europe. The remarkable (lacustrine) Tournaisian Albert shale of E Canada is famous for its well-preserved palaeoniscoids. The fauna include *Rhadinichthys alberti*, *Elonichthys browni*, *Elonichthys ellsi* and *Canobius*, genera which are well known in Europe. Greiner (1974) also claims the Devonian *Latvius* here, which means that by this time his 'Acadian Divide' was presumably no longer effective.

Dipnoi are similarly well known in Europe. *Ctenodus* and *Sagenodus* are genera common in Europe but rare in N American Mississippian and Pennsylvanian rocks (Baird 1978).

From their late Devonian beginnings in the Euramerican Province the tetrapods radiated (as amphibia and then also as reptiles) in the Carboniferous. None is recorded from the Tournaisian in Britain, but the record from higher stages on both sides of the present Atlantic is important if not extensive.

Rare amphibians are known from the Tournaisian of W Virginia and Nova Scotia, and Viséan forms are known from Scotland, Czechoslovakia and Ohio. The two major groups of Palaeozoic amphibia, the labyrinthodonts and the lepospondyls, were well established in Laurussia by Westphalian times (Carroll 1967, Carroll *et al.* 1972, Boyd 1984). Milner & Panchen (1973) and Panchen (1973) listed the known occurrences of the Carboniferous tetrapods, and later the ecological influences for their spread from central Europe westwards as far as Texas were discussed (Panchen 1977, 1980). Johnson (1980, 1981) notes an apparent progressive shift of tetrapod sites southward during the Carboniferous and relates it to the northward drift of the continent. Thus tetrapods appear to have preferred the equatorial environment, with Carboniferous occurrences unknown from Gondwanaland which was presumably enduring older climates. The distribution of the amphibia within the equatorial realm seems likely to have been closely controlled ecologically, rather than by region, and the Caledonides appear to abut an area of a cosmopolitan tetrapod fauna (see Milner 1987).

Continental floras

Floral regions and provinces and the problems of their fossil interpretation

A large number of different terms is used to describe the same units in modern plant biogeography. Good (1974) refers to six floral kingdoms (Boreal, Neotropical, Palaeotropical, Cape, Australian and Antarctic), which are divided into 37 regions. In addition the Mediterranean Region, for example, can further be divided into E Mediterranean, N Mediterranean etc. Cox & Moore (1980) refer to Good's kingdoms as regions and elevate his two Palaeotropical sub-kingdoms to regions. French plant geographers also refer to floral regions at the top of their hierarchy and define them as areas of any size distinguished by certain types of plants, with 50%–70% of the genera being endemic. These are then divided into domains, sectors and sub-sectors. In very few cases is the term 'floral province' used.

A multiplicity of terms is used for palaeophytogeographic units. Chaloner & Meyen (1973) use four orders, kingdom, area, province and district, for the Carboniferous and Permian floras. Other workers refer to suite, zone, flora, floral unit, region, biome etc. Here we use *floral region* as probably equivalent to Chaloner and Meyen's *kingdom* and floral province as equivalent to their *area*.

It is relatively easy to establish modern phyto-geographic units at any hierarchial level. These are influenced in their distribution by altitude, latitude, geographic separation, climate and soils. Similar conditions may result in certain extant genera or species being circumpolar, circumtemperate or circumequatorial in their distribution. Whether or not they form part of a single floral unit will depend upon analysis of the total flora. In any modern area it is possible to record every plant that is growing and, because of the completeness (non-fragmentary nature) of this approach, the results should be totally objective.

With fossil plants, however, it is much more difficult to interpret biogeographic units. The plants will be transported from their area of growth, and their remains will be fragmentary and often difficult to identify. The fossil record will be biased towards those plants growing in lowland areas because upland plants will suffer more microbial decay and may never reach areas of anaerobic deposition. Other problems include lack of outcrop, reworking and, in many continental sections, lack of stratigraphic control. Further investigation may add information to a genus or species which could render it less useful in floral interpretation. For example the Devonian dispersed spore *Samarisporites triangulatus* appeared to be endemic to the Old Red Sandstone continent (McGregor 1979), but more recent work in China (Lu Lichang 1980) shows it to be more widespread in its occurrence (Allen 1982). Initially it seemed significant that the progymnosperm *Svalbardia* occurred to the E of the Caledonian orogenic belt and not to the W, but further work revealed it in Greenland (Friend *et al.* 1983) and New York State (Matten 1981). The distinctive microphyll of the lycopod *Leclercqia* was known only in New York State until Fairon-Demaret (1981) found it in Belgium. Moreover, Fairon-Demaret (1980) has shown that some specimens formerly referred to the widespread genus *Protolepidodendron* have *Leclercqia*-type microphylls. More recently Thomas & Purdy (1982) recorded the lycopsid *Tomiodendron*, a genus previously regarded as being confined to the Angaran Floral Region, from the early Carboniferous of England. Thus, extreme caution must be exercised in recording a fossil floral unit on the presence or absence of certain genera and species.

It is interesting to speculate whether, if Good's (1974) six floral kingdoms of modern plant geography were subjected to fossilization, the worldwide dominance of the four families Leguminosae, Compositae, Poaceae (Graminae) and Cyperaceae would be said to indicate more than one fossil floral region.

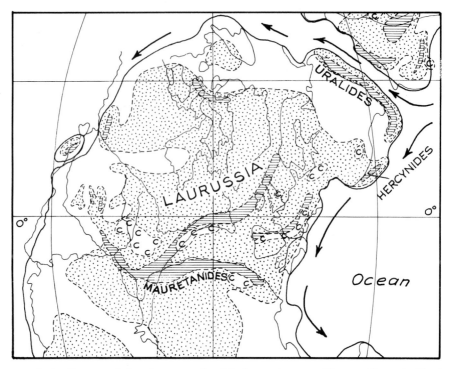

FIG. 4. Late Carboniferous–early Permian geography of the Laurussian part of Pangaea. Key as for Fig. 3.

Devonian

Arber (1921) argued for the existence of two Devonian macrofloras, a lower *Psilophyton* flora and an upper *Archaeopteris* flora, on the basis largely of information from the western hemisphere. Kräusel (1937) added a third and intermediate *Hyenia* flora to these, the three being approximately equivalent to the lower, middle and upper Devonian. Leclercq (1940) supported Kräusel's tripartite division, but recommended that *Protopteridium* (now *Rellimia*) should replace *Hyenia* as the name for the middle assemblage as this genus includes a larger number of species with a wider geographic distribution.

As the result of much recent research, particularly in N America, Europe, the USSR and China, Banks (1980) has described seven biozones for the Siluro-Devonian which are based on macroplant assemblages of diagnostic genera. However, Devonian plants are commonly fragmentary and are not confined by stratigraphic boundaries or good stratigraphic control, and Banks (1980) admits that his zonation is very tentative. The floral zones of Arber, Kräusel and Banks are of course stratigraphic and not geographic, the implication being that at any one

time during the Devonian only one floral region can be identified worldwide.

Middle Devonian

Groups of plants common throughout this timespan were the Lycopsida, the Cladoxylopsida and the Progymnospermopsida. Heterospory, which probably occurred before the close of the lower Devonian, is more marked, and megaspore tetrads in which three partially abhort appear by Givetian times (Allen 1972). Secondary xylem, enabling the pteridophytes and progymnosperms to attain arborescent proportions, is first demonstrated in the Givetian.

Few Eifelian floras are known except in the USSR (Petrosian 1968), but Givetian floras are common. Banks (1980) divided the middle Devonian into two stratigraphic biozones, a lower *Hyenia* zone and an upper *Svalbardia* zone. However, many of the floras are not accurately dated, and genera which occur in the lower zone continue into the upper zone; they will be referred to here only as middle Devonian floras. Within Laurussia, middle Devonian floras have been described from eastern Canada, the eastern

U.S.A., Scotland, Belgium, the F.R.G., Czechoslovakia, Norway and Spitsbergen (see bibliography in Banks (1980)). For comparison, Siberian and Kazakhstanian floras are recorded by Iurina (1969) and Petrosian (1968).

The well-documented floras of the F.R.G. and Belgium include the lycopsids *Leclercqia*, *Estinnophyton* and *Drepanophycus*, the cladoxylopsids *Cladoxylon*, *Pseudosporochunus* and *Calamophyton*, the progymnospermopsids *Aneurophyton* and *Rellimia*, and *Hyenia* which is of debatable affinity. The flora from the F.R.G. also includes a number of flabelliform 'leaves'. The New York State flora contains a high proportion of lycopsids (Grierson & Banks 1963). The petrified New York progymnosperms are difficult to compare with compressed material from other areas.

In broad terms, there seems to be little difference in composition between floras of western and eastern Laurussia or from N to S. Representatives of the Lycopsida, Cladoxylopsida and Progymnospermopsida are common throughout. *Drepanophycus*, *Psilophyton* and *Taeniocrada*, which are more abundant in the lower Devonian, occur in both western and eastern Laurussia and indeed in Kazakhstania. *Aneurophyton* and *Svalbardia* occur over the same area, and many other genera are found throughout Laurussia. The floras recorded from Siberia are rather similar. Floras from Kazakhstania (Senkevich 1961, Petrosian 1968), however, contain a number of endemic genera, particularly lycopsida, suggesting some development in geographical isolation.

In terms of climate, a single floral province is not unexpected. Laurussia probably lay within the tropical belt and had a fairly uniform climate. Any climatic changes with altitude would not be reflected in the plants fossilized which, as mentioned earlier, would have been derived mostly from lowland areas. It is perhaps a little surprising that any geographical isolation between western and eastern Laurussia on either side of the Caledonian mountain ranges is not reflected in the flora.

Upper Devonian

As in the middle Devonian, the Lycopsida, Cladoxylopsida and Progymnospermopsida are dominant. Coenopteridopsida or their precursors are also recorded, together with the first undoubted Sphenopsida. Arborescent Lycopsida, which are relatives of the large Carboniferous lepidodendrids, appear. The first isolated seeds of both radiaspermic (Gillespie *et al.* 1981) and platyspermic (Chaloner *et al.* 1977) construction occur, indicating that both major lines of the gymnosperms had evolved by upper Devonian times. It is possible that some of the radiaspermic seeds may belong to plants at present recorded as progymnosperms.

Banks (1980) divided this epoch into two biozones, a lower *Archaeopteris* zone and an upper *Rhacophyton* zone. Detailed comparison of upper and lower floras is difficult because there are few Frasnian floras; some are recorded as being just upper Devonian. The best-known earlier floras are those from New York State and Pennsylvania (Banks 1966). They are dominated by the progymnosperm *Archaeopteris*, which is an important genus of worldwide distribution, occurring not only throughout Laurussia but in Siberia, Kazakhstania, China and Australia. Other progymnosperms include *Tetraxylopteris* and *Aneurophyton*; the latter also occurs in eastern Laurussia. Of the lycopods, *Colpodexylon* has been found only in the eastern USA whereas *Archaeosigillaria* and *Drepanophycus* also occur in eastern Laurussia. *Pseudosporochnus*, which is common in the middle Devonian of Belgium, is also abundant. *Zosterophyllopsida*, which is so important in the Lower Devonian, continues with *Sawdonia* and *Serrulacaulis*. A lack of well-documented Frasnian floras elsewhere in Laurussia makes comparisons difficult. However, on the evidence to date, only one floral region can be identified in Laurussia and worldwide at this time.

Comparison of Fammenian and lowest Tournaisian floras is more satisfactory. The Bear Island flora is the best known. It includes the lycopsids *Sublepidodendron*, *Pseudolepidodendropsis* and *Cyclostigma*, the probable sphenopsids *Pseudobornia* and *Sphenophyllum*, the progymnosperm *Archaeopteris*, the coenopteridopsid-like *Rhacophyton*, flabelliform 'leaves', seeds and possibly *Leptophloeum* (Nathorst 1902, Schweitzer 1967, 1969). Similar floras with Bear Island elements occur in southern Britain and Ireland, the F.R.G., Belgium and eastern N America. Petrosian (1968) records similar genera in western U.S.S.R.

A comparison of Fammenian and lowest Tournaisian megaspore floras (Winslow 1962, Allen & Robson 1981, Higgs & Scott 1982) also indicates similar assemblages for Laurussian localities. The megaspore assemblages contain a large number of species with an apical prominence (gula) probably indicative of an increase in arborescent lycopsids.

Outside Laurussia there are indications that the Siberian floras are similar, but in Kazakhstania there is a predominance of lycopsids, especially *Leptophloeum*, whilst *Archaeopteris* is absent. There is therefore continuing evidence for the geographical isolation of Kazakhstania at this time. Within Laurussia, all that can be said at present is that at any one time there was probably only one floral region but that the earlier floras differ from the later ones. Distribution maps of middle and upper Devonian floras can be found in Edwards (1973).

Carboniferous and early Permian

Early Carboniferous

Groups of plants which were common during this period were the Lycopsida, which included the first of the very large lepidodendrids, the Sphenopsida, the Coenopteridopsida, the Filicopsida, which were the first true ferns, and the Gymnopermopsida. The progymnosperms continued into the lower Carboniferous, but were not such an important group as in the middle and upper Devonian.

Jongmans (1952) recorded a more or less uniform lower Carboniferous flora as being worldwide in distribution. This was named the *Lepidodendropsis* flora, and *Lepidodendropsis*, *Rhacopteris* and *Triphyllopteris* were cited as characteristic genera.

Pal & Chaloner (1979) comment that subsequent research has generally confirmed that the lower Carboniferous flora was fairly uniform and lycopod rich, and they give generic lists. Since the work of Jongmans (1952), attempts have been made to divide the *Lepidodendropsis* flora into separate floral units.

Using miospore assemblages Sullivan (1967) recorded three Viséan suites, mostly for the northern hemisphere. According to Sullivan (following Van Hilten 1962), these suites lay within broad latitudinal belts parallel to the palaeo-equator, and were climatically controlled. They were named the *Grandispora* suite to 20°N, the *Molinospora* suite to 50°N, and the *Kazakhstan* suite which was more temperate and found only in Kazakhstania. On the basis of the palaeogeographic reconstruction of Bambach et al. (1980) many of the *Molinospora* suite localities fall very near the palaeo-equator, indicating that Sullivan's suites may not be climatically controlled.

Ziegler et al. (1981), in a statistical analysis of genera, refer to three phytogeographic units in the lower Carboniferous which they called the Angaran Unit (northern polar high-latitude temperate), the Gondwanan Unit (southern temperate) and the Circum-Tethyan Unit (equatorial).

Laurussia forms part of the Circum-Tethyan Unit (here called the Circum-Tethyan Region), which according to Ziegler et al. (1981) also includes Kazakhstania and China. There is some evidence for the separation of the Circum-Tethyan Region into N and S Circum-Tethyan Provinces. This is suggested by Ziegler et al. (1981), who included floras from northern Scotland, Spitsbergen and the Donetz Basin together with Kazakhstan, the Malay Peninsula and S China within the N Circum-Tethyan Province. Their S Circum-Tethyan Province encompasses the southern Laurussian localities in the USA and France together with Spiti in India. Within Laurussia, further evidence for this separation into two provinces is shown by the similarity between early Carboniferous anatomically preserved plants (Scott et al. 1984) in the USA and France. In Laurussia, the N Circum-Tethyan Province would include Sullivan's (1967) *Molinospora* suite and the S Province would include his *Grandispora* suite.

Opinions vary as to whether the Kazakhstanian floral localities should be separate from those referred to the N Circum-Tethyan Province here. Sullivan (1967) records a separate Kazakhstan suite, while Chaloner & Meyen (1973) refer to Kazakhstan as having a flora intermediate between the Circum-Tethyan Region and the Angaran Region (see also Vakhrameev et al. 1970).

However, Radchenko refers to a Scottish–Kazakhstanian flora (see Meyen 1976), and Ziegler et al. (1981) include the Kazakhstan localities in the N Circum-Tethyan Province. If the early Carboniferous world maps (Bambach et al. 1980) are correct and if, as suggested, the China floras were similar to those in northern Laurussia, it is unlikely that the flora of Kazakhstania, which is placed geographically between the two, would be different.

In summary, it appears that during the early Carboniferous there were three latitudinal floral regions, a northern Angaran (Siberia) Region, a central Circum-Tethyan Region (Laurussia, Kazakhstania and China) and a southern Gondwanan Region (Gondwana). The Circum-Tethyan Region can be divided (Table 1) into a northern province (N Laurussia, Kazakhstania and China) and a southern province (USA, France and part of India). It is recognized that certain genera occur in more than one region.

The separation of Laurussian floras from those N and S would appear to be climatic. Within Laurussia itself we might have expected the floras to be different on opposing sides of the orogen. The fact that they are N–S suggests a climatic separation.

Late Carboniferous

Within Laurussia, groups of plants common during this epoch are similar to those in the early Carboniferous. Dominant amongst the pterido-phytes are the Lycopsida with the large lepidod-endrids including *Lepidodendron*, *Lepidophloios* and *Sigillaria*, the Sphenopsida with *Calamites* and *Sphenophyllum*, and the Filicopsida with *Acitheca* and *Asterotheca*. The other dominant group is the gymnosperms, with the pteridosper-males including *Alethopteris* and *Neuropteris* and the Cordaitales with *Cordaites*.

With climatic changes, the lycopsid-dominated floras of the Westphalian were replaced in the Stephanian by floras in which tree ferns and pteridosperms were more dominant (Phillips *et al.* 1974). Based on coal palynology and studies of compressions and permineralized peat, there has been much recent work in mid and eastern N America and Europe on climatic changes and palaeo-ecological interpretations of the West-phalian coal-swamp floras (Phillips *et al.* 1974, Scott 1979, Phillips & Peppars 1984, Dimichelle *et al.* 1985). However, in terms of defining floral regions and provinces these upper Carboniferous floras from Laurussia together with those from Kazakhstan, China and Indonesia form a single Circum-Tethyan Floral Region (see Table 1).

Two floral provinces can be recognized in Laurussia. E Laurussia together with Kazakhs-tania form the Euramerian province, whilst W of

the Rocky Mountains the floras show some differences. Unlike those to the E, these floras do not occur in coal basins. They are generally poor in arborescent lycopsids and contain certain Permian elements. Read (1947) referred to these as the Cordilleran flora, and suggested that events within the Rocky Mountain orogenic belt in-creased upland habitats which supported a different flora from the swamp forests further E. Whether or not this Cordilleran flora (here referred to as the Cordilleran Province) occurred further E in more upland areas is unproven, although Permian differences between western and eastern Laurussia suggest that there may have been a geographic barrier between the two areas during the late Carboniferous (Fig. 4).

Early Permian

Worldwide differentiation into floral regions is more marked at this epoch than during any previous time. Laurussia, Kazakhstania and China, which formed a single Circum-Tethyan Floral Region in the Carboniferous, can now be divided into separate floral regions. In Laurussia the area can be divided into E and W regions. The Euramerican Floral Region of eastern Lau-russia includes genera which characterize the area—*Sigillaria*, *Calamites*, *Sphenophyllum*, *Pe-copteris*, *Alethopteris*, *Neuropteris* and *Cordaites*, all of which were present in this area in late

TABLE 1. *Floral regions and provinces in, and associated with, Laurussia*

Age	Laurussia*	Areas outside Laurussia with similar floras
Early Permian	EURAMERICAN FLORAL REGION N AMERICAN FLORAL REGION *Supaia* Floral Province *Glenopteris* Floral Province *Gigantopteris* Floral Province	Distinct floral regions elsewhere
Late Carboniferous	CIRCUM-TETHYAN FLORAL REGION Euramerian Floral Province Cordilleran Floral Province	Kazakhstania and China also in Cir-cum-Tethyan Floral Region Kazakhstania part of Euramerian Floral Province China in Cathaysian Floral Province
Early Carboniferous	CIRCUM-TETHYAN FLORAL REGION N Circum-Tethyan Floral Province S Circum-Tethyan Floral Province	Kazakhstania and China also in Cir-cum-Tethyan Floral Region Kazakhstania and China in N Circum-Tethyan Floral Province Parts of India in S Circum-Tethyan Floral Province
Middle and late Devonian	ONE FLORAL REGION WORLDWIDE, WITH SOME VARIATION IN INDIVIDUAL FLORAS	

*Euramerican refers only to areas in Europe and America; Euramerian also includes Kazakhstania.

Carboniferous time—together with the more typically Permian species *Callipteris*, *Lebachia* and *Ernestiodendron*. Lower Permian floras typical of this floral region occur throughout Europe. The dating of the flora of the eastern USA as lower Permian is more doubtful.

In western Laurussia, in what is now the southwestern USA, the floras include *Callipteris*, *Sphenophyllum*, *Walchia*, *Taeniopteris*, *Supaia*, *Glenopteris* and *Gigantopteris*, and were referred to as the N American Kingdom and Area by Chaloner & Meyen (1973). We refer to it here as the N American Region. Read & Mamay (1964) separated this region into three separate floras: a more western *Supaia* flora occurring in Arizona, New Mexico and Utah, a more eastern *Glenopteris* flora in Kansas, and a slightly older *Gigantopteris* flora in Oklahoma and N Texas. Read & Mamay (1964) suggested that the separation of the *Supaia* flora from the *Giganopteris* flora may be due to a topographic (Rocky Mountains) barrier. These three floras are called floral provinces here (Table 1).

With reference to early Permian floras worldwide, a number of general points emerge. The continued separation of Siberia, Kazakhstania and lands further E is reflected in an increasing regionality in floras E of Laurussia. The appearance of two floral regions in Laurussia suggests that, as climatic conditions were probably similar throughout, there may have been geographical isolation between western and eastern Laurussia. Finally, the totally dissimilar flora of Gondwanaland may reflect a change in climatic conditions there rather than geographic isolation from Laurussia. Distribution maps of Carboniferous and Permian floras have been given by Chaloner & Lacey (1973) and Chaloner & Meyen (1973).

Summarizing comments

In summary, the region around the Caledonide–Appalachian orogen was subjected to repeated marine transgressions throughout the period from mid-Devonian to the end of the Carboniferous and widely different sedimentary environments existed within relatively small areas. The region lay within the tropics and was probably influenced by strongly-flowing westward ocean currents and weather systems. Transport of organisms westwards from the Moscovian Sea would have been relatively swift and effective; minor currents may have transported organisms eastwards. N–S transport between Laurussia and NW Africa was not greatly inhibited during this period. Continental habitats were regulated by climate, relief and the evolution of vascular terrestrial floras. Amphibia and, somewhat later, reptiles appear to have been able to migrate throughout the southern coastal belt of Laurussia, and in the Permian they spread S into Gondwana.

References

ALLEN, K. C. 1972. Devonian megaspores from East Greenland: their bearing on the development of certain trends. *Review of Palaeobotany and Palynology*, **14**, 7–17.

—— 1982. *Samarisporites triangulatus* Allen 1965, an important Devonian miospore, and its synonymous species. *Pollen et Spores*, **24**, 157–66.

—— & ROBSON, J. 1981. Megaspores with multifurcate and bifurcate processes from Old Red Sandstone Facies of Tournaisian age, from the Taft Gorge, South Glamorgan, Wales. *New Phytology*, **88**, 387–98.

ARBER, E. A. N. 1921. *Devonian Floras*. Cambridge University Press, Cambridge, 100 pp.

BAILEY, J. B. 1978. Provincialism and migration in Lower Devonian Pelecypods. *Palaeogeography, Palaeoclimatology, Palaeoecology*, **23**, 119–30.

BAIRD, D. 1978. Studies on Carboniferous freshwater fishes. *American Museum Novitates No. 2641*, pp. 1–22.

BAMBACH, R. K., SCOTESE, C. R. & ZIEGLER, A. M. 1980. Before Pangaea: the geographies of the Paleozoic world. *American Scientist*, **68**, 26–38.

BANKS, H. P. 1966. Devonian flora of New York State. *Empire State Geogram*, **4**(3), 10–24.

—— 1980. Floral assemblages in the Siluro-Devonian. *In*: DILCHER, D.L. & TAYLOR, T.B. (eds) *Biostratigraphy of Fossil Plants*, pp. 1–24, Dowden, Hutchinson & Ross, Philadelphia, PA.

BARDACK, D. & RICHARDSON, E. S. 1977. New agnathous fishes from the Pennsylvanian of Illinois. *Fieldiana, Geology*, **33**, 489–510.

—— & ZANGERL, R. 1971. Lampreys in the fossil record. *In*: HARDISTY, M.W. & POTTER, I.C. (eds) *The Biology of Lampreys*, pp. 67–84.

BLESS, M. J. M. & WINKLER-PRINS, C. F. 1972. Palaeoecology and palaeogeography of the Aegir Marine Band and its equivalents in North-western Europe. *Comptes Rendus du 7ème Congrès International sur la Stratigraphie et Géologie du Carbonifère, Krefeld, 1971*, Vol. 1, pp. 231–9.

BOUCOT, A. J. 1975. *Evolution and Extinction Rate Controls*, Elsevier, Amsterdam, 427 pp.

—— & GRAY, J. 1979. Epilogue: A Paleozoic Pangaea? *In*: BOUCOT, A.J. & GRAY, J. (eds) *Historical Biogeography, Plate Tectonics and the Changing Environments*, pp. 465–82, Oregon State University Press, Corvallis, OR.

—— & —— 1983. A Paleozoic Pangaea. *Science*, **222**, 571–81.

BOWEN, Z. P., RHOADS, D. C. & MCALESTER, A. L. 1974. Marine benthic communities in the upper Devonian of New York. *Lethaia*, **7**, 93–120.

BOYD, M. J. 1984. The upper Carboniferous tetrapod assemblage from Nesham, Northumberland. *Palaeontology*, **27**, 367–92.

BRIGGS, D. E. G. & CLARKSON, E. N. K. 1983. The Carboniferous Granton Shrimp-bed, Edinburgh. *In*: BRIGGS, D.E.G. & LANE, P.D. (eds) *Trilobites and other Early Arthropods, Papers in Honour of Professor H.B. Whittington, F.R.S. Palaeontological Association Special Papers in Palaeontology No. 30*, 161–78.

BURCHETTE, T. P. 1981. European Devonian reefs: a review of current concepts and models. *In*: TOOMEY, D.F. (ed.) *European Fossil Reef Models. Special Publication of the Society of the Economics of Mining and Palaeontology No. 30*, pp. 85–142.

CALVER, M. A. 1968. Distribution of Westphalian marine faunas in Northern England and adjacent areas. *Proceedings of the Yorkshire Geological Society*, **37**, 1–72.

CAMPBELL, K. S. W. & BELL, M. W. 1977. A primitive amphibian from the Late Devonian of New South Wales. *Alcheringa*, **1**, 369–81.

CARROLL, R. L. 1967. Labyrinthodonts from the Goggins Formation. *Journal of Palaeontology*, **41**, 111–42.

——, BELT, E. S., DINELEY, D. L., BAIRD, D. & MCGREGOR, D. C. 1972. *Vertebrate Paleontology of Eastern Canada, Excursion A59 Guidebook, 24th International Geological Congress, Montreal*, 113 pp.

CHALONER, W. G., HILL, A. J. & LACEY, W. S. 1977. First Devonian platyspermic seed and its implications in gymnosperm evolution. *Nature, London*, **265**, 233–5.

—— & LACEY, W. S. 1973. The distribution of late palaeozoic floras. *Organisms and Continents through Time. Palaeontological Association Special Papers in Palaeontology No. 12*, pp. 271–89.

—— & LAWSON, J. D. 1985. Evolution and environments in the late Silurian and early Devonian. *Philosophical Transactions of the Royal Society, Series B*, 309.

—— & MEYEN, S. V. 1973. Carboniferous and Permian floras of the northern continents. *In*: HALLAM, A. (ed.) *Atlas of Palaeobiogeography*, pp. 169–86, Elsevier, Amsterdam.

COX, C. B. & MOORE, P. D. 1980. *Biogeography, an Ecological and Evolutionary Approach*, Blackwell Scientific Publications, Oxford, 234 pp.

DIMICHELE, W. A., PHILLIPS, T. L. & PEPPARS, R. A. 1985. The influence of climate and depositional environment on the distribution and evolution of Pennsylvanian coal-swamp plants. *In*: TIFFNEY, B.H. (ed.) *Geological Factors and the Evolution of Plants*, pp. 223–56, Yale University Press, New Haven, CT.

DINELEY, D. L. & LOEFFLER, E. J. 1979. Early vertebrates and the Caledonian earth movements. *In*: HARRIS, A.L., HOLLAND, C.H. & LEAKE, B.E. (eds) *The Caledonides of the British Isles Reviewed.*

Special Publication of the Geological Society of London No. 8, pp. 411–14.

EAGAR, R. M. C. 1961. A summary of the results of recent work on the palaeoecology of Carboniferous non-marine lamellibranchs. *Comptes Rendus du Congrès d'Avances Etudes de la Stratigraphie et Géologie du Carbonifère, Heerlen, 1958*, Vol. 1, pp. 137–49.

EDWARDS, D. 1973. Devonian floras. *In*: HALLAM, A. (ed.) *Atlas of Palaeobiogeography*, pp. 105–15, Elsevier, Amsterdam.

ERBEN, H. K. 1964. Facies developments in the marine Devonian of the Old World. *Proceedings of the Ussher Society*, **1**, 92–118.

FAHREUS, L. 1976. Conodontophorid ecology and evolution related to global tectonics. *Geological Association of Canada Special Paper No. 15*, pp. 11–26.

FAIRON-DEMARET, M. 1980. A propos des spécimens déterminés *Protolepidodendron scharianum* par Kräusel et Weyland, 1932. *Review of Palaeobotany and Palynology*, **29**, 201–20.

—— 1981. Le genre *Leclercqia* Banks, Bonamo et Grierson 1972 dans le Devonien Moyen de Belgique. *Bulletin de l'Institut Royal des Sciences Naturelles de Belgique Sciences de la Terre*, **31**(12), 1–10.

FRIEND, P. F., ALEXANDER-MARRACK, P. D., ALLEN, K. C., NICHOLSON, J. & YEATS, A. K. 1983. Devonian sediments of East Greenland VI. Review of results. *Meddelelser om Grønland*, **206**, 1–96.

GARDINER, B. G. 1966. Catalogue of Canadian fossil fishes. *Royal Ontario Museum Life Sciences Contributions No. 68*, 154 pp.

GILLESPIE, W. H., ROTHWELL, G. W. & SCHECKLER, S. E. 1981. The world's oldest seeds. *Nature, London*, **293**, 462–4.

GOLDRING, R. & LANGENSTRASSEN, F. 1979. Open shelf and near-shore clastic facies in the Devonian. *In*: HOUSE, M.R., SCRUTTON, C.T. & BASSETT, M.G. *The Devonian System. Palaeontological Association Special Papers in Palaeontology No. 23*, pp. 81–98.

GOOD, R. 1974. *The Geography of Flowering Plants*, 4th edn, Longman, London, 557 pp.

GREINER, H. 1974. The Albert Formation of New Brunswick; a Palaeozoic lacustrine model. *Geologische Rundschau*, **63**, 1102–13.

—— 1978. Late Devonian facies interrelationships in bordering areas of the North Atlantic and their palaeogeographic implications. *Palaeogeography, Palaeoclimatology, Palaeoecology*, **25**, 24–263.

GRIERSON, J. D. & BANKS, H. P. 1963. Lycopods of the Devonian of New York State. *Paleontographica Americana IV*, **31**, 210–95.

GROSS, W. 1950. Die paläontologische und stratigraphische Bedeutung der Wirbeltierfaunen des Old Reds und der marinen Altpaläozoischen Schichten. *Abhandlungen der Deutschen Akademie der Wissenschaften zu Berlin, Jahrbuch 1949*, Vol. 1, 130 pp.

HAILWOOD, E. A. 1974. Palaeomagnetism of the Msissi Norite (Morocco) and the Palaeozoic reconstruction of Gondwanaland. *Earth and Planetary Science Letters*, **23**, 376–86.

HECKEL, P. H. & WITZKE, B. J. 1979. Devonian world palaeogeography determined from distribution of carbonates and related lithic climatic indicators. *In*: HOUSE, M.R., SCRUTTON, C.T. & BASSETT, M.G. (eds) *The Devonian System. Palaeontological Association Special Papers in Palaeontology No. 23*, pp. 99–124.

HIGGS, K. & SCOTT, A. C. 1982. Megaspores from the uppermost Devonian (Strunian) of Hook Head, Co. Wexford, Ireland. *Palaeontographica B*, **181**, 79–108.

HILL, D. 1973. Lower Carboniferous corals. *In*: HALLAM, A. (ed.) *Atlas of Palaeobiogeography*, pp. 133–42, Elsevier, Amsterdam.

HODSON, F. & RAMSBOTTOM, W. H. C. 1973. The distribution of Carboniferous goniatite faunas in relation to suggested continental reconstructions for the period. *Organisms and Continents through Time. Palaeontological Association Special Papers in Palaeontology No. 12*, pp. 321–9.

HOUSE, M. R. 1971. Devonian faunal distributions. *In*: MIDDLEMISS, F.A., RAWSON, P.F. & NEWALL, G. (eds) *Faunal Provinces in Space and Time. Geological Journal Special Issue No. 4*, pp. 77–94.

—— 1973. Devonian goniatites. *In*: HALLAM, A. (ed.) *Atlas of Palaeobiogeography*, pp. 97–104, Elsevier, Amsterdam.

—— 1975. Facies and time in Devonian tropical areas. *Proceedings of the Yorkshire Geological Society*, **40**, 233–87.

IURINA, A. L. 1969. The Devonian flora of Central Kazakhstan. *Materraly po Geologii Tsentral'nogo Kazakhstana*, **8**, 1–43 (in Russian).

JANVIER, P. & LUND, R. 1983. *Hardistiella montanensis* N. gen. et sp. (Petromyzontida) from the Lower Carboniferous of Montana, with remarks on the affinities of the Lampreys. *Journal of Vertebrate Palaeontology*, **2**, 407–13.

JARVIK, E. 1948. Note on the Upper Devonian vertebrate fauna of East Greenland and on the age of the ichthyostegid stegocephalians. *Arkiv før Zoologi*, **41A**, 1–8.

JOHNSON, G. A. L. 1980. Carboniferous geography and terrestrial migration routes. *In*: PANCHEN, A. L. (ed.) *The Terrestrial Environment and the Origin of Land Vertebrates. Systematics Association Special Volume 15*, pp. 39–54, Academic Press, New York.

—— 1981. Geographical evolution from Laurasia to Pangaea. *Proceedings of the Yorkshire Geological Society*, **43**, 221–52.

JONGMANS, W. J. 1952. Some problems of carboniferous stratigraphy. *Comptes Rendus du 3ème Congrès d'Avances Etudes de la Stratigraphie et Géologie du Carbonifère*, Vol. 1, pp. 295–306.

KLAPPER, G. & BARRICK, J. E. 1977. Conodont ecology: pelagic versus benthic. *Lethaia*, **11**, 15–23.

—— & JOHNSON, J. G. 1980. Endemism and dispersal of Devonian conodonts. *Journal of Paleontology*, **54**, 400–55.

KRÄUSEL, R. 1937. Die Verbreitung der Devonfloren. *Comptes Rendus du 2ème Congrès sur la Stratigraphie du Carbonifère, Heerlen, 1935*, pp. 527–37.

KŘÍŽ, J. 1979. Devonian Bivalvia. *In*: HOUSE, M.R., SCRUTTON, C.T. & BASSETT, M.G. (eds) *The Devonian System. Palaeontological Association Special Papers in Palaeontology No. 23*, pp. 255–8.

LECLERCQ, S. 1940. Contribution à l'étude de la flore du Dévonien de Belgique. *Académie Royale de Belgique, Memoires de la Classe des Sciences*, **12**, 1–65.

LU LICHANG. 1980. Devonian miospores from the Lunghuashan section in Xhanyi of Yunnan and their stratigraphic significance. *Academia Sinica, Memoirs of the Institute of Geology and Palaeontology, Nanking*, **14**, 1–50 (in Chinese, English abstract).

LUND, R. 1983. On a dentition of *Polyrhizodus* (Chondreichthyes, Petalodontiformes) from the Namurian Bear Gulch Limestone of Montana. *Journal of Vertebrate Paleontology*, **3**, 1–6.

LYARSKAYA, L. A. 1981. *Studies on Devonian Fish from the Prebaltic: Asterolepididae*, Zinatne, Riga, 152 pp.

MCGHEE, G. R., JR & SUTTON, R. G. 1976. Late Devonian benthic marine communities of the central Appalachian Allegheny Front. *Lethaia*, **9**, 111–36.

—— 1981. Late Devonian marine ecology and zoogeography of the central Appalachians and New York. *Lethaia*, **14**, 27–43.

MCGREGOR, D. C. 1979. Spores in Devonian stratigraphic correlation. *In*: HOUSE, M. R., SCRUTTON, C. T. & BASSETT, M. G. (eds) *The Devonian System. Palaeontological Association Special Papers in Palaeontology No. 23*, pp. 163–84.

MCKERROW, W. S. (ed.) 1978. *The Ecology of Fossils*, Duckworth, London, 384 pp.

MCLAREN, D. J. 1970. Time, life and boundaries. *Journal of Paleontology*, **44**, 801–15.

—— 1982. Frasnian–Famennian extinctions. *Geological Society of America Special Paper No. 190*, pp. 477–84.

—— 1983. Bolides and biostratigraphy. *Geological Society of America Bulletin*, **94**, 313–24.

MATTEN, L. C. 1981. *Svalbardia banksii* sp. nov. from the upper Devonian (Frasnian) of New York State. *American Journal of Botany*, **68**, 1383–91.

MEYEN, S. V. 1976. Carboniferous and Permian Lepidophytes of Angaraland. *Palaeontographica B*, **157**, 112–57.

MILNER, A. R. 1987. The Westphalian tetrapod fauna; some aspects of its geography and ecology. *Journal of the Geological Society*, **144**, 495–506.

—— & PANCHEN, A. L. 1973. Geographical variation in the tetrapod fauna of the Upper Carboniferous and lower Permian. *In*: TARLING, D. H. & RUNCORN, S. K. (eds) *Implications of Continental Drift to the Earth Sciences*, Vol. 1, pp. 353–68, Academic Press, New York.

NATHORST, A. G. 1902. Zur Oberdevonische flora der Bäreninsel. *K. Sven. Vetensk. Akad. Handl.*, **36**, 1–60.

OLIVER, W. A., JR 1976. Presidential address: Biogeography of Devonian Rugose corals. *Journal of Paleontology*, **50**, 365–73.

—— 1977. Biogeography of late Silurian and Devonian

rugose corals. *Palaeogeography, Palaeoclimatology, Palaeoecology*, **22**, 85–135.

PAL, A. K. & CHALONER, W. G. 1979. A lower Carboniferous *Lepidodendropsis* flora in Kashmir. *Nature, London*, **281**, 295–7.

PANCHEN, A. L. 1973. Carboniferous tetrapods. *In*: HALLAM, A. (ed.) *Atlas of Palaeobiogeography*, pp. 117–26, Elsevier, Amsterdam.

—— 1977. Geographical and ecological distribution of the earliest tetrapods. *In*: HECHT, M. K., GOODY, P. C. & HECKT, B. K. (eds) *Major Patterns in Vertebrate Evolution*, pp. 723–9, Plenum, New York.

—— (ed.) 1980. *The Terrestrial Environment and the Origin of Land Vertebrates. Systematics Association Special Volume 15*, Academic Press, New York, 633 pp.

PETROSIAN, N. M. 1968. Stratigraphic importance of the Devonian flora of the U.S.S.R. *In*: OSWALD, D. H. (ed.) *International Symposium on the Devonian System*, Vol. 1, pp. 579–86, Alberta Society of Petroleum Geology, Calgary.

PHILLIPS, T. L. & PEPPARS, R. A. 1984. Changing patterns of Pennsylvanian coal-swamp vegetation and implications of climatic control on coal occurrence. *International Journal of Coal Geology*, **3**, 205–55.

——, PEPPARS, R. A., AVCIN, M. J. & LAUGHNAN, P. F. 1974. Fossil plants and coal. Patterns of change in Pennsylvanian coal swamps of the Illinois Basin. *Science*, **184**, 1367–9.

RAUP, D. M. 1976. Species diversity in the Phanerozoic: a tabulation. *Palaeobiology*, **2**, 279–88.

RAYNER, D. H. 1971. Data on the environment and preservation of late Palaeozoic tetrapods. *Proceedings of the Yorkshire Geological Society*, **38**(4, No. 20), 437–95.

READ, C. B. 1947. Pennsylvanian floral zones and floral provinces. *Journal of Geology*, **55**, 271–9.

—— & MAMAY, S. H. 1964. Upper Paleozoic floral zones and floral provinces of the United States. *United States Geological Survey Professional Paper No. 454K*, pp. 1–35.

ROLFE, W. D. I. 1980. Early invertebrate terrestrial faunas. *In*: PANCHEN, A. L. (ed.) *The Terrestrial Environment and the Origin of Land Vertebrates. Systematics Association Special Volume 15*, pp. 117–57, Academic Press, New York.

—— 1982. Ancient air breathers. *Field· Museum of Natural History Bulletin*, **53**, 12–16.

ROSS, C. A. 1973. Carboniferous Foraminiferida. *In*: HALLAM, A. (ed.) *Atlas of Palaeobiogeography*, pp. 127–32, Elsevier, Amsterdam.

SÄVE-SÖDERBERGH, G. 1932. Preliminary note on Devonian stegocephalians from East Greenland. *Meddelelser om Grønland*, **94**, 1–107.

SCHOPF, T. J. M. 1979. The role of biogeographic provinces in regulating marine faunal diversity through geologic time. *In*: BOUCOT, A. J. & GRAY, J. (eds) *Historical Biogeography, Plate Tectonics and the Changing Environment*, pp. 449–58, Oregon State University Press, Corvallis, OR.

SCHWEITZER, H.-J. 1967. Die Oberdevon—flora der Bäreninsel. I. *Pseudobornia ursina* Nathorst. *Palaeontographica*, **120B**, 116–37.

—— 1969. Die Oberdevon—flora der Bäreninsel. II. Lycopdiinae. *Palaeontographica*, **126**, 101–37.

SCOTESE, C. R. 1984. Plate reconstructions from Paleozoic paleomagnetism. *In*: VAN DER VOO, R., SCOTESE, C. R. & BONHOMMET, N. (eds) *Geodynamic Series No. 12*. American Geophysics Union, Washington, DC.

SCOTT, A. C. 1979. The ecology of coal measure floras from Northern Britain. *Proceedings of the Geological Association*, **90**, 97–116.

——, GALTIER, J. & CLAYTON, G. 1984. Distribution of anatomically-preserved floras in the lower Carboniferous in Western Europe. *Transactions of the Royal Society of Edinburgh, Earth Sciences*, **75**, 311–40.

SENKEVICH, M. A. 1961. Description of the Devonian flora of Kazakhstan. *Materraly po Geologii i Poleznym Iskopaemym Kazakhstana*, **1**(26), 1–58 (in Russian).

SIGNOR, P. W., III & BRETT, C. E. 1984. The mid-Paleozoic precursor to the Mesozoic marine revolution. *Paleobiology*, **10**, 229–45.

SMITH, A. G., HURLEY, A. M. & BRIDEN, J. C. 1981. *Phanerozoic, Palaeocontinental World Maps*. Cambridge University Press, 102 pp.

SOKOLOV, B. S., LYARSKAYA, L. A. & SAMAITOVA, L. S. 1981. *Devonian and Silurian of the Prebaltic*, Zinatne, Riga, 502 pp.

STANLEY, S. M. 1984. *Earth and Life through Time*. W. H. Freeman, New York, 690 pp.

SULLIVAN, H. J. 1967. Regional differences in Mississippian spore assemblages. *Review of Palaeobotany and Palynology*, **1**, 185–92.

SUTTON, R. G., BOWEN, Z. P. & MCALESTER, A. L. 1970. Marine shelf environments of the upper Devonian Sonyea Group of New York. *Geological Society of America Bulletin*, **88**, 2975–92.

TELFORD, P. G. 1972. Conodonts. *Journal of the Geological Society of Australia*, **19**, 81–97.

THAYER, C. W. 1974. Marine palaeoecology in the Upper Devonian of New York. *Lethaia*, **7**, 121–55.

THOMAS, B. A. & PURDY, H. M. 1982. Additional fossil plants from the Drybrook Sandstone, Forest of Dean, Gloucestershire. *Bulletin of the British Museum (Natural History), Geology*, **36**(2), 131–42.

TOOMEY, D. F. (ed.) 1981. European Fossil Reef Models. *Special Publication of the Society of Economic Mining and Paleontology No. 30*.

VAKHRAMEEV, V. A., DOBRUSKINA, I. A., ZAKLINSKAYA, G. D. & MEYEN, S. V. 1970. Palaeozoic and Mesozoic floras of Eurasia and phytogeography of this time. *Transactions of the Geological Institute of the Academy of Sciences, U.S.S.R.*, **208**, 1–426 (in Russian).

VAN HILTEN, D. 1962. Presentation of magnetic data, polar wandering, and continental drift. *American Journal of Science*, **206**, 401–26.

WINSLOW, M. R. 1962. Plant spores and other micro-fossils from upper Devonian and lower Mississippian rocks of Ohio. *United States Geological Survey Professional Paper No. 364*, 99 pp.

WHITE, E. I. 1927. The fish fauna of the cementstones of Foulden, Berwickshire. *Transactions of the Royal Society of Edinburgh,* **55**, 255–7.

WOOD, S. 1982. New basal Namenian (U. Carboniferous) fishes and crustaceans found near Glasgow. *Nature, London,* **297**, 574–7.

WOODROW, D. L., FLETCHER, F. W. & AHRNSBRAK, W. F. 1973. Paleogeography and paleoclimate at the deposition site of the Devonian Catskill and Old Red facies. *Geological Society of America Bulletin,* **84**, 3051–64.

YOUNG, G. C. 1981. Biogeography of Devonian vertebrates. *Alcheringa,* **5**, 225–43.

ZANGERL, R. & RICHARDSON, E. S. 1963. The paleoecological history of two Pennsylvanian black shales. *Fieldiana Geology Memoirs,* **4**, 352 pp.

ZIEGLER, P. A. 1982. *Geological Atlas of Western and Central Europe.* Shell International Petroleum Maatsch. B.V. Two volumes. Elsevier, Amsterdam.

——, BAMBACH, R. K., PARRISH, J. T., BARRETT, G. F., GIERLOWSKI, E. H., PARKER, W. C., RAYMOND, A. & SEPKOSKI, J. J. 1981. Paleozoic biogeography and climatology. *In*: NIKLAS, K. (ed.) *Paleobotany, Paleoecology and Evolution,* Vol. 2, pp. 231–66, Praeger, New York.

——, SCOTESE, C. R., MCKERROW, W. S., JOHNSON, J. G. & BAMBACH, R. 1977. Paleozoic biogeography of continents bordering the Iapetus (pre-Caledonian) and Rheic (pre-Hercynian) oceans. *Paleontology and Plate Tectonics with Special References to the History of the Atlantic Ocean,* pp. 1–22. Milwaukee Public Museum, Milwaukee, WI.

Addendum

Since the submission of this chapter, a paper by Raymond (1985) has been published, which gives a phytogeographical analysis of three early Carboniferous intervals on a global basis. Our paper, however, is concerned pedominantly with Laurussia and our approach is therefore different.

RAYMOND, A. 1985. Floral diversity, phytogeography and climatic amelioration during the Early Carboniferous (Dinantian). *Paleobiology,* **11**, 293–309.

K. C. ALLEN, Department of Botany, Woodland Road, University of Bristol, Bristol BS8 1UE, UK.

D. L. DINELEY, Department of Geology, Wills Memorial Building, Queens Road, University of Bristol, Clifton, Bristol BS8 1RY, UK.

Devono–Carboniferous river systems and sediment dispersal from the orogenic belts and cratons of NW Europe

Michael Robert Leeder

SUMMARY: Facies, palaeocurrent and provenance analysis combine to give vital information concerning hinterland tectonic events, particularly when continental facies are used to assess orogenic and/or epeirogenic uplift. In Palaeo-Europa steady progress has been made in this area but much integrative tectono-sedimentary study is still needed. Six palaeogeographic maps are presented in the paper with continental/alluvial facies ('molasse') and turbiditic continental margin facies ('flysch') mapped out. Palaeocurrent data is 'distilled' to highlight impressions of terrestrial drainage trends. Clastic wedges are identified within basins caused by major tectonic events, and include the following: (a) Lower—Middle Devonian successor basins within the Caledonides (fore-arc and inter-arc types, and Pannonian types); (b) Lower Devonian–Lower Carboniferous back-arc and foreland tilt block basins related to lithospheric stretching caused by Acado-Ligerian subduction and collision; (c) Upper Devonian–Upper Carboniferous foreland basins formed by diachronous closure of the Rheno-Hercynian back-arc successions by thrust stacking; (d) Middle–Upper Carboniferous passive thermal cooling of the stretched Caledonian lithosphere; (e) final Upper Carboniferous collision of Gondwanaland and tightening of the Ibero-Armorican arc. No tectonic explanation is yet forthcoming for the growth and development of the huge 'Pennine' drainage system which dominated sedimentation over large areas of Ireland, Scotland, England and the North Sea during Middle–Upper Carboniferous times.

The 'degradation' of an orogenic or epeirogenic uplift begins immediately after emergence. Sediment is liberated, transported and deposited in a variety of continental, coastal and oceanic environments. Molasse and flysch deposits attest to these processes, but the terms cannot be used more precisely because of controversy over their scope, meaning and application. Modern sedimentological studies (facies, palaeocurrent and provenance analysis) can provide detailed information concerning hinterland evolution.

In the present paper I seek to draw together from a large published literature the major palaeogeographic elements of Devono-Carboniferous Europe. The resulting maps may have subconsciously drawn upon Ziegler's recent synthesis (Ziegler 1982), but were assembled independently from an extensive original literature, with greater emphasis placed upon river dispersal systems as deduced from published palaeocurrent data. The text which follows is provided simply as an adjunct to the maps; space is available for neither a full discussion of each reconstruction nor a full list of data sources. In any case the reconstructions must be treated only as crude templates for future refinement.

Lower Devonian (408–387 Ma) (Fig. 1)

Internal drainage basins are prominent within the Caledonides, chiefly the well-studied volcan-

ogenic Scottish Midland Valley inter-arc basin (I follow Bluck's (1984) terminology), the Dingle basin and the developing Orcadian basin. The former two show evidence of marginal alluvial fans. Basin centre axial drainage is well established for the Midland Valley (Bluck 1978). The ultimate fate of the Midland Valley rivers is more controversial. Simon & Bluck (1982) postulate a course through the area of the present-day North Channel between Antrim and Galloway to link up with tributaries from the Welsh Caledonides— the system eventually flowing into the external depocentre of developing Rheno-Hercynia. There is no direct evidence for this hypothesis, which is also made more difficult if we accept Thirlwall's (1981) proposal that an active subduction zone intervened between the two areas. Figure 1 accordingly shows the Scotto-Irish Midland Valley drainage terminating internally, but again no direct evidence exists and the problem still remains open.

A major external depocentre, stretching from S Wales to Poland, was receiving the eroded detritus from the southern Caledonides. Although N—S flow is known (Allen 1974), the ultimate source lands provide problems. Allen (1974) postulates drainage extending northwards over the Iapetus line into northern Ireland to tap garnetiferous source lands (see also Allen & Crowley 1983). Thirlwall's active subduction zone again raises difficulties here. Sm–Nd dating of the garnets would be helpful in resolving this dilemma.

From HARRIS, A. L. & FETTES, D. J. (eds), 1988, *The Caledonian–Appalachian Orogen*, Geological Society Special Publication No. 38, pp. 549–558.

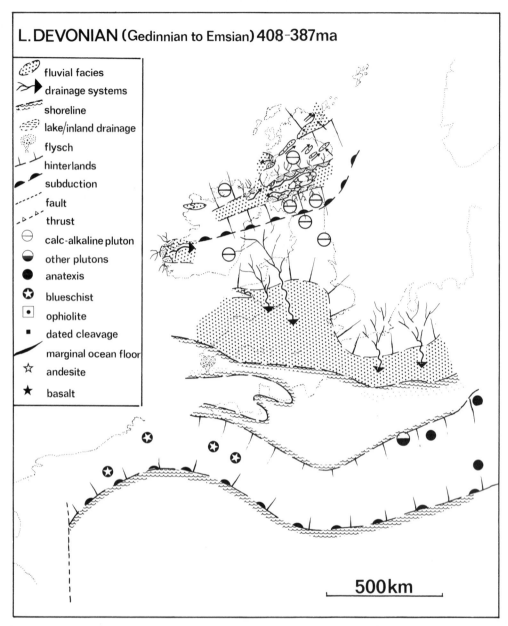

FIG. 1. Palaeogeographic reconstruction of NW Europe in Lower Devonian times. In this and subsequent base maps some attempt has been made to restore the Rheno-Hercynian zone palinspastically by allowing for 50% contraction on major thrust faults and in internal strain. The Ibero-Armorican arc has also been unfolded to various degrees in line with palaeomagnetic constraints (see Leeder (1987) for further discussion). The palaeocurrent data used as a basis for drainage trends are taken from Allen (1974), Bluck (1978), Gardiner & McCarthy (1981), Simon & Bluck (1982) and Mykura (1983). Other geological data in this and subsequent maps are from many sources. All ages are from Harland *et al.* (1982). Note that no attempt is made to outline drainage basin areas other than in a highly schematic way.

Active subsidence at this time in Rheno-Hercynia may reflect the beginnings of lithospheric stretching caused by Ligerian subduction in Ibero-Armorica to the S (Cogné 1976).

Middle Devonian (387–374 Ma) (Fig. 2)

A number of important tectonic events correlate with sedimentation trends in this interval. The Lower Devonian internal and external depocentres were gently deformed and uplifted, restricting deposition to a narrow fringe on the northern shores of the Rheno-Hercynian sea. Incision and erosion occurred widely, perhaps reflecting final orogenic uplift within the Caledonides as collisional strain ceased and late orogenic plutonic magma 'buoyed-up' the orogen isostatically.

By way of contrast, the Orcadian basin subsided rapidly and extensive lake systems developed. No convincing basin subsidence model has yet been published although Astin (1985) has recently postulated extensional processes. Certain aspects of the basin's evolution resemble development of the Tertiary Pannonian basin in the Carpathians (Royden *et al.* 1983).

The back-arc stretching process in the Rheno-Hercynian zone (Leeder 1982) developed to the extent that marginal ocean crust was formed in the Lizard (Styles & Rundle 1984) and basaltic activity was widespread elsewhere. Major marine transgression occurred, possibly as a result of this extension, and reached into the central North Sea. Towards the end of the period rapid subsidence changed many carbonate reef complexes into pelagic sea mounts. Tilt-block tectonics is suspected in parts of marine Rheno-Hercynia (Engel *et al.* 1983, fig. 4).

Upper Devonian 374–360 Ma (Fig. 3)

Depocentres were widely re-established and new basins were developed following the demise of the Middle Devonian uplift of the Caledonides. The Midland Valley basin reappears as an asymmetrically subsiding half-graben with reversed axial drainage compared with that of the lower Devonian (Bluck 1978, figs 9 and 15). The Borders basin appears for the first time. Both drainage systems appear to trend into the North Sea where no upper Devonian marine facies are known. The major Munster basin has developed, with its radial drainage from the Irish Caledonides into an internal drainage system (Gardiner

& McCarthy 1981, Graham 1983). The Craven–Bowland basin also developed for the first time, although little is known of sediment source lands. Renewed subsidence in S Wales, S England and N France trapped the alluvial products of the rivers draining the southern Caledonides, the Welsh rivers now containing much less garnet than during the Lower Devonian (Allen 1974).

The widespread subsidence noted above has been attributed to the northward spread of lithospheric stretching consequent upon active subduction around the Ibero-Armorican arc to the S (Leeder 1982, 1987). We now see, for the first time, evidence for synchronous closure from the S of the short-lived Rheno-Hercynian marginal ocean since the Lizard ophiolite was obducted at this time (Davies 1984, Styles & Rundle 1984). Southern derived flysch is recognized in the Saar (Fluck *et al.* 1980) and in the greywacke of the Giessen, Werra, Sudharz and Selke nappes. These give evidence for tectonic thickening in the area of the mid-German Rise (Engel *et al.* 1983).

Lower Carboniferous (360–330 Ma) (Fig. 4)

Active tilt-block tectonics became dominant in northern Britain and over much of central Ireland as the effects of lithospheric stretching spread from the S (Leeder 1982, 1987). Local drainage systems were widely established on the footwall portions of these tilt blocks. The first signs of a major drainage system coming from the N and NE are seen in the E Midland Valley (Fife) and Northumberland basins. Initially sediment supply was dominated by mature detritus. Major marine transgression during the early Carboniferous was undoubtedly aided by extensional processes.

Continued subduction, microplate collision and calc-alkaline pluton intrusion around Ibero-Armorica caused molasse to accumulate in numerous small basins in Brittany and the northern Massif Central (Peterlongo 1971; Renouf 1974).

Middle Carboniferous (333–315 Ma) (Fig. 5)

Broad regional 'sag'-type subsidence of suspected thermal origin occurred in a broad belt from central Ireland to the central North Sea (Leeder 1982). A huge river system, which had begun to tap a hinterland rich in regional metamorphic

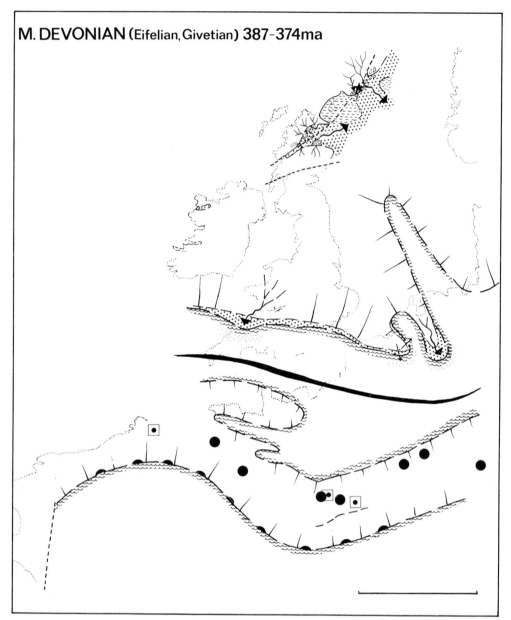

FIG. 2. Palaeogeographic reconstruction of NW Europe in Middle Devonian times. Drainage trends are
reconstructed from data given by Allen (1974), P. A. Allen (1982), Langenstrassen (1983), Mykura (1983) and
Astin (personal communication). The southern North Sea Gulf is due to Ziegler (1982). See also caption to Fig. 1.

and igneous detritus, flowed into this system from
the N.

This Pennine drainage system deposited a
major clastic wedge over previously active tilt
blocks. This major clastic influx cannot be
correlated with any known tectonic event either
in the Caledonides or in the Proterozoic or

Archaean basement. It is possible that climatic
change from arid to humid caused drainage-
system growth at this time. Provenance studies
(Drewery *et al.* 1987) indicate a persistent
Archaean contribution to the detrital zircon
population.

Further S, active thrust tectonics had already

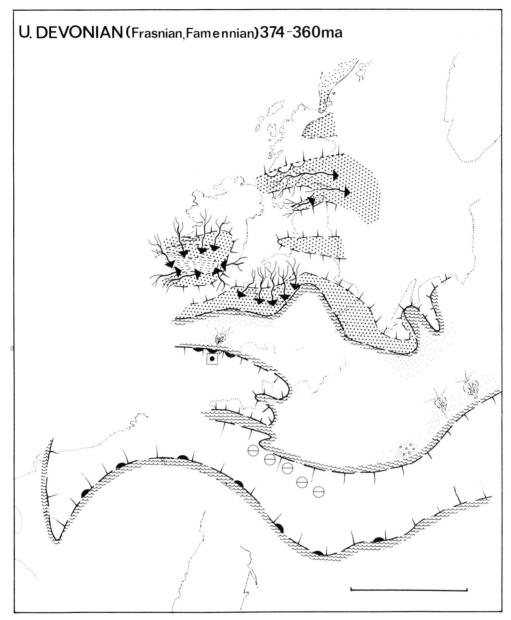

U. DEVONIAN (Frasnian, Famennian) **374-360ma**

FIG. 3. Palaeogeographic reconstruction of NW Europe in Upper Devonian times. Drainage trends reconstructed from data given by Allen (1965), Leeder (1973), Bluck (1978) and Gardiner & McCarthy (1981). See also caption to Fig. 1.

begun on the southern fringes of the Rheno-Hercynian back-arc complex since mica neo-formed cleavage planes in both Cornwall and the Rhenish Schiefergebirge has been dated as Namurian by K–Ar analysis (Dodson & Rex 1970, Ahrendt *et al.* 1983). Flysch sedimentation occurred to the N of the advancing thrust sheets in the Schiefergebirge, giving rise to a back-arc subduction complex (Engel *et al.* 1983, Weber & Behr 1983). Interior molasse basins developed in Brittany and the Saar. Tightening of the Ibero-Armorican arc caused gradual advance of turbiditic mud plumes into southern Cantabria. Microplate collisions in the Montagne Noire–Mouthoumet region caused southward nappe translation with flysch fans and melange deposits.

FIG. 4. Palaeogeographic reconstruction of NW Europe in Lower Carboniferous times. Drainage trends are reconstructed from data given by Greensmith (1965) and Leeder (1974) (see Leeder (1987) for a full discussion of the basis for this reconstruction). Note that the fluvio-deltaic wedges were frequently subject to marine transgressions in the Northumberland basin. See also caption to Fig. 1.

Upper Carboniferous (315–296 Ma) (Fig. 6)

By now much of NW Europe was dominated by the advancing clastic wedges laid down as alluvial plains by the Pennine–N Atlantic drainage systems. Much of Ireland, northern Britain and the North Sea was probably subsiding owing to thermal contraction (Leeder 1982). However, the future coal basins of S Wales, SE England, N France and N Germany almost certainly owed their subsidence to crustal flexuring of foreland type caused by the gradual northward migration

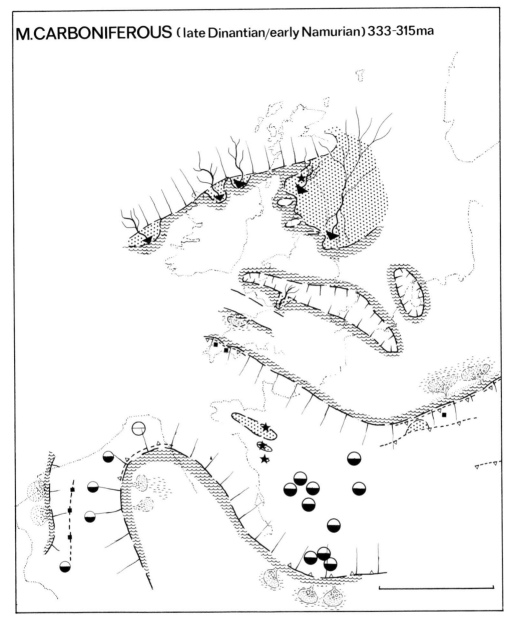

M.CARBONIFEROUS (late Dinantian/early Namurian) 333-315ma

FIG. 5. Palaeogeographic reconstruction of NW Europe in Middle Carboniferous times (actually for late Dinantian–early Namurian). Cantabrian data are taken from Bowman (1980) and Portuguese data are taken from De Souza & Oliveira (1983). Flysch fans are very schematic; little facies work and palaeocurrent data are available. Mica dates in the Coimbra–Cordoba shear zone are taken from Blatrix & Burg (1981). Note that the northern British fluvio-deltaic wedges are frequently subject to marine transgressions. See also caption to Fig. 1.

of major nappes and thrust sheets, e.g. Faille de Midi. Sediment wedges in these southern areas were derived from emergent thrust sheets rather in the manner of the development of the Alberta–Saskatchewan coal basins in relation to Rocky Mountain foreland thrusting.

In the S the spread of molasse and flysch fans had reached well into Cantabria by this time. As the Carboniferous period drew to an end the terminal collision of Gondwanaland with Pangaea tightened the Ibero-Armorican arc still further and initiated a phase of strike-slip

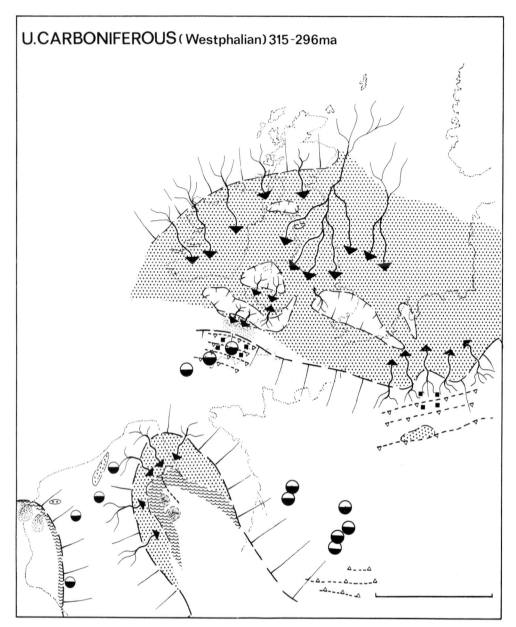

FIG. 6. Palaeogeographic reconstruction of NW Europe in upper Carboniferous times to show the maximum extent of the alluvial plains. Drainage trends are based on data taken from Mackowsky (1968), Kelling (1974), Scott (1979), Bowman (1980) and Haszeldine & Anderton (1980). Note that virtually all of the Coal Measures fluvio-deltaic plains were subject to repeated marine transgressions, probably of glacioeustatic origins. See also caption to Fig. 1.

movements causing pull-apart basins to form extensively in Cantabria during the Stephanian (Heward & Reading 1980), and also along faults such as the Sillon Houiller in central France. The vast alluvial plains of NW Europe were gradually inverted by this terminal collision and thus converted into arid uplands by the lower Permian climatic shift.

Conclusions

Much work remains to be done on the clastic wedges of Upper Palaeozoic Europe. Many outcrops, particularly in mainland Europe, have not been analysed for palaeocurrents or for the environment of deposition. The current 'unfashionable' status of provenance studies in Britain hinders modern integrative work on Caledonide hinterland geology. Exciting possibilities exist for radiometric dating of heavy minerals, and such results, when properly combined with facies and palaeocurrent work, should shed much light on the ultimate origins of the various clastic wedges described in this paper (Drewery *et al.* 1987).

ACKNOWLEDGMENT: I thank Texaco USA for their support of this work.

References

AHRENDT, H., CLAVER, N., HUNZIKER, J. C. & WEBER, K. 1983. Migration of folding and metamorphism in the Rheinisches Schiefergebirge deduced from K–Ar and Rb–Sr age determinations. *In:* MARTIN, H. & EDER, F. W. (eds) *Intercontinental Fold Belts*, pp. 323–38, Springer, Berlin.

ALLEN, J. R. L. 1965. Upper Old Red Sandstone (Farlovian) palaeogeography in South Wales and the Welsh Borderland. *Journal of Sedimentary Petrology*, **35**, 167–95.

—— 1974. Sedimentology of the Old Red Sandstone (Siluro-Devonian) in the Clee Hills area, Shropshire, England. *Sedimentary Geology*, **12**, 73–167.

—— & CROWLEY, S. F. 1983. Lower Old Red Sandstone (Siluro-Devonian) in the Clee Hills area, Shropshire, England. *Sedimentary Geology*, **12**, 73–167.

ALLEN, P. A. 1982. Cyclicity of Devonian fluvial sedimentation, Cunningsburgh Peninsula, S.E. Shetland. *Journal of the Geological Society, London*, **139**, 49–58.

ASTIN, T. R. 1985. The palaeogeography of the Middle Devonian Lower Eday Sandstone. *Scottish Journal of Geology*, **21**, 353–76.

BLATRIX, P. & BURG, J. P. 1981. $^{40}Ar–^{39}Ar$ dates from Sierra Morena (Southern Spain): Variscan metamorphism and Cadomian orogeny. *Neues Jahrbuch für Mineralogie, Monatshefte*, **10**, 470–8.

BLUCK, B. J. 1978. Sedimentation in a late orogenic basin: the Old Red Sandstone of the Midland Valley of Scotland. *In:* BOWES, D. R. & LEAKE, B. E. (eds) *Crustal Evolution in Northwestern Britain and Adjacent Regions. Special Publication of the Geological Society of London No. 10*, pp. 249–78.

—— 1984. Pre-Carboniferous history of the Midland Valley of Scotland. *Transactions of the Royal Society of Edinburgh*, **75**(2), 257–96.

BOWMAN, M. B. J. 1980. The sedimentology and stratigraphy of the San Emiliano Formation and associated sequences, Carboniferous, N.W. Spain. *Ph.D. Thesis*, University of Sheffield (unpublished).

COGNÉ, J. 1976. La châine Hercynienne ouest-Européenne, correspond-elle à un orogène par collision? Propositions pour une interprétation géodynamique globale. *Colloque International du CNRS No. 268*, pp. 111–29.

DAVIES, G. R. 1984. Isotopic evolution of the Lizard Complex. *Journal of the Geological Society, London*, **141**, 3–14.

DE SOUZA, M. J. L. & OLIVEIRA, J. T. (eds) 1983. *The Carboniferous of Portugal. Memorias dos Servicios Geologicos, Portugal, No. 29*, 211 pp.

DODSON, M. H. & REX, D. C. 1971. Potassium-argon ages of slates and phyllites from S.W. England. *Journal of the Geological Society, London*, **126**, 465–99.

DREWEREY, S., CLIFF, R. A. & LEEDER, M. R. 1987. Provenance of Carboniferous sandstones from U-Pb dating of detrital zircons. *Nature, London*, **325**, 51–3.

ENGEL, W., FRANKE, W. & LANGENSTRASSEN, F. 1983. Palaeozoic sedimentation in the northern branch of the mid-European Variscides—essay of an interpretation. *In:* MARTIN, H. & EDER, F. W. (eds) *Intracontinental Fold Belts*, pp. 9–42, Springer, Berlin.

FLUCK, P., MAASS, R. & VON RAUMER, J. F. 1980. The Variscan units east and west of the Rhine graben. *Memoires du Bureau de Recherches Géologiques et Minières*, **108**, 112–31.

GARDINER, R. R. R. & McCARTHY, I. A. J. 1981. The Late-Palaeozoic evolution of southern Ireland in the context of tectonic basins and their transatlantic significance. *In:* KERR, J. W. & FERGUSSON, A. J. (eds) *Geology of the North Atlantic Borderlands. Canadian Society of Petroleum Geology Memoir No. 7*, pp. 683–725.

GRAHAM, J. R. 1983. Analysis of the Upper Devonian Munster Basin, an example of fluvial distributary system. *In:* COLLINSON, J. D. & LEWIN, J. (eds) *Modern and Ancient Fluvial Systems. Special Publication of the International Association of Sedimentology No. 6*, pp. 473–83.

GREENSMITH, J. T. 1965. Calciferous Sandstone Series sedimentation at the eastern end of the Midland Valley of Scotland. *Journal of Sedimentary Petrology*, **35**, 223–42.

HARLAND, W. B., COX, A. V., LLEWELLYN, P. G., PICKTON, C. A. G., SMITH, A. G. & WALTERS, R. 1982. *A Geologic Time Scale*, Cambridge University Press, Cambridge.

HASZELDENE, S. & ANDERTON, R. 1980. A braid plain facies model for the Westphalian-B Coal Measures of NE England. *Nature, London*, **284**, 51–3.

HEWARD, A. & READING, H. G. 1980. Deposits associated with a Hercynian to late Hercynian continental strike-slip system, Cantabrian Mountains, northern Spain. *In:* BALLANCE, P. F. &

READING, H. G. (eds) *Sedimentation in Oblique-Slip Mobile Zones. Special Publication of the International Association of Sedimentology No. 4.* Blackwell Scientific Publications, Oxford.

KELLING, G. 1974. Upper Carboniferous sedimentation in South Wales, *In*: OWEN, T. A. (ed.) *The Upper Palaeozoic and Post-Palaeozoic Rocks of Wales*, pp. 185–224, University of Wales Press, Cardiff.

LANGENSTRASSEN, E. 1983. Neritic sedimentation of the Lower of the Lower and Middle Devonian in the Rheinische Schiefergebirge East of the River Rhine. *In*: MARTIN, H. & EDER, F. W. (eds) *Intracontinental Fold Belts*. pp. 43–70, Springer, Berlin.

LEEDER, M. R. 1973. Sedimentology and palaeogeography of the Upper Old Red Sandstone in the Scottish Border Basin. *Scottish Journal of Geology*, **9**, 117–44.

—— 1974. Lower Border Group (Tournaisian) fluvio-deltaic sedimentation and palaeogeography of the Northumberland Basin. *Proceedings of the Yorkshire Geological Society*, **40**, 129–80.

—— 1982. Upper Palaeozoic basins of the British Isles—Caledonide inheritance versus Hercynian plate margin processes. *Journal of the Geological Society, London*, **139**, 479–91.

—— 1987. Plate tectonics, palaeogeography and sedimentation in Lower Carboniferous Europe. *In*: MILLER, J., ADAMS, A. E. & WRIGHT, V. P. (eds) *European Dinantian Environments*, 1–20, Wiley, London.

MACKOWSKY, M.-TH. 1968. European Carboniferous coalfields and Permian Gondwana Coalfields. *In*: MURCHISON, D. & WESTOLL, T. S. (eds) *Coal and Coal-bearing Strata*, pp. 325–46, Oliver & Boyd, Edinburgh.

MYKURA, W. 1983. Old Red Sandstone. *In*: CRAIG, G.

Y. (ed.) *Geology of Scotland*, pp. 205–252, Oliver & Boyd, Edinburgh.

PETERLONGO, J.-M. 1971. Le Paleozoique ante-Houiller dans le Massif Central. *Geologie, Geomorphologie et Structure Profonde du Massif Central, Francais 9J, Jung Symposium*, pp. 157–68, Plein Air Service, Clermont Ferrand.

RENOUF, J. T. 1974. The Proterozoic and Palaeozoic development of the Armorican and Cornubian Provinces. *Proceedings of the Ussher Society*, **3**, 6–43.

ROYDEN, L., HORVATH, F. & RUMPLER, J. 1983. Evolution of the Pannonian Basin system. 1. Tectonics. *Tectonics*, **2**(1), 63–90.

SCOTT, A. C. 1979. Sedimentological and zoological control of Westphalian B plant assemblages from West Yorkshire. *Proceedings of the Yorkshire Geological Society*, **41**, 461–508.

SIMON, B. & BLUCK, B. J. 1982. Palaeodrainage of the southern margin of the Caledonian mountain chain in the northern British Isles. *Transactions of the Royal Society of Edinburgh, Earth Sciences*, **73**, 11–15.

STYLES, T. & RUNDLE, C. C. 1984. The Rb–Sr isochron age of the Kennack Gneiss and its bearing on the age of the Lizard Complex, Cornwall. *Journal of the Geological Society, London*, **141**, 15–20.

THIRLWALL, M. F. 1981. Implications for Caledonian plate tectonic models of chemical data from volcanic rocks of the British Old Red Sandstone. *Journal of the Geological Society, London*, **138**, 123–38.

WEBER, K. & BEHR, H.-J. 1983. Geodynamic interpretation of the mid-European Variscides. *In*: MARTIN, H. & EDER, F. W. (eds) *Intracontinental Fold Belts*, pp. 427–72, Springer, Berlin.

ZIEGLER, P. A. 1982. *Geological Atlas of Western and Central Europe*, Shell, The Hague.

M. R. LEEDER, Department of Earth Sciences, University of Leeds, Leeds LS2 9JT, UK.

Middle Devonian to Permian plutonism and volcanism in the N American Appalachians

O. Don Hermes & Daniel P. Murray

SUMMARY: Mid-Devonian to late Palaeozoic igneous activity in the N American Appalachians occurs in the eastern portions of the orogen. Represented radiometric ages are almost continuous from 250 to 370 Ma and older, thus overlapping Acadian and Alleghanian orogenic events. In many instances igneous activity is generally similar to that initiated earlier in the Palaeozoic. Plutonic rocks consist of granitoids with subordinate intermediate to mafic rocks. Plutonism is mainly of 'Caledonian' or alkalic variety and is dissimilar to subduction-related magmatism of the Andean type. Regional synthesis indicates that some general distinctions of plutonism occur across strike as well as along strike from S to N within the orogen in eastern N America.

In the southern Appalachians granites and minor contemporaneous gabbros occur in all lithotectonic zones between the Blue Ridge and the Coastal Plain. These plutons are commonly syn-kinematic in the eastern Piedmont where Alleghanian deformation and metamorphism are best exhibited, but are late- to post-kinematic to the W. The rocks include metaluminous biotite and megacrystic granites and lesser peraluminous two-mica granites. Late Palaeozoic igneous activity is sparse to absent in the central Appalachians.

In New England several kinds of mid-Devonian to Carboniferous igneous activity are represented. Biotite and biotite + muscovite granitoids dominate the central terranes, whereas the more easterly Avalon zone is intruded by alkalic–peralkalic plutonic rocks and contains minor bimodal volcanics. Final Permian plutonism includes intrusion of homogeneous metaluminous to peraluminous granite.

Within the Canadian Maritimes biotite and megacrystic granites followed by mildly alkalic varieties dominate the Devonian–Carboniferous plutons of New Brunswick and Newfoundland, whereas muscovite + biotite rocks are prominent in the Meguma terrane of Nova Scotia. Volcanism, which is bimodal, is best documented in New Brunswick and northern Nova Scotia. Igneous activity of Permian age is not recognized in the Canadian Maritimes.

The petrological diversity together with the considerable span of time represented by the late Palaeozoic igneous activity in the N American Appalachians indicates repeated and locally prolonged anatexis of a variety of heterogeneous crustal sources. The alkalic and bimodal suites are characteristic of extensional or anorogenic tectonics. The more aluminous rocks are generally compositionally similar to the Caledonian and, to a lesser extent, the Hercynian suites of Europe. Overall the igneous activity may reflect relatively independent rifting and accretion of small crustal plates of diverse thicknesses and compositions in which magmatism was not related to a simple subduction island-arc setting.

Igneous activity ranging in age from mid-Devonian to late Palaeozoic is common within the eastern portion of the N American Appalachian orogen. Abundant, but localized, plutonism is reported from the southern Appalachian Piedmont, New England and the Maritime Provinces of Canada. Volcanism is much less common and is well documented only in New England (alkalic and/or bimodal) and the Maritime provinces of Canada (bimodal). The most common plutonic rocks consist of biotite-rich granitoids that are associated in some cases with smaller volumes of more aluminous muscovite + biotite granites. The overall character of this magmatism is difficult to relate directly to orthodox continental margin models that involve simple subduction- or collision-related mechanisms (Fullagar & Butler 1979, Wones 1980, Pitcher 1983), and in fact may represent processes somewhat unique to an Appalachian–Caledonide model. In many respects these biotite-rich granitoids exhibit features which are transitional and intermediate between Cordilleran I- and S- types (Chappell & White 1974). Such transitional granitoids have been referred to as Caledonian I-types by Pitcher (1983), who suggested that magmatism of this variety may be characteristic of post-orogenic closure and uplift. Markedly different from these relatively aluminous rocks are the more alkalic–peralkalic granitoids so prominent in southeastern New England and more rarely present in the Canadian Maritimes. In this paper we summarize the major occurrences and characteristics of the igneous varieties in the

From HARRIS, A. L. & FETTES, D. J. (eds), 1988, *The Caledonian–Appalachian Orogen,* Geological Society Special Publication No. 38, pp. 559–571.

N American Appalachians and raise some speculative issues regarding their tectonic setting, petrogenesis and relationship to orogenesis.

Southern Appalachians

In the southern Appalachians (Fig. 1) granitoid plutons that range in age from 265 to 330 Ma are widespread from Georgia to Maryland (Fullagar & Butler 1979, Sinha *et al.* 1980, Snoke *et al.* 1980, Speer *et al.* 1980, Glover *et al.* 1983). These plutons crop out in every lithotectonic belt E of the Brevard Zone and W of the Coastal Plain, within a region that consists primarily of Proterozoic to Ordovician crystalline rocks metamorphosed during the lower Palaeozoic Taconic orogeny. Plutons in the central and western parts of the Piedmont are mainly post-kinematic, whereas those to the E are variably deformed by ductile shear zones of Alleghanian age.

Outcrop areas of the post-kinematic plutons commonly range from a few tens to several hundred square kilometres, but include some of up to several thousand square kilometres. Most plutons occur as dispersed isolated composite complexes with at least two mappable facies that may exhibit gradational, intrusive or faulted internal contacts. Textures range from coarse- to fine- grained and commonly include porphyritic and megacrystic feldspar varieties. In many cases a fine-grained facies cuts an earlier coarse-grained lithology. Primary igneous flow layering characterized by alignment of elongate feldspars and mafic-rich bands is common in some units. Inclusions of autoliths or mixed-metamorphic xenoliths comparable with adjacent country rock are abundant in some plutons, especially near marginal contacts. The restite-like inclusions which are so common in Cordilleran batholiths are absent or rare in the plutons of the Appalachians.

Most post-kinematic plutons are rounded to elongate, and are generally in sharp contact with the country rocks which consist of schists, gneisses, amphibolites or metavolcanics. Contacts may be discordant, *lit-par-lit* or faulted. Where intrusive contacts are exposed in the Inner Piedmont, the plutons commonly have superposed metamorphic aureoles (in places kyanite-bearing) on the country rock, thus post-dating an earlier pre-Alleghanian regional metamorphism. Those plutons in the central part of the southern orogen tend to be massive and largely unfoliated, except at margins where faulted or along localized cross-cutting ductile shear zones (Fullagar & Butler 1979). This mylonitic deformation, which

appears to be of Alleghanian age, is generally restricted to localized zones of shearing and is not pervasive and penetrative in this part of the orogen. One reported exception is a thoroughly deformed pluton (High Shoals) located within the centralized Kings Mountain belt along the eastern border of the Inner Piedmont in the Carolinas (Horton & Stern 1983). In contrast with most central and western stocks, many of the easternmost plutons within the Kiokee belt (Snoke *et al.* 1980) and the Raleigh belt (Russell *et al.* 1985) (Fig. 1) exhibit penetrative fabrics which locally transect lithological boundaries between different plutonic units (Glover *et al.* 1983). Here the plutons appear to be predominantly pre- or syn-kinematic and are associated within the northwestern edge of a localized zone of late Palaeozoic penetrative deformation and regional metamorphism (Murray 1988).

In broad terms the granitic plutons represent two major varieties: (a) more common metaluminous biotite granites which contains minor hornblende and tend to have relatively low initial strontium ratios (0.702–0.708) generally similar to the Caledonian I-types described by Pitcher (1983); (b) less abundant peraluminous biotite + muscovite granites with higher initial strontium ratios (above 0.708) which more closely resemble the S-types of Chappell & White (1974). Transitional varieties also occur. Few systematic compositional variations across the orogen have been recognized, except that the western plutons tend to be higher in strontium (Fullagar & Butler 1979), are enriched in ^{18}O (Wenner 1981) and exhibit neodymium isotopic signatures indicating a greater continental crustal influence (Sando & Hart 1982) compared with plutons farther E. The ^{18}O-enriched plutons, which correlate with areas of negative-gravity anomalies, tend to be more aluminous S-types with higher initial strontium ratios. These compositional distinctions have been interpreted to reflect different magma source rocks and hence distinct basement terranes as well as a greater crustal involvement for the western plutons during magma genesis (Snoke *et al.* 1980, Wenner 1981). The significance of such E–W compositional trends should be considered with caution in the light of the COCORP seismic reflection data. These suggest that the Piedmont is rootless, as it has been thrust westward over continental margin strata along shallow detachment surfaces (Cook *et al.* 1979, Cook & Oliver 1981). Notably absent in the southern Appalachians are middle to late Palaeozoic alkalic to peralkalic rocks comparable with those in southeastern New England as well as hornblende-rich granite–tonalite typical of the Cordilleran I-types that characterize the circum-Pacific orogen

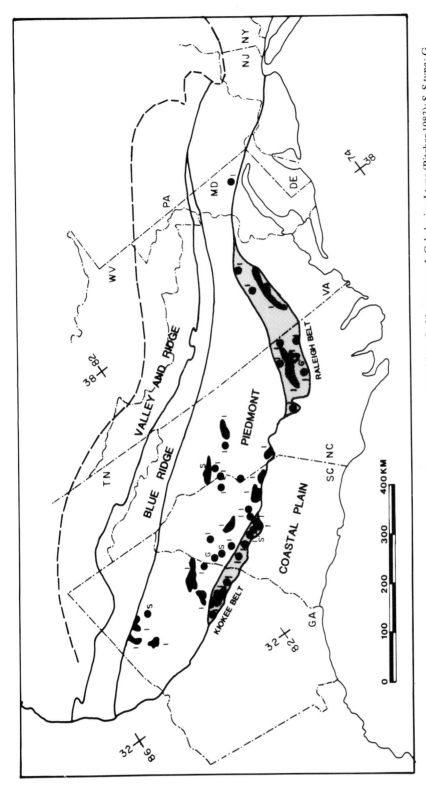

FIG. 1. Distribution of mid-Devonian to Permian igneous rocks in the southern and central Appalachian orogen: I, Caledonian I type (Pitcher 1983); S, S type; G, gabbro; stippled regions are characterized by Alleghanian regional metamorphism and ductile deformation. The Piedmont here includes undivided terranes of the Brevard, Inner Piedmont, King's Mountain, Charlotte and Carolina Slate Belts. The basis for classification and sources for data are given in the text.

(Chappell & White 1974, Pitcher 1983). Coeval volcanic rocks are also absent.

A few mafic plutonic rocks are spatially associated with the late Palaeozoic granites. Some of these belong to an earlier (350–410 Ma) pre-metamorphic gabbro–diorite–syenite series (Fullagar & Butler 1979, McSween *et al.* 1984) (not shown in Fig. 1), whereas others have superimposed contact metamorphic signatures upon fabrics in the country rocks, demonstrating that they are younger than 350 Ma (Speer *et al.* 1980), and several cut late Palaeozoic granite plutons (Fig. 1). For example, the Pee Dee gabbro intrudes the Lilesville pluton (326 Ma), and norite–diorite cuts the Coronaca granite (287 Ma) (Fullagar & Butler 1979). Although coeval mafic rocks appear few in number, just how many are of late Palaeozoic age is unclear because of a paucity of radiometric data and clear-cut field relationships. At least some mafic magmatism was coeval with granite magmatism, but whether the felsic and mafic rocks are petrogenetically related or if their simultaneous production was coincidental is unclear. However, intermediate rocks are generally absent, and it appears likely that the two groups locally represent a bimodal plutonic suite somewhat comparable with the granite and gabbro–diorite association in the northern Appalachians (Fyffe *et al.* 1981) and Europe (Michard-Vitrac *et al.* 1980, Pitcher 1983) instead of a compositionally continuous rock series.

No late Palaeozoic plutonic or volcanic rocks have been recognized in the central Appalachians from N of Maryland to New England, perhaps because the easternmost Piedmont is not exposed.

New England

In New England two distinct kinds of igneous activity can be distinguished to the NW and SE of a fault system that separates the Avalon zone from terranes to the W (Fig. 2). Metaluminous to peraluminous granitoids occur NW of this fault system, whereas to the SE the igneous activity is mainly alkalic to peralkalic, except for the more aluminous Permian Narragansett Pier granite.

Gander zone

NW of the fault zone, post-kinematic granites broadly define two groups of mid-Devonian to Carboniferous-age and one suite of Permian-age. The oldest group (not shown in Fig. 2) ranges in age from 360 to 395 Ma (Wones & Sinha 1988) and consists of biotite-rich or biotite + muscovite granitoids of the New Hampshire plutonic series. Although all plutons included here have been described as post-kinematic, some are reported to be syn-metamorphic whereas others have superimposed contact aureoles on the country rock and truncate metamorphic gradients (Naylor 1971, Dallmeyer 1982, Dallmeyer *et al.* 1982). Compositionally, these rocks are not notably distinct from slightly older pre- or syn-tectonic Acadian granites (390–410 Ma) in the region (Wones & Sinha 1988).

A younger plutonic group, which exhibits radiometric ages of 310–340 Ma (Fig. 2), includes the massive muscovite + biotite granites of the Concord sub-series in New Hampshire (Lyons & Livingston 1977, Lyons 1979), the slightly less aluminous Biddeford, Lyman and Sebago plutons, and the more mafic Saco pluton in Maine (Gaudette *et al.* 1982, Aleinikoff 1984, Hayward & Gaudette 1984). As in the southern Appalachians, intermediate rocks are sparse or absent. Initial $^{87}Sr/^{86}Sr$ ratios for the biotite granitoids cluster between 0.7031 and 0.7067, whereas higher ratios of 0.7107–0.7144 are exhibited by the Concord plutons. The binary Concord granitic rocks generally resemble S-types, whereas several of the plutons in Maine appear more comparable with Caledonian I-types. U–Pb isotopic systematics on zircon separated from the Concord granites show a mild inheritance from older late Proterozoic Z crust which so far has not been detected in older plutonic rocks within the Merrimack synclinorium (Lyons 1979). Again, these rocks are similar compositionally to both the syn-kinematic Acadian granites and the older post-kinematic (360–395 Ma) age group. Distinction between magmatism of Acadian- and Alleghanian-age is rather arbitrary and may reflect more or less continuous igneous activity from late early Devonian to the Carboniferous. In fact, Chamberlain & England (1985) have suggested that the Concord granites may be the delayed result of crustal thickening during the Acadian orogeny. No contemporaneous volcanic rocks have been recognized to be associated with either the 310–340 or 360–395 Ma age groups.

The youngest rocks consist of a single Permian pluton, the Milford Pluton, which occurs in the Merrimack synclinorium of New Hampshire (Aleinikoff *et al.* 1979). This granite is a massive homogeneous biotite granite with little or no primary muscovite. It contains a zircon suite that exhibits mild inheritance consistent with a late Proterozoic crustal source considerably younger than that indicated by the Permian Narragansett Pier granite described below.

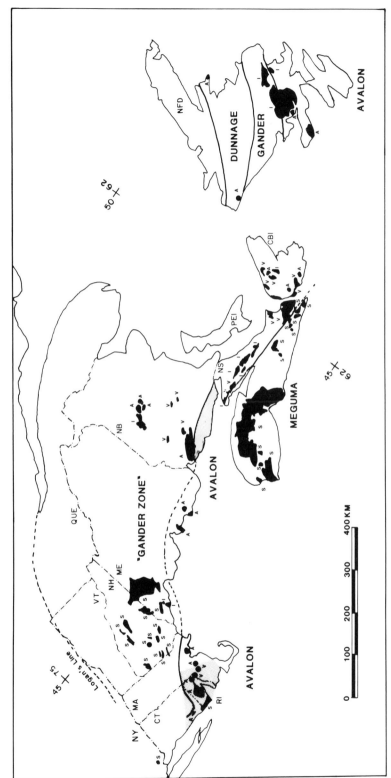

Fig. 2. Distribution of mid-Devonian to Permian igneous rocks in the New England and Maritime Appalachian orogen: I, Caledonian I type; S, S type; A, A type; V, volcanic rock; stippled regions are characterized by Alleghanian regional metamorphism and ductile deformation (the northern and western termini of such regions in southeastern New England remain poorly constrained). Terrane W of the Avalon zone in New England and New Brunswick is referred to collectively here as the Gander zone. The basis for classification and sources for data are given in the text.

Avalon zone

Aluminous muscovite-bearing granitoids of Devono-Carboniferous age are conspicuously absent SE of the fault system in New England where there is no evidence for Taconic or Acadian orogenic events. Instead alkalic igneous rocks are prominent. These include the large Scituate–E Greenwich Complex (370 Ma) and other smaller plutonic bodies (about 345 Ma) in Rhode Island (Hermes & Zartman 1985), the Rattlesnake pluton (380 Ma) in eastern Massachusetts (Lyons & Kruger 1976) and the Joshua Rock gneiss (about 300 Ma) of southern Connecticut (Murray 1987; Fig. 1) (Zartman *et al.*, in press). A few intermediate monzodiorites and quartz diorites are present in the Scituate Complex (Jordan 1983), but most rocks of these plutons are alkali feldspar granites which contain accessory sodic amphibole and pyroxene, fluorite, allanite, zircon and astrophyllite. In addition to exhibiting high ratios of $Na_2O + K_2O$ to Al_2O_3, the rocks characteristically are high in trace elements such as zirconium, niobium, yttrium and zinc. Mineralogically and chemically they are similar to older alkalic plutons in eastern Massachusetts and the Gulf of Maine (Zartman 1977, Hermes *et al.* 1978, Zen 1983a, b) that range in age from late Ordovician to early Devonian. All these rocks are comparable with anorogenic A-type granites (Loiselle & Wones 1979, Collins *et al.* 1982, Pitcher 1983). Moreover, to the N in coastal Maine a number of lesser-studied plutons are known to consist of rapakivi and hypersolvus granite (Chapman 1968, Brookins 1976, Metzger *et al.* 1982), implying that the A-type granites continue northward (Fig. 2). Other workers have also pointed out compositional differences between the Devonian to Carboniferous granitoids of the Gander zone described earlier and these anorogenic granitoids within the coastal zone of Maine (Loiselle & Ayuso 1980, Andrew *et al.* 1983). Collectively, these observations suggest that coastal Maine may have a plutonic history more comparable with southeastern New England than with terranes to the W, an interpretation consistent with its classification as part of the Avalon zone.

In Rhode Island and eastern Massachusetts subordinate volcanic rocks are associated with some of the alkalic plutons (Fig. 2). The Spencer Hill volcanics, which consist of quartz-feldspar porphyry and volcaniclastic rocks, exhibit major- and trace-element chemistry identical with that of associated plutonic rocks and are interpreted to be coeval with rocks of the Scituate pluton (Jordan 1983, Olson & Hermes 1983). The volcanic and epiclastic suite demonstrates the shallow level nature of the alkalic rocks and the concurrent deposition of sediment in associated basins. Likewise, quartz-feldspar felsite porphyry is associated spatially with the Quincy granite of northern Rhode Island. Quinn *et al.* (1949) interpreted the felsite to be a concordant sill intrusive into Carboniferous sediments of the Narragansett Basin and contemporaneous with rhyolite flows and basalt layers enclosed in Carboniferous sediments in adjacent Massachusetts (Quinn 1971). The Diamond Hill silicified zone may represent a zone of hydrothermal alteration of the felsite unaccompanied by movement instead of a shear zone as previously believed. The source of the fluids is conjectural, but could be from the aforementioned volcanism, dewatering of sediments undergoing metamorphism or crystallization of slightly younger granite. Although not studied in detail, the intimate association of these rocks with sediments of the Narragansett Basin confirms that mainly alkalic and/or bimodal plutonism and volcanism was essentially episodically continuous in southeasternmost New England from the late Ordovician to the Carboniferous (Zartman 1977, Hermes & Zartman 1985).

Most of the volcanic and plutonic rocks in southeasternmost New England are variably deformed to a greater extent than the more massive rocks to the NE in Massachusetts. The Scituate and Rhode Island Quincy granites are cut locally by ductile shear zones, and the western and southern parts of the Scituate are pervasively lineated and foliated where they are in close proximity to the Hope Valley shear zone, which is a post-370 Ma (Permian?) deformational feature (O'Hara & Gromet 1985). This shear zone is considered to divide the composite Avalon zone of southeastern New England into two regions. The western Hope Valley terrane is thought to have underthrust the Merrimack synclinorium during the Taconian or Acadian orogenies (Rodgers 1981, Hall & Robinson 1982), while the relatively southeastern Esmond–Dedham terrane (which includes the Scituate granite) is interpreted to have been tectonically juxtaposed during the Alleghanian orogeny. The foliated Joshua Rock gneiss (within the Hope Valley terrane) south of the Honey Hill fault in southern Connecticut is conformable with Proterozoic gneissic rocks that appear to have been deformed in the late Palaeozoic (Zartman *et al.* in press). U–Pb isotopic systematics on zircons from the rocks in southern Rhode Island and Connecticut (Hermes *et al.* 1981b, Hermes & Zartman 1985, Zartman *et al.*, in press) as well as $^{40}Ar/^{39}Ar$ release patterns (Dallmeyer 1982) also indicate a late Palaeozoic deformation of the crystalline rocks to the W of the deformed Narragansett Basin. Such characteristics constitute evidence of an Alleghanian deformational front along the southern coastline of southeastern New England which post-dates the mid-Devonian to early Carboniferous emplacement of these rocks.

Also present in southern Rhode Island–Connecticut are several post-kinematic plutons of Permian age (Fig. 2), of which the most important are the 275 Ma E–W-trending Naragansett Pier and Westerly granites (Hermes *et al.* 1981a, Zartman & Hermes 1987). Massive Narragansett Pier granite may crop out as far W as the Stony Creek Dome where undeformed granite appears in the core (McLellan & Stockman 1985), while to the E it intrudes Carboniferous rocks of the Narragansett Basin, post-dating the peak metamorphic and deformational features in these rocks (Murray & Skehan 1979, Murray 1988). It is mainly a homogeneous biotite granite–granodiorite that includes a leucocratic muscovite + garnet-rich facies where it is in contact with carbonaceous-rich sediments. The lack of a contact aureole coupled with evidence for widespread fluid exchange between granite and metasedimentary rock suggests that ambient temperatures were high at the time of emplacement. The Westerly granite represents a slightly later pulse of magma of similar composition that occurs as southerly-dipping dykes which cut the Narragansett Pier granite and older gneissic rocks. The emplacement of both granites appears to have been controlled by fracture systems. Unlike any other igneous rocks in the N American Appalachians, zircon suites from the Westerly and Narragansett Pier granites show substantial inheritance from a much earlier crustal source which appears to be as old as Archaean (Zartman & Hermes 1987). As such, the source material for these granites represents the only example of crustal material older than Proterozoic beneath the Appalachians. The presence of a similar Permian pluton within the New Hampshire–Massachusetts 'Gander' zone and of those of the Avalon zone described here is consistent with the juxtapositioning of these two terranes along the Hope Valley shear zone prior to emplacement of the plutons. However, the strong contrast in the lead isotopic signatures of their respective zircon suites implies that, although of similar age and composition, they are derived through the melting of very different sources.

Recently, two-mica tourmaline granites of Carboniferous age have been recognized (Brock & Brock 1985) in the Manhatten Prong of southeasternmost New York State. These small bodies were syn-kinematically emplaced along extensional ductile shear zones. Whether these late Palaeozoic rocks contain older inherited crustal signatures similar to slightly younger Narragansett Pier Granite is not known.

Canadian Maritime Provinces

In New Brunswick (Fig. 2) a few post-orogenic (337–352 Ma) granites were intruded into deformed rocks of the Fredericton trough (Fyffe *et al.* 1981). These early Carboniferous granites, which are shallow-level coarse-grained biotite granites associated with small volumes of quartz-feldspar porphyry and granophyre, are generally comparable with the Caledonian I-type varieties to the S in the USA. Some of these plutons are similar to an older plutonic suite that includes pre-, syn- and post-Acadian plutons that contain hornblende-bearing intermediate rocks (Ruitenberg & Fyffe 1983). Small masses of mafic rock that were intruded shortly before the felsic varieties are associated with the post-orogenic granitoids. The younger plutons, along with related hypabyssal and volcanic rocks, are mildly alkalic (Fyffe 1986, personal communcation) and locally contain mineralized zones of tin and tungsten. Overall, there appears to be a gradual change from earlier Caledonian I-type magmatism to mildly-alkalic varieties in the late Palaeozoic. Significantly, no important break is apparent in the early Devonian to Carboniferous plutonism, once again indicating that igneous activity was more or less continuous from Devonian (and earlier) to Carboniferous time. As in the Appalachians of the USA, rocks of intermediate composition are of small areal extent.

Apparently coeval with some of this magmatism are several plutons of calc-alkaline affinity and a bimodal volcanic suite in the Avalon terrane near St John, New Brunswick (not shown in Fig. 2). Unfortunately the ages of these rocks have not been confirmed by radiometric methods, but they are reported to have been deformed in the late Palaeozoic (Rast *et al.* 1978, 1984, Rast 1983, Mosher & Rast 1984). The volcanic suite may be similar to Devono-Carboniferous basalts and rhyolites described from the Antigonish and Cobequid Highlands of Nova Scotia and from Cape Breton Island (Fig. 2), N of the Chedabucto fault (Dostal *et al.* 1983). Locally on Cape Breton Island, sub-volcanic syenogranite may be coeval and petrologically related to some of the volcanic rocks (Barr *et al.* 1985). Chemically, the basaltic rocks are comparable with either continental tholeiites or alkali basalts, whereas the felsic rocks are similar to calc-alkali rhyolites. These volcanics, which in places are reported to be spatially and temporally associated with plutonism, have been interpreted (Dostal *et al.* 1983) to be emplaced immediately after the compressive phase of the Acadian orogeny during incipient development of the Magdalen pull-apart basin.

The bimodal volcanics and metaluminous granitoids of northern Nova Scotia contrast with the predominantly more peraluminous muscovite-bearing S-type granitoids of the Meguma terrane S of the Chedabucto fault (Clarke *et al.* 1980). Included here are the well-known peraluminous S Mountain batholith and other plutons that contain magmatic andalusite, cordierite and garnet (Clarke & Halliday 1980, MacDonald & Clarke 1985) and are perhaps the best eastern N American analogues of the typical S-type granites of southwestern Australia (Chappell & White 1974). Most plutons in the Meguma terrane are of middle Devonian age. Apparently absent are younger representatives of Devono-Carboniferous age similar to those in the Avalon of northern Nova Scotia.

Northward, in Newfoundland, a few Devono-Carboniferous megacrystic biotite granites occur in both the Avalon zone and the central mobile belt (Fig. 2). Many of these occur along the Hermitage flexure near the Gander–Avalon boundary and have markedly higher initial strontium ratios (0.715–0.722) compared with the older granites (0.704–0.709) (not shown in Fig. 2) which are considered to be Acadian (Bell & Blenkinsop 1975, 1977). As in New Brunswick, the older Devonian plutons appear to be typical of Caledonian I-types, whereas the younger rocks tend to be mildly alkalic (O'Brien 1986, personal communication). The youngest Palaeozoic igneous activity is represented by the peralkalic St. Lawrence granite in the Avalon zone and by hypabyssal alkalic rocks at Cape Brule in the NW Dunnage zone (Fig. 2). Somewhat older alkalic rocks are also present in the southern (Devonian (Wilton 1985)) and central (Ordovician–Silurian, Taylor 1979) parts of the Dunnage zone. Thus, in both New Brunswick and Newfoundland alkalic plutons occur in the central mobile belt and are not restricted to the Avalon zone as they are in southeastern New England.

Discussion

Relationship of igneous activity to orogenesis

Just how the middle to late Palaeozoic igneous activity is related to orogenesis is complex and poorly understood. Whereas the mechanical properties of rocks are such that deformational features in them may develop rapidly in response to orogenic stresses, the considerably longer time necessary to raise the ambient temperatures sufficiently to generate partial melts and subsequently to emplace the resultant magmas at higher crustal levels may far outlive the associated orogenic processes (England & Thompson 1984, Thompson & England 1984, Chamberlain & England 1985). In general, the ages of the igneous rocks in this paper overlap both the Acadian and Alleghanian orogenies in the Appalachians.

The Acadian appears to be diachronous in N America (Rodgers 1983), generally from 340–380 Ma in the southern Appalachians (Fullagar & Butler 1979, Glover *et al.* 1983) to 380–410 Ma in New England and perhaps slightly younger in the Maritimes (Naylor 1971, Lyons & Livingston 1977, Robinson & Hall 1980, Fyffe *et al.* 1981, Dallmeyer *et al.* 1982, Gaudette *et al.* 1982, Dostal *et al.* 1983). Acadian deformation is most intense in S central New England, less so in Canada and quite feeble within the plutonic terrane of the southern Appalachians. The Alleghanian orogeny in the southern Appalachians (Glover *et al.* 1983) ranges from 230–330 Ma (and in fact is based mainly on the age spread of the igneous activity), but is slightly later (late Carboniferous–early Permian) in the N (Quinn 1971, Skehan & Murray 1980). Like the Acadian, intense Alleghanian tectonothermal features are localized within the orogen, being most intense along the E edge of the orogen in the southern Appalachians and within southeastern New England to the N (Murray 1988).

It may be significant that the rocks discussed in this time-slice are not markedly different from slightly older plutonic rocks distributed throughout the orogen. We, as well as earlier workers, have problems understanding how these igneous rocks can be related to any simple plate-tectonic model. We raise the question of whether much (all?) of the middle to late Palaeozoic igneous activity may possibly be a consequence of considerably earlier subduction, continental accretion and crustal thickening leading to increased heat flow accompanying radioactive decay and frictional movements. For example, slightly older igneous activity in the southern Appalachians includes leucocratic granitoids of the Salisbury group (Butler & Fullagar 1978) as well as a granite–syenite–gabbro group of rocks. These plutons tend to yield radiometric ages that range from 350–410 Ma and are distinctly older than the 250–330 Ma ages of plutons from the southern Appalachians emphasized here. Although these older plutons tend to be associated with more abundant intermediate and mafic rocks and the granites tend to be more sodic, overall the rocks are similar to Caledonian suites and may represent igneous activity precursory to emplacement of the younger plutons.

Likewise, in the northern Appalachians, the 310–340 Ma plutons are similar to the older post-kinematic plutons (360–390 Ma), and in fact are not notably distinct from the Acadian pre- and syn-kinematic igneous rocks. All age groupings include Caledonian I- and S-types. Even the age groupings adopted here may be artificial, for as more radiometric age data become available it seems that such igneous activity in the northern Appalachians was generally episodically continuous from the earliest Acadian events to Alleghanian time (Lyons 1979, Clarke *et al.* 1980, Fyffe *et al.* 1981, Dallmeyer *et al.* 1982, Dostal *et al.* 1983). It appears that the igneous activity represents a relatively broad time continuum that may not directly correlate with the more time-restrictive pulses of deformation and metamorphism that characterize Acadian and Alleghanian events.

Summary of varieties and patterns of magmatism

For the purposes of discussion the magmatic activity can be classified into the categories described below. The Gander zone is considered to include terranes W of Avalonia *sensu stricto* as indicated in Figs 1 and 2.

1 Mid-Devonian to Permian Caledonian I-type granitoids are mainly confined to the Gander zone in southern New England (i.e. Merrimack synclinorium), but occur within both the Gander and Avalon zones elsewhere. The country rock near these intrusions has undergone an earlier relatively intense Acadian and/or Taconic orogenic event whereas, except locally (e.g. Kiokee–Raleigh belt, Kings Mountain belt, southern Narragansett Basin area of Rhode Island), these regions exhibit a relatively weak Alleghanian metamorphic and deformational event. In fact most of the plutons are post-kinematic and occur within terranes cut by major structural lineaments and strike-slip faults. Overall, we agree with Pitcher (1983) that the tectonic setting for this style of pluton emplacement is more typical of the late uplift stage of orogenesis and that the plutons need to be distinguished from Andean I- or Hercynian S-types. The mineralogy, compositions, rock types, field relationships, lack of mineralization etc. collectively show greater affinity to Caledonian plutons than to Cordilleran rock types. Permian granitoids occur in both the

Gander and Avalon zones of the U.S. Appalachians, but not at all in Canada. However, only in the Avalon zone of southeastern New England, within Narragansett Pier and Westerly granites, have inherited lead patterns in zircons indicative of Archaean crustal source rocks, been recognized.

2 Devonian to Permian S-type and metaluminous granitoids transitional to Caledonian I-types are most common in the Meguma terrane of Nova Scotia and the Gander zone of New England. As indicated by isotopic data, they may be more common in the western part of the southern Appalachians. Their tendency to be coeval and geographically interspersed with Caledonian I-types may reflect local heterogeneities of the crustal source materials.

3 Mid-Devonian to early Carboniferous alkalic granite plus coeval volcanics are found in the Avalonian terrane *sensu stricto* of New England. Mildly-alkalic rocks are also present in coastal Maine and in the Avalon of Newfoundland, as well as in the Gander zone of New Brunswick and Newfoundland. Older Ordovician–Silurian plutonism of similar composition occurs in the Gander zone of Newfoundland, but is present only in the Avalon zone of New England. These rocks have most of the petrological features which characterize classic A-type granitoids, and are well documented to be characteristic of end-stage orogenic events or of extensional tectonic regimes.

4 Bimodal volcanism, which is confined to parts of New Brunswick and Nova Scotia and to the NW part of the Narragansett Basin in New England, may be related to lithospheric stretching or pull-apart basin evolution.

Constraints on tectonic models

Even given the simplifications implicit in the above classification and discussion, we are most impressed with the range of late Palaeozoic magmatic activity. Such diversity may be as much a function of the variety of crust present along the eastern flank of the Appalachians as of different tectonic regimes. Although the alkalic versus the aluminous igneous rocks of adjacent lithotectonic units in New England may represent juxtaposed terranes, some of the patterns of magmatism elsewhere may reflect variations in crustal thickness, composition and prior involvement in episodes of partial melting. Moreover, the variations in magmatic activity among regions in the Appalachians preclude (at least at present) their interpretation in terms of one unified model. For the southern Appalachians in particular, the major observable trend is the restriction of Caledonian-type igneous activity to the eastern third of the Appalachians. In New England, spatial, temporal and compositional patterns are more clearly defined. A tentative model for this region which relates igneous activity to tectonism is presented below. Although at present the model is quite tentative, it may serve to indicate significant lines of inquiry.

Stage 1. The production of Caledonian I-type and transitional S-type granitoids in the Gander zone began during the relaxation of Acadian tectonism, while alkalic igneous activity took place elsewhere in Avalonia within a thick crustal block that had undergone previous melting episodes. The emplacement of the alkalic rocks was controlled by tensional tectonics related to the detachment (from Africa?) and subsequent transit of this block towards New England.

Stage 2. Extensive crustal melting, other than that reflected in alkalic granitoids, does not seem to have occurred at the exact time and site of docking of Avalonia, perhaps because the angle of collision was very small or because the Avalonian block itself was areally small. Alternatively, crustal thickening caused by the collision of Avalonia with the Gander terrane of southern New England may have been indirectly responsible for the generation of granitoids such as the Narragansett Pier granite, as it would have caused a thermal perturbation of the crust. In any case, Caledonian I-type and transitional S-type magmatism continued unabated to the N and W.

Stage 3. In New England there appears to have been a pause in igneous activity from 310–275 Ma. Such an *apparent* hiatus in igneous activity can be interpreted in several ways. One possibility is that the Permian metaluminous to peraluminous granites (i.e. the Narragansett Pier and Westerly granites) are the only true 'Hercynian' granites in the region and formed as a consequence of collision of the eastern flank of Avalonia with Gondwanaland during the final closure of the Rheic Ocean. Contemporaneous structural and metamorphic phenomena in the region are best interpreted as forming on the lower plate, with Gondwanaland overriding N America. If true, the unusual inherited lead in zircon indicative of Archaean source rocks in southeasternmost New England must be derived either from previously unmelted crust or from yet another crustal fragment that was under-plated

to the Avalonian crust during this event. The reason for such an interpretation is that there is no crust older than 1.5 Ga in the northeastern United States.

Comparison of Appalachian to Hercynian igneous activity

In Europe middle to late Palaeozoic igneous activity falls into two distinct categories. The first occurs N of the Variscan front, and is characterized by predominantly tholeiitic volcanism indicative of tensional tectonics in an essentially anorogenic regime (Francis 1988). In contrast, S of the Variscan front the dominant rocks are S-type Hercynian granites (Michard-Vitrac *et al.* 1980, Pitcher 1983) associated with low-pressure regionally metamorphosed terranes. These granites have traditionally been interpreted as the result of continent–continent collision, and their absence or scarcity in the Appalachians may indicate that in N America accretion of a collage of microplates was the dominant mechanism of continental growth, as opposed to continent–continent collision in Europe.

Thus, for both sides of the Atlantic, igneous activity of middle to late Palaeozoic age can be treated as the consequence of three overlapping processes: (1) the thermal decay of the Caledonian–Acadian orogenic system, which produced predominantly Caledonian-type granitoids; (2) alkalic plutonism and subordinate volcanism formed within a tensional or strike-slip tectonic regime in microplates in transit; (3) Hercynian S-type granitoids that formed as a consequence of continent–continent collision involving Gondwanaland and Laurussia. The first two are best developed within the Appalachians, while the latter dominates within the European Hercynides.

ACKNOWLEDGMENTS: Oversimplifications of ideas and omissions of complete credits necessarily occur in a broad synthesis such as this paper. For these we apologize. We are grateful for critical comments on an earlier draft made by P. H. Osberg, J. Rodgers, D. T. Secor and D. R. Wones. Special thanks are given to A. K. Sinha who shared his unpublished detailed compiled data on igneous rocks from the southern Appalachians. One of us (ODH) was supported by National Science Foundation grant EAR–8206149 during the preparation of this paper.

References

ALEINIKOFF, J. N. 1984. Carboniferous uranium–lead age of the Sebago batholith, southwestern Maine. *Geological Society of America Abstracts with Programs*, **16**, 23.

——, ZARTMAN, R. E. & LYONS, J. B. 1979. U–Th–Pb geochronology of the granite near Milford, south-central New Hampshire: new evidence for Avalonian basement and Taconic and Alleghanian disturbances in eastern New England. *Contributions to Mineralogy and Petrology*, **71**, 1–11.

ANDREW, S. S., LOISELLE, M. C. & WONES, D. R. 1983. Granitic plutonism as an indicator of microplates in the Palaeozoic of central and eastern Maine. *Earth and Planetary Science Letters*, **66**, 151–65.

BARR, S. M., JAMIESON, R. A. & RAESIDE, R. P. 1985. *Igneous and Metamorphic Geology of the Cape Breton Highlands: Excursion 10*, Geological Association of Canada and Mineralogical Association of Canada, University of New Brunswick, 48 pp.

BELL, K. & BLENKINSOP, J. 1975. Geochronology of eastern Newfoundland. *Nature, London*, **254**, 410–11.

—— & —— 1977. Geochronological evidence of Hercynian activity in Newfoundland. *Nature, London*, **265**, 616–18.

BROCK, P. C. & BROCK, P. W. G. 1985. Carboniferous (D6) and Permian? (D7) shear zones of the northern Manhattan Prong, S.E. N.Y. *Geological Society of America Abstracts with Programs*, **17**, 8.

BROOKINS, D. G. 1976. Geochronologic contributions to stratigraphic interpretation and correlation in the Penobscot Bay area, eastern Maine. *Geological Society of America Memoir*, **148**, 129–45.

BUTLER, J. R. & FULLAGAR, P. D. 1978. Petrochemical and geochronological studies of plutonic rocks in the southern Appalachians: III. Leucocratic adamellites of the Charlotte belt near Salisbury, North Carolina. *Geological Society of America Bulletin*, **89**, 460–6.

CHAMBERLAIN, C. P. & ENGLAND, P. C. 1985. The Acadian thermal history of the Merrimack synclinorium in New Hampshire. *Journal of Geology*, **93**, 593–602.

CHAPMAN, C. A. 1968. A comparison of the Maine coastal plutons and the magmatic central complexes of New Hampshire. *In*: ZEN, E-AN, WHITE, W. S., HADLEY, J. B. & THOMSON, J. B. (eds) *Studies of Appalachian Geology: Northern and Maritime*, pp. 385–96, Wiley-Interscience, New York.

CHAPPELL, B. W. & WHITE, A. J. R. 1974. Two contrasting granite types. *Pacific Geology*, **8**, 173–4.

CLARKE, D. B. & HALLIDAY, A. N. 1980. Strontium isotope geology of the South Mountain batholith, Nova Scotia. *Geochimica et Cosmochimica Acta*, **44**, 1045–58.

——, BARR, S. M. & DONOHOE, H. V. 1980. Granitoid and other plutonic rocks of Nova Scotia. *In*: WONES, D. R. (ed.) *The Caledonides in the USA: Proceedings of the International Geological Correlation Program—Caledonide Orogen Project 27, Blacksburg, VA. Department of Geological Sciences, Virginia Polytechnic Institute and State University, Memoir No. 2*, pp. 107–16.

COLLINS, W. J., BEAMS, S. D., WHITE, A. J. R. & CHAPPELL, B. W. 1982. Nature and origin of A-type granites with particular reference to southeastern Australia. *Contributions to Mineralogy and Petrology*, **80**, 189–200.

COOK, F. A. & OLIVER, J. E. 1981. The late Precambrian–early Paleozoic continental edge in the Appalachian orogen. *American Journal of Science*, **281**, 993–1008.

——, ALBAUGH, D. S., BROWN, L. D., KAUFMAN, S., OLIVER, J. E. & HATCHER, R. D. 1979. Thin-skinned tectonics in the crystalline southern Appalachians: COCORP seismic reflection profiling of the Blue Ridge and Piedmont. *Geology*, **7**, 563–7.

DALLMEYER, R. D. 1982. $^{40}Ar/^{39}Ar$ ages from the Narragansett basin and southern Rhode Island basement terrain: their bearing on the extent and timing of Alleghanian tectonothermal events in New England. *Geological Society of America Bulletin*, **93**, 1118–30.

——, VAN BREEMEN, O. & WHITNEY, J. A. 1982. Rb–Sr whole-rock and $^{40}Ar/^{39}Ar$ mineral ages of the Hartland stock, south-central Maine: a post-Acadian representative of the New Hampshire Plutonic Series. *American Journal of Science*, **282**, 79–93.

DOSTAL, J., KEPPIE, J. D. & DUPUY, C. 1983. Petrology and geochemistry of Devono-Carboniferous volcanic rocks in Nova Scotia. *Maritime Sediments and Atlantic Geology*, **19**, 59–71.

ENGLAND, P. C. & THOMPSON, A. B. 1984. Pressure–temperature–time paths of regional metamorphism I. Heat transfer during the evolution of regions of thickened continental crust. *Journal of Petrology*, **25**, 894–928.

FRANCIS, E. H. 1988. Mid-Devonian to early Permian volcanism: Old World. *This volume*.

FULLAGAR, P. D. & BUTLER, J. R. 1979. 325 to 265 m.y.-old granitic plutons in the Piedmont of the southeastern Appalachians. *American Journal of Science*, **279**, 161–85.

FYFFE, L. R., PAJARI, G. E. & CHERRY, M. E. 1981. The Acadian plutonic rocks of New Brunswick. *Maritime Sedimentology and Atlantic Geology*, **17**, 23–36.

GAUDETTE, H. E., KOVACH, A. & HUSSEY, A. M., II 1982. Ages of some intrusive rocks of southwestern Maine, U.S.A. *Canadian Journal of Earth Sciences*, **19**, 1350–7.

GLOVER, L., III, SPEER, J. A., RUSSELL, G. S. & FARRAR, S. S. 1983. Ages of regional metamorphism and ductile deformation in the central and southern Appalachians. *Lithos*, **16**, 223–45.

HALL, L. M. & ROBINSON P. 1982. Stratigraphic-tectonic subdivisions of southern New England. *In*: ST-JULIEN, P. & BELAND, J. (eds) Major Structural Zones and Faults of the Northern Appalachians. *Geological Association of Canada Special Paper No. 24*, pp. 15–44.

HAYWARD, J. A. & GAUDETTE, H. E. 1984. Carboniferous age of the Sebago and Effingham plutons, Maine and New Hampshire. *Geological Society of America Abstracts with Programs*, **16**, 23.

HERMES, O. D. & ZARTMAN, R. E. 1985. Late Precambrian and Devonian plutonic terrane within the Avalon Zone of Rhode Island. *Geological Society of America Bulletin*, **96**, 272–82.

——, BALLARD, R. D. & BANKS, P. O. 1978. Upper Ordovician peralkalic granites from the Gulf of

Maine. *Geological Society of America Bulletin*, **89**, 176–74.

——, BAROSH, P. J. & SMITH, P. V. 1981. Contact relationships of the late Paleozoic Narragansett Pier granite and country rock. *In*: HERMES, O. D. & BOOTHROYD, J. C. (eds) *Guidebook to Field Studies in Rhode Island and Adjacent Areas. New England Intercollegiate Geological Conference, 73rd Annual Meeting*, pp. 125–52. University of Rhode Island, Kingston, RI.

——, GROMET, L. P. & ZARTMAN, R. E. 1981. Zircon geochronology and petrology of plutonic rocks in Rhode Island. *In*: HERMES, O. D. & BOOTHROYD, J. C. (eds) *Guidebook to Field Studies in Rhode Island and Adjacent Areas. New England Intercollegiate Geological Conference, 73rd Annual Meeting*, pp. 315–38. University of Rhode Island, Kingston, RI.

HORTON, J. W., JR & STERN, T. W. 1983. Late Paleozoic (Alleghanian) deformation, metamorphism, and synthectonic granite in the central Piedmont of the southern Appalachians. *Geological Society of America Abstracts with Programs*, **15**, 599.

JORDAN, B. C. 1983. Petrology of the East Greenwich Pluton. *M.S. Thesis*, University of Rhode Island, Kingston, 270 pp. (unpublished).

LOISELLE, M. C. & AYUSO, R. A. 1980. Geochemical characteristics of granitoids across the Merrimack synclinorium, eastern and central Maine. *In*: WONES, D. R. (ed.) *The Caledonides in the USA: Proceedings of the International Geological Correlation Program—Caledonide Orogen Project 27, Blackburg, VA. Department of Geological Sciences, Virginia Polytechnic Institute and State University, Memior No. 2*, pp. 97–121.

—— & WONES, D. R. 1979. Characteristics of anorogenic granites. *Geological Society of America Abstracts with Programs*, **11**, 539.

LYONS, J. B. 1979. Stratigraphy, structure, and plutonism east of the Bronson Hall Anticlinorium, New Hampshire. *In*: SKEHAN, J. W., S. J. & OSBERG, P. H. (eds) *The Caledonides in the USA: Geological Excursions in the Northeast Appalachians*, pp. 73–92, Weston Observatory, Boston College, Weston, MA.

—— & KRUGER, H. W. 1976. Petrology, chemistry and age of the Rattlesnake pluton and implications for other alkalic granite plutons of southern New England. *In*: LYONS, P. C. & BROWNLOW, A. H. (eds) *Studies in New England Geology. Geological Society of America Memoir*, **146**, 71–192.

—— & LIVINGSTON, D. E. 1977. Rb–Sr age of the New Hampshire plutonic series. *Geological Society of America Bulletin*, **88**, 1808–12.

MACDONALD, M. A. & CLARKE, C. B. 1985. Petrology, geochemistry and economic potential of the Musquadoboit batholith, Nova Scotia. *Canadian Journal of Earth Sciences*, **22**, 1633–42.

McLELLAN, E. L. & STOCKMAN, S. 1985. Age and structural relations of granites, Stony Creek area, Connecticut. *In*: TRACY, R. J. (ed.) *Guidebook for Field Trips in Connecticut and Adjacent Areas of New York and Rhode Island. New England Intercol-*

legiate Geologic Conference, 77th Annual Meeting, pp. 61–114. Yale University, New Haven, CT.

McSWEEN, H. Y., JR, SANDO, T. W., CLARK, S. R., HARDEN, J. T. & STRANGE, E. A. 1984. The gabbro–metagabbro Association of the southern Appalachian Piedmont. *American Journal of Science*, **284**, 437–61.

METZGER, W. J., MOSE, D. G. & NAGEL, M. S. 1982. Rb–Sr whole-rock ages of igneous rocks in the vicinity of Mt. Desert Island, coastal Maine. *Northeastern Geology*, **4**, 33–8.

MICHARD-VITRAC, A., ALBAREDE, F., DUPUIS, C. & TAYLOR, H. P., JR 1980. The genesis of Variscan (Hercynian) plutonic rocks: inferences from Sr, Pb, and O studies on the Maladeta Igneous Complex, central Pyrenees (Spain). *Contributions to Mineralogy and Petrology*, **72**, 57–72.

MOSHER, S. & RAST, N. 1984. The deformation and metamorphism of Carboniferous rocks in Maritime Canada and New England. *In*: HUTTON, D. & SANDERSON, D. (eds) *Variscan Tectonics of the North Atlantic Region. Special Publication of the Geological Society of London No. 14*, 233–43.

MURRAY, D. P. 1988. Post-Acadian metamorphism in the Appalachians. *This volume*.

—— & SKEHAN, J. W., S. J. 1979. A traverse across the eastern margin of the Appalachian–Caledonian orogen, southeastern New England. *In*: SKEHAN, J. W., S. J. & OSBERG, P. H. (eds) *Geological Excursions in the Northeast Appalachians*, pp. 1–35, Western Observatory, Boston College, Weston, MA.

NAYLOR, R. S. 1971. Acadian Orogeny: an abrupt and brief event. *Science*, **172**, 358–60.

O'HARA, K. D. & GROMET, L. P. 1985. Two distinct late Precambrian (Avalonian) terranes in southeastern New England and their late Paleozoic juxtaposition. *American Journal of Science*, **285**, 673–709.

OLSON, A. C. & HERMES, O. D. 1983. Petrologic relations of felsic volcanic rocks in central Rhode Island. *Geological Society of America Abstracts with Programs*, **15**, 187.

PITCHER, W. S. 1983. Granite type and tectonic environment. *In*: HSU, K. J. (ed.) *Mountain Building Processes*, pp. 9–40, Academic Press, New York.

QUINN, A. W. 1971. Bedrock geology of Rhode Island. *United States Geological Survey Bulletin No. 1265*, 68 pp.

——, RAY, R. G. & SEYMOUR, W. L. 1949. Bedrock geology of the Pawtucket Quadrangle, Rhode Island–Massachusetts. *United States Geological Survey Geologic Quadrangle Map No. CQ–1*.

RAST, N. 1983. Variscan orogeny. *In*: HANCOCK, P. L. (ed.) *The Variscan Fold Belt in the British Isles*, Adam Hilger, Bristol, pp. 1–19.

——, DICKSON, L. W. & TENG, H. C. 1984. Precambrian and Carboniferous igneous rocks of the Avalon platform, southwestern New Brunswick, Canada. *Geological Society of America Abstracts with Programs*, **16**, 57.

——, GRANT, R. H., PARKER, J. S. D. & TENG, H. C. 1978. The Carboniferous deformed rocks west of

St. John, New Brunswick. *In*: LUDMAN, A. (ed.) *Guidebooks for Field Trips in SE Maine and SW New Brunswick. New England Intercollegiate Conference, 70th Annual Meeting. Geological Bulletin No. 6*, pp. 162–74, Queen's College Press, Flushing, NY.

ROBINSON, P. & HALL, L. M. 1980. Tectonic synthesis of southern New England. *In*: WONES, D. R. (ed.) *The Caledonides in the USA: Proceedings of the International Geological Correlation Program—Caledonide Orogen Project 27, Blacksburg, VA. Department of Geological Sciences, Virginia Polytechnic Institute and State University, Memoir No. 2*, pp. 73–82.

RODGERS, J. 1981. The Merrimack synclinorium in northeastern Connecticut. *American Journal of Science*, **281**, 176–86.

——, 1983. The life history of a mountain range—the Appalachians. *In*: HSU, K. J. (ed.) *Mountain Building Processes*, pp. 229–41, Academic Press, New York.

RUITENBERG, A. A. & FYFFE, L. R. 1983. Metallic mineral zonation related to tectonic evolution of the New Brunswick Appalachians. *In*: SCHENK, P. E. (ed.) *Regional Trends in the Geology of the Appalachian–Caledonian–Hercynian–Mauritanide Orogen*, pp. 363–73, Reidel, Dordrecht.

RUSSELL, G. S., RUSSELL, C. W. & FARRAR, S. S. 1985. Alleghanian deformation and metamorphism in the eastern North Carolina Piedmont. *Geological Society of America Bulletin*, **96**, 381–7.

SANDO, T. W. & HART, S. R. 1982. Nd isotope geochemistry of Hercynian granitic rocks of the southeastern Piedmont, U.S.A. *Geological Society of America Abstracts with Programs*, **14**, 79.

SINHA, A. K., HANAN, B. B., SANS, J. R. & HALL, S. T. 1980. Igneous rocks of the Maryland Piedmont: indicators of crustal evolution. *In*: WONES, D. R. (ed.) *The Caledonides in the USA: Proceedings of the International Geological Correlation Program—Caledonide Orogen Project 27, Blacksburg, VA. Department of Geological Sciences, Virginia Polytechnic Institute and State University, Memoir No. 2*, pp. 131–5.

SKEHAN, J. W., S. J., & MURRAY, D. P. 1980. Geologic profile across southeastern New England. *Tectonophysics*, **69**, 285–319.

SNOKE, A. W., KISH, S. A. & SECOR, D. T. 1980. Deformed Hercynian granite rocks from the Piedmont of South Carolina. *American Journal of Science*, **280**, 1018–34.

SPEER, J. A., BECKER, S. W. & FARRAR, S. S. 1980. Field relations and petrology of the postmetamorphic, coarse-grained granitoids and associated rocks of the southern Appalachian Piedmont. *In*: WONES, D. R. (ed.) *The Caledonides in the USA: Proceedings of the International Geological Correla-*tion Program—Caledonide Orogen Project 27, Blacksburg, VA. Department of Geological Sciences, Virginia Polytechnic Institute and State University, Memoir No. 2*, pp. 137–48.

TAYLOR, R. P. 1979. Topsoils igneous complex—further evidence of middle Palaeozoic epeirogeny and anorogenic magmatism in the northern Appalachians. *Geology*, **7**, 488–90.

THOMPSON, A. B. & ENGLAND, P. C. 1984. Pressure–temperature–time paths of regional metamorphism II. Their inference and interpretation using mineral assemblages in metamorphic rocks. *Journal of Petrology*, **25**, 929–55.

WENNER, D. B. 1981. Oxygen isotopic compositions of the late orogenic granites in the southern Piedmont of the Appalachian Mountains, U.S.A., and their relationship to subcrustal structures and lithologies. *Earth and Planetary Science Letters*, **54**, 186–99.

WILTON, D. H. C. 1985. Tectonic evolution of southwestern Newfoundland as indicated by granitoid petrogenesis. *Canadian Journal of Earth Sciences*, **22**, 1080–92.

WONES, D. R. 1980. a comparison between granitic plutons of New England, U.S.A. and the Sierra Nevada batholith, California. *In*: WONES, D. R. (ed.) *Proceedings of the International Geological Correlation Program—Caledonide Orogen Project 27, Blacksburg, VA. Department of Geological Sciences, Virginia Polytechnic Institute and State University, Memoir No. 2*, pp. 123–30.

—— & SINHA, A. K. 1988. A brief review of early Ordovician to Devonian plutonism in the N American Caledonides. *This volume*.

ZARTMAN, R. E. 1977. Geochronology of some alkalic rock provinces in eastern and central United States. *Annual Review of Earth and Planetary Sciences*, **5**, 257–86.

ZARTMAN, R. E. & HERMES, O. D. 1987. Archean inheritance in zircon from late Paleozoic granites from the Avalon zone of south-eastern New England: an African Connection. *Earth Planetary Science Letters*, **82**, 305–15.

——, —— & PEASE, M. H., Jr., in press. Igneous zircon ages, and subsequent isotopic disturbance events, in ghessic rocks of eastern Connecticut and western Rhode Island. *American Journal of Science*.

ZEN, E-AN (ed.) 1983a. *Bedrock Geologic Map of Massachusetts* (three sheets). United States Geological Survey, Washington, DC.

ZEN, E-AN 1983b. Exotic terranes in the New England Appalachians—limits, candidates, and ages: a speculative essay. *In*: HATCHER, R. D., JR, WILLIAMS, H. & ZIETZ, I. (eds) *Tectonics and Geophysics of Mountain Chains. Geological Society of America Memoir*, **158**, 55–81.

O. D. HERMES & D. P. MURRAY, Geology Department, University of Rhode Island, Kingston, RI 02881, USA.

Mid-Devonian to early Permian volcanism: Old World

E. H. Francis

SUMMARY: Three major episodes of activity are distinguished in each of three volcano-tectonic provinces. The provinces are represented by a craton to the N and the Moldanubian zone (including central Iberia) in the S separated by the orogen which combines the inner Saxothuringian–Ossa Morena zone with the outer Rhenohercynian–S Portuguese zone. During the first episode (380–325 Ma) activity did not begin on the craton until early Carboniferous and was then continental, alkaline and mainly basaltic; in the orogen, however, bimodal mainly tholeiitic activity assumed to be back-arc in character continued from early in the Devonian, while the southern province was experiencing calc-alkaline volcanism probably related to northwards subduction of the proto-Tethys ocean crust. The second episode saw the alkaline activity of the craton becoming volumetrically reduced and largely more phreatic, while the orogen became volcanologically inactive and calc-alkaline activity probably continued in the S, although the evidence (distal ash-fall farther N) is indirect. In the third episode the orogen, now accreted to the northern craton, experienced, with the craton, renewed and more silica-undersaturated alkaline activity related to newly formed fracture patterns, while in the southern province there was a resurgence of calc-alkaline activity.

The content of this paper lends itself to a threefold division in both time and space. Both dimensions require definition.

In terms of northern European stratigraphy the earliest of the three time bands (about 380–325 Ma) extends up to the end of the Viséan stage of the Lower Carboniferous (Dinantian), thereby including all the N American Mississippian except for the uppermost Chesterian. The 325 Ma upper limit is not merely a compromise between the time-scales of De Souza (1982) and Harland *et al.* (1982); it coincides more significantly with the age given by the more detailed radiometric sampling of Lippolt & Hess (1985). The volcanologically distinctive middle time band (about 325–295 Ma) includes virtually the whole of the N European Namurian and Westphalian, corresponding to the remaining upper sector of the N American Chesterian and the lower part of the Pennysylvanian (up to mid-Desmoinesian). The 295 Ma upper limit conforms with the time-scales of both De Souza (1982) and Harland *et al.* (1982). Thus the third period (about 295–270 Ma) includes the Stephanian (mid–Desmoinesian to end Virgilian), Autunian (Wolfcampion) and Rotliegendes (Lower Permian); the correlation problems inherent where volcanics of this age are interbedded with intermontane or other sediments of continental red bed facies should be noted in passing.

The spatial distribution coincides in part with the structural zonation established for central and northern Europe (Read & Watson 1975, fig. 3.2) extrapolated by Andrews (1982) and Rast (1983) to link with the Iberian structural zones of Julivert *et al.* (1972). As seen in Fig. 1 this comprises northern and southern cratons separated by a two-zoned orogenic belt.

The northern post-Caledonian craton is distinguished by deltaic to shallow marine Carboniferous sediments which, though faulted and locally gently folded, were not subjected to subsequent metamorphism. In contrast the outer Rhenohercynian zone (RHZ) of the orogenic belt with its S Portuguese zone (SPZ) extension represents the sub-Variscan foredeep where flysch (e.g. culm) was deposited during the Devonian and Carboniferous; late Westphalian to Stephanian deformation resulted in major overfolding and thrusting, particularly along the Variscan front adjacent to the northern craton, although metamorphism is nowhere higher than greenschist facies. Deformation in the inner Saxothuringian zone (STZ) and its presumed Ossa Morena zone (OMZ) correlative was earlier with perhaps two episodes, one 'Bretonic' (late Devonian to early Carboniferous) and one 'Sudetic' (Viséan to Namurian), superimposed on Upper Devonian volcanics and intrusives which themselves rest on Precambrian basement. The southern craton, the Moldanubian zone (MZ), is formed of lower Palaezoic rocks on a Precambrian basement; Cadomian, Caledonian and Variscan phases of deformation together with super-tectonic and post-tectonic granitoids make this the most highly metamorphosed of the zones.

The three regions are distinctive as much in the timing as in the nature of their volcanism (Fig. 2). Activity in the northern craton, for instance, started much later than elsewhere, but it then continued sporadically up to the end of the third period, giving a suite of unmetamor-

From HARRIS, A. L. & FETTES, D. J. (eds), 1988, *The Caledonian–Appalachian Orogen,*
Geological Society Special Publication No. 38, pp. 573–584.

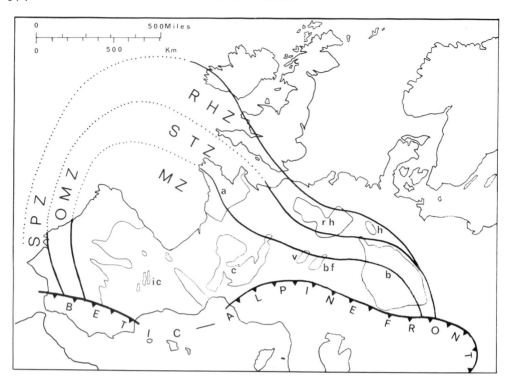

FIG. 1. Map of tectonic zones corresponding to volcanic belts (see text for sources): RHZ, Rhenohercynian zone; STZ, Saxothuringian zone; MZ, Moldanubian zone; OMZ, Ossa Morena zone; SPZ, S Portuguese zone. The massifs are identified as follows: a, Armorican; rh, Rheinische Schiefergebirge; h, Harz Mountains; ic, Iberian Cordillera; c, Massif Central; v, Vosges; bf, Black Forest; b, Bohemian.

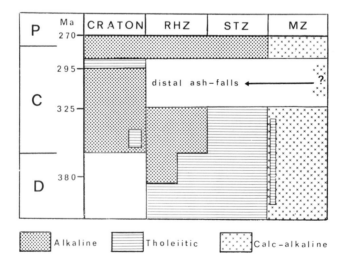

FIG. 2. Time–space distribution of magmatic types: D, Devonian; C, Carboniferous; P, Permian. Zones as for Fig. 1.

phosed mainly alkaline rocks of unequivocally inter-continental type. The central orogenic belt saw activity during the first and third periods, with the first starting even earlier than the time-span under consideration here; the rocks are metamorphosed so that determination of their generally tholeiitic intra-plate back-arc affinities depends on analysis of the immobile incompatible elements (not everywhere available as yet). The rocks produced in the orogen during the third period, after the hiatus, are mainly inter-continental and alkaline like those of the northern craton to which the orogen had by then accreted. The volcanism of the southern region started early, as it did in the orogen, and the rocks are similarly metamorphosed. They were erupted sub-aerially, however, on crystalline basement and are subduction related and calc-alkaline in their affinities. Such rocks are preserved at outcrop in both the first and third period, but there is evidence to suggest that they were also produced in this region during the middle phase, thereby indicating a continuous influence of subduction (assumed in most current models to have been northward dipping) throughout all three periods.

Figure 1 makes no allowance for either the strike-slip movement or the rotation of Iberia relative to mainland Europe required by some some current plate-tectonic models (Ziegler 1984), although movement of either kind would need to have been substantial if the correlation between the N European and Iberian zones is to be invalidated. The same considerations do not apply to the mid-Devonian to early Permian volcanic rocks of the allochthonous Betic–Alpine ranges to the S. Their spatial relationship to the rest of Europe at the time of eruption is so uncertain that it is sufficient to note the following. Firstly, the Malaguide Formation of the Subbetics contains such an abundance of carbonated diabase dykes that it indicates a crustal extension during the late Devonian (Herbig 1983). Secondly, extension also obtained from Devonian to Namurian times in the present day S Alpine region as indicated by metasomatized acid and basic rocks of alkaline affinity (Castellarin & Vai 1981). Thirdly, andesites, diorites and rhyolites (including ignimbrites) were produced early in the Permian in Corsica (Bebien & Gagny 1980).

Mid-Devonian to end Dinantian (about 380–325 Ma)

Craton

After the mainly subduction-related calc-alkaline magmatism which accompanied the end Cale-

donian orogeny and which appears to have ranged in age from late Silurian in the Scottish Highlands to early Devonian in northern England (Thirwall 1981), the record shows no sign of volcanism in the uplands or the sedimentary cuvettes of the craton for virtually the whole of the remaining Devonian period. When activity recommenced early in the Carboniferous it was mainly alkaline and intra-plate (Fig. 3). The only apparent exception to this pattern of timing comes from the Orkney islands in northern Scotland in the form of the alkali basalts of Eday and Hoy, which are of middle and upper Old Red Sandstone age respectively. However, the uncertainties as to the exact equivalence between Old Red Sandstone and Devonian apply as much to the upper boundary as to the lower, and the Hoy rocks, at least, have an early Carboniferous age (Halliday *et al.* 1979) comparable with the first alkaline lavas (the Birrenwarks and Kelso Traps) of the Scottish borders (De Souza 1982).

Dinantian activity spread sporadically across most of the craton and even extended in the form of dyke swarms across the Highlands (Baxter & Mitchell 1984). It reached its peak in the Scottish Midland Valley where the Viséan Clyde Plateau lavas alone extend over 3000 km^2 and are up to 1 km thick. Although there are a few pillow lavas, most of the activity was Hawaiian-type basaltic effusion. These rocks are dominantly mildly undersaturated and hypersthene-normative (transitional) alkali basalts with spatial variations evidencing considerable mantle inhomogeneity (Macdonald 1975, 1980). Locally there was late-stage fractionation to mugearites, quartz-trachytes and rhyolites, and some of these engendered ash-flow activity in E Lothian (Upton 1982).

S of the Midland Valley and its extension into Ireland, activity was entirely basaltic, and as it was sporadic, less voluminous and located in areas of shelf-sea carbonate sedimentation many of the flows are submarine and spilitized. The Derbyshire rocks resemble those of Scotland in indicating polybaric fractionation and mantle inhomogeneity, but differ by including tholeiites among the alkali basalts (Ineson *et al.* 1983, Macdonald *et al.* 1984). The palaeogeographic setting and petrology of the basalts of County Cork and Limerick (Strogen 1973) are like those of Derbyshire, and they can also be compared with Dinantian basalts similarly located towards the southern margin of the craton near Lublin, Poland, although the chemical affinities of the latter are less well known (Lendzion *et al.* 1970).

In most parts of the craton the location of activity is at the margins of sedimentary basins rather than in the depocentres (Francis 1978). These hinge lines follow crustal fractures which,

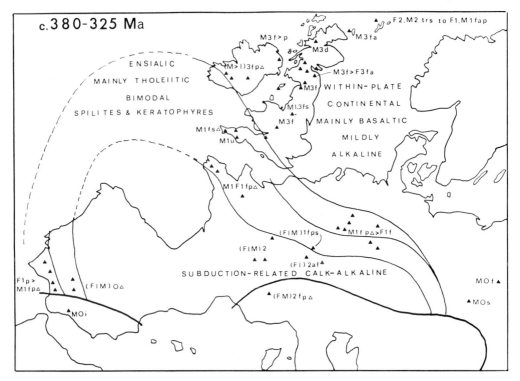

FIG. 3. Distribution (▲) of Devono-Dinantian volcanic rocks: F, felsic; I, intermediate; M, mafic; 1, tholeiitic; 2, calc-alkaline; 3, alkaline; a, ash-flows; d, dykes; f, lavas; p, pyroclastics; s, sills; u, ultrabasics; *, sub-aerial; △, submarine.

in Scotland at least, are inherited Caledonide lineaments, and the half-graben control exerted over both volcanism and sedimentation is attributed by Leeder (1982) to lithospheric stretching. Macdonald et al. (1984) accept such stretching, but not fracturing, as controls of the Derbyshire activity.

Rhenohercynian zone

By mid-Devonian times, the peak of the first phase of volcanic activity had already passed in SW England, where Floyd (1982a, b) finds the earliest spilites to have some of the features of incompatible-element-enriched oceanic basalts, suggesting initial continental rifting in an ensialic back-arc basin. The rifting was abortive in Cornwall (Floyd 1984), but somewhere to the S there seems to have been spreading comparable with that of the present-day Red Sea before almost immediate closure and obduction of the newly formed (375 ± 34 Ma) ocean crust represented by the Lizard complex (Davies 1984).

In the second Upper Devonian–Lower Carboniferous phase activity was volumetrically

greater and different in character. Although the basalts in different areas have their own incompatible-element characteristics reflecting both variable melting and mantle hetereogeneity, they are entirely intra-plate and tholeiitic with development of alkaline varieties along trough margins, particularly later, during the Dinantian, and along the northern part of the area (Floyd 1983).

Bimodal activity farther E, in the Rheinische Schiefergebirge massif and the Harz Mountains, differs only in the larger proportion of metasomatized acid rocks, especially early in the Devonian, followed late in the period by voluminous metabasalts which, from their rare-earth-element contents, resemble those of SW England in being mainly within-plate tholeiites (Hermann et al. 1974; Wedepohl et al. 1983).

S Portuguese zone

The Volcano-Sedimentary Complex, which is nowhere more than 800 m thick and is generally much less, has always attracted particular attention from its relationship to metallogenesis in the Iberian pyrite belt (Schermerhorn 1981). The activity began later than in the RHZ *sensu stricto*, perhaps ranging from Fammenian in the N to Tournaisian in the S, although the evidence for that degree of diachronism is not wholly convincing (Oliveira 1983).

As in the German sector of the RHZ the products are bimodal—spilites and keratophyres. Their distribution is laterally very variable, although a generalized sequence (Laraña 1983) allows for three phases of felsic volcanism with the first being followed by the main phase of basaltic activity (Strauss *et al.* 1981). The basic rocks, which are considerably the least in total volume, include high-level diabase sills (Schermerhorn 1970a) as well as pillow lavas and hyaloclastites. Although spilitized, their ratios of large-ion-lithophile elements to high-field-strength elements indicate original intra-plate tholeiitic compositions according to Munhá (1983) who postulates a back-arc spreading model like that proposed by Floyd (1982a) for the RHZ.

The more voluminous felsic rocks include dust tuffs and tuffisites, but more importantly pyroclastic flows. Schermerhorn (1970b) interprets them as being entirely submarine, but Munhá (1983) identifies some as ignimbrites indicative of at least periodic sub-aerial activity—a view substantiated by textures seen by the present author. Munhá (1983) describes the composition of these rocks as quartz-keratophyres (dacitic to rhyolitic) which, since they are unrelated to the tholeiites by fractionation, must have been derived by crustal anatexis. They were erupted from centres located on linear alignments.

Saxothuringian zone

Although the sedimentary troughs of the STZ are separated from those of the RHZ by the Normanic–Mid German High, the pattern of volcanism is broadly similar apart from variations in the chronology. In the Armorican massif the earliest Devonian spilitized tholeiites appear to have oceanic affinities (Floyd 1982a), like those of SW England, but are otherwise of intra-plate continental affinity; they are followed by late Devonian and Dinantian metarhyolites and acid pyroclastics including ignimbrites (Bebien & Gagny 1980, Bebien *et al.* 1980). Farther E, in the northern sector of the Vosges, the rocks are again bimodal with a high proportion of felsic rocks and lesser volumes of metabasalts once thought to be alkaline but now reinterpreted by Floyd (1982a) as tholeiitic. Bimodalism is also evident still farther E in the Bavarian sector of the Bohemian massif where the sequence starts with metasomatized acid lavas and pyroclastics as well as spilitized continental tholeiites—all of

Givetian to Frasnian age—followed by acid tuffites in the Dinantian culm (Behr *et al.* 1982).

Ossa Morena zone

Unlike other zones discussed so far, the OMZ lacks adequate geochemistry for discrimination between original alkaline, tholeiitic and calcalkaline compositions. The setting of the volcanics in the zone, however, complements that of the SPZ in so similar a fashion to those of the STZ and RHZ that perhaps no great difference in petrology should be expected. As in the SPZ the activity was mainly Dinantian and was located along two volcanic lineaments lying within and parallel to the margins of a marine basin (Quesada 1983); the northern lineament (the Varas–Guadalbarbo) consists almost entirely of pillow basalts, whereas along the southern axis (Villaviciosa–La Coronada) early basic, possibly earliest Devonian, activity was followed during the Viséan by intense acid volcanism—mostly lavas—as well as some intrusions.

Moldanubian zone

In contrast with the zones to the N and W, the volcanic rocks of the MZ were erupted mainly sub-aerially on Precambrian basement. They also differ in their petrochemistry in being calcalkaline and are generally assumed to be related to an underlying shallow northward-dipping subduction zone (Bebien *et al.* 1980, Floyd 1982a)—a view strengthened by rare-earth-element compositions of the Devono-Dinantian *complex andesitique* of the Massif Central which are typical of island arcs or continental margins and show a northern enrichment in incompatible elements (Pin *et al.* 1982).

Namurian and Westphalian (about 325–295 Ma)

In the craton the pattern and controls over volcanism show little change during middle to later Carboniferous times, although there was some decline in the geographical extent and volume of outpouring (Fig. 4). In W Lothian the effusion of alkaline basalts continued through the late Viséan into early Namurian times, but most Namurian activity in the Scottish Midland Valley is represented by emplacement of high-level alkaline dolerite sills and multiple pipes which fed subsequently buried or eroded Surtseyan-type basaltic ash-rings. Basaltic pyroclastics are also found interbedded with Namurian sediments in the English Midlands (Francis 1978). Such activity continued beneath the Firth of Forth

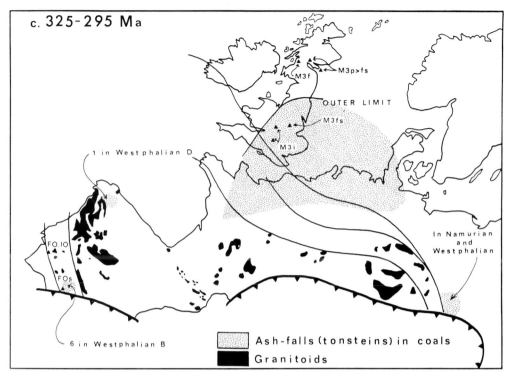

FIG. 4. Distribution of Westphalian and Namurian volcanic rocks (for lithological symbols see Fig. 3). The outer limit of the ash-fall is based on Francis (1969, fig. 2); the Hercynian granitoids are after Autran & Cogné (1980) and Julivert *et al.* (1980).

into early Westphalian times, whilst almost simultaneously in Ayrshire (Macdonald *et al.* 1977) and the E Midlands of England (Kirton 1984) basalts of mildly alkaline to transitional (tholeiitic) composition accumulated to thicknesses of 160 m and 150 m respectively. Basaltic activity continued even to Westphalian B and C times, although by then it was reduced to the minor episodes, mainly intrusive, of alkaline rocks in Oxfordshire and the W Midlands (Kirton 1984).

In the orogen, in contrast, superficial activity seems virtually to have ceased from the very start of this period as the areas formerly covered by Dinantian sedimentation became uplifted into active fold belts (with only intermontane sedimentary basins) progressively from the S, the STZ–OMZ during the Namurian and the RHZ–SPZ during the Westphalian (Ziegler 1984). Recorded rocks from the OMZ can be assumed to have some relationship with the extensive emplacement of granitoids during this period, for the Toca da Moura volcano-sedimentary complex (probably Namurian) of the Santa Susana Basin passes laterally into acid and intermediate por-

phyries (Domingos *et al.* 1983) while the sill intruded into limnic Westphalian B and C sediments of the Guadiato Basin near Cordoba is also a quartz-porphyry (Ortuño 1970).

However, there is a good reason to suppose that the lack of extrusive rocks of these ages in the southern MZ may be attributable less to quiescence than to non-preservation of proximal products. The evidence is to be found in the distribution of distal ash-falls not only among the more complete successions of sediments found in the N but also in the partial sequences of the internal limnic basins farther S. In the paralic coalfields the ash layers, which were generally less than 5 cm thick, were diagenetically altered by the humic environment to kaolinite, thereby forming the intensely researched tonsteins of NW Europe (Burger 1979, 1985). These layers offer two indications of their source. One is their geochemistry, which in NW Europe differentiates between mainly basaltic ash in Westphalian A and mainly silicic in Westphalian B and D (Spears & Kanaris-Sotiriou 1979); the importance of this is in the broad equation of silicic with Plinean activity and of basaltic with mainly

Strombolian or Surtseyan activity (Francis 1985). The other is their distribution, which correlates well with the geochemistry. Thus the abundance of basaltic tonsteins in Westphalian A in the English E Midlands reflects the short-range dispersal of the local basaltic volcanism and contrasts with the more widespread silicic tonsteins of Westphalian B, C and D. Given the down-wind carry of more than 1000 km recorded in historic Plinean eruptions, the northwestern limit shown in Fig. 4 (based on the virtual absence of tonsteins in Wales and Scotland) assumes added significance from the easterly wind system presumed from palaeolatitude evidence to have prevailed at the time; it suggests that the stratovolcano sources were more likely to have been located above the penecontemporaneous granitoids of the Bohemian massif than above those of the Massif Central. This inference is supported by the presence of thick deposits of wetzsteins (whetstones, i.e. silicic high-K tuffs) in the Lower Namurian of the Silesian–Cracow upland and by records of both basic and acid tonsteins in the Namurian and Westphalian of neighbouring Polish coalfields (Ryszka & Wilk 1974, Środoń 1976) as well as in those of Czechoslovakia (Dopita & Králík 1967).

The Iberian evidence does not accord so well with this view of a wind-directed Bohemian source (Fig. 4); for this reason as well as the uncertainty in the palaeogeographical position of the peninsula relative to the rest of Europe at the time it might be safer to assume that stratovolcanoes located over penecontemporaneous Spanish and Portuguese granitoids generated the Westphalian B tonsteins in the limnic coal measures of the Villanueva coalfield, near Seville (Garcia-Loygorri & Dollé 1971) and the Westphalian D *Tonstein Lozanita* in Cantabria (Feys *et al.* 1974).

Stephanian–early Permian (about 295–270 Ma)

The post-orogenic period saw the whole European region uplifted, with sedimentation continuing only in intermontane basins, apart from Cantabria, and with new stress patterns expressed by fractures controlling volcanism (Fig. 5). When activity recommenced in the RHZ and STZ, after the quiesence of Namurian–Westphalian times, it was indistinguishable from that continuing in the older craton to the N, although the Moldanubian zone retained its separate identity.

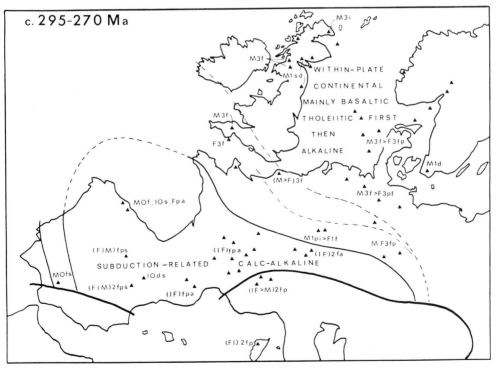

FIG. 5. Distribution of Stephanian to early Permian volcanic rocks. For lithological symbols see Fig. 3.

N Europe

The new regime was heralded by an apparently single pulse of tholeiitic volcanism represented by an E–W dyke-sill belt 200 km wide which extends across Scotland and N England and reappears in Sweden and Norway, where it has its only known extrusive expression in the form of the lowest lava in the Oslo Rift (Macdonald *et al.* 1981) and where most of the succession is alkaline although some of the later plateau basalts revert to tholeiite (Oftedahl 1978, Segalstad 1978). It may be that the supra-batholithic rhyolites near Plymouth were contemporaneous for, although stratigraphical evidence is lacking (Cosgrove & Elliott 1976), pebbles in molasse deposits give a date of 295 Ma (Hawkes 1981).

Elsewhere in the British Isles this first phase was followed by continued alkaline-basalt activity. It took the form of pipes and dykes in northern and E central Scotland (MacIntyre *et al.* 1981) and effusion of lavas in Mauchline, Ayrshire, the 170 m thickness of which is now known from drilling to be greatly exceeded beneath younger rocks at Larne in Northern Ireland, where lavas form more than half of a 617 m volcanic sequence (Penn *et al.* 1983).

The olivine basalts and high-K basalts of the Exeter Traps in SW England (Knill 1982) appear to conform with this pattern of intra-plate alkaline activity, and it may be that the lamprophyric composition of many of the dykes of this age cutting the Armorican massif is an indication of similar affinities in northern France. There, 'basalts and andesites' are also reported from the Stephanian–Autunian coal basin of Cotentin and Littry in Normandy (Bebien & Gagny 1980), and a 169 m sequence of metabasalts, andesites and rhyolites has been drilled at Arton et d'Orville in the Pas de Calais (Morre 1964). Although these assemblages might not normally be considered intra-plate, the basalts are so described by Bebien & Gagny (1980) and certainly their major-element chemistry is similar to that of their mildly-alkaline counterparts in Britain.

The most extensive volcanism of this age in N Europe, however, has been proved by hydrocarbon exploration to extend northwards from outcrop in the Saar–Nahe and Halle districts of mid-Germany beneath Holland and the N German plain to the northern flank of the mid-North Sea–Ringkøbing-Fyn high (see Ziegler 1978, encl. 12 for map) linking beyond that to the Oslo Graben. The products of eruption are bimodal—mainly basaltic, with minor silicic extrusives. Presenting new data from wells and reviewing previous literature, Dixon *et al.* (1981) refute Ekhart's (1979) interpretation of the German

sector rocks as calc-alkaline, describing them all instead as intra-plate mildly-alkaline (transitional) basalts and hawaiites with the composition of the acid rocks made uncertain (dacite or rhyodacite?) by silicification. They follow Nicholls & Lorenz (1973) in interpreting the whole of the region from central Germany northwards to, and including, the Oslo Rift as a strike-slip-dominated province analogous to the Rio Grande Rift–Basin and Range region of the western USA, invoking lithospheric stretching to explain basin sagging and mantle melting.

S Europe

In the S the subduction-related calc-alkaline volcanism of Devonian–Dinantian (and inferred Namurian–Westphalian) times appears to have continued. Dziedzic (1980) records andesites (some intrusive) and ignimbrite-like rhyolites in a bimodal suite in the southern Sudetan sector of the Bohemian Massif. In Vosges, late Stephanian trachyandesites are succeeded by early Permian rhyolites (Bebien & Gagny 1980), while most of the intermontane Stephanian–Autunian coal basins of the Massif Central contain tuffs (some ashflows) of andesitic and rhyolitic composition (Bouroz *et al.* 1983).

The pattern of activity in the Iberian Cordillera is similar, with emplacement of Stephanian quartz-diorite dykes and sills at Cuenca and Ternel (Desparmet *et al.* 1972) followed by abundant calc-alkaline rhyolites and rhyodacites at Atienza and Albarracín (Navidad 1983). This mainly Pelean volcaniclastic suite also includes basalts and andesites—all with potassic tendencies (Muñoz *et al.* 1985). Smaller outcrops farther S in the Cuenca del Viar near Seville are basalts and diabase sills of undefined affinity.

It is problematical how far Cantabria and the Pyrenees should be viewed as separate from the Iberian Massif or even from each other at this time. In Cantabria, bimodal acid-basic lavas seem to be related to NE–SW fracturing and basin formation in a pattern very like the extensional regime invoked for northern Europe (Garcia 1983). However, it appears to contrast with the calc-alkaline andesites and rhyolites (including ignimbrites) forming part of, or locally the whole of, Stephanian–Autunian sequences lying unconformably on Hercynian basement in the Pyrenees (Gisbert 1983, Marti & Gisbert 1985).

Discussion

Relatively fresh rocks are found only in parts of the northern craton. Even there spilitization is common in places, whilst further S such alteration has been overprinted by regional metamorphism up to greenschist facies. Research over the last decade or more has consequently been focused on the immobile incompatible-element abundances and ratios in basalts and, while variations are apparent, these seem subordinate to an otherwise relatively simple gross pattern.

Among the variations, for instance, Macdonald (1980), Floyd (1982a), Franke & Engel (1982) and Wedepohl *et al.* (1983) have all observed trace-element hallmarks distinctive for each separate sedimentary basin, and explanations, including mantle inhomogeneity, changes in heat flow and dehydration of subducted lithosphere, have been invoked. Similarly in several regions there is evidence of changes in the trend of basalt magma composition with time including a greater undersaturation with respect to silica which may be progressive (Macdonald 1975, Floyd 1982b) or even cyclical (Macdonald *et al.* 1977).

The gross pattern (Fig. 2), however, remains as follows.

1 In the Devono-Dinantian there is a broad S to N change from calcalkaline through tholeiitic to alkaline (Floyd 1982a); it reflects progression from destructive margin through back arc to inter-continental respectively.

2 A middle period followed when Andean-type calc-alkaline activity probably continued in the S and intra-plate alkaline in the N, with the two regions separated by a volcanologically (although not tectonically) inactive orogen.

3 Finally the northern type of activity spread southwards over the orogen while the southern region saw continued subduction of the oceanic crust first of proto-Tethys and then of Tethys (Ziegler 1984).

There is little that is novel about this view of the type of volcanism in the northern and southern regions as intra-plate and Andean respectively, but the unified concept for the orogen—and particularly for its Iberian arm—is new and possibly still contentious. The wide acceptance of a back-arc interpretation for most of the volcanics is compatible with the limited extent of spreading allowed for in Davies' (1984) analogy with the present-day Red Sea. However, this does not imply total revival of Johnson's (1973) 'mid-European Ocean', for while there are no geochemical constraints in modelling the demise of such a narrow strip of oceanic crust by obduction (e.g. the Lizard), the same is not true for any subduction model. Indeed, Schermerhorn (1975), Floyd (1982a) and Munhá (1983) have argued forcibly that the southwards subduction of oceanic crust beneath the STZ in N Europe or correspondingly northeastwards in Iberia (Bard *et al.* 1973, 1980) does not accord with either the bimodality of the volcanism or the minor-element chemistry. Perhaps the most intriguing problem posed by the volcanic petrology is its lack of support for the identification as sutures of both the southwestern and northeastern boundaries of the OMZ (Bard *et al.* 1973, 1980, Oliveira 1983); if they are sutures they must be early or pre-Devonian.

References

ANDREWS, J. R. 1982. The Iberian pyrite belt, southwest England and Hercynian geotectonics. *Proceedings of the Ussher Society*, **5**, 387–9.

AUTRAN, A. & COGNÉ, J. 1980. La zone interne de l'orogène varisque dans l'Ouest de la France et sa place dans le développement de la chaîne hercynienne. *Memoires du Bureau de Recherches Géologiques et Minières*, **108**, 90–111.

BARD, J.-P., BURG, J. P., MATTE, P. & RIBEIRO, A. 1980. La chaîne hercynienne d'Europe occidentale en termes de tectonique des plaques. *Memoires du Bureau de Recherches Géologiques et Minières*, **108**, 233–46.

——, CAPDEVILA, R., MATTE, P. & RIBEIRO, A. 1973. Geotectonic model for the Iberian Variscan Orogen. *Nature, London, Physical Science*, **241**, 50–52.

BAXTER, A. N. & MITCHELL, J. G. 1984. Camptonite–Monchiquite dyke swarms of northern Scotland—age relationships and their implications. *Scottish Journal of Geology*, **20**, 297–308.

BEBIEN, J. & GAGNY, C. 1980. Volcanites du Précambrien au Crétacé et leur signification géostructurale. *Memoires du Bureau de Recherches Géologiques et Minières*, **107**, 99–135.

——, —— & ROCCI, G. 1980. La place du volcanisme devono-dinantien dans l'évolution magmatique et structurale de l'Europe moyenne varisque au Palaéozoïque. *Memoires du Bureau de Recherches Géologiques et Minières*, **108**, 213–25.

BEHR, H.-J., ENGEL, E. & FRANKE, W. 1982. Variscan wildflysch and nappe-tectonics in the Saxothuringian Zone (NE Bavaria, W. Germany). *American Journal of Science*, **282**, 1438–70.

BOUROZ, A., SPEARS, D. A. & ARBEY, F. 1983. Review of the formation and evolution of petrographic markers in coal basins. *Memoires de la Société Géologique du Nord No. 16*, 74 pp.

BURGER, K. 1979. Vorkommen und Stratigraphische Verteilung der Kaolin-kohlentonsteine in der Kohlenrevieren der Erde. *Comptes Rendus du 8ème Congrès International de Stratigraphie et de Géologique du Carbonifère, Moscow, 1975*, Vol. 5, pp. 21–9.

—— 1985. Kohlentonsteine im Oberkarbon NW-

Europas ein beitrag zur Geochronologie. *Comptes Rendus du 10ème Congrès International de Stratigraphie et de Géologique du Carbonifère, Madrid, 1983*, Vol. 3, pp. 433–47.

CASTELLARIN, A. & VAI, G. B. 1981. Importance of Hercynian tectonics within the framework of the Southern Alps. *Journal of Structural Geology*, **3**, 477–86.

COSGROVE, M. E. & ELLIOTT, M. H. 1976. Suprabatholithic volcanism of the southwest England granites. *Proceedings of the Ussher Society*, **3**, 391–401.

DE SOUZA, H. A. F. 1982. Age data from Scotland and the Carboniferous time scale. *In:* ODIN, G. S. (ed.) *Numerical Dating in Stratigraphy*, pp. 455–65, Wiley, New York.

DAVIES, G. R. 1984. Isotopic evolution of the Lizard Complex. *Journal of the Geological Society of London*, **141**, 3–14.

DESPARMET, R., MONROSE, H. & SCHMITZ, U. 1972. Zur Altersstellung der Eruptive-Gesteine und Tuffite in Nordteil der Westlichen Iberischen Ketten (NE-Spanien). *Münstersche Forschung zur Geologie und Palaeontologie*, **24**, 3–14.

DIXON, J. E., FITTON, J. G. & FROST, R. T. C. 1981. The tectonic significance of post-Carboniferous igneous activity in the North Sea basin. *In:* ILLING, L. V. & HOBSON, G. V. (eds) *Petroleum Geology of the Continental Shelf of North-west Europe*, pp. 121–37, Institute of Petroleum, London.

DOMINGOS, L. C. G., FREIRE, J. L. S., DA SILVA, F. G., GONCALVES, F., PEREIRA, E. & RIBEIRO, A. 1983. The structure of the intermontane Upper Carboniferous basins in Portugal. *In:* DE SOUZA, M. J. L. & OLIVEIRA, J. T. (eds) *The Carboniferous of Portugal. Memorias dos Servicios Geologicos, Portugal, No. 29*, pp. 187–94.

DOPITA, M. & KRÁLÍK, J. 1967. Zur Frage der Tonsteine im oberschlesischen Steinkohlenbecken. *Comptes Rendus du 6ème Congrès International de Stratigraphie et de Géologique du Carbonifère, Sheffield*, Vol. 2, pp. 647–61.

DZIEDZIC, K. 1980. Subvolcanic intrusions of Permian volcanic rocks in the central Sudetes. *Zeitschrift für Geologische Wissenschaften*, **8**, 1181–1200.

ECKHART, F. J. 1979. Geochemical investigation of Permian andesites from central Europe. *Physics and Chemistry of the Earth*, **11**, 527–32.

FEYS, R., GARCIA-LOYGORRI, A. & ORTUÑO, G. 1974. Stratigraphie des faisceaux productifs du Bassin Central des Asturies (Espagne). *Comptes Rendus du 7ème Congrès International de Stratigraphie et de Géologique du Carbonifère, Krefeld, 1971*, Vol 3, pp. 27–44.

FLOYD, P. A. 1982a. Chemical variation in Hercynian basalts relative to plate tectonics. *Journal of the Geological Society, London*, **139**, 505–20.

—— 1982b. The Hercynian Trough: Devonian and Carboniferous volcanism in south-western Britain. *In:* SUTHERLAND, D. S. (ed.) *Igneous Rocks of the British Isles*, pp. 227–42, Wiley, New York.

—— 1983. Composition and petrogenesis of the Lizard Complex and preorogenic basaltic rocks in southwest England. *In:* HANCOCK, P. L. (ed.) *The Variscan Fold Belt in the British Isles*, pp. 130–52, Adam Hilger, Bristol.

—— 1984. Geochemical characteristics and comparison of the basic rocks of the Lizard Complex and the basaltic lavas within the Hercynian troughs of SW England. *Journal of the Geological Society, London*, **141**, 61–70.

FRANCIS, E. H. 1969. Les tonstein du Royaume-Uni. *Annales de la Société Géologique du Nord*, **89**, 209–14.

—— 1978. Igneous activity in a fractured craton: Carboniferous volcanism in northern Britain. *In:* BOWES, D. R. & LEAKE, B. E. (eds) *Crustal Evolution in North-western Britain and Adjacent Regions. Geological Journal Special Issue No. 10*, pp. 279–95.

—— 1985. Recent ash-fall: a guide to tonstein distribution. *Comptes Rendus du 10ème Congrès International de Stratigraphie et de Géologique du Carbonifère, Madrid, 1983*, Vol 4, 189–95.

FRANKE, W. & ENGEL, W. 1982. Variscan sedimentary basins on the Continent and relations with south west England. *Proceedings of the Ussher Society*, **5**, 259–69.

GARCIA, E. M. 1983. El Pérmico de la Cordillera Cantabrica. *In:* DIAZ, C. M. (ed.) *Carbonífero y Pérmico de España*, pp. 389–402. Instituto Geologico y Minero de España.

GARCIA-LOYGORRI, A. & DOLLÉ, P. 1971. Les tonsteins du Bassin houiller de Villanueva del Rio y Minas. (Westphalian B) (Province de Seville—Espagne). *Annales de la Société Géologique du Nord*, **91**, 17–24.

GISBERT, J. 1983. El permico de los Pirineos Españoles. *In:* DIAZ, C. M. (ed.) *Carbonífero y Pérmico de España*, pp. 403–20, Instituto Geologico y Minero de España.

HALLIDAY, A. N., McALPINE, A. & MITCHELL, J. G. 1979. The age of the Hoy Lavas, Orkney. *Scottish Journal of Geology*, **15**, 80.

HARLAND, W. B., COX, A. V., LLEWELLYN, P. G., PICKTON, C. A. G., SMITH, A. G. & WALTERS, R. 1982. *A Geologic Time-scale*, Cambridge University Press, Cambridge, 131 pp.

HAWKES, J. R. 1981. A tectonic 'watershed' of fundamental importance in post-Westphalian evolution of Cornabia. *Proceedings of the Ussher Society*, **5**, 128–31.

HERBIG, H.-G. 1983. El Carbonifero de las Cordilleras Béticas. *In:* DIAZ, C. M. (ed.) *Carbonífero y Pérmico de España*, pp. 343–56. Instituto Geologico y Minero de España.

HERMANN, A. G., POTTS, M. J. & KNAKE, D. 1974. Geochemistry of the rare earth elements in spilites from the oceanic and continental crust. *Contributions to Mineralogy and Petrology*, **44**, 1–16.

INESON, P. R., WALTERS, S. G. & SIMON, R. M. 1983. The petrology and geochemistry of the Waterswallows Sill, Buxton, Derbyshire. *Proceedings of the Yorkshire Geological Society*, **44**, 341–54.

JOHNSON, G. A. L. 1973. Closing of the Carboniferous Sea in Western Europe. *In:* TARLING, D. H. & RUNCORN, S. K. (eds) *Implications of Continental*

Drift to the Earth Sciences, Vol. 2, pp. 845–50, Academic Press, New York.

JULIVERT, M., FONTBOTE, J. M., RIBEIRO, A. & CONDE, L. E. 1972. Mapa tectónico de la Península Ibérica y Baleares E. 1:1,000,000. *Instituto Geologico y Minero de Espana Memoria Explicativa 1974*, 113 pp.

——, MARTINEZ, F. J. & RIBEIRO, A. 1980. The Iberian segment of the European Hercynian fold belt. *Memoires du Bureau de Recherches Géologiques et Minières*, **108**, 132–58.

KIRTON, S. R. 1984. Carboniferous volcanicity in England, with special reference to the Westphalian of the east and west Midlands. *Journal of the Geological Society, London*, **141**, 161–70.

KNILL, D. C. 1982. Permian volcanism in south-western England. *In:* SUTHERLAND, D. S. (ed.) *Igneous Rocks of the British Isles*, pp. 329–32, Wiley, New York.

LARAÑA, P. F. 1983. Carbonifero Marino de la zona 'Sudportuguesa'. *In:* DIAZ, C. M. (ed.) *Carbonífero y Pérmico de España*, pp. 223–42. Instituto Geologico y Minero de España.

LEEDER, M. R. 1982. Upper Palaeozoic basins of the British Isles—Caledonide inheritance versus Hercynian plate margin process. *Journal of the Geological Society, London*, **139**, 479–91.

LENDZION, K., NIEMCZYCKA, T., KIEZEL, W. & CEBULAK, S. 1970. Volcanic rocks in the Lublin district. *In:* SOKOLOWSKI, S., CIEŚLIŃSKI, S. & CZERMIŃSKI, J. (eds) *Geology of Poland*, Vol. 1, pp. 497–8, Warsaw.

LIPPOLT, H. J. & HESS, J. C. 1985. $^{40}Ar/^{39}Ar$ dating of sanidines from Upper Carboniferous tonsteins. *Comptes Rendus du 10ème Congrès International de Stratigraphie et de Géologique du Carbonifère, Madrid, 1983*. Vol 4, 175–81.

MACDONALD, R. 1975. Petrochemistry of the early Carboniferous (Dinantian) lavas of Scotland: a review. *Scottish Journal of Geology*, **11**, 269–314.

—— 1980. Trace element evidence for mantle heterogeneity beneath the Scottish Midland Valley in the Carboniferous and Permian. *Philosophical Transactions of the Royal Society of London*, Ser. A, **297**, 245–57.

——, GASS, K. N., THORPE, R. S. & GASS, I. G. 1984. Geochemistry and petrogenesis of the Derbyshire Carboniferous basalts. *Journal of the Geological Society of London*, **141**, 147–59.

——, GOTTFRIED, D., FARRINGTON, M. J., BROWN, F. W. & SKINNER, N. G. 1981. Geochemistry of a continental tholeiite suite: late Palaeozoic quartz dolerite dykes of Scotland. *Transactions of the Royal Society of Edinburgh, Earth Sciences*, **72**, 57–74.

——, THOMAS, J. E. & RIZZELLO, S. A. 1977. Variations in basalt chemistry with time in the Midland Valley province during the Carboniferous and Permian. *Scottish Journal of Geology*, **13**, 11–22.

MACINTYRE, R. M., CLIFF, R. A. & CHAPMAN, N. A. 1981. Geochronological evidence for phased volcanic activity in Fife and Caithness. *Transactions of the Royal Society of Edinburgh, Earth Sciences*, **72**, 1–7.

MARTI, J. & GISBERT, J. 1985. Secuencias ignimbríticas y lahares calientes en el estefano-autuniense del Pirineo Catalán, *Comptes Rendus du 10ème Congrès International de Stratigraphie et de Géologique du Carbonifère, Madrid, 1983*, Vol 3, pp. 197–212.

MORRE, N. 1964. Principaux charactères pétrographiques des laves permo-Carbonifères du nord de la France. *Comptes Rendus Hebdomadaires des Séances de l'Académe des Sciences*, **258**, 4100–1.

MUNHÁ, J. 1983. Hercynian magnetism in the Iberian Pyrite Belt. *In:* DE SOUZA, M. J. L. & OLIVEIRA, J. T. (eds) *The Carboniferous of Portugal. Memorias dos Servicios Geologicos, Portugal*, No. 29, pp. 39–81.

MUÑOZ, M., ANCOCHEA, E., SAGREDO, J., DE LA PEÑA, J. A., BRANDLE, J. L. & MARFIL, R. 1985. Vulcanismo permo-carbonífero de la Cordillera Ibérica. *Comptes Rendus du 10ème Congrès International de Stratigraphie et de Géologique du Carbonifère, Madrid, 1983*, Vol 3, pp. 27–52.

NAVIDAD, M. 1983. El vulcanismo Permocarbonifero de la península Ibérica. *In:* DIAZ, C. M. (ed.) *Carbonífero y Pérmico de España*, pp. 471–82. Instituto Geologico y Minero de España.

NICHOLLS, I. A. & LORENZ, V. 1973. Origin and crystallization of Permian tholeiites from the Saar-Nahe trough, S.W. Germany. *Contributions to Mineralogy and Petrology*, **40**, 327–44.

OFTEDAHL, C. 1978. Origin of the magmas of the Vestfold lava plateau. *In:* NEUMANN, E.-R. & RAMBERG, I. B. (eds) *Petrology and Geochemistry of Continental Rifts*, pp. 193–208, Reidel, Dordrecht.

OLIVEIRA, J. T. 1983. The marine Carboniferous of south Portugal: a stratigraphical and sedimentological approach. *In:* DE SOUZA, M. J. L. & OLIVEIRA, J. T. (eds) *The Carboniferous of Portugal. Memorias dos Servicios Geologicos, Portugal*, No. 29, pp. 3–37.

ORTUÑO, M. G. 1970. Middle Westphalian strata in south-west Spain. *Comptes Rendus du 6ème Congrès International de Stratigraphie et de Géologique du Carbonifère, Sheffield, 1967*, Vol. 3, pp. 1275–92.

PENN, I. E., HOLLIDAY, D. W., KIRBY, G. A., KUBALA, M., SOBEY, R. A., MITCHELL, W. I., HARRISON, R. K. & BECKINSALE, R. D. 1983. The Larne No. 2 borehole: discovery of a new Permian volcanic centre. *Scottish Journal of Geology*, **19**, 333–46.

PIN, C., DUPUY, C. & PETERLONGO, J.-M. 1982. Répartition des terres rares dans les rockes volcaniques basiques dévono-dinantiennes du Nord-Est du Massif Central. *Bulletin de la Société Géologique de France*, **24**, 669–76.

QUESADA, C. 1983. El Carbonifero de Sierra Morena. *In:* DIAZ, C. M. (ed.) *Carbonífero y Pérmico de España*, pp. 243–78. Instituto Geologico y Minero de España.

RAST, N. 1983. Variscan orogeny. *In:* HANCOCK, P. L. (ed.) *The Variscan Fold Belt in the British Isles*, pp. 1–19, Adam Hilger, Bristol.

READ, H. H. & WATSON, J. 1975. *Introduction to Geology*, Vol. 2, *Earth History*, Part II, *Later Stages of Earth History*. Macmillan, London, 371 pp.

RYSZKA, J. & WILK, A. 1974. Mineralogy of tonsteins from the Flora (Hrusov) beds in Grodziec Mine.

Polska Akademia Nauk, Oddzial w Krakowie, Komisja Nauk Mineralogicznych, Prace Mineralogiczne, **38**, 29–40.

SCHERMERHORN, L. J. G. 1970a. Mafic geosynclinal volcanism in the lower Carboniferous of south Portugal. *Geologie en Mijnbouw*, **49**, 439–50.

—— 1970b. The deposition of volcanics and pyrite in the Iberian Pyrite Belt. *Mineralium Deposita*, **5**, 273–9.

—— 1975. Spilites, regional metamorphism and subduction in the Iberian pyrite belt: some comments. *Geologie en Mijnbouw*, **54**, 23–35.

—— 1981. Framework and evolution of Hercynian mineralization in the Iberian Meseta. *Leidse Geologische Mededelingen*, **52**, 23–56.

SEGALSTAD, T. V. 1978. Petrology of the Skien basaltic rocks and the early basaltic (B1) volcanism of the Permian Oslo Rift. *In:* NEUMANN, E.-R. & RAMBERG, I. B. (eds) *Petrology and Geochemistry of Continental Rifts*, pp. 209–16, Reidel, Dordrecht.

SPEARS, D. A. & KANARIS-SOTIRIOU, R. 1979. A geochemical and mineralogical investigation of some British and other European tonsteins. *Sedimentology*, **26**, 407–25.

ŚRODOŃ, J. 1976. Mixed-layer smectite–illites in the bentonites and tonsteins of the Upper Silesian Coal basin. *Polska Akademia Nauk, Oddzial w Krakowie, Komisja Nauk Mineralogicznych, Prace Mineralogiczne*, **49**, 83 pp. (in English).

STRAUSS, G. K., ROGER, G., LECOLLE, M. & LOPERA, E. 1981. Geochemical and geologic study of La Zarza, Huelva Province, Spain. *Economic Geology*, **76**, 1975–2000.

STROGEN, P. 1973. The volcanic rocks of the Carrigogunnel area, Co. Limerick. *Scientific Proceedings of the Royal Dublin Society*, **25**, 169–92.

THIRLWALL, M. F. 1981. Implications for Caledonian plate tectonic models of chemical data from volcanic rocks of the British Old Red Sandstone. *Journal of the Geological Society, London*, **138**, 123–38.

UPTON, B. G. J. 1982. Carboniferous to Permian volcanism in the stable foreland. *In:* SUTHERLAND, D. S. (ed.) *Igneous Rocks of the British Isles*, pp. 255–75, Wiley, New York.

WEDEPOHL, K. H., MEYER, K. & MUECKE, G. K. 1983. Chemical composition and genetic relations of meta-volcanic rocks from the Rhenohercynian Zone. *In:* MARTIN, H. & EDER, F. W. (eds) *Intracontinental Fold Belts*, pp. 231–56, Springer, Berlin.

ZEIGLER, P. A. 1978. Northwestern Europe: tectonics and basin development. *Geologie en Mijnbouw*, **57**, 589–626.

—— 1984. Caledonian and Hercynian crustal consolidation of western and central Europe—a working hypothesis. *Geologie en Mijnbouw*, **63**, 93–108.

E. H. FRANCIS, Department of Earth Sciences, University of Leeds, Leeds LS2 9JT, UK.

Tectonic implications of the timing of the Variscan orogeny

Nicholas Rast

Terminology

This paper is written in memory of Sir Edward Bailey, whose tectonic perception was outstanding. He was one of the pioneers in demonstrating the geological unity of stratigraphic and tectonic events. In 1935 he stated that 'The Ardennes of Belgium and much of the Appalachians of America are alike members of the Hercynian System' (Bailey 1935), although this had already been foreseen by Bertrand (1887). A few years earlier, in 1928, he developed the concept of intersection of the Caledonian and Hercynian orogenic belts in America (Fig. 1) (Bailey 1929). He also pointed out (Bailey 1935) that the term Hercynian (from the Harz Mountains of Germany), as defined by Bertrand, involved a time-dependent orogenic process as distinct from the earlier definition of the same term by Leopold von Buch who referred to the direction of fault structures. In western Europe, particularly Britain, Hercynian structures, which are well developed in Cornwall and Brittany, have often been referred to as Armorican (Suess 1887), with particular reference to the ancient Armorica but also applied to Cornubia. Although again a specific time-dependent orogeny was assumed, a measure of directional sense entered the definition. As a result the WNW–ESE to E–W trend became known as 'Armoricanoid' (Wills 1929). Furthermore, since in Germany most geologists followed von Buch rather than Bertrand, the term 'Variscan' became entrenched as a synonym of 'Hercynian' and was proselytized by Stille (1924). In an attempt to formalize the usage, Bailey (1929, 1935), following Suess, employed 'Hercynian' as a term for the orogeny and 'American' and 'Variscan' to define two principal orogenic arcs. Coe (1962, p. vii) reported that in 1961 it was decided by a meeting of interested geologists that the term 'Variscan' should be used in a geographical sense for the whole belt of late Palaeozoic deformation in Europe (from Ireland to Czechoslovakia), while 'Hercynian' should be used only in the time sense. Such a separation of place and time in orogeny is not satisfactory. Rutten (1969, p. 66) stated that Hercynian and Variscan are synonymous, although he pointed out that in Germany Hercynian direction (*Richtung*) refers to the post-Hercynian faults, as applied originally by von Buch. At this juncture it should be noted that neither Armorica nor the Harz Mountains covers a large part of the orogenic belt, whereas in central Europe (Rhineland–Bohemia) the Variscan deformed rocks show a much more comprehensive cross-section

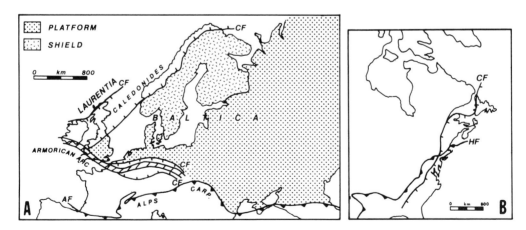

FIG. 1. Bailey's concept of transatlantic correlation.
(A) European scheme Z (note Caledonides intersected by the Armorican arc that continues into central Europe as the Variscan arc): CF, Caledonian fronts in Caledonides proper and in Central Europe; AF, Alpine front.
(B) American scheme: note the Hercynian front (HF) intersecting the Caledonian front (CF).
Note that in Britain the platform (dotted) is Avalonian.

From HARRIS, A. L. & FETTES, D. J. (eds), 1988, *The Caledonian–Appalachian Orogen,* Geological Society Special Publication No. 38, pp. 585–595.

of the belt. Therefore, the term 'Variscan' is preferable for the European part of the orogenic belt, and, since conventionally orogenic belts and most orogenies responsible for their generation have the same linguistic roots, the term 'Variscan orogeny' should always be employed in preference to 'Hercynian orogeny'. As Bailey (1935) recognized, the southern and central Appalachians have been affected by the Variscan (Hercynian) orogenic movements, and therefore America and Europe were sites of a single orogenic belt prior to the Mesozoic drift. Subsequent correlations by Rast & Grant (1973, 1977), Lefort & Van der Voo (1981), Rast (1983) and Lefort (1983), while varying in detail (Fig. 2), largely confirm Bailey's earlier ideas. The correlations imply that the N American late Palaeozoic orogenic belt should be referred to as Variscan. A difficulty arises in this respect since the Alleghanian orogeny (sometimes spelled Alleghenian in error) is often quoted as a terminal orogenic episode in N America, whereas in Europe the Variscan (Hercynian) orogeny is usually assumed to be a lengthy sequence of events starting at the end of the Devonian and ending in the Permian or, as reported by Simpson (1962), even in the Triassic! Stille (1924) divided the Variscan orogeny into phases: *Bretonic* (late Devonian–early Carboniferous), *Sudetic* (Namurian) and *Asturic* (Westphalian to Stephanian). Since then, other sub-phases or new phases have been introduced by Stille's students (Rast 1983). Thus, in European nomenclature the Variscan orogeny covers not only the Alleghanian but also, in some cases, the Acadian movements (Lefort 1983), although this is not completely accepted in this paper. Furthermore, the actual stratigraphy or upper Devonian–Carboniferous–

lower Permian rocks correlates badly between the USA and Europe. Correlations between the USA and the USSR are somewhat better because essentially platformal sequences are compared. Therefore recent attempts to use mixed W European and Soviet international chronostratigraphy accord better with the American stratigraphic scheme (Rast 1983). The main significance of the scheme rests in the division of the Namurian (A, B and C), so that the lower Namurian (A) is now referred to as Serpukhovian and the upper Namurian (B and C) as Bashkirian. The junction between the Bashkirian and the Serpukhovian coincides with the N American divisions of the Mississippian and Pennsylvanian. Other junctions, however, do not correspond.

The European usage of the term orogeny and its cyclically developed phases has in general topographic, tectonic and petrological connotations. Each major orogenic episode (Rast & Crimes 1969) is considered to be associated with uplift producing mountains, with tectonism resulting in folding, cleavage, thrusting etc. and with intrusion of syn-tectonic and post-tectonic granitoids into generally metamorphosed rocks. How local or general these events were is determined by geological circumstances. Stille (1924) tended to associate the development of angular unconformities with orogenic episodes, but such unconformities can be related to very localized manifestations of deformation, such as some early Palaeozoic unconformities in Wales, that are associated with faults (Rast 1969). Thus the association of orogenic phases with unconformities can only be valid if such unconformities have an extensive lateral continuity.

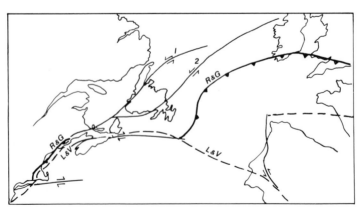

FIG. 2. Differing recent views regarding possible transatlantic correlations of the Variscan orogenic front: L & V, Lefort & Van der Voo (1981); R & G, Rast & Grant (1973); 1 and 2 represent possible American continuations of the Great Glen fault (1, Cabot fault; 2, Hare Bay–Dover fault).

Comparison of depositional events

Despite the large separations between eastern Europe and the southern Appalachians, there is at first sight a remarkable similarity in the successions of Carboniferous rocks along the Variscan orogen. This similarity can be demonstrated in terms of the lithological sequence (Fig. 3). However, examination of the complex relationship of lithologies either in Europe (Weber & Behr 1983) or in the southern Appalachians (Hatcher 1978) immediately reveals that depositional belts, which are parallel to strike, show rapid changes and variability across it. For instance in the Harz Mountains, over a distance of a mere 70 km, there is a highly diachronous flysch (greywacke) which in the SE begins its deposition in the upper Devonian and in the NW in the Namurian (Walliser & Alberti 1983). Since the flysch originates in response to a tectonic event, this means that such events and concomitant sedimentation have geologically prolonged histories. Therefore precise chronological positioning of tectonic episodes is probably unjustifiable. Similarly there is evidence for a close relation between sedimentation and thrust tectonism in the Appalachians (Rast 1984a), so that packages of coarse clastic deposits can be related to distinctive movements in the belt (Donaldson & Shumaker 1981).

Another problem with the interpretation of orogenic sedimentation in time and place is that the interiors of orogenic belts are usually deeply eroded and therefore successions are truncated, thus removing evidence for their original depositional continuity. Furthermore, since fossils are rare and many facies belts are margined by major dislocations, the resulting distinctive terranes cannot be interpreted without ambiguity and have been called 'suspect terranes' (Williams & Hatcher 1982, 1983). In the Appalachians, this concept was adopted from Cordilleran geology (Coney *et al.* 1980). The recognition of distinctive belts (zones) as components of the Variscan orogenic belt in Germany dates from Kossmat (1927), who divided the Variscan orogenic belt into stratotectonic belts or zones on the basis that there is a connection between Variscan orogenic phases, the successions involved and the nature of the underlying basement. The three most important zones recognized were the Rhenohercynian, the Saxothuringian and the Moldanubian. Their extension away from central Europe is disputed by different workers (Fig. 4). Attempts have been made to correlate these zones across the Atlantic Ocean (Rast 1983, fig. 14, Skehan & Rast 1984). In the type locality (central Germany and Bohemia) the zones have the following significance.

The *Rhenohercynian zone* includes the Harz Mountains, the Rheish massif, most of the Devon and Cornwall region of the British Isles, parts of southern Ireland and South Portugal. The rocks of the zone have undergone late Carboniferous deformation. The 'Variscan' strata commence with diverse Devonian rocks (4000 m thick), ranging from non-marine red beds to shallow marine clastics and carbonates (reefs) deposited in isolated basins, and end with the upper Carboniferous molasse. The Rhenish rocks have been described by Langenstrassen (1983) and Eder *et al.* (1983). The latter workers also discuss

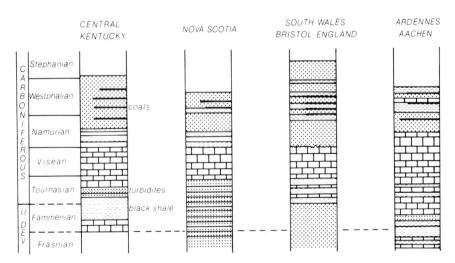

FIG. 3. Comparisons of Carboniferous lithostratigraphy between America, British Isles and continental Europe. Brick shading, carbonates; dots and lines, turbidites.

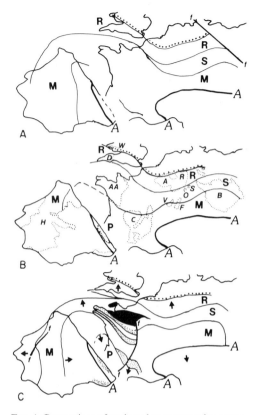

FIG. 4. Comparison of projected stratotectonics zones in Europe according to: (A) Weber & Behr (A, Alpine front; M, Moldanubian zone; R, Rhenohercynian zone; S, Saxothuringian zone; ft, Tornquist line; dotted line, sub-Variscan fore deep); (B) Kossmat, Rutten and followers (AA, Armorican Massif; A, Ardennes; B, Bohemian Massif; C, Central Massif; D, Devon and Cornwall; F, Black Forest; H, Hisperide Massif; O, Odenwald; P, Pyrenees; R, Rheinisches Schiefergebirge; S, Spessart; V, Vosges; W, Welsh Massif; other symbols as in (A)); (C) Autran & Cogné (f, major faults; black areas, undeformed masssifs; dotted areas, Icartian and Cadomian areas in France where nappes have been recognized recently including Montagne Noire, A–A (Alpine front), other symbols as in (A) and (B)).

Carboniferous carbonate flysch of that area, which later on was overrun by clastic flysch advancing from the SE. According to Voll (1979), the underlying basement in the Eifel area consists of rocks of greenschist and amphibolite facies on the basis of xenoliths in Quaternary and Tertiary volcanic rocks of the area. It is speculatively suggested that the basement is of Cadomian rocks (Schulz-Dobrick & Wedepohl 1983). In the southern part of the Rhenish massif nappe tectonics have been proposed by Engel *et al.*

(1983), as indeed they have been in the Harz Mountains (Walliser & Alberti 1983). According to Ahrendt *et al.* (1983), the deformation in the Rhenish Massif is time transgressive, varying from 326 Ma in the S to 305 Ma in the N of the massif. These dates suggest a Namurian–lower Westphalian event in which the rocks suffered 50% shortening. These movements have in the past been called Asturian.

To the N of the Rhenohercynian zone, separated by an overthrust (Faille de Midi) well identified in the Belgian Ardennes, lies the so-called sub-Variscan foredeep. Its rocks in Belgium (Namur megasyncline) consist of Devonian and Carboniferous carbonates and clastics with a thick coal-bearing upper Carboniferous section (Fig. 3). The Carboniferous rocks are internally strongly folded and over-thrust. The megasyncline and particularly the Faille de Midi are usually assumed to mark the front of Variscan deformation.

To the S of the Rhenohercynian zone lies the mid-German crystalline rise, which Kossmat (1927) included in the Saxothuringian zone. The Saxothuringian zone has been defined by Kossmat from the northern part of the Bohemian Massif (Fig. 4B); it includes parts of the Vosges and Black Forest and continues into the Massif Central and central and northern Brittany (Fig. 4B). The crystalline rise consists of metamorphic and granitic rocks thought to have been affected by lower Devonian deformation and pre-370 Ma metamorphism. The Odenwald and Spessart pre-tectonic granites of the zone yield late Silurian to early Devonian (398–419 Ma) Rb–Sr ages (Kreuzer *et al.* 1973, Lippolt *et al.* 1976).

Still later, during uplift, relatively shallow 3–5 km gabbros and granodiorites were intruded; these give a hornblende cooling age of 335 Ma. Since metamorphism was deep (15 km) and the granodiorites are partly syn-tectonic, there may have been a gradual elevation of the rise throughout Devonian time. The current interpretation is that this is due to thrusting and that the resultant uplift of the crystalline rise supplied material for the greywacke flysch of the Rhenohercynian zone (Weber & Behr 1983).

The *Saxothuringian zone* has a complex pre-Devonian history. It is characterized by assemblages of rocks subjected to different degrees of metamorphism and includes large granulitic complexes, of which the latest, according to Weber & Behr (1983), are Silurian in age (430 Ma). They suggest that the initial sedimentation occurred about 900 Ma ago. It was followed by mafic and ultramafic intrusions (Luecke & Rein 1972), and later granites margined by anatexites (Anatexis I?) and metamorphism (525–580 Ma). These effects were related to crustal stretching, which lasted from the late Precambian to the Ordovician (460 Ma) and was succeeded in 430 Ma by a generation of granulites. The late Devonian to early Carboniferous metamorphism led to Anatexis II (380–430 Ma), followed by later gentler Carboniferous deformation. Fluck *et al.* (1980) report that in the Saar 1 borehole a granite similar to those of the Black Forest part of the Saxothuringian zone is overlain by undeformed middle Devonian rocks. In the Vosges and Black Forest, granulites about 430 Ma old are present among the gneisses.

Autran & Cogné (1980) interpret the highest-grade *Moldanubian zone* as the internal zone of the orogen. It is characterized by middle and upper Devonian deformation and metamorphism (Ligerian and Bretonic orogenic episodes) and lower and middle Ordovician granites. Therefore in this sense the Saxothuringian zone represents the metamorphosed external zone. It is characterized by the mid-Dinantian (Nassau) episode of deformation and metamorphism. The Rhenohercynian zone is external and essentially unmetamorphosed and is characterized by the Asturian (late Carboniferous) episode of deformation (Shackleton *et al.* 1982) which also affects the pre-Variscan fore deep.

The Variscan zone of central Europe, once traced southward across the belt (Fig. 4C), shows changes of vergence of folding and thrusting from that to the N to that to the S (e.g. Montagne Noire). Matte (1983) has recently discussed this point, and the same behaviour is observed in Spain (Julivert *et al.* 1980). Thus it appears that the Variscan orogenic domain of Europe is two-sided and that vergence reverses across the internal Moldanubian belt.

The trans-Moldanubian Palaeozoic rocks show features and isotopic dates similar to those of central Europe (Flugel 1975, Satir & Mortiane 1980), but since they mainly lie S of the Alpine front they have not been so thoroughly investigated. Nevertheless, the evidence of deformation and metamorphism of both lower Palaeozoic and upper Palaeozoic (Asturian) ages is widely recognized and can even be detected in Morocco (Clauer *et al.* 1980), where isotopic ages of 330–305 Ma are recorded for various granitoids.

Tectonic interpretations of Variscan chronology

There are three groups of tectonic interpretations of the Variscan orogen in Europe.

1 Weber & Behr (1983) consider the orogen as an intra-continental fold belt that began sedimentation in the late Precambrian, underwent deep extension in the Ordovician and Silurian and collapsed compressionally from middle Devonian times onward to the late Carboniferous.

2 Arthaud & Matte (1977) interpreted the late Variscan tectonics of both Europe and N America in terms of strike-slip movement on conjugate faults. This interpretation was extended by Badham (1982) to suggest the interaction of small plates of continental aspect throughout all episodes of deformation.

3 Dewey & Burke (1973) suggested a collisional hypothesis analogous to that used by them to interpret the Himalayan–Tibetan belt. There are numerous followers of this interpretation, among whom Autran & Cogné (1980), Bard *et al.* (1980) and Lorenz & Nicholls (1984) should be mentioned in particular.

The hypothesis of Weber & Behr has problems in that it is ambiguous about the events in the trans-Moldanubian parts of the belt. For instance, was the European crust continuous with the African crust? Can high-pressure granulites, which are incidentally associated with ultramafic and eclogitic rocks, be produced in a rift environment? The interpretation, which is plausible for central Germany, cannot easily be applied to France where the Saxothuringian-type rocks do not form a continuous belt (Fig. 4C) and the Moldanubian belt is surrounded by several large blocks interpreted as microplates (Autran & Cogné 1980). At present, therefore, this hypothesis appears to be incomplete.

Badham's hypothesis suggests, on the basis of Cornubian geology, the existence of long-lived strike-slips which generate dextral shear zones that involve multiple microplates at oblique plate-interaction junctions. This hypothesis does not incorporate the timing of European Variscan events, and it does not analyse metamorphism, intrusive activity, nappe tectonics (which are now widely demonstrated) or details of deformation. At present it has the status of an interesting and possibly only partly applicable speculation.

The collisional hypothesis also has some defects. Post-Precambrian pre-Alpine ophiolites normally found in collisional environments are rare. Zwart & Dornsiepen (1980) suggest that the Variscan crust which, at present, is no more than 30 km thick could not have been thicker in Variscan times by more than another 15 km, which is incompatible with collisional duplication of the crust. This difficulty, however, becomes less significant if, following Autran & Cogné (1980), it is assumed that there were several intervening microplates. Lorenz & Nicholls (1984) propose a lower Carboniferous volcanic arc on the site of present southern Europe, which also accounts for the thin Variscan crust. They consider that the collision of the southern and northern European masses was diachronous. The interpretation of an island arc is doubtful, since under these conditions obduction and continental accretion of ophiolites is likely in the suture zone. Therefore the only solution is that if an oceanic area (Rheic Ocean?) separated the Baltic craton from the African craton and the associated microplates, it was entirely subducted under the surrounding cratonic areas and the only localities where obduction may have occurred were micro-oceans between some microplates, as in southern Brittany (Matte 1983). Despite the general absence of ophiolites, a collisional origin of the Variscan orogenic belt is, at present, the best interpretation. It accounts not only for compressional tectonics, volcanism and granite emplacement, but also for the preservation of occasional 'foreign' blocks of Precambrian basement which cannot be easily related to the European craton (e.g. Icartian and Cadomian blocks) (Fig. 4C) and are difficult to explain by the intra-continental hypotheses. It also explains the extremely arcuate shape of large parts of the orogenic belt that are not amenable to strike-slip interpretations.

Appalachian orogen and its correlation with Europe

The manifestations of the Variscan cycle in the Appalachian chain are recognized mainly in the southern and central Appalachians. In the Canadian northern Appalachians the orogenic effects, although noticed (Gussow 1953, Poole 1967), were not recorded as Variscan (Hercynian) until the 1970s (Rast & Grant 1973, Keppie 1981), possibly because, unlike the southern Appalachians, the deformed and metamorphosed Carboniferous rocks were found only to the SE of the main orogenic belt affected by the mid-Devonian Acadian orogenies. Three provinces (zones) of deformation are recognized in the southern and central Appalachians (Hatcher et al. 1980). To the W and NW lies the non-metamorphic Valley and Ridge province (Rodgers 1970), which is a wide essentially single-phase imbricate zone of thrusting and folding affecting strata ranging from the early Cambrian to the early Permian. This episode of deformation is referred to as the Alleghanian orogeny. To the E and SE of the Valley and Ridge lies the metamorphosed Blue Ridge where the strata range from Grenville Precambrian to the Ordov-

ician but the complex deformation is attributed mainly to the Grenvillian, Taconian and Alleghanian orogenies. To the E of the Blue Ridge lies the Piedmont which consists of rocks ranging from Precambrian to upper Ordovician (Silurian?) age and where Acadian orogenic effects have also been claimed. Acadian thrust movements have also been described from the central Appalachians (Drake 1980). The Piedmont consists of a great variety of meta-igneous and metasedimentary rocks intruded by granites varying in age from Precambrian to upper Palaeozoic. Although in this region no Carboniferous sediments have been recognized, dated Carboniferous granites of both syn-tectonic and post-tectonic ages are well known (Speer et al. 1980, Sinha & Zietz 1982). Sinha and Zietz have suggested that an arc of Carboniferous calc-alkaline granites existed in the southeastern part of the Piedmont area.

From the point of view of metamorphism, the frontal overthrust of the Blue Ridge in the widest part of the southern Appalachians is affected by Taconian (mid-Ordovician) metamorphism of about 470–460 Ma (Dallmeyer 1975) which rises in grade from the NW to the SE (Butler 1972), where it is in the upper amphibolite facies. The metamorphism is syn-tectonic and is associated with major thrusting (Hatcher et al. 1980). In the Piedmont, except for some belts such as the Carolina Slate Belt, metamorphism is high and there is much migmatization. In the central Appalachians, lower Palaeozoic as well as Precambrian granulities are reported.

Rast (1983) correlated the Valley and Ridge Province with the Rhenohercynian (non-metamorphic external zone), the Blue Ridge with the Saxothuringian (metamorphic external zone) and the Piedmont with the Moldanubian (internal zone) belts. There are, however, considerable differences. The continuation of the central European Variscan belt into western and south-western Europe, away from the Alps proper, indicates that the orogen is two-sided (Autran & Cogné 1980), with the Moldanubian zone representing the interior of the orogen. The two-sidedness, especially in France, is strongly supported by the divergent sense of tectonic movement on either side of the Moldanubian belt (Matte 1983). In the southern and central Appalachians the main sense of tectonic translation (overthrusting) is uniformly to the NW (Cook et al. 1979), and this is so not only in relation to the Alleghanian but also to the Taconian and possibly the Acadian thrusts. The Acadian movements are suggested on the basis of the chronology of mylonites (Bartholomew & Lewis 1984). Thus if the Appalachian orogen was two-sided, the other side of it has to be sought under the so-called Coastal Plain deposits or the Atlantic continental shelf or in Africa (Lefort 1984).

Furthermore, while in Central Europe the presence and the extent of the unquestioned Precambrian basement is debatable (Weber & Behr 1983), in the soutern Appalachians Grenville rocks dated 1000 Ma are known from both the Blue Ridge and the Piedmont (Rast *et al.* 1988). Of course, the presence of Grenville intercalations in the Piedmont may be the product of extreme allochthonous movements over Grenville massifs during Palaeozoic deformations. According to many of the aforementioned workers the Variscan orogenic episodes in Europe, in both Germany and France, become younger towards the orogenic front: Bretonic (Acadian?)–Sudetic–Asturian. No such feature has been noticed in the Appalachians, although successive mid-Ordovician, Devonian and Carboniferous thrusting is recognized (Rast & Kohles 1984). In

the USA it can be explained by the development of thrusting forward, towards the craton. In the southern Appalachians earlier episodes of thrusting affect the underlying basement, whereas the Alleghanian thrusting is thin skinned although it carries previously-thrust crystalline basement.

The frequent and successive thrusting in the USA has led to the progressive development of associated clastic wedges (Donaldson & Shumaker 1981, Rast 1984b, Thomas & Schenk 1987). Where the clastic wedges are exposed on the Kentucky–West Virginia–Tennessee platform, the sediments consist essentially of clastic rocks (conglomerates, sandstones and shales) ranging in age from middle Devonian to lower Permian and divisible into several wedges, each probably representing an important Variscan thrust movement. The total succession is variable and has often been referred to as molasse, but in comparison with the Swiss Alpine molasse (Fig. 5) it is both thin and of a much longer time-

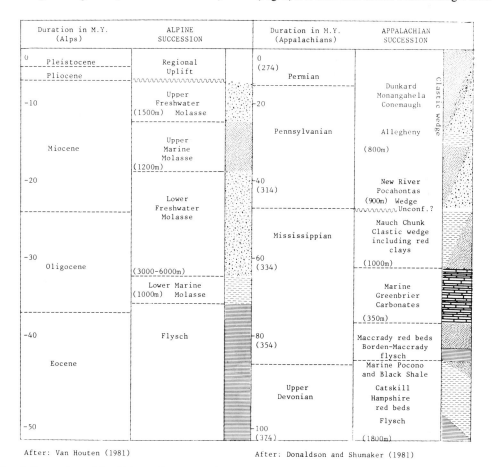

FIG. 5. Comparison of the Alpine molasse succession with the Carboniferous section in the central–southern Appalachians. Conglomeratic wedges are indicated.

span. Only at the beginning of the cycle is there an indication of turbidite deposition. Thus there is an indication of Variscan episodicity, but in the absence of granites or volcanics in the Valley and Ridge and the western Blue Ridge, this episodicity cannot be recognized in the orogenic belt. It may be that ultimately correlations of low- to medium-grade metamorphic rocks from Valley and Ridge to Blue Ridge would supply the answer.

Despite uncertainties there still seems to be a broad tectono-stratigraphic zonal correlation with Europe. Nevertheless the zonal correlation has to be judged in the light of major movements that shaped the Appalachian system.

Plate-tectonic kinematics

If the continuity of the southern and central Appalachians with the European Variscan orogenic belt is accepted, the following inferences can be made.

1 The Appalachian–Variscan orogen had been affected by sequential deformations prior to the Variscan proper, i.e. the Cadomian and 'Caledonian' in central Europe, and the Avalonian (Virgilian) and Taconian in the southern Appalachians. The Variscan cycle proper began after the associated Acadian (essentially early to middle Devonian) in America and Acado-Ligerian in Europe, although the Acadian rather than the Variscan may include the *Bretonic* in Europe (340–360 Ma). The Variscan continued to the end Pennsylvanian (Stephanian) on both continents (about 280 Ma). Thus it appears that the orogen was continuous, and what is claimed for the Variscan of Europe is in general true for the Appalachian belt of N America.
2 The Variscan–Appalachian cycle involved the approach to and collision with Africa of Europe and N America. The sinuous shape of the Variscan orogen in Europe suggests the existence of intervening microplates. The more linear shape

of the southern central Appalachians implies that if there were intervening microplates they were elongated, as for example the Avalonian terrane (Rast & Skehan 1983) which has been claimed to have been in sinistral motion during late Devonian–Mississippian times (Kent & Opdyke 1979, Van der Voo 1982), although this is now denied (Kent & Opdyke 1985). The motion and interaction of European microplates (Badham 1982) has also been used to explain some Variscan movement (Sudetic), and therefore in principle the situation appears similar. However, the Avalon terrane of N America extends into Newfoundland and Britain and therefore cuts across the boundary of the Variscan orogen (Fig. 2), which suggests that any possible sinistral movements at the America-facing edge of the Avalon terrane must have occurred prior to the inception of the Variscan cycle. The ambiguity is unresolved at present, but Mississippian movements in N America were certainly significant as is demonstrated by the development of major basins of deposition in eastern Canada (Schenk 1978).
3 The main collision leading to major overthrusting in both Europe (Germany, Belgium, UK) and N America (eastern Canada, Rhode Island, Massachusetts and southern Appalachians) that affected coal-bearing upper Carboniferous or lower Permian strata occurred in Westphalian to Stephanian times (Asturian and Alleghanian movements). Thus Dallmeyer (1981) reported hornblende cooling ages of about 260 Ma from Rhode Island.
4 Lastly, as pointed out by Arthaud & Matte (1977) and Lefort & Van der Voo (1981), the pervasive shear affecting most Variscan domains is attributable to the lower Permian movements.

ACKNOWLEDGMENTS: The author wishes to express his thanks to Dr J. Rodgers for his useful advice, K. M. Kohles for help with reading and drafting and Brenda Phillips for typing the manuscript. The contributions by the National Science Foundation (grant EAR 8200047) and the Chevron Oil Company are acknowledged.

References

AHRENDT, H., CLAUER, N., HUNZIKER, J. C. & WEBER, K. 1983. Migration of folding and metamorphism in the Rheinisches schiefergebirge deducted from K–Ar and Rb–Sr age determinations. *In:* MARTIN, H. & EDER, F. W. (eds) *Intracontinental Fold Belts,* pp. 323–38, Springer-Verlag, Berlin.

ARTHAUD, F. & MATTE, Ph. 1977. Late Paleozoic strike-slip faulting in southern Europe and northern Africa: result of a right lateral shear zone between the Appalachians and the Urals. *Geological Society of America Bulletin,* **88,** 1305–20.

AUTRAN, A. & COGNÉ, J. 1980. La zone interne de l'orogéne varisque dans l'Ouest de la France et sa place dans le développement de la chaine hercynienne. *26th International Geological Congress, Colloque C6,* pp. 90–111.

BADHAM, J. P. N. 1982. Strike-slip orogens—an explanation for the Hercynides, *Journal of the Geological Society, London,* **139**, 495–506.

BAILEY, E. B. 1929. The Palaeozoic mountain systems of Europe and America. *Report to the British Association for the Advancement of Science (1928),* pp. 57–76.

—— 1935. *Tectonic Essays, Mainly Alpine,* Clarendon Press, Oxford, 200 pp.

BARD, J. P., BURG, J. P., MATTE, Ph. & RIBEIRO, A. 1980. The Variscan tectonic evolution of Central and Western Europe. *26th International Geological Congress, Colloque C6,* pp. 233–48.

BARTHOLOMEW, M. J. & LEWIS, S. E. 1984. Evolution of Grenville massifs in the Blue Ridge geologic province, southern and central Appalachians. *Geological Society of America Special Paper No. 194,* pp. 229–54.

BERTRAND, M. 1887. La Chaine des Alpes, et la formation du continent européen. *Bulletin de la Société Géologique de France, Série 3,* **15**, 423–57.

BUTLER, J. R. 1972. Age of Paleozoic regional metamorphism in the Carolinas, Georgia and Tennessee southern Appalachians. *American Journal of Science,* **272**, 319–33.

CLAUER, N., JEANNETTE, D. & TISSERANT, D. 1980. Datation isotopique des cristallisations successives d'un socle cristallin et crystallophyllien (Haute Moolouya, Moyen Maroc). *Geologische Rundschau,* **69**, 63–83.

COE, K. (ed.) 1962. *Some Aspects of the Variscan Fold Belt,* Manchester University Press, Manchester, 163 pp.

CONEY, P. J., JONES, D. D. & MONGER, J. W. H. 1980. Cordilleran suspect terranes. *Nature, London,* **288**, 329–33.

COOK, F. A., ALBAUGH, D. S., BROWN, L. D., KAUFMAN, S., OLIVER, J. E. & HATCHER, R. D., JR 1979. Thin-skinned tectonics in the crystalline southern Appalachians; COCORP seismic-reflection profiling of the Blue Ridge and Piedmont. *Geology,* **7**, 563–7.

DALLMEYER, R. D. 1975. Incremental Ar^{40}/Ar^{39} ages of biotite and hornblende from retrograded basement gneisses of the southern Blue Ridge: their bearing on the age of Paleozoic metamorphism. *American Journal of Science,* **275**, 444–60.

—— 1981. The extent of Hercynian metamorphism in southern New England. *Geological Society of America Abstracts with Programs,* **13**, 129–30.

DEWEY, J. F. & BURKE, K. C. 1973. Tibetan, Variscan, and Precambrian basement reactivation products of continental collision. *Journal of Geology,* **81**, 683–92.

DONALDSON, A. C. & SHUMAKER, R. C. 1981. Late Paleozoic molasse of Central Appalachians. *In:* MAILL, A. D. (ed.) *Sedimentation and Tectonics in Alluvial Basins. Geological Association of Canada Special Paper No. 23,* pp. 199–224.

DRAKE, A. A., JR 1980. The Taconides, Acadides and Alleghenides in the Central Appalachians. *In:* WONES, W. R. (ed.) *The Caledonides in the USA: Proceedings of the International Geological Correlation Program—Caledonide Orogen Project 27,*

Blacksburg, VA. Department of Geological Sciences, Virginia Polytechnic Institute and State University, Memoir No. 2, pp. 179–87.

EDER, F. W., ENGEL, W., FRANKE, W. & SADLER, P. M. 1983. Devonian and Carboniferous limestone-turbidites of the Rheinisches Schiefergebirge and their tectonic significance. *In:* MARTIN, H. & EDER, F. W. (eds) *Intracontinental Fold Belts,* pp. 93–124, Springer, Berlin.

ENGEL, W., FRANKE, W., GROTE, W., WEBER, K., AHRENDT, H. & EDER, F. W. 1983. Nappe tectonics in the southeastern part of the Rehinisches Schiefergebirge 1983. *In:* MARTIN, H. & EDER, F. W. (eds) *Intracontinental Fold Belts,* pp. 267–88, Springer, Berlin.

FLUCK, P., MAASS, R. & VON RAUMER, J. F. 1980. The Variscan units east and west of the Rhine graben. *26th International Geological Congress, Colloque C6,* pp. 112–31.

FLUGEL, H. W. 1975. Einige Preobleme des Variszikums von Neo-Europa. *Geologische Rundschau,* **64**, 1–62.

GUSSOW, W. C. 1953. Carboniferous stratigraphy and structural geology of New Brunswick, Canada. *American Association of Petroleum Geologists,* **37**, 1713–816.

HATCHER, R. D., JR 1978. Synthesis of the Southern and Central Appalachians, USA. *In:* TOZER, E. T. & SCHENK, P. E. (eds) *Caledonian–Appalachian Orogen of the North Atlantic Region. Geological Survey of Canada Paper No. 78–13,* pp. 149–58.

——, BUTLER, J. R., FULLAGER, P. D., SECOR, D. T. & SNOKE, A. W. 1980. Geological synthesis of the Tennessee–Carolinas–northeast Georgia Southern Appalachians. *In:* WONES, D. R. (ed.) *The Caledonides in the USA: Proceedings of the International Geological Correlation Program—Caledonide Orogen Project 27, Blacksburg, VA. Department of Geological Sciences, Virginia Polytechnic Institute and State University, Memoir No. 2,* pp. 63–6.

JULIVERT, M., MARTINEZ, F. J. & RIBEIRO, A. 1980. The Iberian segment of the European Hercynian foldbelt. *26th International Geological Congress, Colloque C6,* pp. 132–58.

KENT, D. V. & OPDYKE, N. D. 1979. The Early Carboniferous palaeomagnetic field for North America and its bearing on the tectonics of the northern Appalachians. *Earth and Planetary Science Letters,* **44**, 365–72.

—— & —— 1985. Multicomponent magnetization from the Mississippian Mauch Chunk formation of the Central Appalachians and their tectonic implications. *Journal of Geophysical Research,* **90**, 5371–83.

KEPPIE, J. D. 1981. Tectonics of Nova Scotia—a review. *Geological Society of America Abstracts with Programs,* **13**, 140.

KOSSMAT, F. 1927. Gliederung des varistischen Gebirgesbaues. *Abhandlungen des Sächsischen Geologischen Landesamtes,* **1**, 39 pp.

KREUZER, H., LENZ, H., HARRE, W., MATTHES, S., OKRUSCH, M. & RICHTER, P. 1973. Zur Altersstellung der Rotgneisse im Spessart, Rb/Sr Gesamtgestems-datierungen. *Geologisches Jahrbuch, Rerhe A*, **9**, 69–88.

LANGENSTRASSEN, F. 1983. Neritic sedimentation of the Lower and Middle Devonian in the Rheinishe Schiefergebirge east of the river Rhine. *In*: MARTIN, H. & EDER, F. W. (eds) *Intracontinental Fold Belts*, pp. 43–76, Springer, Berlin.

LEFORT, J. P. 1983. A new geophysical criterion to correlate the Acadian and Hercynian orogenies of western Europe and eastern America. Geological Society of America, Memoir, **158**, 3–18.

—— 1984. Mise en évidence d'une virgation carbonifère induite par la dorsale Reguibat (Mauritanie) dans les Appalaches du Sud (U.S.A.). Arguments géophysiques. *Bulletin de la Société Géologique de France*, **26**, 1293–303.

—— & VAN DER VOO, R. 1981. A kinematic model for the collision and complete suturing between Londevanal and Laurussia in the Carboniferous. *Journal of Geology*, **89**, 537–50.

LIPPOLT, H. J., BARANY, J. & RACZEK, J. 1976. *Rb/Sr chronology of Orthogneisses in the Eastern Odenwald and Southern Spessant (Germany)*, Abstract ECO-GIV, Amsterdam.

LORENZ, V. & NICHOLLS, I. A. 1984. Plate and intraplate processes of Hercynian Europe during the late Palaeozoic. *Tectonophysics*, **107**, 25–56.

LUECKE, W. & REIN, G. 1972. Gabbroide, metamorphite and ultramafitite in Sudschwerzwald. *Fortschritte der Mineralogie*, **50**, 19–33.

MATTE, Ph. 1983. Two geotraverses across the Ibero-Armorican Variscan of Western Europe. *In*: RAST, N. & DELANEY, F. M. (eds) *Profiles of the Orogenic Belt*, pp. 83–96, American Geophysical Union and Geological Society of America.

POOLE, W. H. 1967. Tectonic evolution of Appalachian region in Canada. Geology of the Atlantic region. *Royal Society of Canada Special Paper No. 4*, pp. 9–51.

RAST, N. 1969. The relationship between Ordovician structures and volcanicity in Wales. *In*: WOOD, A. (ed.) *The Pre-Cambrian and Lower Palaeozoic Rocks of Wales*, pp. 305–35, University of Wales Press, Cardiff.

—— 1983. Variscan orogeny. *In*: HANCOCK, P. L. (ed.) *Variscan Fold Belt of the British Isles*, pp. 1–19, Adam Hilger, Bristol.

—— 1984a. Alleghanian deformation as a sediment-generating event in the Southern Appalachians. *Geological Society of America Abstracts with Programs*, **16**, 188.

—— 1984b. The Alleghanian orogeny in North America. *In*: HUTTON, D. & SANDERSON, D. (eds) *Variscan Tectonics in the North Atlantic. Special Publication of the Geological Society of London No. 14*, pp. 197–217.

—— & CRIMBES, T. P. 1969. Caledonian orogenic episodes in the British Isles and Northwestern France and their tectonic and geochronological interpretation. *Tectonophysics*, **7**, 277–307.

—— & GRANT, R. H. 1973. Transatlantic correlation of the Variscan–Appalachian orogeny. *American Journal of Science*, **273**, 272–9.

—— & —— 1977. Variscan–Appalachian and Allegh-

enian deformation in the Northern Appalachian. *Colloquium Volume: Contributions to International Colloquium on the Variscan system, Rennes, 1974. CNRS Publication No. 243*, pp. 583–6.

—— & KOHLES, K. M. 1984. The Late Precambrian sediments at the eastern margin of the Laurentian shield in the Southern Appalachians. *Geological Society of America Abstracts with Programs*, **16**, 188.

—— & SKEHAN, J. W., S. J. 1983. The evolution of the Avalonian plate. *Tectonophysics*, **100**, 257–86.

——, STURT, B. A. & HARRIS, A. L. 1988. Early deformation in the Caledonian–Appalachian orogen. *This volume*.

RODGERS, J. 1970. *The Tectonics of the Appalachians*. Wiley-Interscience, New York, 271 pp.

RUTTEN, M. 1969. *The Geology of Western Europe*. Elsevier, Amsterdam, 520 pp.

SATIR, M. & MORTIANE, G. 1980. Radiometrische and petrologische Untersuchungen zur praealpidischen migmatit-Bildung zur alpidischen metamorphose in westlichen Tauernfenster (Ostalpen). *Berliner Geowissenschaftliche Abhandlungen, Reihe A*, **29**, 194.

SCHENK, P. E. 1978. Synthesis of the Canadian Appalachians. *Geological Survey of Canada Paper 78–13*, pp. 111–36.

SCHULZ-DOBRICK, B. & WEDEPOHL, K. H. 1983. The chemical composition of sedimentary deposits in the Rhenohercynian belt of Central Europe. *In*: MARTIN, H. & EDER, F. W. (eds) *Intracontinental Fold Belts*, pp. 211–29, Springer, Berlin.

SHACKLETON, R. M., RIES, A. C. & COWARD, M. P. 1982. An interpretation of the Variscan structures in SW England. *Journal of the Geological Society, London*, **139**, 535–44.

SIMPSON, S. 1962. Variscan orogenic phases. *In*: COE, K. (ed.) *Some Aspects of the Variscan Fold Belt*, pp. 65–75, Manchester University Press, Manchester.

SINHA, A. K. & ZIETZ, I. 1982. Geophysical and geochemical entrance for a Hercynian magmatic arc, Maryland to Georgia. *Geology*, **10**, 593–6.

SKEHAN, J. W., S. J. & RAST, N. 1984. Correlation of Carboniferous tectonostratigraphic zones in Europe and North America. *Neuvième Congrés International de Stratigraphic et de Géologie Carbonifère, Compte Rendu, Washington and Champlain-Urbana*, Vol. 3, pp. 13–22.

SPEER, J. A., BECKER, S. W. & FARRAR, S. S. 1980. Field relations and petrology of the post-metamorphic, coarse-grained granitoids and associated rocks of the southern Appalachian Piedmont. *In*: WONES, D. R. (ed.) *The Caledonides in the USA. Proceedings of the International Geological Correlation Program—Caledonide Orogen Project 27, Blacksburg, VA. Department of Geological Sciences, Virginia Polytechnic Institute and State University, Blacksburg, VA. Memoir No. 2*, pp. 137–48.

STILLE, H. 1924. *Grundfragen der Vergleichenden. Tectonik*, Gebrueder Borntrager, Berlin, 322 pp.

SUESS, E. 1887. Ueber unterbrochene Gebirgsfaltung. *Sitzungsberichte der Kaiserlich Akademie der Wissenschaften*, **94**, 111.

THOMAS, W. A. & SCHENK, P. E. 1987. Late Palaeozoic

sedimentation along the Appalachian orogen. *This volume.*

VAN DER VOO, R. 1982. Pre-Mesozoic palaeomagnetism and plate tectonics. *Annual Review of Earth and Planetary Sciences,* **10,** 191–200.

VOLL, G. 1979. Untersuchung von vulkanischen Auswurflingen aus Kruste und Mantel in Raum der Eifel. *DEG Protokoll uber das 4. Kolloquium im Schwerpunkt Vertikalbewegungen und ihre Ursachen am Beispiel des Rheinischen Schildes,* 93–5.

WALLISER, O. H. & ALBERTI, H. 1983. Flysch, olistostromes and nappes in the Harz Mountains. *In:* MARTIN, H. & EDER, F. W. (eds) *Intracontinental Fold Belts,* pp. 145–70, Springer, Berlin.

WEBER, K. & BEHR, H. J. 1983. Geodynamic interpretation of the Mid-European Variscides. *In:* MARTIN, H. & EDER, F. W. (eds) *Intracontinental Fold Belts,* pp. 427–69, Springer, Berlin.

WILLIAMS, H. & HATCHER, R. D., JR 1982. Suspect terranes and accretionary history of the Appalachian orogen. *Geology,* **10,** 530–6.

—— & —— 1983. Appalachian suspect terranes. *Geological Society of America, Memoir,* **150,** 33–54.

WILLS, L. J. 1929. *The Physiographic Evolution of Britain,* Arnold, London, 376 pp.

ZWART, H. J. & DORNSIEPEN, V. F. 1980. The Variscan and pre-Variscan tectonic evolution of Central and Western Europe; a tentative model. *26th International Geological Congress, Colloque C6,* pp. 233–48.

N. RAST, Department of Geological Sciences, University of Kentucky, Lexington, KY 40506–0059, USA.

Post-Acadian metamorphism in the Appalachians

Daniel P. Murray

SUMMARY: Well-documented post-Acadian metamorphism occurs at three locales along the eastern flank of the Appalachians, where it has affected Avalonian basement and/or Carboniferous cover. Carboniferous rocks of coastal New Brunswick display a greenschist-facies metamorphism of Pennsylvanian to Permian age which largely post-dates associated Alleghanian ductile deformation. In southeastern New England sedimentary rocks of late Pennsylvanian age have undergone an amphibolite-facies Barrovian metamorphic event (275–290 Ma) that is syn- to post-ductile deformation and is truncated by peraluminous granite. Considerations of patterns of metamorphism in surrounding crystalline rocks implies that at least two distinct late Palaeozoic tectonothermal events have affected New England. In the Piedmont of Virginia and the Carolinas amphibolite-facies metamorphism (roughly 260–310 Ma) is synchronous with the emplacement of syn-kinematic granitoids. In all three areas isogradic patterns are complex, reflecting the effects of later faulting and fault-controlled retrograde metamorphism.

In the USA at least, Alleghanian metamorphism also affected areas well beyond the boundaries of Avalonian terranes *sensu stricto* into the polydeformed crystalline terrane to the W (Inner Piedmont, Merrimack synclinorium). Within these crystalline rocks the Permian thermal overprint appears to be focussed along shear zones. Late Palaeozoic regional metamorphism in the Appalachians probably reflects crustal thickening related to continent–continent or continent–microcontinent collisions characterized by heat transfer along fundamental tectonic boundaries, and not simply proximity to late Palaeozoic igneous activity or subduction-zone tectonics.

Traditionally, regional metamorphism within the Appalachians was attributed almost entirely to the Taconic and Acadian orogenies, and effects of the Alleghanian orogeny were considered to be of only local importance. In the last few years, however, many independent studies have demonstrated that late Palaeozoic ductile deformation accompanied by greenschist- to amphibolite-grade metamorphism is widespread along the eastern flank of the Appalachians from New Brunswick to Georgia. The metamorphism was only recognized recently because at the current erosion level it has, with few exceptions, affected crystalline basement that is relatively unresponsive to additional metamorphism. Progress has taken place primarily through the integration of isotopic dating of deformed granitoids intrusive into crystalline basement. In the southern Appalachians in particular this approach has allowed the recognition that extensive tracts of crystalline rocks of Proterozoic or Ordovician–Devonian age underwent ductile deformation and regional metamorphism during Carboniferous to Permian times. In this paper we describe the Alleghanian metamorphism in three areas along the eastern flank where it is best documented: coastal New Brunswick, southeastern New England, and the eastern Piedmont of the southern Appalachians (Hermes & Murray 1988, figs 1 and 2). The extent and nature of the thermal overprint upon contig-

uous basement terranes and the very-low-grade metamorphism of the western flank are then considered. For additional relevant information on the American Appalachians, the reader is also directed to Hatcher *et al.* (in press) for a recent review of the Alleghanian deformation and metamorphism, and to Secor *et al.* (in press) for a summary of pre-Carboniferous geological activity in Avalonian terranes.

Maritime provinces

Late Palaeozoic dynamothermal metamorphism is only documented along the coast of New Brunswick near St. John (Hermes & Murray 1988, fig. 2), where it has affected Avalonian basement (Proterozoic Z) and Carboniferous sedimentary rocks. Deformation there is complex, consisting of two periods of folding plus one period in which kink bands were formed (Rast *et al.* 1978, Mosher & Rast 1984). The first two folding events dominate and trend NE; they are roughly coaxial and are associated with thrusting. Tectonic transport was initially to the NW and then to the SE. They are synchronous with M_1, a phyllite-producing regional metamorphism that is uniform throughout the region. M_2 is largely post-kinematic and, proceeding SE, increases

From HARRIS, A. L. & FETTES, D. J. (eds), 1988, *The Caledonian–Appalachian Orogen,* Geological Society Special Publication No. 38, pp. 597–609.

from lower to upper greenschist facies culminating in the production of small garnets (Rast *et al.* 1978). Temporal relationships among metamorphism, deformation, magmatism and time are approximate for this area. This is because at present the exact geological ages and duration of events are constrained only by stratigraphic control based upon megaflora within the deformed and metamorphosed Lancaster Formation (Rast 1983) and not by radiometric ages. Alleghanian deformed and metamorphosed rocks are truncated by the Belle Isle and associated faults, which are taken to represent the Appalachian equivalent of the Variscan front of southwestern England (Rast 1983). Garnet increases in abundance away from the fault system (i.e. to the SE), and this is interpreted to indicate an increase in metamorphic grade to the SE (Rast *et al.* 1978). Carboniferous granites (Caledonian I type. (Hermes & Murray 1987)) within this coastal belt are post-kinematic and have no well-defined contact aureole.

Elsewhere in the Maritime Provinces late Palaeozoic metamorphism is limited to the Meguma terrane, where it occurs as contact metamorphic aureoles and muscovite plus biotite-bearing fabrics developed along shear zones (Dallmeyer & Keppie 1986). Unlike the Appalachians in the U.S.A., the rest of the crystalline rocks of the Maritime Provinces show no evidence of retrogression or disturbed isotopic systems that cannot be adequately explained in terms of normal uplift and cooling of Acadian terranes.

New England

Alleghanian metamorphism is best displayed in southeastern New England, which consists of an Avalonian basement overlain or intruded by a variety of other lithologies (Skehan & Murray 1980, Boothroyd & Hermes, 1981, Rast & Skehan 1983, Hermes & Zartman 1985, Secor *et al.*, in press). This terrane contains several Carboniferous basins, of which the Narragansett Basin of Rhode Island and Massachusetts is the largest and best known (Fig. 3). In this section we focus on the history of this basin (the only place within the Appalachians containing an almost complete record of Alleghanian sedimentation, deformation, metamorphism and plutonism) and the adjacent basement rocks. Moreover, recent dating of granitoids and incremental argon studies elsewhere in New England imply that Alleghanian metamorphism extends well to the W and NE.

Southeastern New England

Narragansett Basin

The Narragansett Basin is an arcuate structural basin of area 1600 km^2 composed of Pennsylvanian to early Permian coal-bearing non-marine clastic sediments that have been variably deformed and metamorphosed, and intruded by the Permian Narragansett Pier granite (Murray & Skehan 1979, Burks *et al.* 1981, Hermes *et al.* 1981a, Murray *et al.* 1981, Mosher 1983). The basin is generally considered to have formed by simple rifting, or possibly as a composite pull-apart basin within an active megashear system (Bradley 1982, Mosher 1983). Both regional metamorphism and deformation increase to the SW, culminating in multiple episodes of folding and amphibolite-facies metamorphism (Fig. 1).

The northern half of the basin is characterized by ENE-trending upright open folds accompanied by anchizone to lower greenschist (chlorite without biotite) metamorphism accompanied by thrusting to the NNW along axial planes. Attempts have been made using coal petrology (Murray *et al.* 1981) and mica crystallinity (Hepburn & Rehmer 1981) to subdivide and quantify metamorphic conditions within the anchizone. The resulting patterns are complex, and indicate the importance of not only the depth of burial and temperature but also fluid chemistry and kinetics. Shearing is often confined to coal seams, and coals from these anomalously deformed seams imply temperatures in excess of 350°C, perhaps in part a consequence of frictional heating. Quartz grains in folded rocks from the northwestern part of the basin show a preferred orientation that can be related to the axial plane of folds in the region. On the basis of microfabric analysis of deformation mechanisms in quartz from these rocks, Bristol *et al.* (1984) argue that a temperature of 200–250°C occurred during the development of the preferred orientation as well as the associated folding. Such an estimate appears to be broadly consistent with values obtained from coal petrology (180–200°C). In general, a comparison of the data given in the aforementioned references indicates that temperatures of metamorphism inferred from coal reflectivity and deformation mechanisms are higher than those obtained from consideration of illite crystallinity.

The southern half of the basin displays two episodes of NE-trending tight to isoclinal folding, the first (D_1) verging to the W and the second (D_2) verging to the E. Subsequent multiple deformation, probably related to dextral and/or sinistral shear systems (D_3 and D_4), is at least locally important (Murray & Skehan 1979, Burks

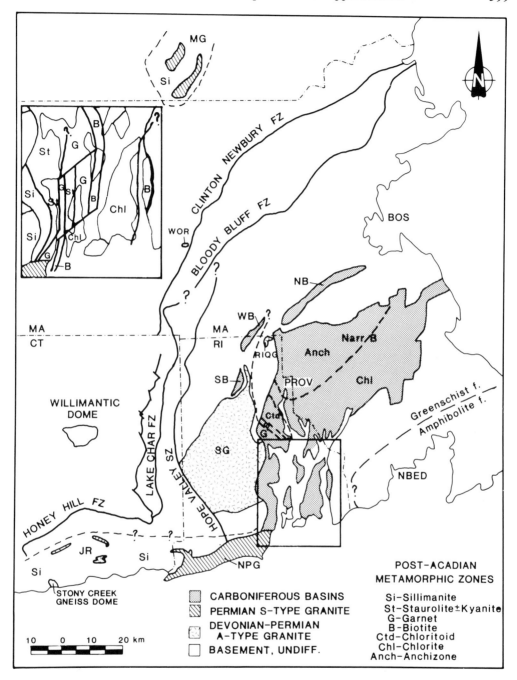

FIG. 1. Distribution of post-Acadian igneous, metamorphic and tectonic features in southeastern New England compiled from Quinn (1971), Grew & Day (1972), Murray & Skehan (1979), Day *et al.* (1980), Burks *et al.* (1981), Hepburn & Rehmer (1981), Hermes *et al.* (1981a, b), Murray *et al.* (1981), Mosher (1983), Robinson (1983), Zen (1983), O'Hara & Gromet (1985), Rodgers (1985) and Murray (unpublished data). BOS, Boston; PROV, Providence; NBED, New Bedford; JR, Joshua Rock gneiss; SG, Scituate granite; RIQG, Rhode Island Quincy granite; NPG, Narragansett Pier granite; MG, Milford granite; NarrB, Narragansett Basin; NB, Norfolk Basin; SB, Scituate Basin; WS, Woonsocket Basin; WOR, Worcester Basin; FZ, fault zone. As described in the text, the metamorphic zones are in part fault bounded.

et al. 1981, Mosher 1983, Burks 1984). Both the kinematic history and the style of deformation within the Narragansett Basin are considered to reflect repeated reactivation of basement structures during Alleghanian deformation (Murray & Mosher 1984, Mosher 1985, Hatcher *et al.* in press). The associated Barrovian metamorphism in the southern part of the basin ranges from chlorite to kyanite or sillimanite grade, with intensity increasing to the S and W. Farther E a low-grade trough extends southwards, but metamorphic grade rises again to biotite grade along the southeastern margin of the basin (Fig. 1). The basement terrane to the E is at staurolite or higher grade and could represent the continuation of prograde metamorphism to the E of the basin. The isograd pattern presented in Fig. 1 is based upon a small number of well-exposed and well-studied outcrops, and consequently the exact location of isograds or the orientation of isogradic surfaces is poorly constrained, but the apparent pattern is complex and at least partially reflects later faulting (Mosher 1983, 1985). Those faults for which there is strong evidence are shown in Fig. 1; others may exist as well. Moreover, it is difficult to evaluate the extent to which the isograds have been folded from their map distribution, although fabric analysis would imply that they have been deformed by all but the first period of folding. Mineral assemblages (Quinn 1971, Grew & Day 1972) and garnet–biotite barometry and thermometry (Murray *et al.* 1981, unpublished data) imply peak metamorphic conditions of 600°C and 5 kbar. Retrograde metamorphism is ubiquitous in the southern portion of the Narragansett Basin and is spatially associated with post-D_2 shear zones. Abundant veining, the occurrence of thermally deformed coals throughout the basin and structural trends controlled by the reactivation of basement faults imply the presence of large deviatoric stresses and widespread fluid migration. Dehydration of basinal sediments during metamorphism may have provided the fluids needed for hydration of shear zones within contiguous granitic basement which contains relatively abundant mica. Interestingly, there are other amphibole- and garnet-rich shear zones within the basement which suggest relatively higher metamorphic grade than the surrounding terrane. It may be that retrogression occurred where shear zones within the basement served as a conduit for fluids. Otherwise shear zones may have functioned simply as zones of dehydration.

Although in a gross sense metamorphism increases towards the contact with the peraluminous Narragansett Pier granite, in detail it appears that the thermal maxima are displaced to the N of the contact and that the isograds are truncated by the granite. There is no obvious contact metamorphic aureole surrounding the granite, and the ambient temperature of the metasediments apparently was high at the time of granite emplacement (Murray & Skehan 1979, Burks *et al.* 1981, Hermes *et al.* 1981a). On the basis of Pb–Pb isotopic (Zartman & Hermes 1984) and petrological arguments, the granite is considered to be derived through partial melting of metasedimentary rocks of Archaean age whose source is the African craton. The contact with Carboniferous metasediments is characterized by abundant roof pendants, and here the granite is bleached white owing to the breakdown of exsolved hematite within feldspars and contains primary muscovite plus garnet instead of biotite. These variations in granite petrology are taken as evidence of widespread fluid interchange between carbonaceous metasediments and granite (Murray & Skehan 1979), and indicate the reduction of iron-bearing phases within the granite and possible hydration of metasedimentary rocks in the vicinity of the contact.

The presence of megaflora within the metasediments (Lyons & Chase 1976, Brown *et al.* 1978), isotopic ages (Hermes *et al.* 1918a, Dallmeyer 1982, Zartman & Hermes 1984), and mesoscopic and microscopic fabric relationships (Murray & Skehan 1979, Burks *et al.* 1981, Murray *et al.* 1981, Mosher 1983, 1985) permit the following chronology to be established for the various elements of the Alleghanian orogeny.

1 Deposition of coal-bearing sediments through Stephanian A or B. Coals in the northern part of the Narragansett Basin appear to have remained on normal coalification paths into meta-anthracite (lower- to middle-greenschist-facies conditions), while those to the S display thermal alteration textures that indicate early hydrothermal metamorphism.

2 Prograde metamorphism (M_1) was synchronous with or later than D_1 in the southwestern part of the basin. Apparently M_1 occurred relatively later to the N and E, where it is associated with D_2 (Mosher 1983).

3 Emplacement of the Narragansett Pier granite (275 Ma (Hermes *et al.* 1981a, Zartman & Hermes 1984)) was followed by additional episodes of deformation (D_3 and D_4) that are related to strike-slip faulting (Mosher 1983). The depth of emplacement was approximately 4 kbar near the contact with the metasediments (Hermes *et al.* 1981a).

4 Retrograde metamorphism was synchronous with post-D_3 and D_4.

5 Argon-release patterns from metasediments

and Narragansett Pier granite indicate that both hornblende and biotite cooled below argon retention temperatures by 250–255 Ma and 239–250 Ma respectively (Dallmeyer 1982).

Other Carboniferous basins

In addition to the Narragansett Basin, several other smaller occurrences of known or possible Carboniferous rocks are found in southeastern New England (Fig. 1). The Norfolk Basin extends northeastward from the Narragansett Basin to the Boston Basin of Proterozoic Z age. It consists of anchizone to lower-greenschist-facies rocks which are considered to be correlatable with the Narragansett Basin stratigraphy. In general, rocks in the Boston area are only feebly metamorphosed and appear to have escaped any of the effects of Alleghanian metamorphism observed to the S or N (in Maine). The Scituate and Woonsocket Basins are fault-bounded grabens along the northern border of Rhode Island that record a garnet-grade prograde and chlorite-grade retrograde metamorphism (Rose & Murray 1984). Their age is uncertain, although a Carboniferous age is preferred for stratigraphic reasons. The Worcester Basin in E central Massachusetts also contains garnetiferous schists, as well as plant fossils (Grew 1973). It is of interest because it represents the only occurrence of late Palaeozoic stratified rocks in New England that lies outside the Avalonian terrane.

Pre-Carboniferous basement

The dominant rocks W of the Narragansett Basin are a suite of variably deformed granites that in the field are deceptively similar to each other and whose age relationships have proved surprisingly difficult to unravel. A major breakthrough was the recognition that many ductilely deformed granites previously considered to be Precambrian are actually mid-Devonian in age (Hermes *et al.* 1981b, Hermes & Zartman 1985, O'Hara & Gromet 1985), and this has enabled a more accurate delineation of late Palaeozoic tectonothermal activity. A tentative set of 'isograds' within this terrane was developed by Day *et al.* (1980) on the basis of variations in the structural state of alkali feldspars and annealing textures, which indicate a decrease in sub-solidus reheating proceeding broadly northward from the Narrangansett Pier granite to central Rhode Island. Dallmeyer (1982) determined ^{39}Ar/^{40}Ar release patterns for phyllites, biotite and hornblende from metasediments within the Narragansett Basin, the Narragansett Pier granite and the adjoining crystalline basement in a swathe along the southern coast of Rhode Island and southeastern Connecticut that has as its approximate northern limit the region examined by Day *et al.* (1980). Dallmeyer found argon retention ages ranging from 239–258 Ma which confirmed the ideas of previous workers (Lundgren 1966, Zartman *et al.* 1970, Murray & Skehan 1979, Day *et al.* 1980) of a pervasive Permian thermal overprint that characterized the region. Drier (1984) has also shown that the Precambrian Blackstone Series of northeastern Rhode Island has been affected by two periods of folding and metamorphism to biotite grade that post-date the Carboniferous age Rhode Island Quincy granite (Fig. 1). Together with the observations of Rose & Murray (1984) for the nearby Woonsocket Basin, they suggest a prograde metamorphic gradient increasing towards the W that can be related to the Hope Valley shear zone (see next section).

In a recent paper Wintsch & Lefort (1984) present an intriguing though speculative model for late Palaeozoic tectonics that attempts to integrate metamorphic petrological data from the Willamantic Dome region of eastern Connecticut with palaeomagnetic data. They argue that variations in mineral lineations observed in eastern Connecticut formed during the late Palaeozoic cooling and uplift of that region. In the presence of a changing stress field. According to their hypothesis, temporal variations in this stress field are the result of the collision of Africa with eastern N America followed by sinistral rotation of Africa. One of the more important ramifications of their work is the strong suggestion that upper Alleghanian amphibolite-facies metamorphism extends to the W and N of the Honey Hill–Lake Char fault systems.

One of the least understood areas in southern New England is the New Bedford area, which is the basement terrane between the Narragansett Basin and Cape Cod (Fig. 1). It consists of undeformed to multiply-deformed granitoids and gneissic rocks (Zen 1983, Goldsmith 1985, personal communication, Murray, unpublished data) which, if the age of metamorphism and complex ductile deformation proves to be Alleghanian, would require substantial revisions in current models for Alleghanian orogenesis in southern New England.

Shear zones

Although the numerous brittle to ductile shear zones of southeastern New England have been the subject of many investigations over the years, there is still little agreement about their relative timing, sense of movement and importance

(Lundgren & Ebblin 1972, Robinson & Hall 1980, Skehan & Murray 1980, Goldstein 1982, 1986, Zen 1983, Hamidzada & Hermes 1984, Gromet & O'Hara 1985, O'Hara & Gromet 1985, Rodgers 1985). Traditionally, the Honey Hill, Lake Char, Clinton–Newbury and Bloody Bluff fault zones (Fig. 1) were considered to be the most significant in the region, and all have been suggested as candidates for possible sutures.

For the Honey Hill Fault system, O'Hara & Gromet (1983) have combined isotopic dating of micas and careful examination of recovery textures in minerals within the shear zone in order to determine the timing and temperature of mylonite formation. On the basis of the results, they argue that the mylonitic fabric within the fault formed during the Permian, under upper-greenschist-facies conditions, thus proving that in this region the Alleghanian metamorphism is not simply a thermal overprint. These results are consistent with observations made by Goldstein (1982) on the Lake Char fault.

More recently O'Hara & Gromet (1985) have presented a strong case for a fundamental tectonic boundary in western Rhode Island which separates the Esmond–Dedham terrane (Avalonian basement *sensu stricto*) from the Merrimack synclinorium plus its basement, the Hope Valley Alaskite terrane. The criteria for its identification include the newly recognized patterns in isotopic dates in granitic rocks plus a probable increase in ductile deformation approaching it. This boundary, the Hope Valley shear zone (Fig. 1), would be a possible southern extension of the Bloody Bluff fault and would be distinct from the Lake Char fault. As discussed by O'Hara & Gromet, the presence of this tectonic boundary would reconcile a major conflict in the interpretation of the geological relationships of southeastern New England, i.e. whether the Avalonian stratigraphy in Rhode Island and eastern Massachusetts can be traced into the stratigraphy of the Merrimack synclinorium of Connecticut. Not all accept the Hope Valley shear zone as a major tectonic boundary, and an alternative explanation for the tectonic history of the faults in this region has been presented by Goldstein & Owens (1985). Regardless of the tectonic significance attached to a particular fault, there is an emerging consensus among those working in the region that at least the Honey Hill fault (O'Hara & Gromet 1983), the Lake Char fault (Goldstein 1982) and the Hope Valley shear zone (O'Hara & Gromet 1985, Getty & Gromet 1986) underwent ductile deformation accompanied by upper-greenschist- to amphibolite-facies metamorphism during late Palaeozoic times. What is unclear at present is the age of the metamorphic patterns

spatially associated with these fault systems and whether they are evidence of a metamorphism distinct from the more widespread Permian thermal overprint recorded throughout the basement terrane of southern New England.

Southern Connecticut and New York

A variety of metasedimentary basement rocks whose presently observed sillimanite grade has been considered to represent an Alleghanian metamorphosed terrane (Lundgren 1966, Robinson 1983) rather than Taconic or Acadian metamorphism occur along the southern coast of Rhode Island and eastern Connecticut. In the New London area the Joshua rock gneiss occurs as several discrete stratigraphic horizons of mildly to highly deformed alkalic granite, which are strictly concordant with multiply-folded gneisses. If these rocks are of Permo-Carboniferous age, as their isotopic ages suggest (Hermes 1985, personal communication, O'Hara 1986), significant ductile deformation of Permian age is implied in S central Connecticut. McLellan & Stockman (1985), in their investigation of the Stony Creek Dome along the Connecticut coast, describe granitoids that are petrologically similar to the Permian age Narragansett Pier granite. Brock & Brock (1985) have documented the presence of pegmatitic granites of Carboniferous age in southeastern New York which record at least an episode of extensional ductile deformation. Collectively, these data suggest that Alleghanian metamorphism and ductile deformation have affected southern New England in a swathe that extends from E of the Narragansett Basin to southeastern New York, a trend that is highly discordant with the ductile deformation associated with the aforementioned fault systems. K–Ar dates (Zartman *et al.* 1970) and incremental argon dates (Dallmeyer 1982, Wintsch & Sutter 1985, personal communication) also indicate a Permian thermal overprint along coastal New England that dies out to the N.

Southern New Hampshire and Maine

K–Ar and Rb–Sr mineral ages (primarily micas) from Maine and New Hampshire often give Permian ages, and these have been taken as evidence of a Permian disturbance (Faul *et al.* 1963). Subsequently Zartman *et al.* (1970) argued that K–Ar isotopic ages represented cooling ages, an interpretation supported by incremental argon studies of micas in Maine (Dallmeyer *et al.* 1982) and consistent with the assignment of all metamorphism in New Hampshire and Maine to the Acadian or older orogenies. Recent whole-rock dating of the Concord suite of S-type granites in New Hampshire (Lyons *et al.* 1982) and the petrologically similar Sebago Lake, Maine (Aleinikoff 1984, Hayward & Gaudette 1984) has shown them to be of Carboniferous to Permian age, implying that spatially associated contact metamorphism and low-pressure regional metamorphism is Alleghanian aged. The presence of a well-defined late Palaeozoic thermal disturbance gains further support from new incremental argon ages from hornblendes in western Maine, which indicate that regional metamorphism occurred during the Carboniferous (Lux & Guidotti 1985) in contrast with the Permian age recognized for metamorphism in the Narragansett Basin area. The Milford granite of southern New Hampshire is also of Permian age, and has a contact aureole (Aleinikoff *et al.* 1979, Robinson 1983). Taken together, these data indicate a discontinuous zone of Alleghanian metamorphism across southern New Hampshire and southwestern Maine that is at least partially attributable to the emplacement of S-type granitoids.

Central and southern Appalachians

No Palaeozoic sedimentary rocks younger than lower Palaeozoic are exposed along the eastern flank of the Appalachians, and the evidence for late Palaeozoic metamorphism in this region is based entirely upon the presence of deformed granitoids of Devonian or younger age. They occur in a discontinuous belt along the eastern margin of the southern Appalachians, and have been the subject of several recent studies. One of the earliest well-documented examples was the Kiokee belt of South Carolina (Snoke *et al.* 1980) in which it was demonstrated that plutonism ranging from 313 to 254 Ma was roughly synchronous with ductile deformation accompanied by amphibolite-facies metamorphism. In the last 5 years similar results have been found along the eastern Piedmont in a zone extending from the Kiokee belt to Maryland. To the W, in the Carolina slate belt and the Piedmont belt, Alleghanian metamorphism is confined to discrete shear zones. The Valley and Ridge records an anchizone metamorphism associated with the long-recognized folding and faulting. The reader is also directed to two extended reviews of Alleghanian deformation, magmatism and metamorphism in the southern Appalachians (Glover *et al.* 1983, Hatcher *et al.* in press, Secor *et al.* 1986).

Kiokee belt

As discussed by Snoke *et al.* (1980), Alleghanian metamorphism in the Kiokee belt can be divided into two zones, an eastern amphibolite belt and an adjacent western greenschist belt. The former is either locally overlain unconformably by undisturbed Mesozoic sedimentary rocks of the Coastal Plain or over-thrust by phyllites of the Belair zone. Prograde Barrovian metamorphism to at least kyanite grade at approximately 300 Ma was associated with the first two episodes of W-directed folding and was followed by additional milder deformation that lasted until roughly 250 Ma. The two belts are separated by the Medoc fault, which in fact may be only a boundary separating amphibolite-facies remobilized basement to the E from non-pervasively deformed greenschist-facies basement to the W. To the W, this greenschist belt consists of ductile to brittle shear zones that sporadically cut the basement rocks and late Palaeozoic granites.

Raleigh belt

Similar observations have been made for the Raleigh belt and eastern North Carolina Piedmont (Farrar 1985, Russell *et al.* 1985), where foliated granites range in age from 315 to 285 Ma. Isotopic studies coupled with fabric analysis indicate that upper-greenschist- to middle-amphibolite-grade metamorphism is roughly synchronous with granite emplacement, folding and development of ductile shear zones. An eastern as well as western boundary to the Alleghanian metamorphism is recognized here, based upon variations in cooling history and intensity of deformation recorded in a granite (Butterwood granite) that straddles the contact between the Raleigh belt (to the W) and the eastern Carolina slate belt (Russell *et al.* 1985). Thus, in the Raleigh belt at least it can be demonstrated that Alleghanian metamorphism is confined to a narrow zone within the eastern margin of the Appalachians that is probably fault bounded on both eastern and western margins. A continuation of this zone of Alleghanian metamorphism northward into Virginia is indicated by the occurrence of foliated Carboniferous granite (Bobyarchick & Glover 1979) and incremental argon patterns in micas and hornblende from basement gneisses (Durrant *et al.* 1980).

Southern Appalachians, outside the Raleigh and Kiokee belts

More generally, the patterns observed in the two areas described above probably hold for the entire eastern flank of the southern Appalachians, including the Kiokee and Raleigh belts and their along-strike continuations. Within the zone metamorphism to kyanite grade is ubiquitous, with upper sillimanite grade attained in contact aureoles. Although regions of relatively intense metamorphism are spatially and temporally associated with granitoids of Carboniferous age, it would be an oversimplification to treat them as contact metamorphism for several reasons: (1) granitoids are often foliated, and detailed field and isotopic studies (Snoke *et al.* 1980, Glover *et al.* 1983, Russell *et al.* 1985) suggest that ductile deformation, metamorphism and intrusion are all of late Palaeozoic age; (2) assemblages diagnostic of depth of metamorphism, where found, invariably imply pressures of 5 kbar or more; (3) within the zone amphibolite-facies metamorphism occurs both in close proximity to plutons and elsewhere.

In the Inner Piedmont and Carolina slate belt, evidence for Alleghanian metamorphism is confined to regions of relatively intense ductile deformation where mineral assemblages observed within shear zones define amphibolite-facies metamorphic conditions (Glover *et al.* 1983). Except within the vicinity of these shear zones, granitoids in the Inner Piedmont of Georgia were intruded into rocks whose ambient temperature, for the most part, may have been no greater than approximately 300 °C, a value that can be accounted for by slow cooling of rocks metamorphosed during the Taconic orogeny (Dallmeyer 1978). Recently Horton & Stern (1983) have demonstrated that pervasively deformed granite of Pennsylvanian age occurs within the Kings Mountain belt of the central Piedmont, and that the granite has imparted a deep-seated contact aureole onto the surrounding gneissic basement terrane. It remains to be seen to what extent their observations are applicable to other areas within the central Piedmont belt, and Glover (1986, personal communication) has suggested that the amphibolite-facies metamorphism in the King's Mountain area may be concentrated along the central Piedmont suture which is a zone of basement reactivation. These results, if typical of the central Piedmont, dramatically increase the westward extension of the upper greenschist or higher-grade metamorphism of Carboniferous or younger age in the southern Appalachians.

The Valley and Ridge Province along the western flank of the central and southern Appalachians traditionally has been synonymous with the Alleghanian orogeny, yet relatively little effort has been directed towards deciphering the thermal structure of this region. Ongoing investigations of conodont coloration and anthracite reflectivity confirm previous assignments of anchizone metamorphism there. The Appalachian Plateau (i.e. the foreland) has also been the subject of ongoing studies of very-low-grade metamorphism in which an attempt has been made to date layered silicates observed as 'clay' coatings along joint sets through examination of incremental argon-release patterns. Preliminary results indicate that the coatings are detrital, and there is no evidence for the growth of new mineral species (P. Geiser 1983, personal communication).

Relation of metamorphism to tectonism

Despite the obvious need for additional data, several patterns emerge for the Alleghanian metamorphism within the Appalachians. With the exceptions of some of the contact metamorphic aureoles in Maine and the Maritime Provinces, metamorphism is Barrovian style, with kyanite (and not andalusite and/or cordierite) commonly found in pelitic assemblages. As pointed out by Fisher (1983) and Rodgers (1983) the Palaeozoic isograd patterns within the orogen are in large part fault controlled, and this is particularly true for the Alleghanian tectonothermal event. Moreover, the presently observed metamorphic record in most areas represents an integration of an Alleghanian metamorphism together with a thermal signature inherited primarily from the Taconic and Acadian orogenies. The Alleghanian metamorphism is widespread along the eastern flank of the Appalachians, and unlike earlier metamorphisms (Fisher 1983) bears no simple relation to the pattern of late Palaeozoic magmatism (Hermes & Murray 1988), suggesting that convective heat transfer to the crust from crystallization of igneous bodies was not the only factor.

Going from the Maritime Provinces to the southern Appalachians, changes in patterns of Alleghanian metamorphism may be attributable to the change in tectonic style from types dominated by the oblique accretion of microplates (Maritime Provinces) to one characterized by continental collision (southern Appalachians). In this sense, the complex patterns of ductile deformation and metamorphism may represent the cumulative results of both processes.

Maritime Provinces

In the Maritime Provinces Alleghanian metamorphism is of minor importance. Contact metamorphic aureoles associated with granitoids are common in the Meguma and Avalon zones, and dynamically recrystallized micas occur in some shear zones. Unlike the US Appalachians, these faults are related to either uplift or strike-slip movement and not to thrusts associated with crustal thickening, suggesting that head-on collision of large continental masses did not occur in this section of the Appalachians.

New England

In contrast, the record in the USA implies a more intense collisional event in which crustal thickening caused by large-scale thrusting was responsible for much of Alleghanian tectonism. Southern New England displays a complex and probably diachronous pattern of post-Acadian metamorphism and ductile deformation, which includes the following areas.

1 *Southern coast of New England.* The emerging pattern of igneous activity, superposition of new metamorphic fabrics on basement gneisses and widespread resetting of isotopic systems implies an intense Alleghanian metamorphism throughout this region.
2 *Shear zones.* Metamorphic intensity also increases approaching (to the W and N) the Hope Valley shear zone–Lake Char fault zone–Bloody Bluff fault zone. The general trend of these zones of ductile deformation is at a high angle to the E–W–trending isograds in the previous area.
3 *Narragansett Basin.* Patterns of metamorphism and tectonism are complex here, and at present there is little consensus as to how they relate to the first two areas.
4 *New Bedford.* Another ductilely deformed basement terrane of unknown age which could represent yet another Alleghanian metamorphic terrane occurs SE of the Narragansett Basin.
5 *Maine and New Hampshire.* Metamorphism in this area, although not strictly a contact phenomenon, is nevertheless associated with abundant plutonism.

Although much more work needs to be done in this area before we have a clear picture of Permian palaeogeography, it is interesting to speculate on the implications of the metamorphism and the constraints it may place on tectonic models. Apparently, in this region we observe a thermal history that is the result of at least two semi-independent events. The first event may be the juxtapositioning from the NE of the Esmond–Dedham terrane along the Hope Valley shear zone during the late Palaeozoic, as suggested by O'Hara & Gromet (1985). The second event could be the continent–continent collision involving NW Africa (i.e. the Hercynian orogeny) and could be responsible for the late Palaeozoic deformation, plutonism and metamorphism in the region that is not spatially related to the Hope Valley shear zone. According to this interpretation, the rapid burial, regional metamorphism and development of sub-horizontal axial planes associated with D_1 and D_2 in the southern Narragansett Basin may be the consequence of the tectonic loading of this terrane and the contiguous basement with a thrust sheet of major proportions such as that indicated by COCORP data for the southern Appalachians (Ando *et al.* 1983). These two events may be correlative with the two periods of late Palaeozoic deformation described by Geiser & Engelder (1983) for the Valley and Ridge and Plateau regions of the Appalachians.

Early lithospheric stretching may also have been an important factor in southeastern New England if, prior to Permian compressional tectonics, the Avalon zone consisted of a series of horsts and grabens (the Carboniferous basins of the region) formed through crustal thinning. Collision of the eastern margin of this southeastern Avalon terrane with a larger crustal plate would have two consequences. Intense ductile deformation would develop along the leading (western) edge of Avalon, resulting in the formation of the Hope Valley shear zone. Moreover, the horst and graben terrane could have buckled, with the eastern portion overriding the western part, in a manner similar to that described by Oxburgh (1982, fig. 8). In this scenario most or all of the upper plate would have been removed, exposing the metamorphosed basement and basinal sediments of the lower plate. Underplating of the eastern margin (i.e. flake tectonics) may also have occurred, with wet sediments emplaced under the Carboniferous basins providing the source for peraluminous granite (e.g. Narragansett Pier granite (Hermes & Zartman 1985, Hermes & Murray 1988)). Further collision of the region with Africa would result in ductile deformation and metamorphism along the southern coast of New England.

Although these models are speculative, they serve the purpose of helping the more precise formulation of goals for subsequent work. Four problems stand out: (1) determination of the relative timing and possible overprinting of fabrics associated with the Hope Valley shear zone with those observed elsewhere in the region, such as along the southern coast of New England; (2) determination of the northern and western extent of the Permian thermal overprint; (3) determination of the metamorphic and structural history of the region S and E of the Narragansett

Basin; (4) determination of the role of the problematic Joshua Rock alkalic complex in southern Connecticut. Moreover, data on mineral chemistry are still sparse for both Carboniferous metasediments and basement rocks. Because of these limitations, it is not feasible at present to develop pressure–temperature–time paths for critical lithologies in this region in the way that has been done so effectively for other parts of New England (Chamberlain & England 1985, Chamberlain 1986, Spear 1986).

Southern Appalachians

Pervasive Alleghanian metamorphism is limited to a discrete zone within the eastern flank of the Appalachians that is characterized by abundant late Palaeozoic granitoids and separated from greenschist-facies metamorphism on each side by faults. Surprisingly, E of this zone (i.e. the eastern slate belt) metamorphism decreases to greenschist facies. To the W of this zone, recrystallization of basement rocks is confined to the vicinity of discrete shear zones. A possible model for this region argues that the crust of the entire eastern flank of the southern Appalachians was tectonically thickened and that, where bulk compositions were appropriate, melts of lower crustal granitic rocks formed that migrated upwards along surfaces that may represent reactivated faults. These melts would efficiently transfer heat to shallower crustal levels, not only causing contact metamorphic aureoles but also facilitating the dynamic recrystallization of basement rocks along ductile shear zones. The cause of the episode of crustal thickening was presumably the collision of Africa with N America, as manifested by eastward-thickening thrust

sheet(s), and consequently metamorphic effects would have decreased to the W. Thus crystalline rocks of the Blue Ridge and western Piedmont would not be expected to respond to the Alleghanian metamorphism. Previously unmetamorphosed sedimentary rocks of the Valley and Ridge do record a feeble metamorphism since, in contrast with the crystalline rocks to the E, they were capable of sensitively responding to slight increases in temperature or depth of burial.

Comparison of Alleghanian metamorphism with Variscan/Hercynian metamorphism

The Permian metamorphism in N America also appears to be fundamentally distinct in style from the Variscan metamorphism of Europe, which tends to be of lower pressure and more clearly associated with S-type granitoids (Martínez & Rolet 1988). The European Variscan metamorphism can be best interpreted in terms of a Tibetan type of basement reactivation (Dewey & Burke 1973). In contrast, the Appalachian 'Variscides' may have developed in a tectonic regime in which microplate accretion and large-scale horizontal translation dominated, and this may be reflected in the different style of metamorphism.

ACKNOWLEDGMENTS: I am grateful to R. Goldsmith, A. Goldstein, L. P. Gromet, S. Mosher, K. O'Hara, N. Rast, J. Rodgers, and J. Skehan, S. J., R. Wintsch and especially Don Hermes for valuable discussions of southern New England geology. The paper has also benefited substantially from thoughtful reviews by L. Glover III, J. Rodgers and D. Secor.

References

ALEINIKOFF, J. N. 1984. Carboniferous uranium–lead age of the Sebago batholith, southwestern Maine. *Geological Society of America Abstracts with Programs*, **16**, 23.

——, ZARTMAN, R. E. & LYONS, J. B. 1979. U–Th–Pb geochronology of the granite near Milford, south-central New Hampshire: new evidence for Avalonian basement and Taconic and Alleghanian disturbances in eastern New England. *Contributions to Mineralogy and Petrology*, **71**, 1–11.

ANDO, C. J., COOK, F. A., OLIVER, J. E., BROWN, L. D. & KAUFMAN, S. 1983. Crustal geometry of the Appalachian Orogen from seismic reflection studies. *In*: HATCHER, R. D., JR, WILLIAMS, H. & ZIETZ, I. (eds) *Tectonics and Geophysics of Mountain Chains. Geological Society of America Memoir No. 158*, pp. 83–101.

BOBYARCHICK, A. R. & GLOVER, L. III 1979. Deformation and metamorphism in the Hylas zone and adjacent parts of the eastern Piedmont in Virginia. *Geological Society of America Bulletin, Part 1*, **90**, 739–52.

BOOTHROYD, J. & HERMES, O. D. (eds) 1981. *Guidebook for Field Trips in Rhode Island and Adjacent Areas. New England Intercollegiate Geological Conference, 73rd Annual Meeting*, University of Rhode Island, Kingston, RI, 383 pp.

BRADLEY, D. C. 1982. Subsidence in late Palaeozoic basins in the Northern Appalachians. *Tectonics*, **1**, 107–23.

BRISTOL, D., TULLIS, J. & TULLIS, T. 1984. Nature of distributed faulting in the Dighton Conglomerate of SE Massachusetts. *Geological Society of America Abstracts with Programs*, **16** (1), 6.

BROCK, P. C. & BROCK, P. W. G. 1985. Carboniferous (D6) and Permian?(D7) shear zones of the northern Manhatten Prong, S.E. N.Y. *Geological Society of America Abstracts with Programs*, **17** (1), 8.

BROWN, A., MURRAY, D. P. & BARGHORN, E. 1978. Pennsylvanian fossils from metasediments within the Narragansett Pier Granite, Rhode Island. *Geological Society of America Abstracts with Programs*, **10**, 35–6.

BURKS, R. J. 1984. Alleghanian shear zones in the Narragansett Basin and adjacent basement, Rhode Island. *Geological Society of America Abstracts with Programs*, **16** (1), 7.

——, MOSHER, S. & MURRAY, D. 1981. Alleghanian deformation and metamorphism of southern Narragansett Basin. *In*: BOOTHROYD, J. C. & HERMES, O. D. (eds) *Guidebook for Field Trips in Rhode Island and Adjacent Areas. New England Intercollegiate Geological Conference, 73rd Annual Meeting*, pp. 265–75, University of Rhode Island, Kingston, RI.

CHAMBERLAIN, C. P. 1986. *P–T* paths in the root-zone of the Fall Mountain Nappe: constraints on the thermal budget of Acadian metamorphism. *Geological Society of America Abstracts with Programs*, **18** (1), 8.

—— & ENGLAND, P. C. 1985. The Acadian thermal history of the Merrimack synclinorium in New Hampshire. *Journal of Geology*, **93**, 593–602.

DALLMEYER, R. D. 1978. ^{40}Ar/^{39}Ar incremental-release ages of hornblende and biotite across the Georgian Inner Piedmont: their bearing on late Paleozoic-early Mesozoic tectono-thermal history. *American Journal of Science*, **278**, 124–49.

—— 1982. ^{40}Ar/^{39}Ar ages from the Narragansett Basin and southern Rhode Island basement terrain: their bearing on the extent and timing of Alleghanian tectonothermal events in New England. *Geological Society of America Bulletin*, **93**, 1118–30.

—— & KEPPIE, J. D. 1986. Polyphase late Palaeozoic tectonothermal evolution of the Meguma Terrane, Nova Scotia. *Geological Society of America Abstracts with Programs*, **18** (1), 11.

——, & WHITNEY, J. A. 1982. Rb–Sr whole-rock and ^{40}Ar/^{39}Ar mineral ages of the Hartland stock, south-central Maine: a post-Acadian representative of the New Hampshire Plutonic Series. *American Journal of Science*, **282**, 79–93.

DAY, H. W., BROWN, V. M. & ABRAHAM, K. 1980. Precambrian(?) crystallization and Permian(?) metamorphism of hypersolvus granite in the Avalonian terrain of Rhode Island, Parts I and II, *Geological Society of America Bulletin*, **91**, 389–91, 1669–741.

DEWEY, J. F. & BURKE, K. G. A. 1973. Tibetan, Variscan, and Precambrian basement reactivation: products of continental collision. *Journal of Geology*, **81**, 683–92.

DRIER, R. B. 1984. The Blackstone Series: evidence for Alleghanian deformation in an Avalonian terrane. *Geological Society of America Abstracts with Programs*, **16** (1), 13.

DURRANT, J. M., SUTTER, J. F. & GLOVER, L. III 1980. Evidence for an Alleghanian (Hercynian?) meta-morphic event in the Piedmont province near Richmond, Virginia. *Geological Society of America Abstracts with Programs*, **12**, 176.

FARRAR, S. S. 1985. Tectonic evolution of the eastern-most Piedmont, North Carolina. *Geological Society of America Bulletin*, **96**, 362–80.

FAUL, H., STERN, T. W., THOMAS, H. H. & ELMORE, P. L. D. 1963. Ages of intrusion and metamorphism in the Northern Appalachians. *American Journal of Science*, **261**, 1–19.

FISHER, G. W. 1983. Metamorphism in the U.S. Appalachians: overview and implications. *In*: SCHENK, P. (ed.) *Geology of the Appalachian-Caledonian-Hercynian-Mauritanide Orogen*, pp. 259–62, Reidel, Dordrecht.

GEISER, P. & ENGELDER, T. 1983. The distribution of layer parallel shortening fabrics in the Appalachian foreland of New York and Pennsylvania: evidence for two non-coaxial phases of the Alleghanian orogeny. *Geological Society of America Memoir*, **158**, 161–75.

GETTY, S. R. & GROMET, L. P. 1986. The southern terminus of the Hope Valley Shear Zone, Rhode Island. *Geological Society of America Abstracts with Programs*, **18** (1), 18.

GLOVER, L. III, SPEER, J. A., RUSSELL, G. S. & FARRAR, S. S. 1983. Ages of regional metamorphism and ductile deformation in the central and southern Appalachians. *Lithos*, **16**, 223–45.

GOLDSTEIN, A. G. 1982. Geometry and kinematics of ductile faulting in a portion of the Lake Char mylonite zone, Massachusetts and Connecticut. *American Journal of Science*, **282**, 1378–2405.

—— 1986. A summary of fault motion histories for eastern Massachusetts and Connecticut. *Geological Society of America Abstracts with Programs*, **18** (1), 19.

—— & OWENS, J. O. 1985. Mesoscopic and microscopic structure of the lake Char–Honey Hill mylonite zone. *In*: TRACY, R. J. (ed.) *Guidebook for Field Trips in Connecticut and Adjacent Areas of New York and Rhode Island. New England Intercollegiate Geologic Conference, 77th Annual Meeting*, pp. 61–114, Yale University, New Haven, CT.

GREW, E. S. 1973. Stratigraphy of the Pennsylvanian and Prepennsylvanian rocks of the Worcester area, Massachusetts. *American Journal of Science*, **273**, 113–29.

—— & DAY, H. W. 1972. Staurolite, kyanite, and sillimanite from the Narragansett Basin of Rhode Island. *U.S. Geological Survey Professional Paper No. 800-D*, pp. 151–7.

GROMET, L. P. & O'HARA, K. D. 1985. The Hope Valley Shear Zone—a major late Paleozoic ductile shear zone in southeastern New England. *In*: TRACY, R. J. (ed.) *Guidebook for Field Trips in Connecticut and Adjacent Areas of New York and Rhode Island. New England Intercollegiate Geologic Conference, 77th Annual Meeting*, pp. 61–114, Yale University, New Haven, CT.

HAMIDZADA, N. & HERMES, O. D. 1984. Ductile shear zones in north-central Rhode Island and their bearing on Devonian plutonism and basin formation. *Geological Society of America Abstracts with Programs*, **16**, 22.

HATCHER R. D., THOMAS, W. A. & VIELE, G. W. (eds) in press. *The Appalachian–Ouachita Synthesis Volume: The Geology of North America, F2.* Geological Society of America, Boulder, Co.

HAYWARD, J. A. & GAUDETTE, H. E. 1984. Carboniferous age of the Sebago and Effingham plutons, Maine and New Hampshire. *Geological Society of America Abstracts with Programs*, **16**, 23.

HEPBURN, J. C. & REHMER, J. 1981. The diagenetic to metamorphic transition in the Narragansett and Norfolk Basins, Massachusetts and Rhode Island. *In*: BOOTHROYD, J. C. & HERMES, O. D. (eds) *Guidebook for Field Trips in Rhode Island and Adjacent Areas. New England Intercollegiate Geological Conference, 73rd Annual Meeting*, pp. 47–67, University of Rhode Island, Kingston, RI.

HERMES, O. D. & MURRAY, D. P. 1988. Middle Devonian to Permian plutonism and volcanism in the N American Appalachians. *This volume.*

—— & ZARTMAN, R. E. 1985. Late Precambrian and Devonian plutonic terrane within the Avalon Zone of Rhode Island. *Geological Society of America Bulletin*, **96**, 272–82.

——, BAROSH, P. J. & SMITH, P. V. 1981a. Contact relationships of the Late Paleozoic Narragansett Pier Granite and country rock. *In*: BOOTHROYD, J. C. & HERMES, O. D. (eds) *Guidebook for Field Studies in Rhode Island and Adjacent Areas. New England Intercollegiate Geological Conference, 73rd Annual Meeting*, pp. 125–52, University of Rhode Island, Kingston, RI.

——, GROMET, L. P. & ZARTMAN, R. E. 1981b. Zircon geochronology and petrology of plutonic rocks in Rhode Island. *In*: BOOTHROYD, J. C. & HERMES, O. D. (eds) *Guidebook for Field Trips in Rhode Island and Adjacent Areas. New England Intercollegiate Geological Conference, 73rd Annual Meeting*, pp. 315–38, University of Rhode Island, Kingston, RI.

HORTON, J. W. JR & STERN, T. W. 1983. Late Paleozoic (Alleghanian) deformation, metamorphism, and syntectonic granite in the central Piedmont of the southern Appalachians. *Geological Society of America Abstracts with Programs*, **15**, 599.

LUNDGREN, L. W., JR. 1966. Muscovite reactions and partial melting in southeastern Connecticut. *American Journal of Science*, **7**, 421–53.

—— & EBBLIN, C. 1972. Honey Hill fault in eastern Connecticut: regional relations. *Geological Society of America Bulletin*, **83**, 2773–94.

LUX, D. R. & GUIDOTTI, C. V. 1985. Evidence for extensive Hercynian metamorphism in western Maine. *Geology*, **13**, 696–700.

LYONS, J. B., BOUDETTE, E. L. & ALEINIKOFF, J. N. 1982. The Avalonian and Gander zones in central eastern New England. *In*: ST. JULIEN, P. & BELAND, J. (eds) *Major Structural Zones and Faults of the Northern Appalachians. Geological Association of Canada Special Paper No. 24*, pp. 43–66.

LYONS, P. C. & CHASE, H. B. 1976. Coal stratigraphy and flora of the northwestern Narragansett Basin. *In*: CAMERON, B. (ed.) *Guidebook for Field Trips to the Boston Area and Vicinity. New England Intercollegiate Geologic Conference, 68th Annual Meeting*, p. 513, Boston University, Boston, MA.

MCLELLAN, E. L. & STOCKMAN, S. 1985. Age and structural relations of granites, Stony Creek area, Connecticut. *In*: TRACY, R. J. (ed.) *Guidebook for Field Trips in Connecticut and Adjacent Areas of New York and Rhode Island. New England Intercollegiate Geologic Conference, 77th Annual Meeting*, pp. 61–114, Yale University, New Haven, CT.

MARTÍNEZ, F. J. & ROLET, J. 1988. Late Palaeozoic metamorphism in the northwestern Iberian Peninsula, Brittany and related areas in SW Europe. *This volume.*

MOSHER, S. 1983. Kinematic history of the Narragansett Basin, Massachusetts and Rhode Island: constraints on Late Palaeozoic plate reconstructions. *Tectonics*, **21** (4), 327–44.

—— 1985. Effects of Alleghanian accretion of the Boston Platform on the Western Narragansett Basin, RI. *Geological Society of America Abstracts with Programs*, **17** (7), 670.

—— & RAST, N. 1984. The deformation and metamorphism of Carboniferous rocks in Maritime Canada and New England. *In*: HUTTON, D. H. W. & SANDERSON, D. J. (eds) *Variscan Tectonics of the North Atlantic Region. Special Publication of the Geological Society of London No. 14*, pp. 233–43.

MURRAY, D. P. & MOSHER, S. 1984. Permian deformation and metamorphism in southeastern New England. *Geological Society of America Abstracts with Programs*, **16** (1), 51.

—— & SKEHAN, J. W., S. J. 1979. A traverse across the eastern margin of the Appalachian–Caledonian orogen, southeastern New England. *In*: SKEHAN, J. W., S. J. & OSBERG, P. H. (eds) *The Caledonides in the USA. Geological Excursions in the Northeast Appalachians*, pp. 1–35, Weston Observatory, Boston College, Boston, MA.

——, RABEN, J. D., LYONS, P. C. & CHASE, H. B., JR 1981. The geologic setting of coal and carbonaceous material, Narragansett Basin, southeastern New England. *In*: BOOTHROYD, J. C. & HERMES, O. D. (eds) *Guidebook for Field Trips in Rhode Island and Adjacent Areas. New England Intercollegiate Geological Conference, 73rd Annual Meeting*, pp. 175–95, University of Rhode Island, Kingston, RI.

O'HARA, K. D. 1986. The role of the Joshua Rock gneiss (JR) in the tectonic evolution of southern Connecticut. *Geological Society of America Abstracts with Programs*, **18** (1), 59.

—— & GROMET, L. P. 1983. Textural and Rb–Sr isotopic evidence for late Paleozoic mylonitization within the Honey Hill fault zone in southeastern Connecticut. *American Journal of Science*, **283**, 762–79.

—— & —— 1985. Two distinct late Precambrian (Avalonian) terranes in southeastern New England and their late Paleozoic juxtaposition. *American Journal of Science*, **285**, 673–709.

OXBURGH, E. R. 1982. Heterogeneous lithospheric stretching in early history of orogenic belts. *In*: HSU, K. J. (ed.) *Mountain Building Processes*, pp. 85–93, Academic Press, New York.

QUINN, A. W. 1971. Bedrock geology of Rhode Island. *U.S. Geological Survey Bulletin No. 1265*, 68 pp.

RAST, N. 1983. The northern Appalachian traverse in the Maritime Provinces. *American Geophysical Union, Geodynamics Series*, **10**, 243–74.

—— & SKEHAN, J. W., S. J. 1983. The evolution of the Avalonian plate. *Tectonophysics*, **100**, 257–86.

——, GRANT, R. H., PARKER, J. S. D. & TENG, H. C. 1978. The Carboniferous deformed rocks west of St. John, New Brunswick. *In:* LUDMAN, A. (ed.) *Guidebooks for Field Trips in SE Maine and SW New Brunswick. New England Intercollegiate Geologic Conference, 70th Annual Meeting. Geological Bulletin No. 6*, pp. 162–74, Queen's College Press, Flushing, NY.

ROBINSON, P. 1983. Realms of regional metamorphism in southern New England, with emphasis on the eastern Acadian metamorphic high. *In:* SCHENK, P. (ed.) *Geology of the Appalachian–Caledonian–Hercynian–Mauritanide Orogen*, pp. 249–58. Reidel, Dordrecht.

—— & HALL, L. M. 1980. Tectonic synthesis of southern New England. *In:* WONES, D. R. (ed.) *The Caledonides in the USA; Proceedings of the International Geological Program—Caledonide Orogen Project 27, Blacksburg, VA. Department of Geological Sciences, Virginia Polytechnic Institute and State University, Memoir No. 2*, pp. 73–82.

RODGERS, J. 1983. The life history of a mountain range—the Appalachians. *In:* HSU, K. J. (ed.) *Mountain Building Processes*, pp. 229–41, Academic Press, New York.

—— (compiler) 1985. *Bedrock Geological Map of Connecticut* (scale 1:125 000; two map sheets), U.S. Geological Survey and Connecticut Geological and Natural History Survey.

ROSE, S. & MURRAY, D. P. 1984. Age relationships in the Woonsocket and Scituate Basins, southeastern New England. *Geological Society of America Abstracts with Programs*, **16** (1), 60.

RUSSELL, G. S., RUSSELL, C. W. & FARRAR, S. S. 1985. Alleghanian deformation and metamorphism in the eastern North Carolina Piedmont. *Geological Society of America Bulletin*, **96**, 381–7.

SECOR, D. T., SNOKE, A. W. & DALLMEYER, R. D. 1986. Character of the Alleghanian orogeny in the southern Appalachians: Part III. Regional tectonic relations. *Geological Society of America Bulletin*, **97**, 1345–53.

——, MURRAY, D. P. & GLOVER, L., in press. Avalonian rocks in the U.S. Appalachians. *In:* HATCHER, R. D., THOMAS, W. A. & VIELE, G. W. (eds). *The Appalachian—Ouachita Synthesis Volume: The Geology of North America, F.2.* Geological Society of America, Boulder, Co.

SKEHAN, J. W., S. J. & MURRAY, D. P. 1980. Geologic profile across southeastern New England. *Tectonophysics*, **69**, 285–319.

SNOKE, A. W., KISH, S. A. & SECOR, D. T. 1980. Deformed Hercynian granite rocks from the Piedmont of South Carolina. *American Journal of Science*, **280**, 1018–34.

SPEAR, F. S. 1986. *P–T* paths in central New England: the evolution of a paired metamorphic belt. *Geological Society of America Abstracts with Programs*, **18** (1), 68.

WINTSCH, R. & LEFORT, J. P. 1984. A clockwise rotation of Variscan strain orientation in SE New England and regional implications. *In:* HUTTON, D. H. W. & SANDERSON, D. J. (eds) *Variscan Tectonics of the North Atlantic Region. Special Publication of the Geological Society of London No. 14*, pp. 245–51.

ZARTMAN, R. E. & HERMES, O. D. 1984. Evidence from inherited zircon for Archean basement under the southeastern New England Avalon terrane. *Geological Society of America Abstracts with Programs*, **16**, 704.

——, HURLEY, P. M., KRUEGER, H. W. & GILETTI, B. J. 1970. A Permian disturbance of K–Ar radiometric ages in New England: its occurrence and cause. *Geological Society of America Bulletin*, **81**, 3359–74.

ZEN, E-AN (ed.) 1983. *Bedrock Geologic Map of Massachusetts* (scale 1:250 000; three map sheets), U.S. Geological Survey and Commonwealth of Massachusetts.

D. P. MURRAY, Geology Department, University of Rhode Island, Kingston, RI 02881, USA.

Late Palaeozoic metamorphism in the northwestern Iberian Peninsula, Brittany and related areas in SW Europe

Francisco J. Martínez & Joël Rolet

SUMMARY: In the NW of the Iberian Peninsula elongated and coalescent thermal domes are centred in P_3 antiforms and associated with granite plutonism. After the Emsian and before the Namurian, assemblages with garnet, staurolite and kyanite changed into others with andalusite–sillimanite, biotite and cordierite giving evidence of heating and/or decompression related to syn-metamorphic granite intrusion. The Namurian is roughly the metamorphic peak of low-pressure conditions in the inner zones. In the central Armorican domain in Brittany the main metamorphic event has an age between 330 and 345 Ma. There is also a pressure decrease with time and the earlier zones are telescoped in the W by sub-autochthonous leucogranites associated with high-grade zones. Contact aureoles affecting the Dinantian basins in Brittany must be late Carboniferous. In the other areas, i.e. Catalonia, the Pyrenees, Montagne Noire and the French Massif Central, the history is essentially the same, with the low-pressure metamorphic peak being Namuro-Westphalian.

Regional setting and aims

The general link, trend and zoning of the Hercynian Chain in western and central Europe can be deduced from the outcrops of pre-Mesozoic basement in the various massifs (Matte 1976, Engel & Franke 1983, Julivert & Martínez 1983). Some of those in southwestern Europe will be discussed below.

The Iberian Peninsula shows, from NE to SW, the best section through the Hercynian in western Europe, outcropping in a belt 770 km wide. The link between this sector of the chain and that in Brittany is now firmly established, with the two forming the Ibero-Armorican arc. The following description and model of Variscan metamorphism will be mainly focussed on NW Iberia and, to a lesser extent, on Brittany, although the Pyrenees, Catalonian Chains, Montagne Noire and French Central Massif (Fig. 1) are closely related and are considered at the end of the paper for purposes of comparison.

The northwestern part of the Iberian Peninsula

The metamorphic areas in the Iberian Massif form generally elongated belts parallel to the main structural trends which form the arcuate shape of the Hercynian fold belt in the Iberian Peninsula (Fig. 2). Careful examination of these belts shows that they are not longitudinally continuous but join or are linked to one another. From NE to SW the most conspicuous are (see Fig. 2) Novellana–Pola de Allande–Degaña, Boal–Los Ancares, Vivero–Lugo–Sarria, Puentes de Garcia Rodriguez–Sanabria, Santa Comba–Santiago–Bande, Finisterre–La Guardia, Vila Real–Moncorvo–Vitigudino (continuing in the Guadarrama area) and Porto–Viseu.

These metamorphic belts coincide essentially with antiforms produced by the upright refolding of earlier structures during the P_3 deformation phase. In the cores of the westernmost antiforms, i.e. in the inner parts of the chain, the oldest rocks belonging to Palaeozoic and/or upper Proterozoic sequences crop out. This is particularly clear along the Ollo de Sapo antiform (Puentes–Sanabria belt) and in the areas of Celanova, Finisterre and Moncorvo–Vitigudino (Fig. 2) and Guadarrama (Fig. 1). The metamorphic zoning in each of the belts shows a broadly symmetrical pattern with respect to its axis. In some places there are one or more elongated, sometimes coalescent, thermal domes with the same symmetrical zoning. In most cases the centre of those domes is marked by S-type (Chappel & White 1974) aluminium-rich granite plutonism of alkaline affinity (muscovite or two-mica- and albite-rich leucogranites and inhomogeneous diatexitic granites). These granites are variably deformed and closely related to the metamorphism. Away from the thermal axis the metamorphism decreases very quickly, reaching the chlorite zone in a few kilometres. In the high-grade areas this S-type plutonism is accompanied by a group of deformed metamorphism-related I-type granitoids (diorites, tonalites, granodiorites etc.) which form part of a calc-alkaline series. These granitoids, which are usually the oldest syn-metamorphic intrusives, have ages clustering between 335 and 320 Ma (Pinto 1983, Priem &

From HARRIS, A. L. & FETTES, D. J. (eds), 1988, *The Caledonian–Appalachian Orogen,*
Geological Society Special Publication No. 38, pp. 611–620.

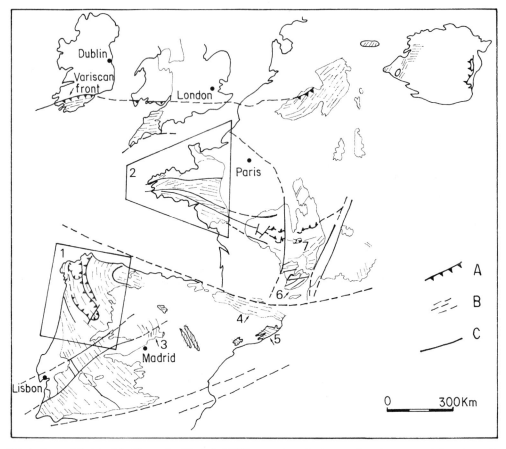

FIG. 1. General sketch of the Hercynian Chain in SW Europe: A, main thrusts; B, main structural directions; C, major faults; 1, NW Iberia; 2, Brittany; 3, Guadarrama area; 4 Pyrenean axial zone; 5, Catalonian massifs; 6, Montagne Noire; 7, French Massif Central. The relative positions of the Iberian Peninsula and the rest of Europe restored before the opening of the Bay of Biscay in the Mesozoic are shown. The framed areas are NW Iberia and Brittany (Figs 2 and 3). Based on Matte (1976).

Den Tex 1984). Sometimes the antiformal cores are almost filled with granitoids with, locally, inliers of migmatitic augen-gneisses and banded gneisses as well as high-grade pelite–greywacke sequences containing calc-silicate layers. There is also a group of younger post-tectonic granitoids of both I- and S-type bodies. The age of these younger granitoids is 280 Ma.

Three main phases of deformation related to the metamorphic evolution can be seen in the NW of the Peninsula (Noronha et al. 1981, Gil Ibarguchi et al. 1983, Martínez & Gil Ibarguchi 1983). The first phase (P$_1$) resulted in the formation of the most important structures in the area such as the isoclinal folds verging towards the concave side of the arc; these have an associated slaty cleavage or a schistosity (S$_1$) in the higher-metamorphic-grade areas. The second phase (P$_2$) gives rise to very tight minor folds

with gentle plunging axial planes verging like those of the first phase and associated with a strong crenulation cleavage (S$_2$) which, when well developed in amphibolite-facies conditions, forms a true new schistosity obliterating S$_1$. In certain areas, such as the Mondonedo nappe (Vivero–Lugo–Sarria belt), this second phase seems to be related to highly deformed shear zones associated with thrusting of the limbs of the first-phase isoclinal folds. In the third deformation phase (P$_3$) folds with almost vertical axial planes deform or reshape the P$_1$ or P$_2$ structures.

Characteristics and evolution of the metamorphic areas

The eastern edge of metamorphism in the outermost zone of the orogen lies close to the onset of cleavage which is situated near the

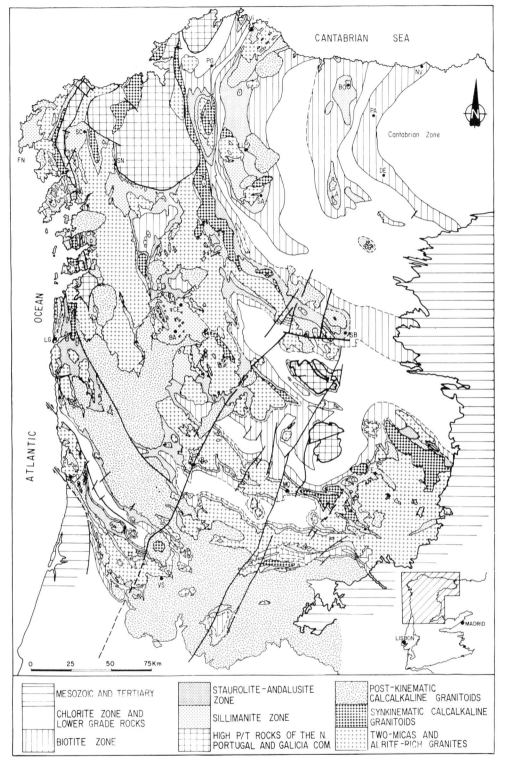

MESOZOIC AND TERTIARY	STAUROLITE–ANDALUSITE ZONE	POST-KINEMATIC CALCALKALINE GRANITOIDS
CHLORITE ZONE AND LOWER GRADE ROCKS	SILLIMANITE ZONE	SYNKINEMATIC CALCALKALINE GRANITOIDS
BIOTITE ZONE	HIGH P/T ROCKS OF THE N. PORTUGAL AND GALICIA COM.	TWO-MICAS AND ALBITE-RICH GRANITES

FIG. 2. Distribution of the main metamorphic belts and their relation to the granite intrusion in the northwestern Iberian Peninsula: NV, Novellana; PA, Pola de Allande; DE, Degaña; BO, Boal; LA, Los Ancares; V, Vivero; LU, Lugo; SA, Sarria; PG, Puentes de García Rodriguez; SB, Sanabria; SC, Santa Comba; SN, Santiago; FN, Finisterre; LG, La Guardia; VR, Vila Real; MO, Moncorvo; VT, Vitigudino; PO, Porto; VS, Viseu; CE, Celanova; BA, Bande; FE, Fermoselle.

eastern boundary of the Novellana–Degana belt (Narcea antiform) (Fig. 2). Low-grade metamorphic minerals, essentially chlorite and muscovite, are developed syn-P_1 (first Hercynian deformation phase in that area) and outline the axial plane cleavage (S_1) of the folds.

The outermost thermal dome or axis is situated in the Narcea antiform where biotite and muscovite develop mimetically with S_1 and quartz recrystallizes statically. The second metamorphic belt, Boal–Los Ancares, lies further to the W (Fig. 2) where, in addition to the above-mentioned minerals, andalusite and cordierite are found. These minerals are not only developed close to the granitic stocks which appear in this belt but they also show a wide regional distribution as areas of spotted and nodular slates. The recrystallization in this area is essentially post-kinematic, although in some instances pressure shadows and rotated schistosites in metamorphic porphyroblasts suggest a syn-kinematic mineral growth, at least locally. In this marginal belt the metamorphism already presents a characteristic which is common in the inner zones of the orogen, i.e. a close relationship in space and time between the development of the belt and the intrusion of the older S- and I-type granitic rocks.

The type of metamorphism found in the Boal–Los Ancares belt is relatively simple with well-defined biotite and andalusite–cordierite assemblages, characteristic of a high thermal gradient. The style of metamorphism becomes increasingly complicated to the W and SW with the widespread development of higher-grade phenomena and a more complex evolution in time.

The Vivero–Lugo–Sarria zone (Fig. 1) is the most easterly of these more complex higher-grade metamorphic belts. It shows prograde metamorphic zoning with biotite, almandine, staurolite and locally kyanite, which is evidence of Barrovian-style medium-pressure metamorphism (Capdevila 1969). These assemblages are overprinted by andalusite and sillimanite. The andalusite overgrows earlier garnet and staurolite which are found as relics inside the andalusite porphyroblasts (Bastida & Pulgar 1978, Bastida *et al.* 1986). Other examples of overlapping metamorphic zones and variations in the pressure gradients are found in many areas such as the schistose region S of Lalin, the Santa Comba–Santiago–Bande and Finisterre–La Guardia belts, the Guadarrama area etc. (Van Meerbeke *et al.* 1973, Lopez Ruiz *et al.* 1975, Gil Ibarguchi 1978, Marquínez 1984). All the belts mentioned show complex evolutionary sequences, with the final metamorphic pattern of most of these areas being the result of a complex interplay through time of the metamorphism and the associated granitic intrusions. In fact granitic rocks (generally two-mica granites) have been intruded in an extended process with, locally, the granitic contacts cutting across the metamorphic zones and the metamorphic rocks frequently forming roof pendants in the granite bodies. The granites lying along the thermal axis of the belts are only slightly discordant to the metamorphic isograds cutting and modifying them, with new metamorphic minerals developed close to the contact with the granites. This spatial and temporal parallelism between granite intrusion and metamorphic development was called plutono-metamorphism by Oen (1970) in northern Portugal, and the superposition of low-pressure metamorphism related to granitoid intrusion upon intermediate-pressure metamorphism constitutes a variation of it. Examples are found in the Porto–Viseu (low-pressure) and Albergaria–Oliveira (intermediate-pressure) belts; the latter is immediately to the SW of the former and is not shown in Fig. 2.

In the zones with such superposition, relic kyanite from the earlier episode is found inside andalusite porphyroblasts (Atherton *et al.* 1974). The continuous development of the style of metamorphism in the same area means that sometimes only the final part of this process is well represented, as in the Vila Real–Moncorvo–Vitigudino belt (Martínez 1974, Oen 1974) where only andalusite–cordierite and sillimanite belonging to the low-pressure metamorphic phase is seen. In these areas isograds are more closely spaced as a result of the higher metamorphic gradient. Even in these areas, however, careful analysis of the mineral assemblages may show a similar increase with time in the thermal gradient with or without a decrease in pressure; for example, assemblages with biotite–staurolite–andalusite are found locally (Godinho 1974, Martínez 1974, Bastida & Pulgar 1978, Marquínez & Klein 1982) and provide evidence that the continuous reaction (in an Fe–Mg system) staurolite + muscovite + quartz → andalusite/fibrolite + biotite + H_2O took place. However, in the thermal core of some belts or domes such as El Tormes, which forms part of this Vila Real–Vitigudino belt, garnet–cordierite–biotite–sillimanite–K-feldspar–plagioclase metatexitic gneisses occur in which garnets reacted with sillimanite and quartz to give cordierite and plagioclase; this reaction represents decompression and cooling in the core of the dome (Gil Ibarguchi & Martínez 1982). Moreover, during the metamorphic climax much melt is generated in the higher-grade zones of the domes, occasionally giving rise to broad migmatitic areas (Finisterre–La Guardia, Celanova–Bande, Sanabria and Fermoselle–Vitigudino (see Fig. 2)). Migmatites are the result of partial melting of pelite–greywacke sequences as well as of augen-gneisses and banded gneisses in the cores of the antiforms on which these metamorphic belts are centred.

Mineral growth in the various metamorphic areas mentioned above took place at different times in the deformational sequence (P_1, P_2 and P_3) depending on the type of metamorphism. Mineral parageneses with garnet, staurolite or kyanite representing Barrovian metamorphic gradients (Spear *et al.* 1984) are the oldest (syn-P_1 to syn-P_2), while those indicative of lower pressure and/or higher temperature, with andalusite, cordierite and sillimanite, developed later along the thermal axis or directly related to the granitic intrusions (syn-P_2 to syn-post-P_3 depending on locality).

Remnants of the former Barrovian episodes are best seen where they are not overprinted by younger events, i.e. in those areas where there was no change in peak conditions. This situation can be found away from the domes, as in the synformal areas of Calicia and Northern Portugal. Some of these synforms contain klippen of granulite- or blueschist-facies complexes, recording an older probably Siluro-Devonian event (Robinson *et al.* 1988). These klippen, for example, in Cabo Ortegal, Ordenes, Malpica-Tuy, Morais and Braganca (cross pattern in Fig. 2) were placed in their present position before the doming (P_3) episode and suffered heterogeneous retrogression under medium-pressure amphibolite-facies conditions but were undisturbed by the younger lower-pressure events.

In the areas where andalusite–cordierite and sillimanite assemblages were superimposed on garnet, staurolite and kyanite assemblages without obliterating the latter, the overall metamorphic gradient can be deduced as a curve concave towards the temperature. This reflects the progressive increase of the temperature–pressure ratio with time at any point throughout the area owing to syn–metamorphic intrusion (Spear *et al.* 1984, Martínez *et al.*, in preparation). The last part of the pressure–temperature trajectory followed by the core of some domes or belts such as El Tormes represents mainly a fall in pressure coupled to a lesser extent with a decrease in temperature (Gil Ibarguchi & Martínez 1982). This path may account for uplift related to P_3 doming.

The age of the metamorphism can be estimated from the stratigraphy and tectonics as well as from its relation to the granite intrusion. In the first pair of thermal highs, the Novellana–Degaña (Narcea antiform) and Boal–Los Ancares belts, the metamorphic imprint is related to potassium-

rich S-type granites and granodiorites which crop out as small stocks but most probably form a wider mass below. The age of these post-P_3 granites, and thus that of the associated metamorphism, ranges between 284 ± 8 and 287 ± 8 Ma (Suarez *et al.* 1978), i.e. late Stephanian.

The age of the lower-pressure metamorphic imprint with andalusite–cordierite and sillimanite in the inner zones of Galicia and northern Portugal can be inferred from the spatial relation between the growth of these minerals and the intrusion of either deformed I-type granitoids or two-mica albite-rich S-type leucogranites; these syn-metamorphic syn-tectonic intrusions cover a wide span of time, starting pre-syn-P_2 and going up to late P_3.

The climax of granite intrusion is roughly syn-P_3, which corresponds to the doming stage and the coeval shearing associated with major transcurrent shear zones (Iglesias & Choukroune 1980), much as in the central part of Brittany (Hanmer *et al.* 1982). A group of later completely post-tectonic shallow mainly I-type intrusives have distinct contact aureoles (Oen 1970).

The Rb–Sr whole-rock ages of the syn-metamorphic leucogranites, near which the low-pressure minerals recrystallize, range between 318 ± 21 Ma for the syn-P_3 deformed leucogranites of Finisterre–La Guardia (Van Calsteren 1977, Buiskool-Toxopeus *et al.* 1978) and 327 ± 5 Ma for the granite near Vitigudino in the Vila Real–Vitigudino belt (Priem *et al.* 1984). Given the close relation between this group of granites and the related anatexites it can be concluded that the metamorphic peak in these areas, corresponding to the lowest-pressure event and coinciding with the doming phase, is intra-Namurian. Nevertheless there exists proof that in some areas, such as in the vicinity of the Vivero leucogranite near the Cantabrian coast, the change to low pressure had already started syn-P_2 as the S_2 schistosity flattens around andalusites which include relics of staurolite (Bastida & Pulgar 1978). Further support for the intra-Namurian age of the thermal peak is given by the 325 ± 2 Ma age deduced from the lower intercept with the Concordia curve of zircons from the Ollo de Sapo gneiss in Sanabria (Lancelot *et al.* 1985). That age should represent the main Hercynian thermal event and is in excellent agreement with the Rb–Sr ages mentioned above.

Muscovite and biotite K–Ar cooling ages from 17 samples of S-syn-metamorphic and I-type granites and granodiorites from the belts to the W of Boal–Los Ancares (Ries 1979) and several samples of the same types of granitoids in NE Portugal (Mendes 1968) range between 270 and

313 Ma. Some of these ages reflect reheating caused by the younger post-tectonic intrusives mentioned above, but in other cases they imply that medium- to lower-grade amphibolite-facies conditions probably prevailed around these granites until the upper Westphalian.

Thus the metamorphic peak seems to have migrated; it is Namurian in the W and in the inner parts of the chain, but can be as young as Stephanian in the more external parts such as Boal–Los Ancares.

The age of the Barrovian event is more problematic. It is younger than the lower Devonian rocks involved in the Mondoñedo and El Caurel recumbent folds (Vivero–Lugo–Sarria belt) (Drot & Matte 1967, Pérez Estaún 1978, Martínez Catalán 1981). Furthermore, the Mamoa orthogneisses in the schistose region S of Lalín, which have suffered P_1 deformation and metamorphic recrystallization, give a lower mid-Devonian Rb–Sr age of 387 ± 16 Ma (Marquínez 1984, pp. 36–37). Another constraint is that the Barrovian minerals have grown between P_1 and P_2, and in the Mondoñedo nappe the isograds are cut by the basal thrust (P_2) of the nappe (Bastida *et al.* 1986). The Barrovian event should therefore be dated immediately before the thrusting phase representing the end of a continuous process of deformation starting with P_1. The age of P_1–P_2, which is that of the Barrovian event, can be deduced from the fact that in the most external parts of the chain, such as the Cantabrian zone (Fig. 2), the first and possibly second deformation phases are represented by decollement nappes whose time of thrusting ranges from Bashkirian to the end of Podolskian (Julivert & Arboleya 1986). This age for P_1 seems to correspond to the P_3 doming phase coeval with the low-pressure metamorphic peak in the inner parts, where the age of P_1–P_2 should be older than Namurian and consequently older than the age of the corresponding phase in the Cantabrian zone.

The beginning of deformation in the inner zones should be datable by the syn-orogenic flysch-like deposits of San Clodio and Guadramil, the age of which has been considered as no older than upper Devonian and most likely lower Carboniferous (possibly Viséan as in Catalonia) (Matte 1968, Teixeira & Pais 1973, Pérez Estaún 1974, Ribeiro & Ribeiro 1974). These sediments contain pebbles of gneisses, schists and granites, and it is uncertain whether these pebbles come from rocks deformed a short time before their erosion and deposition or from the erosion of an older basement. In the first case, the deformation and subsequent Barrovian metamorphism event should have started some time between lower Devonian (Emsian) and lower Carboniferous. In the second case the Barrovian metamorphism would be younger than these upper Devonian or lower Carboniferous syn-orogenic deposits. In any case an upper limit for the Barrovian event must be the Namurian age of the doming and the climax of the lower-pressure metamorphism.

Characteristics and timing of the Hercynian metamorphic episodes (upper Devonian–Carboniferous) in the Armorican Massif

Two regions belonging to the Bretonian phase (354–330 Ma) of the Hercynian as developed in the central Armorican domain can be distinguished. The eastern region (Fig. 3), including the Cotentin Peninsula, the Bocage Normand, Mancellia, the Laval synclinorium and the Block of Rennes, is only slightly affected by the Bretonian metamorphism, which reaches greenschist facies, and shows a well-developed slaty cleavage. This region presents local thermal anomalies related to either granitic domes like the Flamanville granite (Ledru & Brun 1977) or the shear zone that forms the southern boundary of the Block of Rennes (Le Corre 1978). Similar events could well have affected some parts of the Vendée at the same time. The western region (Fig. 3) underwent a stronger deformation than the eastern region but is still largely affected by only a greenschist-facies metamorphism characterized by a widespread development of chloritoid in aluminium-rich metasediments (Montagnes Noires, Arrée, S Morlaix, Elorn). However, the metamorphism increases quickly to the N and S in Léon, Briec and Pontivy, with very closely spaced isograds marking the progressive appearance of the following parageneses in pelitic rocks:

quartz, muscovite, chlorite, albite, $\pm$ chloritoid
quartz, muscovite, biotite, $\pm$ andalusite
quartz, muscovite, biotite, staurolite, $\pm$ almandine

The earlier zones are obliquely cut by a late sillimanite isograd and by the onset of melting, resulting in anatexites which are associated with sub-autochthonous leucogranites (Locronan, Landudal, Pontivy). Index minerals do not always appear in the same order, testifying to lateral variations in pressure and temperature (Hanmer *et al.* 1982). This is exactly the same relationship described above for NW Iberia, i.e. the systematic relationship between granitic intrusions and metamorphic evolution. Kyanite closely related

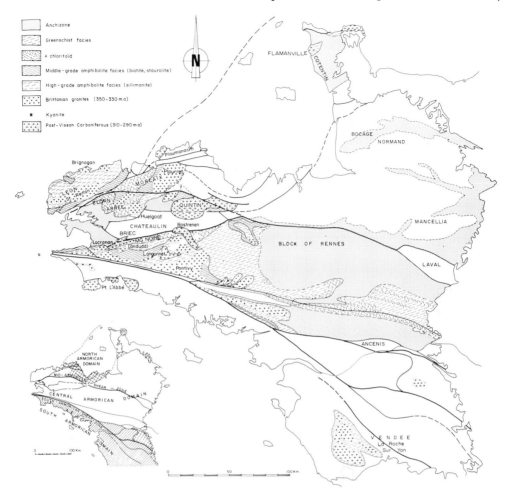

FIG. 3. Distribution of the lower Carboniferous (Bretonian) metamorphism in Brittany.

to shear zones seems to be independent of the regional isograds. It can be found with staurolite or associated with andalusite as in Briec or the Montagnes Noires. Cordierite as a late mineral is associated with biotite, sillimanite and sometimes almandine in high-grade pelitic gneisses found as enclaves to the N of the Pontivy granite. Cordierite is also found in anatexites related to the Brignogan granite (N of Léon). These high-grade parageneses with low-pressure minerals mark the metamorphic peak and seem to indicate a progressive pressure decrease as metamorphism prograded and temperature increased. The high-grade metamorphism and melting is related to crustal thickening, which is an intra-crustal process (with under-thrusting of the Léon) during the Devonian (Rolet *et al.* 1986).

In some areas, such as the Briec region, the Bretonian age of metamorphism is based on the

sillimanite grade of the middle Devonian (perhaps upper Devonian) rocks. The Bretonian age is not so clear in the Léon area, but lower Devonian rocks are affected and the isograds are modified by the late-kinematic granite of Saint Renan (345 Ma).

The Dinantian basins of Morlaix, Chateaulin, Laval and Ancenis (Fig. 3) have suffered a Namuro-Westphalian greenschist facies or even weaker metamorphism coupled with the development of a slaty cleavage (Rolet 1982, 1984). The Chateaulin basin is affected by the thermal aureole of the Rostrenen and Quintin granites (291 ± 9 Ma). The easternmost basins such as Laval seem to have been less affected, suggesting that the highest-grade zones of western Brittany remained hot throughout the middle Carboniferous. The last thermal events are also connected with the reactivation of some strike-slip faults along which granite was intruded in places with low-grade contact aureoles such as those in the Ploumanac'h and Langonnet granites. All tectono-metamorphic events are closely associated with either aluminium-rich S-type syn-Bretonian granites or late Hercynian sub-alkaline granites (Barrière *et al*. 1983).

Away from the central Armorican domain there may be some Carboniferous thermal anomalies such as those in La Roche-sur-Yon or around the Pont L'Abbé granite in the S Armorican domain.

The metamorphic picture in related areas

The history of the Catalonian coastal massifs (Julivert & Martínez 1980), axial zone of the Pyrenees and Montagne Noire (Fig. 1) is similar to that of the northwestern Iberian peninsula. In these areas staurolite and garnet grew between two stages of isoclinal folding and shearing, but later, up to or even beyond the upright folding or doming stage, they were overgrown by lower-pressure minerals such as cordierite and andalusite (Thompson & Bard 1982). Sillimanite or sillimanite–K-feldspar anatectic zones developed in the same prograde sequence as these younger minerals (Zwart 1976, Carreras & Santanach 1983); in some areas, such as the N Pyrenean massif of Agly, even low-pressure anatectic granulitic gneisses and related charnockitic granite appear (Fonteilles 1970, Pin & Vielzeuf 1983). These facts point once more to a pressure decrease related to a temperature increase with time (Thompson & Bard 1982). U–Pb ages ranging between 295 and 315 Ma for these granulitic rocks (Respaut 1984) confirm a Westphalian age for the low-pressure metamorphic peak in the Pyrenees. In the Montagne Noire muscovite in medium- and upper-amphibolite-facies gneisses gives ages between 330 and 335 Ma, and the syn-metamorphic Laouzas granite intruded in the axial zone of the dome provides an Rb–Sr age of 340 ± 22 Ma (Demange 1982), implying an upper

Visean or lower Namurian age for the thermal peak that post-dates the main deformation phase in the axial zone and the nappe emplacement in the cover (Thompson & Bard 1982).

In the French Massif Central, where nappe tectonics are important (Burg *et al*. 1984), the late metamorphic syn- to post-P_3 (doming phase) evolution fits well within the last part of the above-mentioned history. Chlorite, muscovite, biotite, garnet, andalusite, cordierite and sillimanite cross-cut S_1 and S_2. This low-pressure event could be related to syn-tectonic intrusion of granitoids in the nappe, and the beginning of the process is slightly older than 335 ± 5 Ma (Respaut 1984), the age of the Margeride granite, which in its turn is younger than the P_3 folding (Burg *et al*. 1984). Later events include the contact metamorphism of the Margeride granite, where former staurolite breaks down to give andalusite and hercynite (Burg *et al*. 1984), and the thermal imprint of the Velay dome at 300 Ma (Caen-Vachette *et al*. 1982). An intermediate-pressure (Barrovian) to medium-low-pressure metamorphism developed here prior to the low-pressure event described above. Although both these have almost the same formal relations as in the areas already described, the older Barrovian episode would have a lower Devonian age here (Robinson *et al*. 1988).

As the Barrovian event seems to be linked everywhere to an episode of syn-collisional isoclinal folding and nappe emplacement, its age, and that of the subsequent 'dome-stage' refolding, may be different in different parts of the chain: lower–middle Devonian in the S of Brittany and the Massif Central, and upper Devonian to lower Carboniferous in NW Iberia and Catalonia (Central Armoricain domain), the Pyrenees and Montagne Noire.

ACKNOWLEDGMENTS: F. J. Martínez is most grateful to M. Julivert and M. L. Arboleya for their comments and help. John Rodgers is deeply thanked for his thorough revision of the text and knowledge of 'Spanglish'. J. Rolet thanks L. Dupret and R. Wyns for their help concerning Normandy and Vendée. We are also indebted to D. Santallier and to an anonymous referee for comments that improved the manuscript.

References

ATHERTON, M. P., ATKIN, B. P. & NAGGAR, M. H. 1974. Kyanite in the Hercynian metamorphic rocks of the Porto–Viseu belt, North Portugal. *Geologie en Mijnbouw*, **53**, 189–92.

BARRIÈRE, M., ROLET, J. & THONON, P. 1983, Le magmatisme, marqueur de l'évolution orogénique, en domaine hercynien ouest-armoricain. *Comptes*

Rendus Hebdomadaires des Séances de l'Académie des Sciences, **296**, 917–22.

BASTIDA, F. & PULGAR, J. A. 1978. La estructura del manto de Mondoñedo entre Burela y Tapia de Casariego (Costa Cantábrica, NW de España). *Trabajos de Geología* **10**, 75–159.

——, MARTÍNEZ CATALÁN, J. R. & PULGAR, J. A. 1986.

Structural, metamorphic and magmatic history of the Mondoñedo nappe (Hercynian belt, NW Spain). *Journal of Structural Geology*, **8**, 415–30.

BUISKOOL-TOXOPEUS, J. M. A., HAALEBOS, P. E. M. & VAN OVERMEEAEN, F. A. 1978. An outline of the petrology and structural geology of the Hercynian complex South of Vigo (Pontevedra, Spain). *In*: HOMENAJE, I. (ed.) *Geología de la Parte Norte del Macizo Ibérico*, pp. 93–110, Parga Pondal El Castro, La Coruña.

BURG, J. P., LEYRELOUP, A., MARCHAND, J. & MATTE, PH. 1984. Inverted metamorphic zonation and large-scale thrusting in the Variscan Belt: an example in the French Massif Central. *In*: HUTTON, D. H. W. & SANDERSON, D. J. (eds) *Variscan Tectonics of the North Atlantic Orogen. Special Publication of the Geological Society of London No. 14*, pp. 47–61.

CAEN-VACHETTE, M., COUTURIE, J. P. & DIDIER, J. 1982. Ages radiométriques des granites anatectiques et tardimigmatiques du Velay (Massif Central français). *Comptes Rendus Hebdomadaires des Séances de l'Académie des Sciences*, **294**, 135–8.

CAPDEVILA, A. 1969. Le métamorphisme régional progressif et les granites dans le segment Hercynien de Galice Nord Orientale (NW de l'Espagne). *Thesis*, Université de Montpellier, 430 pp. (unpublished).

CARRERAS, J. & SANTANACH, P. 1983. El hercínico de los Pirineos. *In*: IGME (ed.) *Geología de España*, Vol. 1, pp. 536–50, Libro Jubilar J. M. Rios, Madrid.

CHAPPELL, B. W. & WHITE, A. J. R. 1974. Two contrasting granite types. *Pacific Geology*, **8**, 173–4.

DEMANGE, M. 1982. Etude géologique du Massif de l'Agout, Montagne Noire—France. *Thesis*, Université de Paris VI, 407 pp.

DROT, J. & MATTE, P. 1967. Sobre la presencia de capas del Devoniano en el límite de Galicia y Leon (NW de España). *Notas y Comunicaciones del Instituto Geológico y Minero de España*, **93**, 87–92.

ENGEL, W. & FRANKE, W. 1983. Flysch-sedimentation: its relations to tectonism in the European Variscides. *In*: MARTIN, H. & EDER, W. (eds) *Intracontinental Fold Belts*, pp. 289–321, Springer, Berlin.

FONTEILLES, M. 1970. Géologie des terrains métamorphiques et granitiques du Massif Hercynien de l'Agly (Pyrénées Orientales). *Bulletin du Bureau de Recherches Géologiques et Minières (France)*, **2**, 21–72.

GIL IBARGUCHI, J. I. 1978. Metamorfismo y plutonismo en la región de Muxia–Finisterre (NO de España). *Thesis*, Universidad Autónoma de Barcelona, 220 pp. (unpublished).

—— & MARTÍNEZ, F. J. 1982, Petrology of garnet-cordierite–sillimanite gneisses from the El Tormes thermal dome, Iberian Hercynian fold-belt (W Spain). *Contributions to Mineralogy and Petrology*, **80**, 14–24.

—— JULIVERT, M. & MARTÍNEZ, F. J. 1983. La evolución de la Cordillera Herciniana en el tiempo. *In*: IGME (ed.), Vol 1, *Geología de España*, pp. 607–612, Libro Jubilar J. M. Rios, Madrid.

GODINHO, M. M. 1974. Sobre o plutonometamorfismo da região de Guardão (Caramulo–Portugal). *Memorias e Noticias Publicacoes do Museu e Laboratorio Mineralogico e Geologico da Universidade de Coimbra*, **78**, 37–77.

HANMER, S. K., LE CORRE, G. & BERTHE, D. 1982. The role of Hercynian granites in the deformation and metamorphism of Brioverian and Palaeozoic rocks of Central Brittany. *Journal of the Geological Society*, London, **139**, 85–93.

IGLESIAS, M. & CHOUKROUNE, P. 1980. Shear zones in the Iberian arc. *Journal of Structural Geology*, **2**, 63–8.

JULIVERT, M. & ARBOLEYA, M. L. 1986. Areal balancing and estimate of areal reduction in a thin-skinned fold-and-thrust-belt (Cantabrian zone, NW Spain): constraints on its emplacement mechanism. *Journal of Structural Geology*, **8**, 407–14.

—— & MARTÍNEZ, F. J. 1980. The Paleozoic of Catalonian Coastal Ranges (NW Mediterranean). *IGCP Project 5 Newsletter No. 2*, pp. 124–8.

—— & —— 1983. Estructura de conjunto y visión global de la Cordillera Herciniana. *In*: IGME (ed.) *Geología de España*, Vol. 1, pp. 612–30, Libro Jubilar J. M. Rios, Madrid.

LANCELOT, J. R., ALLEGRET, A. & IGLESIAS PONCE DE LEON, M. 1985. Outline of Upper Precambrian and Lower Palaeozoic evolution of the Iberian Peninsula according to U–Pb dating of zircons. *Earth and Planetary Science Letters*, **74**, 325–37.

LE CORRE, C. 1978. Approche quantitative des processus synschisteux. L'exemple du segment hercynien de Bretagne centrale. *D.Sc. Thesis*, Université de Rennes, 381 pp.

LEDRU, P. & BRUN, J. P. 1977. Utilisation des fronts et des trajectoires de schistosité dans l'étude des relations entre tectonique et intrusion granitique: exemple du granite de Flamanville (Manche). *Comptes Rendus Hebdomadaires des Séances de l'Académie des Sciences*, **285**, 1199–208.

LOPEZ RUIZ, J., APARICIO, A. & GARCIA CACHO, L. 1975. El metamorfismo de la Sierra de Guadarrama, Sistema Central Español. *Memoria del Instituto Geológico y Minero de España*, **85**, 1–127.

MARQUÍNEZ, J. L. 1984. La geología del area esquistosa de Galicia Central (Cordillera Herciniana, NW de España). *Memoria del Instituto Geológico y Minero España*, **100**, 1–231.

—— & KLEIN, E. 1982. Evolución temporal y distribución del metamorfismo en el área esquistosa de Galicia Central (NO de España). *Trabajos de Geología*, **12**, 227–42.

MARTÍNEZ, F. J. 1974. Estudio del area metamórfica del NW de Salamanca (Cordillera Herciniana, España). *Trabajos de Geología*, **7**, 3–59.

—— & GIL IBARGUCHI, J. I. 1983. El metamorfismo en el Macizo Ibérico. *In*: IGME (ed.) *Geología de España*, Vol. 1, pp. 555–69, Libro Jubilar J. M. Rios, Madrid.

——, JULIVERT, M., SEBASTIAN, A., ARBOLEYA, M. L. & GIL IBARGUCHI, J. I. Structural and thermal evolution of high-grade areas in the Northwestern parts of the Iberian Massif. Submitted to *American Journal of Science*.

MARTÍNEZ CATALAN, J. R. 1981. Estratigrafía y estructura del domo de Lugo (sector Oeste de la zona Asturoccidental Leonesa). *Thesis*, Universidad de Salamanca, 317 pp.

MATTE, PH. 1968. La structure de la virgation hercynienne de Galice (Espagne). *Travaux du Laboratoire de Géologie de la Faculté des Sciences de Grenoble*, **44**, 1–128.

—— 1976. Raccord des segments hercyniens de l'Europe sud-occidentale (Îles Britanniques, France, Péninsule Ibérique, bloc Corso-Sard): Les differents marqueurs utilisables. *In*: *F. Kossmat Symposium, Nova Acta Leopoldina N.F.*, **224** (45), 239–62.

MENDES, F. 1968. Contribution à l étude géochronologique par la méthode au strontium des formations cristallines du Portugal. *Boletim de Museo Laboratorio Geologico, Facultade de Ciencias, Lisboa*, **11**, 1–155.

NORONHA, F., RAMOS, J. M. F., REBELO, J. A., RIBEIRO, A. & RIBEIRO, M. L. 1981. Essai de corrélation des phases de déformation hercynienne dans le Nord-Ouest Péninsulaire. *Leidse Geologische Mededelingen*, **52**, 87–91.

OEN, I. S. 1970. Granite intrusion, folding and metamorphism in Central Portugal. *Boletín Geológico y Minero*, **81**, 271–98.

—— 1974. A note on lower pressure and higher pressure metamorphic belts in North Portugal. *Geologie en Mijnbouw*, **53**, 193–4.

PÉREZ ESTAÚN, A. 1974. Aportaciones al conocimiento del Carbonifero de San clodio (prov. de Lugo). *Breviora Geológica Astúrica*, **18**, 3–8.

PIN, G. & VIELZEUF, D. 1983. Granulites and related rocks in Variscan median Europe: a dualistic interpretation. *Tectonophysics*, **93**, 47–74.

PINTO, M. S. 1983. Carboniferous granitoids of Portugal: some geochemical and geochronological aspects. *Papers on the Carboniferous of the Iberian Peninsula. Anales de la Facultad de Ciencias, Porto, Supplemento*, **64**, 15–33.

PRIEM, H. N. A. & DEN TEX, E. 1984. Tracing crustal evolution in the NW Iberian Peninsula through the Rb–Sr and U–Pb systematics of Palaeozoic granitoids: a review. *Physics of the Earth and Planetary Interiors*, **35**, 121–30.

——, SCHERMERHORN, L. J. G., BOELRIJK, N. A. I. M. & HEBEDA, E. H. 1984. Rb–Sr geochronology of Variscan granitoids in the tin-tungsten province of Northern Portugal: a progress report. *Terra Cognita*, **4**, 212–213 (abstract).

RESPAUT, J. R. 1984. Age and genetic relationship of two Variscan granites and their associated basic xenoliths. *Terra Cognita*, **4**, 196 (abstract).

RIBEIRO, M. L. & RIBEIRO, A. 1974. Signification paléogéographiquhle et tectonique de la présence de galets de roches métamorphiques dans un flysch d'âge Dévonien supérieur du Trás-Os-Montes oriental (Nord-Est du Portugal). *Comptes Rendus*

Hebdomadaires des Séances de l'Académie des Sciences, **278**, 3161–3.

RIES, A. C. 1979. Variscan metamorphism and K–Ar dates in the Variscan foldbelt of S Brittany and NW Spain. *Journal of the Geological Society, London*, **136**, 89–103.

ROBINSON, P., TRACY, R. J., SANTALLIER, D. S., ANDREASSON, P.-G. & GIL IBARGUCHI, J. I. 1988. Scandian–Acadian–Caledonian *sensu strictu* metamorphism in the age range 430–360 Ma. *This volume.*

ROLET, J. 1982. La 'phase bretonne' en Bretagne: état des connaissances. *Bulletin de la Société Géologique et Minéralogique de Bretagne*, **14**, 63–71.

—— 1984. Grabens losangiques (pull-apart) en régime de décrochement. Le rôle des coulissements hercyniens dans l'individualisation des bassins carbonifères du Massif Armoricain. *Annales de la Société Géologique du Nord, Série C*, **3**, 209–20.

——, LE GALL, B., DARBOUX, J. R., THONON, R. & GRAVELLE, M. 1986. L'évolution géodynamique dévono-carbonifère de l'extrémité occidentale de la Chaine Hercynienne d'Europe sur le transect Armorique–Cornwall. *In*: *Structure Profonde et Évolution de la Croûte Hercynienne d'Europe. Bulletin de la Société Géologique de France*, (8), t II, **1**, 43–54.

SPEAR, F. S., SELVERSTONE, J., HICKMOTT, D., CROWLEY, P. & HODGES, K. V. 1984. P–T paths from garnet zoning: a new technique for deciphering tectonic processes in crystalline terranes. *Geology*, **12**, 87–90.

SUAREZ, O., RUIZ, F., GALAN, F. & VARGAS, I. 1978. Edades Rb–Sr de granitoides del Occidente de Asturias (NW de España). *Trabajos de Geología*, **10**, 437–42.

TEIXEIRA, C. & PAIS, J. 1973. Sobre a presencia de Devónico na regiao de Bragança (Guadramil e Mofreita) é de Alcañices (Zamora). *Boletin da Sociedade Geologica de Portugal*, **18**, 199–202.

THOMPSON, P. H. & BARD, J. P. 1982. Isograds and mineral assemblages in the eastern axial zone, Montagne Noire (France): implications for temperature gradients and P–T history. *Canadian Journal of Earth Sciences*, **19**, 129–43.

VAN CALSTEREN, P. W. C. 1977. Geochronological, geochemical and geophysical investigations in the high-grade mafic–ultramafic complex at Cabo Ortegal and other pre-existing elements in the Hercynian basement of Galicia (NW Spain). *Leidse Geologische Mededelingen*, **51**, 57–61.

VAN MEERBEKE, G. L. E., HILGEN, J. D. & FLOOR, P. 1973. Preliminary results of the investigation of the Central Galician schist area (prov. of Orense and Pontevedra, NW Spain). *Leidse Geologische Mededelingen*, **49**, 3–37.

ZWART, H. J. 1976. Regional metamorphism in the Variscan orogeny of Europe. *F. Kossmat Symposium. Nova Acta Leopoldina N. F.*, **224**(45), 361–7.

F. J. MARTÍNEZ, Departamento de Petrología, Facultad de Ciencias, Universidad Autónoma de Barcelona, 08193 Bellaterra, Barcelona, Spain.

J. ROLET, Université de Bretagne Occidentale, Département des Sciences de la Terre, Laboratoire de Géologie Structurale, Avenue le Gorgeu, 29283 Brest Cédex, France.

Fourth time-slice: mid-Devonian to Permian synthesis

John Rodgers

SUMMARY: By some time in the middle Devonian, the Iapetus Ocean between Laurentia and Baltica was entirely closed (Acadian orogeny in the Maritimes and New England) and the Rheic Ocean between Baltica and proto-Gondwana was mostly closed (Devonian orogeny in France), although some relict oceanic basins (*cf.* Black Sea) may have remained. The Theic Ocean between Laurentia and proto-Gondwana (Africa) may well have remained partly open for much longer, but probably contained already consolidated continental blocks of various sizes. Where closing was fairly complete, late Palaeozoic deformation took the form of relatively narrow zones, often rift zones containing pull-apart basins whose sediments were later strongly deformed (sometimes with plutonism and metamorphism), lacing between larger blocks that remained barely affected but moved *en bloc* by strike-slip (Maritimes, Armorica) or large-scale thrust movement (southern Appalachians, Mauritanides). Certain zones however, are former continental passive margins, e.g. the Appalachian Valley and Ridge and the folded belt from southern Ireland to the Rheinische Schiefergebirge. Remaining oceanic areas presumably closed diachronously during the Carboniferous or early Permian, but few are available for inspection (Lizard?). The Theic suture is apparently traceable by geophysics beneath the coastal plains and shelves from southern Portugal to Florida. Deformation in any one area was episodic (Stillean phases), but no consistent episodes can be followed over the whole orogen.

The third time-slice finished (as agreed between the convenors of the third and fourth time-slice sessions) with the Acadian and related Devonian orogenies, which in our opinion marked the final closure of the Iapetos Ocean between proto-N America (Laurentia) and Baltica, creating what is commonly called Laurussia or the Old Red Continent. In discussing the fourth time-slice, therefore, we should begin by describing the situation after that 'event'.

The three Palaeozoic oceans or parts of oceans that appear in Fig. 1 have been named after three Titans of the generation that preceded Atlas, after whom the present (Cenozoic and later Mesozoic) Atlantic Ocean is named. Iapetos was Atlas's father, and Rheia and Theia were his aunts (Hesiod, *Theogonia*, lines 133–5, 507–9).

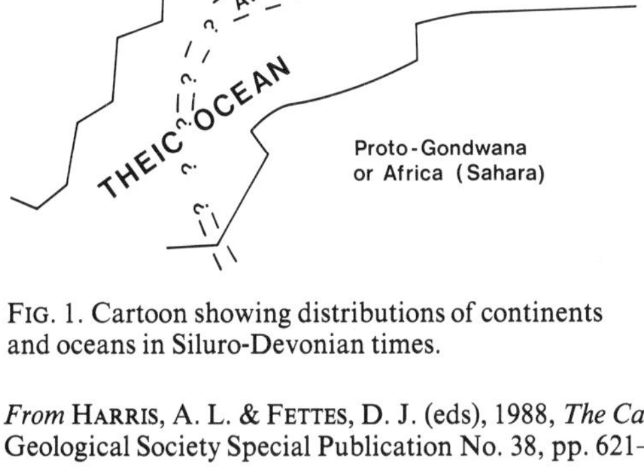

The closing of Iapetos was almost certainly diachronous. If the earlier Cambro–Ordovician wave of orogenic episodes (Finnmarkian, Grampian, Penobscot, Taconic etc.) is left out of account, the later Siluro–Devonian wave seems to have progressed, although probably not very regularly, from NE to SW. The climax of the Scandian was probably early Silurian in northern Norway but later Silurian farther S in Scandinavia, the climax of the Caledonian in Great Britain was latest Silurian, the climax of the so-called Acadian of Newfoundland was perhaps latest Silurian or early Devonian*, the climax of the 'type' Acadian of the Maritime Provinces and Gaspé was early Devonian, the climax of that of New England (as recorded in the Catskill delta and precursor deposits) was late early to middle Devonian, and the climax of the corresponding episode in the northern part of the southern Appalachians (recorded by the Price and Grain-

FIG. 1. Cartoon showing distributions of continents and oceans in Siluro-Devonian times.

* The data do not permit very precise dating; the youngest rocks involved in N central Newfoundland are early Ludlow, and the oldest not involved are highest Devonian or lower Carboniferous (Tournaisian). The only obvious candidate for a syn-orogenic deposit is the Clam Bank formation of the Port-au-Port peninsula on the W coast, red arkosic sandstone and conglomerate containing a bed of limestone with fossils dated as Pridoli; these strata were overturned before the deposition of lower Carboniferous conglomerate.

From HARRIS, A. L. & FETTES, D. J. (eds), 1988, *The Caledonian–Appalachian Orogen,*
Geological Society Special Publication No. 38, pp. 621–626.

ger formations) was late Devonian or earliest Carboniferous (Thomas & Schenk 1988). I conclude that Iapetos closed from N to S over a time of the order of the length of the Devonian period.

Absolutely critical to this discussion is the Devonian location of Avalonia–Armorica. For several years now, the students of palaeomagnetism have been assuring us that it then lay far from either border of Iapetos, although various geological considerations suggest that it may be a sort of southwestern peninsula or appendage of Baltica, at least in Silurian and later time. However, the workers who originally proposed that Avalonia was at least 20° farther S than the presently adjacent part of proto-N America, at least until late in the Carboniferous (Kent & Opdyke 1978), have changed their minds; new data have convinced them that nothing prevents its having approached N America during the Devonian (Kent & Opdyke 1985). If so, the discrepancies between the palaeomagnetic description and the geological description (late Devonian granite sealing the NW border fault of Avalonia for example) fall away, and the Iapetos Ocean could be considered to have closed by the collision of Baltica *and* its Avalonia–Armorica appendage with proto-N America. No ocean would be left, at least as far SW as southern New England (Fig. 2, no. 1).

The ocean between Baltica and proto-Gondwana (whatever is done with Avalonia–Armorica) has been called the Rheic Ocean. Here again the orogeny that ends the third time-slice was very significant, at least in France although much less obviously so in Iberia or farther SW ('Caledonide' movements in the Mauritanides appear to belong to the earlier 'Taconic' group of orogenies). Did it completely close the Rheic Ocean? Probably it did not; various oceanic basins may have remained, especially in and around the present Armorican massif, perhaps like the present-day Black Sea and southern Caspian oceanic relicts of 'Tethys'. Nevertheless, provincialism became weak to absent in the marine fauna and even in the continental flora and fauna, being more a function of latitude than of oceanic barriers (Allen & Dineley 1988).

Southwestward, beyond the end of Avalonia–Armorica or perhaps only by connections across its southern continuation, Iapetos merged with the Rheic Ocean into the Theic Ocean. Here much true ocean probably remained well into the fourth time-slice, although the evidence is equivocal and debated, and SW of Iberia it is hidden, if it exists, under the wide coastal plains and continental shelves on each side of the central Atlantic. Moreover, it was certainly not much like the present-day Atlantic; probably the

present SW Pacific is a better analogue, i.e. it contained several consolidated or partially consolidated but perhaps mainly submarine blocks or plateaux (Fig. 2, no. 7) like the present Lord Howe Rise and the ridge connecting the North Island of New Zealand to New Caledonia. On the present N American side most of the Piedmont of the central and southern Appalachians was consolidated by the mid-Devonian if not earlier, although granite in considerable abundance continued to be intruded there through the Carboniferous (Hermes & Murray 1988). (A later analogue, on an even larger scale, is the cortège of later Mesozoic granites that extends into northeastern China and eastern Mongolia nearly 2000 km westward of the belt of Mesozoic orogeny along the Pacific coast.) But this consolidated block was separated from N America by the passive margin now represented by the Valley and Ridge province on which marine (shallow-water) deposits accumulated until the late Carboniferous. On the present African side the *môle cotière* of Morocco formed the W border of the deep sedimentary basin or basins whose Palaeozoic deposits are now exposed in the Moroccan Meseta and the High Atlas (the Anti-Atlas is the S border); nevertheless it lay E of the true Theic suture suggested by geophysics (Lefort 1981). Farther S, some of the higher thrust sheets of the inner Mauritanides may represent another such intra-oceanic continental block now thrust across the passive margin of the Saharan or African continent; this margin certainly remained marine until the late Devonian.

The further history of the various parts of the orogen was obviously conditioned by whether they were already consolidated into 'continent' or remained truly oceanic. In the consolidated parts, probably including most of the northern regions as far S as S central France and southern New England (and probably much of the Appalachian Piedmont as well), areas of deposition took one of several forms or gradations between these forms. One end-member is that of a relatively simple down-warp or locally downfaulted basin (Fig. 2, no. 2) in which non-marine sediments were deposited, commonly red-beds but later also coal measures with or without basaltic or rhyolitic volcanics. Middle or late Devonian examples are the upper Old Red Sandstone basins of the British Isles and various small basins in eastern Canada and Maine (the Pirate Cove–Escuminac basin on the Restigouche estuary, the Mapleton sandstone basin, the Trout Valley conglomerate basin beside the Traveller volcanic pile, and the Perry basin). More widespread are the broad little-deformed Carboniferous basins (Fig. 2, no. 3) which the sea invaded

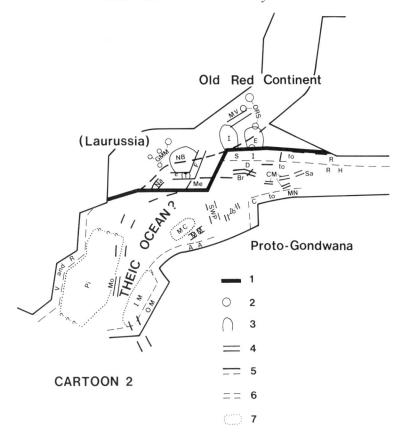

FIG. 2. Cartoon showing the framework of sedimentary basins in mid-Devonian to Permian times. 1, southern margin of Old Red Continent or Laurussia; 2, smaller basin, mainly Devonian; 3, larger basin, mainly Carboniferous; 4, rift zone, graben or half-graben; 5, passive margin with or without adjacent Culm trough; 6, isolated Culm trough; 7, already consolidated block within a mainly oceanic domain. Letters (the numbers in parentheses refer to the tectonic setting): AA, Anti-Atlas passive margin (5); Br, Brittany 'rift zone' (4); CM, graben and half-graben in the Massif Central (4); C to MN, Cantabria to Montagne Noire passive margin and Culm trough (5); D to RH, Devon to Rheno-Hercynian Culm trough (5); E, central and northern England larger basin (3); F, Fundy rift (4); GMM, smaller basins in Gaspé, Maritime Provinces and Maine (2); I, central Ireland larger basin (3); Ib, late graben in Iberia (4); IM, inner Mauritanide block (7); MC, *môle cotière* block (7); Me, Meguma block (of Old Red Continent) (1); MM, Moroccan Meseta basin(s) (6 or 4); Mo, Modoc 'rift' (4); MV, Midland Valley (4); Na, Narragansett basin (4); NB, New Brunswick–Gulf of St Lawrence larger basin (3); OM, outer Mauritanide passive margin (5); ORS, middle and upper Old Red Sandstone smaller basins (2); Pi, Appalachian Piedmont block (7); Sa, Saar half-graben (4); SI to R, southern Ireland to Ruhr passive margin (5); SWP, SW Portugal Culm trough (6); (T), Truro rift (part of Fundy rift) (4); V and R, Valley and Ridge province passive margin (5).

once or several times; examples of these are the Carboniferous basins of central and northern England and central Ireland (if indeed they were separate) and the basin in E central New Brunswick and eastward under the Gulf of St Lawrence (not to mention the foreland basins outside the orogen on each side, over the N American and the Saharan or African cratons).

All gradations from such basins to strongly faulted relatively narrow rift valleys or pull-apart basins (Fig. 2, no. 4) exist, e.g. the Midland Valley of Scotland and northern Ireland and the Fundy rift system extending from the present S coast of New Brunswick across central Nova Scotia (Truro rift or Minas basin) into Cape Breton Island and on across western Newfoundland along the Cabot Fault (Thomas & Schenk 1988). The Modoc fault zone on the E edge of the Piedmont in the southern Appalachians may be part of a similar system. The coal basins of central France and the Narragansett basin of southeastern New England are comparable, although less long-lived and mostly if not entirely non-marine. The relative importance of normal and strike-slip faulting in forming these basins needs to be worked out for each case. Many of the rift valleys were later strongly deformed or even metamorphosed and intruded by granite. Moreover, volcanics are widely if sporadically distributed along the borders of both the broad basins and the narrower rift valleys and coal basins (Francis 1988). To the S these basins may well grade into extensional basins of the 'marginal sea' or 'back-arc' type, notably in the area of the former Rheic Ocean (Leeder 1988).

In the more oceanic regions marine sedimentation continued through the Devonian and well into the Carboniferous. In the later Devonian and earlier Carboniferous in particular, thick flyschoid or Culm-type clastic sediments (Fig. 2, nos 5 and 6) were common, in contrast with the widespread non-marine to shallow marine strata (carbonates in at least the lower Carboniferous) of the broader basins in the consolidated areas. Some of the Culm sediments contain pebbles of schist and gneiss, which are evidence of already consolidated blocks nearby.

The belts of sediment deposited on passive continental margins (Fig. 2, no. 5) that had been there earlier in the Palaeozoic or had been created by the Siluro-Devonian orogenies are of particular interest. An example of the latter type is the geosynclinal wedge on the N side of the Variscan orogenic belt (the S margin of the Old Red Continent) which is now exposed in southern Ireland, across S Wales and SW England, in the Belgian and N French coal basin and the Ardennes, and in the Ruhr and the Rheinisches Schiefergebirge. The former type includes the entire Appalachian Valley and Ridge province, the Montagne Noire (and part of southern Sardinia ?), the Cantabrian zone in Iberia, and probably the Anti-Atlas and a belt along the W side of the W African craton, now partly incorporated into the lower thrust sheets of the outer Mauritanides. In some places (e.g. Galicia and SW England) there may have been 'true' ocean outboard of the passive margin; in others this is improbable (the Valley and Ridge province) or the evidence one way or the other has been destroyed. However, almost throughout, belts of strongly deformed (and locally metamorphosed (Murray 1988)) middle Devonian to Carboniferous strata are relatively narrow and are set between broader blocks where such strata are little deformed. The Truro rift or Minas basin of central Nova Scotia is a particularly clear example set between the only locally deformed coal basins along the N coast and the even less

deformed and shallower basins on the Meguma block (Thomas & Schenk 1988).

As time proceeded through our time-slice more and more areas that had remained oceanic were progressively deformed and consolidated (Hatcher 1988), and some were metamorphosed (Martínez & Rolet 1988) and intruded by granite, often more than once (Hermes & Murray 1988). As these areas joined the others, the style of deposition and deformation appropriate to the areas which were already consolidated—rift valleys, coal basins and, more rarely, broader basins—spread over them as well. Examples are the Westphalian coal basins and the mainly post-Westphalian red beds and conglomerate basins of Iberia and Morocco.

In some areas deformation may have been extensional rather than compressional, either incidentally to strike-slip movements or by the actual opening of new marginal basins of considerable size and depth which in their turn were deformed and consolidated. The progress of consolidation was evidently spasmodic, probably irregularly so. In any one area it may lend itself to Stillean phase analysis: Stille's 'Variscan' phases are based on Iberia, Armorica and middle Germany. The history of the Maritime Provinces of Canada during our time-slice was equally jerky (the Maritime disturbance), but I do not believe that the times of deformation fit the same pattern (see Rast 1988). In other belts, e.g. the central and southern Appalachians and the Mauritanides, the evidence on which the separation of phases is based is much more equivocal or entirely absent; the obvious angular unconformities have very wide ranges, and 'phases' are probably best dated on the basis of wedges of clastic sediments in the stratigraphic sequence.

As the remaining ocean basins closed (diachronously), the consolidated blocks found themselves no longer relatively free to move, as they had been earlier in the Palaeozoic, but increasingly constrained. They creaked and jostled and fought for space, and deformed the narrower belts between—the rift zones and the old passive margins—with special intensity. In the rift zones the result was generally large networks of strike-slip faults as the blocks worked past each other; on the passive margins it was spectacular far-travelled thrust sheets or nappes like those of the northern Ardennes (Faille du Midi) and the Montagne Noire, the two flanks of the Iberian chain, and the Mauritanides and southern Appalachians. Perhaps the most extraordinary result is the great sub-surface thrust fault (Cook *et al.* 1988) along which the consolidated Inner Piedmont with the present Blue Ridge attached was driven 200 km (or even more) over the passive margin of N America. Although the rocks of the Piedmont and the Blue Ridge were probably not as cold at that time (Murray 1988) as I believed previously, they were still relatively rigid.

By the end of our time-slice—in the early Permian, say—all the continental blocks and masses had merged into the single continent of Pangaea (broken only by the proto-Tethyan indentation E of the area that concerns us), and our orogen was part of a great complex mountain chain crossing that continent (Fig. 3) in the same way that the mountain chain from Anatolia to China and Malaysia crosses the present Asian continent. The former passive margins were probably the highest and most continuous mountain ranges within the chain (Fig. 3, no. 1), and the southern Appalachians must have included a great altiplano (Fig. 3, no. 5) or plateau of Tibetan type (although perhaps not as large), for the depth of the sub-surface décollement fault, even after differential uplift and erosion of the core of the mountain range, ranges from 8 or 10 km under

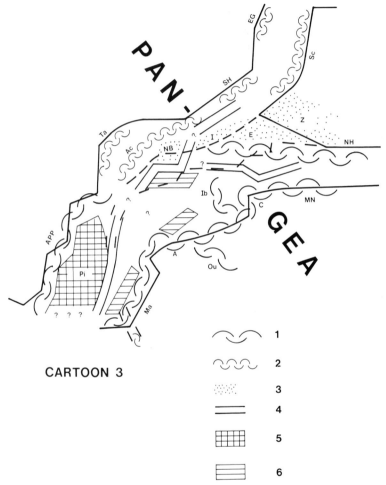

CARTOON 3

FIG. 3. Cartoon showing the pattern of orogenic highlands and lowlands in late Carboniferous and early Permian times. 1, new presumably rugged mountain range; 2, older presumably somewhat lower mountain range; 3, larger basin or plain; 4, rift zone and zone of particularly prominent strike-slip faulting; 5, high plateau (altiplano); 6, plateau (possible intermontane basin); unornamented areas probably contained groups of smaller ranges and basins. Letters (the numbers in parentheses refer to the tectonic setting): A, Atlas and Anti-Atlas range (1); Ac, Acadian range (2); APP, Appalachian range (1); C, Cantabrian range (1); E, basin of central and northern England (3); EG, Greenland range (2); I, basin of central Ireland (3); Ib, Iberian range (1); Ma, Mauritanide range (1); MN, Montagne Noire range (1); NB, New Brunswick basin (3); NH, North Hercynian range (1); Ou, Ougarta range (1); Pi, Piedmont altiplano (5); Sc, Scandinavian range (2); SH, Scottish Highlands range (2); Ta, Taconic range (2); Z, Zechstein basin or plain (3).

J. Rodgers

the Inner Piedmont to 4 or 5 km under the Valley and Ridge so that the 200 km of lateral thrusting along it would have been accompanied by 4 or 5 km of vertical uplift of the entire hanging-wall block. The former broad Carboniferous basins, however, remained as intermontane basins (Fig. 3, no. 3); a present-day analogue might be the Tarim or Takla Makan basin in central Asia whose surface is close to sea level even though it is surrounded by mountains reaching elevations of 7 km. During the Permian the sea entered the desert Zechstein basin near the edge of the old Baltica, leading to the accumulation of great salt deposits there and nearby; this basin probably lay between two arms of the mountain chain, the older but rejuvenated Caledonian arm on the site of Iapetos (Leeder 1988) and the younger Variscan arm on the site of the Rheic Ocean (Rast 1988). Areas containing narrow rift zones, pull-apart basins and strike-slip faults (Fig. 3, no. 4) may have resembled present-day California, as Wilson (1962) suggested about two decades ago for the Maritime Provinces of Canada during the Carboniferous.

Since then, the orogen has passed through a mild Great Basin stage (Triassic to mid-Jurassic) and has been torn apart as the present Atlantic Ocean began to open in various stages from late middle Jurassic to early Tertiary.

ACKNOWLEDGMENTS: I thank all those who took part in the day devoted to the fourth time-slice for accepting and carrying out their assignments. Naturally my attempt at synthesis is greatly indebted to them, even where they are not specifically cited. I am also grateful to Andrew Reid of the University of Durham, who drafted the cartoons.

References

ALLEN, K. C. & DINELEY, D. L. 1988. Mid-Devonian to mid-Permian floral and faunal regions and provinces. *This volume.*

COOK, F. A., MATTHEWS, D. H. & JACOB, A. W. B. 1988. Crustal and upper mantle structure of the Appalachian–Caledonide orogen from seismic results. *This volume.*

FRANCIS, E. H. 1988. Mid-Devonian to early Permian volcanism: Old World. *This volume.*

HATCHER, R. D. 1988. Basement–cover relationships in the Appalachian–Caledonian–Variscan orogen: mid-Devonian (end of Acadian orogeny) to end of Permian. *This volume.*

HERMES, O. D. & MURRAY, D. P. 1988. Middle Devonian to Permian plutonism and volcanism in the N American Appalachians. *This volume.*

KENT, D. V. & OPDYKE, N. D. 1978. Paleomagnetism of the Devonian Catskill red beds: evidence for motion of the coastal New England–Canadian maritime region relative to cratonic North America. *Journal of Geophysical Research*, **83**, 4441–50.

—— & —— 1985. Multicomponent magnetizations from the Mississippian Mauch Chunk Formation of the Central Appalachians and their tectonic implications. *Journal of Geophysical Research*, **90**, 6371–83.

LEEDER, M. R. 1988. Devono–Carboniferous river systems and sediment dispersal from the orogenic belts and cratons of NW Europe. *This volume.*

LEFORT, J.-P. 1981. La limite méridionale de la Laurussia entre la Floride et le Bassin d'Aquitaine. *Bulletin de la Société Géologique de France, Série 7*, **23**, 565–70.

MARTÍNEZ, F. J. & ROLET, J. 1988. Late Palaeozoic metamorphism in the northwestern Iberian Peninsula, Brittany and related areas in SW Europe. *This volume.*

MURRAY, D. P. 1988. Post-Acadian metamorphism in the Appalachians. *This volume.*

RAST, N. 1988. Tectonic implications of the timing of the Variscan orogeny. *This volume.*

THOMAS, W. A. & SCHENK, P. E. 1988. Late Palaeozoic sedimentation along the Appalachian orogen. *This volume.*

WILSON, J. T. 1962. Cabot fault, an Appalachian equivalent of the San Andreas and Great Glen faults and some implications for continental displacement. *Nature, London*, **195**, 135–8.

J. RODGERS, Kline Geology Laboratory, Yale University, New Haven, CT 06511, USA.

Index